The University of Chicago School Mathematics Project

Geometry

Teacher's Edition

Authors

Arthur Coxford
Zalman Usiskin
Daniel Hirschhorn

About the Cover
A bicycle wheel exhibits segments, angles, parallel lines, concentric circles,
chords, tangents, congruence, circumference, translations, rotations, and curves of the cycloid family.
Each UCSMP secondary text discusses some of these ideas, and all but the cycloid are
brought together in this text.

Scott, Foresman and Company
Editorial Offices: Glenview, Illinois Regional Offices: Sunnyvale, California •
Atlanta, Georgia • Glenview, Illinois • Oakland, New Jersey • Dallas, Texas

Acknowledgments

Authors

Arthur Coxford
Professor of Education, The University of Michigan

Zalman Usiskin
Professor of Education, The University of Chicago

Daniel Hirschhorn
UCSMP

UCSMP Production and Evaluation

Series Editors: Zalman Usiskin, Sharon Senk

Technical Coordinator: Susan Chang

Director of the Field Trial Evaluation: Sandra Mathison

Director of the Nationwide Evaluation: Penelope Flores

Teacher's Edition Additional Author: Jerry Smith
Niles Township High School West, Skokie, Illinois

Editorial Development and Design

Scott, Foresman staff, Rusty Kane

We wish to acknowledge the generous support of the **Amoco Foundation** in helping to make it possible for these materials to be developed and tested, and the additional support of the **Carnegie Corporation of New York** in the nationwide field-testing of these materials.

Contents · Teacher's Edition

T4-T18 **Highlights of UCSMP *Geometry***

vi-x **Contents of the Student Edition**

The complete Contents for the Student Edition begins on page *vi*.

2	Chapter 1	Points and Lines
58	Chapter 2	Definitions and If-then Statements
104	Chapter 3	Angles and Lines
154	Chapter 4	Reflections
204	Chapter 5	Polygons
252	Chapter 6	Transformations and Congruence
302	Chapter 7	Triangle Congruence
354	Chapter 8	Measurement Formulas
414	Chapter 9	Three-Dimensional Figures
466	Chapter 10	Surface Areas and Volumes
520	Chapter 11	Coordinate Geometry
562	Chapter 12	Similarity
628	Chapter 13	Logic and Indirect Reasoning
682	Chapter 14	Trigonometry and Vectors
732	Chapter 15	Further Work with Circles
792	Glossary	
800	Symbols	
801	Postulates	
803	Theorems	
809	Formulas	
810	Conversion Formulas	
811	Selected Answers	

T19-T52 **Professional Sourcebook for UCSMP**

Section 1: Overview of UCSMP
T19	The Reasons for UCSMP
T24	The UCSMP Secondary Curriculum
	Content Features, General Features, Target Populations, Starting in the Middle of the Series
T29	Development Cycle for UCSMP Texts

Section 2: UCSMP *Geometry*
T31	Problems UCSMP *Geometry* is Trying to Address
T34	Goals of UCSMP *Geometry*

Section 3: General Teaching Suggestions
Optimizing Learning:
T35	Pace
T36	Review
T36	Mastery
T37	Reading
T38	Understanding — The SPUR Approach

Using Technology:
T40	Calculators
T41	Computers and Automatic Drawers

Evaluating Learning:
T42	Grading
T43	Standardized Tests
T44	**Section 4: Research and Development of UCSMP *Geometry***
T50	**Section 5: Bibliography**

T53	Additional Answers
T67	Index

Note:
The **Professional Sourcebook** is located at the back of the Teacher's Edition.

UCSMP Helps You Update Your Curriculum and Better Prepare Your Students!

As reports from national commissions have shown, students currently are not learning enough mathematics, and the curriculum has not kept pace with changes in mathematics and its applications.

In response to these problems, UCSMP has developed a complete program for grades 7-12 that upgrades the school mathematics experience for the average student. The usual four-year high-school mathematics content — and much more — is spread out over six years. The result is that students learn more mathematics and students are better prepared for the variety of mathematics they will encounter in their future mathematics courses and in life.

In addition, UCSMP helps students view their study of mathematics as worthwhile, as full of interesting information, as related to almost every endeavor. With applications as a hallmark of all UCSMP materials, students no longer ask, "How does this topic apply to the world I know?"

For a complete description of the series, see pages **T19-T49** at the back of the **Teacher's Edition**.

In short, UCSMP...

■ Prepares students to use mathematics effectively in today's world.

■ Promotes independent thinking and learning.

■ Helps students improve their performance.

■ Provides the practical support you need.

> **"**I like the way it uses real life problems. The book is very easy to follow and understand.**"**
>
> **Geometry** student, Niles West High School, Skokie, Illinois

Imagine using a text that has been developed as part of a coherent 7–12 curriculum design, one that has been tested on a large scale *before* publication, and most important, has bolstered students' mathematical abilities, which is reflected in test scores. Read on to find out how UCSMP has done that, and more.

For a detailed discussion of the development and testing of **Geometry**, see pages **T44-T49**.

Years of field-testing and perfecting have brought impressive results!

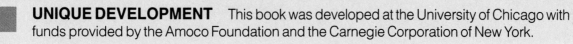

UNIQUE DEVELOPMENT   This book was developed at the University of Chicago with funds provided by the Amoco Foundation and the Carnegie Corporation of New York.

PLANNING   Initial planning was done with input from professors, classroom teachers, school administrators, and district and state supervisors of mathematics, along with the recommendations by national commissions and international studies. In particular, the UCSMP secondary curriculum is the first full mathematics curriculum to implement the recommendations of the NCTM Standards committees.

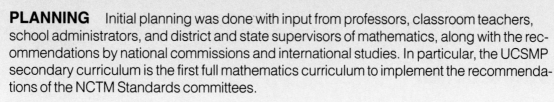

AUTHORSHIP   All UCSMP authors were chosen for expertise in the relevant areas of school mathematics and for classroom experience. All of the authors of **Geometry** are experienced high school teachers. Two of the authors had previously written a geometry text known for its integration of various approaches to geometry and its ability to reach a wide variety of students.

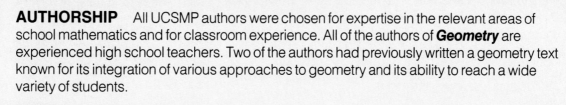

FIELD-TESTING AND EVALUATION   Pilot testing began with local studies in a variety of schools. Then, the materials were revised. Further evaluation and revisions were based on two years of national studies. The Scott, Foresman input includes enhancements, such as color photography and nearly 600 blackline masters, to better meet the needs of teachers and students.

Offers a Wide Variety of Content and Applications

Geometry is designed to attract and keep students in mathematics — not weed them out. The content connects the physical and visual world with the algebra students know, and arranges it in a clear logical framework.

Consistent organization leads to mastery

The following features are built into every lesson, providing a consistent path for learning.

Lesson Introduction

gets students reading mathematics on a daily basis. Provided are key concepts, relevant vocabulary, and meaningful examples for students to read and discuss. Topics are placed in real-world settings so students know why they are studying them.

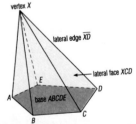

T6

Four Kinds of Questions

provide a variety of contexts, encouraging students to think about each problem.

1 **COVERING THE READING** offers a variety of types of questions that allow students to try out what they've learned in the lesson introduction.

2 **APPLYING THE MATHEMATICS** offers real-world and other applications of the lesson concepts.

3 **REVIEW** keyed to past lessons, helps students acquire, maintain, and improve performance on important skills and concepts, and previews ideas to prepare students for topics that will be studied later.

4 **EXPLORATION** extends the lesson content, offering an interesting variety of applications, generalizations, and extensions, including open-ended experiments, research, and much more.

Questions

Covering the Reading

1

In 1–6, use the figure below when necessary. Give the distance between the named points.

1. A and B

2. B and C

3. A and C

4. A and the origin

5. B and D

6. (x_1, y_1) and (x_2, y_2)

[Figure: coordinate grid with points $C = (6, 7)$, $A = (-5, 2)$, $B = (6, 2)$, $D = (2, -4)$]

7. To get to a hospital from the middle of a nearby town, you can drive 8 miles east, turn and go 4 miles south, and then go 1 mile west. By helicopter, how far is it from the middle of the town to the hospital?

Applying the Mathematics

2

8. Let $J = (-5, 0)$, $K = (5, 8)$, and $L = (4, -1)$.
   a. Prove that $\triangle JKL$ is isosceles by using the Distance Formula.
   b. Is $\triangle JKL$ equilateral?

9. Given: $A = (4, -7)$, $B = (6, -3)$, $C = (4, 1)$, and $D = (-10, -3)$.
   Prove: $ABCD$ is a kite.

10. On a map, it can be seen that Charles lives 1 mile east and 1.5 miles south of school, while Cynthia lives 2 miles west and 0.8 miles south of school. By air, how far do Charles and Cynthia live from each other?

11. Tell whether the statement is *true* or *false*. If false, give a counterexample.
   a. $|x_2 - x_1| = (x_2 - x_1)$
   b. $|x_2 - x_1|^2 = (x_2 - x_1)^2$
   c. $|x_2 - x_1| = |x_1 - x_2|$
   d. $(x_1 - x_2)^2 = (x_2 - x_1)^2$

12. a. Find the distance between $(1, 2)$ and $(3, 4)$.
   b. Is the answer to part **a** the same as the distance between $(3, 4)$ and $(1, 2)$?
   c. Generalize the result.

13. Let $A = (-1, 3)$ and $B = (11, 2)$. Prove that the point $C = (3, -7)$ is on the circle with center B and radius BA.

Review

14. Prove: $A = (0, 0)$, $B = (4, 0)$, $C = (5, 1)$, and $D = (3, 3)$ are vertices of a trapezoid. *(Lesson 11-1)*

15. Prove that the triangle with vertices $P = (3z, 4z)$, $Q = (7z, 2z)$, and $R = (2z, -8z)$ is a right triangle. *(Lesson 11-1)*

3

In 16 and 17, find the point of intersection of the lines by solving a system. *(Lesson 11-1, Previous course)*

16. $\begin{cases} -2x + y = 11 \\ x + 2y = 6 \end{cases}$

17. $\begin{cases} y = 13 \\ 4x - 3y = 10 \end{cases}$

18. a. A square has sides of length 100. What is the length of either diagonal?
   b. Generalize part **a**. *(Lesson 8-7)*

19. A parallelogram and triangle have the same base and same altitude. How are their areas related? *(Lessons 8-6, 8-5)*

20. The measure of one acute angle of a right triangle is 45° more than the measure of the other.
   a. Is this possible?
   b. If so, find the measures. If not, tell why not. *(Lessons 5-7, 3-2)*

21. Lynne has scored 92, 83, and 95 on her three tests so far this grading period. What is her average (or mean) score? *(Previous course)*

Exploration

4

22. The distance from point X to $(2, 8)$ is 17.
   a. Show that X could be $(10, 23)$.
   b. Name five other possible locations of point X. (Hint: Draw a picture.)

Prepares Students to Use Mathematics Effectively in Today's World

Real-World Applications

Students study each mathematical idea in depth through applications and practical problems, providing opportunities to develop skills and to understand the importance of mathematics in everyday life.

Wider Scope

Geometry integrates standard approaches, coordinates, and transformations, making use throughout of the algebra students know. It presents the history of major ideas and examples of recent developments in geometry and its applications, which both teachers and students really like and appreciate.

Lesson Integrating Coordinates

LESSON

11-1

Proofs with Coordinates

rectangular region with length 14, width 8

Figures can be described with or without coordinates. Above and below are three descriptions of congruent rectangular regions. Tw of these descriptions use coordinates.

rectangular region with vertices (0, 0), (14, 0), (14, 8), and (0, 8)

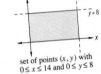

set of points (x, y) with $0 \le x \le 14$ and $0 \le y \le 8$

Any polygon or polygonal region can be described using a des tion like the one just above on the left. Just list its vertices in Some polygons can be proved to be special.

Example 1 Consider quadrilateral *ABCD* with vertices *A* = (0, 0), *B* = (8, *C* = (11, 12), and *D* = (3, 12). Prove that *ABCD* is a parallelo

Solution 1 First draw a picture, as done at the left. In the dra appears that *ABCD* is a parallelogram. The idea is to use slo prove opposite sides parallel. Here is what you might write.

Using the slope formula, $\overline{AD}$ and $\overline{BC}$ have slope 4 and $\overline{DC}$ an and Slopes Theorem parallelogram (suffic

statement, written i

Justifications
definition of slope

Parallel Lines and Slopes Theorem definition of para sufficient conditi

Lesson Integrating Transformations

(bottom) Lesson Using Standard Approach

LESSON

4-2

Reflecting Figures

Power-generating windmills reflected in a pond

In Lesson 4-1 each point in the image dog correspon point in the preimage dog. The reflection image of t set of all the individual image points. This is why t In general, the **reflection image of a figure** is the s reflection images of points in the figure.

Below is ∠*AEH* and its image, ∠*A'E'H'*. Individua ∠*AEH* are black and their reflection images are sho

Several striking features of this figure are evident. L *collinear* points *E*, *D*, and *C*. Their images *E'*, *D'*, collinear. Also, *D* is *between E* and *C*, and its imag between the images of *E* and *C*. This observation is *G*, and *H*. Is it true for *E*, *G*, and *A*?

LESSON

7-3

Triangle Congruence Proofs

To use any triangle congruence theorem, you need to know that three parts (SSS, SAS, ASA, or AAS) of one triangle are congruent to the corresponding three parts of another. The particular theorem then enables you to conclude that the triangles are congruent. Be-cause the triangles are congruent, all their corresponding parts are congruent due to the CPCF Theorem. Thus the SSS, SAS, ASA, and AAS theorems enable you to get six pairs of parts congruent where you only had three. That makes them quite powerful.

Example 1 **Given:** ∠*EBA* ≅ ∠*CBD*
$\overline{AB}$ ≅ $\overline{BC}$
∠*A* ≅ ∠*C*.

Prove: $\overline{EB}$ ≅ $\overline{DB}$.

Draw Copy the figure and mark it with the given information.

Technology

Students learn how to use calculators and computers — tools they'll need in the real world. The evidence shows that the appropriate use of technology enhances student mathematical understanding and improves problem-solving skills.

LESSON

4-3

Using an Automatic Drawer

Drawing or constructing figures can be time-consuming and difficult. If you do not have a good compass, your circles may start in one place and end in another. Pencil lines have thickness and if a ruler slips just a little, the entire drawing may be off.

Computers have changed the way many people draw. Nowadays, many of the Saturday morning television cartoons are drawn with the aid of a computer. Many commercials on TV use computer graphics. Manufacturers use computer designing to help design new

construc-
software
ing tool or
construct,
of various

the **win-**
options.

LESSON

2-3

If-then Statements in Computer Programs

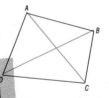

Recall that a diagonal of a polygon is a segment connecting two nonconsecutive vertices of the polygon.

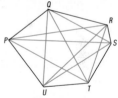

$\overline{AC}$ and $\overline{BD}$ are the two diagonals of quadrilateral *ABCD*.

hexagon *QRSTUP* and its nine diagonals

hen polygons have many sides, it is tedious to count to find the mber of diagonals. Fortunately, there is a simple formula. If *n* is e number of sides of the polygon and *d* the number of diagonals, en

$$d = \frac{n(n-3)}{2}.$$

program can instruct a computer to calculate a value of *d* given a lue of *n*. Consider the following BASIC (Beginners All-purpose mbolic Instructional Code) computer program.

```
10   PRINT "COMPUTE NUMBER OF DIAGONALS IN POLYGON"
20   PRINT "ENTER THE NUMBER OF SIDES"
30   INPUT N
40   IF N >= 3 THEN PRINT "THE NUMBER OF DIAGONALS IS ";
     N *(N − 3)/2
50   END
```

he 10, 20, 30, 40, and 50 are **line numbers.** The computer per-rms the instructions in the order of the line numbers. Any natural umber can be a line number.

LESSON

14-3

The Tangent Ratio

In Example 3 of Lesson 14-1, measures of two angles and a non-included side in a triangle were given. That is the AAS condition. From this information, measures of all other angles and sides could be computed. In general, using trigonometry *all* sides and angles can be found whenever enough information is given for a triangle con-gruence condition. In this book you will learn how to do this with right triangles.

Consider two right triangles *ABC* and *XYZ* with a pair of congruent acute angles. The triangles might be formed by figures and shadows at the same time of day. Following custom, in the drawing at the right the side opposite angle *A* is called *a*, the side opposite angle *B* is called *b*, and so on. You should be careful to write small letters differently from capital letters.

The triangles are similar because of AA Similarity.

rtional $\frac{a}{=} = \frac{b}{}$

Develops Independent Thinking and Learning

Reading

GREAT FOR STUDENTS Well-written explanations and examples enable students to successfully apply what they've read and also serve as a great reference tool, encouraging students to look for answers on their own. The reading also helps to motivate students by connecting mathematics to their world, which makes it more interesting to them.

GREAT FOR TEACHERS Because students can read and understand the text, you have the freedom to teach in a variety of ways. Instead of merely explaining every day what the text says, you can concentrate on developing further examples and explanations tailored to your students' needs.

Problem Solving

Every lesson contains a variety of problem-solving questions applying the mathematics. Students learn about the selection of problem-solving strategies to encourage efficient methods. In addition, requiring students to read helps develop thinkers who are more critical and aware.

LESSON 7-1
Drawing Triangles

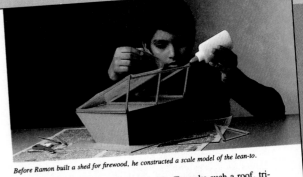

Before Ramon built a shed for firewood, he constructed a scale model of the lean-to.

A lean-to roof has only one slanted side. To make such a roof, triangular supports (shown in orange) are often used. In order for the lean-to roof to be a plane, and to fit snugly with the walls, the triangular supports must be congruent. Since roofs and their supports are often made of wood, these triangles cannot be made by machine; they have to be measured and cut.

Ramon was building a lean-to to serve as a shed for firewood on his farm. He cut long pieces of wood into lengths of 2, 4, and 5 feet. Using one piece of each length, he made triangles out of them. He did this by cutting and nailing the ends together. He made four triangular frames for his shed.

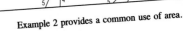

Example 2 provides a common use of area.

Example 2 A carpet dealer advertises a particular carpet for yard. How much will it cost to carpet a room that

Solution Since the price of carpeting is in square dimensions of the room must be converted from 9 feet = 3 yards and 12 feet = 4 yards. Thus, in area of the room is 3 yards · 4 yards = 12 yards carpeting is 12 · $18.95 = $227.40. This is befo charges such as installation or padding.

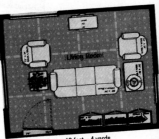

12 feet = 4 yards

Questions

Covering the Reading

1. Below, two different unit squares are used to large congruent rectangles.

   unit A

   a. What is the area using unit A?
   b. What is the area using unit B?

2. Rectangle *ABCD* has dimensions 8.3 cm a
   a. What is an appropriate unit of area in t
   b. Find Area (*ABCD*).

Example 2 A standard bowling ball cannot be more than 27 inches in circumference. What is the maximum volume of such a ball (to the nearest cubic inch) before the holes are drilled?

Solution First find the radius of the ball. Use the circumference formula.

$$C = 2\pi r$$
$$27 = 2\pi r$$
$$r = \frac{27}{2\pi} \approx 4.3''.$$

So

Now substitute into the volume formula $V = \frac{4}{3}\pi r^3$.

$$V \approx \frac{4}{3} \cdot \pi (4.3)^3$$
$$\approx \frac{4}{3} \cdot \pi \cdot 79.507$$
$$\approx 333 \text{ cubic inches}$$

Even after drilling the holes, there are more than 300 cubic inches of rubber or plastic in a standard bowling ball.

Questions

Covering the Reading

In 1–3, use this drawing of a sphere, cylinder, and two cones. Sections formed by their intersections with a plane four units above and parallel to the horizontal plane through the figures' middles are colored.

Chapter Review

The main objectives for the chapter are organized into sections corresponding to the four main types of understanding this book promotes: Skills, Properties, Uses, and Representations. Thus, the Chapter Review extends the multi-dimensional approach to understanding, offering a broader perspective that helps students put everything in place.

1 SKILLS range from the carrying out of procedures for drawings and constructions to the study of algorithms.

2 PROPERTIES range from the mathematical justifications for conclusions to the writing of proofs.

3 USES range from simple real-world applications of the mathematics to the modeling of real situations.

4 REPRESENTATIONS range from graphs and diagrams to the invention of other metaphors to describe mathematics.

Notice that the four types of understanding are not in increasing order of difficulty. There may be hard skills and easy representations; some uses may be easier than anything else; and so on.

All of these views combine to contribute to the deep understanding of mathematics that students need to have in today's world.

CHAPTER 2

Chapter Review

Questions on **SPUR** Objectives

SPUR stands for **S**kills, **P**roperties, **U**ses, and **R**epresentations.
The Chapter Review questions are grouped according to the SPUR Objectives for this chapter.

1

SKILLS deal with the procedures used to get answers.

■ Objective A: *Distinguish between convex and nonconvex regions. (Lessons 2-1, 2-7)*

In 1–3, characterize each region as convex or nonconvex.

1.   2.   3.

6. Draw a convex octagonal region.
7. Draw a nonconvex nonagonal region.
8. Match each term with the most appropriate drawing.
   a. decagon   **b.** pentagon   **c.** quadrilateral

(i)   (ii)   (iii)   (iv)

9. Trace the polygon (i) in Question 8 above. Draw the polygon formed by connecting the midpoints of consecutive sides.

■ Objective B: *Draw and identify polygons. (Lesson 2-7)*

4. Draw an equilateral triangle.
5. Draw an isosceles triangle.

2

PROPERTIES deal with the principles behind the mathematics.

■ Objective C: *Write the converse of a conditional. (Lesson 2-4)*

In 10–12, **a.** write the converse of the statement. **b.** Tell whether the converse is true.

10. If $x = 3$, then $x^2 = 9$.
11. If $AM = MB$, then M is the midpoint of $\overline{AB}$.
12. All Hawaiians live in the U.S.

■ Objective D: *Apply the properties of a good definition. (Lessons 2-1, 2-5)*

13. Why is it important to carefully define terms?
14. "Polygon" is defined using what three previously defined terms?

In 15 and 16, tell which definition is violated by

15. The midpoint M of $AM = BM$.
16. A triangle is a clos
17. Here is a definition A secant to a circle the circle in two po This definition mak previously defined
18. Break the definitio into its meaning an halves.

■ Objective E: *Write and interpret statements in "if-then" form. (Lesson 2-2)*

In 19–21, rewrite in "if-then" form.
19. Every radius is a segment.
20. All hexagons have 9 diagonals.
21. Given $AB = 7$, you can conclude $BA = 7$.

In 22 and 23, copy the statement and underline the antecedent once and consequent twice.
22. A figure is a rectangle if it is a square.
23. If p, then q.

In 24 and 25, refer to this statement: If a figure is a union of four segments, then it is a quadrilateral.
24. Draw an instance of the antecedent for which the consequent is also true.
25. Draw a counterexample.

■ Objective F: *Determine the union and intersection of sets. (Lesson 2-6)*

26. If A = { 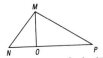 } and B = {5, 13, 9}, find A ∩

27. Let D = the solution set to $n \leq 15$, and E = the solution set to $n \geq -15$.
   a. Describe D ∩ E.
   b. Describe D ∪ E.

28. Triangle MNO below is x and triangle MOP is y. Name the segments of:
   a. x ∩ y;   **b.** x ∪ y.

(triangle MNO P diagram)

■ Objective G: *Use logical ($p \Rightarrow q$) notation. (Lessons 2-2, 2-3, 2-4)*

29. Let $p =$ "$\triangle ABC$ is equilateral." $q =$ "$\triangle ABC$ has three 60° angles." Write in words. **a.** $q \Rightarrow p$;   **b.** $p \Leftrightarrow q$.

In 30 and 31, p and q may be any statements.
30. If $p \Rightarrow q$ is true, must $q \Rightarrow p$ be true?
31. A counterexample for $p \Rightarrow q$ is a situation in which p is __?__ and q is __?__.

USES deal with applications of mathematics in real situations.

■ Objective H: *Apply properties of if-then statements in real situations. (Lessons 2-3, 2-4)*

35. An umpire has just swept off home plate in the picture below. What polygon is the shape of home plate?

REPRESENTATIONS deal with pictures, graphs, or objects that illustrate concepts.

■ Objective J: *Read computer programs with IF-THEN statements. (L___3)*

In 36–38, consider this ___am.

```
10  PRINT "COMPUTE NUMBER OF
    DIAGONALS IN POLYGON"
20  INPUT N
30  IF N >= 3 THEN PRINT "THE NUMBER
    OF DIAGONALS IS "; N * (N - 3)/2
40  END
```

36. What will be printed if N is given the value 1?
37. What will be printed if N is given the value 20?
38. What will be printed if N is given the value 3?

In 39 and 40, consider this program.

```
10  INPUT X
20  IF X < .33 THEN PRINT 3 * X
30  IF X >= .33 AND X <= .67 THEN PRINT
    2 * X
40  IF X > .67 THEN PRINT X
50  END
```

39. What will be printed if X is given the value 0.4?
40. What will be printed if X is given the value 20?

■ Objective K: *Draw hierarchies of triangles and polygons. (Lesson 2-7)*

41. Draw the hierarchy relating the following: figure, triangle, isosceles triangle, scalene triangle.
42. Draw the hierarchy relating the following: polygon, triangle, hexagon, isosceles triangle, equilateral triangle.

```
10 INPUT X
20 IF X < .33 THEN PRINT 3*X
30 IF X >= .33 AND X <= .67 THEN PRINT 2*X
40 IF X > .67 THEN PRINT X
50 END
```

Helps Students Improve Their Performance

Strategies for increasing skills are combined in a unique fashion—and there is evidence that the result is a remarkable improvement in student achievement.

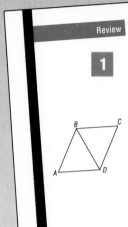

1 **DAILY REVIEW** reinforces skills learned in the chapter and combines and maintains skills from earlier chapters.

2 The **SUMMARY** gives an overview of the entire chapter and helps students consider the material as a whole.

3 The **VOCABULARY** section provides a checklist of terms, symbols, and properties students must know. Students can refer to the lesson, to the Glossary, or to the lists of Theorems, Postulates, and Formulas for additional help.

T12

Review

1

15. A regular pentagon has perimeter 13. What is the length of a side? *(Lesson 8-1)*

16. A parallelogram has perimeter 462 cm. One side is 185 cm. Find the lengths of the other three sides. *(Lessons 8-1, 7-7)*

17. What is the measure of each angle of a regular pentagon? *(Lesson 5-7)*

18. A rectangle has vertices at (-2, 5), (-2, -1), (3, -1), and (3, 5). Find its perimeter. (Hint: A drawing may help.) *(Lessons 8-1, 1-3)*

19. Refer to the figure at the left.
Given: $m\angle ABD = m\angle BDC$
$m\angle ADB = m\angle DBC$.
Prove: $AB = CD$. *(Lessons 7-4, 6-7)*

20. Expand: $(a + 5)^2$. *(Previous course)*

21. Solve: $2x^2 = 54$. *(Previous course)*

22. *Multiple choice.* $\sqrt{27} =$
(a) $9\sqrt{3}$ (b) $3\sqrt{9}$ (c) $9\sqrt{9}$ (d) $3\sqrt{3}$. *(Previous course)*

CHAPTER 10

...llations.
...of his work.
...discovered by Rolf
...a sheet of paper.

2 **Summary**

The lateral or surface area of a three-dimensional figure measures its boundary, which is two-dimensional. So these areas, like the areas you studied in Chapter 8, are measured in square units. Volume measures the space enclosed by a three-dimensional figure. Beginning with the formula $V = \ell wh$ for the volume of a box, this chapter developed formulas for the volumes of other figures. Four basic properties of volume and Cavalieri's Principle were employed. The following chart contains a summary of these formulas.

	Volume	Lateral Area Right or regular	Surface Area
Prism (Cylinder)	Bh	ph	L.A. + 2B
Pyramid (Cone)	$\frac{1}{3}Bh$	$\frac{1}{2}p\ell$	L.A. + B
Sphere	$\frac{4}{3}\pi r^3$		$4\pi r^2$
Cube	s^3		$6s^2$

In these formulas, B is the area of a base, p the perimeter of a base, h the height, ℓ the slant height, L.A. the lateral area, and r the radius. You can obtain special formulas for cones and cylinders by substituting πr^2 for B and $2\pi r$ for p.

3 **Vocabulary**

Below are the most important terms and phrases for this chapter.
For the starred (*) terms you should be able to give a definition of the term.
For the other terms you should be able to give a general description and specific example of each.

Lesson 10-1
surface area, S.A.
lateral area, L.A.
Right Prism-Cylinder Lateral
   Area Formula
Prism-Cylinder Surface
   Area Formula

Lesson 10-2
regular pyramid
Regular Pyramid-Right Cone
   Lateral Area Formula
Pyramid-Cone Surface Area
   Formula

Lesson 10-3
volume
unit cube
*cube root, $\sqrt[3]{}$
Volume Postulate (parts **a–d**)
Cube Volume Formula

Lesson 10-5
Cavalieri's Principle
   (Volume Postulate **e**)
Prism-Cylinder Volume Formula

Lesson 10-6
Heron's Formula

Lesson 10-7
Pyramid-Cone Volume Formula

Lesson 10-8
Sphere Volume Formula

Lesson 10-9
Sphere Surface Area Formula

Unique Tools for Mastery

4 **PROGRESS SELF-TEST** provides the opportunity for feedback and correction—before students are tested formally. The Student Edition contains full solutions to questions on this test to enhance accurate self-evaluation.

5 **CHAPTER REVIEW** arranges questions according to the four dimensions of understanding—Skills, Properties, Uses, and Representations—to help students master those concepts that have not yet been mastered. Questions are keyed to objectives and lessons for easy reference.

The **QUIZZES** and **CHAPTER TESTS** in the Teacher's Resource File offer further help to assess mastery. You choose the test format which best suits your needs.

CHAPTER 10

4 Progress Self-Test

Directions: Take this test as you would take a test in class. Use a ruler and calculator. Then check your work with the solutions in the Selected Answers section in the back of the book.

1. An oblique rectangular prism has dimensions 3 cm by 6 cm by 15 cm and height 14 cm.
   a. Draw an appropriate figure and indicate the formula you would use to find its volume.
   b. Find its volume.

2. A regular square pyramid has base edges of length 20 and slant height of length 26.
   a. Draw an appropriate figure and indicate the formula you would use to find its lateral area.
   b. Find its lateral area.

3. The largest asteroid, Ceres, has a diameter of 620 miles. Assuming Ceres is spherical in shape, what is its volume?

4. How much paper is needed for a cone-shaped megaphone with radius 4" and slant height 18"? (Ignore the small open end.)

5. Find the volume of the inside of a pipe 20" long and with an inside radius of 3", as drawn below.

6. Find the volume of this right cone.

In 7 and 8, the base of a right prism has and perimeter 32. Its height is 30.
   7. What is its lateral area?
   8. What is its volume?

In 9 and 10, a box has a volume of 400 a height of 10 cm, and a width of 5 cm.
   9. What is its length?
   10. What is its surface area?

11. A sphere has a surface area of 100π its radius?

12. Give the cube root of 400 to the nea number.

13. State Cavalieri's Principle.

14. A prism and a pyramid have congru and their heights are equal. How do volumes compare?

15. Jupiter has 11 times the diameter of How do their surface areas compare

In 16 and 17, choose from the following box, cube, regular pyramid, prism, right sphere, cone.

16. For which figure does
    S.A. = L.A. + B?

17. For which figure does L.A. = ph?

18. Find the volume of the box pictured

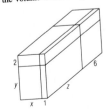

---

5 Chapter Review

Questions on **SPUR** Objectives

SPUR stands for **S**kills, **P**roperties, **U**ses, and **R**epresentations. The Chapter Review questions are grouped according to the SPUR Objectives for this chapter.

SKILLS deal with the procedures used to get answers.

■ Objective A: *Draw 3-dimensional figures, given their dimensions. (Lessons 10-1, 10-2, 10-8)*
In 1–4, show the given information on the figure.
   1. Draw a cylinder whose height is twice its diameter.
   2. Draw a cone with radius 3 and slant height 5.
   3. Draw a sphere with diameter $1\frac{3}{4}''$.
   4. Draw a square pyramid with slant height 15 and height 9.

■ Objective B: *Calculate surface areas and volumes of cylinders and prisms from appropriate lengths, and vice-versa. (Lessons 10-1, 10-3, 10-5)*
   5. Refer to the right cylinder drawn below. Find its **a.** lateral area; **b.** surface area; **c.** volume.

   6. Refer to the right square prism drawn below. Find its **a.** volume; **b.** surface area.

7. The base of the prism drawn below is a right triangle with legs of lengths 5 and 12. The distance between the bases of the prism is 24. Find the volume of the prism.

8. If a cylinder is to have a volume of 30π cubic units and a base with radius 3, what must its height be?

9. Find the surface of a cube whose volume is 125 cubic units.

10. Find the volume of a right cylinder whose lateral area is 60π square centimeters and whose base has diameter 12 centimeters.

■ Objective C: *Calculate surface areas and volumes of pyramids and cones from appropriate lengths, and vice-versa. (Lessons 10-2, 10-7)*
   11. Find the surface area and volume of the right cone drawn below.

516

T13

Provides the Practical Support You Need

"I enjoyed it! I also believe it is a valuable course for the students. It encourages development of critical thinking, reading, realization of geometry's usefulness in the real world, and review of algebra and previously encountered geometry concepts." **Jane Staats,** teacher, North Hunterdon High School, Annandale, New Jersey

Continual involvement of teachers and instructional supervisors — in planning, writing, rewriting, and evaluating — has made this program convenient and adaptable to your needs.

Before each chapter you'll find the following:

1 **DAILY PACING CHART** shows you at a glance two alternate ways to pace the chapter.

2 **TESTING OPTIONS** list the chapter quizzes and tests for ease of planning.

3 **OBJECTIVES** are letter-coded and keyed to Progress Self-Test, Chapter Review, and Lesson Masters, showing a direct correspondence between what is taught and what is tested.

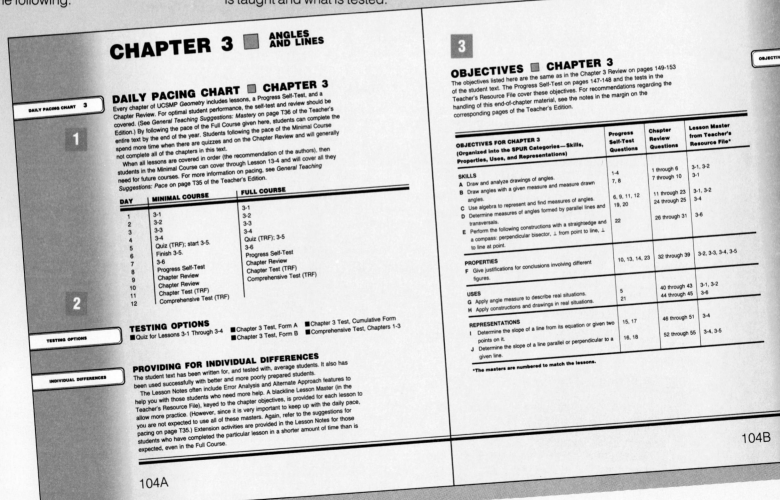

CHAPTER 3 — ANGLES AND LINES

DAILY PACING CHART — CHAPTER 3

Every chapter of UCSMP *Geometry* includes lessons, a Progress Self-Test, and a Chapter Review. For optimal student performance, the self-test and review should be covered. (See *General Teaching Suggestions: Mastery* on page T36 of the Teacher's Edition.) By following the pace of the Full Course given here, students can complete the entire text by the end of the year. Students following the pace of the Minimal Course spend more time when there are quizzes and on the Chapter Review and will generally not complete all of the chapters in this text.

When all lessons are covered in order (the recommendation of the authors), then students in the Minimal Course can cover through Lesson 13-4 and will cover all they need for future courses. For more information on pacing, see *General Teaching Suggestions: Pace* on page T35 of the Teacher's Edition.

DAY	MINIMAL COURSE	FULL COURSE
1	3-1	3-1
2	3-2	3-2
3	3-3	3-3
4	3-4	3-4
5	Quiz (TRF); start 3-5.	Quiz (TRF); 3-5
6	Finish 3-5.	3-6
7	3-6	Progress Self-Test
8	Progress Self-Test	Chapter Review
9	Chapter Review	Chapter Test (TRF)
10	Chapter Review	Comprehensive Test (TRF)
11	Chapter Test (TRF)	
12	Comprehensive Test (TRF)	

TESTING OPTIONS
- Quiz for Lessons 3-1 Through 3-4
- Chapter 3 Test, Form A
- Chapter 3 Test, Form B
- Chapter 3 Test, Cumulative Form
- Comprehensive Test, Chapters 1-3

PROVIDING FOR INDIVIDUAL DIFFERENCES

The student text has been written for, and tested with, average students. It also has been used successfully with better and more poorly prepared students.

The Lesson Notes often include Error Analysis and Alternate Approach features to help you with those students who need more help. A blackline Lesson Master (in the Teacher's Resource File), keyed to the chapter objectives, is provided for each lesson to allow more practice. (However, since it is very important to keep up with the daily pace, you are not expected to use all of these masters. Again, refer to the suggestions for pacing on page T35.) Extension activities are provided in the Lesson Notes for those students who have completed the particular lesson in a shorter amount of time than is expected, even in the Full Course.

104A

OBJECTIVES — CHAPTER 3

The objectives listed here are the same as in the Chapter 3 Review on pages 149-153 of the student text. The Progress Self-Test on pages 147-148 and the tests in the Teacher's Resource File cover these objectives. For recommendations regarding the handling of this end-of-chapter material, see the notes in the margin on the corresponding pages of the Teacher's Edition.

OBJECTIVES FOR CHAPTER 3 (Organized into the SPUR Categories—Skills, Properties, Uses, and Representations)	Progress Self-Test Questions	Chapter Review Questions	Lesson Master from Teacher's Resource File*
SKILLS			
A Draw and analyze drawings of angles.	1-4	1 through 6	3-1, 3-2
B Draw angles with a given measure and measure drawn angles.	7, 8	7 through 10	3-1
C Use algebra to represent and find measures of angles.	6, 9, 11, 12 19, 20	11 through 23 24 through 25	3-1, 3-2 3-4
D Determine measures of angles formed by parallel lines and transversals.	22	26 through 31	3-6
E Perform the following constructions with a straightedge and a compass: perpendicular bisector, ⊥ from point to line, ⊥ to line at point.			
PROPERTIES			
F Give justifications for conclusions involving different figures.	10, 13, 14, 23	32 through 39	3-2, 3-3, 3-4, 3-5
USES			
G Apply angle measure to describe real situations.	5	40 through 43	3-1, 3-2
H Apply constructions and drawings in real situations.	21	44 through 45	3-6
REPRESENTATIONS			
I Determine the slope of a line from its equation or given two points on it.	15, 17	46 through 51	3-4
J Determine the slope of a line parallel or perpendicular to a given line.	16, 18	52 through 55	3-4, 3-5

*The masters are numbered to match the lessons.

104B

DAILY PACING CHART 3

TESTING OPTIONS

INDIVIDUAL DIFFERENCES

OBJECTIVES

T14

OVERVIEW 3

PERSPECTIVES 3

OVERVIEW ■ CHAPTER 3

Chapter 3 presents the terminology and basic properties of angles and lines and their connections with coordinates, constructions, and deduction. It is the shortest chapter in this book, and about half of it will be review for students who have used UCSMP *Transition Mathematics* and *Algebra*.

The first two lessons deal with angles. Lesson 3-1 reviews how to measure angles with a protractor and introduces the Angle Measure Postulate. Students will need protractors for Lesson 3-1. If they are

to use their own protractors, they should have them by the first day of the chapter.

Lesson 3-2 reviews the names given to angles and to pairs of angles.

Lesson 3-3 helps set the stage for deductions and proofs, which appear in later chapters.

Lessons 3-4 and 3-5 provide the necessary work on parallel and perpendicular lines needed to understand reflections in Chapter 4 and polygons in Chapter 5. Properties of parallel lines are given both

synthetically (without coordinates) and analytically (with coordinates), the latter by reviewing slopes.

Lesson 3-6 introduces constructions, which gives students flexibility in locating points and provides the tools for constructing reflection images of points in Chapter 4. Straightedge and compass are required.

Drawing is a major objective in this and succeeding chapters. Students should come to class every day ready to use a protractor, graph paper, ruler, and compass.

PERSPECTIVES ■ CHAPTER 3
The Perspectives provide the rationale for the inclusion of topics or approaches, provide mathematical background, and make connections with other lessons and within UCSMP.

3-1
ANGLES AND THEIR MEASURES
Angles can be defined in various ways. The definition now commonly used in secondary school geometry in the United States is the set theory definition used in the School Mathematics Study Group (SMSG) curriculum of 1960. It is also possible to define an angle as the set of points on or between two rays with the same endpoint, or as the set of rays including or between two rays with the same endpoint. There are nonset-theoretic definitions which are possible as well.

Our Angle Measure Postulate is called the Protractor Postulate in some books, and traces its origin back through SMSG to a postulate set used by George David Birkhoff in the 1920s. His postulate set was designed to use real numbers in geometry and was employed in *Basic Geometry*, a high school text he wrote with Ralph Beatley, published by Scott, Foresman in 1940.

Part **a** of the Angle Measure Postulate (p. 108) ensures that there is an angle for each real number between 0 and 180. But

there is not a 1-1 correspondence between angle measures and numbers unless you restrict yourself to one side of the line. So part **b** also notes that every line has two sides (that's the reason $\overline{BC}$ must intersect $\overrightarrow{VA}$).

We allow zero angles and straight angles (parts **c** and **d** of the Angle Measure Postulate) because later we want to apply angles to rotations. Rotations can certainly be halfway around; in fact, 180° turns are very important rotations. Zero-degree rotations will ensure that when one rotation is followed by another, the composite is a rotation.

Straight angles are found in Euclid's *Elements*. They were not used in some "new math" treatments of geometry because, since an angle was defined as a union of two rays, there would be two interiors of a straight angle, and that might be confusing.

But of all parts of this postulate, the one part that will be applied more than any other is part **e**. This property is analogous to the Be-

tweenness Theorem for distances. It tells when two angle measures can be added to get a third.

3-2
TYPES OF ANGLES
Students who have studied UCSMP *Transition Mathematics* should be familiar with the names given to angles of various measures and also with vertical angles. The terms *supplementary* and *complementary* are used in UCSMP *Algebra*. The other terminology will be new.

The Linear Pair and Vertical Angle theorems begin the reading of formal proofs and lead into the next lesson.

3-3
JUSTIFYING CONCLUSIONS
In this book, a conclusion requires a justification. This is somewhat different from the use of conclusion to mean the same thing as consequent. In Lesson 13-1, we discuss

the Law of Detachment (also called *modus ponens*), the formal logical principle behind the conclusions made in this lesson. By writing a conclusion and its justification, a student has made a one-step proof.

The first proofs for students are found in the next chapter. At this point, we are just trying to give students an idea of why proof is used in mathematics.

3-4
PARALLEL LINES
In algebra, slope is studied as the *rate of change*. In geometry, slope is a measure of tilt. The word "parallel" in Lesson 1-1 meant "go in the same direction," which can also mean "have the same tilt." This lesson applies what students have (or should have) learned in algebra to the geometry of parallel lines.

The formal definition of *parallel lines* given in Lesson 1-7 allowed a line to be parallel to itself. The theorems of this lesson, that lines are parallel if and only if their slopes are equal, and that parallelism is transitive, are very simply stated because of this definition.

The content of this lesson, except for the formal statement of the postulates, should be review for students who have studied UCSMP *Transition Mathematics* and Algebra.

3-5
PERPENDICULAR LINES
The approach taken to define perpendicular lines is analogous to the approach taken with parallel lines. First, there is a definition, next the geometric properties are established, and then the connection is made with slope.

A proof that "the product of the slopes of perpendicular nonvertical lines is -1" is beyond the mathematics students have studied so far. We do not prove the theorem in this book, waiting instead for UCSMP *Advanced Algebra*. The reason for including the statement of the theorem is to indicate that the slope of one direction determines the slope of the direction perpendicular to it. Also, it reviews important algebra and enables students to see perpendicularity in the coordinate plane.

3-6
CONSTRUCTING PERPENDICULARS
Constructions are often studied in grades 7 or 8, sometimes even earlier. Obviously, students with some experience with constructions will be at a great advantage in learning the content of this lesson. If students have never before used a ruler or a compass, you may need two days for this lesson.

We distinguish between *drawings* and *constructions*. The rules given here for constructions are more rigid than those found in some other books. We do not recommend that students be allowed to open their compasses to *any* given radius. There are two reasons for being more rigid: first, these are the rules that are actually followed by mathematicians in the study of constructions; second, we want to describe algorithms, and we need to be certain that circles and lines will intersect at various times. By giving the radius, we can ensure that the described algorithms will always work. The bonus is that constructions become much easier to grade because they are congruent.

The description of constructions by algorithmic steps is something you may not have seen before. We do it here because we are getting students ready for the kinds of statement sequences they will be using in doing proofs. The rules are justifications for the construction steps just as reasons are justifications for steps in proofs. They say that something can be done.

A key idea in this lesson is that of subroutine. The perpendicular bisector construction is a subroutine for the other constructions of perpendiculars.

104C

104D

Super Teaching Support

"Best geometry course I've ever taught!" **Marilyn Wilkerson,** teacher, Walnut Hills High School, Cincinnati, Ohio

1 **RESOURCES** save you time by coordinating all of the ancillaries to the lesson.

2 **OBJECTIVES** are letter-coded for easy reference.

3 **TEACHING NOTES** provide everything you need, including reading tips, suggestions for the examples, dialogue to generate higher-order thinking, suggestions for small groups, and more.

4 **COMPUTER** gives tips for involving students in computer technology. Combine this with the Computer Masters ancillary and the new Scott, Foresman software for worthwhile and interesting computer activities in Geometry.

5 **ALTERNATE APPROACH** offers a different strategy for presenting the lesson, often using concrete materials or cooperative learning.

6 **ADDITIONAL EXAMPLES** provide parallel examples to those in the text for added flexibility.

7 **NOTES ON QUESTIONS** highlight important aspects of questions and provide helpful suggestions to enhance learning.

8 **ERROR ANALYSIS** pinpoints typical student errors and provides remediation strategies for correcting the errors.

9 **MAKING CONNECTIONS** helps you connect present content and ideas to material covered in an earlier or later lesson, chapter, or text.

10 **ADDITIONAL ANSWERS** give easily located answers to the questions in the lesson. Shorter answers are overprinted in red near the questions.

11 **MORE PRACTICE** lists the Lesson Master which can be used for additional practice of the lesson skills and concepts.

12 **EXTENSION** offers high-interest activities for all students, as well as enrichment activities for students needing additional challenge. These well-liked activities provide ideas for technology, connections with other fields of study, and additional applications.

13 **EVALUATION** tells what you need to know about the quizzes and tests. It also provides **Alternative Assessment** suggestions to encourage different evaluation formats, such as oral presentation and cooperative learning.

14 The **LESSON MASTER** is pictured where you can refer to it conveniently.

LESSON 3-4

1 **RESOURCES**
- Lesson Master 3-4
- Quiz for Lessons 3-1 through 3-4.
- Visual for Teaching Aid 17 can be used with **Examples 2** and **3** and **Questions 1-5.**
- Computer Master 3

OBJECTIVES

2 **D** Determine measures of angles formed by parallel lines and transversals.

F Give justifications for conclusions involving different figures.

I Determine the slope of a line from its equation or given two points on it.

J Determine the slope of a line parallel to a given line.

TEACHING NOTES

3 Postulates are chosen for use in a geometry textbook based on tradition, on their ease of understanding, or on the ease of their application. The Corresponding Angles Postulate is natural and easy

Computer An automatic drawer is a powerful motivating and exploring device for the theorem in the middle of page 208. Have students draw triangles that are obviously not isosceles and then draw their angle bisectors, medians, and perpendicular bisectors of the sides. Next, have students try isosceles triangles or ones that are nearly isosceles. Use the Repeat feature to repeat the construction on a variety of triangles. Have them make conjectures leading to the Isosceles Triangle Theorem.

Reading The proof of the Isosceles Triangle Symmetry Theorem is difficult for many students to read. Part of the difficulty is that the theorem seems so obvious that it needs n

Reading You can help students learn how to read for detail by asking them to take notes as they read the lesson. They should pay careful attention to the properties of reflections and make a complete list of all information they discover about reflections.

Alternate Approach An overhead projector can be very useful when discussing reflections. Put the reflecting line on one transparency and the preimage on a second transparency. You can show the fold over the reflecting line and get very accurate images by tracing or by turning over the transparency. Various figures (like triangles or nongeometric shapes) can be cut out of transparency film (colored film makes striking demonstration shapes) and projected along with their images. After flipping the figures over the (projected) reflecting line, have students describe the properties of reflections.

ADDITIONAL EXAMPLES

1. Suppose a triangle has one vertex on the reflecting line. How many images must be located to determine its reflection image?
2

2. Draw the image of *ABCD* over line *m*.

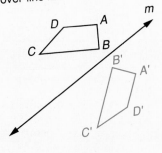

NOTES ON QUESTIONS

Question 4b: There are three different justifications for the three pairs of angles: the median is on the same line as the angle bisector; the median is on the perpendicular bisector; and the Isosceles Triangle Theorem.

Question 6: If students are confused as to which statement is true or false, review the hierarchy of triangles, showing equilateral triangles as a subset of isosceles triangles.

Error Analysis for Question 7b: Students may be confused when matching the triangle with the number of symmetry lines because sometimes there are three symmetry lines, sometimes only one. Begin to stress the requirement that a statement must hold generally. That is, when asked for a characteristic of isosceles triangles, it must hold for *all* isosceles triangles.

Making Connections for Question 10: If two intersecting circles do not contain each other's center, then the quadrilateral formed by connecting the centers to the points of intersection is a kite, which is defined in the next lesson. You may wish to use this question to set up the next lesson.

Question 12: If students cannot find an algebraic solution immediately, try a special case with two vertex angle measures whose sum is 83. Have students try different pairs of numbers.

ADDITIONAL ANSWERS

5.

Conclusions	Justifications
1. m∠1 = m∠XYZ	Vertical Angle Thm.
2. m∠XYZ = m∠2	Isosceles △ Thm.
3. m∠1 = m∠2	Transitive Prop. of Eq. (steps 1 and 2)

FOLLOW-UP

MORE PRACTICE
For more questions on SPUR Objectives, use *Lesson Master 5-4*, shown below.

EXTENSION
Have students interested in kites do research on how to build them and how they are used ceremoniously in certain cultures. They should note how close real-world examples are to textbook examples. Other students can look up "kite" in the dictionary to determine its several interesting usages (a kite is also a bird, a rogue, or the highest sail in a ship).

EVALUATION
A quiz covering Lesson 5-1 through 5-4 is provided in the Teacher's Resource File.

Alternative Assessment
Have students bring closure to the lesson by listing the properties of kites, rhombuses, rectangles, and squares. Ask students to relate the properties to the quadrilateral hierarchy orally.

NAME _____

LESSON MASTER 5-4
QUESTIONS ON **SPUR** OBJECTIVES

■ **SKILLS** *Objective A (See pages 249–251 for objectives.)*

1. Draw a parallelogram that is not a rhombus.
sample:

2. Draw a nonconvex kite *ABCD* with ends *A* and *C*.
sample:

3. Is it possible to draw a nonconvex rhombus? If so, draw one.   No

■ **PROPERTIES** *Objective E*

4. *True or false*? The diagonals of a square bisect each other.   True

In 5 and 6, use the rhombus *UVWX* at the right, in which m∠*VUX* = 46, m∠*WXZ* = 67, and *VX* = 10.

5. Find as many other angle measures as you can.
m∠*XWV* = 46; m∠*XUZ* = m∠*VUZ* = 23; m∠*UXZ* = 67;
m∠*VWZ* = m∠*XWZ* = 23; m∠*UXZ* = 67;
m∠*UVZ* = m∠*WVZ* = 67; m∠*UXW* = 134;
m∠*UVW* = 134; m∠*UZX* = m∠*UZV* = m∠*WZV* = m∠*WZX* = 90

6. Find as many other lengths as you can.
XZ = *VZ* = 5

■ **PROPERTIES** *Objective G*

7. Given: *ABCD* is a kite, with ends *A* and *C*.
Prove: *BE* = *ED*.

Conclusions	Justifications
1. *AC* is a symm. diag.	def. of symm. diag. (suff. cond.)
2. *AC* is the ⊥ bis. of *BD*.	Kite Diag. Thm.
3. *BE* = *ED*	Def. of ⊥ bis. (meaning)

41

Geometry © Scott, Foresman and Company

Components Designed for Ease of Teaching

"This book does a good job of presenting real world applications instead of making something up to fit a topic. I've seen this all throughout." **Robert Mervine,** teacher, Lyons Township High School, LaGrange, Illinois

Student Edition
full color

Teacher's Resource File
About 600 blackline masters
to cover your every classroom need!

Quiz and Test Masters
Quizzes (at least one per chapter)
Chapter Tests, Forms A and B (parallel forms)
Chapter Tests, Cumulative Form
Comprehensive Tests (four per text,
including Final Exam, primarily multiple choice)

Lesson Masters
(one per lesson)

Computer Masters

Answer Masters
(provide answers for questions in student text;
oversized type to enable display in class,
allowing students to grade their own work)

Teaching Aid Masters
(patterns for manipulatives;
masters for overhead transparencies;
forms, charts, and graphs from the P.E.;
coordinate grids; and more)

Teacher's Edition
annotated and with margin notes

Additional Ancillaries

Solutions Manual
Computer Software
Visual Aids

UCSMP
SCOTT, FORESMAN

The University of Chicago School Mathematics Project
Geometry

Authors

Arthur Coxford
Zalman Usiskin
Daniel Hirschhorn

About the Cover
A bicycle wheel exhibits segments, angles, parallel lines, concentric circles,
chords, tangents, congruence, circumference, translations, rotations, and curves of the cycloid family.
Each UCSMP secondary text discusses some of these ideas, and all but the cycloid are
brought together in this text.

Scott, Foresman and Company
Editorial Offices: Glenview, Illinois Regional Offices: Sunnyvale, California •
Atlanta, Georgia • Glenview, Illinois • Oakland, New Jersey • Dallas, Texas

Acknowledgments

Authors

Arthur Coxford
Professor of Education, The University of Michigan

Zalman Usiskin
Professor of Education, The University of Chicago

Daniel Hirschhorn
UCSMP

UCSMP Production and Evaluation

Series Editors: Zalman Usiskin, Sharon Senk

Technical Coordinator: Susan Chang

Director of the Field Trial Evaluation: Sandra Mathison

Director of the Nationwide Evaluation: Penelope Flores

Teacher's Edition Additional Author: Jerry Smith
Niles Township High School West, Skokie, Illinois

Editorial Development and Design

Scott, Foresman staff, Rusty Kane

We wish to acknowledge the generous support of the **Amoco Foundation** in helping to make it possible for these materials to be developed and tested, and the additional support of the **Carnegie Corporation of New York** in the nationwide field-testing of these materials.

It takes many people to put together a project of this kind and we cannot thank them all by name. We wish particularly to acknowledge Carol Siegel, who coordinated the use of these materials in schools; Peter Bryant, Dan Caplinger, Kurt Hackemer, Maryann Kannapan, Mary Lappan and Therese Manst of our technical staff; Sharon Mallo, who wrote some of the ancillary materials; and editorial assistants Matt Ashley, Laura Gerbec, Eric Kolaczyk, Thomas McDougal, and Teri Proske (at Chicago) and Peter Appelbaum (at Michigan).

We wish to acknowledge and give thanks to the following teachers who taught preliminary versions of UCSMP *Geometry*, participated in the pilot and formative research, and contributed many ideas to help improve this book.

Betty Foxx
Collins High School
Chicago Public Schools

Paula Murphy
Corliss High School
Chicago Public Schools

Adrienne Roth
Taft High School
Chicago Public Schools

Kenneth Kerr
Glenbrook South High School
Glenview, Illinois

Rita Belluomini
Jan Moore
Wayne Wirta
Rich South High School
Richton Park, Illinois

Sharon Mallo
Lake Park East High School
Roselle, Illinois

We also wish to acknowledge the following schools which used earlier versions of UCSMP *Geometry* in nationwide studies. Their comments, suggestions, and performance guided the changes made for this version.

Chaparral High School
Scottsdale, Arizona

Irvine High School
Irvine, California

Mendocino High School
Mendocino, California

Marietta High School
Marietta, Georgia

Hyde Park Career Academy
Taft High School
Chicago, Illinois

Lyons Township High School
La Grange, Illinois

Rich South High School
Richton Park, Illinois

Niles Township High School West
Skokie, Illinois

Fruitport High School
Fruitport, Michigan

North Hunterdon High School
Annandale, New Jersey

Aiken High School
Cincinnati Academy of Mathematics and Science
Walnut Hills High School
Cincinnati, Ohio

Carrick High School
Allderdice High School
Pittsburgh, Pennsylvania

We wish to express our thanks and appreciation to the many other schools and students who have used earlier versions of these materials.

UCSMP Geometry

The University of Chicago School Mathematics Project (UCSMP) is a long-term project designed to improve school mathematics in grades K-12. UCSMP began in 1983 with a 6-year grant from the Amoco Foundation. Additional funding has come from the Ford Motor Company, the Carnegie Corporation of New York, the National Science Foundation, the General Electric Foundation, GTE, and Citibank/Citicorp.

The project is centered in the Departments of Education and Mathematics of the University of Chicago, and has the following components and directors:

Resources	Izaak Wirszup, Professor Emeritus of Mathematics
Primary Materials	Max Bell, Professor of Education
Elementary Teacher Development	Sheila Sconiers, Research Associate in Education
Secondary	Sharon L. Senk, Assistant Professor of Mathematics, Michigan State University (on leave)
	Zalman Usiskin, Professor of Education
Evaluation	Larry Hedges, Professor of Education

From 1983 to 1987, the director of UCSMP was Paul Sally, Professor of Mathematics. Since 1987, the director has been Zalman Usiskin.

The text *Geometry* was developed by the Secondary Component (grades 7-12) of the project, and constitutes the third year in a six-year mathematics curriculum devised by that component. As texts in this curriculum complete their multi-stage testing cycle, they are being published by Scott, Foresman and Company. The first four books— *Transition Mathematics, Algebra, Geometry, Advanced Algebra*—are available. *Functions, Statistics, and Trigonometry, with Computers* and *Precalculus and Discrete Mathematics* have their first publication in spring of 1991.

Transition Mathematics	Available, spring, 1989
Algebra	Available, spring, 1989
Geometry	Available, spring, 1990
Advanced Algebra	Available, spring, 1989
Functions, Statistics, and Trigonometry, with Computers	spring, 1991
Precalculus and Discrete Mathematics	spring, 1991

A first draft of *Geometry* was written, and then piloted in six schools during the 1986–87 school year. After incorporating changes based on these pilots and comments from many students and teachers, the 1987–88 field trial of *Geometry* was tested in 16 schools with students who had not had previous UCSMP courses. Further changes were made and a summative evaluation was conducted in 1988–89 both with students who had and students who had not had previous UCSMP courses. Results are available by writing UCSMP. This Scott, Foresman and Company edition is based on improvements suggested by that testing, by the authors and editors, and by some of the many teacher and student users of earlier editions.

Comments about these materials are welcomed. Address queries to Secondary Mathematics Product Manager, Scott, Foresman and Company, 1900 East Lake Avenue, Glenview, Illinois 60025 or to UCSMP, The University of Chicago, 5835 S. Kimbark, Chicago, IL 60637.

UCSMP *Geometry* differs from other geometry books in six major ways. First, it has **wider scope** in content. It integrates algebra with the geometry. It uses coordinates and transformations throughout and in both two and three dimensions. It discusses networks and history and famous problems. These topics are not isolated as separate units of study or as enrichment. Instead they are employed to motivate, justify, extend, and help students with important geometry concepts.

Second, this book has a **different sequence.** Coordinates and transformations, which are critical to building and maintenance of algebra skills and concepts, are studied early. Measurement, area, and volume, topics of importance to all students, are studied earlier than most textbooks. Proof, which requires geometry knowledge and experience, is built up slowly.

Third, this book emphasizes **reading and problem solving** throughout. Students can and should be expected to read this book. The explanations were written for students and tested with them. The first set of questions in each lesson is called "Covering the Reading." These exercises guide the student through the reading and check his or her coverage of critical words, rules, explanations, and examples. The second set of questions is called "Applying the Mathematics." These questions extend the student's understanding of the principles and applications of the lesson. Reading is necessary for the problem solving which pervades this book.

Fourth, there is a **reality orientation** towards both the selection of content and the approaches allowed the student in working out problems. Knowing geometry is of little ultimate use to an individual unless he or she can apply that content. Geometry is rich in applications and problem solving. Real life situations motivate geometric ideas and provide the settings for practice of geometry skills. Calculators are assumed throughout this book (and should be allowed on tests) because virtually all individuals who use mathematics today find it helpful to have them. Scientific calculators are recommended because they use an order of operations closer to that found in algebra and have numerous keys that are needed in certain lessons. Computer exercises show how the computer can be used to develop, verify, and apply geometric concepts. To further widen the student's horizons, "Exploration" questions are found in every lesson.

Fifth, **four dimensions of understanding** are emphasized: skill in drawing, visualizing, and following algorithms; understanding of properties, mathematical relationships, and proofs; using geometric ideas in real situations; and representing geometric concepts with coordinates, networks or other diagrams. We call this the SPUR approach: **S**kills, **P**roperties, **U**ses, **R**epresentations. With the SPUR approach, concepts are discussed in a rich environment which enables more students to be reached.

Sixth, the **instructional format** is designed to maximize the acquisition of geometry skills and concepts. Lessons are intended to be covered in one day. The lessons have been sequenced into carefully constructed chapters which combine gradual practice with a mastery learning approach. Concepts introduced in a lesson are reinforced through "Review" questions in the immediately succeeding lessons. This gives students several nights to learn and practice important concepts. At the end of the chapter, a modified mastery learning scheme is used to solidify acquisition of concepts from the chapter so that they may be applied later with confidence. It is critical that the end-of-chapter content be covered. To maintain skills, important ideas are reviewed in later chapters. Algebra skills are also reviewed throughout the text.

CONTENTS

Acknowledgments	*ii-iii*
UCSMP Geometry	*iv*
To the Teacher	*v*
Table of Contents	*vi-x*
To the Student	1

Chapter 1 **Points and Lines** 2

1-1:	Dots and Points	4		**Summary and Vocabulary**	52
1-2:	Locations as Points	8		**Progress Self-Test**	53
1-3:	Ordered Pairs as Points	14		**Chapter Review**	54
1-4:	Points in Networks	19			
1-5:	Drawing in Perspective	25			
1-6:	The Need for Undefined Terms	30			
1-7:	Postulates	35			
1-8:	One-Dimensional Figures	40			
1-9:	The Triangle Inequality	46			

Chapter 2 **Definitions and If-then Statements** 58

2-1:	The Need for Definitions	60		**Summary and Vocabulary**	98
2-2:	"If-then" Statements	65		**Progress Self-Test**	99
2-3:	If-then Statements in Computer Programs	70		**Chapter Review**	101
2-4:	Converses	76			
2-5:	Good Definitions	81			
2-6:	Unions and Intersections of Figures	87			
2-7:	Terms Associated with Polygons	92			

Chapter 3 **Angles and Lines** 104

3-1:	Angles and Their Measures	106		**Summary and Vocabulary**	146
3-2:	Types of Angles	113		**Progress Self-Test**	147
3-3:	Justifying Conclusions	120		**Chapter Review**	149
3-4:	Parallel Lines	126			
3-5:	Perpendicular Lines	132			
3-6:	Constructing Perpendiculars	140			

Chapter 4 **Reflections** 154

4-1:	Reflecting Points	156
4-2:	Reflecting Figures	163
4-3:	Using an Automatic Drawer	170
4-4:	The First Theorem in Euclid's *Elements*	176
4-5:	The Perpendicular Bisector Theorem	183
4-6:	Reflecting Polygons	187
4-7:	Reflection-Symmetric Figures	192

Summary and Vocabulary	198
Progress Self-Test	199
Chapter Review	200

Chapter 5 **Polygons** 204

5-1:	Isosceles Triangles	206
5-2:	Types of Quadrilaterals	213
5-3:	Conjectures	218
5-4:	Properties of Kites	223
5-5:	Properties of Trapezoids	228
5-6:	Alternate Interior Angles	234
5-7:	Sums of Angle Measures in Polygons	240

Summary and Vocabulary	246
Progress Self-Test	248
Chapter Review	249

Chapter 6 **Transformations and Congruence** 252

6-1:	Transformations	254
6-2:	Translations	259
6-3:	Rotations	266
6-4:	Miniature Golf and Billiards	273
6-5:	Congruent Figures	279
6-6:	Isometries	285
6-7:	Corresponding Parts in Congruent Figures	292

Summary and Vocabulary	296
Progress Self-Test	297
Chapter Review	299

Chapter 7 **Triangle Congruence** 302

7-1:	Drawing Triangles	304
7-2:	Triangle Congruence Theorems	310
7-3:	Triangle Congruence Proofs	317
7-4:	Overlapping Triangles	323
7-5:	The SSA Condition and HL Congruence	327
7-6:	Properties of Special Figures	333
7-7:	Sufficient Conditions for Parallelograms	339
7-8:	The SAS Inequality	344

Summary and Vocabulary	348
Progress Self-Test	349
Chapter Review	350

Chapter 8 **Measurement Formulas** 354

8-1:	Perimeter Formulas	356
8-2:	Tiling the Plane	362
8-3:	Fundamental Properties of Area	367
8-4:	Areas of Irregular Regions	373
8-5:	Areas of Triangles	378
8-6:	Areas of Trapezoids	384
8-7:	The Pythagorean Theorem	390
8-8:	Arc Measure and Arc Length	396
8-9:	The Area of a Circle	402

Summary and Vocabulary	407
Progress Self-Test	408
Chapter Review	410

Chapter 9 **Three-Dimensional Figures** 414

9-1:	Points, Lines, and Planes in Space	416
9-2:	Prisms and Cylinders	421
9-3:	Pyramids and Cones	427
9-4:	Plane Sections	433
9-5:	Reflections in Space	439
9-6:	Views of Solids and Surfaces	444
9-7:	Making Surfaces	449
9-8:	The Four-Color Problem	455

Summary and Vocabulary	460
Progress Self-Test	461
Chapter Review	462

Chapter 10   Surface Areas and Volumes   466

10-1:	Surface Areas of Prisms and Cylinders	468
10-2:	Surface Areas of Pyramids and Cones	473
10-3:	Fundamental Properties of Volume	478
10-4:	Multiplication, Area, and Volume	483
10-5:	Volumes of Prisms and Cylinders	488
10-6:	Remembering Formulas	494
10-7:	Volumes of Pyramids and Cones	499
10-8:	The Volume of a Sphere	505
10-9:	The Surface Area of a Sphere	510

Summary and Vocabulary	514
Progress Self-Test	515
Chapter Review	516

Chapter 11   Coordinate Geometry   520

11-1:	Proofs with Coordinates	522
11-2:	The Distance Formula	527
11-3:	Equations for Circles	532
11-4:	The Midpoint Formula	537
11-5:	The Midpoint Connector Theorem	544
11-6:	Three-Dimensional Coordinates	550

Summary and Vocabulary	557
Progress Self-Test	558
Chapter Review	559

Chapter 12   Similarity   562

12-1:	Size Changes on a Coordinate Plane	564
12-2:	Size Changes Without Coordinates	569
12-3:	Properties of Size Changes	575
12-4:	Proportions	581
12-5:	Similar Figures	586
12-6:	The Fundamental Theorem of Similarity	593
12-7:	Can There Be Giants?	599
12-8:	The SSS Similarity Theorem	604
12-9:	The AA and SAS Similarity Theorems	609
12-10:	The Side-Splitting Theorem	615

Summary and Vocabulary	621
Progress Self-Test	622
Chapter Review	624

Chapter 13	**Logic and Indirect Reasoning** 628				
13-1:	The Logic of Making Conclusions	630		**Summary and Vocabulary**	675
13-2:	Negations	635		**Progress Self-Test**	676
13-3:	Ruling Out Possibilities	640		**Chapter Review**	678
13-4:	Indirect Proof	645			
13-5:	Tangents to Circles and Spheres	651			
13-6:	Uniqueness	658			
13-7:	Exterior Angles	665			
13-8:	Exterior Angles of Polygons	671			

Chapter 14	**Trigonometry and Vectors** 682				
14-1:	Special Right Triangles	684		**Summary and Vocabulary**	725
14-2:	Lengths in Right Triangles	690		**Progress Self-Test**	726
14-3:	The Tangent Ratio	696		**Chapter Review**	728
14-4:	The Sine and Cosine Ratios	702			
14-5:	Vectors	708			
14-6:	Properties of Vectors	714			
14-7:	Adding Vectors Using Trigonometry	720			

Chapter 15	**Further Work with Circles** 732				
15-1:	Chord Length and Arc Measure	734		**Summary and Vocabulary**	785
15-2:	Regular Polygons and Schedules	740		**Progress Self-Test**	786
15-3:	The Inscribed Angle Theorem	745		**Chapter Review**	788
15-4:	Locating the Center of a Circle	752			
15-5:	Angles Formed by Chords or Secants	758			
15-6:	Angles Formed by Tangents	763			
15-7:	Lengths of Chords, Secants, and Tangents	769			
15-8:	The Isoperimetric Inequality	775			
15-9:	The Isoperimetric Theorems in Space	780			

Glossary	792		**Conversion Formulas**	810
Symbols	800		**Selected Answers**	811
Postulates	801		**Index**	875
Theorems	803		**Photo Acknowledgments**	884
Formulas	809			

Geometry is the study of visual patterns. Learning geometry is greatly helped by being able to see these patterns. Poor drawings hide patterns in geometry just as poor computation can hide patterns in arithmetic. Thus for this course you should have good drawing equipment, both for your homework and in class.

In addition to the notebook paper, sharpened pencil, and erasers you should always have, you need to have some drawing equipment.

> Ruler (marked in both centimeters and inches)
> Protractor (to measure angles)
> Compass
> Graph paper

It is best if the ruler and protractor are made of transparent plastic. A good compass is harder to find. We recommend compasses that tighten by using a screw in the middle and can still take regular pencils.

You will need a scientific calculator in many places in this book. We recommend a *solar-powered* calculator so that you do not have to worry about batteries. A good calculator will last for many years. It also helps to have access to a dictionary.

There is another important goal of this book: to assist you to become able to learn mathematics on your own, so that you will be able to deal with the mathematics you see in newspapers, magazines, on television, on any job, and in school. The authors, who are all experienced teachers, offer the following advice.

1. You cannot learn much mathematics just by watching other people do it. You must participate. Some teachers have a slogan:

   Mathematics is not a spectator sport.

2. You are expected to read each lesson. Read slowly, and keep a pencil with you as you check the mathematics that is done in the book. Use the Glossary or a dictionary to find the meaning of a word you do not understand.

3. You are expected to do homework every day while studying from this book, so put aside time for it. Do not wait until the day before a test if you do not understand something. Try to resolve the difficulty right away and ask questions of your classmates or teacher. You are expected to learn many things by reading, but school is designed so that you do not have to learn everything by yourself.

4. If you cannot answer a question immediately, don't give up! Read the lesson again; read the question again. Look for examples. If you can, go away from the problem and come back to it a little later.

We hope you join the many thousands of students who have enjoyed this book. We wish you much success.

DAILY PACING CHART ■ CHAPTER 1

Every chapter of UCSMP *Geometry* includes lessons, a Progress Self-Test, and a Chapter Review. For optimal student performance, the self-test and review should be covered. (See *General Teaching Suggestions: Mastery* on page T36 of the Teacher's Edition.) By following the pace of the Full Course given here, students can complete the entire text by the end of the year. Students following the pace of the Minimal Course spend more time when there are quizzes and on the Chapter Review and will generally not complete all of the chapters in this text.

When all lessons are covered from the beginning (the recommendation of the authors), then students in the Minimal Course can cover through Lesson 13-4 and will cover all they need for future courses. For more information on pacing, see *General Teaching Suggestions: Pace* on page T35 of the Teacher's Edition.

DAY	MINIMAL COURSE	FULL COURSE
1	1-1	1-1
2	1-2	1-2
3	1-3	1-3
4	Quiz (TRF); Start 1-4.	Quiz (TRF); 1-4
5	Finish 1-4.	1-5
6	1-5	1-6
7	1-6	Quiz (TRF); 1-7
8	Quiz (TRF); Start 1-7.	1-8
9	Finish 1-7.	1-9
10	1-8	Progress Self-Test
11	1-9	Chapter Review
12	Progress Self-Test	Chapter Test (TRF)
13	Chapter Review	
14	Chapter Review	
15	Chapter Test (TRF)	

TESTING OPTIONS
■ Quiz for Lessons 1-1 Through 1-3　■ Chapter 1 Test, Form A
■ Quiz for Lessons 1-4 Through 1-6　■ Chapter 1 Test, Form B

PROVIDING FOR INDIVIDUAL DIFFERENCES

The student text has been written for, and tested with, average students. It also has been used successfully with better and more poorly prepared students.

The Lesson Notes often include Error Analysis and Alternate Approach features to help you with those students who need more help. A blackline Lesson Master (in the Teacher's Resource File), keyed to the chapter objectives, is provided for each lesson to allow more practice. (However, since it is very important to keep up with the daily pace, you are not expected to use all of these masters. Again, refer to the suggestions for pacing on page T35.) Extension activities are provided in the Lesson Notes for those students who have completed the particular lesson in a shorter amount of time than is expected, even in the Full Course.

OBJECTIVES ■ CHAPTER 1

The objectives listed here are the same as in the Chapter 1 Review on pages 54-57 of the student text. The Progress Self-Test on page 53 and the tests in the Teacher's Resource File cover these objectives. For recommendations regarding the handling of this end-of-chapter material, see the notes in the margin on the corresponding pages of the Teacher's Edition.

OBJECTIVES FOR CHAPTER 1 (Organized into the SPUR Categories—Skills, Properties, Uses, and Representations)	Progress Self-Test Questions	Chapter Review Questions	Lesson Master from Teacher's Resource File*
SKILLS			
A Analyze networks.	17, 18	1 through 4	1-4
B Make and determine the perspective of drawings.	2	5 through 8	1-5
PROPERTIES			
C Give the dimensions of figures and objects.	8, 9	9 through 14	1-2
D Given a property of points and lines, tell whether it is true for each of the four descriptions of points: dots, locations, ordered pairs, and nodes.	6, 7, 11	15 through 19	1-1, 1-2, 1-3, 1-4
E Recognize the use of undefined terms and postulates.	10, 20, 21	20 through 33	1-6, 1-7
F Apply properties of betweenness.	22, 23	34 through 41	1-8, 1-9
G Determine whether a triangle can be formed with sides of three given lengths.	4	42 through 49	1-9
USES			
H Apply distance to real situations.	12, 13	50 through 53	1-2
I Apply the Triangle Inequality in real situations.	5, 19	54 through 57	1-9
REPRESENTATIONS			
J Determine distance on a number line.	1, 24	58 through 65	1-2
K Graph points and lines in the coordinate plane.	3, 14-16	66 through 74	1-3

*The masters are numbered to match the lessons.

OVERVIEW ■ CHAPTER 1

In Chapter 1, the building blocks of geometry (points, lines, and planes) are introduced in a way that conveys their importance and enables the introduction of coordinate geometry and the geometry of networks. The many applications are intended to motivate students.

Begin this chapter by examining the page entitled "To the Student." From the beginning, students are expected to draw and to examine drawings for properties. All students need to have a straightedge and graph paper by Lesson 1-2.

The content is presented from a unique viewpoint. In many books (and to many teachers), the need for undefined terms is viewed as a weakness of mathematics. In this book, the *power* of undefined terms is emphasized. Because points, lines, and planes are undefined, they may serve a variety of purposes. Points as dots (Lesson 1-1) are the ways that many computers picture geometry. Points as locations (Lesson 1-2) are the standard points usually studied in geometry itself. Points as ordered pairs (Lesson 1-3) are the description used in analytic geometry and in calculus. Points as nodes of networks (Lesson 1-4) form the basis for graph theory. Vanishing points, used in projective geometry, are discussed in Lesson 1-5.

Lesson 1-6 discusses the need for undefined terms, explaining why postulates are necessary; otherwise, nothing could be deduced about those terms. The postulates we choose (Lesson 1-7) delineate the kind of geometry wanted, namely the Euclidean geometry of locations and ordered pairs. By introducing these different conceptions early, we are able to make immediate use of them.

Lesson 1-8 gives definitions for the major one-dimensional figures. This helps set up Chapter 2, where mathematical reasoning and some definitions of two-dimensional figures are discussed.

To explain what happens to distances between noncollinear points, Lesson 1-9 introduces the Triangle Inequality, which we take as a postulate.

PERSPECTIVES ■ CHAPTER 1

The Perspectives provide the rationale for the inclusion of topics or approaches, provide mathematical background, and make connections with other lessons and within UCSMP.

1-1

DOTS AS POINTS

In many geometry books, students are admonished to give up the most common conception of point, the dot. Dots are *not* points, it is said. Points are called idealizations of dots. The dot is a picture of a point, and so on.

Those books are not wrong, but they are taking a more narrow frame of reference. In personal computers, on television sets, and in many photographs, points are dots. There is a geometry to those points, but it is not Euclidean geometry. For example, between two dots there may not be a third dot. In this geometry, it is possible for two oblique lines not to be parallel and not to intersect (because the dots miss each other). But it does share some properties with Euclidean geometry, and if the points are very close to each other (as they are in television screens and in the latest computer monitors), one almost cannot tell the difference.

1-2

LOCATIONS AS POINTS

The location conception of point is the one used in Euclidean geometry. A natural question to ask about location is thus a natural question in Euclidean geometry: What is the distance between two points? The coordinatized line (that is, the number line) connects the location conception of point with the ordered pair conception, which is introduced in Lesson 1-3. It is as natural to get the distance between two points in the coordinatized plane as it is to get the distance between two locations. It is not as natural to ask about the distance between two dots.

1-3

ORDERED PAIRS AS POINTS

The coordinate plane is a model for Euclidean geometry. In this model, a point is an ordered pair of real numbers. A line is a set of points $\{(x, y): Ax + By = C\}$. These points and lines satisfy all the postulates for Euclidean geometry and (in theory) one can prove all the theorems of Euclidean geometry using coordinates. This was actually done by the great mathematician David Hilbert around the turn of this century by using a typically mathematical ploy: he deduced the postulates of Euclidean geometry from coordinates. Then, since the postulates lead to the theorems, he did not have to do any more.

For instance, two lines with equations of the form $Ax + By = C$ give a system, and a system either has no solution (the lines are parallel), exactly one solution (the lines intersect), or infinitely many solutions (the lines coincide). This is a verification of the postulate that two distinct lines intersect in at most one point.

The ordered pair representation of point is exceedingly important in mathematics. Functions and relations are sets of ordered pairs. Ordered pairs can be generalized to ordered triples (x, y, z) which can be graphed, and ordered 4-tuples (x, y, z, w) which cannot be. The idea of n-dimensional space is a natural further extension from the ordered pair conception of point: simply increase the number of components of the point from 2 to n.

The ordered pair representation of point is also very important in applications. One speaks of data points in statistics, economics, and business.

1-4

POINTS IN NETWORKS

The geometry of networks is quite different from Euclidean geometry. A line is an arc. There can be many different arcs between two points, so two points do not determine a line. A line contains only two points, its endpoints. (These ideas are found in Question 19, which is an important question to discuss.) Still, there are occasions to relate the geometry of networks to Euclidean geometry at many places in this book. For instance, a polygon with its diagonals can be considered a network in which each node is connected to every other node.

In this lesson, the points in networks are always idealizations of geography. But in applications, a node in a network can stand for almost anything. In Lesson 15-2, each node stands for a team and the arcs connecting them represent games played between the teams.

1-5

DRAWING IN PERSPECTIVE

The important notion presented in this lesson is the properties of a figure drawn in perspective. The goal is to make students aware of the differences between geometric drawings and perspective drawings. In geometry, perspective is often ignored when drawing congruent three-dimensional figures. Dashes or dots are used to show lines that cannot be seen.

Another goal of this lesson is to begin the study of space geometry. Many students have great trouble visualizing, and some may never have drawn a cube as asked for in the questions.

1-6

THE NEED FOR UNDEFINED TERMS

Students are often told that geometry is based on points, lines, and planes, but that these are undefined. From a student's perspective, this can be very confusing. How can one base a course on ideas that are not even defined? This lesson provides the answer and proceeds naturally into the next lesson.

1-7

POSTULATES

Postulates are necessary because we wish to make the properties of the basic figures precise. There are two reasons we must be precise. The first is that, without postulates, even if one has some idea about concepts such as point and plane, it has been seen in previous lessons that the nonprecise ideas may be in conflict. So postulates are used to remove the conflict.

In this way, postulates determine the kinds of points and lines that are possible. Once one lists all the postulates normally given for Euclidean geometry, the whole geometry has, in theory, been determined.

The second reason for being precise is that we plan to deduce other properties from these assumed properties.

1-8

ONE-DIMENSIONAL FIGURES

This lesson gives building blocks for Chapters 2 through 5 and is a natural extension of the postulates of the previous lesson. Segments are used in the definitions of all the types of polygons; rays are used in defining angles.

1-9

THE TRIANGLE INEQUALITY

Almost all geometry books differ in the postulates they choose. What is a theorem in one book might be a postulate in another.

In this book, the Triangle Inequality is a postulate, even though it could be deduced from all the other postulates we have chosen. The reasons for this are (1) a proof of the Triangle Inequality proposition would involve ideas far more complicated than the proposition itself; (2) the content of the Triangle Inequality is closely related to the idea of betweenness discussed in Lesson 1-8; and (3) students already know the idea of shortest distance.

Students who have studied UCSMP *Algebra* should be familiar with the Triangle Inequality and its applications.

We recommend 12-15 days be spent on this chapter: 9 to 11 days on the lessons and quizzes; 1 day for the Progress Self-Test; 1 or 2 days for the Chapter Review; and 1 day for a Chapter Test. (See the Daily Pacing Chart on page 2A.)

At the beginning of the school year, it is not uncommon to have some teaching periods cut short. Remember that students are expected to read, and do not delay moving on to a new lesson or keep from doing certain questions simply because the material was not covered in class. The shortened period is a wonderful reason to expect students to read on their own.

If you spend more than 15 days on this chapter, you are moving too slowly. Keep in mind that each lesson includes Review questions to help students firm up content studied previously.

MAKING CONNECTIONS
Students who have studied from UCSMP *Algebra* tend to cover this chapter more quickly than other students because they have a better knowledge of graphing.

Points and Lines

1-1: Dots as Points

1-2: Locations as Points

1-3: Ordered Pairs as Points

1-4: Points in Networks

1-5: Drawing in Perspective

1-6: The Need for Undefined Terms

1-7: Postulates

1-8: One-Dimensional Figures

1-9: The Triangle Inequality

2

From 1884 to 1886, Georges Seurat, a French artist, worked on the painting reproduced at the left, entitled *Sunday Afternoon on Grande Jatte Island*. This painting is entirely made up of small dots of about equal size. In it Seurat showed that a painting could be made without long brushstrokes. Even delicate figures and shadows could be formed from dots. The original painting, worth millions of dollars today, hangs in the Art Institute of Chicago.

The geometry that you will study in this book involves many different ideas, but almost all these ideas concern visual patterns of forms or shapes. As in Seurat's painting, any form in geometry may be thought of as being made up of many different points. Geometry is the study of such sets of points.

A surprising thing is that points themselves are not always the same. Nor are lines. In this chapter, you will learn about different ways of describing points and lines.

USING PAGES 2-3
George Seurat (1859-1891) applied the color theories of the painter Delacroix and the scientists Helmholtz and Chevreul in painting *Sunday Afternoon on Grand Jatte Island*. The dots in the large painting (approximately 206 cm by 305 cm) are all about equal size, and there is a precise relationship between primary and complementary colors. Seurat called his method *divisionism,* but the method is usually called *pointillism.* This monumental work is one of the most famous Post-Impressionist paintings in the world and is worth millions of dollars.

You might give the dimensions of the painting and ask students how the painting would fit if it hung in the front of your classroom.

Seurat had no way of knowing it, but the ideas in his art are not too dissimilar to the ways in which computers display art.

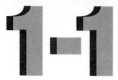

Dots as Points

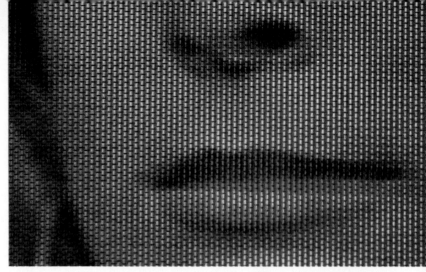

Seurat's actual painting, pictured on the previous page, is over 6 feet high and about 10 feet wide. If you could look at the actual painting from a few feet away, you would see the individual dots that make it up. But if you are far away, or if the picture is reduced in size, you do not see the individual dots.

This also happens with television pictures and computer images. A television screen or computer monitor is made up of tiny dots. Combinations of the dots make up the picture you see. The dots are so numerous and so close together that what you see appears connected. Television and computer people call these dots **pixels.** The pixels are arranged in a rectangular array of rows and columns, called a **matrix.** An IBM PC computer is designed to show its output on a screen having 320 rows and 192 columns of pixels. An Apple Macintosh outputs to a screen with 512 rows and 342 columns. If the screens are the same size, the Macintosh screen will have more pixels per square inch. It would have sharper pictures. We say the Macintosh allows better **resolution.**

Some printers for computers are *dot-matrix printers*. The more rows and columns in the matrix, the better the resolution of the printer, and the better the letters and figures look. For example, a printer might use a matrix with 9 rows and 8 columns. That matrix has $9 \cdot 8 = 72$ cells. To print a letter, the printer puts dots in particular cell centers. One way of making a capital (or upper-case) "A" and a small (or lower-case) "j" is shown below.

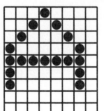 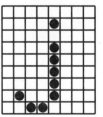

4

Not all dots are small. Signs can be formed by light bulbs arranged in a large matrix. By turning light bulbs on and off quickly, the letters can look like they are moving. In this way, a long message can be put in a little space. Part of a message is shown below.

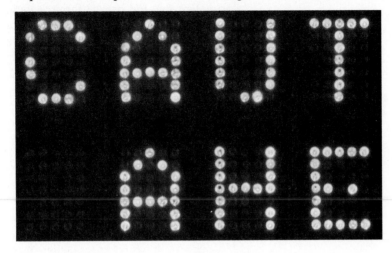

You have seen marching bands form letters and simple pictures. When creating a new band formation, the drillmaster (designer) treats each band member like a dot. The more people in a band, the more complicated the pictures that can be created. The starburst pictured at the left is formed by a large number of performers at the opening ceremonies of the Summer Olympics in Seoul, Korea.

These are all examples of dots as *points*. This is the first of four descriptions of points you will study in this chapter.

First description of a point:

A point is a dot.

Lines are made up of points. When a point is a dot, a line is made up of points with space between their centers. The line is called **discrete.** Every line is either **horizontal, vertical,** or **oblique.** Parallel lines are lines which go in the same direction. Think of lines as going on forever. Drawn below are parts of discrete lines.

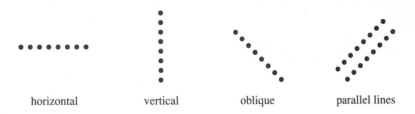

| horizontal | vertical | oblique | parallel lines |

The next day, simply go down the questions in order. In most lessons in this book, going through the questions will review all the important content in a way that teaches the lesson. As you go through the questions, insert any comments you wish about the material and probe students to make sure they understand the ideas. Do not take too much time on any one question, but if you finish the set, go back to questions in which students seemed particularly interested. *Do not spend more than one day on this lesson.*

Reading   If students have not studied UCSMP materials previously, they probably have not been expected to read their math books. Thus, they will need to be taught to read. Emphasize the importance of reading.

Remind students that to read with comprehension they should try to draw an example and a nonexample when they encounter a word that is being defined. Ask them to draw a line, to draw something that is *not* a line, and to draw a "line" that is *not* discrete.

Error Analysis   It is possible that some students will not have firmly established the distinction between *horizontal* and *vertical.* Remind them that *horizontal* lines are parallel to the *horizon.*

ADDITIONAL EXAMPLE
Coins on an overhead projector and students "lined up" are good models for points as dots. They can help students articulate when points are collinear and when they are not.

Points that are part of one line are called **collinear.** When a point is thought of as a dot, then lines have some thickness, and between two points on a line there may or may not be other points. There may be more than one line through two dots depending on whether you require that the line go through their centers. It is possible for two of these lines to cross without having any points in common. Not all lines are like this. As you will later read, when points are not dots, the properties of lines are different.

Questions

Covering the Reading

These questions check your comprehension of the reading. If you cannot answer a question, you should go back in the lesson to find the answer.

1. Who painted *Sunday Afternoon on Grande Jatte Island?*
   Georges Seurat
2. What is a pixel? the dots in a television screen or computer monitor
3. *True* or *false?* If a screen has more pixels than another screen of the same size, it has better resolution. True
4. Why are some printers called "dot-matrix" printers? See margin.
5. *True* or *false?* Two given points can be on several discrete lines. True
6. A dot is one description of a(n) __?__ . point
7. What is a discrete line? a line made up of points with space between their centers
8. A discrete line may be __?__ , __?__ , or oblique.
   horizontal vertical
9. Points that are on the same line are called __?__ . collinear

Applying the Mathematics

These questions extend the content of the lesson. Reread the examples and explanations of the lesson slowly if you cannot answer a question.

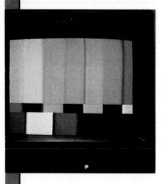

10. How many total pixels are there on:
    a. an IBM PC screen; **b.** an Apple Macintosh screen?
    61,440   175,104
11. Draw two parallel horizontal discrete lines. See margin.
12. Draw two discrete lines which cross, but have no points in common. See margin.
13. If two screens have the same dimensions, which has the better resolution, one with 200 rows and 300 columns of pixels, or one with 150 rows and 310 columns of pixels?
    the one with 200 rows and 300 columns
14. The Mayfield Precision Marching Band wishes to form a block M of the type pictured here. Draw a block M using 60 band members. See margin.

15. Pictured at the left is a horse's head as drawn with the help of a computer. The pixels are square.
   a. Which are used to form this picture, black squares or white squares? black squares (black ink on white paper)
   b. How are some parts made to look darker than others? by clustering the squares

In 16 and 17, use a 9 row by 8 column dot matrix like the one drawn here.

16. Create a dot matrix for the upper-case letters O and R.
See margin.

17. In most typing, the numeral zero is different from the letter O. Create a zero different from your O in Question 16.
See margin.

Review

Review questions practice ideas presented in earlier lessons or previous courses. Review questions which cover ideas from previous courses are marked (Previous course).

18. What is the area in square feet of the Seurat painting? *(Previous course)*
about 60 square feet

19. Suppose $4x - 3y = 12$. What is the value of x if $y = 6$? *(Previous course)* 7.5

20. Graph on a coordinate plane: $(6, 5)$, $(6, -4)$, $(2.5, 0.9)$, and $(-\frac{1}{2}, -\frac{1}{2})$. *(Previous course)* See margin.

21. Evaluate each expression. *(Previous course)*
   a. $|-23|$ **b.** $|4 - 19|$ **c.** $|19.3 - 11|$ **d.** $|7 - -5|$
     23   15   8.3   12

Exploration

Exploration questions often require that you use dictionaries or other sources. Frequently they have many possible answers.

22. Find an example of a picture made up of dots in a newspaper or other reading matter. Answers will vary.

23. In the "light bulb" sign pictured in this lesson. part of a message is given. What might be the complete message?
Answers will vary. Sample: "CAUTION AHEAD"

24. Use a dictionary to find the meaning of the term "pointillism."
Pointillism is a method of painting with tiny dots and no brushstrokes.

FOLLOW-UP

MORE PRACTICE
For more questions on SPUR Objectives, use *Lesson Master 1-1,* shown below.

14. sample:

16. samples:

17. sample:

20. See Additional Answers in the back of this book.

NAME _____

LESSON MASTER 1–1
QUESTIONS ON SPUR OBJECTIVES

■ **PROPERTIES** *Objective D (See pages 54–57 for objectives.)*
In the following questions, consider points as dots. *True or false?*

1. Points have no width, length, or depth.	False
2. Two points determine a single line.	False
3. Between two points on a discrete line there must always be another point.	False
4. Discrete lines may cross even though they have no points in common.	True
5. Any discrete line is made up of an infinite number of points.	True
6. Any two horizontal discrete lines are parallel.	True
7. Any two oblique discrete lines are parallel.	False
8. A vertical and a horizontal discrete line always have a point in common.	False
9. A pixel is a point.	True

1

RESOURCES
■ Lesson Master 1-2
▗ Visual for Teaching Aid 2
can be used with
Questions 15 and **18**.

OBJECTIVES

Letter codes refer to the SPUR Objectives on page 2B.
C Give the dimensions of figures and objects.
D Given a property of points and lines, tell whether it is true for each of the two descriptions of points: dots and locations.
H Apply distance to real situations.
J Determine distance on a number line.

TEACHING NOTES

The definition of distance between two points, $|x - y|$, may not strike students as natural. One way to make it more natural is to take a tape measure and measure the width of a desk. Even though students might put the end of the tape measure at one end of the desk, do *not* do this. Put the tape measure anywhere just so that it stretches the length of the desk. Then ask for the two numbers where the tape measure crosses each end of the desk. The absolute value of their difference is the length of the desk.

The absolute value of a number may be characterized as its distance from the origin. Absolute value tells "how far," not "which direction."

1-2

Locations as Points

A great period of mathematical discovery was during the Greek empire and lasted from about 550 B.C. to 150 A.D. Greek mathematicians of that period made significant advances in number theory and geometry. They considered points not as actual physical dots, but as idealized dots with no size. For them, a point represented an exact location of this idealized dot. A point was considered to be **zero-dimensional,** which means it had no dimensions.

> **Second Description of a Point:**
>
> A point is an exact location.

When two points are locations, it is natural to consider the distance between them. In atlases, maps, and almanacs you can find tables of distances from cities to other cities. For instance, the *1989 World Almanac* gives the road mileage from New York to Los Angeles as 2786 miles. But New York and Los Angeles are both large cities, each many miles across. Some location from which to calculate distances has to be chosen in each city. It may be the city hall, the control tower of an airport, or where two main streets meet.

The road distance from New York to Los Angeles is not the same as the air distance, which the *1989 Information Please Almanac* lists as 2451 miles. Distance between two points depends on the route or path you take.

The shortest path between two locations is along the *line* which contains them. Recall from earlier courses that any line can be made into a **number line.** You can choose any point you want for a zero point and either side of the zero can be the positive side. Every number identifies a point on the line and every point is identified with exactly one number called the **coordinate** of the point. Such a

8

line is said to be **coordinatized.** Drawn below are two views of the same number line ℓ.

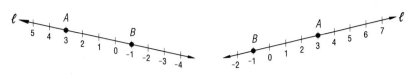

Recall from algebra that the absolute value of a number n is written $|n|$. When n is positive, it equals its absolute value. For instance, $|6.2| = 6.2$. The absolute value of a negative number is the opposite of that number: $|-2500| = 2500$. The absolute value of 0 is 0: $|0| = 0$.

Using the ideas of a coordinatized line and absolute value, *distance* is defined as follows.

Definition:

The **distance** between two points on a coordinatized line is the absolute value of the difference of their coordinates.

In symbols, the distance between two points with coordinates x and y is $|x - y|$. The distance between points A and B is written AB.

■ ■ ■ ■ ■ ■

Example   Find AB on the coordinatized line above.

> **Solution**   The coordinate of A is 3. The coordinate of B is -1.
> $AB = |3 - (-1)| = |4| = 4$.
>
> **Check**   Count the units to verify that there are 4 units between A and B.

Caution: When A and B are points, AB is not their product. You cannot multiply points.

Because of properties of absolute value, if you switch the order of the points, the distance will be the same:

$$BA = |-1 - 3| = |-4| = 4.$$

For any two points A and B, $AB = BA$. The distance from New York to Los Angeles is the same as the distance from Los Angeles to New York.

Tape measures (when stretched) and rulers resemble coordinatized lines. For example, if you wish to buy draperies or blinds for a window, you need the dimensions of the window. Suppose a tape measure crosses the top of a window at the 6 inch mark and the

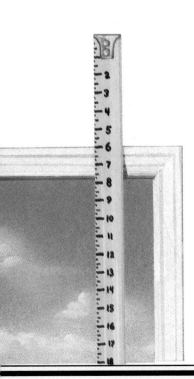

LESSON 1-2 Locations as Points   9

1. Are two desktops in the classroom in the same plane?
Answers depends on desks in the classroom.

2. a. In what way is a wire one-dimensional?
b. In what way is a wire three-dimensional?
When viewed from afar, it seems to have length but no width or breadth, so it seems one-dimensional, but when viewed from very close, it has three dimensions, and if straight, it is like a cylinder.

3. Suppose in a town, each block is $\frac{1}{8}$ of a mile and consists of 100 numbers of addresses. In this town, how far is it from 800N to 300S?
$\frac{11}{8}$ of a mile, or $1\frac{3}{8}$ miles

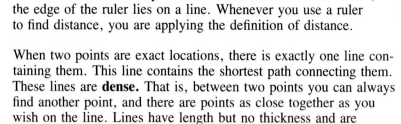

tabletop

two-dimensional

bottom at the 81 in. mark. Then the window is $|6 - 81|$ or $|-75|$ or 75 inches tall. When you connect two locations with a ruler, the edge of the ruler lies on a line. Whenever you use a ruler to find distance, you are applying the definition of distance.

When two points are exact locations, there is exactly one line containing them. This line contains the shortest path connecting them. These lines are **dense.** That is, between two points you can always find another point, and there are points as close together as you wish on the line. Lines have length but no thickness and are **one-dimensional.** A good model for part of this kind of line is a laser beam or other light ray.

A **plane** is a set of points thought of as something flat, like a tabletop. (A carpenter's plane is a tool for making things flat and smooth.) In small spaces, like a classroom, the floor can be considered as a plane. An unbent sheet of paper is part of a plane. The surface of the Earth is *not* a plane because it is curved.

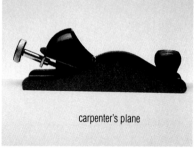

carpenter's plane

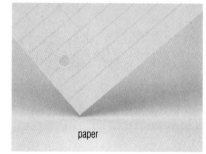

paper

A **plane figure** is a set of points that are all in a plane. Two or more figures that lie in the same plane are **coplanar.** (So all the points of a plane figure are coplanar.) Points, lines, rays, and segments are plane figures.

With other plane figures, such as squares, circles, and triangles, all the points of the figure do not lie on a single line. Those plane figures are **two-dimensional.**

Spheres, boxes, cubes, and other real objects do not all lie in a single plane. They are **three-dimensional** or **space figures.**

sphere   cube

10

ADDITIONAL ANSWERS
13. Sample: The makers of the almanac may have chosen different points within New York and Los Angeles from which to compute the road mileage or they may have used different routes.

Covering the Reading

1. Among ancient Greek mathematicians, what was a point considered to be? They considered points to be idealized dots with no size and no dimensions.

2. According to the *1989 World Almanac,* what is the road mileage from New York to Los Angeles? 2786 miles

3. According to the *1989 Information Please Almanac,* what is the air distance from New York to Los Angeles? 2451 miles

4. Define: distance between two points on a coordinatized line.
   the absolute value of the difference of their coordinates

5. The distance between two points *A* and *B* is written as __?__ . AB

6. Give the distance between two points with the given coordinates.
   a. 5 and 14 9   **b.** 14 and 5 9
   c. -14 and -5 9

In 7-9, give the distance between two points with the given coordinates.

7. -321 and 32 353   8. 3 and -4 7

9. *x* and *y* $|x - y|$ or $|y - x|$

10. Give the number of dimensions for each figure.
    a. point 0   **b.** plane 2
    c. line 1   **d.** space 3

11. What is meant by lines being *dense?*
    There is no space between points on a line.

12. A person stretches a tape measure over a table. At one side of the table the tape measure reads 1″. At the other side the tape measure reads 45″. How long is the table from side to side? 44″

Applying the Mathematics

13. The *1989 Information Please Almanac* gives 2825 miles as the road mileage from New York to Los Angeles. How is it possible that this distance differs from that in Question 2? See margin.

14. Why is the road distance from New York to Los Angeles greater than the air distance? The road distance is measured along roads, which do not always go straight.

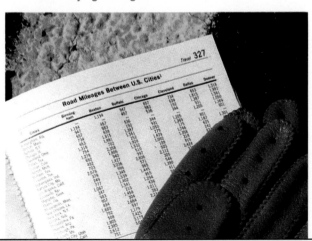

11

15. Use the following road mileage chart for four cities in Ohio.

	Cincinnati	Cleveland	Columbus	Toledo
Cincinnati		244	108	200
Cleveland	244		139	111
Columbus	108	139		133
Toledo	200	111	133	

How much further is the drive from Cincinnati to Cleveland if you stop in Toledo? **67 miles**

16. a. On a drive to Denver, Colorado, you pass a road marker that reads Denver, 88 miles. Along the same road you pass a later marker that reads Denver, 52 miles. How far have you traveled between markers? **36 miles**

b. If the first road marker reads *x* km to Denver and the second reads *y* km to Denver, how far have you traveled? $x - y$ **km**

Tabor Center Shopping Mall in Denver, Colorado

17. Use the number line below.

a. Calculate *AB*, *BC*, and *AC*. **AB = 150, BC = 225, AC = 375**
b. *True* or *false?* *AB* + *BC* = *AC*. **True**

18. Fill in the table with T if the statement is *always* true, F otherwise.

	Description of point	
Statement	Dot	Location
A point has some size.	T	F
If two coplanar lines are not parallel, then they have a point in common.	F	T
Between two points on a line there is always a third point.	F	T

12

Every lesson from here on contains review questions which give practice on ideas presented in earlier lessons. Numbers in parentheses after the questions indicate where the idea was first presented. For example, (Lesson 2-1) indicates the question was based on Chapter 2, Lesson 1. If you can't remember how to do a review question, look back at the indicated lesson. Some skills in review exercises provide practice on ideas you learned in earlier courses. They are marked (Previous course).

19. How many dots are on a computer screen whose dimensions are 380 pixels by 192 pixels? *(Lesson 1-1)* 72,960

20. If two screens have the same dimensions, which screen has a better resolution, one whose pixels are 380 by 192 or one that is 330 by 154? *(Lesson 1-1)* the screen that is 380 by 192

21. What is meant by a *discrete* line? *(Lesson 1-1)*
a line made up of points with space between their centers

22. Graph the line containing (-2,1) and (5,-6) on a coordinate plane. *(Previous course)* See margin.

23. For the equation $x - 3y = 5$, find the value of y for each given value of x. *(Previous course)*

x	3	-2	5
y	$-\frac{2}{3}$	$-\frac{7}{3}$	0

24. Physicists sometimes speak of space-time. How many dimensions does space-time have? 4

25. To the nearest 100 miles, how far do you live from each of the following cities?
   a. New York   **b.** Los Angeles
   c. Honolulu   **d.** Moscow
   Answers will vary; depends on students' locale.

A blend of old and new architecture in Moscow, Russia

MORE PRACTICE
For more questions on SPUR Objectives, use *Lesson Master 1-2*, shown below.

ADDITIONAL ANSWERS
22.

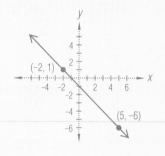

NAME _____

LESSON **MASTER 1–2**
QUESTIONS ON **SPUR** OBJECTIVES

■ **PROPERTIES** *Objective C (See pages 54–57 for objectives.)*
In 1–4, give the dimension for each object, considering points as exact locations.

1. one side of a triangle — one
2. a square — two
3. a point — zero
4. a pyramid — three

■ **PROPERTIES** *Objective D*
In the following questions, consider points as exact locations. *True or false?*

5. Two points determine a unique line. — True
6. A point has a definite size. — False
7. A line is a two-dimensional figure. — False
8. Between any two points on a line there is another point. — True

■ **USES** *Objective H*

9. What is the distance between a fish 8 meters below the surface of a lake and a bird directly above it which is 3 meters above the surface? — 11 meters
10. A truck which is 13 ft 2 in. high enters a tunnel which is 15 ft 6 in. high. What is the clearance of the truck in the tunnel? — 2 ft 4 in.

■ **REPRESENTATIONS** *Objective J*
In 11–13, find the distance between the indicated points.

11. A and C — 4.2
12. A and B — 3
13. B and C — 7.2

2   Geometry © Scott, Foresman and Company

OBJECTIVES

*Letter codes refer to the
SPUR Objectives on page
2B.*
D Given a property of points
and lines, tell whether it is
true for each of the three
descriptions of points:
dots, locations, and or-
dered pairs.
K Graph points and lines in
the coordinate plane.

TEACHING NOTES

To some, a point *is represented by* an ordered pair. In
this book, a point *is* (at certain times) an ordered pair.
We write *A* = (2, 5), not *A:*
(2, 5) or *A*(2, 5), which appear in many books. *A*=(2,
5) indicates that *A* and (2, 5)
are viewed as two different
names for the same point in
the plane. (Because the postulates will guarantee that
any plane can be coordinatized, nothing is lost by this
view.)

LESSON

1-3

Ordered Pairs as Points

Portrait of René Descartes (1596-1650) by Jan Lievens

Around the year 1630, the French mathematicians Pierre de Fermat
and René Descartes realized that a location in a plane can be identified by an **ordered pair** of real numbers. This is the idea behind
coordinate graphing. Below, the three points (0, 0), (3, 2), and
(-5.3, 4.8) are graphed. The plane containing these points is called
the **Cartesian plane** (named after Descartes' Latin name, Cartesius)
or, more simply, the **coordinate plane.** This leads to a third description of a point.

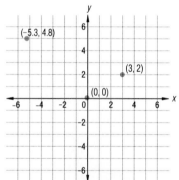

> **Third description of a point:**
>
> A point is an ordered pair of numbers.

When a point is an ordered pair, a line is the set of ordered pairs
(x, y) satisfying the equation
$$Ax + By = C$$
where A, B, and C are specific numbers.

14

Example   Graph the set of ordered pairs satisfying $3x - y = 5$.

Solution   Find two points on the line. Many people like to make a table. You can choose *any* values for x. In this example, 0 and 3 have been selected.

When $x = 0$,
$$3 \cdot \mathbf{0} - y = 5$$
$$-y = 5$$
$$y = -5.$$
Graph $(0, -5)$.

When $x = 3$,
$$3 \cdot \mathbf{3} - y = 5$$
$$9 - y = 5$$
$$y = 4.$$
Graph $(3, 4)$.

Draw the line through $(0, -5)$ and $(3, 4)$. Put arrows at both ends to indicate that the line goes on forever in each direction.

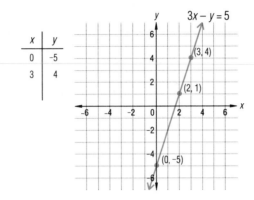

x	y
0	-5
3	4

Check   Find a third point whose coordinates satisfy the equation.
When $x = 2$,
$$3 \cdot \mathbf{2} - y = 5$$
$$6 - y = 5.$$
So $y = 1$. Is the point $(2, 1)$ on the line graphed? Yes, so it checks.

Four important characteristics help to distinguish the various descriptions of points and lines.

1. *Unique line*. Do two points determine a line?

2. *Dimension*. Are points without size? Are lines without thickness? Does the plane have more than one line?

3. *Number line*. Can the points of a line be put into one-to-one correspondence with the real numbers?

4. *Distance*. Is there a unique distance between two points?

Points as dots do not possess the dimension or number line characteristic, and may or may not have the other two characteristics. However, points as locations have all these characteristics. And, since an ordered pair exactly locates a point, points in the coordinate plane have the same characteristics as points as locations.

LESSON 1-3   Ordered Pairs as Points   **15**

MAKING CONNECTIONS
The four characteristics on page 15 anticipate the Point-Line-Plane Postulate of Lesson 1-7.
   All students should have had experience with coordinate graphing before studying this book. Research has shown that UCSMP *Algebra* students are better prepared in coordinate graphing than other students.

Error Analysis   A frequent error that students make when graphing ordered pairs is to confuse the order of locating coordinates. Thus, (2, 1) would be graphed at the location (1, 2). You can help students remember the correct order by arranging H and V alphabetically as the ordered pair *(H, V)*. The first coordinate corresponds with H, the horizontal, and the second coordinate corresponds with V, the vertical.

ADDITIONAL EXAMPLES
1. Graph the set of ordered pairs satisfying $x + 4y = 6$.

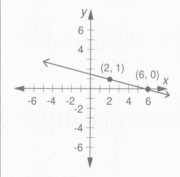

2. Why can't a discrete line be put in one-to-one correspondence with the set of real numbers?
If one were to assign numbers to a discrete line, for example,

where would the real number 3.3 be assigned? the real number 2.65? There are not enough dots for the real numbers.

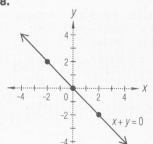
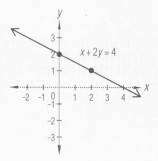
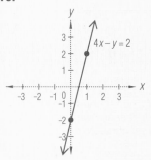
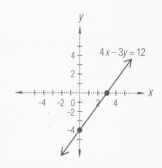
In the general equation for a line, $Ax + By = C$, the values of A, B, and C determine the tilt and location of the line. When neither A nor B is zero, as in the Example, the line is oblique. When $A = 0$, the equation of the line is of the form $y = k$, where k is the specific number $\frac{C}{B}$, and the line is horizontal. When $B = 0$, the equation of the line is of the form $x = h$, where h is the specific number $\frac{C}{A}$, and the line is vertical.

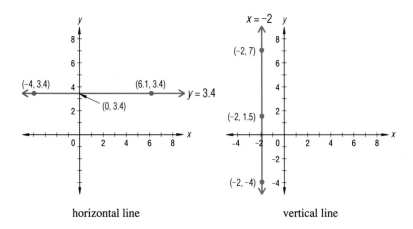

horizontal line   vertical line

Describing points as ordered pairs is very important in mathematics. Sets of ordered pairs may be a curve, and equations can describe that curve. Below are graphed a parabola and an exponential growth curve, two curves that you may have studied or will learn about in other courses. Each curve is described with an equation.

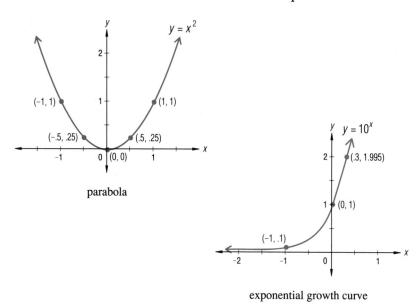

parabola

exponential growth curve

16

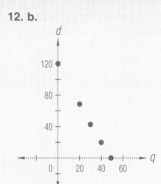

Covering the Reading

1. Give three descriptions of a point. dot, location, ordered pair of numbers
2. **a.** Which two mathematicians developed the idea of using ordered pairs of numbers to represent points?
   b. About how many years ago was this done?
   a) Pierre de Fermat and René Descartes; b) about 360 years ago

In 3-6, classify the line as vertical, horizontal, or oblique.

3. $x - 3y = 5$ oblique   4. $y = -1.234$ horizontal

5. $x = 8$ vertical   6. $14 - 9y = 32x$ oblique

7. **a.** Name the four characteristics of points and lines mentioned in this lesson. uniqueness, dimension, number line, distance
   b. Which are never satisfied by points as dots? dimension, number line
   c. Which are satisfied by points as ordered pairs? all

15. a. and b.

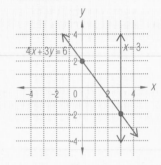

Applying the Mathematics

In 8-11, graph the set of ordered pairs satisfying each equation.

8. $x + y = 0$ See margin.   9. $x + 2y = 4$ See margin.

10. $4x - y = 2$ See margin.   11. $4x - 3y = 12$ See margin.

12. Elaine has $12 in quarters and dimes.
    a. Name five ordered pairs (q, d) of quarters and dimes she might have. Samples: (0, 120), (48, 0), (20, 70), (40, 20), (30, 45), (10, 95)
    b. Graph these points. See margin.
    c. Are these points collinear? Yes

17. The Hitachi resolution is greater than the IBM PC (about 660/square in.) and the Macintosh (about 1100/square in.)

13. Give an equation for the horizontal line that passes through (0, -5). $y = -5$
14. Give an equation for the vertical line that passes through (7, -10). $x = 7$
15. **a.** Graph the line $x = 3$.
    b. Graph the line $4x + 3y = 6$ on the same coordinate plane.
    c. At what point(s) do the lines intersect? a-b) See margin.; c) (3, -2)

18. See the margin on p. 18.

Review

16. Give the distance between two points on a number line with coordinates 1 and 10. *(Lesson 1-2)* 9

17. In April of 1989, Hitachi Ltd. advertised a TV screen with approximately 115,200 pixels. If this screen has the same dimensions as the computer screens mentioned on page 4, how does its resolution compare with those? *(Lesson 1-1)* See margin.

18. Draw two discrete parallel vertical lines. *(Lesson 1-1)* See margin.
19. If the ruler at the left is marked in centimeters, about how long is the segment AB? *(Lesson 1-2)* about 1.8 cm

20. Suppose C has coordinate -7 and D has coordinate -211. Find:
    a. CD; 204   **b.** DC. *(Lesson 1-2)* 204

21. Use the road mileage chart below for the four largest cities in Georgia. Suppose you want to travel from Columbus to Savannah.
    a. How much further is the drive if you stop in Atlanta?
    b. At 55 mph, about how much longer would it take you?
    (Lesson 1-2, Previous course) a) 94 miles; b) about 1.7 hours

	Atlanta	Columbus	Macon	Savannah
Atlanta		108	82	255
Columbus	108		96	269
Macon	82	96		173
Savannah	255	269	173	

Exploration

22. Points in the coordinate plane with integer coordinates are called **lattice points** (integers are {..., -3, -2, -1, 0, 1, 2, 3, ...}). For example, (-4, 11) is a lattice point, but (-2.5, 6) is not.
    a. Name a lattice point on the line $3x + 2y = 5$.
    b. Name a point on the line $4x - y = 8$ that is not a lattice point.
    Answers will vary. Samples: a) (3, -2); b) ($\frac{1}{4}$, -7)

23. The latitude and longitude of a location on Earth are like coordinates of a point. Look on a map to find the latitude and longitude of the place where you live.
    Answers will vary; depends on student's location

18

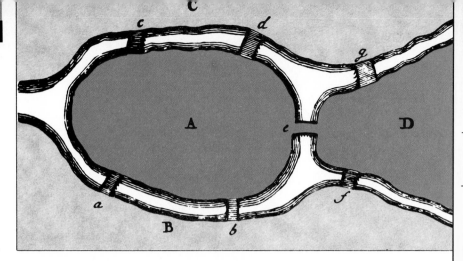

LESSON 1-4

RESOURCES
- Lesson Master 1-4
- Visual for Teaching Aid 5 provides the drawings of the Könisberg Bridge Network.
- Visual for Teaching Aid 6 displays the networks for **Questions 13-16** and **18**.

Through the city of Kaliningrad, in the Soviet Union, flows the Pregol'a River. There are two islands in this river, and seven bridges connect the islands to each other and to the shores. In the drawing above, which first appeared in an article by the great mathematician Leonhard Euler (pronounced "Oiler"), the islands are A and D. The bridges are *a, b, c, d, e, f,* and *g.* The shores of the river are B and C.

In the 1700s this city was part of East Prussia and was known as Königsberg. It was common on Sunday for people to take walks over the bridges. These walks and bridges led to a problem.

> Is there a way to walk across all the bridges
> so that each bridge is crossed exactly once?

You might try to find such a way before reading on.

This question has become known as the **Königsberg Bridge Problem.** Euler solved it in 1736. First he named the islands, shores, and bridges as shown above. He then redrew the map with the islands A and D as very small, and lengthened the bridges. This doesn't change the problem.

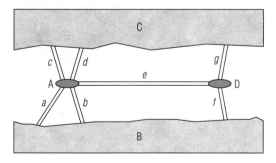

OBJECTIVES

Letter codes refer to the SPUR Objectives on page 2B.
A Analyze networks.
D Given a property of points and lines, tell whether it is true for each of the four descriptions of points: dots, locations, ordered pairs, and nodes.

TEACHING NOTES

This is a fun lesson. Most students enjoy trying to find solutions to tracing problems. For this reason, the questions should be definitely assigned before there is class discussion. Otherwise, the interesting history and the challenge of determining if a network is traversable can be lost.

Even though the criterion for distinguishing a traversable network is easy, many students will not get it until class discussion the next day.

The Königsberg Bridge problem is one of the most famous problems in all of mathematics. It has this eminence because (a) it is easy to state yet not easy to solve (unless you have a hint at the solution); (b) the solution, when known, is remarkably elegant and solves every problem of the same type; (c) the solver, Leonhard Euler, was one of the greatest mathematicians of all time; and (d) the idea used in the solution proved to be the beginning of what is now an entire field of study in mathematics, graph theory.

Encourage students to make the conceptual leap Euler did, that is, to treat land masses as individual points.

To determine whether a network is traversable, here is what you need to do.
(a) Identify its nodes. This is easy; there will always be at least two nodes. (b) By counting, determine whether each node is odd or even. You may wish to put *O*s and *E*s by the nodes, as is done in Question 12. (c) If there are 0 or 2 odd nodes, the network is traversable. If there are 4, 6, 8, . . . odd nodes, the network is not.
(d) In fact, if there are 0 odd nodes (all nodes are even), then a traversable path may start anywhere. If there are 2 odd nodes, the traversable path must start at one of the odd nodes and end at the other.

It is important for students to recognize that this use of point and line is very helpful in making mathematical models of real-world problems, but that they do not satisfy the properties of other contexts, namely points as locations. Emphasize that the only points are the nodes.

Then he realized that the shores B and C could be small. That again distorts the picture but it doesn't change the problem.

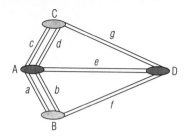

Finally—and this was the big step—he thought of the land areas A, B, C, and D as points and the bridges *a* through *g* as **arcs** connecting them. The result, shown below, is a **network** of points and arcs. In this network there is a path (though not necessarily direct) from any point to any other point. Euler was able to rephrase the original question to become: *Without lifting a pencil off the paper, can the pencil trace over **all** the arcs exactly once?* If the answer is yes, this kind of network is called **traversable.**

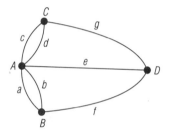

In a network, the *only* points are the endpoints of arcs. These endpoints have no size and are called **nodes** or **vertices.** (The singular of vertices is **vertex.**) Euler noticed that the number of arcs at each node provided a clue as to whether a network was traversable. In the Königsberg Bridge Problem, there are 5 arcs at vertex *A* (*c, d, e, b,* and *a*) and 3 arcs at each of vertices *B, C,* and *D*.

Networks illustrate a fourth way to describe a point.

Fourth description of a point:

A point is a node of a network.

Points and lines in networks have different properties than when points and lines are dots, locations, or ordered pairs. For example, a line in a network is an arc or segment connecting either two nodes or one node to itself. There are no points between the nodes. So an arc cannot be coordinatized. Also, two nodes do not determine exactly one arc.

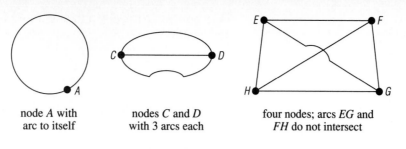

node A with
arc to itself

nodes C and D
with 3 arcs each

four nodes; arcs EG and
FH do not intersect

Before we tell you Euler's answer to the Königsberg Bridge Problem, here are three more networks to consider. In these networks, we draw the arcs as segments.

Example 1 How many arcs are at each node of networks I, II, and III?

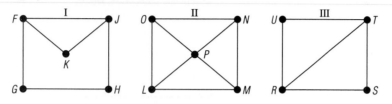

Solution Network I: There are 2 arcs at vertices G, H, and K, and 3 at F and J.

Network II: There are 3 arcs at vertices L, M, N, and O, and 4 arcs at vertex P.

Network III: There are 2 arcs at S and U, 3 arcs at R and T.

Example 2 Which of the networks in Example 1 are traversable?

Solution Network I is traversable. One path begins at F and goes to K and then to J to H to G to F to J.

Network II is not traversable. (Try it.)

Network III is traversable. One path is from R to S to T to R to U to T.

If the number of arcs at a node is even, the node is called an **even node.** Otherwise it is an **odd node.** In the Examples, nodes G, H, K, P, U, and S are even nodes while nodes F, J, L, M, N, O, R, and T are odd nodes. These are sometimes called odd or even **vertices.**

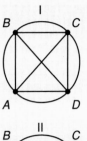

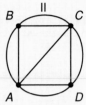

There are five arcs at each node of network I; there are five arcs at nodes A and C of network II, but four nodes at B and D of that network.

2. Which of networks I and II above is traversable?
II

3. Can network I be made traversable by adding one path?
Yes

ADDITIONAL ANSWERS

2. Is there a way to walk across all the bridges in Königsberg so that each bridge is crossed exactly once?

6. A network is traversable when there is a path going over each arc exactly once without lifting the pencil off the paper.

10. a. sample:

b. sample:

17. a.

b.

18.

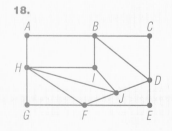

Euler noticed that when a path goes through a vertex, it uses two arcs, one to the vertex, and one from it. This led him to realize that when a network has an odd vertex, it *must* be the starting or finishing point for a traversable path. (Look back at Example 2 and verify that the traversable paths of Networks I and III begin and end at odd nodes.) Euler then realized that all four vertices in the Königsberg network are odd. So the Königsberg network is not traversable. In general, whenever a network has more than two odd nodes, it is *not* traversable.

Problems like the Königsberg Bridge Problem may seem frivolous or silly, but there are important real situations that are similar.

Can a telephone company repair crew inspect all the lines without going over any section twice?

Can a school bus route be set up so that the bus drives on each street only once?

Questions

Covering the Reading

1. How many bridges were there in Königsberg? **7**

2. What is the Königsberg Bridge Problem? **See margin.**

3. Who solved the Königsberg Bridge Problem and when?
   Leonhard Euler in 1736

In 4 and 5, use the Königsberg network.

4. What do the nodes in this network represent?
   A and D islands; B and C shores

5. What do the arcs in this network represent?
   bridges

6. What does it mean for a network to be traversable?
   See margin.

7. What is the description of a point in this lesson?
   a node of a network

8. What is the description of a line in this lesson? **an arc or segment connecting either two nodes or one node to itself**

9. What did Euler notice about networks? **An odd vertex in a network must be the starting or finishing point of a traversable path.**

10. **a.** Draw a traversable network.
    b. Draw a network that is not traversable.
       See margin.

11. Describe a traversable path for Network III of this lesson different from the one in this lesson. **Sample: *T* to *R* to *S* to *T* to *U* to *R***

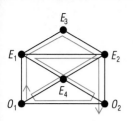

12. The network at the left has 6 nodes.
  a. Copy it. Draw a path that shows that this network is traversable.
  b. At what node does your path begin? O_1 or O_2
  c. At what node does your path end? O_2 or O_1
  d. Why are the vertices called *E*s and *O*s?
     The *E*s are even vertices, the *O*s are odd vertices.

In 13 and 14, the network is traversable. **a.** Describe a traversable path.
b. At what vertices can a traversable path begin?

13.

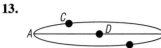

a) Sample: *A* to *C* to *B* to *D* to *A* to
E to *B*; b) either *A* or *B*

14.

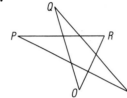

a) Sample: *M* to *F*
to *G* to *H* to *I* to
J to *K* to *L* to *F*
to *H* to *J* to *L* to
M; b) at any vertex.

In 15 and 16, **a.** give the number of even and odd nodes; **b.** tell whether the network is traversable.

15.

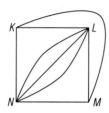

a) 0 even, 4 odd; b) no

16.

a) 5 even, 0 odd; b) yes

17. a. Draw a network with more arcs than nodes.
  b. Draw a network with more nodes than arcs.
     See margin.

18. An architect is planning a museum. Her sketch is shown. Can a security guard completely walk each part of his route once without going through any part of his route twice? (Hint: Represent the intersection of hallways with nodes, and the hallways themselves with arcs.) **Yes, see margin.**

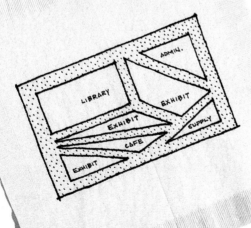

LESSON 1-4 Points in Networks **23**

FOLLOW-UP

MORE PRACTICE
For more questions on SPUR Objectives, use *Lesson Master 1-4*, shown below.

EXTENSION
Each geometric idea presented in this text has accompanying real-world applications which students should recognize as real and noncontrived. Many buildings have hallways which need to be swept or guarded each evening. If your school has hallways, do they form a traversable network? Having more than one floor simply means that there are more arcs connecting the nodes, which could appear at tops of stairs and elevators.

EVALUATION
Alternative Assessment
In order to compare the four descriptions of points in this chapter, call upon several students to explain their answers to **Question 19**.

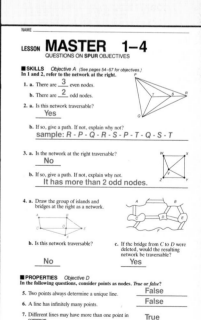

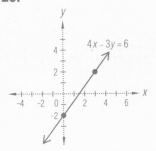

19. Below at the left are statements about points and lines. Fill in each part of the table with A if the statement is always true, S if the statement is sometimes true, or N if the statement is never true.

Statement	Dots	Ordered Pairs	Locations	Node
Between two points on a line there is a third point.	S	A	A	N
A line contains infinitely many points.	A	A	A	N
Through two points there is exactly one line.	S	A	A	S

Review

In 20 and 21, graph the set of ordered pairs satisfying each equation.

20. $4x - 3y = 6$ *(Lesson 1-3)*
See margin.

21. $x = -3$ *(Lesson 1-3)*
See margin.

22. Give an equation for the horizontal line containing (-2, 5). *(Lesson 1-3)*
$y = 5$

23. Suppose A, B, and C are collinear with coordinates -6, 1, and 14, respectively. Calculate $AB + BC$. *(Lesson 1-2)* 20

24. Ignoring small thicknesses, give the number of dimensions for a laser beam. *(Lesson 1-2)* one

25. Using the number line at the right, find CD. *(Lesson 1-2)* 5

Exploration

26. There are many puzzles using networks. Here is one. Start with a network that has n arcs. (The networks below have 4 nodes and 6 arcs.) Name each *node* with a different number from 0 to n. Then number each *arc* by the positive difference of the nodes it connects. For example, in the network below at the right, the arc connecting nodes 5 and 3 is named 2 because $5 - 3 = 2$. The goal is to name the nodes in such a way that the n arcs are numbered with all the integers from 1 to n. Such a network is called a *graceful* network.

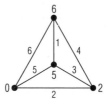

graceful
(arcs are numbered from 1 to 6)

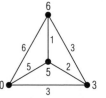

not graceful
(two arcs are numbered 3)

Number the nodes in these three networks so as to make them graceful. Answers will vary. See below for samples.

a.

b.

c.

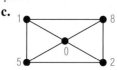

24

1-5

Drawing in Perspective

The drawings in this book are one- and two-dimensional, but the world is three-dimensional. This presents problems. We know that railroad tracks are parallel and thus do not intersect, but in life and in many drawings and photographs they look as if they will meet if extended. The point where they would meet is called a **vanishing point.**

In the painting above, *Overseas Highway,* the artist, Ralston Crawford, has created a feeling of depth, or **perspective,** by the use of a vanishing point. You can see that the sides of the floor of the bridge meet at the vanishing point. Likewise, the railings on both sides of the bridge are drawn to the same vanishing point.

The idea of a vanishing point comes from Renaissance artists. They imagined a clear screen between the viewer and the object they wanted to draw. They connected points on the object to the eye with lines called **lines of sight,** as shown at the left. The points where the lines of sight intersected the screen showed how to draw the object.

LESSON 1-5 *Drawing in Perspective* **25**

LESSON 1-5

RESOURCES
■ Lesson Master 1-5
▣ Visual for Teaching Aid 7
  can be used with
  Questions 9, 11 and **15**.

OBJECTIVE

Letter code refers to the SPUR Objectives on page 2B.
B Make and determine the perspective of drawings.

TEACHING NOTES

In January 1985, *Mathematics Magazine,* a journal of the Mathematical Association of America (MAA), published an astounding article by Branko Grünbaum of the University of Washington. Entitled "Geometry Strikes Again," the article pointed out that the MAA logo, the regular icosahedron, was drawn incorrectly—in reality, it could not occur the way it appeared on MAA stationery and in MAA journals. A comment by the editor indicated the logo has been this way since 1924, when it first appeared. Sixty years and no one had observed the difference!

One goal of this lesson is to provide language which will clear up the paradox of parallel lines (for example, parallel railroad tracks) seeming to meet. The explanation is simple—they intersect at what we call a point at infinity. This is not a point of the plane but a theoretical point beyond the plane.

In mathematics, and even in real life, people are attuned to compensating for perspective. Both the top and bottom drawings on page 26 may be perceived as cubes, even though they are quite different.

The geometry of vanishing points and vanishing lines is called *projective geometry,* a branch of mathematics that began in the 17th century and was motivated by artists' perspective drawings. If you have a student in your class who is interested in art, you might ask the student to bring in a book on art showing how artists use perspective in making drawings.

If properties of points and lines in projective geometry were to be compared with those of Euclidean geometry (something not done in this book), one difference is that there are no parallel lines in projective geometry; they all intersect at points at infinity. Note that points at infinity, being outside the plane, are not the same as vanishing points, which are in the plane.

Drawing good figures will be essential for students throughout the course. Encourage them to develop careful habits and to use a straightedge. The markings on a transparent rule can be used to draw parallel segments better. Hidden lines or lines which are to appear behind others should be dotted.

Unless they have had experience in art, students may find the idea of drawing in perspective confusing at first, but after practice, they will probably enjoy it.

These drawings are called **perspective drawings.** In perspective drawings, horizontal (or vertical) lines remain horizontal (or vertical) and parallel. But oblique parallel lines will intersect if extended. The box below has two vanishing points, *P* and *Q*. Vertical lines on the box remain vertical and parallel, but the box has been tilted to have no horizontal edges.

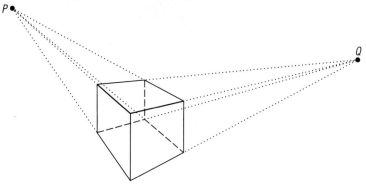

The box drawn below is tilted to have neither horizontal nor vertical edges. It has three collinear vanishing points, *R, S,* and *T*. They lie on the **vanishing line** for this drawing. In realistic drawings, the vanishing line is both the horizon and the height of the viewer's eye.

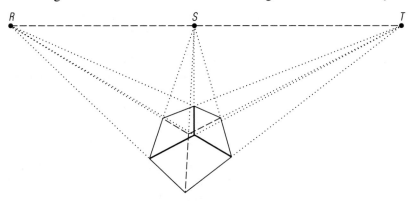

Drawing in perspective can be difficult, so mathematicians often avoid perspective in their drawings. Below, a cube is drawn as most mathematicians would draw it. Notice that the back of the cube, *BCEH,* is the same size as the front, *ADFG*. In the real world, the back of the cube is farther away than the front and it would look smaller. Realist artists would not like this drawing.

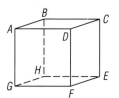

nonperspective drawing
of a cube

26

Geometers (mathematicians who study geometry) use another technique that preserves a feeling of depth. **Hidden lines,** such as the three back edges of the cube, are shown as dashed lines instead of solid to indicate that they would not normally be seen.

In this book, you will often be asked to draw three-dimensional figures. You are not expected to use perspective unless asked. But you should follow the rules that geometers follow, and dot or dash hidden lines to show depth.

Questions

Covering the Reading

1. **a.** In a perspective drawing, do railroad tracks meet in the distance? Yes
   b. In the real world, do railroad tracks meet in the distance? No

2. What is a vanishing point? the point where parallel lines in perspective drawings would meet if extended

3. What are lines of sight? imaginary lines connecting points on an object to the viewer's eye

4. In perspective drawings, tell whether these lines would intersect if extended:
   a. horizontal parallel lines No
   b. vertical parallel lines No
   c. oblique parallel lines. Yes

5. In general, do mathematicians use perspective in drawings? No

6. How are hidden lines in non-perspective drawings drawn? dashed

7. Draw a cube: **a.** in perspective; **b.** not in perspective. See margin.

Applying the Mathematics

8. Of the four descriptions of points mentioned in previous lessons, which best describes a vanishing point? location

9. Consider these four drawings.

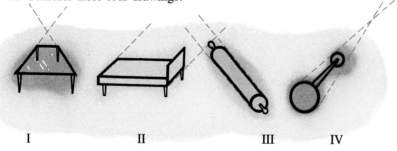

   I   II   III   IV

   a. Which are drawn in perspective? I, IV
   b. Trace each perspective drawing and find its vanishing point.

10. Make a perspective drawing of a square floor tiled with square tiles. See margin.

LESSON 1-5 *Drawing in Perspective* **27**

ADDITIONAL EXAMPLES
1. Draw a box not in perspective.
sample:

2. Draw a box in perspective, as seen from the front.
sample:

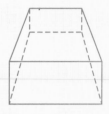

NOTES ON QUESTIONS
Question 7. Students should be encouraged to draw neatly. Discourage freehand drawings. Students who do not have an "eye" for making lines look parallel may require some specific algorithm. It is usually easiest to draw the front face first, pick the vanishing point, and then draw the edges that will meet at that point. Draw the back face last.

Question 10: This idea lends itself to extra credit projects. Filling the plane with tiles, whether squares or some other polygon, drawn in perspective, may interest some students.

ADDITIONAL ANSWERS
7. a. sample: **b. sample:**

10. sample:

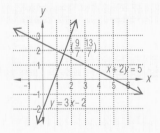
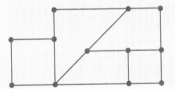

11. Sally's baby brother has a block with ○ ☼ ▲ ✳ ● ✚ on the six faces. Three views of the block are shown here.

Which pictures are on opposites sides of the block? **See margin.**

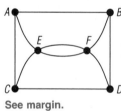

12. Opposite sides of a die add to seven. Here a die is seen from a little above one face.
   a. What is the sum of the numbers that cannot be seen? 13
   b. Where are these numbers? (Call the faces of the die top, bottom, front, back, right, and left.) 4 (bottom), 2 (back), 1 (left) and 6 (right), or 1 (right) and 6 (left)

Review

In 13 and 14, is the network traversable? If so, give a route; if not, tell why not. *(Lesson 1-4)*

13.
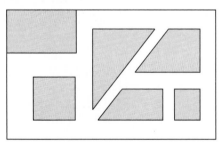

See margin.

14.
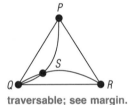

traversable; see margin.

15. a. Represent the floor plan below with a network. **See margin.**
    b. Is it traversable? *(Lesson 1-4)* No

16. Give an equation for the vertical line containing (-1, -6). *(Lesson 1-3)*
    x = -1

17. a. Graph the lines $y = 3x - 2$ and $x + 2y = 5$ on the same coordinate plane. **See margin.**
    b. From the graph, estimate the coordinates of the point of intersection. *(Lesson 1-3)* Answers may vary; the actual point of intersection is $(\frac{9}{7}, \frac{13}{7})$.

18. If A has coordinate 461 and B has coordinate -35, find AB. *(Lesson 1-2)*
496

19. A tape measure was placed against a door. The left side was aligned to the 17 cm mark, and the right side to the 73 cm mark. How wide is the door? *(Lesson 1-2)* 56 cm

Exploration

20. Below is an example of anamorphic art (*Napoleon III with His Children,* artist anonymous), a perspective drawing where the vanishing point is about 1 meter to the left of the page in the same plane as the page.
   a. Look at the drawing from the vanishing point. Briefly describe the picture. **See below.**
   b. Why do you think an artist would use such a device? **See below.**

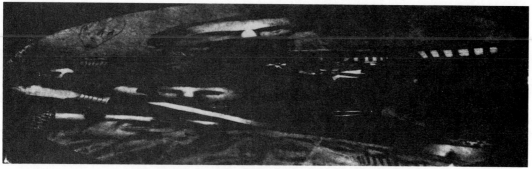

a) a man in a military uniform with a little girl and boy
b) Answers will vary; they were used as puzzles, to convey hidden political views, or to satirize.

LESSON 1-5 Drawing in Perspective **29**

FOLLOW-UP

MORE PRACTICE
For more questions on SPUR Objectives, use *Lesson Master 1-5,* shown below.

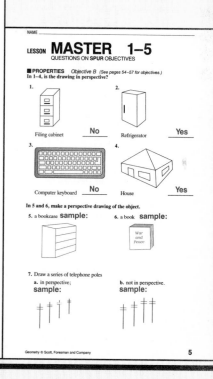

RESOURCES
- Lesson Master 1-6
- Quiz for Lessons 1-4 Through 1-6
- Visual for Teaching Aid 8 can be used with **Question 18**.

OBJECTIVE

Letter code refers to the SPUR Objectives on page 2B.
E Recognize the use of undefined terms and postulates.

TEACHING NOTES

It was recognized by Aristotle that, logically, if terms are to be defined by simpler terms, then some terms must be left undefined. For example, a person cannot use a Russian dictionary to learn Russian because the words have to be defined in terms of each other. But this is not a weakness, as the undefined terms (for example, point, line, and plane in geometry) may have several meanings and thus may be more applicable than if there were specific definitions in the first place!

The first five lessons have set the stage for introducing the need for undefined terms. This section articulates that need and leads naturally to the need for postulates (as given in the next lesson), which remove ambiguity about what will satisfy the concepts of point, line, and plane desired in our geometry.

LESSON

1-6

The Need for Undefined Terms

The famous "freedom march" on Washington in 1963. Does the word "freedom" mean the same thing to all people?

A *set* is a collection of objects called *elements*. If the elements are points, then the set is a *figure*. The set of all points from which points of a figure are selected is called *space*. The study of figures in the two-dimensional space of a plane, such as polygons and circles, is called **plane geometry.** The study of figures in three-dimensional space, such as spheres and pyramids, is called **solid geometry.** In this book you will study both plane and solid geometry.

In the previous paragraph, there are many terms. Here two of them are formally defined.

> **Definitions:**
> **Space** is the set of all possible points.
> A **figure** is a set of points.

These definitions are useful because they state precisely what these words mean in this book.

Careful definitions are not always needed. However, in some fields, defining terms is not just useful, but necessary. Law, economics, philosophy, science, and labor relations, in addition to mathematics, are some of the fields where precise definitions are necessary. For example, disputes may occur because individuals have no definitions or have different definitions for "overtime" or "freedom" or "force" or "obscene."

Mathematicians try to define terms carefully. However, notice that the meanings of the words "space" and "figure" depend on what a point means. Trying to define "point" presents two problems. First, as you have seen in the previous lessons, there are many possible meanings for "point." A point may be a dot, or a location, or an ordered pair, or a node in a network.

30

Second, you get into trouble when you try to select a meaning for "point." For instance, suppose you defined a point to be a *spot*. What about the word "spot"? Well, a spot is a *place*. But a place is an *exact location*. Trying to define this term, you might find that the best description of an exact location is "point"!

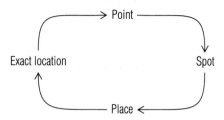

Thus you have returned to the original word which you were trying to define. You have circled back to where you started. When this "circling back" occurs, it usually means you are trying to define basic terms. It is called **circularity.** (Circularity means that you have circled back to any word previously defined, not necessarily the original one.) To avoid circularity, certain basic geometric terms are forced to be *undefined*.

In this book, we choose *point, line,* and *plane* as **undefined terms.** One strength of this is that it allows geometry to be applied to different kinds of points and lines. For instance, we can talk about the distance between (4, 5) and (4, 2), because we can think of (4, 5) and (4, 2) as representing points, and not just pairs of numbers.

Also, very common English words—the articles, prepositions, and conjunctions—are not defined. We assume that you are familiar with many words used in algebra or arithmetic, such as "equation," "number," "equals," "is less than," and so on. So terms like these are left undefined.

Undefined terms (in this book):

Geometric terms: point, line, plane.
Algebraic and arithmetic terms: number, equals, addition,
and so on.
Common English words: the, a, of, into, and, and so on.

If something is not defined, it could mean anything. Point might mean "elephant"! So, to clarify that we are talking about a particular kind of point or line, we will assume points and lines have certain properties. For instance, if we assume that points have no dimensions, you know we are not talking about dots. If we assume that between two points, there is always another point, you know we are not talking about lines in networks. The assumptions about points and lines for this book are given in the next lesson.

LESSON 1-6 The Need for Undefined Terms **31**

NOTES ON QUESTIONS

Questions 9-11: Often when looking up words, the definitions will not circle back to the original word but to the second or third word.

Question 18: This question is far easier than it looks. All one has to do is count the arcs at each node and determine whether there are more than two odd nodes. This is one of the author's favorite problems. It illustrates the power of simple mathematics to solve what would seem to be incredibly difficult problems.

Error Analysis for Question 18: A common error is to think of Queens and Brooklyn as two different land masses.

ADDITIONAL ANSWERS

3. Plane geometry is the study of figures in the two-dimensional space of a plane; solid geometry is the study of figures in three-dimensional space.

15. a.　　　　**b.**

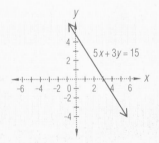

16.

Covering the Reading

1. In geometry, space is the ⟨ ? ⟩. **set of all possible points**

2. In this book, a figure is a(n) ⟨ ? ⟩. **set of points**

3. What is the difference between plane geometry and solid geometry? **See margin.**

4. Name five fields where precise definitions are needed. **Samples: law, economics, philosophy, science, and labor relations**

5. In an attempt to define a simple word, such as "point," you may find the original word is used in the definition. This is called ⟨ ? ⟩. **circularity**

6. Name three geometry terms undefined in this book. **point, line, plane**

7. Name two undefined words or phrases from algebra. **Samples: equation, number**

8. What assumption about points and lines would indicate that the points and lines are not in networks? **Sample: Between two points on a line there is always another point.**

Applying the Mathematics

9. Look up the word "concord" in a dictionary. Try to find a one-word synonym. Look up this synonym. Find a one-word synonym for this second word. Continue this process. How many words did you look up before circularity happened? **Sample: 3; concord, harmony, agreement, concord**

In 10 and 11, follow the directions for Question 9 but begin with the following words.

10. inundate **Sample: 2; inundate, overwhelm, inundate**　　11. satire **Sample: 2; satire, irony, satire**

In 12 and 13, define the word on your own without a dictionary.

12. freedom **Sample: ability to do what you want to do**　　13. number **Sample: quantity**

Review

14. Do mathematicians generally draw in perspective? *(Lesson 1-5)* **No**

15. Draw railroad tracks: **a.** in perspective; **b.** not in perspective. *(Lesson 1-5)* **See margin.**

16. Graph the line with equation $5x + 3y = 15$. *(Lesson 1-3)* **See margin.**

17. Trace the figure below and find the vanishing point. *(Lesson 1-5)* **See margin.**

18. *The New York City Bridge Problem.* Below is a drawing of the five boroughs of New York City, Randall's Island, and New Jersey. (No water separates Brooklyn and Queens.) Bridges and tunnels connect the regions. Draw a network (like the Königsberg bridge network) to represent New York and determine if you could take a driving tour of New York going over each bridge and through each tunnel exactly once. *(Lesson 1-4)* See margin.

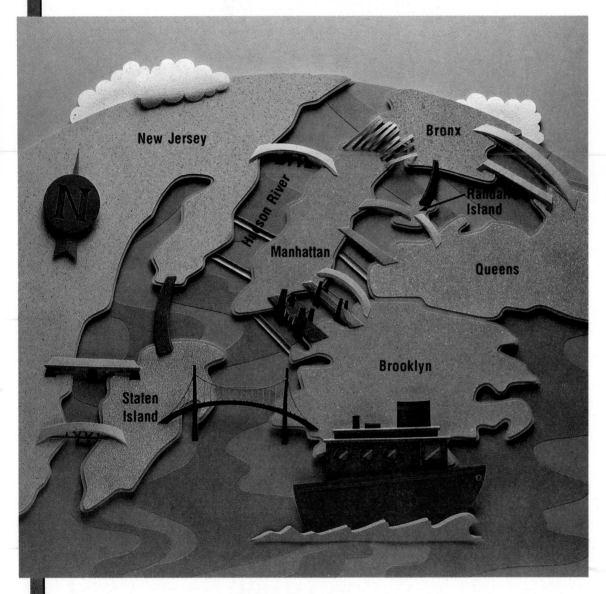

19. Calculate *AB*. *(Lesson 1-2)* 5.3

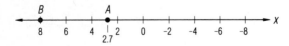

LESSON 1-6 The Need for Undefined Terms **33**

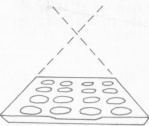
18.

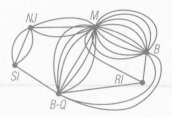

The network is traversable; a path must have Manhattan and Randall's Island as its endpoints.

20. Fill in the table with A if the statement is always true, S if sometimes true, or N if never true. *(Lessons 1-4, 1-3, 1-2, 1-1)*

Statement	Description of a point			
	Location	Ordered Pair	Node	Dot
Through two points, there is exactly one line.	A	A	S	S
A line is an infinite set of points.	A	A	N	A
A point has no size.	A	A	A	N

21. Give the number of dimensions in each figure. Assume points are locations. *(Lesson 1-2)*
    a. line 1
    b. plane 2
    c. point 0
    d. space 3

22. Find the distance between (4, 5) and (4, 2). (Hint: graph them.) *(Lessons 1-3, 1-2)* 3

23. On a number line, graph all solutions to the inequality $x \geq -10$. *(Previous course)*

24. On a number line, graph all numbers t with $\frac{1}{2} \leq t \leq \frac{5}{2}$. *(Previous course).*

Exploration

25. Some words have many definitions.
    a. Look in a dictionary. How many different definitions are given for the word "point"? **See below.**
    b. Find another word with as many definitions.

a) Answers may vary: Sample: in *Webster's II New Riverside University Dictionary,* there are 34. b) Sample: in some dictionaries, "set" has as many as 40 definitions.

34

34

RESOURCES
■ Lesson Master 1-7
▙ Visual for Teaching Aid 9
can be used with
Questions 24 and **25**.

You have now seen four descriptions of points. Others are possible but are not discussed in this book.

Description	Example
dot	computer screens
location	geography
ordered pair	graphs
node of network	airplane routes

These examples show that points and lines do not have the same properties when different descriptions are used. This is one reason why *point* and *line* are undefined. To make clear which description of *point* and *line* is being followed, assumptions or **postulates** are made about them.

Below we state four assumptions about points and lines. These are grouped together and called the *Point-Line-Plane Postulate*. These assumptions were picked to fit the descriptions of point as location and as ordered pair, since these descriptions are the most used in mathematics and its applications. The assumptions may not fit other descriptions of *point* and *line*.

Point-Line-Plane Postulate:

(a) Unique line assumption Through any two points, there is exactly one line.

Sometimes this is read, "Two points determine a line." This assumption does not apply to the node description of point, where there can be more than one line (arc) connecting two points (nodes).

(b) Dimension assumption Given a line in a plane, there exists a point in the plane not on the line. Given a plane in space, there exists a point in space not on the plane.

Thus, a line has more dimensions than a point, a plane has more dimensions than a line, and space has more dimensions than a plane.

(c) Number line assumption Every line is a set of points that can be put into a one-to-one correspondence with the real numbers, with any point on it corresponding to 0 and any other point corresponding to 1.

This part means that any line can be made into a real number line. Any point on the line can be the origin, either direction can be the positive direction, and any length can be the unit length. It also allows points in the plane to be ordered pairs. This part does not apply to the dot or node description of point.

(d) Distance assumption On a number line, there is a unique distance between two points.

If the points have coordinates x and y, we define this distance to be $|x - y|$.

OBJECTIVE

Letter code refers to the SPUR Objectives on page 2B.
E Recognize the use of undefined terms and postulates.

TEACHING NOTES

In Euclidean geometry, like any mathematical system, certain propositions are true and certain others are false. For instance, in Euclidean geometry, "two points determine a line" is true and "the sum of the measures of a triangle is 200°" is false. The truth or falsity of a statement either comes from a postulate, a definition, or a deduction from these. There can be and there have been many different sets of postulates which give rise to Euclidean geometry. The first set of postulates extant today was from Euclid himself.

Put most simply, Euclidean geometry is a geometry of points as locations or as ordered pairs. (There are other geometries of points as locations or as ordered pairs, but the postulates in later chapters—for example, the postulates about parallels—narrow the field down until ultimately the only propositions that can be deduced are those of Euclidean geometry.)

To repeat: The Point-Line-Plane Postulate limits the points in this book to be locations or ordered pairs. A different postulate would have been needed if we wanted the results to be applicable to the dot or node description of point.

The first purpose served by postulates is to explain undefined terms. A second purpose, just as important, is to serve as a starting point for logically deducing or proving other statements about figures.

For instance, in the figure below, if P and Q are points, m and n cannot *both* be lines. If they were, there would be two lines through P and Q, yet from part (a) of the Point-Line-Plane Postulate, there can only be one. We denote the unique line through P and Q by $\overleftrightarrow{PQ}$ or $\overleftrightarrow{QP}$. $\overleftrightarrow{PQ}$ is read "line PQ."

P and Q are points; m and n are different lines.
Impossible.

Theorems are geometric statements that are deduced from postulates, definitions, or previously deduced theorems. The argument above proves the following theorem.

Theorem:

Two different lines intersect in at most one point.

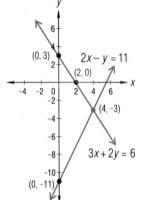

This theorem holds when points are ordered pairs. For instance, in algebra, when you solved the system $\begin{cases} 3x + 2y = 6 \\ 2x - y = 11 \end{cases}$ you found $(4, -3)$ as the point of intersection of the two lines. You also know that sometimes lines do not intersect, and sometimes two equations can describe the same line. When coplanar lines do not intersect in exactly one point, they are called *parallel*. The idea behind parallel is "going in the same direction."

Definition:

Two coplanar lines m and n are **parallel lines**, written $m \parallel n$, if and only if they have no points in common, or they are identical.

The most famous organization of postulates, definitions, and theorems (and perhaps the earliest) was by the Greek mathematician Euclid around 300 B.C. In a set of books called *Elements,* Euclid used five geometric postulates and five arithmetic postulates.

36

The original Elements *were written by Euclid in 300 B.C. No copy of the original exists. Pictured here is a translation by H. Billingsley in the year 1570.*

Postulates from arithmetic and algebra are still used in geometry. Here are the most important postulates for this course. All of these hold for *any* real numbers *a*, *b*, and *c*. These properties also hold for all algebraic expressions and anything that stands for real numbers. You will review other properties and theorems from algebra in later lessons as they are needed.

Some Postulates from Arithmetic and Algebra

Postulates of Equality

Reflexive Property of Equality: $a = a$

Symmetric Property of Equality: *If $a = b$, then $b = a$.*

Transitive Property of Equality: *If $a = b$ and $b = c$, then $a = c$.*

Postulates of Equality and Operations

Addition Property of Equality: *If $a = b$, then $a + c = b + c$.*

Multiplication Property of Equality: *If $a = b$, then $ac = bc$.*

Substitution Property of Equality: *If $a = b$, then a may be substituted for b in any expression.*

Postulates of Inequality and Operations

Addition Property of Inequality: *If $a < b$, then $a + c < b + c$.*

Multiplication Property of Inequality: *If $a < b$ and $c > 0$, then $ac < bc$.*
If $a < b$ and $c < 0$, then $ac > bc$.

Equation to Inequality Property: *If a and b are positive numbers and $a + b = c$, then $c > a$ and $c > b$.*

Transitive Property of Inequality: *If $a < b$ and $b < c$, then $a < c$.*

Postulates of Operations

Commutative Property of Addition: $a + b = b + a$

Commutative Property of Multiplication: $ab = ba$

Distributive Property: $a(b + c) = ab + ac$

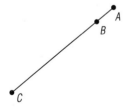

The above postulates should be familiar to you except for the Equation to Inequality Property. This property was worded by Euclid (in Greek) as "the whole is greater than any of its parts." For example, in the figure at the left, suppose $AB + BC = AC$. Then $AC > AB$ and $AC > BC$. The length of the whole segment is greater than the length of any part of it.

The definition of parallel lines given in this lesson is slightly different from definitions in many other books. It allows a line to be parallel to itself. We do this because it enables less language and better theorems later. For example, it can be stated that parallelism is transitive (if *m* ∥ *n* and *n* ∥ *p*, then *m* ∥ *p*) without having to worry about an exception when *m* = *p*. Lines are parallel to their images under translations without exception. Two lines with the same slope are parallel without exception.

With this definition of *parallel lines*, none of the customary theorems is violated. There will still be only one line parallel to a given line through a point not on that line, but now it can be more general—the point can be anywhere. Two lines perpendicular to the same line are parallel (even when the two lines are identical).

Making Connections
Stress the importance of properly stating and applying postulates, theorems, and definitions. This will tie in with later work on the form of a conditional sentence and the use of the hypothesis and conclusion in proof.

ADDITIONAL EXAMPLES
1. To guide a ship into a rocky harbor, two large diamond-shaped signs are mounted, one near the shore and one some distance up the hill. Why not one?
One sign would not be enough to indicate the line that the pilot of the ship should take. The two points determine exactly one line.

2. Can a number line be co-ordinatized as shown here?

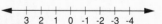

Yes; there seems to be a one-to-one correspondence between the real numbers and the points on the line.

Example   In solving an equation, a student changes $3 = 4x + 2$ into $4x + 2 = 3$. What property justifies the change?

Solution   The right and left sides of the equation have been switched. Thus the Symmetric Property of Equality has been applied: If $3 = 4x + 2$, then $4x + 2 = 3$.

Questions

Covering the Reading

1. What is a postulate? **an assumption**

2. What are the two purposes of postulates? **See margin.**

In 3-6, does the named part of the Point-Line-Plane Postulate hold for the given description of point?

3. part (a) for node **No**

4. part (d) for location **Yes**

5. part (b) for ordered pair **Yes**

6. part (c) for dot **No**

7. *True* or *false?*   Every part of the Point-Line-Plane Postulate holds for points as locations. **True**

8. What part of the Point-Line-Plane Postulate is violated by this figure?
part (a)

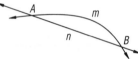

m and *n* are different lines.
m intersects *n* at two points, *A* and *B*.

9. The line through points X and A is written __?__ or __?__ . $\overleftrightarrow{XA}$ or $\overleftrightarrow{AX}$

10. *True* or *false?*   According to the definition in this lesson, every line is parallel to itself. **True**

11. What was Euclid's *Elements?*
a set of books of postulates and theorems by Euclid

12. How did Euclid word the Equation to Inequality Property?
The whole is greater than any of its parts.

Applying the Mathematics

In 13–19, a postulate from arithmetic or algebra is applied. Name the postulate.

13. Since $\frac{1}{4} = .25$ and $.25 = 25\%$, $\frac{1}{4} = 25\%$.
Transitive Property of Equality

14. $4\sqrt{3} = \sqrt{3} \cdot 4$ **Commutative Property of Multiplication**

15. When $2x + 46 = 30$, $2x = -16$. **Addition Property of Equality**

16. When $2x + 46 < 30$, $2x < -16$. **Addition Property of Inequality**

17. In the figure below, since *PQ + QR = PR*, then *PR > PQ*.

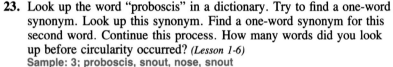

P   Q   R   **Equation to Inequality Property**

18. If *m = 2x + 5* and *x = 4*, then *m = 2 · 4 + 5*.
Substitution Property of Equality

19. $3(x - 2y) = 3x - 3 \cdot 2y$ **Distributive Property**

20. Give the property that justifies each indicated step.
   a. $3x + 4x = x \cdot 3 + x \cdot 4$ **Commutative Property of Mult.**
   b. $= x(3 + 4)$ **Distributive Property**
                 $= x \cdot 7$
   c. $= 7x$ **Commutative Property of Multiplication**

21. One of Euclid's assumptions was (in English translation)
"If equals are added to equals, the sums are equal."
What is the name we give to this property of real numbers?
Addition Property of Equality

22. If points are dots on a number line, and a dot is .001 unit in diameter, how many dots can there be between 0 and 1? (Do not include dots at 0 and 1.) **999**

Review

23. Look up the word "proboscis" in a dictionary. Try to find a one-word synonym. Look up this synonym. Find a one-word synonym for this second word. Continue this process. How many words did you look up before circularity occurred? *(Lesson 1-6)*
Sample: 3; proboscis, snout, nose, snout

24. Refer to the network at the right.
   a. How many nodes does it have? **5**
   b. How many arcs does it have? **10**
   c. Is the network traversable?
       If so, give a route; if not,
       explain why not. *(Lesson 1-4)*
       not traversable, since there are more than 2 odd nodes.

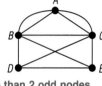

25. **a.** Represent the floor plan at the left with a network. **See margin.**
   b. Is it traversable? *(Lesson 1-4)* **No**

26. **a.** Graph *y = x* and *y = x + 1* on the same set of axes. **See margin.**
   b. Are they parallel? *(Lesson 1-3)* **Yes**

27. Classify the line as vertical, horizontal, or oblique. *(Lesson 1-3)*
   a. *y = 7* **horizontal**   **b.** *2x − y = 9* **oblique**

Exploration

28. Equality satisfies the Transitive Property:
     If *a = b* and *b = c*, then *a = c*.
So does <:
     If *a < b* and *b < c*, then *a < c*.
So does *is an ancestor of*:
     If *a* is an ancestor of *b* and *b* is an ancestor of *c*, then *a* is an ancestor of *c*.
Find two other things that satisfy the Transitive Property.
Answer will vary. Samples: >, "is a subset of," "goes to the same school as"

MORE PRACTICE
For more questions on SPUR Objectives, use *Lesson Master 1-7*, shown below.

EVALUATION
Alternative Assessment
Call upon three or four students to explain the assumptions for the Point-Line-Plane Postulate in their own words. Ask them to summarize the content of this lesson.

26. a.

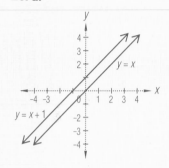

NAME _____

1-8

One-Dimensional Figures

The light rays of fiber optics are one-dimensional.

The location of a point on a line can be described with one number. (This is part (c) of the Point-Line-Plane Postulate.) This is why we say that a line is one-dimensional. Parts or subsets of lines are also one-dimensional figures. The most common subsets of lines are *line segments* and *rays*. *Line* is an undefined term, but the other terms can be defined combining line and a simple idea, betweenness.

A *number* is **between** two others if it is greater than one of them and less than the other. For example, 5 is between -1 and 6.5 since $5 > -1$ and $5 < 6.5$. The number -1 is *not* considered to be between itself and 6.5.

A *point* is **between** two other points on the same line if its coordinate is between their coordinates. Point *U* above, with coordinate 5, is between the other two points *A* and *B*. If you graph -1, 6.5, and *all* points having coordinates between -1 and 6.5, the graph is a *segment*. The points for -1 and 6.5 are the *endpoints* of the segment.

Definition:

The **segment** (or **line segment**) with **endpoints** *A* and *B*, denoted $\overline{AB}$, is the set consisting of the distinct points *A* and *B* and all points between *A* and *B*.

The segment pictured above consists of -1, 6.5, and all points on the line whose coordinates satisfy the inequality $-1 < x < 6.5$.

Recall that AB (with no bar above the A or B) is the distance between A and B, called the **length** of $\overline{AB}$. By the definition of distance, the length is $|-1 - 6.5|$, which is 7.5.

In the example below, point B is between points A and C. Notice the relationship between the three lengths AB, BC, and AC.

■ ■ ■ ■ ■ ■ ■

Example   Suppose A, B, and C are three points on a number line with coordinates -53, 212, and 670. By calculating distances, show that $AB + BC = AC$.

Solution   First draw a picture.

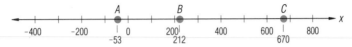

$AB = |-53 - 212| = |-265| = 265$
$BC = |212 - 670| = |-458| = 458$
$AC = |-53 - 670| = |-723| = 723$
So $AB + BC = 265 + 458 = 723$, which equals AC.

The idea shown in the Example can be proved (using algebra) for any three points on a line. It is an important property of betweenness.

Betweenness Theorem:

If B is between A and C, then $AB + BC = AC$.

Player no. 5 is not between players 32 and 26.

Another way to state the Betweenness Theorem is: If B is on $\overline{AC}$, then $AB + BC = AC$. Using the Betweenness Theorem and the Equation to Inequality Property, you can immediately conclude that if B is between A and C, then $AC > AB$ and $AC > BC$.

LESSON 1-8   One-Dimensional Figures   **41**

A similar argument works for the case (2) $x > y > z$.

It should be noted that the distinction between the notations for rays, lines, segments, and distance is one commonly found in high school geometry textbooks but not one used often by mathematicians, or even by practicing geometers. They ignore the distinction, preferring to let context tell which is being discussed. Indeed, virtually every word describing a segment of some special type (radius, diameter, side, leg, hypotenuse, base, and so on) can mean either the segment or its length, and some words (tangent, secant, perpendicular, and so on) stand either for lines or segments. The message in all this is that we try to be consistent in this book and distinct with our notation, but one should not give a picture that mathematics is rigid here when it is not.

Remind students that a segment must be named by its two endpoints; a ray must be named by its endpoint, but may have any other point on it for its second named point; a line may be named by *any* two points on the line.

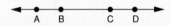

$\overleftrightarrow{AB} = \overleftrightarrow{CD} = \overleftrightarrow{CA}$; $\overline{BC} = \overline{BD}$

In Lesson 1-7, parallel lines were defined. Often it is convenient to refer to segments and rays as parallel as well. Thus, inform students that segments and/or rays which lie in parallel lines are parallel.

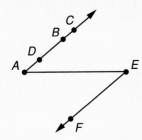

$\overline{AD} \parallel \overline{BC}$
$\overrightarrow{AB} \parallel \overrightarrow{EF}$
$\overline{BD} \parallel \overrightarrow{EF}$

Alternate Approach
Students who do not understand rays and lines may benefit from graphing examples of them. Using the number line below, have students graph each of the following:
$\overrightarrow{AD}; \overrightarrow{DA}; \overleftrightarrow{FB}; \overleftrightarrow{FG};$
$\overleftrightarrow{AG}; \overrightarrow{CD}; \overrightarrow{CE}.$

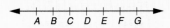

ADDITIONAL EXAMPLES
1. Suppose A, B, C are three points on a number line and the coordinates of A and B are 5 and -2, respectively. State a possible coordinate for C if
a. $AB + BC = AC$;
any number less than -2
b. $AC + BC = AB$.
any number between -2 and 5

2. Why are rays $\overrightarrow{BC}$ and $\overrightarrow{BA}$ not opposite rays?

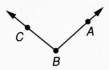

B is not between C and A.

42

A geometric *ray* is like a laser beam. A laser beam starts at a point and, if not blocked, goes forever in a particular direction. In geometry, a ray consists of an endpoint and all points of a line on one side of that endpoint.

Definition:

The **ray** with endpoint A and containing a second point B, denoted $\overrightarrow{AB}$, consists of the points on $\overline{AB}$ and all points for which B is between each of them and A.

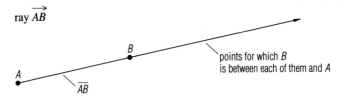

ray $\overrightarrow{AB}$

points for which B is between each of them and A

$\overline{AB}$

You have drawn rays on a number line when solving inequalities. For example, if A has coordinate 5 and B has coordinate 7, then $\overrightarrow{AB}$ consists of all points with coordinates $x \geq 5$. If C has coordinate 4, then $\overrightarrow{AC}$ points in the opposite direction of $\overrightarrow{AB}$. $\overrightarrow{AC}$ consists of all points with coordinates $x \leq 5$. $\overrightarrow{AB}$ and $\overrightarrow{AC}$ are called *opposite rays*.

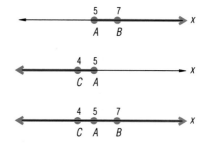

Definition:

$\overrightarrow{AB}$ and $\overrightarrow{AC}$ are **opposite rays** if and only if A is between B and C.

Notice that, for any two points A and B, $\overrightarrow{BA}$ and $\overrightarrow{AB}$ are *not* opposite rays. They have many points in common. $\overrightarrow{BA}$ has endpoint B, while $\overrightarrow{AB}$ has endpoint A.

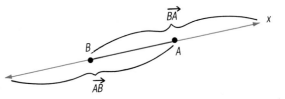

42

Caution: Be careful to distinguish among the following symbols. They may look similar, but their meanings are quite different.

$\overleftrightarrow{AB}$ is the *line* determined by points A and B.

$\overrightarrow{AB}$ is the *ray* with endpoint A and containing B.

$\overline{AB}$ is the *segment* with endpoints A and B.

AB is the *distance* between A and B, or the length of $\overline{AB}$.

   AB is a single number, while $\overline{AB}$ is a set of points.

Questions

Covering the Reading

1. On a number line, point A has coordinate 2, point B has coordinate -2, and point C has coordinate $\sqrt{2}$. Which point is between the other two, and why? **C is between A and B since -2 < $\sqrt{2}$ < 2.**

2. $\overline{AB}$ is the set whose elements are __?__ .
   A, B, and all points between A and B

3. A laser beam is like the geometric figure called a(n) __?__ . **ray**

4. Match each symbol with the correct description.
   a. AB (i) line
   b. $\overline{AB}$ (ii) length
   c. $\overleftrightarrow{AB}$ (iii) ray
   d. $\overrightarrow{AB}$ (iv) segment
   a) (iv); b) (ii); c) (i); d) (iii)

5. $\overrightarrow{MN}$ has endpoint __?__ and contains a second point __?__ .
                            M   **N**

6. *Multiple choice.* If X is between Y and Z, then
   (a) $XY + YZ = XZ$ (b) $XZ + YX = YZ$
   (c) $XY = XZ$ (d) $XZ + YZ = XY$. **(b)**

7. *Multiple choice.* If X is between Y and Z, then
   (a) $XZ > XY$ (b) $XY > YZ$
   (c) $XY > XZ$ (d) $YZ > XZ$. **(d)**

8. *Multiple choice.* Which is not true?
   (a) $\overline{AB} = \overline{BA}$ (b) $AB = BA$
   (c) $\overleftrightarrow{AB} = \overleftrightarrow{BA}$ (d) $\overrightarrow{AB} = \overrightarrow{BA}$ **(d)**

9. A, B, and C are three points on a number line with coordinates 3, 14, and 82. Verify that $AB + BC = AC$. **See margin.**

10. **a.** On a number line, graph the set of numbers satisfying $y \leq 1$.
    See margin.
    b. What one-dimensional figure best describes the graph?
    a ray

11. **a.** On a number line, graph the set of numbers satisfying $7 \leq x \leq 8.3$. **See margin.**
    b. What one-dimensional figure best describes the graph?
    a segment

Applying the Mathematics

In 12 and 13, use the figure below. B is between A and C.

12. If $AC = 100$, find x. 96

13. If $AB = BC$, find x. 38

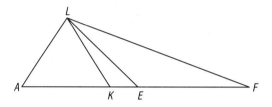

14. Two points are 7 units apart on a number line. The coordinate of one point is -8. What are the possible coordinates of the other? -1 or -15

15. Point Q on a number line has coordinate -5. Find all possibilities for the coordinate of R so that $QR = 21$. 16 or -26

In 16 and 17, use the figure below. K is between A and E. E is between K and F.

16. If $AE = 10$, $KF = 12$, and $AF = 19.6$, find KE. 2.4

17. If $AE = 15x$, $KF = 19x$, and $AF = 30x$, find KE. 4x

Review

In 18–20, name the postulate from arithmetic or algebra that is being applied. *(Lesson 1-7)*

18. $4(3x - 5) = 12x - 20$ Distributive Property

19. If $5x = \frac{1}{5}$, $x = \frac{1}{25}$. Multiplication Property of Equality

20. When $7 = 2 - x$, then $2 - x = 7$. Symmetric Property of Equality

21. m and n are coplanar lines. *True* or *false*?
   a. If $m = n$, then $m \parallel n$. True
   b. If m does not intersect n, then $m \parallel n$. True
   c. If m intersects n in exactly one point, then $m \parallel n$. *(Lesson 1-7)* False

22. Three views of the same cube are given below. Which symbols are on opposite faces of the cube? *(Lesson 1-5)* U opp. M, G opp. S, P opp. C

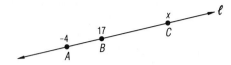

23. Graph $3x - y = 4$ and $7x + 2y = 5$ on the same axes. *(Lesson 1-3)*
See margin.

24. Give an equation for the vertical line containing (7, 3). *(Lesson 1-3)*
$x = 7$

25. Lines on the surface of the earth do not behave like lines in the plane. Suppose only perfectly north-south lines are considered as lines. (These are lines of longitude.) What part or parts of the Point-Line-Plane Postulate would these lines violate? *(Lesson 1-7)*
parts (a), (c)

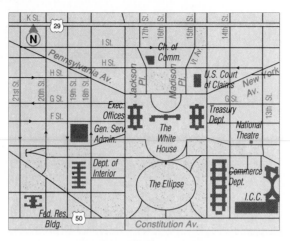

Exploration

26. Two points can be the endpoints of 1 segment. Three points A, B, and C can be endpoints of 3 segments ($\overline{AB}$, $\overline{BC}$, and $\overline{AC}$).
  a. How many segments are determined by 4 points? 6
  b. How many segments are determined by 8 points? 28
  c. How many segments are determined by n points? $\dfrac{n(n-1)}{2}$

MORE PRACTICE
For more questions on SPUR Objectives, use *Lesson Master 1-8,* shown below.

ADDITIONAL ANSWERS
23.

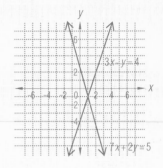

NAME _____

LESSON **MASTER   1–8**
QUESTIONS ON **SPUR** OBJECTIVES

■ **PROPERTIES**   *Objective F (See pages 54–57 for objectives.)*

1. Points A and B lie on a number line. If A has coordinate 3 and $\overline{AB}$ has length 3.7, the possible coordinates of B are ___6.7___ or ___-0.7___ .

2. Suppose B lies between A and C. If $AB = 11$, and $AC = 15$, then $BC =$ ___4___

3. a. Graph the set of numbers satisfying $-3 \leq x \leq 5$.

b. What geometrical figure does this represent? ___line segment___

4. a. Graph the set of numbers satisfying $x \leq -1$.

b. What geometrical figure does this represent? ___ray___

5. If $BC = 5$ and $AD = 12$, find $AB + CD$. ___7___

6. If A, B, and C lie on a line, with $AB = 10$, $AC = 4$, and $BC = 6$, then point ___C___ lies between points ___A___ and ___B___ .

OBJECTIVES

Letter codes refer to the SPUR Objectives on page 2B.
F Apply properties of betweenness.
G Determine whether a triangle can be formed with sides of three given lengths.
I Apply the Triangle Inequality in real situations.

TEACHING NOTES

In the previous section, there is the Betweenness Property: If B is between A and C, then $AB + BC = AC$. It is natural to ask what happens if B is not between A and C. This question leads to the Triangle Inequality.

Although the term *triangle* has not been formally defined, the concept of triangle is understood by students prior to this course, enabling this early discussion of the Triangle Inequality Postulate. The definition of a triangle as a union of segments is discussed in Lesson 2-6.

There is an equivalent statement of the Triangle Inequality that does not mention the term *triangle*: If $A, B,$ and C are noncollinear points, then $AB + BC > AC; AC + CB > AB;$ and $BA + AC > BC$. In words, if three points are noncollinear, then the sum of the distances from any of the

LESSON

1-9

The Triangle Inequality

The bridge and wires form many triangles.

The Betweenness Theorem states that if B is between A and C, then $AB + BC = AC$. A natural question to ask is what happens when B is not between A and C.

If B does not lie on $\overleftrightarrow{AC}$, then $A, B,$ and C form the vertices of a triangle. It seems from this situation that $AB + BC > AC$. That is, it takes longer to travel from A to B to C than to go from A to C directly. This result is called the *Triangle Inequality*. In this book we treat the Triangle Inequality as a postulate. That is, we do not prove it from other postulates.

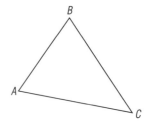

Triangle Inequality Postulate:

The sum of the lengths of two sides of any triangle is greater than the length of the third side.

In $\triangle ABC$ drawn above, this relationship means three inequalities are true:
$$AB + BC > AC \quad \text{and} \quad BC + AC > AB \quad \text{and} \quad AB + AC > BC.$$

■ ■ ■ ■ ■ ■ ■

Example 1 Can a triangle have sides of length 3″, 5″, and 10″?

Solution Is the sum of the lengths of the smaller two sides greater than the length of the third side? Is 3″ + 5″ > 10″? No, so there is no triangle with sides of these lengths.

46

Check If you try to draw such a triangle, you can see that the segments will not meet.

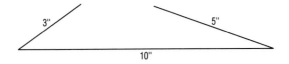

Given two sides of a triangle, the Triangle Inequality Postulate makes it possible to determine the possible lengths of the third side.

■ ■ ■ ■ ■ ■ ■ ■ ■

Example 2 Suppose two sides of a triangle have lengths 19 cm and 31 cm. What are the possible lengths of the third side?

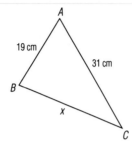

Solution Let x = the length of the third side of the triangle. Substitute into the Triangle Inequality to find the possible values of x.

$$19 + 31 > x \quad \text{and} \quad 19 + x > 31 \quad \text{and} \quad 31 + x > 19.$$

Solve each inequality.

$$50 > x \quad \text{and} \quad x > 12 \quad \text{and} \quad x > \text{-}12.$$

The first two inequalities show that $\overline{BC}$ must be shorter than 50 cm but longer than 12 cm. This can be written as $12 < x < 50$. (The third inequality shows that $\overline{BC}$ must also be longer than -12. But since length is positive, this was already known.)

In this and the last lesson, you have studied two possible locations of B with respect to A and C.

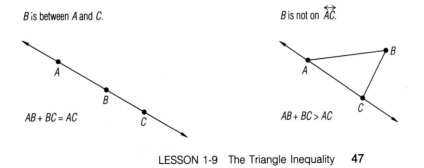

B is between A and C.

$AB + BC = AC$

B is not on $\overleftrightarrow{AC}$.

$AB + BC > AC$

LESSON 1-9 *The Triangle Inequality* **47**

points to the other two is greater than the distance between the other two points.

The complexity of these statements, together with the universal name given to this property, indicate why we decided to use the triangle description.

Some students may assume the concept of sum and not state it. For example, they may say "two sides of a triangle are greater than the third." Encourage the use of the word *sum.*

Making Connections
Students who have studied UCSMP *Algebra* will have had a lesson devoted to this property and will have solved systems of inequalities like those in **Example 2.** If students have not seen inequalities, you will have to proceed carefully, but the content is easy and the end-of-chapter material will make it possible to move on after a single day.

ADDITIONAL EXAMPLES
1. Can a triangle have sides of length
a. 3 cm, 8 cm, and 6 cm?
Yes
b. 3 cm, 8 cm, 5 cm?
No
c. all sides 3 cm?
Yes

2. Two sticks of lengths 10″ and 14″ are joined by a hinge.

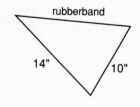

rubberband

14″   10″

a. If a rubberband is attached at their other ends, what is the longest distance the rubberband can be stretched?
24 in.
b. What is the shortest distance that it could ever be?
4 in.

There are two other possibilities for three distinct points A, B, and C.

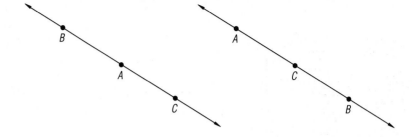

B is on $\overleftrightarrow{AC}$; A is between B and C. B is on $\overleftrightarrow{AC}$; C is between A and B.

It seems obvious from both pictures that $AB + BC > AC$. This can be shown using the algebraic postulates.

Suppose A is between B and C (as on the line drawn above at the left). From the Betweenness Theorem,
$$BC = BA + AC.$$
Adding AB to both sides,
$$AB + BC = AB + BA + AC.$$
Applying the Equation to Inequality Property,
$$AB + BC > AC.$$

In Question 8, you are asked to show that the other possibility also leads to $AB + BC > AC$. (The steps are almost the same.)

When A, B, and C are distinct points, the relationship between AB, BC, and AC can be summarized.

In words	Algebraically
B is between A and C	exactly when $AB + BC = AC$.
B is not between A and C	exactly when $AB + BC > AC$.

Two consequences are important enough to be stated as theorems.

Theorem:

If A, B, and C are distinct points and $AB + BC = AC$, then B is on $\overline{AC}$.

Theorem:

For any three points A, B, and C,
$$AB + BC \geq AC.$$

48

Example 3 Rosalita lives at R, 12 miles from the airport A and 3.5 miles from her office O. What are the possible distances from her office to the airport?

Solution Draw a possible picture.
Using the last theorem with points R, O, and A,

$RO + RA \geq OA$ and $RO + OA \geq RA$ and $RA + OA \geq RO$.
$3.5 + 12 \geq OA$ and $3.5 + OA \geq 12$ and $12 + OA \geq 3.5$.
$15.5 \geq OA$ and $OA \geq 8.5$ and $OA \geq -8.5$.

Combining these statements:
$15.5 \geq OA \geq 8.5$.

The distance from Rosalita's office to the airport is at least 8.5 miles but no more than 15.5 miles.

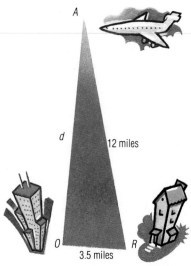

A

12 miles

d

O

3.5 miles

R

Questions

Covering the Reading

1. State the Triangle Inequality Postulate. See margin.

2. Give three inequalities satisfied by the lengths of the sides of $\triangle ABC$.
   $AB + BC > AC$, $BC + AC > AB$, and $AB + AC > BC$

In 3–5, tell whether the numbers can be lengths of the three sides in a triangle.

3. **a.** 2, 2, 2   **b.** 2, 2, 3   **c.** 2, 2, 4   **d.** 2, 2, 5
       Yes   Yes   No   No
4. **a.** 12, 15, 28   **b.** 12, 15, 10   **c.** 12, 15, 2
       No   Yes   No
5. **a.** 1, 2, 3   **b.** 2, 3, 4   **c.** 101, 102, 103
       No   Yes   Yes

6. Suppose two sides of a triangle have lengths 16 inches and 11 inches. What are the possible lengths of the third side?
   shorter than 27 inches but longer than 5 inches

LESSON 1-9 The Triangle Inequality   **49**

NOTES ON QUESTIONS
Question 2: The answer to this question requires verbal articulation; that is, rather than simply saying "AB plus BC is greater than AC," expect "the sum of the lengths AB and BC is greater than the length AC," or something similar.

Questions 3-5: If $a \leq b \leq c$, then obviously $c + b > a$ and $c + a > b$, so one needs only to check whether $a + b > c$.

Questions 7-9: These questions are not simply recall items; it may be advisable to draw pictures as part of the explanation.

Questions 13 and 14: In discussing these questions, point out that the Triangle Inequality tends to hold for time as well as distance. For example, if it takes 10 minutes for Bob to get from home to school and 25 minutes for Sarah to get from home to school, then it will take between 15 and 35 minutes to get from Bob's to Sarah's (assuming constant speeds). However, those who fly often know that there is no Triangle Inequality for airline fares. It can sometimes cost $\$x$ to go from A to B, $\$y$ to go from B to C, and far more than $\$(x + y)$ or far less than $|x - y|$ dollars to go directly from A to C.

Question 15: Use the problem-solving strategy *try a special case*. Ask for values of x and y and then determine z given those values. Then generalize.

ADDITIONAL ANSWERS
1. The sum of the lengths of two sides of any triangle is greater than the length of the third side.

EXTENSION
Small Group Work
Do the following in groups of
2 or 3 students to facilitate
collecting data.
(1) Give each group several
"sticks" of spaghetti.

(2) Have one student hold a
stick behind his or her back
and break it into 3 pieces.

(3) Determine whether or not
the three pieces may form a
triangle:
for example,
——— —— ——————— (No)
——————— ——— ——— (Yes)

(4) Tabulate the results of all
experiments.

(5) From these data, what is
the relative frequency that a
stick broken into three pieces
may form a triangle?

Generally, the relative frequency in experiments like
this is much higher than the
probability (which can be
shown to be $\frac{1}{4}$) because students seldom break the spaghetti into very small pieces.

ADDITIONAL ANSWERS
8. Since *C* is between *A*
and *B*, *AC* + *BC* = *AB* by
the Betweenness Theorem.
From the Equation to
Inequality Property, *AB* >
AC. Since *BC* > 0, *AB* + *BC*
> *AC*.

16. a.

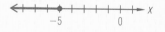

7. Suppose *A* is between *B* and *C*. What can you conclude using the Betweenness Theorem? *BC = BA + AC*

8. Explain why, if *C* is between *A* and *B*, then *AB + BC > AC*.
   See margin.

9. For any three points *A, B,* and *C,* how are the distances related? *AB + BC ≥ AC*

10. In Example 3, suppose Rosalita lives 6.5 miles from the airport and 15.5 miles from her office. What then are the possible distances from her office to the airport?
    at least 9 miles, but no more than 22 miles

11. *True* or *false*? If *PQ* = 17, *QR* = 81, and *PR* = 98, then *Q* must be between *P* and *R*. **True**

Applying the Mathematics

12. Can the numbers be lengths of the three sides in a triangle?
    a. $\frac{1}{2}, \frac{1}{3}, \frac{1}{4}$ **Yes** **b.** $\frac{1}{2}, \frac{1}{3}, \frac{1}{5}$ **Yes** **c.** $\frac{1}{2}, \frac{1}{2}, \frac{1}{4}$ **Yes**

13. Two sides of a triangle have lengths 9 cm and 20 cm.
    a. Must the 9 cm side be the shortest side? **Yes**
    b. Must the 20 cm side be the longest side? **No**

14. According to a Sheraton hotel directory, there is a Sheraton in the Houston area that is 40 miles from the Houston Intercontinental Airport and 10 miles from Hobby Airport. With this information, you know that the airports are between __?__ and __?__ miles apart. **30, 50**

15. In the triangle below, *x* > *y*. Then __?__ < *z* < __?__.
    (Hint: Consider examples and look for a pattern.) *x − y, x + y*

Houston, Texas, skyline

Review

16. **a.** On a number line, graph the set of numbers satisfying *x* ≤ -5.
    b. What one-dimensional figure best describes the graph? *(Lesson 1-8)*
    a) See margin. b) a ray

17. On the number line below, if *WY* = 17, *WZ* = 23, and *XZ* = 21, find *XY*. *(Lesson 1-8)* **15**

18. Two points are 13 units apart on a number line. The coordinate of one point is 81. What are the possible coordinates of the other? *(Lesson 1-8)*
    94 or 68

19. What postulate of algebra guarantees that *PQ* + *QR* = *QR* + *PQ*? *(Lesson 1-7)* **Commutative Property of Addition**

20. What is a postulate? *(Lesson 1-7)* **an assumption**

21. a. Represent the bridges and land pictured below with a network.
b. Is it traversable? *(Lesson 1-4)*   **a) See margin. b) Yes**

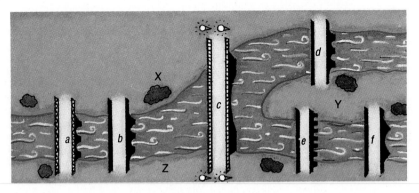

22. Graph $y = 8$ on coordinate axes. *(Lesson 1-3)* **See margin.**

23. If $x = 42$, what is $|14 - x|$? *(Lesson 1-3)* **28**

Exploration

24. The lengths 2″, 2″, 2″, and 2″ can be sides of a quadrilateral, but 2″, 4″, 8″, and 16″ cannot. Is there a "quadrilateral inequality"? That is, is there some general way you can tell when four positive numbers a, b, c, and d can be the lengths of the sides of a quadrilateral?

Sides a, b, c, d of a quadrilateral must satisfy $a + b + c > d$, $b + c + d > a$, $a + b + d > c$, and $a + c + d > b$.

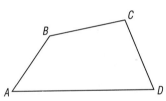

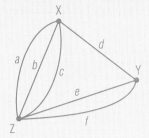

22.

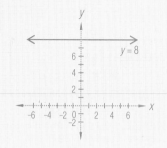

NAME _____

LESSON **MASTER   1–9**
QUESTIONS ON **SPUR** OBJECTIVES

■ **PROPERTIES**   *Objective F   (See pages 54–57 for objectives.)*

1. *Multiple choice.* If X is between Y and Z, which of the following is *not* a valid conclusion?   **(c)**

(a) $XY < YZ$ (b) $XY + XZ \geq YZ$

(c) $XY + XZ > YZ$ (d) $XY + XZ = YZ$

2. What conclusion can you make about points A, B, and C if $AB + BC = AC$?
   B is between A and C.

■ **PROPERTIES**   *Objective G*

3. Two sides of a triangle have lengths 7 and 12. What are the possible lengths of w, the third side?   **$5 < w < 19$**

4. Consider the triangle below. What are the possible values for y?   **$0 < y < 12$**

■ **USES**   *Objective I*

5. Dan and Elaine travel from Cleveland to Los Angeles. They know the distance from Cleveland to Denver is 1370 miles and from Denver to Los Angeles is 1170 miles. Using this information only, what conclusion can they make about the distance from Cleveland to Los Angeles?
   It is between 200 and 2540 miles.

6. Earth orbits the sun at a mean distance of 93,000,000 miles, while Mars orbits at a mean distance of 141,710,000 miles. The orbits are nearly circular and about in the same plane. About what is the minimum distance from Mars to Earth?   **48,710,000 mi**

Geometry © Scott, Foresman and Company   **9**

SUMMARY

The Summary gives an overview of the entire chapter and provides an opportunity for students to consider the material as a whole. Thus, the Summary can be used to help students relate the various concepts presented in the chapter.

VOCABULARY

Terms, symbols, and properties are listed by lesson to provide a checklist of concepts a student must know. Emphasize to students that they should read the vocabulary list carefully before starting the Progress Self-Test. If students do not remember the meaning of a term or a statement of a postulate or theorem, they should refer back to the individual lesson.

Definitions or descriptions of all terms in vocabulary lists may be found in the Glossary or the List of Theorems in the student text.

Summary

Geometry is the study of visual patterns. In two-dimensional geometry, the basic building blocks of these patterns are points and lines. Four conceptions or descriptions of points and lines are studied in this chapter. (1) When points are dots, lines are collections of dots in a row. It is possible that between two dots, there might be no other dots. (2) When points are locations, lines are shortest paths between the locations. (3) When points are ordered pairs, lines are sets of ordered pairs (x, y) satisfying $Ax + By = C$. (4) When points are nodes in networks, lines are arcs joining the nodes. Then lines have only two points on them and there may be many lines connecting two points.

In three-dimensional geometry, planes join points and lines as basic building blocks. It is impossible to show a three-dimensional figure on a page exactly as it is. A person can choose to draw the figure in perspective or not. Mathematicians usually do not use perspective.

It is impossible to define all terms in any system because of circularity. The terms left undefined in geometry are *point, line,* and *plane*. So any of the above conceptions of point might be possible. However, the assumptions in the Point-Line-Plane Postulate apply only to points either as locations or as ordered pairs. This postulate indicates which properties points and lines satisfy. It also forms a starting point for deducing other properties.

The properties of points and lines as ordered pairs and locations are the same, so what you learned in algebra about points and lines can be used in geometry. For instance, if point B is between points A and C, then $AB + BC = AC$. However, if B is not between A and C, then by the Triangle Inequality, $AB + BC > AC$. Thus, the shortest distance between two points is along the line containing them.

Vocabulary

Below are the most important terms and phrases for this chapter.
For the starred (*) terms you should be able to give a definition of the term.
For the other terms you should be able to give a general description and a specific example of each.

Lesson 1-1
pixel, matrix, resolution
discrete line, oblique, *collinear

Lesson 1-2
coordinate, coordinatized
number line, *distance, AB
zero-dimensional
dense line, one-dimensional
two-dimensional, plane figure
*coplanar
three-dimensional, space figure

Lesson 1-3
coordinate plane
Cartesian plane
ordered pair, lattice point

Lesson 1-4
Königsberg Bridge Problem
network, arc
traversable network
node, vertex (vertices)
odd node, odd vertex
even node, even vertex

Lesson 1-5
vanishing point, perspective
perspective drawings
line of sight, vanishing line
hidden lines

Lesson 1-6
plane geometry
solid geometry, *space
*figure, circularity
undefined terms

Lesson 1-7
*postulate, $\overleftrightarrow{AB}$, *theorem
*parallel lines
Point-Line-Plane Postulate
Line Intersection Theorem
Reflexive Property of Equality
Symmetric Property of Equality
Transitive Property of Equality
Addition Property of Equality
Multiplication Property of Equality
Substitution Property of Equality

Addition Property of Inequality
Multiplication Property of
Inequality
Equation to Inequality Property
Transitive Property of Inequality
Commutative Property of Addition
Commutative Property of
Multiplication
Distributive Property

Lesson 1-8
betweenness of numbers
betweenness of points
*line segment, segment, $\overline{AB}$
length of a line segment
*ray, $\overrightarrow{AB}$, *opposite rays
Betweenness Theorem

Lesson 1-9
Triangle Inequality Postulate

52

Progress Self-Test

See margin for answers not shown below.

Directions: Take this test as you would take a test in class. Then check your work with the solutions in the Selected Answers section in the back of the book. You will need graph paper and a ruler. Calculators are allowed.

1. Using the number line below, find AB. 4

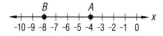

2. Draw a carton:
   a. in perspective;   **b.** not in perspective.

3. Graph the line with equation $3x - 2y = 10$.

4. Can 4.8, 9.2, and 3.7 be the lengths of three sides of a triangle? No

5. It is 1115 km from Hong Kong to Manila and 1229 km from Hong Kong to Shanghai. From only this information, what can you say about the distance d (in km) from Manila to Shanghai? $114 \le d \le 2344$

In 6 and 7, fill in the table with A if the statement is always true, S if sometimes true, or N if never true.

Description of Point

Statement	Dot	Location	Ordered Pair	Node
6. A line contains infinitely many points.	A	A	A	N
7. A point has size.	A	N	N	N

8. How many dimensions does space have? three

9. Ignoring its small thickness, how many dimensions does a flat sheet of paper have? two

10. If in defining a word, you return to the original word, what has occurred? circularity

11. If two computer screens are the same size,
    a. which screen has better resolution, one whose pixels are 180 by 310 or one that is 215 by 350? 215 by 350
    b. How many pixels are on the screen with the better resolution? 75,250

12. A tape measure is stretched across a shelf. If one end reads 4″ and the other 32″, how long is the shelf? 28″

13. The air distance from Chicago to Duluth is 450 miles, but the road distance is 464 miles. Why are the distances different?

14. Graph $y = 4x$ and $x + y = 5$ on the same set of axes.

In 15 and 16, given is an equation of a line. Classify the line as vertical, horizontal, or oblique.

15. $x = \frac{3}{2}$ vertical   16. $11x + y = 3$ oblique

17. **a.** Is the network drawn at the left below traversable? Yes
    b. If so, give a route. If not, explain why not.

18. **a.** Represent the floor plan above with a network. **b.** Is it traversable?

19. It is 8 minutes by subway from Harvard Square to Park Street. It is 6 minutes by subway from Central Square to Park Street. From only this information, how long would it take by subway to get from Harvard Square to Central Square? 2 to 14 minutes

In 20 and 21, a postulate from arithmetic or algebra is applied. Name the postulate.

20. When $3x > 11$, $3x + 6 > 17$.

21. If $AB + BC = 10$ and $AB = 7$, then $7 + BC = 10$.

22. Two points are 19 units apart on a number line. The coordinate of one point is -42. What are the possible coordinates of the other?

23. The graph on a number line of the set of points satisfying $x \ge 40$ is the geometric figure called a(n) __?__. ray

24. *Multiple choice.* If E and F are points, which is a number?
    (a) EF (b) $\overline{EF}$ (c) $\overrightarrow{EF}$ (d) $\overleftrightarrow{EF}$ (a)

Whereas end-of-chapter materials may be considered optional in some texts, they should not be considered optional in UCSMP *Geometry*. The Progress Self-Test provides the opportunity for feedback and correction; the Chapter Review provides additional opportunities for practice. It is at this point that the material "gels" for many students, allowing them to solidify skills and concepts before a test. In general, students performance is markedly improved after doing these pages.

USING THE PROGRESS SELF-TEST
Assign the Progress Self-Test as a one-night assignment. Worked-out *solutions* for all questions are in the Selected Answers section of the student text. Encourage students to take the Progress Self-Test honestly, grade themselves, and then be prepared to discuss the test in class.

Advise students to pay special attention to those Chapter Review questions (pages 54-57) which correspond to questions missed on the Progress Self-Test. A chart provided with the Selected Answers keys the Progress Self-Test questions to the lettered SPUR Objectives in the Chapter Review or to the Vocabulary. It also keys the questions to the corresponding lessons where the material is covered.

3., 13., 14., 17.b., 18.a. and b., 20., 21., 22. See Additional Answers in the back of this book.

CHAPTER REVIEW

The main objectives for the chapter are organized here into sections corresponding to the four main types of understanding this book promotes: Skills, Properties, Uses, and Representations. We call these the SPUR objectives.

Skills range from the carrying out of simple and complicated procedures for drawings and getting answers to the study of algorithms.

Properties range from the mathematical justifications for procedures and other theory to the writing of proofs.

Uses range from simple real-world applications of the mathematics to the modeling of real situations.

Representations range from graphs and diagrams to the invention of other metaphors to describe the mathematics.

Notice that the four types of understanding are not in increasing order of difficulty. There may be hard skills and easy representations; some uses may be easier than anything else; and so on.

USING THE CHAPTER REVIEW
Students should be able to answer questions like these with about 85% accuracy by the end of the chapter.

You may assign these questions over a single night to help students prepare for a test the next day, or you may assign the questions over a two-day period.

Chapter Review

See margin for answers not shown below.

Questions on **SPUR** Objectives

SPUR stands for **S**kills, **P**roperties, **U**ses, and **R**epresentations. The Chapter Review questions are grouped according to the SPUR Objectives for this chapter.

SKILLS deal with the procedures used to get answers.

■ **Objective A:** *Analyze networks.* (*Lesson 1-4*)

In 1 and 2, refer to the network below.

1. **a.** How many even nodes are there? 5
   b. How many odd nodes are there? 2

2. Is the network traversable? Yes

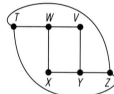

3. **a.** Is the network below traversable? No.
   b. If so, give a path. If not, explain why not.
   It has more than two odd nodes.

4. **a.** Represent the floor plan below with a network.
   b. Is it traversable? No

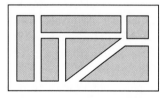

■ **Objective B:** *Make and determine the perspective of drawings.* (*Lesson 1-5*)

In 5 and 6, draw **a.** in perspective; **b.** not in perspective.

5. a cube   6. a table

In 7 and 8, **a.** tell whether the picture is drawn in perspective or not in perspective. **b.** If the figure is drawn in perspective, trace it and show a vanishing point.

7.

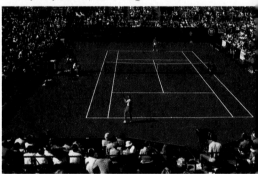

shoe box

size: 7
color: bl

not in perspective

8. in perspective; see margin.

PROPERTIES deal with the principles behind the mathematics.

■ **Objective C:** *Give the dimensions of figures and objects.* (*Lesson 1-2*)

In 9 and 10, tell how many dimensions each object has. Ignore small thicknesses.

9. a mirror 2   10. a tightrope 1

In 11–14, write the number of dimensions for each figure. Assume the points are ordered pairs.

11. point 0   12. plane 2
13. line 1   14. space 3

54

Objective D: *Given a property of points and lines, tell whether it is true for each of the four descriptions of points: dots, locations, ordered pairs, and nodes.* *(Lessons 1-1, 1-2, 1-3, 1-4)*

In 15-19, fill in the table with A if the statement is always true, S if sometimes true, N if never true.

Description of Point

	Dot	Location	Ordered Pair	Node
15.	N	A	A	A
16.	A	A	A	N
17.	S	A	A	N
18.	S	A	A	S
19.	S	N	N	S

15. A point has no size.
16. A line contains infinitely many points.
17. Between two points on a line there is a third point.
18. Two points determine a line.
19. Two different lines can have two points in common.

Objective E: *Recognize the use of undefined terms and postulates.* *(Lessons 1-6, 1-7)*

20. In an attempt to define a simple word, you find the original word used in the definition. What is this called? **circularity**

21. Name three undefined geometric terms.

22. What are the two major reasons for having postulates?

23. Why is the Point-Line-Plane Postulate needed?

In 24-33, a postulate from arithmetic or algebra is applied. Name the postulate.

24. $\frac{2}{7}$ = two sevenths **Reflexive Property of Equality**

25. $4(x + y) = 4x + 4y$ **Distributive Property**

26. When $z > 10$, $-5z < -50$.

27. If $|x| = 5$, then $|x| - 3 = 2$.

28. $8.3 + .09 = .09 + 8.3$

29. Since $25\% < 50\%$, $125\% < 150\%$.

30. If x and y are positive and $x + y = 13$, then $x < 13$. **Equation to Inequality Property**

31. If $a + b = 15$ and $15 = c - 12$, then $a + b = c - 12$.

32. If $x^2 + y^2 = 40$ and $y^2 = 7$, then $x^2 + 7 = 40$.

33. Since $1.5 = \frac{3}{2}$, then $1.5y = \frac{3y}{2}$. **Multiplication Property of Equality**

Objective F: *Apply properties of betweenness.* *(Lessons 1-8, 1-9)*

34. If Q is between P and R, then $\underline{\quad?\quad} + \underline{\quad?\quad} = \underline{\quad?\quad}$. **PQ   QR   PR**

35. **a.** On a number line, graph the set of numbers satisfying $x \geq -3$.
   b. What one-dimensional figure best describes the graph? **ray**

36. On the number line below, if $AC = 15$, $BD = 29$, and $AD = 31.8$, find BC. **12.2**

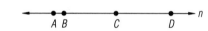

37. In the triangle below, $XW = 46$, $YZ = 39$, and $YW = 6.5$. Find XZ. **78.5**

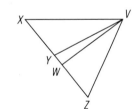

38. Two points are 6 units apart on a number line. The coordinate of one point is -62. What are the possible coordinates of the other? **-68 or -56**

39. Point Q on a number line has coordinate 11. Find all possibilities for the coordinate of R so that $QR = 17$. **-6 or 28**

If you assign the questions over two days, then we recommend assigning the *evens* for homework the first night so that students get feedback in class the next day. Then assign the *odds* for the second night (the night before the test) so that students can use the answers provided in the book as a study aid.

EVALUATION
Two forms of a Chapter Test—Forms A and B—are provided in the Teacher's Resource File. For information on grading, see *General Teaching Suggestions: Grading* on page T44 in the Teacher's Edition.

ASSIGNMENT RECOMMENDATION
We strongly recommend that you assign the reading and questions from Lesson 2-1 for homework the evening of the test. It gives students work to do if they complete the test before the end of the period and keeps the class moving.

If you do not give assignments on the days of tests, you may cover one less *chapter* over the course of the year.

ADDITIONAL ANSWERS
4. a.

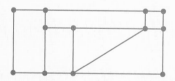

5. a. sample: b. sample:

6.a. and b., 8.b., 21., 22., 23., 26., 27., 28., 29., 31., 32., 35.a. See the margin on p. 56.

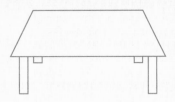

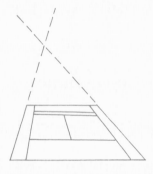

40. If $AB = 19$, $BC = 8$, and $AC = 11$, then __?__ is between __?__ and __?__. **C   A   B**

41. If $XY = 10$, $YZ = 6$, and Y is between X and Z, then $XZ =$ __?__. **16**

■ **Objective G:** *Determine whether a triangle can be formed with sides of three given lengths.* *(Lesson 1-9)*

In 42-47, can the numbers be the lengths of three sides of a triangle?

42. 14, 15, 30 **No**   **43.** 2, 4, 6 **No**

44. 0.8, 0.9, 1.0 **Yes**   **45.** $\frac{1}{3}, \frac{1}{4}, \frac{1}{5}$ **Yes**

46. 2.3, 1.1, 1.1 **No**   **47.** 15, 30, 40 **Yes**

48. Two sides of a triangle have lengths 4 cm and 7 cm. How long can the third side be?

49. You are told two sides of a triangle have lengths 1″ and 10″. **a.** Is this possible? **b.** If so, what are possible lengths for the third side? If not, why not?
a) Yes; b) between 9″ and 11″

USES deal with applications of mathematics in real situations.

■ **Objective H:** *Apply distance to real situations.* *(Lesson 1-2)*

50. A student placed a meter stick on a desk. The front of the desk was aligned to the 13 cm mark, and its back to the 56 cm mark. How wide is the desk? **43 cm**

51. A thermometer reading was -6° at Billings and 2° at Fargo. How far apart are these temperatures? **8°**

52. Jason took a plane from St. Louis to Kansas City and flew 234 miles. Zach took a train from St. Louis to Kansas City and rode 253 miles. Jessica drove 245 miles from St. Louis to Kansas City. Why are all of these distances different?

53. Use the road mileage chart for Florida below. If you drive from Jacksonville to Miami through Tampa, how much longer is it than going directly from Jacksonville to Miami?
96 miles

	J	M	T
Jacksonville (J)		356	198
Miami (M)	356		254
Tampa (T)	198	254	

■ **Objective I:** *Apply the Triangle Inequality in real situations.* *(Lesson 1-9)*

54. It is 151 miles from Chicago to Peoria and 289 miles from Chicago to St. Louis. From only this information, what can you say about the distance from Peoria to St. Louis?

55. It is a fifteen-minute walk from Rudy's place to Vanessa's place. It is a 25-minute walk from Vanessa's place to Theo's place. At this rate, by walking, how long would it take to get from Rudy's place to Theo's place?
at least 10 min., no more than 40 min.

56. Vinh lives 3 blocks from the fire station and 12 blocks from school. How far apart are the fire station and the school?

57. The Earth is 4.3 light years from the star system Alpha Centauri, and 6.1 light years from Barnard's Star, the two closest star systems to us. From this information only, how far are these systems from each other?
at least 1.8 light years, no more than 10.4 light years

56

PRESENTATIONS deal with pictures, graphs, or objects that illustrate concepts.

Objective J: *Determine distance on a number [line]. (Lesson 1-2)*

[In] 58 and 59, using the number lines below, [fin]d *AB*.

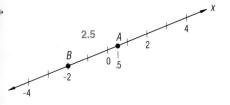

[In] 60 and 61, calculate $|11 - c|$ if

[60.] $c = 15;$ 4 | **61.** $c = -31.$ 42

[In 62]-65, give the distance between two points [wit]h the given coordinates.

[62.] 2 and 9 7 | **63.** -31 and 47 78

[64.] -14 and -90 76 | **65.** x and y
$|x - y|$ or $|y - x|$

Objective K: *Graph points and lines in the coordinate plane. (Lesson 1-3)*

In 66 and 67, graph the set of points satisfying the equation.

66. $4x - y = 8$ **67.** $y = -2x + 1$

68. Graph $y = -2x$ and $4x - 3y = 10$ on the same set of axes.

In 69-72, classify the line as vertical, horizontal, or oblique.

69. $5x + 3y = -19$ **70.** $x = 11$ vertical
71. $y = 3x$ oblique **72.** $y = 3$ horizontal
73. Give an equation for the horizontal line containing (5, 1). $y = 1$

74. Give an equation for the vertical line containing (-2, 10). $x = -2$

48. longer than 3 cm and shorter than 11 cm

52. different routes with different lengths were taken or the measurement of distance was from different points

54. It is at least 138 miles and no more than 440 miles.

56. at least 9 blocks and no more than 15 blocks

66.

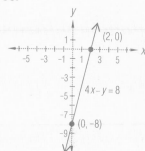

67.

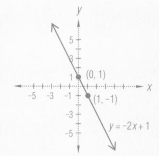

68.

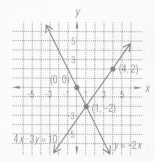

69. oblique

CHAPTER 2 ■ DEFINITIONS AND IF-THEN STATEMENTS

DAILY PACING CHART ■ CHAPTER 2

Every chapter of UCSMP *Geometry* includes lessons, a Progress Self-Test, and a Chapter Review. For optimal student performance, the self-test and review should be covered. (See *General Teaching Suggestions: Mastery* on page T36 of the Teacher's Edition.) By following the pace of the Full Course given here, students can complete the entire text by the end of the year. Students following the pace of the Minimal Course spend more time when there are quizzes and on the Chapter Review and will generally not complete all of the chapters in this text.

When all lessons are covered in order (the recommendation of the authors), then students in the Minimal Course can cover through Lesson 13-4 and will cover all they need for future courses. For more information on pacing, see *General Teaching Suggestions: Pace* on page T35 of the Teacher's Edition.

DAY	MINIMAL COURSE	FULL COURSE
1	2-1	2-1
2	2-2	2-2
3	2-3	2-3
4	2-4	2-4
5	Quiz (TRF); Start 2-5.	Quiz (TRF); 2-5
6	Finish 2-5.	2-6
7	2-6	2-7
8	2-7	Progress Self-Test
9	Progress Self-Test	Chapter Review
10	Chapter Review	Chapter Test (TRF)
11	Chapter Review	
12	Chapter Review (TRF)	

TESTING OPTIONS

■ Quiz for Lessons 2-1 Through 2-4   ■ Chapter 2 Test, Form A   ■ Chapter 2 Test, Cumulative Form
■ Chapter 2 Test, Form B

PROVIDING FOR INDIVIDUAL DIFFERENCES

The student text has been written for, and tested with, average students. It also has been used successfully with better and more poorly prepared students.

The Lesson Notes often include Error Analysis and Alternate Approach features to help you with those students who need more help. A blackline Lesson Master (in the Teacher's Resource File), keyed to the chapter objectives, is provided for each lesson to allow more practice. (However, since it is very important to keep up with the daily pace, you are not expected to use all of these masters. Again, refer to the suggestions for pacing on page T35.) Extension activities are provided in the Lesson Notes for those students who have completed the particular lesson in a shorter amount of time than is expected, even in the Full Course.

OBJECTIVES ■ CHAPTER 2

The objectives listed here are the same as in the Chapter 2 Review on pages 101-103 of the student text. The Progress Self-Test on pages 99-100 and the tests in the Teacher's Resource File cover these objectives. For recommendations regarding the handling of this end-of-chapter material, see the notes in the margin on the corresponding pages of the Teacher's Edition.

OBJECTIVES FOR CHAPTER 2 (Organized into the SPUR Categories—Skills, Properties, Uses, and Representations)	Progress Self-Test Questions	Chapter Review Questions	Lesson Master from Teacher's Resource File*
SKILLS			
A Distinguish between convex and nonconvex regions.	2, 16	1 through 3	2-1, 2-7
B Draw and identify polygons.	14, 15	4 through 9	2-7
PROPERTIES			
C Write the converse of a conditional.	8	10 through 12	2-4
D Apply the properties of a good definition.	1, 12, 13	13 through 18	2-5
E Write and interpret statements in "if-then" form.	3, 4	19 through 25	2-2
F Determine the union and intersection of sets.	5, 6	26 through 28	2-6
G Use logical ($p \Rightarrow q$) notation.	7	29 through 31	2-2, 2-3, 2-4
Uses			
H Apply properties of if-then statements in real situations.	9	32 through 33	2-3, 2-4
I Identify polygons used for real objects.	18	34 through 35	2-7
REPRESENTATIONS			
J Read computer programs with IF-THEN statements.	10, 11	36 through 40	2-3
K Draw hierarchies of triangles and polygons.	17	41 through 42	2-7

*The masters are numbered to match the lessons.

OVERVIEW ■ CHAPTER 2

Chapter 2 contains a great amount of material, some of which is presented in UCSMP *Transition Mathematics* and *Algebra,* so the geometry background of a student will make more of a difference here than it did in Chapter 1. A student who comes in knowing no geometry (for example, a student who has never measured an angle) will take longer to learn this chapter.

The two key ideas in this chapter are in the title. Lesson 2-1 under-scores the need for carefully examining terms. Because every definition is, in theory, an if-and-only-if statement (that is, an if-then statement and its converse), the chapter continues with a discussion of if-then statements (Lesson 2-2), their manifestation in computer programs (Lesson 2-3), and their converses (Lesson 2-4).

These ideas are applied in the many definitions given in Lessons 2-5 through 2-7.

The terms for which students should know definitions are given in the Chapter Summary and in the Vocabulary (page 98). You may wish to give a separate quiz in which students are expected only to write down good definitions of terms. Give no more than ten terms. Include some terms from Chapter 1, and allow one minute for each term.

PERSPECTIVES ■ CHAPTER 2

The Perspectives provide the rationale for the inclusion of topics or approaches, provide mathematical background, and make connections with other lessons and within UCSMP.

2-1

THE NEED FOR DEFINITIONS

Time in this course and in all future mathematics courses will be spent on learning and using definitions of terms. Mathematics is unique among school subjects in requiring such definitions. Establishing the need for careful definitions is the goal of this lesson.

While it is true that, as Lewis Carroll wrote in *Through the Looking Glass,* "when I use a word, it means just what I choose it to mean—neither more nor less," in subjects like geometry, there are certain conventions. Mathematicians generally agree on what they want to be a "rectangle" and what they don't want to be a rectangle. But, even with such agreement, no definition is absolutely correct. Like postulates, definitions are arbitrary.

2-2

"IF-THEN" STATEMENTS

This lesson has a number of simple but important goals. First, there is terminology: the if-then statement (a conditional), antecedent, and consequent; and an instance and counterexample. Secondly, there is the symbolism of variables standing for sentences and ⇒ standing for "implies." (The symbol ⇔ is introduced in a later lesson.)

In some books, the "if" part of an if-then statement is called the *hypothesis,* a word difficult for students because it has a different meaning in science (a theory or guess) than its simpler meaning here. The "then" part is sometimes called the *conclusion.* We introduce that word in Lesson 3-3 and use it throughout this course to mean a justified consequence. Thus, we picked words that are used in logic and may be less confusing to students: antecedent and consequent.

Truth tables are not discussed in this course; they do not have enough payoff here. However, the use of "p," "q," and "⇒" is a wonderful shorthand.

2-3

IF-THEN STATEMENTS IN COMPUTER PROGRAMS

There are many analogies between computer programs and mathematical proofs. Each is a sequence of statements. The statements in a mathematical proof are limited by the postulates, definitions, and theorems of the system in which one is working; the statements in a computer program are limited by hardware and software. Students are not expected to write their own computer programs in this course, so do not spend time on teaching them how to program.

This lesson is more than an application of if-then statements. It helps to emphasize the importance of looking at the truth value of the antecedent p in the conditional $p \Rightarrow q$. The computer ignores the consequent when the antecedent is false. So do mathematicians, because nonsense can be deduced from false statements.

2-4

CONVERSES

One way to get false conclusions is to reason correctly from false premises or antecedents. This was done in Lesson 2-3. Another way is to reason incorrectly. One common example of incorrect reasoning is to "reason the converse," that is, to assume $q \Rightarrow p$ is true just because $p \Rightarrow q$ is true. Such reasoning is often done in the real world.

2-5

GOOD DEFINITIONS

There are four aspects to this lesson: (1) the features of a good definition; (2) the definitions of midpoint and circle; (3) the distinction between the *meaning* and *sufficient condition* parts of a definition; and (4) the introduction of the symbol ⇔.

The third of these is the least familiar, but we use it throughout the remainder of the text, so it needs to be discussed.

When a statement and its converse are both true, as in every definition, then it is called a *biconditional*. This term and the corresponding symbol ⇔ are introduced here. Definitions are not the only biconditionals. Many theorems in geometry are biconditionals; for example, two lines are parallel if and only if interior angles on the same side of the transversal are supplementary; a quadrilateral is a parallelogram if and only if it has a pair of sides that are parallel and equal in length.

When a biconditional involves a property of a figure, that property could be a defining property of the figure. We could define parallelograms as quadrilaterals with one pair of sides parallel and equal in length. We could define parallel lines using supplementary interior angles on the same side of the transversal. We tend to select a particular definition because of tradition or the fact that it is easy to understand or use.

2-6

UNIONS AND INTERSECTIONS OF FIGURES

This lesson gives the language of sets, unions, and intersection. These words are commonly used in geometrical definitions. (Sets of points are more natural, it seems, than sets of numbers.) For example, we define an angle as the union of two rays and a polygon as a particular union of segments; we also speak of the intersection of lines and of half-planes.

Set theory was in vogue in the 1960s but has since dropped out of favor. To computer scientists and mathematicians, however, the concept of a set remains very important. The words "and" and "or" (used with set operations) are fundamental for understanding logic, switching circuits, and many relationships among variables and functions. It is still common to define functions as sets of ordered pairs. It is elegant and useful to be able to write "m and n are parallel" by using the equation "$m \cap n = \emptyset$." In this book, sets are used realistically without overusing them.

2-7

TERMS ASSOCIATED WITH POLYGONS

This is an easy lesson, particularly for students who have studied previous UCSMP texts. However, there is a good deal of terminology, and you should discuss all questions to make certain that students understand the terms.

CHAPTER 2

This is a 10-to-12-day chapter: 7 to 8 days for the lessons and quiz; 1 day for the Progress Self-Test; 1 or 2 days for the Chapter Review; and 1 day for a Chapter test. (See the Daily Pacing Chart on page 58A.)

Definitions and If-then Statements

What is a cookie? According to this column from *USA Weekend*, May 23-25, 1986, the answer is not so simple.

Careful definitions are one of the features of mathematical reasoning. In this chapter, important aspects of that reasoning are applied to simple geometric figures, to some of the other mathematics you know, and to everyday critical thinking.

2-1: The Need for Definitions
2-2: If-then Statements
2-3: If-then Statements in Computer Programs
2-4: Converses
2-5: Good Definitions
2-6: Unions and Intersections of Figures
2-7: Terms Associated with Polygons

58

You could look it up, but that might not help

If it looks like a cookie and tastes like a cookie, it is a cookie, right? Not so fast...

Some of the simplest, everyday things turn out to be not so simple when you try to define them. Everybody knows what "time" is, for example. But if your life depended on coming up with a clear definition of time, you would be in a lot of trouble.

In the news, there are plenty of references to "terrorists," But anybody who tries to spell out what is meant by the word "terrorist" runs into difficulty. We all know what a "terrorist" is, but the United Nations has been unable to come up with a working definition. The State Department and the Pentagon have different definitions, and at least one Congressional Committee finally decided that there is no way of defining the word "terrorist" without making value judgments that not everybody is going to agree with.

One man's "terrorist" is another's "freedom fighter." It's impossible to pass laws against terrorism if you can't spell out with some precision what it is you are talking about.

Definitions are important in the law, of course. In Wilmington, Del., right now, there is a big legal battle being fought in the U.S. District Court. Several giant cookie companies are fighting over the recipe for so-called "dual textured" cookies. That means cookies that are crispy on the outside and soft and chewy on the inside. Procter & Gamble claims it discovered the process, pat-

ented it in 1983, and that Nabisco has infringed on the patent.

Nabisco, Keebler and Frito-Lay claim they were making cookies that were crispy on the outside and chewy on the inside before P&G got its patent. So the Nabisco, Keebler and Frito-Lay lawyers asked P&G to define their terms. Among the terms they wanted defined were "cookie" and "dough."

Now I know what the word cookie means and so do you. My 2-year-old Jamie knows what a cookie is and can ask for it by name.

But the definition turns out to be so important in this case that here are these high-priced lawyers, these learned counselors asking the judge, Joseph Longobardi, to please tell them what a "cookie" is, and what "dough" is.

Judge Longobardi is not a man who shies away from an intellectual exercise, but he declined to oblige the opposing lawyers in their request.

"It should not be the court's burden to supply definitions of the terms," he told them in a memo.

If a wise jurist like Judge Longobardi doesn't want to have to render definitions for such relatively simple concepts as "cookie" and "dough," no wonder the U.N. is bogged down with "terrorist."

If we truly don't know the meaning of "dough," if "cookie" truly is something mysterious, it is surely no wonder that we so often blunder when we're dealing with much more serious matters. ❑

CHARLES OSGOOD

In 1986, Charles Osgood was the anchor of *CBS Sunday Night News*. He is editor and anchor of *Newsbreak* and *The Osgood File* on CBS Radio.

USING PAGES 58-59
This article is referred to in the assignments, so it must be part of the reading.

Students may not realize that there are government agencies which regulate many industries, such as the FDA (Food and Drug Administration), FAA (Federal Aviation Authority), FCC (Federal Communication Commission), EPA (Environmental Protection Agency), AEC (Atomic Energy Commission), and many others. You might have the class compile a list of all the regulatory agencies they can find.

Regulations must be carefully written with terms well understood, so that individuals and companies know what behaviors comply with a regulation and what behaviors do not. The cookie example is one of many that could be given. It was chosen because we believe material in a book should be in good taste.

RESOURCES
■ Lesson Master 2-1
■ Visual for Teaching Aid 11 can be used with **Question 13**.

OBJECTIVE

A Distinguish between convex and nonconvex regions.

TEACHING NOTES

Most of the class time should be spent discussing the questions. Many teachers have reported very rich discussions here.

Discussing **Questions 12-17** is essential. Your students will not agree on definitions of certain figures. Do not try to convince students that some definitions are better than others; even mathematicians do not agree on some definitions. For example, some geometry books (including this one) define "trapezoid" as a quadrilateral having *at least* one pair of parallel sides. Other geometry books define "trapezoid" as a quadrilateral having *exactly* one pair of parallel sides. Some books do not allow angles to have measures of 0 or 180; others (including this one) allow them; before 1960, most geometry books allowed angles to have measures greater than 180.
As a consequence, Questions 12-17 have no correct or incorrect answers. However, they are designed to get students ready to examine the definitions that will follow. For instance, some students might think that in

LESSON

2-1

The Need for Definitions

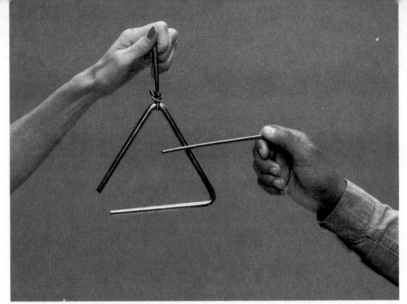

There are many ways to use the word triangle. How would you define a triangle?

You are probably wondering why the column page 59 discussing cookies was put in a book on geometry. The reason is that the column discusses definitions. Careful definitions are found throughout mathematics. When ideas are not carefully defined, people may not agree with what is written about them. Would Nabisco and Procter & Gamble agree on what is meant by a "dual textured cookie"? Do you think everyone in your class would agree on what is (and what is not) a "triangle"? Do you think everyone in the world would agree on what a "circle" is?

Many of the terms that you have seen before this year, including those for the two-dimensional figures shown below, are carefully defined in mathematics and in this book. The drawing above each term pictures one figure of the type the definition should include.

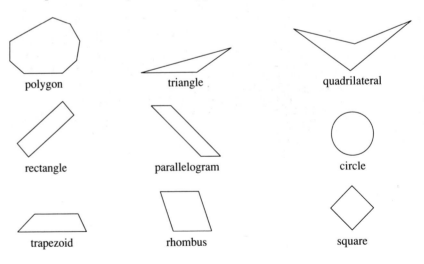

60

You may be skeptical. You may think, "Why is a definition needed for a rectangle? Everyone knows what a rectangle is." Experience has shown that this is not the case. You may not even agree with us! Try this.

Which of the following do you think should be called rectangles? Make choices in your mind before reading on.

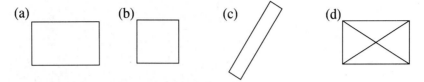

(a)   (b)   (c)   (d)

Almost everyone believes (a) is a rectangle. So do we. Many people think (b) is not a rectangle, because it is a square. Many people think (c) is not a rectangle because it is tilted, or because it is long and thin. Many people think (d) is not a rectangle because there are extra segments drawn. Our view, which agrees with the view of most mathematicians, is that (a), (b), and (c) are rectangles, but (d) is not. That is, all squares are rectangles. A rectangle may be very thin. A rectangle tilted is still a rectangle. But adding segments changes it: (d) is more than a rectangle.

In this lesson, we give only one definition. It distinguishes between sets of points that have "dents" and those that do not. Sets of points that do not have "dents" in them are called *convex sets*.

> **Definition:**
>
> A **convex set** is a set in which all segments connecting points of the set lie entirely in the set.

A set that is not convex is called, quite appropriately, a **nonconvex** set.

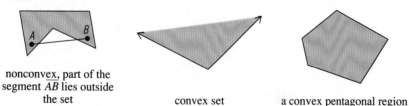

nonconvex, part of the segment *AB* lies outside the set

convex set

a convex pentagonal region

The word "convex" is also used in describing lenses. Lenses which are not convex use the word *concave*.

convex lens   concave lens

LESSON 2-1 The Need for Definitions   **61**

Question 12, the midpoint of $\overline{RT}$ in choice (c) is S. It is possible to come up with a definition of "midpoint" in which that is the case. (Just define midpoint as we have defined "between.")

Warn students that when the definitions for the figures on pages 63-64 and for other terms are established, they will be expected to memorize them. Those terms are marked with asterisks on page 98.

Reading You might ask students to draw and label examples or counterexamples (when appropriate) of the shapes being referred to as they read through the lessons. This should increase their comprehension as well as help them visualize correct diagrams.

Making Connections
The concept of convexity is important because certain later theorems depend on it. For example, the sum of the interior angles of a polygon with n sides is not necessarily $(n-2)180$ if the polygon is not convex, as shown in the example below.

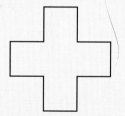

ADDITIONAL EXAMPLES
1. The word "diamond," as in "baseball diamond," is a particular shape.
a. How would you define that shape?
Opinions may vary. Mathematically, a diamond is a synonym for rhombus, a quadrilateral with four sides of the same length.
b. According to your definition, is every square a diamond?
Since a baseball diamond is a square, it would be inconsistent to define "diamond" in such a way

that it did not include squares.

2. Tell whether or not the given set is convex.
a. a ray
Yes
b. a quadrant in the coordinate plane
Yes
c. the letter V
No
d. a triangle
No
e. a bowling ball
Yes, if the holes are ignored; no, if the holes are considered.

NOTES ON QUESTIONS
Question 6: Have students explain why their drawings fail to be rectangles; for example, not right angles, curved sides, do not close up, and so forth.

Questions 7-9: Note that it takes only one segment which has points outside the figure to show that a set is nonconvex.

Question 10: You might ask students to draw a nonconvex three-sided region. Elicit the conjecture that all triangular regions are convex.

Question 12: You may find that some students choose (b) as an example of midpoint. Ask how far *S* can be drawn off the segment *RT* before it is no longer considered to be a midpoint.

Question 13: Without expecting students to be articulate, have them explain why they rejected certain figures.
Students sometimes think that special figures which satisfy more characteristics should be excluded as well; for example, draw a square, rectangle, or parallelogram and ask if it is a quadrilateral.

Question 14: No definition of circle has preceded this question. Elicit a definition from students which includes the figures they have chosen and excludes all others.

In 1–3, refer to the article on the opening page of the chapter.

1. What word did a Congressional committee have trouble defining? terrorist

2. What does "dual textured" mean?
crispy on the outside and soft and chewy on the inside
3. What is the problem that led to a lawsuit involving the cookie companies? Several cookie companies were fighting over the recipe and patent rights for "dual textured cookies."
4. Why is it important to carefully define ideas?
so that everyone will agree with what is written about them
5. How many triangles are pictured in this lesson?
19, not including the pictures at the beginning of the lesson
6. Draw a figure that you think is almost, but not quite, a rectangle.
See margin.

In 7–9, is the set convex?

7.   **8.**   **9.**

No   Yes   Yes

10. Draw a nonconvex 4-sided region. sample:

11. Draw a convex 8-sided region. sample:

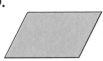

62

12. The word *midpoint* will be carefully defined in Lesson 2-5. But before reading that lesson, in which of the following pictures do you think point S is the midpoint of $\overline{RT}$?

(a)
  •   •   •
  R   S   T

(b)
  •   •
  R   T
      •
      S

(c)
  •
  R   •
      S
        •
        T

(d)
  •   • •
  R   S T

Opinions may vary for each answer; (a) will fit the definition in Lesson 2-5.

13. The word "quadrilateral" has two parts: "quadri" and "lateral." They come from the Latin *quattuor*, meaning "four," and *latus*, meaning "side." So a quadrilateral is meant to be a four-sided figure.
  a. Which of figures I, II, III, IV, and V do you think are quadrilaterals? *See margin.*
  b. If you think the figure is not a quadrilateral, tell why you think so. *Opinions may vary for each answer.*

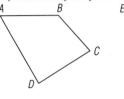

I

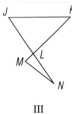

II

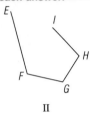

III

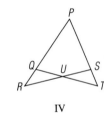

IV

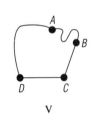

V

14. Which of the following do you think is a picture of a circle?

(a)

(b)

(c)

(d)

Opinions may vary for each answer; (a) will fit our definition.

15. The points (1, 4), (1, 5), (3, 5), (3, 4), and (1, 4) are connected in that order. Do you think the result should be called a rectangle? *Opinions may vary; it will fit our definition.*

16. An orange is cut with one slice of a sharp knife into two pieces. Do you think each piece should be called "half an orange"? *See margin.*

Question 16: Small children, when splitting a candy bar, may ask for "the bigger half." What would their definition of "half" be?

ADDITIONAL ANSWERS
6. sample:

13. a. Opinions may vary. Figure I will fit our definition.

16. Opinions may vary; it will fit our idea of "half an orange" only if the slice is made through the center of the orange.

NAME _____

63

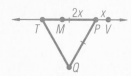
17. A cube is drawn below. The points A, B, C, and D are connected in order. They form a four-sided figure $ABCD$ in which each angle is a right angle. Should $ABCD$ be called a rectangle?

opinions may vary; it will fit our definition.

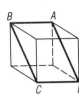

Review

18. Draw a single figure satisfying all of the following conditions.
(1) P is between T and V.
(2) $PM = 2 \cdot PV$
(3) Q is not on $\overleftrightarrow{TV}$.
(4) $QP = PT$ *(Lesson 1-8)* **See margin.**

19. The line $3x + 4y = 6$ contains the point $(10, a)$. What is a? *(Lesson 1-3)* **-6**

20. Give the number of sides of each of these polygons. *(Previous course)*
   a. pentagon **5**   **b.** octagon **8**
   c. decagon **10**   **d.** triangle **3**
   e. heptagon **7**   **f.** quadrilateral **4**

In 21 and 22, solve. *(Previous course)*

21. $x - 23 = 180 - x$ **x = 101.5**

22. $y = 6(90 - y)$ $y = \frac{540}{7}$ or $77\frac{1}{7}$

23. Solve for m: $225z = 15m$. *(Previous course)* **15z = m**

Exploration

24. Consider the article that opens this chapter.
   a. How would you define "cookie"? **sample: a small, flat, sweet cake**
   b. How would you define "terrorist"? **sample: one who uses violence and intimidation to achieve an end**

64

If-then Statements

LESSON 2-2

RESOURCES
■ Lesson Master 2-2

As seen from the Osgood article and in the previous lesson, precise language is often important. The meaning of words is crucial in understanding mathematics. Not only must words such as "rectangle" or "circle" be defined, but you must know meanings for conjunctions such as "and" and "or" and symbols such as "+," "<," or $\overleftrightarrow{AB}$.

The small word "if" is among the most important words in the language of logic and reasoning. It is used in everyday language, but not always carefully. In mathematics it is used *very carefully*. Recall that a hexagon is a six-sided polygon, and consider the following **if-then statement:**

If a figure is a hexagon, then it is a polygon.

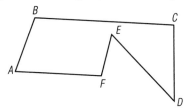

In an if-then statement, the clause following the "if" is called the **antecedent.** The clause following the "then" is the **consequent.** (**Hypothesis** and **conclusion** are alternate names for antecedent and consequent.) The entire if-then statement is called a **conditional.** In the above conditional, the antecedent is *a figure is a hexagon*. The consequent is *it is a polygon*. Notice that both the antecedent and consequent are complete sentences.

The drawing above shows a hexagon, an *instance* of the antecedent. An **instance** of a sentence is a situation for which the sentence is true. For this instance of the antecedent, the consequent of the conditional is true also. The figure is also a polygon.

TEACHING NOTES

As suggested at the bottom of page 67 with the use of *h* and *p,* it is helpful to use appropriate first letters for statements just as it is appropriate to use the variables *A* for area and *w* for width.

Our reasons for using *antecedent* and *consequent* are given in the Perspectives. If you are accustomed to different terms, you may have to avoid them. In particular, avoid the word *conclusion* in this lesson.

Stress that the antecedent and the consequent should be *stand-alone statements,* and that the words "if" and "then" are not part of the statements.

It is good to emphasize repeatedly: One example does not prove; one counterexample does disprove.

The discussion may be clarified by considering the conditional, "If $x < 2$, then $x^2 < 15$." Here, the antecedent A is $x < 2$; the consequent C is $x^2 < 15$. For various values of x, A and C may be true or false. For example,
$x = \text{-}1$: A is true and C is true. This is an instance of the conditional.

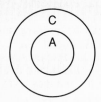
Now consider the following conditional:

If Y is between X and Z, then $XY < YZ$.

The antecedent is *Y is between X and Z*. To get some idea what this conditional means, you should draw instances of the antecedent. Two are drawn below. In the left instance, the consequent is true: XY is less than YZ. In the instance at the right, however, the consequent is not true: XY is not less than YZ. The drawing is not an instance of the consequent. The right drawing shows that the conditional is false. It is a *counterexample* to the conditional.

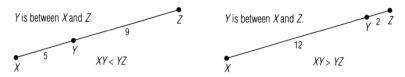

Definition:

> A **counterexample** to a conditional is a situation for which the antecedent (*if* part) is true and the consequent (*then* part) is false.

Proving a conditional false is often easy: you need to find just one counterexample.

Example 1 Show that the conditional "If $x^2 = 9$, then $x = 3$" is false.

Solution You need to look for a counterexample. Look for a situation in which $x^2 = 9$ is true but $x \neq 3$. Such a situation is $x = -3$. When x has the value -3, the antecedent $x^2 = 9$ is true but the consequent $x = 3$ is false. You can say that $x = -3$ is a counterexample to the conditional.

Here is the famous conditional known as *Goldbach's Conjecture*. (Christian Goldbach was a German mathematician who lived from 1690 to 1764.)

If n is an even number greater than 2,
then there are always two primes whose sum is n.

You can rather easily find situations for which both the antecedent and consequent are true. Let $n = 4$; 4 is the sum of the primes 2 and 2. Let $n = 6$; 6 is the sum of the primes 3 and 3. Let $n = 8$; 8 is the sum of the primes 3 and 5. Let $n = 100$; 100 is the sum of the primes 41 and 59. This conjecture has been checked for all even numbers from 2 to well over 100,000,000. No counterexample has ever been found.

66

Unfortunately, a conditional cannot be called true by finding 100 or even a million situations in which the antecedent and consequent are both true. It must be proved true. Goldbach's Conjecture has not yet been proved true.

Conditionals can be written without the words "if" and "then." The following are equivalent to "If a figure is a hexagon, then it is a polygon."

All hexagons are polygons.
Every hexagon is a polygon.
A figure is a polygon if it is a hexagon.

This last statement just has the antecedent, signaled by the word "if," after the consequent.

When statements follow the pattern "All A are B," or "When A occurs, B occurs," they can be rewritten in if-then form as "If something is an A, then something is a B."

Example 2   Rewrite the statement "All triangles have three sides" in if-then form.

Solution   Think of the "something" as a figure: "If a figure is a triangle, then it has three sides."

Single letters can stand for sentences. For instance, with the conditional

If a figure is a hexagon, then it is a polygon,

let h = "a figure is a hexagon" and let p = "a figure is a polygon." Then the conditional may be rewritten:

If h, then p.

A still shorter way of writing this is to use the symbol $\Rightarrow$, which is read "implies."

$$h \Rightarrow p$$
$$h \text{ implies } p$$

With this notation, we can rewrite the definition of counterexample given above. A counterexample to a general conditional $p \Rightarrow q$ is a situation for which p is true and q is false.

LESSON 2-2   "If-then" Statements   **67**

67

ADDITIONAL EXAMPLES
1. Show that the conditional, "If a network has 4 nodes, then it has 6 arcs," is false.
sample counterexample:

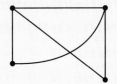

2. Rewrite this statement in if-then form: "All schools must be free of asbestos by January 1, 1988."
"If X is a school, then X must be free of asbestos by January 1, 1988."

3. a. Rewrite the statement "Every bird can fly" in if-then form.
If an animal is a bird, then it can fly.
b. Is the conditional true?
No, there are animals which are birds—for example, ostriches and emus—which cannot fly.

NOTES ON QUESTIONS
Question 7:   You might ask what someone must do to prove the Goldbach conjecture false. (Find an even number which is not the sum of any two primes.)

Question 8:   It is important for students to understand that a conditional may have both instances and counterexamples.

Question 13:   There are 3 sums of two primes that give 40, namely, 37 + 3, 29 + 11, and 23 + 17. The phrase "the sum of two primes" in the conjecture does not mean that there is a unique sum.

Error Analysis for Question 14:   Students may pick (d). Point out that a counterexample of the conditional must be an instance of the antecedent.

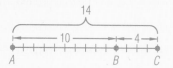
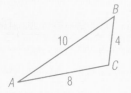

Questions

Covering the Reading

In 1 and 2, copy the statement. Underline the antecedent once and the consequent twice.

1. If a parallelogram has a right angle, then it is a rectangle.

2. Fruit kabob is divine if it is made with watermelon.

3. Let s = "A figure is a square."
   p = "A figure is a polygon."
   $s \Rightarrow p$ refers to what sentence?
   If a figure is a square, then it is a polygon.

4. An instance of a sentence is a situation for which the sentence is __?__.
   true

5. Define: counterexample to a conditional. a situation in an if-then statement for which the antecedent is true and the consequent is false

6. A counterexample to $a \Rightarrow c$ is a situation for which a is __?__ and c is __?__. true, false

7. State Goldbach's Conjecture. If n is an even number greater than 2, then there are always two prime numbers whose sum is n.

8. Consider the statement "If $AB = 10$ and $BC = 4$, then $AC = 14$."
   a. Draw an instance of the antecedent for which the consequent is true.
   b. Draw a counterexample to this statement.
   See margin.

9. How many counterexamples are needed to show that a conditional is false? 1

10. Show that this conditional is false:
    If $x^2 = 16$, then $x = -4$. See margin.

In 11 and 12, rewrite in if-then form.

11. Every square is a quadrilateral. If a figure is a square, then it is a quadrilateral.

12. All Irish setters are dogs. If something is an Irish setter, then it is a dog.

Applying the Mathematics

13. Show that the consequent in Goldbach's Conjecture is true when $n = 40$. 40 = 37 + 3 or 40 = 29 + 11 or 40 = 23 + 17

14. *Multiple choice.* Pick the counterexample to the if-then statement "If a figure is a hexagonal region, then it is convex." (a)

(a)   (b)   (c)   (d)

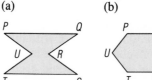

15. Suppose $p \Rightarrow q$ is true. Is it possible to have a counterexample to $p \Rightarrow q$? No

In 16 and 17, **a.** find a situation for which both the antecedent and consequent are true. **b.** Find a counterexample to the statement.

16. If you are in Toledo, then you are in the United States.
a) sample: You are in Toledo, Ohio. b) sample: You are in Toledo, Spain.

17. If a line contains (2, 3), then it is oblique.
a) sample: the line $y = x + 1$; b) the line $x = 2$ or the line $y = 3$

Review

18. Which figures below do you think should *not* be called "triangles"? For each figure you think is not a triangle, explain why you think it isn't. *(Lesson 2 1)*

a.   b.   c.   d.

not 3 segments   not segments   is a triangle   not closed

19. Characterize each region as convex or nonconvex. *(Lesson 2-1)*

a.   b.   c.

nonconvex   nonconvex   convex

20. a. Draw a convex pentagonal region.
    b. Draw a nonconvex pentagonal region. *(Lesson 2-1)*
    See margin.

21. Two sides of a triangle have length $4x$ and $13x$. What are the possible lengths for the third side? *(Lesson 1-9)*
longer than 9x but shorter than 17x

In 22 and 23, solve. *(Previous course)*

22. $15x - 22 + 17x + 1 = 180$ **23.** $90 > 32 + z > 0$
$x = \frac{201}{32} = 6.28125$ $-32 < z < 58$ or $58 > z > -32$

Exploration

24. Consider the antecedent "A network has five nodes."
    a. Make a true conditional with this antecedent.
    b. Make a false conditional with this antecedent.
    See below.

25. Repeat Question 24 for the antecedent "A person is 14 years old."
See below.

26. The words "antecedent" and "consequent" are derived in part from the Latin words *ante* and *sequens*. What do these Latin words mean and how is this related to their mathematical meanings? *Ante* means "before" and *sequens* means "following." The consequent in a conditional normally follows the antecedent.

24. a. sample: If a network has 5 nodes, then it has at least 5 arcs.
    b. sample: If a network has 5 nodes, then it is not traversable.
25. a. sample: If a person is 14 years old, then that person is a teenager.
    b. sample: If a person is 14 years old, then that person is female.

FOLLOW-UP

MORE PRACTICE
For more questions on SPUR Objectives, use *Lesson Master 2-2,* shown below.

EVALUATION
Alternative Assessment
Small group work and oral activities can be used to evaluate whether students understand when a conditional is true. Have each student make up three conditionals relating to sports, hobbies, weather, homework or mathematics. They should then form discussion groups to read their conditionals and discuss them orally. Other members of the group should then (orally) present situations for which the antecedent and consequent are true or offer counterexamples.

NAME

LESSON **MASTER 2-2**
QUESTIONS ON **SPUR** OBJECTIVES

■ **PROPERTIES** *Objective E (See pages 101–103 for objectives.)*
In 1–3, underline the antecedent once and the consequent twice.

1. If it's after the All-Star break, the Cubs will be in last place.
2. If a figure is a triangle, then it has three sides.
3. Louisa will do the dishes if Hernando cooks dinner.

In 4 and 5, rewrite in if-then form.

4. Any student can multiply.
    If someone is a student, then that person can multiply.
5. All cars have transmissions.
If something is a car, then it has a transmission.

■ **PROPERTIES** *Objective G*

6. A counterexample to an if-then statement is a situation where the antecedent is true and the consequent is false.
7. The conditional $a \Rightarrow b$ being true means that when a is true, so is b.

In 8 and 9, let v = "The figure is convex" and w = "The figure is a triangle." *True or false?*
8. $v \Rightarrow w$ False   9. $w \Rightarrow v$ True

11

OBJECTIVES

G Use logical ($p \Rightarrow q$) notation.
H Apply properties of if-then
statements in real situa-
tions.
J Read computer programs
with IF-THEN statements.

TEACHING NOTES

Students who have studied
UCSMP *Transition Mathe-
matics* are familiar with diagonals of polygons. Other
students may not be.

The formula for the number
of diagonals can be deduced
from the principles of counting by using the following
method. Each vertex can be
connected to all but three of
the other vertices, namely,
itself and its two "neighbors."
Since there are *n* vertices,
multiply *n* times 3 less than
n. This counts each diagonal
twice, once at each endpoint.
Hence, divide by 2 to get the
number of diagonals.
A conditional is false if and
only if there is an instance of
the antecedent which is not
an instance of the condi-
tional. Otherwise, it is true.
Hence, if the antecedent has
no instances, the conditional
must be true. Thus, any conditional which would begin
with, "If the moon is made of
green cheese, then. . . ," is
true.

LESSON

2-3

If-then Statements in Computer Programs

Recall that a diagonal of a polygon is a segment connecting two
nonconsecutive vertices of the polygon.

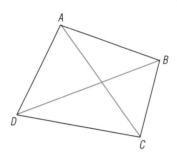
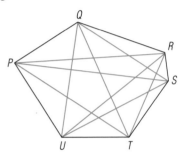

$\overline{AC}$ and $\overline{BD}$ are the two diagonals
of quadrilateral $ABCD$.

hexagon $QRSTUP$ and
its nine diagonals

When polygons have many sides, it is tedious to count to find the
number of diagonals. Fortunately, there is a simple formula. If n is
the number of sides of the polygon and d the number of diagonals,
then

$$d = \frac{n(n - 3)}{2}.$$

A program can instruct a computer to calculate a value of d given a
value of n. Consider the following BASIC (Beginners All-purpose
Symbolic Instructional Code) computer program.

```
10   PRINT "COMPUTE NUMBER OF DIAGONALS IN POLYGON"
20   PRINT "ENTER THE NUMBER OF SIDES"
30   INPUT N
40   IF N >= 3 THEN PRINT "THE NUMBER OF DIAGONALS IS ";
     N *(N − 3)/2
50   END
```

The 10, 20, 30, 40, and 50 are **line numbers.** The computer performs the instructions in the order of the line numbers. Any natural
number can be a line number.

70

The PRINT in lines 10 and 20 instructs the computer to display exactly what is inside the quotation marks. In line 30, INPUT N tells the computer to take the value typed in by a user as the value of N.

Line 40 is an if-then statement. (The $>=$ in line 40 is the computer symbol for $\geq$.) The computer performs the consequent *only* if the antecedent is true. In line 40, if the value input by the user is greater than or equal to 3, then the antecedent is true. Then the computer will first print THE NUMBER OF DIAGONALS IS, and next calculate $N(N - 3)/2$ and print the result of that calculation.

To run this program on a computer, type in the program exactly as indicated. Then type RUN. When the program gets to line 30, you will see a ? on the screen. That is the computer asking for the value for N. Respond by typing the value you want.

■ ■ ■ ■ ■ ■ ■ ■ ■

Example Write what will be printed or shown on the screen when the program on the preceding page is run and

a. N is given the value 7;
b. N is given the value 2.

Solution

a. First the computer prints the messages in lines 10 and 20, and asks for a value of N. When the user enters 7, the computer substitutes 7 for N. In line 40, the antecedent is true ($7 \geq 3$), so the computer prints THE NUMBER OF DIAGONALS IS, then calculates $7 \cdot (7 - 3)/2$ and prints 14. So you will see

> COMPUTE NUMBER OF DIAGONALS IN POLYGON
> ENTER THE NUMBER OF SIDES
> ? 7
> THE NUMBER OF DIAGONALS IS 14

b. The computer substitutes 2 for N. At line 40, because the antecedent is false when N = 2, it skips the consequent. It then goes on to line 50. The final result is

> COMPUTE NUMBER OF DIAGONALS IN POLYGON
> ENTER THE NUMBER OF SIDES
> ? 2

Many people, especially programmers, would fix the program on the preceding page to account for situations such as part **b** of the Example. If a number less than three is input at line 30, there should be a message to indicate that a polygon must have at least three sides.

A more subtle problem is that the program will also accept a mixed number such as 3.62 as an input value of N and calculate the number of diagonals (1.1222). Fixing these problems is part of what is called "debugging."

Show how nonsense begets nonsense (the mathematical analogy of the computer epigram "garbage in, garbage out") by reviewing the reasoning in the **Example** on page 71.

Some students will wonder how the numbers 46 and 85 were found in the "proof" that $131 = 177$ on page 72. Some may even discover how. Here is the generalization. Given $1 = 2$, you can deduce any two numbers a and b are equal. (Here, $a = 131$ and $b = 177$.) First multiply both sides by $b - a$. This yields
$$b - a = 2(b - a).$$
Using the distributive property,
$$b - a = 2b - 2a.$$
Now add $2a - b$ to both sides. This yields
$$a = b.$$
There is no trick here. There is only the fact that we have reasoned from $1 = 2$, a false statement.

Making Connections
Much later, in indirect proof, students will learn that we sometimes reason from statements *whose truth value is not known*. Only when nonsense is reached in a conclusion is it possible to determine that the reasoning started from a false statement.

Error Analysis Students may want to verify the output of the program used for the **Example.** Caution them that programs do not execute predictably unless the statements are typed in exactly as they are written, including the line numbers.

ADDITIONAL EXAMPLE
Write what will be printed or shown on the screen when the program on page 70 is run and
a. N is given the value 5;
5
b. N is given the value 40.
740

In computer programming, a false antecedent causes the machine to ignore the *then* part of the conditional. Outside of computer pro-gramming, conditionals with false antecedents are treated differently. Consider the following true conditional:

If a quadrilateral is a square, then its diagonals have the same length.

What if the antecedent is false and a given quadrilateral is *not* a square? The above statement can tell us nothing. In fact, as the fol-lowing pictures show, some non-square quadrilaterals have diagonals that are the same length, some do not.

not a square

not a square

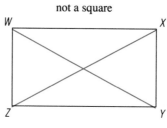 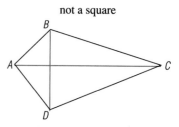

diagonals of same length   diagonals not of same length

When the antecedent of an if-then statement is false, nothing can be determined about the truth of the consequent.

If you reason from a false statement, you may be able to deduce strange things. Assume, for the moment, that $1 = 2$. Then using properties of algebra, you can deduce that any two numbers are equal! Here we show: If $1 = 2$, then $131 = 177$.

$$
\begin{array}{rcll}
1 &=& 2 & \\
46 \cdot 1 &=& 46 \cdot 2 & \text{Multiplication Property of Equality} \\
46 &=& 92 & \text{arithmetic} \\
46 + 85 &=& 92 + 85 & \text{Addition Property of Equality} \\
131 &=& 177 & \text{arithmetic}
\end{array}
$$

Does $131 = 177$? Of course not. But the conditional "If $1 = 2$, then $131 = 177$" is true. It has been proved true.

In a like manner the conditional "If $1 = 2$, then $3 = 3$" can be proved.

$$
\begin{array}{rcll}
1 &=& 2 & \\
2 &=& 1 & \text{Symmetric Property of Equality} \\
1 + 2 &=& 2 + 1 & \text{Addition Property of Equality} \\
3 &=& 3 & \text{arithmetic}
\end{array}
$$

This illustrates that when p is a false antecedent, both true and false consequents q can be deduced. So mathematicians agree that if p is false, the conditional $p \Rightarrow q$ is true regardless of what q is.

72

Questions

Covering the Reading

1. How does a BASIC computer program act when the antecedent of a conditional is true? The program performs the instructions in the "then" statement.
2. How does a BASIC computer program act when the antecedent of a conditional is false? The program ignores the consequent and goes to the next line number.
3. What is the purpose of the number assigned to each line of a BASIC computer program? The numbers order the steps of the program.

In 4–6, refer to the program in the lesson. Tell what will be printed when the program is run and the indicated value of N is substituted.

4. N = 1 See margin.   5. N = 100 See margin.   6. N = 3 See margin.

7. If a polygon has more than 4 sides, it must have more than two diagonals. What does this statement tell you about polygons that have 4 or fewer sides? The statement says nothing about polygons with 4 or fewer sides.
8. **a.** In mathematics, is this statement true or false? If 1 = 2, then 30 = 40. True
   b. Show steps to reason that if 1 = 2, then 30 = 40. See margin.
9. *True* or *false*?   If Paris is in Germany, then London is in France. True

Applying the Mathematics

10. **a.** Diane read an ad: If you use Wonderlashes, your eyes will be more beautiful. Diane used a cheaper brand of artificial eyelashes, and her eyes became more beautiful. Did the ad lie to Diane? No
    b. Flora read the same ad as Diane. Flora already had beautiful eyes, and she used Wonderlashes, but her eyes didn't get any more beautiful. Did the ad lie to Flora? Yes

11. **a.** Mr. Woodward heard an ad: "If you want a cleaner house, then you'll use Magikleen." Mr. Woodward wanted a cleaner house, but did not use Magikleen. Is the ad true? No
    b. How is the answer to part **a** changed if the word "you'll" is changed to "you might"? It is changed to "yes."

---

12. Program starts with
INVENTORY OF
ELECTRO-ROBOT
ENTER THE NUMBER OF
ELECTRO-ROBOT
?
It continues with
a. ?400
PROFIT EQUALS 500
b. ?20
PROFIT EQUALS -1400
ORDER MORE
ELECTRO-ROBOT

13. a. The formula gives an approximation of the area of a circle of radius R.

18. b.

19. A sample counterexample: This network is traversable, but it has no odd nodes.

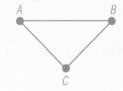

The consequent "it has exactly two odd nodes" is false.

24. b.

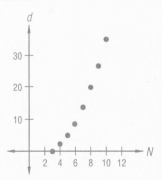

MORE PRACTICE
For more questions on SPUR
Objectives, use *Lesson Master 2-3,* shown on page 75.

EXTENSION
Computer The following
are some suggestions to extend this lesson by using a
computer.
(a) Have students work in
small groups of two or more
at computers. Either have
them type in the short program or have the programs
stored on disk or network
prior to class.
(b) Bring a computer with an
overhead viewer to class.
(c) Make it an out-of-class
computer lab assignment.

1. Run the following program.
What does it do?

```
10  LET SECRET =
    INT(RND(1)*100 + 1)
11  REM SECRET WILL
    BE A "SECRET
    NUMBER"
    FROM 1 TO 100
20  PRINT "PLEASE
    GUESS MY SECRET
    NUMBER: ";
30  INPUT GUESS
40  IF GUESS <
    SECRET THEN
    PRINT "TOO LOW
    . . . TRY AGAIN.":
    GOTO 20
50  IF GUESS >
    SECRET THEN
    PRINT "TOO HIGH
    . . . TRY AGAIN.":
    GOTO 20
60  IF GUESS =
    SECRET THEN
    PRINT
    "CONGRATULATIONS!
    THAT'S RIGHT."
70  END
```

It plays guessing game to
determine the random
number chosen.

12. Consider this computer program.

```
10  PRINT "INVENTORY OF ELECTRO-ROBOT"
15  PRINT "ENTER THE NUMBER OF ELECTRO-ROBOT "
20  INPUT N
25  PRINT "PROFIT EQUALS "; 5 * N − 1500
30  IF N < 300 THEN PRINT "ORDER MORE ELECTRO-
    ROBOT."
35  END
```

a. What is printed if N = 400? See margin.
b. What is printed if N = 20? See margin.

13. This program calculates values from a formula you have studied in
previous years.

```
10  INPUT R
20  LET A = 3.14159 * R * R
30  IF R > 0 THEN PRINT R, A
40  END
```

a. Identify the formula. See margin.
b. For what values of R will nothing be printed? when R ≤ 0

Review

In 14–16, rewrite in if-then form. *(Lesson 2-2)*

14. A polygon has 9 diagonals if it is a hexagon.
If a polygon is a hexagon, then it has 9 diagonals.
15. The volume of a cube with side s is s^3.
If a figure is a cube with side s, then its volume is s³.
16. Every vertical line has an equation of the form $x = h$. If a line is
vertical, then it has an equation of the form x = h.
17. Consider the conditional: If $|x| = 10$, then $x = 10$.
a. If this conditional is $p \Rightarrow q$, what is p? |x| = 10
b. Find a counterexample to this conditional. *(Lesson 2-2)* x = -10

18. Consider this statement:
If D is on $\overline{XY}$, $XD = 11.2$, and $XY = 26.7$, then $DY = \underline{\ ?\ }$.
a. Fill in the blank. 15.5
b. Make a drawing of this situation. *(Lessons 2-2, 1-8)*
See margin.
19. Show that the conditional "If a network is traversable, then it has
exactly two odd nodes" is false. *(Lesson 2-2)* See margin.

20. In the figure below, C is between B and D. If $BC = 4 \cdot CD$ and
$BD = 12$, what is the value of BC? *(Lesson 1-9)* 9.6

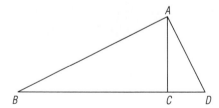

21. Two sides of a triangle are 16 and 41. If x is the length of the third side, graph all possibilities for x on a number line. *(Lesson 1-9)*

In 22 and 23, solve. *(Previous course)*

22. $50z + 3 = 67z + 1$ $z = \frac{2}{17}$

23. $180 > q + 19 > 90$

$161 > q > 71$ or $71 < q < 161$

24. Let N take the values 3, 4, 5, 6, 7, 8, 9, and 10.

a. Find $d = \dfrac{N(N-3)}{2}$ for each N.

b. Plot the ordered pairs (N, d) in a graph. See margin.

c. The points all lie on what curve? *(Previous course)* parabola

a)

N	3	4	5	6	7	8	9	10
d	0	2	5	9	14	20	27	35

Exploration

25. The program given here instructs the computer to print the number of diagonals of polygons with any number of sides from 3 to 20.

```
10  PRINT "NUMBER OF DIAGONALS IN POLYGONS"
20  FOR N = 3 TO 20
30  PRINT "THE NUMBER OF SIDES IS "; N
40  PRINT "THE NUMBER OF DIAGONALS IS "; N * (N - 3)/2
50  NEXT N
60  END
```

Modify this program to give the number of diagonals of polygons with any number of sides from 3 to 50. Run your program.
See below.

26. a. Debug the program on page 70 by adding lines that will print an appropriate message if the input is less than 3.

b. Test your program.
See below.

25. Line 20 should read: 20 for N = 3 to 50
The printout will read:
NUMBER OF DIAGONALS IN POLYGONS
THE NUMBER OF SIDES IS 3
THE NUMBER OF DIAGONALS IS 0
THE NUMBER OF SIDES IS 4
THE NUMBER OF DIAGONALS IS 2
. . . and so on to
THE NUMBER OF SIDES IS 50
THE NUMBER OF DIAGONALS IS 1175

26. a. Lines 10 through 50 can remain the same. Insert the following line:
45 IF N < 3 THEN PRINT "ERROR, A POLYGON MUST HAVE AT LEAST 3 SIDES."
b. The printout will be:
COMPUTE NUMBER OF DIAGONALS IN POLYGON
ENTER THE NUMBER OF SIDES
?2
ERROR, A POLYGON MUST HAVE AT LEAST 3 SIDES.

---

2. Run the following program. What does it do?

```
10  PRINT "ENTER THE
    COORDINATES OF
    TWO POINTS ON
    THE NUMBER
    LINE."
20  INPUT X1, X2
30  If X1 < X2 THEN
    PRINT X1 "IS TO
    THE LEFT OF "X2"
    ON THE LINE."
40  IF X1 > X2 THEN
    PRINT X2 "IS TO
    THE LEFT OF "X1"
    ON THE LINE."
50  IF X1 = X2 THEN
    PRINT "YOU GAVE
    THE COORDINATES
    OF ONE POINT."
60  END
```

It receives input of two points and tells which one is to the left or if the two points are the same.

OBJECTIVES

C Write the converse of a conditional.
G Use logical ($p \Rightarrow q$) notation.
H Apply properties of if-then statements in real situations.

TEACHING NOTES

There is evidence that students confuse statements and their converses. One reason for this is that the word "if" in the real world often is used as if it means "if and only if." The parent who says to a child, "If you don't behave, you will not get your allowance" is also implying, "If you behave, you will get your allowance." This occurs so often that students think that the antecedent and consequent can be treated equivalently. They incorrectly believe that the consequent is true *exactly* when the antecedent is true.

Making Connections
"Reasoning the converse" is a common mistake students will make later when they are doing proofs. They will assume that the converses (the consequents) of certain theorems are true and use them much in the same way they use "givens" in a proof.

LESSON

2-4

Converses

Here is a true if-then statement.

If you are in Los Angeles, then you are in California.
$$LA \Rightarrow C$$

Switching the antecedent and consequent results in a false statement.

If you are in California, then you are in Los Angeles.
$$C \Rightarrow LA$$

The statements $p \Rightarrow q$ and $q \Rightarrow p$ are called *converses* of each other.

Definition:

The **converse** of $p \Rightarrow q$ is $q \Rightarrow p$.

■ ■ ■ ■ ■ ■ ■ ■

Example 1 Consider the conditional:
If a line is horizontal, then it has an equation of the form $y = k$.

a. Write the converse.
b. Is the original statement true? Is the converse true?

Solution

a. The antecedent is "a line is horizontal." The consequent is "it has an equation of the form $y = k$." Switch these to form the converse. The converse is: "If a line has an equation of the form $y = k$, then it is horizontal."
b. Both the original statement and its converse are true.

Knowing that $p \Rightarrow q$ is true *does not* tell you whether $q \Rightarrow p$ is true or false. So unless you have other evidence, you cannot tell whether the converse of a true statement is true. Here are examples.

"If you are in Los Angeles, then you are in California."
$p \Rightarrow q$ true
$q \Rightarrow p$ false

"If a line is horizontal, then it has an equation of the form $y = k$."
$p \Rightarrow q$ true
$q \Rightarrow p$ true

76

Example 2   Mrs. Wilson's will stated: "Every one of my children shall receive ten percent of my estate." When Mrs. Wilson died, Sheri received ten percent of Mrs. Wilson's estate. Is Sheri a child of Mrs. Wilson?

Solution   When put in if-then form, the will states "If someone is Mrs. Wilson's child, then he or she shall receive ten percent of the estate." The *converse* is "If someone receives ten percent of the estate, then that person is Mrs. Wilson's child." This converse describes Sheri's situation. Since you cannot tell if the converse of a true statement is true or false, it is impossible to tell whether Sheri is Mrs. Wilson's child.

Sometimes $p \Rightarrow q$ is false. When this happens, $q \Rightarrow p$ may be true or it may be false. Here are examples.

"If $x^2 = 9$, then $x = 3$."	"If a man has blue eyes, then he weighs over 150 lb."	"If a figure is a circle, then it is a rectangle."
$p \Rightarrow q$ false	$p \Rightarrow q$ false	$p \Rightarrow q$ false
$q \Rightarrow p$ true	$q \Rightarrow p$ false	$q \Rightarrow p$ false

Thus, unless you have other evidence, accepting the converse of a false statement as false is also using incorrect reasoning. The truth or falsity of $p \Rightarrow q$ does not tell you whether $q \Rightarrow p$ is true or false. You must examine converses as independent statements.

■ ■ ■ ■ ■ ■ ■ ■ ■

Example 3   Suppose p = a rectangular floor has perimeter 18 feet
                            q = a rectangular floor has area 20 square feet.
Show that both $p \Rightarrow q$ and its converse are false.

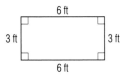

Solution $p \Rightarrow q$ is the statement: If a rectangular floor has perimeter 18 feet, then its area is 20 square feet. A counterexample will show it is false. Here is a figure whose perimeter is 18 ft and whose area is not 20 sq ft.

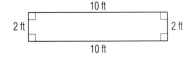

6 ft
3 ft   3 ft
6 ft

The converse is the statement $q \Rightarrow p$: If a rectangular floor has area 20 sq ft, then its perimeter is 18 ft. Here is a counterexample. It has the right area, but the wrong perimeter.

10 ft
2 ft   2 ft
10 ft

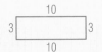

Converses are present whenever equations are solved in algebra. You reason $p \Rightarrow q$ when you solve an equation. You reason the converse $q \Rightarrow p$ when you check the solution. Both $p \Rightarrow q$ <u>and</u> $q \Rightarrow p$ must be true for an equation to be solved correctly. This is why a check is necessary.

■■■■■■■■■

Example 4 Let p: $6x - 10 = 20$.
Let q: $x = 5$.

a. Is $p \Rightarrow q$ true?
b. Is $q \Rightarrow p$ true?

Solution

a. To show $p \Rightarrow q$ is true, solve the equation $6x - 10 = 20$. Justifications for the major steps are given.

$$6x = 30 \qquad\qquad \text{Addition Property of Equality}$$
$$x = 5 \qquad\qquad \text{Multiplication Property of Equality}$$

b. To show $q \Rightarrow p$ is true, you need to show if $x = 5$, then $6x - 10 = 20$. This is the check.

$$6 \cdot 5 - 10 = 30 - 10 = 20$$

Distinguishing between a statement and its converse can be tricky. You should be very careful when doing the Questions.

Questions

Covering the Reading

1. Define: converse. The converse of $p \Rightarrow q$ is $q \Rightarrow p$.

In 2 and 3, the statement is true.
a. Write the converse.   **b.** Tell whether the converse is true.
2. If a line is vertical, then it has an equation of the form $x = h$. a) If a line has an equation of the form $x = h$, then it is vertical. b) True
3. If you are a teenager, then you are at least 13 years old. See margin.

4. *Multiple choice.*   Suppose a statement is true. Then its converse:
   (a) must be true;
   (b) must be false;
   (c) may be either true or false. (c)

5. Suppose $p =$ a rectangular floor has perimeter 26 feet
           $q =$ a rectangular floor has area 42 square feet.
   a. Show that $p \Rightarrow q$ is false. See margin.
   b. Show that the converse of $p \Rightarrow q$ is false. See margin.

6. Ms. Hibrough saw an advertisement which read, "Everyone who attends the dance will receive Eau D'or perfume." Ms. Hibrough received some Eau D'or perfume. Did she attend the dance? *There is not enough information to tell.*

In 7–11, **a.** write $p \Rightarrow q$ and $q \Rightarrow p$. **b.** Tell whether these conditionals are true or false.

7. p: $2x + 31 = 4 - x$ a) $p \Rightarrow q$: If $2x + 31 = 4 - x$, then $x = -9$.
q: $x = -9$ $q \Rightarrow p$: If $x = -9$, then $2x + 31 = 4 - x$.
b) $p \Rightarrow q$ and $q \Rightarrow p$ are both true.

8. p: the perimeter of a particular square is 40 cm.
q: the area of the same square is 100 cm^2.
a) See margin. b) $p \Rightarrow q$ and $q \Rightarrow p$ are both true.

9. A, B, and C are collinear points.
p: $AB + BC = AC$.
q: B is between A and C.
a) See margin. b) $p \Rightarrow q$ and $q \Rightarrow p$ are both true.

10. p: $s^2 = 40,000$ a) $p \Rightarrow q$: If $s^2 = 40,000$, then $s = 200$.
q: $s = 200$ $q \Rightarrow p$: If $s = 200$, then $s^2 = 40,000$.
b) $p \Rightarrow q$ is false, $q \Rightarrow p$ is true.

11. p: B is between A and C.
q: A is between C and B.
a) See margin. b) Both $p \Rightarrow q$ and $q \Rightarrow p$ are false.

12. Refer to Example 3. Find an instance of p for which the consequent q is true. *See margin.*

13. Mr. Chu had lived under communist rule in mainland China but recently immigrated to the province of Ontario in Canada. He knew that communist countries always have socialized medicine. He found out that Ontario has socialized medicine. He concluded that Ontario's provincial government is communist. Is his reasoning correct? *No*

8. a. $p \Rightarrow q$: **If the perimeter of a particular square is 40 cm, then the area of the same square is 100 cm^2.**
$q \Rightarrow p$: **If the area of a particular square is 100 cm^2, then the perimeter of the same square is 40 cm.**

9. a. $p \Rightarrow q$: **If $AB + BC = AC$, then B is between A and C.**
$q \Rightarrow p$: **If B is between A and C, then $AB + BC = AC$.**

11. a. $p \Rightarrow q$: **If B is between A and C, then A is between C and B.**
$q \Rightarrow p$: **If A is between C and B, then B is between A and C.**

12. An instance of $p \Rightarrow q$ and $q \Rightarrow p$ is:

Review

14. **a.** How many diagonals does an *n*-sided polygon have? $\frac{n(n-3)}{2}$
    b. How many diagonals does an octagon have? *(Lesson 2-3)* 20

15. Refer to the following computer program.

```
10  PRINT "COMPUTE SUM OF ANGLE MEASURES IN
    POLYGON"
20  PRINT "ENTER THE NUMBER OF SIDES"
21  INPUT N
30  IF N >=3 THEN PRINT "THE SUM OF THE ANGLE
    MEASURES (IN DEGREES) IS "; (N − 2) * 180
40  END
```

a. What will be printed when N = 6? See margin.
b. What will be printed when N = 1? *(Lesson 2-3)* See margin.

In 16 and 17, write in if-then form. *(Lesson 2-2)*

16. A figure is a quadrilateral whenever it is a square.
    If a figure is a square, then it is a quadrilateral.

17. Any person born in New York City is a U.S. citizen. If a person was
    born in New York City, then that person is a U.S. citizen.

In 18 and 19, graph on a number line and describe the graph. *(Lesson 1-9)*

18. all numbers *x* satisfying $x \geq 7$
    ray

19. all numbers *y* satisfying $3 \leq y \leq 3.01$
    segment

20. Give one reason for undefined terms. *(Lesson 1-6)*
    sample: to avoid circularity

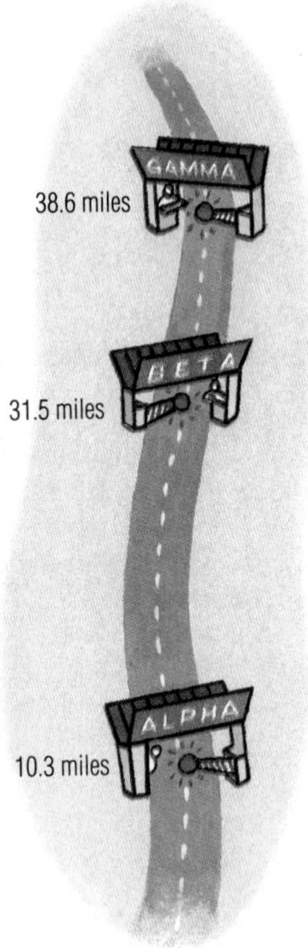

In 21 and 22, Alpha, Beta, and Gamma are three toll booths on a
highway. A headquarters building is planned with one of its functions
being to collect money from the booths. To save on gas, the sum of the
distances from that building to the booths should be as small as possible.
Pictured at the left are three mileage markers. (They are like coordinates
on a number line; for example, Alpha is 10.3 miles from the end of the
highway.) *(Lesson 1-2, Previous course)*

38.6 miles

31.5 miles

10.3 miles

21. Is it more cost efficient to put the headquarters at Alpha, or at Beta,
    or at Gamma? Beta

22. **a.** What is the mean of the mileage markers? 26.8
    b. What is the median of the mileage markers? 31.5
    c. Is it more cost efficient to put the headquarters at the mean or the
    median? median

Exploration

23. Make up a nonmathematical conditional that is false, but whose
    converse is true.
    sample: If you spend money, then you are buying a concert ticket.

80

Good Definitions

Good definitions in geometry, just as good definition in a photograph, help to clarify what is being discussed. Without good definition(s), the subject can be a blur.

Osgood's column discussing cookies on the first page of the chapter illustrates the need for precise definitions outside mathematics. By now, you should be convinced that careful definitions are needed inside mathematics in order for everyone to agree on what they are talking about.

In Chapter 1, we gave good definitions for several words, including "distance," "between," and "segment." In this lesson, we give other careful (or good) definitions. These good definitions have the following properties.

A good definition must:
   I. include only words either commonly understood, defined earlier, or purposely undefined;
   II. accurately describe the idea being defined;
   III. include no more information than is necessary.

Consider the term "midpoint." We want "midpoint" to refer to a special point on a segment, the "halfway point." Such points are important. In a commercial flight over water, if there is trouble before the halfway point, the plane goes back to its point of origin. If there is trouble after that point, the plane goes on to its destination. Here is a good definition.

Definition:

The **midpoint** of a segment AB is the point M on $\overline{AB}$ with $AM = MB$.

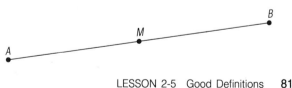

LESSON 2-5

RESOURCES
■ Lesson Master 2-5
▣ Visual for Teaching Aid 12 displays the terms that define midpoint of a segment.

OBJECTIVE

D Apply the properties of a good definition.

TEACHING NOTES

The criteria for a good definition do not tell students how to write a definition. Some teachers like the following:

To define a term (or phrase), (1) name the term, (2) place it in the smallest possible class, and (3) tell how it differs from other members of that class. The definition of midpoint on page 81 is given in that form. The smallest possible class is the set of points on the segment, and it differs because its distance is the same from each endpoint.

Trace the definition of *circle* back to undefined terms as follows:

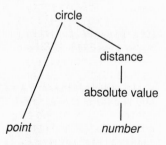

The italicized words are undefined; the other terms have been been defined previously.

The definition of midpoint uses only words commonly understood (The, of, a, is, . . .), defined earlier (segment, $\overline{AB}$, AM, …), or purposely undefined (point). We can trace the phrase "midpoint of a segment" back to these earlier or undefined terms.

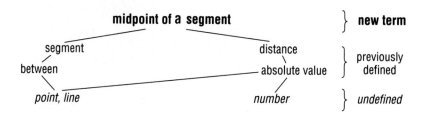

The definition of midpoint distinguishes the midpoint of a segment from other points that are not midpoints. From the definition, the midpoint must be on the segment. Below, $AM = MB$ but M is not on $\overline{AB}$. So M is not the midpoint of $\overline{AB}$. However, since $AM = MB$, we say that M is **equidistant** from A and B.

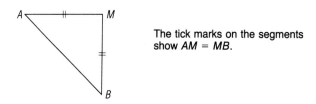

The tick marks on the segments show $AM = MB$.

Some true statements about midpoints are not good definitions. You should be able to tell why they are not good.

Example 1 Why is each of these statements not a good definition of "midpoint"?
  a. The midpoint of a segment is a point between the endpoints.
  b. The midpoint M of $\overline{AB}$ is the point M on $\overline{AB}$ between A and B, the same distance from A and B, and with $MA = MB$.
  c. The midpoint M of $\overline{AB}$ is the intersection of $\overline{AB}$ and a bisector of $\overline{AB}$.

Solution

  a. The statement does not accurately describe midpoint (violates property II).
  b. The statement contains too much information (violates property III).
  c. The statement uses a term, "bisector," not previously defined or understood (violates property I).

A good definition does the job of two conditionals. First, it tells you the characteristics of the defined term. For *midpoint*:

> If M is the **midpoint** of $\overline{AB}$, then M is on $\overline{AB}$ and AM = MB.
> defined term ⇒ characteristics of term
> (in antecedent)

This is the *meaning* half of the definition, because it tells you what the term means.

Second, a good definition tells you the characteristics that allow you to use the defined term. For *midpoint*:

> If M is on $\overline{AB}$ and AM = MB, then M is the **midpoint** of $\overline{AB}$.
> characteristics of term ⇒ the defined term

This is the *sufficient condition* half of the definition, because it tells you when you can use the name of the new term.

Notice that the meaning half and the sufficient condition half of a definition are converses of each other and both are true.

This can be expressed symbolically. In a definition, the meaning half is

$$p \Rightarrow q$$

where *p* contains the term being defined. The sufficient condition half is

$$q \Rightarrow p.$$

The definition consists of both of these: $p \Rightarrow q$ and $q \Rightarrow p$. We then write $p \Leftrightarrow q$, and say *p* **if and only if** *q*. So, for the definition of midpoint, we can say:

> M is the **midpoint** of $\overline{AB}$ if and only if M is on $\overline{AB}$ and AM = MB.

■ ■ ■ ■ ■ ■

Example 2 Let p = "A is between C and D."
Let q = "CA + AD = CD."
Write $p \Leftrightarrow q$ in words.

Solution A is between C and D if and only if CA + AD = CD.

b. A triangle is a rigid figure which encloses space on three sides.
Words are used which have not been defined.
c. If *A, B, C* are three points which are not collinear, then the three segments $\overline{AB}$, $\overline{AC}$, and $\overline{BC}$, and the three angles, one at each point, form a triangle.
More is stated than is needed.

3. Let p = "A country is democratic." Let q = "The power resides with the people." Write $p \Leftrightarrow q$ in words.
A country is democratic if and only if the power resides with the people.

4. Give the meaning half of a good definition of "circle."
If a figure is a circle, then it is a set of points in a plane at a given distance from a given point.

NOTES ON QUESTIONS
Making Connections for Question 9. Parts **c** and **d** are important preparation for the study of size transformations in Chapter 12.

Small Group Work for Questions 10-19: These questions can be done in small groups so that students can discuss the properties of a good definition. Students should also be encouraged to make up their own examples and to discuss them within their groups.

Questions 18 and 19:
Occasionally, we define a term or phrase in the Questions. Students should not be expected to memorize these definitions, but they should be able to draw these figures and distinguish them from other figures.

NOTES ON QUESTIONS

Now consider a familiar figure, the circle. Here is a good definition of *circle*.

> **Definition:**
>
> A **circle** is the set of all points in a plane at a certain distance (its radius) from a certain point (its center).

This definition can be reworded to describe each point on a circle. The **circle with center C and radius r** is the set of all points P in a plane with PC = r. A circle with center C is often called **circle C** or ⊙C.

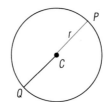

Circle with center C, radius r
PC = r
P is on the circle.
C, the center, is not on the circle.

Example 3 Use the above definition of circle.

    a. Write the meaning of circle.
    b. Write the sufficient condition for a circle.
    c. Write the definition of circle as a biconditional (in if-and-only-if form).

Solution

a. The meaning is a conditional with the defined term "circle" in the antecedent: If a figure is a circle, then it is the set of all points in a plane at a certain distance from a certain point.
b. The sufficient condition is the converse of the meaning: If a figure is the set of all points in a plane at a certain distance from a certain point, then it is a circle.
c. Connect the antecedent and consequent with the words *if and only if*: A figure is a circle if and only if it is the set of all points in a plane at a certain distance from a certain point.

As in English, terms in mathematics may have more than one meaning. The term "radius of a circle" is one such term. It means *the distance* from the center to a point on the circle. It also can mean *a segment* connecting the center with a point on the circle. The situation almost always will indicate which meaning is appropriate. The same is true for the term **diameter of a circle,** which can mean either (a) a segment connecting two points on the circle and which contains the center of the circle, or (b) the length of that segment, which is twice the radius.

84

1. List three properties of a good definition. **See margin.**

2. Define: midpoint of a segment.
   The midpoint of a segment *AB* is the point *M* on *AB* with *AM* = *MB*.

3. The definition of "midpoint of a segment" uses two ideas that have been defined earlier. What are they? **segment and distance**

4. Break the definition of "midpoint" into its meaning and sufficient condition halves. **See margin.**

5. When $a \Rightarrow b$ and $b \Rightarrow a$, we write $a \underset{\Leftrightarrow}{\underline{\quad ? \quad}} b$.

6. The symbol "$\Leftrightarrow$" is read __?__ . **If and only if**

7. If point Q is on circle C with radius r, then $QC = \underline{\quad ? \quad}$. *r*

8. What two meanings does the word "diameter" have? **See margin.**

9. Given: Q is the midpoint of $\overline{RT}$ and $RT = 14$. Fill in each blank with a number. (Hint: draw a picture.)
   a. $RQ = \underline{\quad ? \quad}$ 7
   b. $TQ = \underline{\quad ? \quad}$ 7
   c. $TQ = \underline{\quad ? \quad} \cdot RT$ ½
   d. $\dfrac{RQ}{RT} = \underline{\quad ? \quad}$ ½

   14

   R   *Q*   *T*

10. Why is each of these *not* a good definition of *circle*?
    a. A circle is the set of points at a certain distance from a certain point and it goes around the center.
    b. A circle is a plane section of a sphere.
    c. A circle is the set of points away from a certain point.
    See margin.

11. Refer back to Question 14 of Lesson 2-1. According to the definition of circle, why is choice (d) not a circle? **See margin.**

In 12–15, halves of some previous definitions are written in if-then form. Tell whether the statement is the meaning or the sufficient condition half. (After each question is the lesson where the original definition appears.)

12. If S is space, then S is the set of all possible points. *(Lesson 1-6)* **meaning**

13. If A is between B and C, then $\overrightarrow{AB}$ and $\overrightarrow{AC}$ are opposite rays. *(Lesson 1-8)* **sufficient condition**

14. If points lie on the same line, then they are collinear. *(Lesson 1-5)* **sufficient condition**

15. If two lines are parallel, then they have no points in common or are identical. *(Lesson 1-7)* **meaning**

16. Let p = "The lawn mower needs gas," and q = "The lawn mower doesn't start on 3 pulls." Write $p \Leftrightarrow q$ out in words. **The lawn mower needs gas if and only if it doesn't start on 3 pulls.**

17. Write the definition of "convex set" from Lesson 2-1 in if-and-only-if form. **A set is convex if and only if all segments connecting points of the set lie entirely in the set.**

Margin notes:

4. Meaning: If *M* is the midpoint of $\overline{AB}$, then *M* is on $\overline{AB}$ and *AM* = *MB*. Sufficient Condition: If *M* is on $\overline{AB}$ and *AM* = *MB*, then *M* is the midpoint of $\overline{AB}$.

8. a segment connecting two points on the circle which contains the center of the circle; the length of such a segment

10. a. The definition contains more information than is necessary (violates property III).
b. The definition uses terms not yet defined (violates property I).
c. The definition is inaccurate (violates property II).

11. Choice (d) contains all the points inside the circle as well as the circle itself, so it violates the definition.

18. *Multiple choice.* The shaded portion of the figure at the left is the **interior of the circle** with center A, radius r. Which of these is a good definition of "interior of a circle"?
   (a) The interior of a circle with center A is the set of points inside the circle.
   (b) The interior of a circle with center A, radius r, is the set of points whose distance from A is less than r. **(b)**

19. In the figure at the left, T is the midpoint of $\overline{DQ}$. $DT = TQ$. Let m be any plane, line, ray, or segment containing T and containing *no* other points of $\overline{DQ}$. m is called a **bisector** of $\overline{DQ}$. Write a good definition of "bisector of a segment." **See margin.**

20. M is equidistant from A and B. $AM = 4x + 10$ and $BM = 5x - 7$. Find x. **$x = 17$**

Review

In 21–23, a true statement is given. **a.** Give its converse. **b.** Is the converse true? *(Lesson 2-4)*

21. If $x = -\frac{2}{3}$, then $x^2 = \frac{4}{9}$.   a) If $x^2 = \frac{4}{9}$, then $x = -\frac{2}{3}$. b) No

22. When you read this book, you are studying geometry.   a) If you are studying geometry, then you are reading this book. b) No

23. If $\overrightarrow{AB}$ and $\overrightarrow{AC}$ are opposite rays, then A is between B and C.
   a) If A is between B and C, then $\overrightarrow{AB}$ and $\overrightarrow{AC}$ are opposite rays. b) Yes

24. A line in a computer program reads
   30   IF X >= 25 THEN PRINT 3*X − 75
   What will the computer do at this line if X has the value
   a. 20; ignore line 30 and   **b.** 25;   **c.** 30? *(Lesson 2-3)*
       go to the next program line   print "0"   print "15"

25. Find a counterexample to the conditional "If P, Q, and R are on the same line and $PQ = 20$ and $QR = 6$, then $PR = 26$." *(Lesson 2-2)* **See margin.**

Exploration

26. Sometimes the meaning of a word can be found by taking it apart. For instance, *geometer* originally meant "Earth measurer," from *geo* meaning Earth and *meter* meaning measure. What do these words mean? **See margin.**
   a. geology   **b.** geothermal
   c. geography   **d.** geocentric

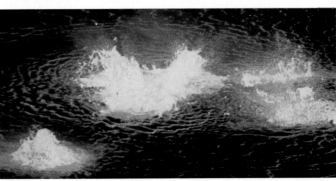

Unions and Intersections of Figures

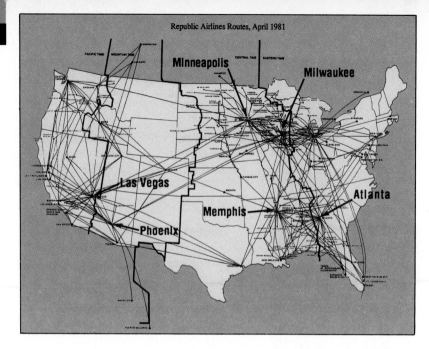

Network of airline routes of Republic Airlines in April, 1981.

Points, lines, segments, and rays are the building blocks of more complex figures. The two most common ways of combining figures or any other sets is to take their *union* or their *intersection*.

Definitions:

The **union of two sets A and B,** written **A ∪ B,** is the set of elements which are either in A or in B, or both.
The **intersection of two sets A and B,** written **A ∩ B,** is the set of elements which are in both A and B.

Here are some examples of unions and intersections of sets.

Set	A	B	A ∪ B	A ∩ B
Example 1	{4, 6, 8}	{10, 6, 4}	{4, 6, 8, 10}	{4, 6}
Example 2	set of numbers x with $x \geq 3$	set of numbers x with $x \leq 7$	set of all real numbers	set of numbers x with $3 \leq x \leq 7$
Example 3	rectangle P Q S R	P Q S R	P Q S R	P Q S R

LESSON 2-6 Unions and Intersections of Figures **87**

LESSON 2-6

RESOURCES
■ Lesson Master 2-6
▱ Visual for Teaching Aid 13 can be used with Questions **7, 8, 14, 15,** and **26.**

OBJECTIVE

F Determine the union and intersection of sets.

TEACHING NOTES

The notation in this lesson can be confusing. When two lines *m* and *n* intersect in a point *P,* we should write *m* ∩ *n* = {*P*}, but sometimes we write the simpler *m* ∩ *n* = *P.* The reason the former is correct is that *m* and *n* are sets of points, and their intersection should also be a set of points, not just a point. However, notation can be whatever you wish it to be, and the latter is often used because it is simpler and easier to understand, and because it does not seem to cause problems.

Make sure students examine the Republic Airlines network example closely. Is it traversable? (No, there are more than two nodes with an odd number of edges from them.)

Remind students that unions and intersections are fundamentally connected with the words *or* and *and.* (Students who have studied UCSMP *Algebra* will have seen this.) X is in the union of A and B ⇔ X is in A **or** X is in B. X is in the intersection of A and B ⇔ X is in A **and** X is in B.

Both the union and intersection of figures occur in practical situations. The next example is with networks. An airline has a *route* between two cities when it flies between them. The set of all routes of an airline forms a network. Shown on page 87 is the network for Republic Airlines in April, 1981.

Example 4 In the late 1970s, North Central Airlines (based in Minneapolis) and Southern Airlines (based in Memphis) merged to form Republic Airlines. Let N = the network of routes for North Central Airlines and S = the network for Southern Airlines. What did N ∪ S and N ∩ S mean in this merger?

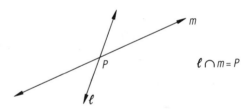

Solution N ∪ S consisted of the routes either in North Central or Southern Airlines or both. It became the starting network of the new merged airline, Republic. N ∩ S consisted of the routes in both North Central and Southern Airlines. It was the overlap between them and indicated places where the new merged airline might think of eliminating repetition of flights.

Look closely at the network for Republic on page 87. The nodes are cities and the arcs are routes. The clusters around Milwaukee and Atlanta show where North Central and Southern had the majority of their routes. Notice that there is a third cluster of routes on the west coast. This is because a third airline, Air West, was later merged into Republic. If W stands for the network for Air West, the routes of Republic became W ∪ N ∪ S.

Unions and intersections are important in geometry. Often we speak of *intersections* of lines. Below, the intersection of lines ℓ and m is point P.

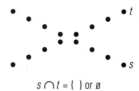

$$\ell \cap m = P$$

If figures have no points in common, then their intersection is the **null set** or **empty set.** That set is written $\emptyset$, or { }. Below are parts of discrete lines s and t. They cross but do not have any points in common.

$$s \cap t = \{ \} \text{ or } \emptyset$$

Complicated figures, such as the Republic Airlines network, are often unions of simpler figures. A triangle is the *union* of simpler figures; specifically, it is the union of three segments.

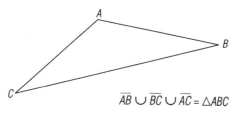

$$\overline{AB} \cup \overline{BC} \cup \overline{AC} = \triangle ABC$$

Questions

NOTES ON QUESTIONS
Making Connections for Question 7: Ask students what the possible intersections of a line and a circle are. (a single point, in which case the line is called a *tangent;* two points, in which case the line is called a *secant;* no points; the term tangent is defined in Lesson 11-3; the term secant in Lesson 15-5)

Question 8: Students who have not named polygons by their vertices may have difficulty with this question. You will have to indicate how polygons may be named.

Question 10: Note that solving the system gives the solution without graphing.

Question 17: Ask how many students know the definition of *sanctions.* Even though some may, using it violates our requirement that we use only words known to all.

Making Connections for Question 24: Later, students will be asked to find an angle whose measure is twice its supplement. That can be done by solving this equation.

Question 25: Ask students if the graph is a ray. (It is not; it lacks an endpoint.) Some may still insist that "there must be a last point just to the right of coordinate of 158."

Question 26: This problem intrigues many students; do not skip it. If they complain that it is too tricky, remind them that it was created and published as a puzzle and many puzzles are supposed to be tricky.

Covering the Reading

1. Define: union of two sets A and B. **The union of two sets A and B is the set of elements which are either in A or in B or in both.**

2. Define: intersection of two sets A and B. **The intersection of two sets A and B is the set of elements which are in both A and B.**

In 3 and 4, find $A \cup B$ and $A \cap B$.

3. A = {-3, 2, 5, 8}, B = {-3, 0, 2}
   $A \cup B = \{-3, 0, 2, 5, 8\}$; $A \cap B = \{-3, 2\}$

4. A = solution set to $x \geq 40$, B = solution set to $x \leq 50$
   $A \cup B =$ the set of all real numbers; $A \cap B = \{x: 40 \leq x \leq 50\}$

5. Choose the correct words from those in parentheses. The Republic Airline route network is the (union, intersection) of the networks of (two, three) airlines.
   union, three

6. If W stands for the network of Air West and N for the network of North Central Airlines, what is the meaning of $W \cap N$?
   routes covered by both Air West and North Central Airlines

7. Suppose *m* is the line and *n* is the circle pictured below. What are the elements of $m \cap n$? **the points A and B**

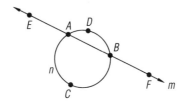

8. *SPED* and *PACE* below are rectangles.
   a. $SPED \cap PACE = $ __?__ $\overline{PE}$ b. $SPED \cup PACE = $ __?__ **the union of rectangle *SACD* and segment $\overline{PE}$**

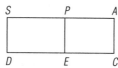

9. A symbol for the null set is __?__ or __?__ . $\emptyset$, { }

LESSON 2-6 Unions and Intersections of Figures   **89**

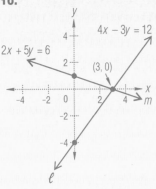

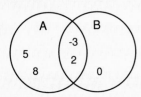
Applying the Mathematics

10. Line ℓ has equation $4x - 3y = 12$. Line *m* has equation $2x + 5y = 6$. Graph ℓ and *m* on the same pair of axes. From the graph, determine the coordinates of ℓ ∩ *m*.
See margin for graph; the actual point of intersection is (3, 0).

In 11–13, describe G ∪ H and G ∩ H.

11. G = set of residents of Indonesia.
H = set of residents of Jakarta, Indonesia.
G ∪ H = all residents of Indonesia; G ∩ H = all residents of Jakarta

12. G = ages of people who are eligible to drive in your state.
H = ages of people who are eligible to vote in your state.
See margin.

13. G = set of students in your geometry class.
H = set of students in other geometry classes.
G ∪ H = students in all geometry classes; G ∩ H = ∅

In 14 and 15, x is triangle *GHI* pictured below and y is triangle *IJG*. Name the segments of:

14. x ∩ y; $\overline{GI}$

15. x ∪ y. $\overline{GH}, \overline{HI}, \overline{IJ}, \overline{GJ}, \overline{GI}$

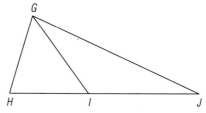

16. Refer to the figure in Question 7. Suppose one of the points from *A, B, C, D, E,* or *F* is chosen at random. What is the probability that it will
a. lie on line *m*? $\frac{2}{3}$
b. lie on circle *n*? $\frac{2}{3}$
c. lie on *m* ∩ *n*? $\frac{1}{3}$

Review

17. Tell why each of the following is not a good definition of speed limit. *(Lesson 2-5)*
a. A speed limit tells how fast you must go.
b. A speed limit gives the highest speed you can go. If you go faster the police may give you a speeding ticket. On some roads it may be dangerous to go faster than the speed limit.
c. A speed limit is the maximum legal speed to avoid prosecution under the state's legislative sanctions.
a) violates prop. II; b) violates prop. III; c) violates prop. I

18. Write as two conditionals: *P* is on circle *O* with radius *r* if and only if *PO* = *r*. *(Lessons 2-5, 2-2)* See margin.

19. Is the statement "If Q is the set of elements in both set A and set B, then Q is the intersection of sets A and B," the meaning or sufficient condition half of the definition of the intersection of two sets? *(Lesson 2-5)* the sufficient condition half

20. Draw a convex hexagonal region. *(Lesson 2-1)* See margin.

21. Draw a nonconvex decagonal region. *(Lesson 2-1)* See margin.

22. a. Write the converse of the statement, "If B is on $\overrightarrow{AC}$, but not between A and C, then $AC = AB - BC$."
  b. Is the statement true?
  c. Is its converse true? *(Lessons 2-4, 1-9)* Yes
    a) If $AC = AB - BC$, then B is on $\overrightarrow{AC}$, but not between A and C.

23. Give the antecedent and consequent of this statement: Should you work more than 40 hours a week, you will receive time-and-a-half for overtime. *(Lesson 2-2)* See margin.

24. Solve for x and check: $x = 2(180 - x)$. *(Previous course)*
  $x = 120$; Check: Does $120 = 2(180 - 120)$? Yes, $120 = 2(60)$.

25. Graph all possibilities for q on a number line: $22 + q > 180$.
  (Previous course)

Exploration

26. Here is a puzzle that combines some ideas of union, intersection, and networks (from *Mathematical Puzzles of Sam Loyd,* edited by Martin Gardner).

It is told that three neighbors who shared a small park, as shown in the sketch, had a falling out. The owner of the large house, complaining that his neighbors' chickens annoyed him, built an enclosed pathway from his door to the gate at the bottom of the picture. Then the man on the right built a path to the gate on the left, and the man on the left built a path to the gate on the right. None of the paths crossed. Can you draw the three paths correctly?

Use the Venn diagram below to list each of the following sets.

R
$R \cup S$
$S \cap T$
$(R \cup S) \cap T$
$(R \cap S) \cup T$
$(R \cap S) \cap T$

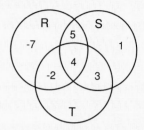

$R = \{-7, -2, 4, 5\}$
$R \cup S = \{-7, -2, 1, 3, 4, 5\}$
$S \cap T = \{3, 4\}$
$(R \cup S) \cap T = \{-2, 3, 4\}$
$(R \cap S) \cup T = \{-2, 3, 4, 5\}$
$(R \cap S) \cap T = \{4\}$

23. Antecedent: You work more than 40 hrs per wk. Consequent: You will receive time-and-a-half for overtime.

OBJECTIVES

A Distinguish between convex and nonconvex regions.
B Draw and identify polygons.
I Identify polygons used for real objects.
K Draw hierarchies of triangles and polygons.

TEACHING NOTES

You may motivate the idea of polygon by describing a path joining three or more coplanar points such that (a) you travel along a line from any one point to another, (b) you never cross any previous point of the path, and (c) you end where you start. Given a set of points, have students determine paths. Usually, there is not a unique solution.

On page 92, some students may think there is an error in the answers for the middle figure at the bottom of the page. The rectangle shown does lie in an oblique plane.

On page 93, you may point out that there are 6! = 720 ways to arrange the 6 letters P,O,L,Y,G,N, but only 12 ways to correctly name the figure. In general, there are 2*n* names for an *n*-gon using its vertices, because there are *n* choices for the first vertex, and you can proceed in either direction.

LESSON

2-7

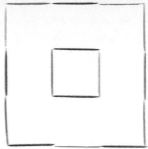

Terms Associated with Polygons

Here is a polygon puzzle.

Move 4 of the 16 toothpicks to create three overlapping squares.

Triangles and other polygons are basic to the study of geometry. So good definitions are necessary. In the last lesson, there is the statement "a triangle is the union … of three segments." This statement is not a good definition because there are unions of three segments that do not look like the figures we want to be triangles.

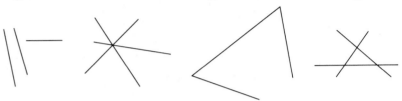

unions of three segments that are not triangles

Clearly a triangle is not the union of *any* three segments. Each segment must intersect the others. Also, the intersections should be at endpoints. These criteria help not only to get a good definition of "triangle," but also the more general term *polygon*.

Definition:

A **polygon** is the union of three or more segments in the same plane such that each segment intersects exactly two others, one at each of its endpoints.

Breaking up the definition clarifies what is and what is not a polygon. A polygon is …

a union of three or more segments,

yes   no   no

in the same plane.

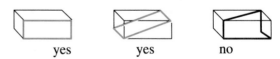

yes   yes   no

92

Each segment intersects exactly two others.

yes   no   no

Intersections are only at the endpoints of the segments.

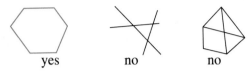

yes   no   no

To describe polygons, terminology is needed. The segments which make up a polygon are its **sides.** The endpoints of the sides are the **vertices** of the polygon. The singular of vertices is **vertex.** A polygon can be named by giving its vertices in order. Many names are possible; two names for the polygon shown here are *POLYGN* and *GYLOPN*.

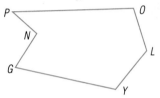

$$POLYGN \quad \overline{PO} \cup \overline{OL} \cup \overline{LY} \cup \overline{YG} \cup \overline{GN} \cup \overline{NP}$$

Consecutive vertices are endpoints of a side. For instance, G and Y are consecutive vertices of *POLYGN*. **Consecutive sides** are sides which share an endpoint, for instance $\overline{PO}$ and $\overline{OL}$ above. A **diagonal** is a segment connecting nonconsecutive vertices. Two of the diagonals of *POLYGN* are $\overline{NY}$ and $\overline{NL}$. Neither they nor any other diagonals of *POLYGN* are drawn above.

A polygon with n sides is called an **n-gon.** When n is small, there are special names: a **triangle** has 3 sides; a **quadrilateral** has 4, a **pentagon** has 5, a **hexagon** has 6, a **heptagon** has 7, an **octagon** has 8, a **nonagon** has 9, and a **decagon** has 10. The boundaries of many things are polygons; below is an outline of a house whose boundary is an 8-gon or octagon. A number of such houses were built in the last century.

By this time, students should be familiar with the names of certain polygons. Still, it is fun to ask for other words with the same prefixes. Three places where these prefixes are found are:
The calendar: *Sept*ember, *Oct*ober, *Nov*ember, *Decem*-ber (The prefix stands for the number of the month beginning with March, when the Roman year originally started.)
Hydrocarbons: *pent*ane, *hept*ane, *oct*ane, *non*ane, *dec*ane (Students will have heard of "octane," at least; the prefix stands for the number of atoms of carbon in the hydrocarbon molecule.)
Sports: *tri*athlon, *pent*athlon, *hept*athlon, . . ., *dec*athlon (The prefix stands for the number of events in these multi-event competitions.) There is also a *bi*athlon.

Throughout this book, hierarchical diagrams are used to help students visualize the relationship among concepts. For example, students have difficulty remembering that isosceles does not mean *exactly two* sides equal. The diagram helps imprint the notion that the set of all triangles separates into two sets, scalene and isosceles. Equilateral is a subset of isosceles.

Reading There is so much new terminology in this lesson that students may need to take notes as they read. They may also need to draw various polygons in order to learn their characteristics. Encourage students to organize their notes on the various polygons in chart form, listing the name of each polygon and its number of sides and vertices.

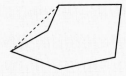
From its definition, every polygon lies entirely in one plane. It separates the plane into three sets—the polygon, its interior, and its exterior. The union of a polygon and its interior is a **polygonal region.**

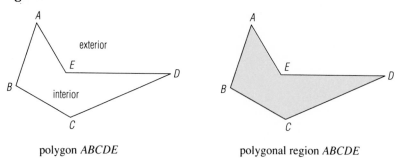

polygon *ABCDE*   polygonal region *ABCDE*

A polygon is **convex** if and only if its corresponding polygonal region is convex. Many commonly used polygons, such as squares and parallelograms, are convex.

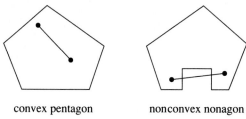

convex pentagon   nonconvex nonagon

Triangles with special characteristics are given specific names. When lengths of the three sides are considered, three possibilities occur: all are equal, two are equal, or no two are equal. An **equilateral triangle** has all three sides equal. An **isosceles triangle** has two (or more) sides of equal length. (An equilateral triangle is also isosceles.) A triangle with no sides of the same length is called **scalene.**

equilateral

isosceles
(two sides equal)

scalene
(no sides equal)

The classification of triangles by sides is shown below in a **family tree** or **hierarchy.** Each name includes all the shapes below it to which it is connected. Thus an equilateral triangle is an isosceles triangle, a triangle, a polygon, and a figure, but an equilateral triangle is not a scalene triangle.

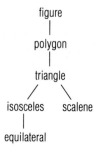

94

94

Question 28: Note the progression to the general solution in part **c**, which is as follows: Find the distance between the two points. Divide it by 2. Add that number to the smaller of the two coordinates and subtract it from the larger. In either case, you obtain the coordinate of the midpoint. In general, suppose $x > y$. Then, we note that
$$y + \frac{(x - y)}{2}$$
$$= x - \frac{(x - y)}{2} = \frac{(x + y)}{2}.$$

Covering the Reading

In 1–4, why is each figure not a polygon? See margin for answers 1-4.

1. 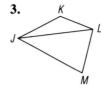   2.   3.   4.

5. Use the polygon *ABCDE* below.
   a. Name its vertices. *A, B, C, D,* and *E*
   b. Name a pair of consecutive sides. sample: $\overline{AB}, \overline{AE}$
   c. Name a pair of consecutive vertices. sample: *A* and *B*

6. a. How many vertices has an octagon? 8
   b. How many vertices has an *n*-gon? *n*

7. How do polygons and polygonal regions differ? See margin.

8. When is a polygon considered to be convex?
   if and only if its corresponding polygonal region is convex
   In 9–12, characterize the polygonal regional as convex or nonconvex.

9.   10. 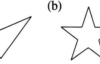   11.   12.

   convex   nonconvex   convex   nonconvex

13. *Multiple choice.* Which figure is shaped like a nonconvex quadrilateral?
    (a)   (b)   (c)   (d) (a)

14. Draw a convex hexagon. See margin.

15. Arrange from most general to most specific: isosceles triangle, figure, polygon, equilateral triangle, triangle, two-dimensional figure.
    See margin.
16. Draw a convex 12-gon. See margin.

ADDITIONAL ANSWERS
1. Segments intersect more than 2 other segments, or segments intersect at points other than endpoints.

2. Not every segment intersects 2 segments.

3. Segments intersect more than 2 other segments.

4. One side is not a segment.

7. A polygonal region is the union of a polygon and its interior. The polygon itself does not include its interior.

14. sample:

15. figure, two-dimensional figure, polygon, triangle, isosceles triangle, equilateral triangle

16. sample:

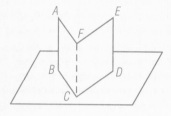

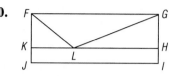

Applying the Mathematics

17. Draw a union of five segments that is not a pentagon. See margin.

18. How many diagonals does a pentagon have? 5

In 19 and 20, the figure includes segments which form more than one polygon. Name the convex polygons.

19.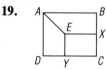

AEYD, ABXE, EXCY, ABCD

20.

See margin.

21. Write the sufficient condition half of the definition of a polygon. (Hint: Begin "If a figure is … .") See margin.

In 22 and 23, use the four conditions for a polygon:
  I. a union of three or more segments
  II. in the same plane
  III. each segment intersects exactly two others
  IV. intersections are only at the two endpoints.

22. Draw a figure satisfying conditions I, II, and III, but not IV. See margin.

23. Draw a figure satisfying conditions I, III, and IV, but not II. See margin.

In 24 and 25, how does the given dictionary definition of *polygon* differ from the definition given in this lesson? (Each of these dictionaries gives more than one definition of *polygon*.)

24. "A closed plane figure having many (more than four) angles and sides." (*American College Dictionary,* 1953 edition) This definition excludes 3-sided and 4-sided polygons.

25. "A closed figure on a sphere bounded by great circle arcs." (*Webster's New Collegiate Dictionary,* 1977 edition) Sides are not segments in this definition.

Review

26. S = {-5, 0, 5, 10} and T = {-3, 0, 3}. *(Lesson 2-6)*
  a. Find S ∪ T. {-5, -3, 0, 3, 5, 10}
  b. Find S ∩ T. {0}

27. Draw an example of two convex sets C and D whose union C ∪ D is nonconvex. *(Lessons 2-6, 2-1)* See margin.

28. **a.** On a number line, suppose A has coordinate 19, B has coordinate 8, and M has coordinate 13.5. Verify that M is the midpoint of $\overline{AB}$ by showing that AM = MB. See margin.
  b. If M has coordinate -2, A has coordinate -43, and B has coordinate 39, verify that M is the midpoint of $\overline{AB}$. See margin.
  c. If A has coordinate x and B has coordinate y, then what is the coordinate of M, the midpoint of $\overline{AB}$? *(Lessons 2-5, 1-2)* $\frac{x+y}{2}$

29. On Interstate 80, Des Moines is 1849 miles from Sacramento. Salt Lake City is between them, 638 miles from Sacramento. If you wanted to drive halfway from Des Moines to Salt Lake City on this highway, **a.** how far would you have to drive and **b.** how far would you be from Sacramento? *(Lessons 2-5, 1-2)* a) 605.5 miles; b) 1243.5 miles

96

30. Give the symbol for each. *(Lesson 1-8)*
  a. line through points X and Y $\overleftrightarrow{XY}$
  b. line segment with endpoints X and Y $\overline{XY}$
  c. distance between X and Y XY

31. Some names for polygons are no longer used or are used only rarely. For each of the following names of polygons, guess how many sides the polygon has, and then check your guesses by looking in a large dictionary.
  a. dodecagon 12
  b. duodecagon 12
  c. enneagon 9
  d. pentadecagon 15
  e. quadrangle 4
  f. tetragon 4
  g. trigon 3
  h. undecagon 11

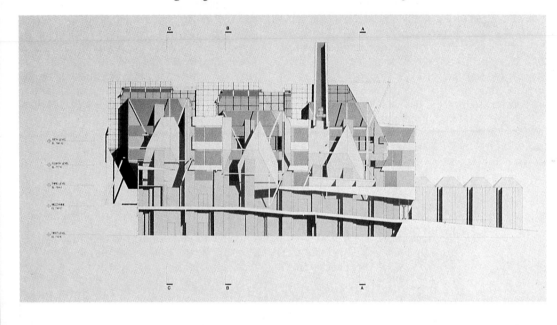

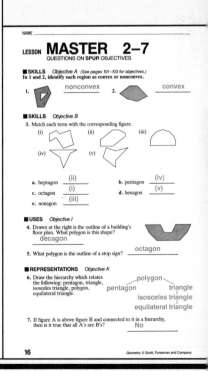

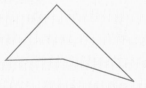
Summary

Every if-then statement (conditional) has an antecedent, the "if" part, and a consequent, the "then" part. If the antecedent is p and the consequent is q, the conditional is $p \Rightarrow q$. This chapter is concerned with the following questions: (1) How can you tell if $p \Rightarrow q$ is false? (2) How are $p \Rightarrow q$ and $q \Rightarrow p$ related? (3) What happens when both $p \Rightarrow q$ and $q \Rightarrow p$ are true? In this chapter, these ideas are applied to segments, circles, and polygons, and also to algebra and everyday reasoning.

(1) How can you tell if $p \Rightarrow q$ is false? A counterexample is needed. A counterexample is a situation for which p is true and q is false. Reasoning from a false statement leads to conclusions which may be true or false. For this reason, computers skip the consequents of any conditional with a false antecedent. Mathematicians consider as true any conditional $p \Rightarrow q$ in which p is false.

(2) $p \Rightarrow q$ and $q \Rightarrow p$ are converse statements. The truth of one does not tell you anything about the truth of the other.

(3) The statement $p \Rightarrow q$ and its converse $q \Rightarrow p$ together form the biconditional $p \Leftrightarrow q$. We then say "p if and only if q." Every definition can be reworded as an "if and only if" statement and can be separated into two if-then statements, the meaning (where the term being defined is in the antecedent) and the sufficient condition (the converse of the meaning). Good definitions are accurate descriptions which involve only words defined earlier, words commonly understood, or words purposely undefined; and good definitions include no more information than is necessary. Good definitions are needed in many fields, not only in mathematics.

Vocabulary

Many terms were defined in this chapter.
For the starred terms (*) below, you should be able to produce a *good* definition.
For the other terms, you should be able to give a general description and a specific example, including a drawing where appropriate.

Lesson 2-1
convex set
nonconvex set

Lesson 2-2
conditional
if-then statement, $\Rightarrow$
antecedent, if part
consequent, then part
instance of a sentence
*counterexample to a
  conditional
Goldbach's Conjecture

Lesson 2-4
*converse

Lesson 2-5
*midpoint, equidistant
meaning half of a definition
sufficient condition half of
  a definition
if and only if
biconditional, $\Leftrightarrow$
*circle, $\odot$
center, radius,
  diameter of a circle

Lesson 2-6
*union of sets, $\cup$
*intersection of sets, $\cap$
null set, empty set, $\varnothing$, { }

Lesson 2-7
*polygon, side of polygon
vertex of polygon
consecutive vertices
consecutive sides
diagonal, n-gon
triangle, quadrilateral,
  pentagon, hexagon,
  heptagon, octagon,
  nonagon, decagon
polygonal region
convex polygon
*equilateral triangle
*isosceles triangle
*scalene triangle
hierarchy, family tree

98

Progress Self-Test

See margin for answers not shown below.

Directions: Take this test as you would take a test in class. Use a ruler and a protractor. Then check your work with the solutions in the Selected Answers section in the back of the book.

1. Tell which property of a good definition is violated by this "bad" definition: The **midpoint of a segment** AB is the point M on $\overline{AB}$ for which $AM = MB$, $\frac{1}{2} AB = AM$, and $\frac{1}{2} AB = MB$. includes too much information

2. Draw a nonconvex quadrilateral region.

3. In the following statement, underline the antecedent once and the consequent twice: Two angles have equal measure if they are vertical angles.

4. Rewrite in if-then form: Every trapezoid is a quadrilateral.

In 5 and 6, use the figure below. If r is rectangle $ABCD$ and t is triangle ADC, name the segments of

5. $r \cup t$; 6. $r \cap t$. $\overline{AD}$ and $\overline{CD}$

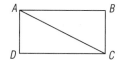

7. Let $p =$ "There are over 10 books on that shelf." $q =$ "The shelf falls." Write $p \Leftrightarrow q$ in words.

8. Consider the statement: If a figure is a triangle, then it is a polygon.
   a. Is the statement true? Yes
   b. Write the converse of this statement.
   c. Show that the converse is false by drawing a counterexample.

9. Mr. Hawkins told his class, "If you do your homework every night, you will be guaranteed a passing grade." Liane, a student in Mr. Hawkins' class, received a passing grade. Did Liane do homework every night? impossible to tell

In 10 and 11, consider this program.

```
10   INPUT V
20   IF V > 5 THEN PRINT V * V
30   IF V <= 5 THEN PRINT "TOO SMALL"
40   END
```

10. What will be printed if 6 is entered for V? 36
11. What will be printed if V is given the value 5?
12. In the following if-then statement from the definition of convex set, tell whether the conditional is the meaning half or the sufficient condition half.

   If S is a set in which a segment connecting any two points of S lies entirely in S, then S is convex. the sufficient condition half

99

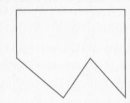

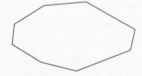

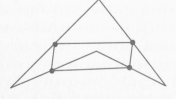
13. M is the midpoint of $\overline{AB}$. N is the midpoint of $\overline{MB}$. If $AB = 40$, what is the length of $\overline{AN}$? **30**

14. Match each term with the most appropriate drawing.
   a. hexagon **iii**
   b. quadrilateral **i**
   c. octagon **iv**

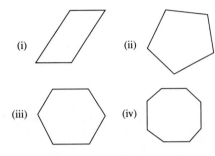

(i)   (ii)   (iii)   (iv)

15. Define: isosceles triangle. **a triangle with two (or more) sides of equal length**

16. Draw a nonconvex hexagon.

17. Draw the hierarchy relating the following: polygon, equilateral triangle, scalene triangle, triangle.

18. Pictured here is a floor plan of the Baha'i House of Worship in Wilmette, Illinois. What is the name given to the polygon outlined? **18-gon**

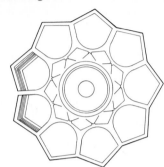

Chapter Review

Questions on **SPUR** Objectives

See margin for answers not shown below.

SPUR stands for **S**kills, **P**roperties, **U**ses, and **R**epresentations. The Chapter Review questions are grouped according to the SPUR Objectives for this chapter.

SKILLS deal with the procedures used to get answers.

■ **Objective A:** *Distinguish between convex and nonconvex regions.* *(Lessons 2-1, 2-7)*

In 1–3, characterize each region as convex or nonconvex.

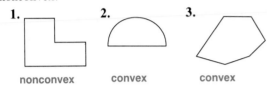

1. nonconvex   2. convex   3. convex

■ **Objective B:** *Draw and identify polygons.*
(Lesson 2-7)

4. Draw an equilateral triangle.

5. Draw an isosceles triangle.

6. Draw a convex octagonal region.

7. Draw a nonconvex nonagonal region.

8. Match each term with the most appropriate drawing.
   a. decagon   **b.** pentagon   **c.** quadrilateral
   iv   ii   i

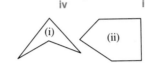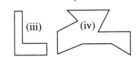

9. Trace the polygon (i) in Question 8 above. Draw the polygon formed by connecting the midpoints of consecutive sides.

PROPERTIES deal with the principles behind the mathematics.

■ **Objective C:** *Write the converse of a conditional.*
(Lesson 2-4)

In 10–12, **a.** write the converse of the statement. **b.** Tell whether the converse is true.

10. If $x = 3$, then $x^2 = 9$.

11. If $AM = MB$, then M is the midpoint of $\overline{AB}$.

12. All Hawaiians live in the U.S.
    a) See margin. b) False

■ **Objective D:** *Apply the properties of a good definition.* *(Lessons 2-1, 2-5)*

13. Why is it important to carefully define terms?

14. "Polygon" is defined using what three previously defined terms?
    union, segment, endpoint

In 15 and 16, tell which property of a good definition is violated by these "bad" definitions.

15. The midpoint M of $\overline{AB}$ is a point such that $AM = BM$. It is inaccurate.

16. A triangle is a closed path with three sides.

17. Here is a definition of a *secant to a circle:*
    A secant to a circle is a line which intersects the circle in two points.
    This definition makes use of five undefined or previously defined terms. Name them.

18. Break the definition of secant in Question 17 into its meaning and sufficient condition halves.

CHAPTER 2 Chapter Review **101**

CHAPTER REVIEW

The main objectives for the chapter are organized here into sections corresponding to the four main types of understanding this book promotes: Skills, Properties, Uses, and Representations.

The four types of understanding are not in increasing order of difficulty. There may be hard skills and easy representations; some uses may be easier than anything else; and so on.

USING THE CHAPTER REVIEW
Students should be able to answer questions like these with about 85% accuracy by the end of the chapter.

You may assign these questions over a single night to help students prepare for a test the next day, or you may assign the questions over a two-day period.

If you assign the questions over two days, then we recommend assigning the *evens* for homework the first night so that students get feedback in class the next day. Then assign the *odds* for the second night (the night before the test) so that students can use the answers provided in the book as a study aid.

10. a. If $x^2 = 9$, then $x = 3$.
b. Not true
11. a. If M is the midpoint of $\overline{AB}$, then $AM = MB$.
b. True
12., 13., 16., 17., 18.
See the margin on p. 102.

■ **Objective E:** *Write and interpret statements in "if-then" form. (Lesson 2-2)*

In 19–21, rewrite in "if-then" form.

19. Every radius is a segment.

20. All hexagons have 9 diagonals.

21. Given $AB = 7$, you can conclude $BA = 7$.
If $AB = 7$, then $BA = 7$.

In 22 and 23, copy the statement and underline the antecedent once and consequent twice.

22. A figure is a rectangle if it is a square.

23. If p, then q.

In 24 and 25, refer to this statement: If a figure is a union of four segments, then it is a quadrilateral.

24. Draw an instance of the antecedent for which the consequent is also true.

25. Draw a counterexample.

■ **Objective F:** *Determine the union and intersection of sets. (Lesson 2-6)*

26. If $A = \{2, 5, 9\}$ and $B = \{5, 13, 9\}$, find $A \cap B$. {5, 9}

27. Let D = the solution set to $n \leq 15$, and E = the solution set to $n \geq -15$.
a. Describe D $\cap$ E. $-15 \leq n \leq 15$
b. Describe D $\cup$ E. all real numbers

28. Triangle *MNO* below is x and triangle *MOP* is y. Name the segments of:
a. x $\cap$ y; MO   b. x $\cup$ y.

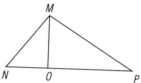

■ **Objective G:** *Use logical ($p \Rightarrow q$) notation. (Lessons 2-2, 2-3, 2-4)*

29. Let p = "$\triangle ABC$ is equilateral."
        q = "$\triangle ABC$ has three 60° angles."
Write in words. a. $q \Rightarrow p$;   b. $p \Leftrightarrow q$.

In 30 and 31, p and q may be any statements.

30. If $p \Rightarrow q$ is true, must $q \Rightarrow p$ be true? No

31. A counterexample for $p \Rightarrow q$ is a situation in which p is __?__ and q is __?__. true, false

---

USES deal with applications of mathematics in real situations.

■ **Objective H:** *Apply properties of if-then statements in real situations. (Lessons 2-3, 2-4)*

32. A sign on the highway states: "The fine for littering is $100." Mr. Woodson was stopped by police on the highway and fined $100. Was he guilty of littering? not enough given to tell

33. A person says: "If the moon is made of green cheese, I'll eat my hat." According to the logic of mathematics, is the statement true or false? True

■ **Objective I:** *Identify polygons used for real objects. (Lesson 2-7)*

34. The edge of a tape dispenser is magnified and drawn below. What polygon is this shape?

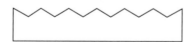

nonconvex 15-gon

35. An umpire has just swept off home plate in the picture below. What polygon is the shape of home plate? pentagon

REPRESENTATIONS deal with pictures, graphs, or objects that illustrate concepts.

■ **Objective J:** *Read computer programs with IF-THEN statements. (Lesson 2-3)*

In 36–38, consider this program.

```
10   PRINT "COMPUTE NUMBER OF
     DIAGONALS IN POLYGON"
20   INPUT N
30   IF N >= 3 THEN PRINT "THE NUMBER
     OF DIAGONALS IS "; N * (N - 3)/2
40   END
```

36. What will be printed if N is given the value 1? See below.

37. What will be printed if N is given the value 20? See below.

38. What will be printed if N is given the value 3? See below.

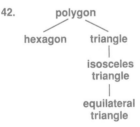

```
10 INPUT X
20 IF X < .33 THEN PRINT 3*X
30 IF X >= .33 AND X <= .67 THEN PRINT 2*X
40 IF X >.67 THEN PRINT X
50 END
```

In 39 and 40, consider this program.

```
10   INPUT X
20   IF X < .33 THEN PRINT 3 * X
30   IF X >= .33 AND X <= .67 THEN PRINT
     2 * X
40   IF X > .67 THEN PRINT X
50   END
```

39. What will be printed if X is given the value 0.4? 0.8

40. What will be printed if X is given the value 20? 20

■ **Objective K:** *Draw hierarchies of triangles and polygons. (Lesson 2-7)*

41. Draw the hierarchy relating the following: figure, triangle, isosceles triangle, scalene triangle. See below.

42. Draw the hierarchy relating the following: polygon, triangle, hexagon, isosceles triangle, equilateral triangle. See below.

EVALUATION
Three tests are provided for this chapter in the Teacher's Resource File. Chapter 2 Test, Forms A and B cover just Chapter 2. The third test is Chapter 2 Test, Cumulative Form. Two-thirds of this test covers Chapter 2; one-third covers Chapter 1. For information on grading, see *General Teaching Suggestions: Grading* on page T44 in the Teacher's Edition.

ASSIGNMENT RECOMMENDATION
We strongly recommend that you assign the reading and questions from Lesson 3-1 for homework the evening of the test. It gives students work to do if they complete the test before the end of the period and keeps the class moving.

If you do not give assignments on the days of tests, you may cover one less *chapter* over the course of the year.

36. COMPUTE NUMBER OF DIAGONALS IN POLYGON
? 1

37. COMPUTE NUMBER OF DIAGONALS IN POLYGON
? 20
THE NUMBER OF DIAGONALS IS 170

38. COMPUTE NUMBER OF DIAGONALS IN POLYGON
? 3
THE NUMBER OF DIAGONALS IS 0

41.
```
              figure
                |
             triangle
            /         \
     isosceles        scalene
     triangle         triangle
```

42.
```
              polygon
            /         \
      hexagon        triangle
                         |
                     isosceles
                     triangle
                         |
                     equilateral
                     triangle
```

CHAPTER 3 ■ ANGLES AND LINES

DAILY PACING CHART ■ CHAPTER 3

DAILY PACING CHART   3

Every chapter of UCSMP *Geometry* includes lessons, a Progress Self-Test, and a Chapter Review. For optimal student performance, the self-test and review should be covered. (See *General Teaching Suggestions: Mastery* on page T36 of the Teacher's Edition.) By following the pace of the Full Course given here, students can complete the entire text by the end of the year. Students following the pace of the Minimal Course spend more time when there are quizzes and on the Chapter Review and will generally not complete all of the chapters in this text.

When all lessons are covered in order (the recommendation of the authors), then students in the Minimal Course can cover through Lesson 13-4 and will cover all they need for future courses. For more information on pacing, see *General Teaching Suggestions: Pace* on page T35 of the Teacher's Edition.

DAY	MINIMAL COURSE	FULL COURSE
1	3-1	3-1
2	3-2	3-2
3	3-3	3-3
4	3-4	3-4
5	Quiz (TRF); start 3-5.	Quiz (TRF); 3-5
6	Finish 3-5.	3-6
7	3-6	Progress Self-Test
8	Progress Self-Test	Chapter Review
9	Chapter Review	Chapter Test (TRF)
10	Chapter Review	Comprehensive Test (TRF)
11	Chapter Test (TRF)	
12	Comprehensive Test (TRF)	

TESTING OPTIONS

TESTING OPTIONS

- Quiz for Lessons 3-1 Through 3-4
- Chapter 3 Test, Form A
- Chapter 3 Test, Cumulative Form
- Chapter 3 Test, Form B
- Comprehensive Test, Chapters 1-3

PROVIDING FOR INDIVIDUAL DIFFERENCES

INDIVIDUAL DIFFERENCES

The student text has been written for, and tested with, average students. It also has been used successfully with better and more poorly prepared students.

The Lesson Notes often include Error Analysis and Alternate Approach features to help you with those students who need more help. A blackline Lesson Master (in the Teacher's Resource File), keyed to the chapter objectives, is provided for each lesson to allow more practice. (However, since it is very important to keep up with the daily pace, you are not expected to use all of these masters. Again, refer to the suggestions for pacing on page T35.) Extension activities are provided in the Lesson Notes for those students who have completed the particular lesson in a shorter amount of time than is expected, even in the Full Course.

OBJECTIVES ■ CHAPTER 3

The objectives listed here are the same as in the Chapter 3 Review on pages 149-153 of the student text. The Progress Self-Test on pages 147-148 and the tests in the Teacher's Resource File cover these objectives. For recommendations regarding the handling of this end-of-chapter material, see the notes in the margin on the corresponding pages of the Teacher's Edition.

OBJECTIVES FOR CHAPTER 3 (Organized into the SPUR Categories—Skills, Properties, Uses, and Representations)	Progress Self-Test Questions	Chapter Review Questions	Lesson Master from Teacher's Resource File*
SKILLS			
A Draw and analyze drawings of angles.	1-4	1 through 6	3-1, 3-2
B Draw angles with a given measure and measure drawn angles.	7, 8	7 through 10	3-1
C Use algebra to represent and find measures of angles.	6, 9, 11, 12	11 through 23	3-1, 3-2
D Determine measures of angles formed by parallel lines and transversals.	19, 20	24 through 25	3-4
E Perform the following constructions with a straightedge and a compass: perpendicular bisector, ⊥ from point to line, ⊥ to line at point.	22	26 through 31	3-6
PROPERTIES			
F Give justifications for conclusions involving different figures.	10, 13, 14, 23	32 through 39	3-2, 3-3, 3-4, 3-5
USES			
G Apply angle measure to describe real situations.	5	40 through 43	3-1, 3-2
H Apply constructions and drawings in real situations.	21	44 through 45	3-6
REPRESENTATIONS			
I Determine the slope of a line from its equation or given two points on it.	15, 17	46 through 51	3-4
J Determine the slope of a line parallel or perpendicular to a given line.	16, 18	52 through 55	3-4, 3-5

*The masters are numbered to match the lessons.

OVERVIEW ■ CHAPTER 3

Chapter 3 presents the terminology and basic properties of angles and lines and their connections with coordinates, constructions, and deduction. It is the shortest chapter in this book, and about half of it will be review for students who have used UCSMP *Transition Mathematics* and *Algebra*.

The first two lessons deal with angles. Lesson 3-1 reviews how to measure angles with a protractor and introduces the Angle Measure Postulate. Students will need protractors for Lesson 3-1. If they are to use their own protractors, they should have them by the first day of the chapter.

Lesson 3-2 reviews the names given to angles and to pairs of angles.

Lesson 3-3 helps set the stage for deductions and proofs, which appear in later chapters.

Lessons 3-4 and 3-5 provide the necessary work on parallel and perpendicular lines needed to understand reflections in Chapter 4 and polygons in Chapter 5. Properties of parallel lines are given both synthetically (without coordinates) and analytically (with coordinates), the latter by reviewing slopes.

Lesson 3-6 introduces constructions, which gives students flexibility in locating points and provides the tools for constructing reflection images of points in Chapter 4. Straightedge and compass are required.

Drawing is a major objective in this and succeeding chapters. Students should come to class every day ready to use a protractor, graph paper, ruler, and compass.

PERSPECTIVES ■ CHAPTER 3

The Perspectives provide the rationale for the inclusion of topics or approaches, provide mathematical background, and make connections with other lessons and within UCSMP.

3-1

ANGLES AND THEIR MEASURES

Angles can be defined in various ways. The definition now commonly used in secondary school geometry in the United States is the set theory definition used in the School Mathematics Study Group (SMSG) curriculum of 1960. It is also possible to define an angle as the set of points on or between two rays with the same endpoint, or as the set of rays including or between two rays with the same endpoint. There are nonset-theoretic definitions which are possible as well.

Our Angle Measure Postulate is called the Protractor Postulate in some books, and traces its origin back through SMSG to a postulate set used by George David Birkhoff in the 1920s. His postulate set was designed to use real numbers in geometry and was employed in *Basic Geometry,* a high school text he wrote with Ralph Beatley, published by Scott, Foresman in 1940.

Part **a** of the Angle Measure Postulate (p. 108) ensures that there is an angle for each real number between 0 and 180. But there is not a 1-1 correspondence between angle measures and numbers unless you restrict yourself to one side of the line. So part **b** also notes that every line has two sides (that's the reason $\overline{BC}$ must intersect $\overleftrightarrow{VA}$).

We allow zero angles and straight angles (parts **c** and **d** of the Angle Measure Postulate) because later we want to apply angles to rotations. Rotations can certainly be halfway around; in fact, 180° turns are very important rotations. Zero-degree rotations will ensure that when one rotation is followed by another, the composite is a rotation.

Straight angles are found in Euclid's *Elements.* They were not used in some "new math" treatments of geometry because, since an angle was defined as a union of two rays, there would be two interiors of a straight angle, and that might be confusing.

But of all parts of this postulate, the one part that will be applied more than any other is part **e.** This property is analogous to the Be-tweenness Theorem for distances. It tells when two angle measures can be added to get a third.

3-2

TYPES OF ANGLES

Students who have studied UCSMP *Transition Mathematics* should be familiar with the names given to angles of various measures and also with vertical angles. The terms *supplementary* and *complementary* are used in UCSMP *Algebra.* The other terminology will be new.

The Linear Pair and Vertical Angle theorems begin the reading of formal proofs and lead into the next lesson.

3-3

JUSTIFYING CONCLUSIONS

In this book, a conclusion requires a justification. This is somewhat different from the use of conclusion to mean the same thing as consequent. In Lesson 13-1, we discuss the Law of Detachment (also called *modus ponens*), the formal logical principle behind the conclusions made in this lesson. By writing a conclusion and its justification, a student has made a one-step proof.

The first proofs for students are found in the next chapter. At this point, we are just trying to give students an idea of why proof is used in mathematics.

3-4

PARALLEL LINES

In algebra, slope is studied as the *rate of change.* In geometry, slope is a measure of *tilt.* The word "parallel" in Lesson 1-1 meant "go in the same direction," which can also mean "have the same tilt." This lesson applies what students have (or should have) learned in algebra to the geometry of parallel lines.

The formal definition of *parallel lines* given in Lesson 1-7 allowed a line to be parallel to itself. The theorems of this lesson, that lines are parallel if and only if their slopes are equal, and that parallelism is transitive, are very simply stated because of this definition.

The content of this lesson, except for the formal statement of the postulates, should be review for students who have studied UCSMP *Transition Mathematics* and *Algebra.*

3-5

PERPENDICULAR LINES

The approach taken to define perpendicular lines is analogous to the approach taken with parallel lines. First, there is a definition, next the geometric properties are established, and then the connection is made with slope.

A proof that "the product of the slopes of perpendicular nonvertical lines is -1" is beyond the mathematics students have studied so far. We do not prove the theorem in this book, waiting instead for UCSMP *Advanced Algebra.* The reason for including the statement of the theorem is to indicate that the slope of one direction determines the slope of the direction perpendicular to it. Also, it reviews important algebra and enables students to see perpendicularity in the coordinate plane.

3-6

CONSTRUCTING PERPENDICULARS

Constructions are often studied in grades 7 or 8, sometimes even earlier. Obviously, students with some experience with constructions will be at a great advantage in learning the content of this lesson. If students have never before used a ruler or a compass, you may need two days for this lesson.

We distinguish between *drawings* and *constructions.* The rules given here for constructions are more rigid than those found in some other books. We do not recommend that students be allowed to open their compasses to *any* given radius. There are two reasons for being more rigid: first, these are the rules that are actually followed by mathematicians in the study of constructions; second, we want to describe algorithms, and we need to be certain that circles and lines will intersect at various times. By giving the radius, we can ensure that the described algorithms will always work. The bonus is that constructions become much easier to grade because they are congruent.

The description of constructions by algorithmic steps is something you may not have seen before. We do it here because we are getting students ready for the kinds of statement sequences they will be using in doing proofs. The rules are justifications for the construction steps just as reasons are justifications for steps in proofs. They say that something can be done.

A key idea in this lesson is that of subroutine. The perpendicular bisector construction is a subroutine for the other constructions of perpendiculars.

RESOURCES
🔦 Visual for Teaching Aid 16 shows the veins of a leaf.

We recommend 10 to 12 days for this chapter: 6 to 7 for the lessons and quiz; 1 for the Progress Self-Test; 1 or 2 for the Chapter Review; 1 for a Chapter Test; and 1 for the Comprehensive Test, which can serve as a quarterly exam. (See the Daily Pacing Chart on page 104A.) If you spend more than 12 days on this chapter, you are moving too slowly. Keep in mind that each lesson includes Review questions to help students firm up content studied previously.

USING PAGES 104-105
All students by this time realize that angles appear in many places. The photograph of the veins of a leaf shows that angles can appear in very small objects. You might note that angles are also used over large stretches of space, as in the location of a star or comet in the sky.

Students may not know that the network of veins in a leaf brings water and nutrients to its cells, much in the same way that blood vessels bring oxygen to our cells.

Nature has evolved an efficient network for doing this, creating veins that meet at 90° and 120° angles. The 90° angles apply the shortest distance property of perpendiculars: to get from a line (a big vein) to a point (a cell) not on the line, travel the perpendicular.

The 120° angles apply to the shortest path property of networks: the network with the shortest total length joining

Angles and Lines

3-1: Angles and Their Measures   **3-4:** Parallel Lines
3-2: Types of Angles   **3-5:** Perpendicular Lines
3-3: Justifying Conclusions   **3-6:** Constructing Perpendiculars

104

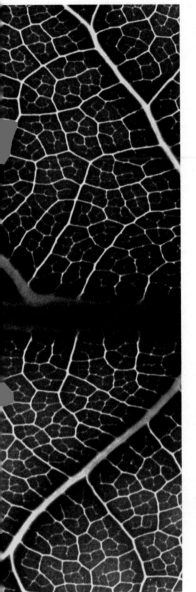

the three vertices of a triangle *ABC* is, for all triangles with no angle with measure greater than 120°, formed by connecting the vertices to a point *F* in the interior such that 120° angles are formed by the three connectors, as shown here.

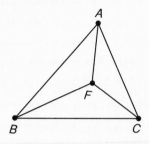

At point *F*, the Fermat point of the triangle, a figure resembling the letter Y is formed.

Notice the similarity between the patterns in the leaf and in the mud flat pictures. This exhibits the power of the same geometry to apply to widely diverse situations. Geometry is used both in studying objects as small as atoms and objects as large as outer space.

Lines all look the same except for their direction, or *tilt*. Angles give a way of measuring the tilt of a line, and also of measuring the differences in the tilts or directions of two lines. Angles occur everywhere, in both living and inanimate objects. Three examples are pictured here.

The leaf exhibits a network of veins. From the largest vein in the middle, smaller and smaller veins branch out. For particular species of trees, these veins are set at characteristic angles, and often the smaller veins are parallel.

When mud dries, it cakes and separates, often at angles that have measures of 90°, showing perpendicular segments.

Folding chairs have legs which make angles with each other and with the plane of the floor.

In geometry, angles are found in all sorts of figures. They occur whenever lines intersect. And they are found in all polygons. There are also angles between curves and between planes, but in this chapter we concentrate on the basic angles of the plane—those formed by lines and those found in polygons.

There are simple relationships between angles, parallel lines, and perpendicular lines, and surprising connections with the slopes of lines you studied in algebra. These too are studied in this chapter.

CHAPTER 3 Angles and Lines   105

Angles and Their Measures

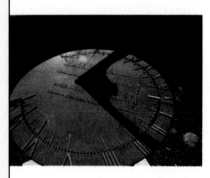

Definition:

An **angle** is the union of two rays that have the same endpoint.

  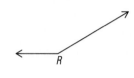

Pictured above are three angles. The **sides** of angles are the two rays; the **vertex** is the common endpoint of the two rays. The symbol for angle is $\angle$.

Angles may be formed by segments, as in the polygons in the photographs on the previous page, but you should still consider the sides of the angle to be rays.

Angles are named in various ways. When there is only one angle at a given vertex, the angle can be named by the vertex. Above are pictured $\angle P$, $\angle Q$, and $\angle R$.

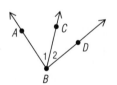

When several angles have the same vertex, each one needs a unique name. At the left there are three angles. Each can be named by giving a point on each side, with the vertex point in between: $\angle ABC$, $\angle CBD$, and $\angle ABD$. The smaller angles can also be named by numbers: $\angle 1$ is $\angle ABC$, $\angle 2$ is $\angle CBD$.

Pictured below are two special angles. $\angle STV$ is a straight angle, and $\angle XWY$ is a zero angle. They are special because some different properties apply to them. In identifying angles in a given figure or problem, both straight and zero angles *are ignored unless specifically mentioned.*

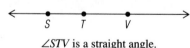 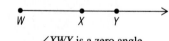

$\angle STV$ is a straight angle. $\angle XWY$ is a zero angle.

Every angle other than a zero angle separates the other points of the plane into two sets. Except for a straight angle, exactly one of the two sets is convex. The convex set is called the **interior** of the angle and the nonconvex set is the **exterior.**

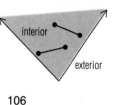

106

For a straight angle, both sets are convex and either set may be its interior. A zero angle has no interior.

The **measure** of an angle indicates the amount of openness of the angle. For example, suppose you want to know how wide your angle of vision is. To say it is large is not precise enough to compare your angle with someone else's. The unit of measure used in this book is the **degree,** denoted °. A 1° angle is determined by dividing a circle into 360 equal parts and taking the angle determined by two consecutive subdivision points and the center. The circle itself has a measure of 360°.

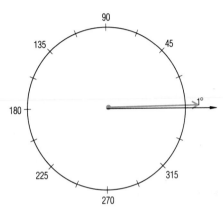

an angle with measure equal to one degree

Since other units of measure for angles are not used in this book, the ° sign is sometimes omitted with angle measures. Thus we can say that the measure of the angle is a unique real number from 0 to 180.

A tool commonly used to measure angles is the **protractor.** It usually contains a scale from 0 to 180 that stretches over a half circle. The **center** V and **base line** $\overleftrightarrow{RV}$ are marked. Angles are measured by performing the three steps shown in the diagram, which shows how to measure $\angle AVB$.

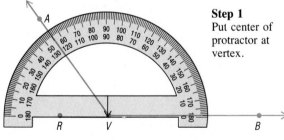

Step 1
Put center of protractor at vertex.

Step 2
Align line $\overleftrightarrow{RV}$ of protractor with one side $\overrightarrow{VB}$ of angle. Note 0 on scale.

Step 3
Read the measure where the other side ($\overrightarrow{VA}$) intersects the protractor.

The steps show that $\angle AVB$ measures about 126. The symbol **m$\angle AVB$** means the measure of angle AVB. So we write $m\angle AVB \approx 126$.

If angle measures greater than 180° were allowed, then an angle could measure both 120° and 240°. In situations where the direction of a turn is used, angles are measured differently. If the interior were considered part of an angle, then angles could have any measure from 0° to 360°.

In the Angle Measure Postulate, part **a** ensures uniqueness, while the other parts ensure existence. That is, **a** states: For every angle there is a unique number; while **b-d** state: For every number between 0 and 180, inclusively, there is an angle.

Error Analysis   Students who have never measured angles often have some initial confusion about which scale to read on the protractor. Emphasize that they should place the protractor with one ray passing through 0. The measure is the number which the other ray passes through on the scale beginning with that 0. It is also important to have a general sense of which number to choose from the two scales. Encourage students to use the larger number if the angle seems to be larger than the corner of a sheet of paper and to use the smaller number if the angle seems to be smaller than the corner of a sheet of paper.

Small Group Work
Students who need more practice measuring angles could be given worksheets to practice in a group. The group should first discuss the proper usage of the protractor. One group member could estimate the sizes of the angles while another could support those estimates or dispute them. A third person could use his/her protractor to verify the actual measurement. Estimates within 10° are good.

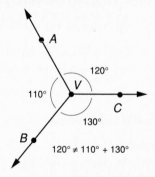
The basic properties of angles and their measures are assumed.

Angle Measure Postulate:

a. Unique measure assumption
Every angle has a unique measure from 0° to 180°.

b. Two sides of line assumption
Given any ray $\overrightarrow{VA}$ and any number x between 0 and 180, there are unique rays $\overrightarrow{VB}$ and $\overrightarrow{VC}$ such that $\overline{BC}$ intersects line $\overleftrightarrow{VA}$ and m∠BVA = m∠CVA = x.

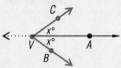

c. Zero angle assumption
If $\overrightarrow{VA}$ and $\overrightarrow{VB}$ are the same ray, then m∠AVB = 0.

d. Straight angle assumption
If $\overrightarrow{VA}$ and $\overrightarrow{VB}$ are opposite rays, then m∠AVB = 180

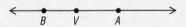

e. Angle Addition Property
If $\overrightarrow{VC}$ (except for point V) is in the interior of ∠AVB, then m∠AVC + m∠CVB = m∠AVB.

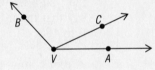

In drawings, an angle's measure is often written in its interior. For instance, in the drawing below at the left, m∠APB = 45.

Example In the drawing at the left, determine

a. m∠APC; **b.** m∠CPD.

Solution

a. $\overrightarrow{PB}$ (except for point P) is in the interior of ∠APC. Using the Angle Addition Property,

m∠APC = m∠APB + m∠BPC
= 45 + 80
= 125.

108

108

b. The measures of the angles about P add to 360°. (Think of P as the center of a circle.) The given angles add to 215°.
$$m\angle CPD = 360 - 215 = 145$$

A special case of the Angle Addition Property occurs with straight angles. Suppose $\overrightarrow{VA}$ and $\overrightarrow{VB}$ are opposite rays. Then, because of the straight angle assumption, $m\angle AVB = 180$. By the Angle Addition Property, $m\angle 1 + m\angle 2 = 180$. For instance, if $m\angle 1 = 43$, then $m\angle 2 = 180 - 43 = 137$. If $m\angle 1 = x$, then $m\angle 2 = 180 - x$. This situation often occurs since it happens whenever lines intersect.

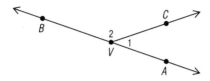

3. Why isn't this an angle?

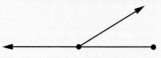

It is the union of two rays and a segment, not just of two rays.

ADDITIONAL ANSWERS
3. b. $\overrightarrow{PR}$ or $\overrightarrow{PT}$ and $\overrightarrow{PS}$ or $\overrightarrow{PM}$ or $\overrightarrow{PN}$

Questions

Covering the Reading

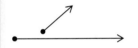

1. Choose the correct words. An angle is the (intersection, union) of two (rays, segments) with the same (endpoint, midpoint).
   union, rays, endpoint

2. Pictured at the left is the union of two rays. Why does this not picture an angle? endpoints are not the same

3. Use the angle shown at the right.
   a. Name the vertex of the angle. P
   b. Name the sides. See margin.
   c. Give 5 different names for this angle.
   Sample: $\angle 1$, $\angle RPM$, $\angle TPS$, $\angle NPT$, $\angle P$

4. In this book, in what unit are angles measured?
   degrees

5. $m\angle A$ is short for __?__. the measure of angle A

In 6 and 7, use the drawing of a protractor shown below. Find the approximate measure of each angle.

6. **a.** $\angle PQS \approx 58°$ **b.** $\angle SQR \approx 122°$

7. **a.** $\angle SQT \approx 22°$ **b.** $\angle TQR \approx 100°$

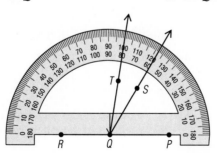

LESSON 3-1   Angles and Their Measures   **109**

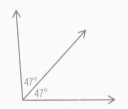
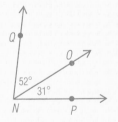
8. Use the drawing below.
   a. Name two straight angles. ∠AEC, ∠DEB
   b. Name two angles with measure 0. **Sample: ∠AEA, ∠DED**
   c. m∠CED + m∠CEB = __?__ 180
   d. If m∠1 = x, m∠2 = __?__. 180 − x

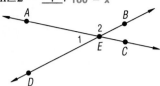

9. Use the figure at the left.
   a. If m∠3 = 80 and m∠4 = 40, then m∠FGH = __?__ .
   b. What property did you apply to get the answer to **a**?
   a) 120; b) Angle Addition Property

10. In the situation pictured below, find the value of x. 120

100°
x° 140°

11. In this photograph of three hexagonal cells of a beehive, the three angles with vertex A have the same measure.
    a. Name these angles. ∠CAB, ∠BAD, and ∠DAC
    b. What is that measure? 120°

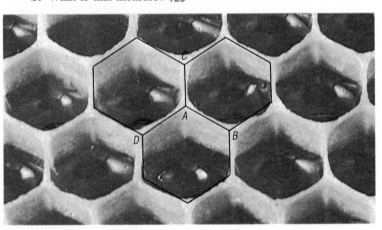

In 12 and 13, use a protractor.

12. a. Draw a 166° angle.
    b. Shade the interior of the angle you have drawn.
    See margin.

13. a. Draw two angles with measure 47° that share a common side.
    b. What part of the Angle Measure Postulate assures that this can be done? a) See margin. b) part (b) of the postulate (two sides of line assumption)

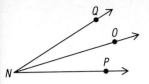

14. Refer to the figure at the left. Suppose m∠QNO = 9x − 2 and m∠ONP = 4x + 7. If m∠QNP = 83, find x and draw a more accurate figure. **x = 6. See margin for drawing.**

15. If you bend your elbow, an angle is formed by the ulna (a bone leading to your wrist) and the humerus (the bone from the shoulder).
  a. When your arm is straight, what is the measure of this angle?
  b. Approximate the measure of the smallest angle you can make with your ulna and humerus. **a) Sample: 175°; b) Sample: 30°**

In 16-18, **a.** guess the measure of the angle. **b.** Measure each with a protractor and compare with your estimate. (You are doing well if your estimate is within 10°.)

16.

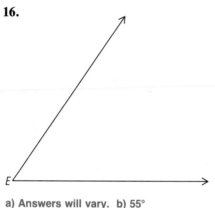

a) Answers will vary. b) 55°

17.

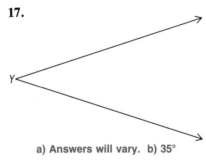

a) Answers will vary. b) 35°

18.

a) Answers will vary. b) 155°

Question 24: Some calculators express angle measures in minutes and seconds. Discuss some real-world activities that may require measuring as accurately as seconds, especially since drawing to the nearest degree is difficult. (examples: surveying, constructing dartboards)

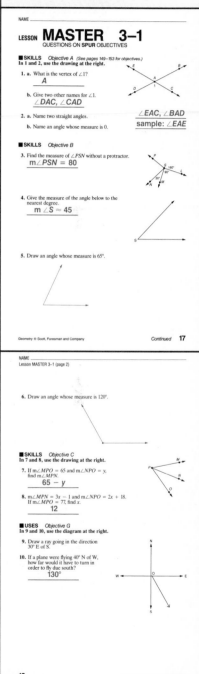

NAME _____

LESSON **MASTER   3–1**
QUESTIONS ON **SPUR** OBJECTIVES

■ **SKILLS**   Objective A (See pages 149–153 for objectives.)
In 1 and 2, use the drawing at the right.

  1. a. What is the vertex of ∠1?
    A

  b. Give two other names for ∠1.
    ∠DAC, ∠CAD

  2. a. Name two straight angles.   **∠EAC, ∠BAD**

  b. Name an angle whose measure is 0.   **sample: ∠EAE**

■ **SKILLS**   Objective B

  3. Find the measure of ∠PSN without a protractor.
    m∠PSN = 80

  4. Give the measure of the angle below to the nearest degree.
    m ∠S ≈ 45

  5. Draw an angle whose measure is 65°.

Geometry © Scott, Foresman and Company   Continued   **17**

NAME _____
Lesson MASTER 3–1 (page 2)

  6. Draw an angle whose measure is 120°.

■ **SKILLS**   Objective C
In 7 and 8, use the drawing at the right.

  7. If m∠MPO = 65 and m∠NPO = y, find m∠MPN.
    65 − y

  8. m∠MPN = 3x − 1 and m∠NPO = 2x + 18. If m∠MPO = 77, find x.
    12

■ **USES**   Objective G
In 9 and 10, use the diagram at the right.

  9. Draw a ray going in the direction 30° E of S.

  10. If a plane were flying 40° N of W, how far would it have to turn in order to fly due south?
    130°

18   Geometry © Scott, Foresman and Company

19. The points of a compass are labeled clockwise in degrees like a protractor. Airport runways are numbered with their compass direction, except that the final zero is dropped. The runway heading north is labeled 36 at the bottom, for 360°. North-south and east-west runways are labeled as shown below.
    a. The Orchard Airport Expansion Project planners want to add a runway labeled 32. Draw a possible runway. See below.
    b. What number would be at the other end of the runway numbered 32? 14

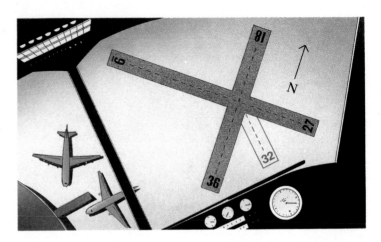

Review

20. In at most how many points do the diagonals of a convex hexagon intersect? *(Lesson 2-7)* 21

21. In at least how many points do the diagonals of a convex hexagon intersect? *(Lesson 2-7)* 19

22. An angle is a union of two rays. What are the possible *intersections* of two rays? *(Lesson 2-6)* point, segment, ray, { }

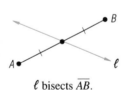

ℓ bisects $\overline{AB}$.

23. Here is a definition of *bisector of a segment*: A line, ray, or segment is a bisector of $\overline{AB}$ if and only if it contains the midpoint of $\overline{AB}$ and no other points of $\overline{AB}$.
    a. Write the meaning half of this definition. See margin.
    b. Write the sufficient condition half of this definition. *(Lesson 2-5)* See margin.

Exploration

24. Degrees can be divided into minutes and seconds.
    a. From a dictionary or other source, find out how many minutes are in one degree. 60
    b. How many seconds are in one degree? 3600
    c. The moon covers an angle of about 30 minutes in the sky. How many moons placed next to each other would extend from one point on the horizon to the point on the opposite side of the horizon? 360

112

3-2

Types of Angles

Semaphore signals are determined by the angles at which the flags are held.

LESSON 3-2

RESOURCES
■ Lesson Master 3-2

OBJECTIVES

A Draw and analyze drawings of angles.
C Use algebra to represent and find measures of angles.
F Give justifications for conclusions involving different figures.
G Apply angle measure to describe real situations.

TEACHING NOTES

A good way to learn the terminology in this lesson is to note that many of the terms have similar definitions outside mathematics. For example, "acute" pains are very sharp pains; an "obtuse" person is very dull. Two ideas "complement" each other if one idea is different from but supports the other. "Supplements" are things that add on to something else. Two lots are "adjacent" if they share a common boundary. You might wish to graph the measures of angles on a number line and label the types as shown.

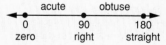

Angles may be classified by measure into one of five types.

Definitions:

If m is the measure of an angle, then the angle is:

a. zero if and only if $m = 0$;
b. acute if and only if $0 < m < 90$;
c. right if and only if $m = 90$;
d. obtuse if and only if $90 < m < 180$;
e. straight if and only if $m = 180$.

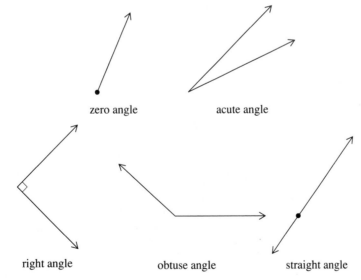

zero angle   acute angle

right angle   obtuse angle   straight angle

To identify a right angle, a "⌐" is drawn in the angle to form a square.

Reading Students should read this lesson carefully, take notes, and draw and label examples and counterexamples (when appropriate) of the many different types of angles and angle pairs. This should help them visualize the various possibilities and increase their comprehension. The proof of the

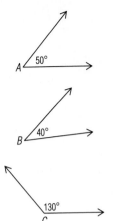

Pairs of angles are special if the sum of their measures is 90 or 180.

> **Definitions:**
>
> If the measures of two angles are m_1 and m_2, then the angles are:
> **a. complementary** if and only if $m_1 + m_2 = 90$;
> **b. supplementary** if and only if $m_1 + m_2 = 180$.

In the figures at the left, $\angle A$ and $\angle B$ are complementary angles while $\angle A$ and $\angle C$ are supplementary angles. It is also said that $\angle A$ and $\angle B$ are **complements** and $\angle A$ and $\angle C$ are **supplements.** At the left, $\angle A$ is a complement to $\angle B$ and a supplement to $\angle C$. If the measure of an angle is x, then any complement to it has measure $(90 - x)$ and any supplement has measure $(180 - x)$.

Example 1 An angle has 3 times the measure of a complement to it. Find the measure of the angle.

Solution Let the angle have measure x. Its complement must have measure $90 - x$. But from the given information, three times the measure of the complement equals x. Thus,

$$x = 3(90 - x)$$
$$x = 270 - 3x$$
$$4x = 270$$
$$x = 67.5.$$

The measure of the angle is 67.5°.

Check $90 - 67.5 = 22.5$. Since 67.5 is $3 \cdot 22.5$, it checks.

Pairs of angles may also be classified by their positions relative to each other.

> **Definitions:**
>
> Two non-straight and non-zero angles are:
> **a. adjacent angles** if and only if a common side ($\overrightarrow{OB}$ in the left figure on page 115) is interior to the angle formed by the non-common sides ($\angle AOC$);
> **b. a linear pair** if and only if they are adjacent and their non-common sides are opposite rays;
> **c. vertical angles** if and only if their sides form two lines.

114

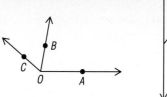
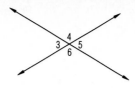
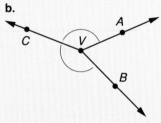

∠COB and ∠BOA
are adjacent angles.

∠1 and ∠2 are
a linear pair.

∠3 and ∠5 are vertical angles.
∠4 and ∠6 are vertical angles.

Identification of adjacent angles can be tricky. Below, angles D and E are not adjacent. They do not have a common side since $\overrightarrow{DE} \neq \overrightarrow{ED}$. Angles 7 and 8 below are not adjacent because $\overrightarrow{ZY}$ is not in the interior of ∠XZW.

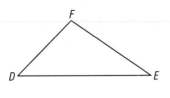
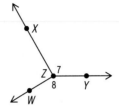

Examine angles 1 and 2 at the top of the page, a linear pair of angles. Their measures add to 180°, since the opposite rays form a line. So they are also supplementary. This argument works for any linear pair. It proves a theorem which you will use later, so we give it a name.

Linear Pair Theorem:

If two angles form a linear pair, then they are supplementary.

Finally, examine the vertical angles 5 and 3 above. Each forms a linear pair with ∠6. So, by the Linear Pair Theorem, they are supplementary. Thus m∠5 + m∠6 = 180 and m∠3 + m∠6 = 180. From the Substitution Property of Equality, m∠5 + m∠6 = m∠3 + m∠6. Adding -m∠6 to each side, m∠5 = m∠3. So the vertical angles have the same measure. This argument works for any vertical angles and proves a second theorem.

Vertical Angle Theorem:

If two angles are vertical angles, then they have equal measures.

1. An angle has a supplement which is 3 times the measure of a complement of the angle. What is the measure of the angle?
45

2. $\overrightarrow{VC}$ is a common side of ∠AVC and ∠BVC. Why are the identified angles not adjacent angles?
a.

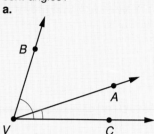

The common side is not in the interior of ∠AVB.
b.

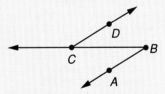

The common side is not in the interior of ∠AVB.

3. Are ∠ABC and ∠BCD adjacent angles?

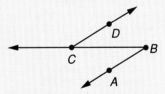

No, ∠ABC and ∠BCD do not have a common side.

In 4-6, a situation is given.
a. Is this situation possible?
b. If so, draw a picture and determine the angle measures. If not, explain why not.

4. A pair of vertical angles is supplementary.
Yes; 90, lines are perpendicular.

115

5. A pair of vertical angles is complementary.
Yes; 45

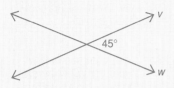

6. A linear pair of angles is complementary.
No; measures of angles in a linear pair add to 180, not 90.

7. Find x if $\overrightarrow{AB}$ bisects ∠CAD.

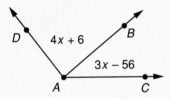

Impossible. The angle measures become negative. This teaches students that you must go back to the original situation after solving and check your answer.

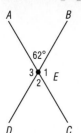

Example 2 Find the measures of as many angles as you can in the figure at the left, given m∠AEB = 62.

Solution With this information, the measures of all drawn angles with vertex E can be found. Using the Vertical Angle Theorem, m∠2 = 62. Since ∠AEB and ∠1 form a linear pair, by the Linear Pair Theorem they are supplementary. Thus m∠1 = 180 − 62 = 118. By a similar argument, m∠3 = 118.

Example 3 Given ∠5 and ∠6 are complementary and adjacent angles, with m∠5 = 47.
a. Sketch a possible situation.
b. Find m∠6.

Solution

a. Since ∠5 and ∠6 are adjacent, they have a common side, so a figure could look like that drawn below.

b. Since ∠5 and ∠6 are complementary,
$$m∠5 + m∠6 = 90.$$
Substitute 47 for m∠5.
$$47 + m∠6 = 90$$
So m∠6 = 43.

This lesson concludes with one last definition concerning angles.

Definition:
> $\overrightarrow{VR}$ is a **bisector** of ∠PVQ if and only if $\overrightarrow{VR}$ is in the interior of ∠PVQ and m∠PVR = m∠RVQ.

Informally, an angle bisector splits an angle into two angles of equal measure.

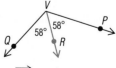

$\overrightarrow{VR}$ bisects ∠PVQ.

Questions

Covering the Reading

1. When classified by measure, there are five types of angles. Name them. **zero, acute, right, obtuse, straight**

2. An angle has 4 times the measure of a supplement to it. Find the measure of the angle. **144°**

In 3 and 4, refer back to the picture of vertical angles on page 115.

3. Does ∠6 appear to be zero, acute, obtuse, right, or straight? **obtuse**

4. Does ∠5 appear to be zero, acute, obtuse, right, or straight? **acute**

In 5–7, use the figure at the left.

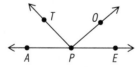

5. ∠1 and ∠3 are __?__ angles. **vertical**

6. If m∠1 = 121, find:
   a. m∠2; **59**   b. m∠3; **121**   c. m∠4. **59**

7. If m∠1 = x, find:
   a. m∠2; **180 − x**   b. m∠3; **x**   c. m∠4. **180 − x**

8. ∠V and ∠W are supplementary, and m∠V = 103.
   a. Find m∠W. **77**
   b. Is ∠V acute, obtuse, or right? **obtuse**
   c. Is ∠W acute, obtuse, or right? **acute**

Applying the Mathematics

In 9–11, sketch a possible drawing of ∠1 and ∠2.

9. ∠1 and ∠2 are supplementary and adjacent. **See margin.**

10. ∠1 and ∠2 are complementary and not adjacent. **See margin.**

11. ∠1 and ∠2 are adjacent, complementary, and have the same measure. **See margin.**

12. In the figure below, m∠APE = 180.
    a. ∠OPE is supplementary to __?__ . **∠OPA**
    b. Name another pair of supplementary angles. **∠APT and ∠TPE**

13. a. Write the converse of the Linear Pair Theorem.
    b. Draw a counterexample to the converse.
    c. What can you conclude about the converse?
    See margin.

14. Let m be the measure of an angle which is less than its complement. Find all possibilities for m. **0 < m < 45**

LESSON 3-2   Types of Angles   117

---

question asks you to draw an element of A ∩ B. Similarly, **Question 11** can be interpreted as drawing angles that are in the intersection of three sets.

Small Group Work for Questions 9-11: Some students will have trouble drawing the various combinations of complementary and supplementary angles. Have students work in groups of three to discuss these questions. Each student should practice the drawings and answer the questions. The group can then evaluate the drawings and answers and offer alternatives.

Question 13: Because so many of the supplementary angles students see are in linear pairs, this question needs to be discussed. It is also a good review of the term *converse*.

ADDITIONAL ANSWERS
9. sample:

10. sample:

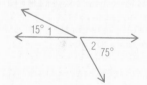

11.

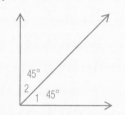

13. a. If two angles are supplementary, then they form a linear pair.
b. sample counterexample:

c. The converse is not true.

15. A triangle is called an **acute, right,** or **obtuse triangle** depending on the measure of its largest angle. Without measuring, does the triangle appear to be acute, right, or obtuse?

a.

right

b.

acute

c.

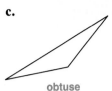

obtuse

16. Use the figure at the right. If $\overrightarrow{BC}$ is the bisector of $\angle ABD$, find m$\angle ABD$. **30**

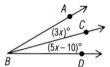

17. The famous Leaning Tower of Pisa has been shifting on its foundation since it was built in the 12th century. At this time the smallest angle it makes with the ground measures about 85°. What is x, the measure of the largest angle it makes with the ground? **95**

Review

18. Measure $\angle D$ below. *(Lesson 3-1)* **60°**

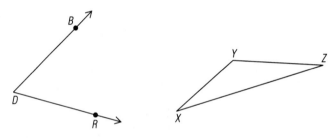

19. Measure $\angle Z$ above. *(Lesson 3-1)* ≈**19°**

20. The plane pictured below is heading in a direction 10° north of east, written 10° N of E, as indicated by the ray. How many degrees would it have to turn in order to head due north? *(Lesson 3-1)* **80°**

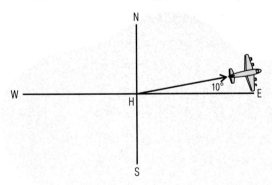

118

21. Give the number of sides of each type of polygon. *(Lesson 2-7)*
  a. octagon 8
  b. hexagon 6
  c. pentagon 5
  d. triangle 3
  e. quadrilateral 4
  f. heptagon 7
  g. nonagon 9
  h. decagon 10
  i. 35-gon 35
  j. *n*-gon *n*

22. Give a counterexample to this statement: If A has 3 elements and B has 2 elements, then A ∪ B has 5 elements. *(Lessons 2-6, 2-2)*
Sample: A = {2, 4, 6}, B = {1, 2}; A ∪ B = {1, 2, 4, 6}

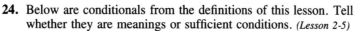

23. If p is rectangle *ABEG* and q is rectangle *ABCD* as shown at the left, how many segments are in each set? *(Lesson 2-6)*
  a. p ∪ q 7
  b. p ∩ q 1

24. Below are conditionals from the definitions of this lesson. Tell whether they are meanings or sufficient conditions. *(Lesson 2-5)*
  a. If x is the measure of an angle and $x = 180$, then the angle is a straight angle.
  b. If m_1 and m_2 are the measures of two supplementary angles, then $m_1 + m_2 = 180$.
  c. If two angles are vertical angles, then their sides form two lines.
  a) sufficient condition; b) meaning; c) meaning

Exploration

25. The words "acute" and "obtuse" have nonmathematical meanings, as in these sentences.
  a. A person has an *acute* sense of smell.
  b. That argument is *obtuse*.
  What do these words mean in these sentences and how do they relate to the corresponding names for angles?
  See below.

26. The words "compliment" and "complement" sound alike but mean different things. They are called *homonyms*.
  a. What is the meaning of "compliment"?
  b. Give a homonym for "right."
  c. Find other mathematical terms that have homonyms.
  See below.

25. Samples:
    a. acute—having a sharp point; intense
    b. obtuse—lacking sharpness, dull, blunt; acute angles are more pointed, thus sharper, than obtuse angles.

26. a. Sample: "an expression of admiration or praise"
    b. write or rite
    c. Sample: pi, arc, sum

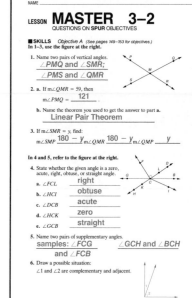
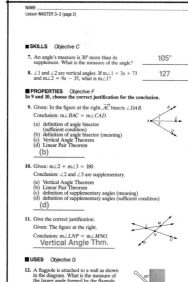

LESSON 3-3

RESOURCES
■ Lesson Master 3-3

OBJECTIVE

F Give justifications for conclusions involving different figures.

TEACHING NOTES

This is not an easy lesson for students, many of whom have seldom had to justify any conclusion. Many have been trained that getting a correct answer quickly is the only thing that matters. Furthermore, even though this is only Chapter 3, there have been many possible justifications for conclusions.

Do not expect a student to realize that a given statement can be a justification in a situation until that student has missed it once! Furthermore, sometimes complete statements are used as justifications. For example, if two angles are vertical angles, then they have the same measure. Sometimes only abbreviations are used (Vertical Angle Theorem). Thus, the task of this lesson, even though it is only justifying one-step conclusions, is by no means trivial. Have patience. Justifying is a skill which will be worked on throughout the next few chapters. Concentrated work with proof does not come for some time.

To emphasize the need for proof, consider the statement: If n is a nonnegative integer, then $n^2 + n + 41$ is a prime number. Make a chart.

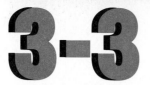

Justifying Conclusions

Recall that you can show that an if-then statement is false by producing a counterexample to it. However, to show that it is true, a *proof* is needed.

> **Definition:**
>
> The **proof** of an if-then statement is a sequence of justified conclusions, leading from the antecedent to the consequent.

To understand this definition, you need to know specifically what is meant by *justified conclusions*. That is what this lesson is about. In the last lesson, two statements were proved—first the Linear Pair Theorem and then the Vertical Angle Theorem. Below, the proof of the Vertical Angle Theorem from the last lesson is repeated, but with the sequence of conclusions and the justifications for them numbered. Notice how each statement follows from previous ones. Notice also that each geometric conclusion is justified either by (1) a particular definition, (2) a particular postulate, or (3) a theorem that has already been proved. These are the only justifications that are allowed in a proof.

Recall the statement of the Vertical Angle Theorem to be proved: *If two angles are vertical angles, then they have equal measures.* We begin with the antecedent of the statement: Angles 3 and 5 are vertical angles.

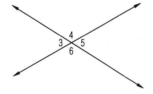

Conclusion 1: Angles 3 and 6 form a linear pair. Angles 5 and 6 form a linear pair.
Justification for 1: If two angles have a side in common and the noncommon sides are opposite rays, then the angles form a linear pair. (definition of linear pair—sufficient condition)

Conclusion 2: ∠3 and ∠6 are supplementary.
∠5 and ∠6 are supplementary.
Justification for 2: If two angles form a linear pair, they are supplementary. (Linear Pair Theorem)

Conclusion 3: m∠3 + m∠6 = 180.
m∠5 + m∠6 = 180.
Justification for 3: If two angles are supplementary, then the sum of the measures of the angles is 180. (definition of supplementary angles—meaning)

Conclusion 4: m∠3 + m∠6 = m∠5 + m∠6.
Justification for 4: Substitution Property of Equality (m∠5 + m∠6 has been substituted for 180 in the first part of conclusion 3.)

Conclusion 5: m∠3 = m∠5.
Justification for 5: Addition Property of Equality (-m∠6 has been added to both sides of the equation of conclusion 4.)

120

Conclusion 5 is the consequent of the theorem. The measures of vertical angles are equal. The proof shows that the statement is true based on the definitions and postulates agreed upon.

Theorems such as the Linear Pair Theorem and the Vertical Angle Theorem may look rather obvious. So why are they proved? Mathematicians generally have three reasons for proving theorems.

The first reason is very important: What is obvious to one person may not be obvious to another person. Sometimes people disagree.

A second reason for proving statements is also important: If a statement cannot be proved after many people have worked on it for a long time, it is quite possible that either (1) the statement cannot be proved or disproved from the postulates, or (2) the statement is not true even though it looks true.

A third reason for proof is that unexpected results can be verified. For instance, in Chapter 1 you learned Euler's Theorem concerning traversable networks. The Pythagorean Theorem also is not an obvious theorem, but it will be proved later in this book. In algebra, the Quadratic Formula is proved, and that formula is not at all obvious.

Simplifying expressions, solving equations, and applying techniques are all series of justified steps. If the given information (p) and the conclusion following from it (q) are important enough, then the statement $(p \Rightarrow q)$ is labeled as a theorem. Showing that from the given p, the conclusion q follows *proves the conditional $p \Rightarrow q$.*

In the Questions, you are asked to provide a justification for one conclusion, the first conclusion one might make from given information. The given p is the antecedent; the conclusion q is the consequent. The justification is a particular definition, postulate, or theorem which asserts that p implies q. In Example 1 the justification is a definition. Later in this course, the sequences of justified conclusions may have many steps.

▪ ▪ ▪ ▪ ▪ ▪ ▪ ▪▪

Example 1   Given: X is the midpoint of $\overline{MT}$ as pictured at the right.

Conclusion: $XM = XT$.
Justify this conclusion.

Solution   The "Given" is the antecedent and the "Conclusion" is the consequent of the conditional: "If X is the midpoint of $\overline{MT}$, then $XM = XT$." This is the meaning half of the definition of midpoint. We thus write as the justification: definition of midpoint (meaning).

LESSON 3-3   *Justifying Conclusions*   **121**

---

n	$n^2 + n + 41$
0	41
1	43
2	47
3	53
4	61
5	71 etc.

Ask the students if they require a proof that the statement is true or if they are satisfied that it works. (All numbers through 39 work.) Then, show them the calculation for $n = 40$.
$(40^2 + 40 + 41)$
$= 40(40 + 1) + 41$
$= (40 + 1)41$
$= 41^2$

Here is another example: Draw a very large circle, a diameter, and a small chord perpendicular to the diameter. Have students measure the four lengths of the parts of the chord and diameter. Do they believe that the length of either half of the chord is the square root of the product of the two lengths on the diameter, one of which is many times longer than the other?

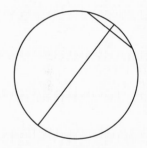

This conclusion requires proof. (It follows from the Power of Point Theorem in Lesson 15-7.)

The list of postulates and theorems at the back of the book is very useful for students. Some teachers make copies for students to use on tests until they become more comfortable with the process of writing proofs. The Summary and Vocabulary pages for each chapter are helpful, also; they include names of theorems or postulates and terms defined in the chapter.

ADDITIONAL EXAMPLES
In 1-4, state a justification for the conclusion.

1. Given: m∠BAC = m∠CAD.
Conclusion: $\overrightarrow{AC}$ is the bisector of ∠BAD.

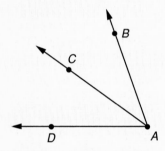

definition of angle bisector (sufficient condition)

2. Given: ∠RPS and ∠RPU are a linear pair.
Conclusion: ∠RPS and ∠RPU are supplementary.

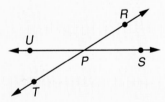

Linear Pair Theorem

3. Given: ∠A and ∠B are supplementary and m∠A = x.
Conclusion: m∠B = 180 − x.

definition of supplementary angles (meaning)

In Example 2, the justification is a theorem already proved.

Example 2 Given: ∠AEC and ∠DEB are vertical angles as pictured below.
Conclusion: m∠AEC = m∠DEB.
Justify this conclusion.

Solution The given statement and the conclusion are instances of the antecedent and the consequent of the Vertical Angle Theorem. So the justification is: The Vertical Angle Theorem.

In Example 3, the justification is one of the postulates from algebra mentioned in Lesson 1-7.

Example 3 Given: x + y = 180. Justify the conclusion y = 180 − x.

Solution -x has been added to both sides of x + y = 180 to get the conclusion. The Addition Property of Equality says you can add the same number to both sides of an equality without changing the solutions. So the justification is: the Addition Property of Equality.

To name or categorize figures, a common justification is to use the sufficient condition half of the definition of that kind of figure.

Example 4 Given: m∠LOG = 80.
Justify the conclusion that ∠LOG is an acute angle.

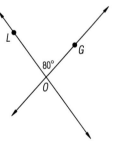

Solution "If m∠LOG = 80, then ∠LOG is an acute angle." This is an instance of the sufficient condition half of the definition of acute angle. Answer: definition of acute angle (sufficient condition).

To find justifications, you obviously need to be familiar with the definitions, postulates, and theorems that you have had. In the back of the book is a list of postulates and a list of theorems. At the back of each chapter is a vocabulary list with the terms you need to know. At this point you can only use justifications that have been presented prior to this lesson. As each new theorem, definition, or postulate is presented in the text, they become added to the list of possible justifications.

122

1. Define: proof. **See margin.**

2. Name the three kinds of statements which can be used as justifications in a proof.
   definitions, postulates, previously proved theorems

3. Can a postulate from algebra be used as a justification in geometry? **Yes**

In 4 and 5, consider the drawing as given.

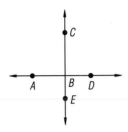

4. *Multiple choice.* Which statement justifies the conclusion?
   Given: $m\angle ABC = 90$.
   Conclusion: $\angle ABC$ is a right angle.
   (a) definition of complementary angles (meaning)
   (b) definition of complementary angles (sufficient condition)
   (c) definition of right angle (meaning)
   (d) definition of right angle (sufficient condition) **(d)**

5. State the justification for the conclusion.
   Given: $\angle ABC$ and $\angle EBD$ are vertical angles.
   Conclusion: $m\angle ABC = m\angle EBD$.
   Vertical Angle Theorem

6. If an important conditional is proved true, it is called a(n) __?__ .
   theorem

7. Give three reasons why mathematicians feel it is important to have proofs. **See margin.**

8. *Multiple choice.* In going from $4x + 3 = 12$ to $4x = 9$, what is the major justification?
   (a) Associative Property of Addition
   (b) Additive Identity Property of Zero
   (c) Definition of Opposites
   (d) Addition Property of Equality **(d)**

In 9 and 10, **a.** make a conclusion based on the given information.
b. Give the justification for that conclusion.

9. $4y = 32$ **Sample: a)** $y = 8$; **b) Multiplication Property of Equality**

10. In the figure below, I is between E and F.

Sample: a) $FI + IE = FE$;
b) Betweenness Theorem

---

4. Given: $m\angle MNQ + m\angle PNQ = 180$.
Conclusion: $m\angle MNQ < 180$.

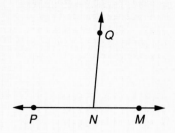

Equation to Inequality Postulate

NOTES ON QUESTIONS
Question 7: Use this question to discuss the reasons for proof that are given on page 121. A fourth reason for proof is the desire to build an axiomatic system, with each consequent demonstrably supported by the postulates. At this point, it is difficult for most students to appreciate that reason.

Questions 9 and 10: We cannot overemphasize the importance of this type of question. All too often, the conclusion is given to the students. The first step in creating mathematics is to *conceive of* the conclusion; only then is there anything to *prove*. Encourage students frequently to state all conclusions they think can be justi-ᵉᵈ in given situations.

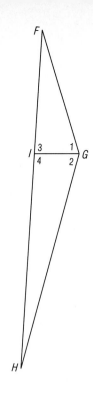

In 11 and 12, *multiple choice*. Use the figure at the left. Which statement justifies the conclusion?

11. Given: $m\angle 1 = 73$; $m\angle 2 = 74$.
Conclusion: $m\angle FGH = 147$.
(a) Angle Addition Property
(b) Linear Pair Theorem
(c) definition of obtuse angle (meaning)
(d) Vertical Angle Theorem (a)

12. Given: $\angle 3$ and $\angle 4$ form a linear pair.
Conclusion: $\angle 3$ and $\angle 4$ are supplementary angles.
(a) Angle Addition Property
(b) Linear Pair Theorem
(c) definition of supplementary angles (meaning)
(d) definition of supplementary angles (sufficient condition) (b)

In 13–15, state the justification for the conclusion. Use the figure at the left.

13. Given: $\angle 3$ and $\angle 4$ are supplementary angles.
Conclusion: $m\angle 3 + m\angle 4 = 180$.
definition of supplementary angles (meaning)

14. Given: $\overrightarrow{GI}$ bisects $\angle FGH$.
Conclusion: $m\angle 1 = m\angle 2$.
definition of angle bisector (meaning)

15. Given: $m\angle 1 = m\angle 2$.
Conclusion: $\overrightarrow{GI}$ bisects $\angle FGH$.
definition of angle bisector (sufficient condition)

Review

In 16–18, give the definition.

16. acute angle *(Lesson 3-2)* See margin.

17. segment *(Lesson 1-8)* See margin.

18. circle *(Lesson 2-5)* See margin.

19. A complement of $\angle T$ has five times the measure of $\angle T$. What is $m\angle T$? *(Lesson 3-2)* $m\angle T = 15$

20. $\overrightarrow{HF}$ and $\overrightarrow{HI}$ are opposite rays. Find $m\angle FHG$. *(Lesson 3-2)* $m\angle FHG = 30$

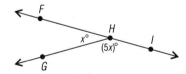

21. An angle is $13°$ less than its complement. Find its measure. *(Lesson 3-2)*
38.5°

22. Let v be the measure of an obtuse angle. Graph all possibilities for v on a number line. *(Lesson 3-2)*

23. $\overrightarrow{XW}$ bisects right angle YXZ. What is the measure of $\angle YXW$? *(Lesson 3-2)* 45°

24. $\angle 2$ and $\angle 3$ are vertical angles. If $m\angle 2 = 12q$ and $m\angle 3 = 4z$, solve for q in terms of z. *(Lesson 3-2)* $q = \frac{z}{3}$

25. If m∠ABC = 101 in the situation below, find m∠DBC.
(Lesson 3-1) 59

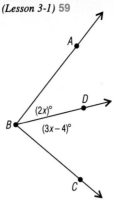

In 26 and 27, rewrite each statement as a conditional. *(Lesson 2-2)*

26. All squares are rectangles.
If a figure is a square, then it is a rectangle.

27. Two angles cannot be both acute and supplementary. If X and Y are two angles, then X and Y cannot be both acute and supplementary.

Exploration

28. The given information is from outside mathematics.
  a. Make a conclusion from the given information.
  b. How sure (in percent) are you of your conclusion?
   i. Today is Monday.
   ii. Last week the football team won its game.
   iii. You toss a coin nine times and it shows "heads" each time.
   See below.

   i. Sample: a) Tomorrow is Tuesday. b) 100%
   ii. Sample: a) This week the team will win. b) sample: 50%
   iii. Sample: a) It will be "heads" on the tenth toss. b) sample: 50%

MORE PRACTICE
For more questions on SPUR Objectives, use *Lesson Master 3-3*, shown below.

EVALUATION
Alternative Assessment
Questions 1-5 can be evaluated by using the following **oral activities:** have students read the questions and give the answers out loud, discuss the answers (correct and incorrect), and summarize the key lesson ideas found in these questions.

NAME _____

LESSON **MASTER   3-3**
QUESTIONS ON **SPUR** OBJECTIVES

■ **PROPERTIES** *Objective F (See pages 149–153 for objectives.)*
In 1–5, $\overleftrightarrow{OJ}$ intersects $\overleftrightarrow{KN}$ at *M*, as shown in the figure below. Give the justification for the conclusion stated.

1. m∠KMJ = m∠OMN	Vertical Angle Thm.
2. m∠LMO = 90°	def. of right angle (meaning)
3. m∠LMN = m∠LMO + m∠OMN	Angle Addition Prop.
4. ∠KMJ is adjacent to ∠LMK.	def. of adj. ∠s (suff. cond.)
5. m∠JMK + m∠KMO = 180°	Linear Pair Thm.

In 6–8, use the figure below, in which $\overleftrightarrow{AE}$ intersects $\overleftrightarrow{DF}$ at *C* and m∠ACB = 40. Give the justification for the stated conclusion. Caution: One conclusion is not valid.

6. m∠BCE = 140	Linear Pair Thm.
7. m∠ACE = 180	def. of straight angle (meaning)
8. $\overrightarrow{CA}$ bisects ∠BCF.	not valid

21

125

3-4

Parallel Lines

Lines have **tilt.** The tilt of a line can be measured by an angle it makes with some line of reference. Often the reference line is horizontal. A road might be described as having a *grade* of 7°, which means that the angle it makes with the horizontal has a measure of 7°.

Now consider angles formed when *two* lines *m* and *n* are intersected by a third line, a **transversal.** Eight angles are formed, as numbered below; four by *m* and the transversal, four by *n* and the transversal. Any pair of angles in similar locations with respect to the transversal and each line is called a pair of **corresponding angles.** In the draw-ing, angles 1 and 5 are corresponding angles, as are angles 2 and 6, 3 and 7, and 4 and 8.

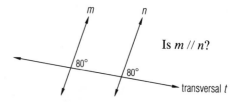

Recall that two coplanar lines are parallel if and only if they are the same line or they do not intersect. (In symbols, $\ell \parallel m \Leftrightarrow \ell = m$ or $\ell \cap m = \varnothing$.) If two lines have the same tilt, that is, if they make the same angle with a transversal, you would definitely think they are parallel.

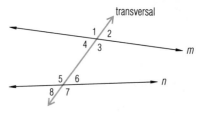

Is $m \parallel n$?

Yet, on Earth, two north-south streets make the same angle with any east-west street, but they would intersect at the North Pole (and

126

South Pole!) if extended. Also, in perspective drawings, some parallel lines meet at a vanishing point. Assumptions about parallel lines are needed to ensure that the geometry you are studying is not the geometry of the curved surface of Earth or the geometry of perspective drawings. The first postulate says that lines with the same tilt are parallel.

Corresponding Angles Postulate:

If two coplanar lines are cut by a transversal so that two corresponding angles have the same measure, then the lines are parallel.

When using this postulate as a justification, you may abbreviate it:
$$\text{corr.} \angle s = \Rightarrow \text{ // lines.}$$

The second postulate is the converse of the first.

Parallel Lines Postulate:

If two lines are parallel and are cut by a transversal, corresponding angles have the same measure.

This postulate may be abbreviated: // lines $\Rightarrow$ corr. $\angle s =$.

Information about linear pairs and vertical angles can be used with the Parallel Lines Postulate to determine measures of angles formed by parallel lines.

■ ■ ■ ■ ■ ■ ■ ■

Example 1 s // t as pictured below. (The >s on the lines s and t indicate that s is parallel to t.) What is m∠8?

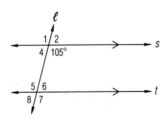

Solution   Here are the steps in the thinking, with justifications.

m∠7 = 105	because // lines $\Rightarrow$ corr. ∠s =. (Parallel Lines Postulate)
m∠7 + m∠8 = 180	because of the Linear Pair Theorem.
105 + m∠8 = 180	because of substitution.
m∠8 = 75	because of the Addition Property of Equality.

LESSON 3-4 Parallel Lines   **127**

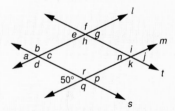

In the coordinate plane, the tilt of a nonvertical line is indicated by the number called the *slope* of the line. You learned about slope in algebra; some ideas are reviewed here.

Definition:

The **slope** of the line through (x_1, y_1) and (x_2, y_2), with $x_1 \neq x_2$, is $\dfrac{y_2 - y_1}{x_2 - x_1}$.

The slope is the change in *y*-values divided by the corresponding change in *x*-values. It tells how many units the line goes up or down for every unit the line goes to the right. The slope of a horizontal line is equal to zero, while the slope of a vertical line is undefined.

Example 2 Find the slope of the line through (7, 5) and (2, 4).

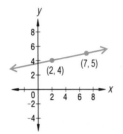

Solution Use the definition. Here $(x_1, y_1) = (7, 5)$ and $(x_2, y_2) = (2, 4)$, so the slope $= \dfrac{4 - 5}{2 - 7} = \dfrac{-1}{-5} = \dfrac{1}{5}$.

Check The line goes up $\frac{1}{5}$ unit for each unit you move to the right. Thus, as you move right 5 units (from 2 to 7), the line goes up 1 unit (from 4 to 5). So it checks.

Example 3 Find the slope of the line with equation $4x + 3y = -12$.

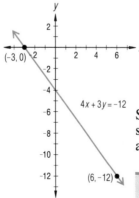

Solution Find two points on the line. We find (-3, 0) and (6, -12). Now use the definition of slope with these two points.

$$\text{slope} = \frac{-12 - 0}{6 - -3} = \frac{-12}{9} = \frac{-4}{3}$$

Check This line should go down 4 units for every 3 units moved to the right. An accurate·graph shows it does.

Since slope is a measure of the tilt of a line, the next theorem should come as no surprise. A proof requires quite a bit of algebra and is omitted.

Parallel Lines and Slopes Theorem:

Two nonvertical lines are parallel if and only if they have the same slope.

128

All vertical lines, of course, are parallel as well. Thus, to determine whether lines are parallel, you only have to know their slopes.

The Parallel Lines and Slopes Theorem is two conditionals. When using it to justify that lines are parallel, you can abbreviate it: = slopes $\Rightarrow$ // lines. When using it to justify equal slopes, write: // lines $\Rightarrow$ = slopes.

Suppose two lines ℓ and n are each parallel to a third line m. Then, because // lines $\Rightarrow$ = slopes, ℓ and m have the same slope, and so do m and n. Thus ℓ and n have the same slope. Then, since = slopes $\Rightarrow$ // lines, ℓ and n are parallel. This argument proves a simple theorem.

Transitivity of Parallelism Theorem:

In a plane, if $\ell \parallel m$ and $m \parallel n$, then $\ell \parallel n$.

In words, if two lines are parallel to a third line, then they are parallel to each other.

Questions

Covering the Reading

In 1–3, refer to the drawing below. Consider line ℓ as a transversal to lines m and n.

1. $\angle 5$ and __?__ are corresponding angles. ∠3

2. $\angle 1$ and __?__ are corresponding angles. ∠7

3. If $m\angle 4 = m\angle 6$, what is wrong with the drawing?
   Lines *m* and *n* should be drawn parallel.

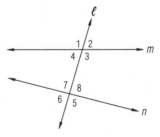

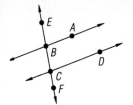

In 4 and 5, use the drawing at the left.

4. If $\overline{AB} \parallel \overline{CD}$ and m∠*ABE* = 80, find m∠*DCB*. 80

5. *True* or *false*? If m∠*ABC* = m∠*FCD*, then $\overline{AB} \parallel \overline{CD}$. True

6. *True* or *false*? The Corresponding Angle Postulate is true on the surface of the earth. False

In 7 and 8, find the slope of the line containing the two points.

7. (1, 4) and (6, 2) $-\frac{2}{5}$

8. (3, -7) and (-7, 3) -1

9. If two nonvertical lines are parallel, what can you say about their slopes? They are equal.

In 10 and 11, find the slope of a line parallel to the line with the given equation.

10. $y = 4x - 5$ 4

11. $12x - 3y = 10$ 4

12. For what lines is slope not defined? vertical lines

13. What justifies the fact that when two lines are parallel to the same line they are also parallel to each other?
Transitivity of Parallelism Theorem

Applying the Mathematics

In 14 and 15, use the figure below. $m \parallel n$.

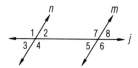

14. If m∠1 = 122, find the measures of as many other angles as you can.
m∠2 = m∠3 = m∠8 = m∠5 = 58; m∠4 = m∠6 = m∠7 = 122

15. a. Name all angles with the same measure as ∠6. ∠1, ∠4, ∠7
b. Name all angles supplementary to ∠6. ∠2, ∠3, ∠5, ∠8

In 16 and 17, use the figure below. A, B, C, and D are collinear.
$\overline{BE} \parallel \overline{CF}$.

16. If m∠*ABE* = 106, then m∠ _?_ = 106. BCF

17. ∠*EBC* and _?_ are corresponding angles. ∠FCD

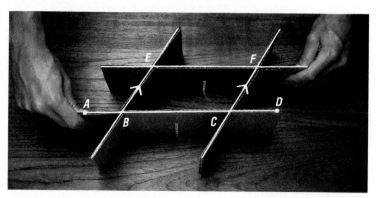

18. Use the coordinate plane sketched below.
  a. Which line has the largest slope? *u*
  b. Which line has negative slope? *w*

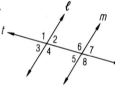

19. *True* or *false*? The slope of the line containing (x_1, y_1) and (x_2, y_2) equals the slope of the line containing (x_2, y_2) and (x_1, y_1). **True**

20. Which would probably be easier to climb, a cliff with a grade of 65° or one with a grade of 80°? **the grade of 65°**

In 21 and 22, state the justification for the conclusion.

21. Given: $m\angle 1 = m\angle 6$ as shown at the right.
  Conclusion: $\ell \parallel m$.
  corr. ∠s = ⇒ ∥ lines

22. Given: the figure at the right.
  Conclusion: $m\angle 2 = m\angle 3$. *(Lessons 3-3, 3-2)*
  Vertical Angle Theorem

Review

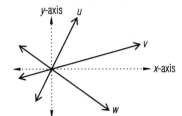

23. Draw an obtuse scalene triangle. *(Lessons 3-2, 2-7)* **See margin.**

24. M is the midpoint of $\overline{AB}$. N is the midpoint of $\overline{MB}$. Fill in the blanks with numbers. (Hint: Draw a picture.)
  a. If $AB = 5$, then $MN = \underline{\ ?\ }$. $\frac{5}{4}$
  b. If $AN = x$, then $NB = \underline{\ ?\ }$. *(Lesson 2-5)* $\frac{x}{3}$

25. M is the midpoint of $\overline{RS}$. If M has coordinate -2 and S has coordinate 31, find the coordinate of R. *(Lessons 2-5, 1-2)* **-35**

Exploration

26. With a ruler, draw three rays $\overrightarrow{OP}$, $\overrightarrow{OQ}$ and $\overrightarrow{OR}$. Let A be any point on $\overrightarrow{OP}$. Let B be any point on $\overrightarrow{OQ}$. Let C be any point on $\overrightarrow{OR}$. Draw six lines: $\overleftrightarrow{AB}$, $\overleftrightarrow{BC}$, $\overleftrightarrow{AC}$, $\overleftrightarrow{PQ}$, $\overleftrightarrow{PR}$, and $\overleftrightarrow{QR}$. Verify the incredible discovery of Gerard Desargues in the early 1600s, that either (1) $\overleftrightarrow{AB} \parallel \overleftrightarrow{PQ}$, $\overleftrightarrow{AC} \parallel \overleftrightarrow{PR}$, or $\overleftrightarrow{BC} \parallel \overleftrightarrow{QR}$; or (2) the three points of intersection of these pairs of lines are collinear. (This result is known as Desargues' Theorem.)   **Sample: For this diagram, the three points of intersection are collinear.**

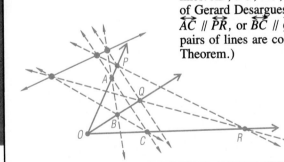

RESOURCES
■ Lesson Master 3-5
■ Visual for Teaching Aid 18 can be used with **Question 26**.
■ Computer Master 4

OBJECTIVES

F Give justifications for conclusions involving different figures.
J Determine the slope of a line perpendicular to a given line.

TEACHING NOTES

Students have great difficulty thinking of perpendicular lines that are neither horizontal nor vertical. Indeed, many students think that "perpendicular" and "vertical" are synonyms. As we have done in this lesson, try to give many examples of perpendicular lines that are not horizontal and vertical.

You may wish to draw an oblique line on the chalkboard (with a meter stick or yardstick) and have a student come to the board to try to draw a second line perpendicular to it. Some students will not be able to do this, and you will have motivated the next lesson, that is, to construct perpendiculars.

The properties relating perpendicularity to parallelism are very much like the multiplication of positive and negative numbers. Think of parallelism as positive and perpendicularity as negative.

LESSON

3-5

Perpendicular Lines

A bookcase is pictured above. There are many right angles in the bookcase (though, due to perspective, they don't all look that way). The angles at the corner of this page are right angles. Right angles are very common. As you know, the sides of right angles are called *perpendicular*.

Definition:

Two segments, rays, or lines are **perpendicular** if and only if the lines containing them form a 90° angle.

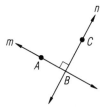

Perpendicular lines need not be horizontal and vertical. ∠*ABC* above is a right angle, so *m* and *n* are perpendicular. The ⌐ sign in the drawing indicates perpendicularity. The symbol ⊥ is read "is perpendicular to." You can write $m \perp n$, $\overline{AB} \perp \overleftrightarrow{BC}$, $\overrightarrow{AB} \perp \overleftrightarrow{BC}$, or $m \perp \overleftrightarrow{BC}$ to indicate perpendicularity.

When lines form one right angle, the Vertical Angle and Linear Pair Theorems force the other three angles to be right angles. So you can put the ⌐ symbol by any of the angles.

132

The two edges of this page are each perpendicular to the bottom edge. If the edges are extended, corresponding 90° angles appear. By the Corresponding Angles Postulate, the side edges are parallel. This argument proves a useful theorem.

page

90°   90°

Two Perpendiculars Theorem:

If two coplanar lines ℓ and m are each perpendicular to the same line, then they are parallel to each other.

In symbols, if $\ell \perp n$ and $m \perp n$, then $\ell \parallel m$. "Is perpendicular to" does not satisfy the transitive property.

Suppose you are given these lines as shown below with one perpendicular relation ($\ell \perp m$) and one parallel relation ($m \parallel n$) among the lines. There are 90° angles where ℓ intersects m. Since $\parallel$ lines $\Rightarrow$ corr. $\angle$s =, there are also 90° angles where ℓ intersects n. So $\ell \perp n$. This simple argument proves: if $\ell \perp m$ and $m \parallel n$, then $\ell \perp n$.

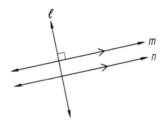

In words, this relation is stated as follows.

Perpendicular to Parallels Theorem:

In a plane, if a line is perpendicular to one of two parallel lines, then it is perpendicular to the other.

As you think of parallel lines as having the same tilt, so you may think of two perpendicular lines as having the most different tilts imaginable. Since you know that parallel lines have the same slope,

If two numbers are positive, their product is positive.

$k \parallel m$ and $m \parallel n \Rightarrow k \parallel n$

If one number is positive and one is negative, their product is negative.

$k \parallel m$ and $m \perp n \Rightarrow k \perp n$
$k \perp m$ and $m \parallel n \Rightarrow k \perp n$

If two numbers are negative, their product is positive.

$k \perp m$ and $m \perp n \Rightarrow k \parallel n$

When discussing the Two Perpendiculars Theorem, you might ask why the word *coplanar* modifies "lines" in the theorem. Use lines in a room as an example. The line which is the intersection of the front wall and floor is not parallel to the line which is the intersection of the side wall and the back wall, even though both are perpendicular to the line which is the intersection of the side wall and the floor.

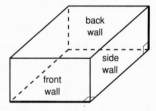

back wall
side wall
front wall

Students definitely need a ruler and compass every day for the rest of the chapter. We strongly recommend a good compass, like the Circle Master, or other kinds that have pins in the middle.

Reading Perpendicularity is a difficult concept for many students, even though it should be review. Have students read through this lesson very carefully, and encourage them to draw diagrams and ask questions. Ask students to think of real-world examples of the Two Perpendiculars Theorem and the Perpendicular to Parallels Theorem.

133

ADDITIONAL EXAMPLE
Give the slope for a line perpendicular to the graph of
$4x - 3y = 5$.

$-\frac{3}{4}$

you might expect that the slopes of two perpendicular lines are about as different as two related numbers can be. What numbers are most different? Opposites? Reciprocals? In fact, the slopes of perpendicular lines are both. Each slope is the opposite of the reciprocal of the other. In symbols, if the slope of a given line is m, the slope of any line perpendicular to it is $-\frac{1}{m}$. Since $m \cdot -\frac{1}{m} = -1$, the next theorem is simply stated as follows.

> **Perpendicular Lines and Slopes Theorem:**
>
> Two nonvertical lines are perpendicular if and only if the product of their slopes is -1.

A proof of this theorem requires quite a bit of algebra, and is omitted.

If one of two perpendicular lines is vertical (with undefined slope), it is perpendicular to a horizontal line (with 0 slope). Since one of the lines has undefined slope, there is no product of slopes in this case.

■ ■ ■ ■ ■ ■ ■■

Example   A line has slope 5. What is the slope of a line perpendicular to it?

Solution   All lines perpendicular to a given line are parallel (Two Perpendiculars Theorem), thus they have the same slope. Let that slope be s. By the Perpendicular Lines and Slopes Theorem,
$$5s = -1.$$
Solving the equation, $s = -\frac{1}{5}.$

Check   Note that $-\frac{1}{5}$ is the opposite of the reciprocal of the given slope 5.

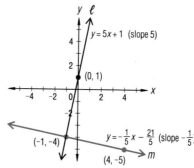

An instance of the Example is graphed above. Line ℓ has equation $y = 5x + 1$. Line m has equation $y = -\frac{1}{5}x - \frac{21}{5}$. $y = 5x + 1$ contains $(0, 1)$ and $(-1, -4)$ and has slope 5. $y = -\frac{1}{5}x - \frac{21}{5}$ contains $(-1, -4)$ and $(4, -5)$ and has slope $-\frac{1}{5}$. Lines ℓ and m are perpendicular.

134

In Lessons 3-4 and 3-5 you have seen how parallel and perpendicular lines can be determined either through angle measures or by slopes. The table below shows how parallelism and perpendicularity relate to the ideas in Chapters 1 and 2 of points as locations and points as ordered pairs.

	a point as a location	a point as an ordered pair (x, y)
line		$Ax + By = C$
measure of tilt of line	angle measure	slope
parallel lines	corresponding angles = in measure	slopes equal
perpendicular lines	lines form 90° angles	product of slopes = −1

NOTES ON QUESTIONS
Question 2: Students are expected to use a protractor to draw 90° angles. Also, perpendiculars may be created by folding the paper through *P* and holding it up to the light to ensure the rays coincide. In the next lesson, perpendiculars will be constructed. Check that the perpendicular is not vertical.

ADDITIONAL ANSWERS
1. a. Two lines are perpendicular if and only if they form a 90° angle.
b. If two lines are perpendicular, then they form a 90° angle.

Questions

Covering the Reading

1. **a** Define: perpendicular lines. **See margin.**
   b. Write the meaning half of the definition. **See margin.**

2. Trace line ℓ below. Draw a line through point P perpendicular to ℓ.

3. What are the *two* symbols indicating perpendicularity? ⊥ **and** ⌐

4. **a.** Trace the figure below. Draw a line t perpendicular to line m. **See below.**
   b. If $m \parallel n$, must t also be perpendicular to n? **Yes**

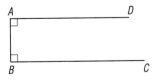

5. In the drawing below, $\overline{AD} \perp \overline{AB}$ and $\overline{BC} \perp \overline{AB}$. What theorem justifies the conclusion that $\overline{AD} \parallel \overline{BC}$? **Two Perpendiculars Theorem**

LESSON 3-5 Perpendicular Lines   **135**

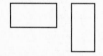
6. In the drawing below, $\ell \parallel m$ and $m \perp n$. What theorem justifies the conclusion that $\ell \perp n$? **Perpendicular to Parallels Theorem**

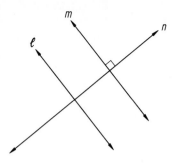

7. A line has slope $\frac{2}{3}$. What is the slope of a line perpendicular to it? **$-\frac{3}{2}$**

8. A line has slope x. What is the slope of a line perpendicular to it?
$-\frac{1}{x}$, if $x \neq 0$. If $x = 0$, the slope is not defined.

9. Write the two conditionals making up the Perpendicular Lines and Slopes Theorem. **See margin.**

10. Line s is perpendicular to line t below. What is the slope of s? **-2**

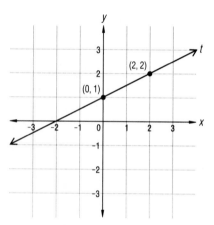

11. Below, $\overrightarrow{AD} \perp \overrightarrow{AC}$. Answer with numbers.
   a. m$\angle DAC = \underline{\ ?\ }$ **90**
   b. m$\angle DAE = \underline{\ ?\ }$ **50**

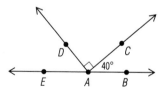

12. Why are street intersections often planned so the streets are perpendicular, even when one has to be bent to do so, as in the diagram below? sample: so no driver's head needs to turn more than 90° at an intersection to see traffic

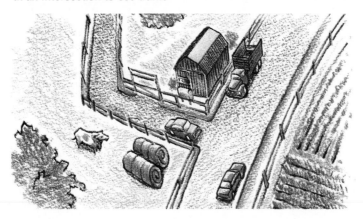

In 13 and 14, use the figure below, given $\overline{QR} \parallel \overline{SU}$, $\overline{QT} \parallel \overline{UP}$, and $\overline{QT} \perp \overline{TU}$ as indicated.

13. Justify each conclusion using one of the following justifications.
  $\parallel$ lines $\Rightarrow$ corr. $\angle$s $=$
  corr. $\angle$s $=$ $\Rightarrow$ $\parallel$ lines
  $\ell \perp n$ and $m \perp n \Rightarrow \ell \parallel m$
  $\ell \perp m$ and $m \parallel n \Rightarrow \ell \perp n$
  $\ell \perp m \Rightarrow$ 90° angle
  90° angle $\Rightarrow \ell \perp m$
  a. $m\angle S = m\angle PQR$ **b.** $\overline{QT} \perp \overline{QR}$
  c. $m\angle SQT = m\angle P$ **d.** $m\angle QTU = 90$ See margin.

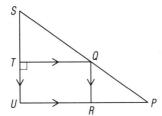

14. If $m\angle PQR = 65$, give the measure of each angle.
  a. $\angle S$ 65° **b.** $\angle TQR$ 90°
  c. $\angle TQS$ 25° **d.** $\angle P$ 25°

15. A line has equation $9y + 2x = 180$. What is the slope of any line perpendicular to this line? $\frac{9}{2}$

16. Consider this statement: If $\overline{AB} \perp \overline{BC}$ and $\overline{BC} \perp \overline{CD}$, then $\overline{AB} \perp \overline{CD}$.
  a. Draw an instance of this statement in a plane, or tell why the drawing is impossible. See margin.
  b. Draw an instance of this statement in space, or tell why the drawing is impossible. See margin.

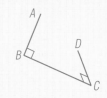

NOTES ON QUESTIONS
Questions 23 and 24:
These questions prepare students for the next lesson and should be discussed.

Question 26: This question is by no means easy. The Dell book gives a goal time of 8 minutes for experts.

ADDITIONAL ANSWERS
24.

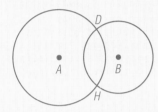

17. Lines *r*, *s*, and *t* intersect as shown below. m∠1 = 70 and *s* ∥ *r*. Find the measures of angles 2 through 8. *(Lesson 3-4)*

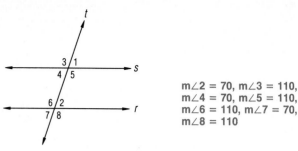

m∠2 = 70, m∠3 = 110,
m∠4 = 70, m∠5 = 110,
m∠6 = 110, m∠7 = 70,
m∠8 = 110

18. A line contains (4, -7) and (-10, -9). Find its slope. *(Lesson 3-4)*
$\frac{2}{14} = \frac{1}{7}$

In 19-21, use the figure below. State the justification for the conclusion. *(Lessons 3-4, 3-3, 3-2)*

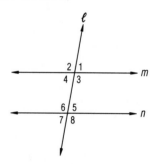

19. Given: m∠3 = m∠8.
Conclusion: *m* ∥ *n*. **corr. ∠s = ⇒ ∥ lines**

20. Given: the figure.
Conclusion: ∠7 and ∠8 are supplementary angles.
Linear Pair Theorem

21. Using a protractor, find m∠6. *(Lesson 3-1)* |m∠6 ≈ 100

22. Which of the if-then statements of Question 13 refers to the meaning half of the definition of perpendicular lines? *(Lesson 2-5)*
ℓ ⊥ *m* ⇒ 90° angle

23. In the figure below, identify the points on ⊙*A* ∩ ⊙*B*. *(Lesson 2-6)*
{D, H}

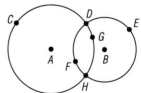

24. Draw the figure of Question 23 using a compass. *(Previous course)*
See margin.

25. Draw a 24° angle. *(Lesson 3-1)*

24°

26. Mazes or labyrinths are puzzles where you try to find a path from the start to the finish. Mazes are usually designed so the walls are either horizontal or vertical.

    a. Try to find the way from the START to the FINISH in the maze pictured below. (From *The Dell Big Book of Crosswords and Pencil Puzzles #5*, Dell Publishing Co., 1985) See below.

    b. Design your own maze. Answers will vary.

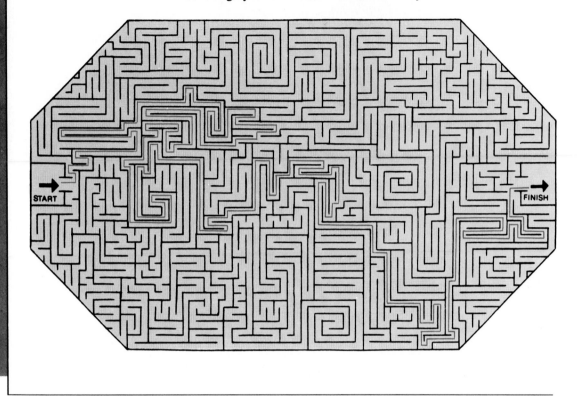

FOLLOW-UP

MORE PRACTICE
For more questions on SPUR Objectives, use *Lesson Master 3-5,* shown below.

LESSON 3-5 Perpendicular Lines **139**

RESOURCES
■ Lesson Master 3-6
⬛ Computer Master 4

TEACHING NOTES

A proof that the perpendicular is the shortest distance from a point to a line is derived from the Pythagorean Theorem discussed in Lesson 8-7.

Algorithm is a concept which has increasing importance in mathematics. Encourage its use in the students' vocabularies. Recall examples from arithmetic; for example, the long division algorithm.

The construction of the perpendicular to a line through a point on the line is a classic example of reducing a problem to one already solved. While you may associate the term "subroutine" with computers, the concept is much broader. It is the idea one uses to shorten long proofs and to solve hard problems. Even as early as page 143, it shortens the description of the construction from six steps to three.

A key question is: Do students have to do all the steps in a subroutine? It's the same

---

Constructing Perpendiculars

You are in a park when someone gets hurt and needs help. (Below is drawn a picture of this situation as seen from the air.) You want to run to the nearest road as fast as you can to flag down a car. What is the shortest route to the road?

● Your location

The answer is that you should run along the line through your location perpendicular to the road.

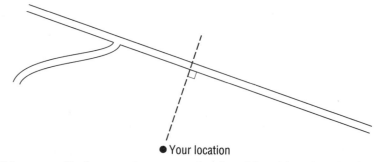

● Your location

This perpendicular may be accurately placed by either drawing it or constructing it. In a **drawing,** you may use any tools. You can use a ruler, a protractor, a computer drawing program, a compass, a T square, or any other tool.

A **construction** is a precise way of drawing which uses specific tools and follows specific rules. From the time of the ancient Greeks, only two tools have been permitted in making a construction. They are the **unmarked straightedge** and the **compass.**

Use of these tools follows three specific rules.

Point rule:

A point must either be given or be the intersection of figures that have been already constructed.
If a figure is given, you can assume as many points are given as will determine the figure.

Straightedge rule:

A straightedge can draw the line $\overleftrightarrow{AB}$ through two points A and B.
A ruler can substitute for the straightedge, but the marks on the ruler must be ignored.

Compass rule:

A compass can draw a circle with center at a point A and containing a second point B.
Also, a compass can be lifted keeping the same radius.

Constructing a geometric figure is like playing a game with rules telling you what is legal and what is illegal. In this book we describe a construction by showing you the steps in it. A sequence of steps leading to a desired end is called an **algorithm.** When we describe a construction, we show you the algorithm for it.

One of the most important constructions is of the line passing through the midpoint of a segment and perpendicular to it. This is the **perpendicular bisector** or **⊥ bisector** of the segment. (A **bisector** of a segment is its midpoint or any plane, line, ray, or segment which intersects it at its midpoint only.)

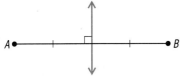

the ⊥ bisector of $\overline{AB}$

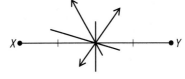

some of the many bisectors of $\overline{XY}$

unmarked straightedge and compass

Example 1 Construct the perpendicular bisector of a given segment $\overline{AB}$.

Solution Here are the algorithm steps.
Step 1. $\odot A$ containing *B*   (Compass rule)
Step 2. $\odot B$ containing *A*   (Compass rule)
Step 3. $\odot A$ and $\odot B$ intersect at
         new points *C* and *D*.   (Point rule)
Step 4. $\overleftrightarrow{CD}$ (Straightedge rule)

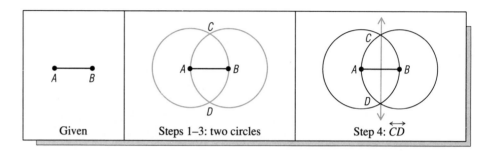

Given	Steps 1–3: two circles	Step 4: $\overleftrightarrow{CD}$

A bonus is that the midpoint of $\overline{AB}$ has also been constructed. It is the intersection of $\overline{AB}$ and $\overleftrightarrow{CD}$ in Step 4.

The steps in Example 1 will give the ⊥ bisector of any given segment. Although at this point you cannot prove that this algorithm works, later in this course you will have enough information to do so. For now, you should be able to repeat the steps of the construction for any segment $\overline{AB}$.

The construction of the perpendicular bisector is a building block for many other constructions.

■ ■ ■ ■ ■ ■ ■ ■

Example 2 Construct the line perpendicular to $\overleftrightarrow{AP}$ through point *P* on the line.

Solution 1 The idea is to locate the point *B* on the other side of *P* from *A*, so that *P* is the midpoint of $\overline{AB}$. Then construct the ⊥ bisector of $\overline{AB}$. That is the desired line. Here is an algorithm for this construction.

Step 1. $\odot P$ containing *A*   (Compass rule)
Step 2. $\odot P$ intersects $\overleftrightarrow{AP}$ at *A* and *B*.   (Point rule)
Steps 3–6. Construct the ⊥ bisector of $\overline{AB}$ as in Example 1.
Step 3. $\odot A$ containing *B*   (Compass rule)
Step 4. $\odot B$ containing *A*   (Compass rule)
Step 5. $\odot B$ intersects $\odot A$ at *D* and *E*.   (Point rule)
Step 6. $\overleftrightarrow{DE}$ (Straightedge rule)

142

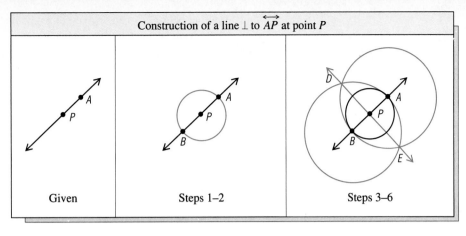

Construction of a line ⊥ to $\overleftrightarrow{AP}$ at point P

| Given | Steps 1–2 | Steps 3–6 |

A **subroutine** is an algorithm you already know that you use in another algorithm. Computer programs often have subroutines. It saves having to write the same steps over and over again. Since Steps 3–6 of Solution 1 are the ⊥ bisector construction, you can write the algorithm in a shorter way. Steps 1 and 2 are the same as in Solution 1. But Step 3 is different.

Solution 2　Step 1.　⊙P containing A
　　　　　　　　Step 2.　⊙P intersects $\overleftrightarrow{AP}$ at A and B.
　　　　　　　　Step 3.　Subroutine: $\overleftrightarrow{DE}$, the ⊥ bisector of $\overline{AB}$.

What about the injured person in the park? In Question 11 you are asked to follow an algorithm to construct the unique line perpendicular to a given line through a point not on that line. That line gives the path you should take.

Questions

Covering the Reading

1. What tools may you use in drawings? Any tools may be used.

2. What tools may you use in constructions?
   an unmarked straightedge and a compass
3. What are the three rules of a construction?
   Point rule, Straightedge rule, and Compass rule
4. In constructions, what points can be used? points that are given or are the intersections of figures that have already been constructed
5. What is an algorithm? a sequence of steps leading to a desired end

6. What is the perpendicular bisector of a segment? the one line through the midpoint of a segment and perpendicular to it

In 7 and 8, use the figure at the left.

7. Trace $\overline{YZ}$. Draw a bisector that is not a perpendicular bisector.
   See margin.
8. Trace $\overline{YZ}$. Construct its perpendicular bisector. See margin.

LESSON 3-6　Constructing Perpendiculars　**143**

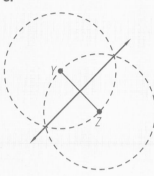
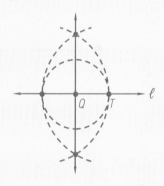

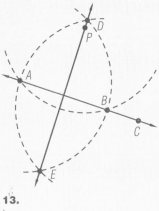
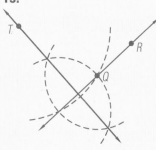

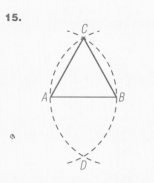
9. Trace the line below. Construct the perpendicular to ℓ through point Q. **See margin.**

10. What is a subroutine?
an algorithm you already know that you use in another algorithm

11. Trace the figure below. Then follow this algorithm to construct the perpendicular to $\overleftrightarrow{AC}$ from P. **See margin.**
Step 1. ⊙P containing A
Step 2. ⊙P intersects $\overleftrightarrow{AC}$ at A and B.
Step 3. Subroutine: $\overleftrightarrow{DE}$, the ⊥ bisector of $\overline{AB}$.
P lies on $\overleftrightarrow{DE}$.

12. Give the rule justifying the first two steps in Question 11.
Step 1: Compass Rule; Step 2: Point Rule
13. Trace the figure below. Use the algorithm of Question 11 to construct the perpendicular to $\overleftrightarrow{QR}$ through T. **See margin.**

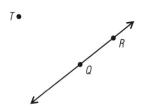

14. Trace the road and the clubhouse dot. Construct the shortest path from the clubhouse to the road.
See margin.

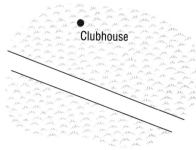

15. Trace $\overline{AB}$ below. Follow the steps. What have you constructed?
Step 1. ⊙A containing B
Step 2. ⊙B containing A
Step 3. ⊙A and ⊙B intersect at C and D.

Step 4. $\overline{AC}$, $\overline{BC}$ △ABC **is an equilateral triangle. See margin for construction.**

144

144

16. a. Measure $\overline{GH}$, $\overline{GI}$, $\overline{GJ}$, $\overline{GK}$, $\overline{GL}$, and $\overline{GM}$ to the nearest millimeter.
b. Which is the shortest?

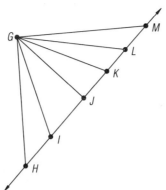

a) **GH ≈ 38 mm, GI ≈ 31 mm,
GJ ≈ 27 mm, GK ≈ 29 mm,
GL ≈ 33 mm, GM ≈ 39 mm;**
b) **$\overline{GJ}$**

Review

17. Break the definition of perpendicular lines into its meaning and sufficient condition halves. *(Lessons 3-5, 2-5)* **See margin.**

18. a. What is the slope of the line with equation $x - 2y = 15$?
(Lesson 3-4) $\frac{1}{2}$
b. What is the slope of a line perpendicular to it? *(Lesson 3-5)* **·2**

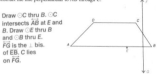

19. In the figure at the left, $\ell \parallel m$. If $m\angle 6 = m\angle 1 + 12$, find $m\angle 1$. *(Lessons 3-4, 3-2)* **m∠1 = 84**

20. Fill in the table with $\ell \parallel n$, $\ell \perp n$, or *can't tell*. *(Lessons 3-5, 3-4)*

	$m \parallel n$	$m \perp n$
$\ell \parallel m$	_?_ $\ell \parallel n$	_?_ $\ell \perp n$
$\ell \perp m$	_?_ $\ell \perp n$	_?_ $\ell \parallel n$

Exploration

21. Because the rules for constructions are quite specific, there are some figures that can be drawn but cannot be constructed. The Greeks were very puzzled by this and three problems became famous. They are called "squaring the circle," "duplicating the cube," and "trisecting an angle." Find out what one of these problems was. **See below.**

21. "Squaring the circle" = **Given any circle, construct a square of exactly the same area.**
"Duplicating the cube" = **Given any cube, construct a cube with twice the volume.**
"Trisecting an angle" = **Given any angle, construct an angle with $\frac{1}{3}$ of its measure.**

MORE PRACTICE
For more questions on SPUR Objectives, use *Lesson Master 3-6,* shown below.

NAME _____

LESSON **MASTER 3–6**
QUESTIONS ON **SPUR** OBJECTIVES

■**SKILLS** *Objective E (See pages 149–153 for objectives.)*

1. Construct the perpendicular bisector to $\overline{CD}$ below.

Draw ⊙C thru D and ⊙D thru C. The intersection of ⊙C and ⊙D is $\overleftrightarrow{EF}$, the ⊥ bis. of $\overline{CD}$.

2. Construct the line perpendicular to $\overleftrightarrow{LM}$ through L.

Draw ⊙L thru M intersecting $\overleftrightarrow{LM}$ at N. Draw ⊙N thru M and ⊙M thru N. The intersections of ⊙N and ⊙M is $\overleftrightarrow{XY}$, the ⊥ to $\overleftrightarrow{LM}$ at L.

3. Construct the line perpendicular to $\overline{AB}$ through C.

Draw ⊙C thru B. ⊙C intersects $\overline{AB}$ at E and B. Draw ⊙E thru B and ⊙B thru E. $\overline{FG}$ is the ⊥ bis. of $\overline{EB}$. C lies on $\overline{FG}$.

Geometry © Scott, Foresman and Company   *Continued* **25**

NAME _____
Lesson MASTER 3–4 (page 2)

In 4 and 5, consider the following construction.

Step 1: subroutine: $\overleftrightarrow{CD}$, the perpendicular bisector of $\overline{AB}$.
Step 2: subroutine: $\overleftrightarrow{BE}$, perpendicular to $\overleftrightarrow{AB}$ through B.

4. Do the construction.

5. Are $\overleftrightarrow{CD}$ and $\overleftrightarrow{EB}$ parallel? Why or why not?
Yes, by the Two Perpendiculars Thm.

■**USES** *Objective H*

6. You are in a forest at point A and want to set up your camp on the other side of the river. You also want to travel the shortest distance to the camp since it is getting dark. Find the camp's location by doing a construction.

Construct the ⊥ to the river bank through point A.

26   *Geometry © Scott, Foresman and Company*

145

Summary

To show $p \Rightarrow q$ is true, you must show that whenever p is true, so is q. One way to do this is to give a general property for which $p \Rightarrow q$ is a special case. This general property is a justification for the truth of $p \Rightarrow q$. The justification must be a postulate, a definition, or a theorem already proved. Then q is a conclusion from p; q has been proved from p; q follows from p.

The basic properties of angles are found in the Angle Measure Postulate. Angles may be classified by their measure as zero, acute, right, obtuse, or straight. Some pairs of angles are vertical angles, in which case their measures are equal. If they form a linear pair, then they are supplementary.

The later results of this chapter stem from two assumptions: the Corresponding Angle Postulate and the Parallel Lines Postulate. These postulates lead to the following theorems:

Transitivity of Parallelism Theorem:
If $\ell \parallel m$ and $m \parallel n$, then $\ell \parallel n$.

Two Perpendiculars Theorem:
If $\ell \perp m$ and $n \perp m$, then $\ell \parallel n$.
Perpendicular to Parallels Theorem:
If $\ell \perp m$ and $m \parallel n$, then $\ell \perp n$.

The word "construction" has a special meaning in geometry. Perpendicular lines, perpendicular bisectors, reflection images, and angle bisectors can all be constructed following specific rules of construction laid down by the ancient Greeks. With these rules, only given or intersecting points of figures can be used and only a straightedge and compass are allowed. In contrast, any instruments, even computers, can be used to make drawings.

In the coordinate plane, the tilt of a nonvertical line is measured by its slope. Nonvertical lines are parallel if and only if they have the same slope. Nonvertical lines are perpendicular if and only if the product of their slopes is -1.

Vocabulary

Below are the new terms and phrases for this chapter. You should be able to give a general description and specific example of each. For those terms that are starred, you should be able to give a *good* definition. You should also be able to rewrite each named theorem or postulate in if-then or if-and-only-if form, as appropriate.

Lesson 3-1
*angle, vertex of angle
sides of angle
$\angle$, $\angle A$, $\angle ABC$, $\angle 1$
interior of angle, exterior of angle
measure of angle, m$\angle ABC$
degree, °, protractor
Angle Measure Postulate
Angle Addition Property

Lesson 3-2
*zero angle, *acute angle,
*right angle, *obtuse angle,
*straight angle
*complementary angles

*supplementary angles
complements, supplements
*adjacent angles, *linear pair
*vertical angles
Linear Pair Theorem
Vertical Angle Theorem

Lesson 3-3
*proof, conclusion, justification

Lesson 3-4
transversal, corresponding angles
*slope
Corresponding Angles Postulate
Parallel Lines Postulate
Parallel Lines and Slopes Theorem
Transitivity of Parallelism Theorem

Lesson 3-5
*perpendicular, $\perp$, $\neg$
Two Perpendiculars Theorem
Perpendicular to Parallels Theorem
Perpendicular Lines and
    Slopes Theorem

Lesson 3-6
drawing, construction
Point rule in constructions
Straightedge rule in constructions
Compass rule in constructions
algorithm
*perpendicular bisector, *bisector
subroutine

146

Progress Self-Test

See margin for answers not shown below.

Directions: Take this test as you would take a test in class. Use a ruler, compass and a protractor. Then check your work with the solutions in the Selected Answers section in the back of the book.

1. Sketch two angles $\angle 1$ and $\angle 2$ that are a linear pair.

In 2–4, refer to the figure below.

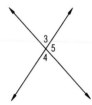

2. If $m\angle 3 = 77$, find $m\angle 4$. **77**

3. Because of their positions, $\angle 3$ and $\angle 4$ are called __?__. **vertical angles**

4. If $m\angle 3 = 2x$, then $m\angle 5 = $ __?__. **180 − 2x**

5. A movie goer has to look 15° above eye level to see the movie screen. How many more degrees would the movie goer have to bend his or her head to be staring straight up at the ceiling? **75°**

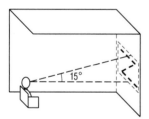

6. $\angle 1$ and $\angle 2$ are complementary. If $m\angle 1 = 5x - 7$ and $m\angle 2 = 4x + 16$, find $m\angle 1$. **38**

7. Use a protractor to find the measure of $\angle A$ below. **40°**

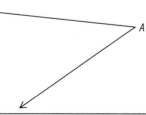

8. Draw a 72° angle.

In 9 and 10, use the figure below.

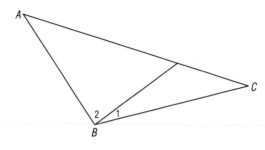

9. If $m\angle ABC = 110$ and $m\angle 2 = 4 \cdot m\angle 1$, find $m\angle 1$. **22**

10. *Multiple choice.* Tell which property justifies the conclusion: $m\angle 1 + m\angle 2 = m\angle ABC$.
(a) definition of supplementary angles (meaning)
(b) definition of supplementary angles (sufficient condition)
(c) Linear Pair Theorem
(d) Angle Addition Property **(d)**

11. Let $m\angle 1 = 21 + x$. If $\angle 1$ is acute, graph all possibilities for x on a number line.

12. $\overrightarrow{BC}$ is the bisector of angle ABD below. If $m\angle ABC = 14y - 3$ and $m\angle CBD = 37 - y$, what is y? $\frac{8}{3}$

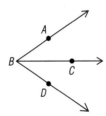

In 13 and 14, complete the statement.

13. If two lines are perpendicular to the same line, then they are __?__. **parallel**

14. If two lines are parallel to the same line, then they are __?__. **parallel**

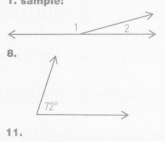

22.

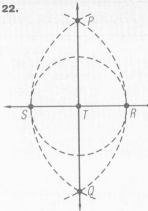

In 15 and 16, consider $\overline{AB}$ drawn below.

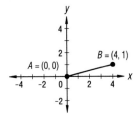

15. What is its slope? $\frac{1}{4}$

16. What is the slope of the perpendicular bisector of $\overline{AB}$? -4

In 17 and 18, a line has equation $2x - y = 6$.

17. What is the slope of this line? 2

18. What is the slope of any line perpendicular to this line? $-\frac{1}{2}$

In 19 and 20, if $\ell \parallel m$ below, give the measure of the indicated angle.

19. ∠4 140   **20.** ∠5 40

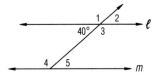

21. *Multiple choice.* Hank has to get quickly to the street for help. Which path should he take?
(a) w   (b) x
(c) y   (d) z (b)

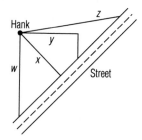

22. Trace the figure below. Construct the perpendicular to $\overleftrightarrow{RT}$ containing T.

23. Justify the conclusion.
Given: Q is the midpoint of $\overline{OP}$.
Conclusion: $OQ = QP$
definition of midpoint (meaning)

Chapter Review

Questions on **SPUR** Objectives

SPUR stands for **S**kills, **P**roperties, **U**ses, and **R**epresentations. The Chapter Review questions are grouped according to the SPUR Objectives for this chapter.

See margin for answers not shown below.

SKILLS deal with the procedures used to get answers.

Objective A: *Draw and analyze drawings of angles.* *(Lessons 3-1, 3-2)*

In 1 and 2, use the drawing below.

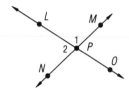

1. **a.** Name a straight angle.
   b. Name an angle with measure 0°.
   c. Name a linear pair.
   d. Give two other names for ∠1.
2. Does ∠2 appear to be acute, right, or obtuse?

In 3 and 4, sketch possible angles 5 and 6.
3. ∠5 and ∠6 are supplementary and adjacent.
4. ∠5 and ∠6 are complementary and have the same measure.

In 5 and 6, refer to the figure below.
Find **a.** m∠1, **b.** m∠3, **c.** m∠4:

5. if m∠2 = 78;
6. if m∠2 = 3*x*.

Objective B. *Draw angles with a given measure and measure drawn angles.* *(Lesson 3-1)*

In 7 and 8, measure the angles to the nearest degree using a protractor.
7. Angle *R* ⏌ m∠R ≈ 52

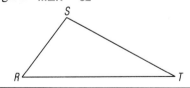

8. m∠Q ≈ 147

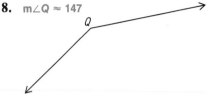

9. Draw two angles with measure 58° that share a common side.
10. Draw an angle with measure 92°.

Objective C: *Use algebra to represent and find measures of angles.* *(Lessons 3-1, 3-2)*

11. Let *m* be the measure of an acute angle. Graph all possibilities for *m* on a number line.
12. Point *D* is in the interior of ∠*ABC*. If m∠*ABD* = 5*t* and m∠*DBC* = 3*t* and m∠*ABC* = 72, find the value of *t*. t = 9
13. Let m∠3 = 12 − *x*. If ∠3 is straight, what is *x*? x = -168
14. Let m∠4 = 31 + *y*. If ∠4 is obtuse, graph the possible values for *y* on a number line.

In 15 and 16, ∠1 and ∠2 below form a linear pair.

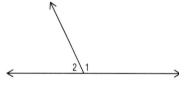

15. If m∠2 is one-fourth m∠1, find the measures of ∠1 and ∠2. m∠1 = 144, m∠2 = 36
16. If m∠1 = 7*x* − 6 and m∠2 = 5*x* + 18, find m∠1 and m∠2. m∠1 = 92, m∠2 = 88

CHAPTER REVIEW

The main objectives for the chapter are organized here into sections corresponding to the four main types of understanding this book promotes: Skills, Properties, Uses, and Representations.

The four types of understanding are not in increasing order of difficulty. There may be hard skills and easy representations; some uses may be easier than anything else; and so on.

USING THE CHAPTER REVIEW
Students should be able to answer questions like these with about 85% accuracy by the end of the chapter.

You may assign these questions over a single night to help students prepare for a test the next day, or you may assign the questions over a two-day period.

If you assign the questions over two days, then we recommend assigning the *evens* for homework the first night so that students get feedback in class the next day. Then assign the *odds* for the second night (the night before the test) so that students can use the answers provided in the book as a study aid.

11.

14.

149

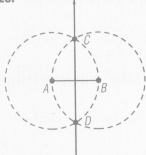
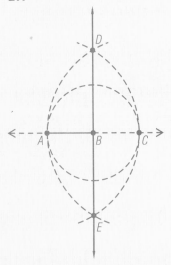
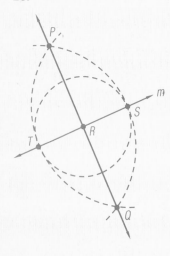
In 17 and 18, use the figure below.

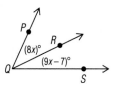

17. If $m\angle PQS = 40$, find x. $x = \frac{47}{17}$

18. If $\overrightarrow{QR}$ is the bisector of $\angle PQS$, find $m\angle PQS$.

19. Lines ℓ and m intersect as in the diagram below. Find y. **16**

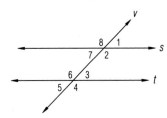

20. An angle has a measure 9 times that of its complement. What is the measure of the angle? **81°**

21. An angle's measure is 42° less than the measure of a supplement to it. What is the measure of the angle? **69°**

22. Let q be the measure of an angle which is less than its supplement. Find all possibilities for q.

23. $\angle 5$ and $\angle 6$ are vertical angles. If $m\angle 5 = 17z$ and $m\angle 6 = 2w$, solve for w in terms of z.

■ **Objective D:** *Determine measures of angles formed by parallel lines and transversals.*
(Lesson 3-4)

In 24 and 25, use the figure below where $s \parallel t$.

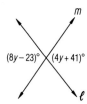

24. If $m\angle 1 = 83$, find the measures of angles 2 through 8.

25. If $m\angle 2 = 3 \cdot m\angle 5$, find $m\angle 2$. **135**

■ **Objective E:** *Perform the following constructions with a straightedge and a compass: perpendicular bisector, $\perp$ from point to line, $\perp$ to line at point.*
(Lesson 3-6)

In 26–30, first trace the figure.

26. Construct the perpendicular bisector of $\overline{AB}$ below.

27. Construct the $\perp$ to $\overleftrightarrow{AB}$ above through B.

28. Construct the perpendicular to line m below through R.

29. Construct the perpendicular to $\overleftrightarrow{AB}$ below from Q.

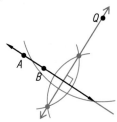

30. Construct the line $\perp$ to $\overline{WV}$ through U.

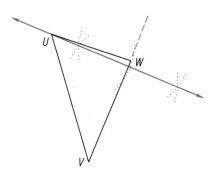

31. a. Follow the algorithm below and perform this construction on any 3 points on a circle of your choosing.

Step 1. $\overleftrightarrow{XY}$

Step 2. Subroutine: $\overleftrightarrow{PQ}$, the ⊥ bisector of $\overline{XY}$

Step 3. $\overleftrightarrow{XZ}$

Step 4. Subroutine: $\overleftrightarrow{RS}$ the ⊥ bisector of $\overline{XZ}$

Step 5. $\overleftrightarrow{PQ}$ intersects $\overleftrightarrow{RS}$ at T, the desired point.

b. What is point T? the center of the circle

c. Give the rule justifying steps 1, 3, and 5 in part **a** above.

31. a.
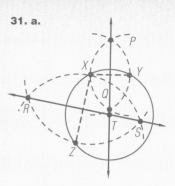

c. Step 1. Straightedge rule
Step 3. Straightedge rule
Step 5. Point rule

37. Linear Pair Theorem

38. Point-Line-Plane Postulate

Properties deal with the principles behind the mathematics.

▨ **Objective F:** *Give justifications for conclusions involving different figures. (Lessons 3-2, 3-3, 3-4, 3-5)*

In 32–34, *multiple choice.* Which statement justifies the conclusion?

32. Given: m∠ABD = m∠DBC in the figure below.
Conclusion: $\overrightarrow{BD}$ bisects ∠ABC.
(a) Angle Addition Property
(b) definition of angle bisector (meaning)
(c) definition of angle bisector (sufficient condition)
(d) Linear Pair Theorem **(c)**

33. Given: A is on a circle with radius 5 and center C.
Conclusion: $AC = 5$. **(a)**
(a) definition of a circle (meaning)
(b) definition of a circle (sufficient condition)
(c) definition of distance (meaning)
(d) definition of distance (sufficient condition)

34. Given: ∠3 and ∠5 are vertical angles.
Conclusion: m∠3 = m∠5.
(a) definition of acute angle (meaning)
(b) definition of acute angle (sufficient condition)
(c) Linear Pair Theorem
(d) Vertical Angle Theorem **(d)**

In 35 and 36, *multiple choice.* Choose the correct justification from this list.
(a) If ℓ ∥ m and m ⊥ n, then ℓ ⊥ n.
(b) If ℓ ⊥ m and m ⊥ n, then ℓ ∥ n.
(c) If ℓ ∥ m and m ∥ n, then ℓ ∥ n.

35. Given: $\overline{MJ}$ ⊥ $\overline{JK}$
$\overline{MJ}$ ∥ $\overline{KL}$.
Conclusion: $\overline{KL}$ ⊥ $\overline{JK}$. **(a)**

36. Given: $\overline{MJ}$ ⊥ $\overline{JK}$
$\overline{KL}$ ⊥ $\overline{JK}$.
Conclusion: $\overline{JM}$ ∥ $\overline{KL}$. **(b)**

In 37–39, justify the conclusion.

37. Given: ∠4 and ∠5 are a linear pair.
Conclusion: m∠4 + m∠5 = 180.

38. Given: A and B are distinct points.
Conclusion: There is only one line containing A and B.

39. Given: the figure below.
Conclusion: m∠EFG + m∠GFH = m∠EFH. **Angle Addition Property**

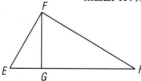

USES deal with applications of mathematics in real situations.

■ **Objective G:** *Apply angle measure to describe real situations. (Lessons 3-1, 3-2)*

40. The latitude of a point *P* on Earth is often described as the measure of the angle *PCE*, where *C* is the center of the earth and *E* is the point on the equator directly north or south of *P*. On a diagram like the one below, draw a point *Q* at 35° latitude.

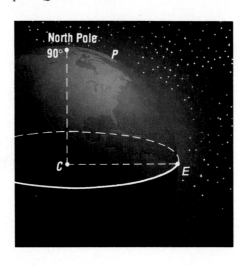

In 41 and 42, trace the diagram at the right.

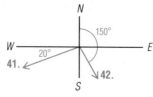

41. Draw a ray going in the direction 20° S of W.

42. A plane is taking off to go 30° E of S. How much would it have to turn to fly due north?

43. A nail is being driven into a wall to hang a picture. If the measure of the smaller angle is 45°, what is the measure of the larger angle? **135°**

■ **Objective H:** *Apply constructions and drawings i real situations. (Lesson 3-6)*

44. Some girls are having a race to the river. Trace the river's edge and the starting point and *draw* the shortest path to run.

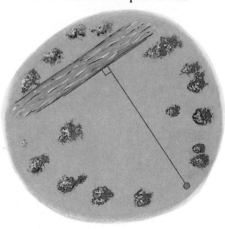

45. A scale drawing of a football field is being made. Many lines perpendicular to $\overleftrightarrow{AB}$ are needed. Trace $\overleftrightarrow{AB}$ and construct the ⊥ to $\overleftrightarrow{AB}$ through *C*.

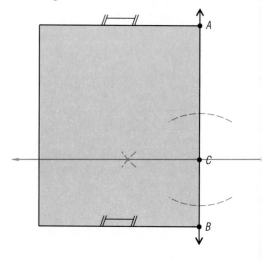

REPRESENTATIONS deal with pictures, graphs, or objects that illustrate concepts.

■ **Objective I:** *Determine the slope of a line from its equation or given two points on it. (Lesson 3-4)*

46. Give the slope of the line through (-5, -2) and (6, 1). $\frac{3}{11}$

47. Give the slope of the line through (4, -3) and (-3, 4). **-1**

In 48 and 49, find the slope of the line with the given equation.

48. $y = -\frac{3}{5}x + 11$ $-\frac{3}{5}$

49. $5x - 3y = 45$ $\frac{5}{3}$

50. Which line below has the greater slope, $2y = x + 1$ or $25y = 5x + 1$? **2y = x + 1**

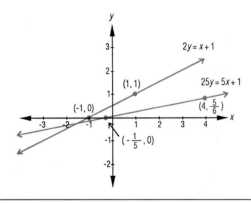

51. Which line has the greater slope, $y = 3x$ or $x = 3y$? **y = 3x**

■ **Objective J:** *Determine the slope of a line parallel or perpendicular to a given line.* *(Lessons 3-4, 3-5)*

52. If a line has slope 10, each line parallel to it has slope __?__ and each line perpendicular to it has slope __?__. **10, $-\frac{1}{10}$**

53. If a line has slope $-\frac{2}{3}$, each line parallel to it has slope __?__ and each line perpendicular to it has slope __?__. **$-\frac{2}{3}, \frac{3}{2}$**

54. Line m goes through points (8, -1) and (-6, -3). If line n is perpendicular to m, what is the slope of n? **-7**

55. *Multiple choice.* The lines with equations $y = 2x + 1$ and $y = -2x + 1$ are
(a) parallel;
(b) perpendicular;
(c) neither parallel nor perpendicular. **(c)**

EVALUATION
Three forms of a Chapter Test are provided in the Teacher's Resource File. Chapter 3 Test, Forms A and B cover just Chapter 3. The third test is Chapter 3 Test, Cumulative Form. About 50% of this test covers Chapter 3, 25% covers Chapter 2, and 25% covers Chapter 1. A fourth test, Comprehensive Test, Chapters 1-3, that is primarily multiple choice in format, is also provided. For information on grading, see *General Teaching Sugges-tions: Grading* on page T44 in the Teacher's Edition.

ASSIGNMENT RECOMMENDATION
We strongly recommend that you assign the reading and questions from Lesson 4-1 for homework the evening of the test. It gives students work to do if they complete the test before the end of the period and keeps the class moving.

If you do not give assign-ments on the days of tests, you may cover one less *chapter* over the course of the year.

CHAPTER 4 ■ REFLECTIONS

DAILY PACING CHART ■ CHAPTER 4

Every chapter of UCSMP *Geometry* includes lessons, a Progress Self-Test, and a Chapter Review. For optimal student performance, the self-test and review should be covered. (See *General Teaching Suggestions: Mastery* on page T36 of the Teacher's Edition.) By following the pace of the Full Course given here, students can complete the entire text by the end of the year. Students following the pace of the Minimal Course spend more time when there are quizzes and on the Chapter Review and will generally not complete all of the chapters in this text.

When all lessons are covered from the beginning (the recommendation of the authors), then students in the Minimal Course can cover through Lesson 13-4 and will cover all they need for future courses. For more information on pacing, see *General Teaching Suggestions: Pace* on page T35 of the Teacher's Edition.

DAY	MINIMAL COURSE	FULL COURSE
1	4-1	4-1
2	4-2	4-2
3	4-3	4-3
4	4-4	4-4
5	Quiz (TRF); Start 4-5.	Quiz (TRF); 4-5
6	Finish 4-5.	4-6
7	4-6	4-7
8	4-7	Progress Self-Test
9	Progress Self-Test	Chapter Review
10	Chapter Review	Chapter Test (TRF)
11	Chapter Review	
12	Chapter Test (TRF)	

TESTING OPTIONS

■ Quiz for Lessons 4-1 Through 4-4   ■ Chapter 4 Test, Form A   ■ Chapter 4 Test, Cumulative Form
   ■ Chapter 4 Test, Form B

PROVIDING FOR INDIVIDUAL DIFFERENCES

The student text has been written for, and tested with, average students. It also has been used successfully with better and more poorly prepared students.

The Lesson Notes often include Error Analysis and Alternate Approach features to help you with those students who need more help. A blackline Lesson Master (in the Teacher's Resource File), keyed to the chapter objectives, is provided for each lesson to allow more practice. (However, since it is very important to keep up with the daily pace, you are not expected to use all of these masters. Again, refer to the suggestions for pacing on page T35.) Extension activities are provided in the Lesson Notes for those students who have completed the particular lesson in a shorter amount of time than is expected, even in the Full Course.

OBJECTIVES ■ CHAPTER 4

The objectives listed here are the same as in the Chapter 4 Review on pages 200-203 of the student text. The Progress Self-Test on page 199 and the tests in the Teacher's Resource File cover these objectives. For recommendations regarding the handling of this end-of-chapter material, see the notes in the margin on the corresponding pages of the Teacher's Edition.

OBJECTIVES FOR CHAPTER 4 (Organized into the SPUR Categories—Skills, Properties, Uses, and Representations)	Progress Self-Test Questions	Chapter Review Questions	Lesson Master from Teacher's Resource File*
SKILLS			
A Perform drawings and constructions applying the definition of reflection image.	8, 10	1 through 4	4-1, 4-3
B Draw reflection images of segments, angles, and polygons over a given line.	11	5 through 8	4-2, 4-3, 4-6
C Draw all symmetry lines of segments and angles.	12	9 through 11	4-7
D Determine measures of angles in figures and their reflection images.	7	12 through 13	4-2, 4-6
PROPERTIES			
E Apply properties of reflections to make conclusions, using one or more of the following justifications: definition of reflection Reflections preserve distance. Reflections preserve angle measure. Reflections switch orientation. Figure Reflection Theorem Flip-Flop Theorem Side-Switching Theorem	1-5	14 through 21	4-1, 4-2, 4-6, 4-7
F Apply properties of symmetry to make conclusions about symmetric figures.	6	22 through 28	4-7
G Given appropriate information, write proofs, using theorems, postulates, or definitions you have studied in this book as justifications.	14, 15	29 through 32	4-4, 4-5
USES			
H Locate and make symmetry lines in designs.	13	33 through 36	4-7
REPRESENTATIONS			
I Find coordinates of reflection images of points over the coordinate axes.	9	37 through 40	4-1, 4-2

*The masters are numbered to match the lessons.

154B

OVERVIEW □ CHAPTER 4

Reflections and symmetry are often studied informally before geometry and used in mathematics courses after geometry. The NCTM Standards and other national reports strongly recommend increased attention to these topics. Only tradition keeps this important content from occupying the place it deserves in geometry courses.

This chapter and Chapter 5 demonstrate the power of transformations in describing and developing properties of figures and relationships between figures. In Chapters 6-8, the ideas are applied further. Two decades ago, two of the authors began their use of transformations in geometry and remain convinced that, without these ideas, students are missing an exceedingly powerful instrument for understanding the ideas of congruence and similarity. With the study of transformations, there is evidence (from the 1970 doctoral dissertation of Anthone Kort) of better learning of function ideas and graphing in later mathematics.

The fundamental reason for using transformations is that they enable geometrical ideas, such as congruence, similarity, and symmetry, to apply to all figures. This makes it possible to make the geometry more intuitive, yet have a tool for later study. This *is* Euclidean geometry. In fact, because congruence will be developed for all figures (Chapter 6), and because no triangle congruence theorem is assumed as a postulate, this development is closer to Euclid's original way of thinking than the present day approaches that assume one or more of the triangle congruence theorems.

Lessons 4-1 and 4-2 provide the basics of reflections: how to find images and how figures and their images compare. Lesson 4-3 shows how recent computer software can draw figures. Lesson 4-4 continues the slow introduction to proof in the context of the construction of an equilateral triangle. Lessons 4-5 through 4-7 apply the ideas of the earlier lessons to deduce properties of reflection-symmetric figures.

If you have never taught transformations, your first and natural reaction will be that this material is more difficult. You may be surprised at the ease students have with these ideas.

PERSPECTIVES □ CHAPTER 4

The Perspectives provide the rationale for the inclusion of topics or approaches, provide mathematical background, and make connections with other lessons and within UCSMP.

4-1

REFLECTING POINTS

The most important reason for discussing transformations is that they apply to all figures, not merely those that are made up of segments and arcs. Any figure in the plane can be reflected, from a single point to a complicated figure like the dog pictured on page 156.

This lesson gives two ways to locate reflection images of points: using a protractor and drawing, and constructing. It also introduces the r( ) notation for reflections, the customary function notation used worldwide.

4-2

REFLECTING FIGURES

Since figures are infinite sets of points, there must be shortcuts to reflect them. The Reflection Postulate and Figure Reflection Theorem introduced in this lesson provide the means for the shortcuts and at the same time give all the background needed for later work with congruence.

That reflections preserve distance is equivalent to the SAS proposition assumed by Hilbert and assumed in most geometry books today. The preservation of all these properties is equivalent to the fourth common notion of Euclid, that things which coincide with one another are equal. Euclid allowed himself the (unstated) privilege of picking up figures and moving them without changing their size or shape. Transformations provide the modern rigorous equivalent.

Related to the Figure Reflection Theorem is the idea of the number of points which determine a figure.

4-3

USING AN AUTOMATIC DRAWER

Just as there exists computer software which graphs functions rather easily, there now exists software which enables the user to obtain many of the kinds of figures which are customarily constructed, such as perpendicular bisectors, angle bisectors, reflection images, congruent copies of segments, angles, triangles, and so on. Some of this software allows the student user to explore by enabling him/her to repeat a "computer construction" with a different figure of the same type as the original. Although this book does not require the use of such drawers, we feel that the learning of geometry is enhanced by their use.

4-4

THE FIRST THEOREM IN EUCLID'S *ELEMENTS*

This lesson continues to build the student's sense of the need and the form of proof. The approach is gradual: Lesson 1-6 discussed the need for undefined terms. Lesson 2-1 developed the need for definitions, and Lesson 2-2 developed a precision of language with if-then statements. Lesson 3-3 gave justifications for conclusions. Here, the need for proof is presented with a historical first: Euclid's first theorem. Not only is it visually appealing, but its logic is clear, and its historical significance can help to motivate students' acceptance of proof.

The first theorem in Euclid's *Elements* is a proof that a particular construction of an equilateral triangle works, namely, that it gives an equilateral triangle. The key justifications in the proof are the definition of a circle and the Transitive Property of Equality. The proofs in this lesson all make use of the Transitive Property.

In this lesson, we also explicitly mention what can be assumed from a figure.

4-5

THE PERPENDICULAR BISECTOR THEOREM

In this lesson, the preservation of distance property of a reflection is applied to prove that if a point is on the perpendicular bisector of a segment, then it is equidistant from the endpoints of the segment. This takes only three steps, and two of those steps are merely using the definition of reflection. So, it is an appropriate second multistep proof.

Next, the Perpendicular Bisector Theorem itself is applied (in a paragraph proof in the middle of page 184) to show how to construct a circle through three noncollinear points.

4-6

REFLECTING POLYGONS

Only one basic property of reflections has not been discussed before this lesson: reflections switch orientation. To discuss this idea, notation is needed because the order of vertices is important.

The idea of orientation does not even arise with segments, angles, lines, or rays, because each of these figures is reflection-symmetric. Only with a figure as complicated as a triangle can images look reversed. And, of course, looking reversed is a fundamental property of mirror images.

It's hard to realize that a figure does not have an orientation except if you identify points on it. Even a clock hand that is turning clockwise looks like it is turning counterclockwise if it is seen from the back. When you explain clockwise and counterclockwise to a class, you must look in the same direction as the students. If you face them when you turn your hand clockwise, they will see a hand turning counterclockwise.

Because of the difficulty of assessing orientation when a polygon is not convex, the best rule is "if you walk around the polygon and its interior is on your right, then the orientation is clockwise." This idea works for all polygons.

4-7

REFLECTION-SYMMETRIC FIGURES

Symmetry is a geometric idea. Many students first formally encounter symmetry while studying graphs of parabolas. They then associate symmetry with horizontal and vertical lines and coordinates and do not realize the intimate connection with reflections.

For every transformation, symmetry with respect to the transformation can be defined. There is reflection symmetry, rotation symmetry, and translation symmetry, and mathematicians (both pure and applied) recognize other kinds of symmetry as well. Whenever something is preserved under a transformation, there is symmetry.

In this lesson, the simplest figures are found to be symmetric, the angle with its one symmetry line and the segment with its two symmetry lines. In Chapter 5, the symmetry of isosceles triangles will be used to deduce properties of those triangles and of kites.

154D

CHAPTER 4

Reflections

4-1: Reflecting Points

4-2: Reflecting Figures

4-3: Using an Automatic Drawer

4-4: The First Theorem in Euclid's *Elements*

4-5: The Perpendicular Bisector Theorem

4-6: Reflecting Polygons

4-7: Reflection-Symmetric Figures

154

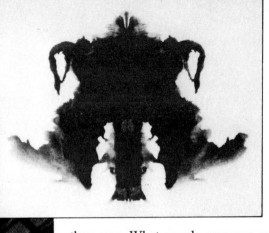

Hermann Rorschach, a Swiss psychiatrist born in 1884, invented a technique for investigating the inner workings of the human mind. He presented ink blots to people and asked them to describe what images they saw. What people saw was supposed to indicate how they thought of themselves and the world in which they lived.

Rorschach ink blots are reflection-symmetric figures like the one shown above.

Reflection-symmetric figures are common in the world of business also. Many companies have logos or trademarks that are reflection-symmetric. Can you name the company associated with the trademark at the right?

Many living creatures have reflection-symmetric shapes. Examples include starfish, manta rays, the leaves and fruits of many trees, beetles, and butterflies. Stars, orbits of planets, sound waves, and crystals are also reflection-symmetric. Because geometry studies these and other real things, many important shapes in geometry are reflection-symmetric. You will examine some of these shapes and their properties in this chapter.

USING PAGES 154-155
Newspapers and books are often printed from plates. The images on these plates are reversed from the original; they are what you see when you hold a piece of paper to the light and you look through the back side. The transformation that helps to explain that reversal is the reflection.

The Rorshach diagram shows a reflection-symmetric figure. Generally, one thinks of either side of the figure as a preimage and the other side as its reflection image. Students may not know what ink blots are; they have probably never used fountain pens. They are more familiar with paint splotches.

The logo is that of the Chrysler Corporation. The starfish has similar symmetry. Of course, animals do not possess as perfect symmetry as manufactured designs, but some are remarkably close.

You might ask students for examples of objects that have symmetry. This will simultaneously stimulate discussion and help you determine what they know about the idea.

OBJECTIVES

A Perform drawings and constructions applying the definition of reflection image.

E Apply properties of reflections to make conclusions, using the following justification: definition of reflection.

I Find coordinates of reflection images of points over the coordinate axes.

TEACHING NOTES

Students should be able to find reflection images by folding figures over the line, by drawing using a ruler and/or protractor, and by construction. Which method to use depends on the question. If the figure is complicated, as in **Question 2,** folding is the desired method. If there are only a couple of points to be reflected, then either drawing or construction may be used. You should expect students to be able to construct a reflection image, but you should not expect them to construct all images. For anything more than a single point, drawing is more realistic and more intuitive.

Some people use the word "reflection" to refer to the image. We think this use confuses the transformation with its image. We always use the phrase "reflection image," because later there will be other kinds of images.

LESSON

4-1

Reflecting Points

The inkblot on the first page of this chapter is an example of a figure and its *reflection image*. It provides still another application of perpendicular lines. Examine the figure below. Think of the picture at the left as the original. It is called the **preimage.** The *reflection image* at the right can be drawn by folding over the line *m* and then tracing. Line *m* is called the **reflecting line** or **line of reflection.**

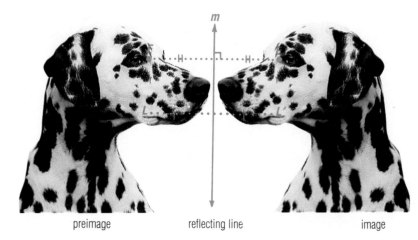

preimage   reflecting line   image

The apostrophe (') indicates corresponding points; *E'* (read "*E* prime") corresponds to *E*. Line *m* is the perpendicular bisector of the segments connecting the corresponding eyes *E* and *E'* and the corners of the lips *L* and *L'*.

156

Definition:

For a point P not on a line m, the **reflection image of P over line m** is the point Q if and only if m is the perpendicular bisector of $\overline{PQ}$.

For a point P on m, the **reflection image of P over line m** is P itself.

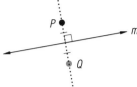

P is not on m.
Q is the reflection image of P.

P is on m.
P is its own reflection image.

In the figures above, let P' be the image of P. Then, at the left, $Q = P'$. At the right, $P = P'$.

Recall that drawing is different than constructing. For *drawing* reflection images of complicated figures, folding and tracing is a good procedure. So is putting a mirror on the reflecting line and sighting the image behind the mirror. For individual points, a quick way of drawing utilizes a protractor.

■ ■ ■ ■ ■ ■ ■

Example 1   Draw the reflection image P' of point P over line m.

Solution   Here is an algorithm.
1. Place your protractor so that its 90° mark and the center of the protractor are on m.
2. Slide the protractor along m so that the edge line (the line through the 0° and 180° marks) goes through P.
3. Measure the distance d from P to m along the edge line. You may wish to draw the line lightly.
4. Locate P' on the other side of m along the edge, the same distance from P.

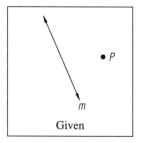

Given

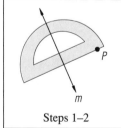

Steps 1–2

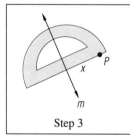

Step 3

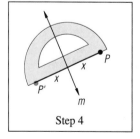

Step 4

Reflection images can also be constructed following the rules for constructions, as shown on the next page.

Do not give students the false impression that reflecting lines must be horizontal or vertical. It is a by-product of thinking of perpendicular lines as horizontal and vertical. Be careful to point out to students that *any* line can be a reflecting line. The figures on page 157 are designed to show that any line can be the reflecting line.

Reading   As students are reading this lesson, make sure they can distinguish the following terminology:
the *preimage* (what you start with);
the *image* (what you end up with);
the *reflection* (the correspondence between preimage and image, described by the rule given in its definition);
reflecting (finding a reflection image).

Students also should pay careful attention to the notation, because it is used throughout the remainder of this book. The notation is standard function notation for transformations. Students generally find the symbols $r(A)$ and $r_m(A)$ easy to understand because the letters indicate what transformation the symbol represents. In contrast, the symbol $f(x)$ is more abstract.

Making Connections
Students who have studied UCSMP *Transition Mathematics* are familiar with the definition of *reflection image over the line m* and have studied the relationship between a preimage, a reflecting line, and the reflection image.

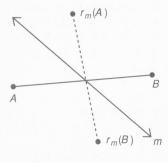
Example 2 Construct the reflection image of point *B* over line *m*.

Solution Shown are steps in the algorithm of the construction.
Step 1. Identify a point on *m*. Call it *Q*. (Point rule)
Step 2. ⊙*B* containing *Q* (Compass rule)
Step 3. ⊙*B* intersects *m* in *Q* and *S*. (Point rule)
Step 4. ⊙*Q* containing *B* (Compass rule)
Step 5. ⊙*S* containing *B* (Why?)
Step 6. ⊙*Q* intersects ⊙*S* in *B* and *B'*. (Point rule)

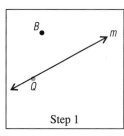
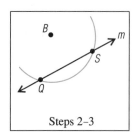
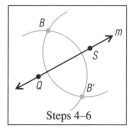

| Step 1 | Steps 2–3 | Steps 4–6 |

Connecting *B* and *B'* yields a bonus, the ⊥ to *m* through *B*.

You can use abbreviations instead of writing statements like "*P* is the reflection image of *R* over line *m*" and "*A'* is the reflection of *A*." Use the lower case letter r to refer to a reflection. When discussing reflections in general, or when the reflecting line is obvious, you can write

$$r(A) = A'$$

for "The reflection image of *A* is *A'*." It is read "r of *A* equals *A'*." When you want to emphasize the reflecting line *m*, write

$$r_m(Q) = P$$

for "The reflection image of *Q* over line *m* is *P*." It is read "r of *Q* over line *m* equals *P*."

Example 3 The reflection image of *A* over line *m* is *B*. Name *B* in two ways using reflection notation.

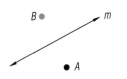

Solution You can write $B = r(A)$ since the reflecting line is obvious. Or specify the line: $B = r_m(A)$.

Reflecting images are often needed for points in the coordinate plane. If the reflecting line is one of the axes, the image is found using the definition of reflection.

158

Example 4 Find the image of (2, 5) when reflected over the *x*-axis.

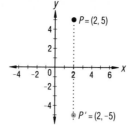

Solution Draw a coordinate plane and let $P = (2, 5)$. Since P is 5 units from the *x*-axis, its image will be 5 units away on the other side. So $P' = (2, -5)$.

In Example 4, $P' = r_x(P)$. So you could write $r_x(P) = (2, -5)$ or $r_x(2, 5) = (2, -5)$.

Questions

1. A figure that is to be reflected is called the __?__ . **preimage**

2. Trace the figure below onto your paper. Then find its reflection image over line *m* by folding and tracing.

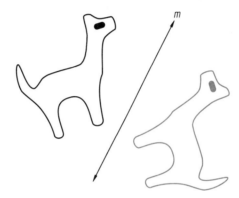

3. Suppose *B* is the reflection image of *A* over line *m*. How are *m*, *A*, and *B* related? *m* **is the perpendicular bisector of** $\overline{AB}$.

4. When a point *P* is on the reflecting line ℓ, then the reflection image of *P* is __?__ . **P**

5. Trace the drawing at the left.
   a. *Draw* the reflection image of *Q* over line ℓ. **See drawing.**
   b. *Construct* the reflection image of *P* over line ℓ. **See margin.**

6. What is the justification for Step 5 in Example 2? **Compass rule**

7. What letter is used to denote a reflection? **r**

8. If *P* is a point, write in words:
   a. $r(P)$ **b.** $r_m(P)$.
   the reflection image of *P*   **the reflection image of *P* over line *m***

LESSON 4-1 Reflecting Points   **159**

---

2. In the diagram below, *k* is the perpendicular bisector of $\overline{AB}$ and $\overline{DC}$. Name r(*A*), r(*C*), and r(*E*).

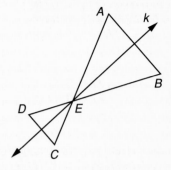

B, D, E

3. What is the reflection image of (2, 7) over the *y*-axis? **(-2, 7)**

NOTES ON QUESTIONS
Question 2: We use a complicated figure for two reasons. First, it forces students to fold rather than to draw or construct images of individual points. Second, complicated figures convey the intuition of reflections more than single points do. Ask students: Does it look like you are seeing the right or left eye of the preimage animal? (right) What eye seems to be visible on the image? (left) Advise students to check the accuracy of their images by seeing whether *m* is the perpendicular bisector of a segment connecting a preimage and image point.

Question 3: Direct students to use the definition, for they often do not think of the *segment AB*.

ADDITIONAL ANSWERS
5. b.

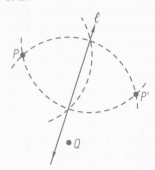

In 9 and 10, trace the drawing, then draw or construct the reflection
images of the points over line *m*.

9.

10.

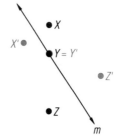

11. In the figure at the right,
give the coordinates of:
a. $r_x(P)$; (3, -5)
b. $r_y(P)$. (-3, 5)

12. Find the image of (-4,1)
when reflected over
a. the *x*-axis; (-4, -1)
b. the *y*-axis. (4, 1)

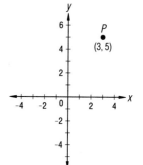

13. Find the image of (*c, d*) when reflected over **a.** the *x*-axis;
b. the *y*-axis a) (*c, -d*); b) (*-c, d*)

14. a. *B*, *C*, and *D* are three reflection images of point *A*. Match each
image with the correct reflecting line. *B* and *ℓ*, *C* and *m*, *D* and *n*

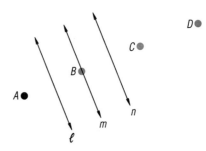

b. Name each image of *A* using reflection notation.
$r_ℓ(A) = B$; $r_m(A) = C$; $r_n(A) = D$

160

15. Below, $r_\ell(P) = T$. Construct ℓ. **See margin.**

• T

• P

16. Trace the figures below. Find the line so that one of the figures is the reflection image of the other.

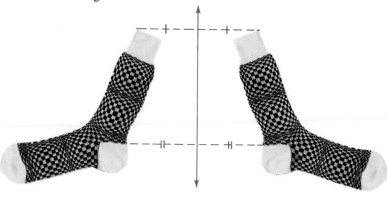

17. a. Decipher the message below.
b. Which letter is written incorrectly?
a) HELP! I'M TRAPPED INSIDE THIS PAGE! b) N

ᕼᗴᒪᑭ! I'M Tᖇᗩᑭᑭᗴᗪ
IᑎᔕIᗪᗴ TᕼIᔕ ᑭᗩGᗴ!

Review

In 18 and 19, trace the figure below.

• A

18. Construct the perpendicular to $\overleftrightarrow{BC}$ through point A. *(Lesson 3-6)*
See margin.
19. Construct the ⊥ bisector of $\overline{BC}$. *(Lesson 3-6)* **See margin.**

LESSON 4-1   Reflecting Points   **161**

18.

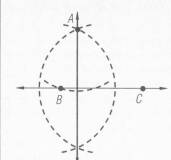

19.

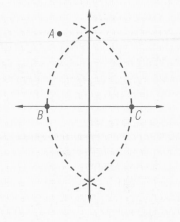

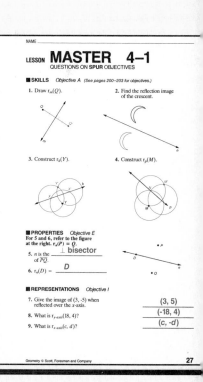

NAME _____

LESSON **MASTER   4-1**
QUESTIONS ON **SPUR** OBJECTIVES

■**SKILLS**   *Objective A (See pages 200–203 for objectives.)*

1. Draw $r_m(Q)$.

2. Find the reflection image of the crescent.

3. Construct $r_k(Y)$.

4. Construct $r_p(M)$.

■**PROPERTIES**   *Objective E*
For 5 and 6, refer to the figure
at the right. $r_n(P) = Q$.

5. n is the ____⊥ bisector____
of $\overline{PQ}$.

6. $r_n(D) =$ ____D____

■**REPRESENTATIONS**   *Objective I*

7. Give the image of (3, -5) when
reflected over the *x*-axis.   (3, 5)

8. What is $r_{y\text{-axis}}(18, 4)$?   (-18, 4)

9. What is $r_{x\text{-axis}}(c, d)$?   (c, -d)

Geometry © Scott, Foresman and Company   **27**

20. Use the coordinate plane below.
   a. Is $\ell \parallel m$? Justify your answer.
   b. Is $\ell \perp n$? Justify your answer. *(Lessons 3-5, 3-4)* **See margin.**

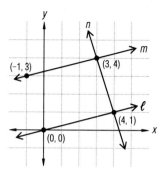

21. *Multiple choice.* The lines with equations $x + 2y = 6$ and $2x - y = 8$ are
   (a) parallel
   (b) perpendicular
   (c) neither parallel nor perpendicular. *(Lessons 3-5, 3-4)* **(b)**

22. Use the figure at the left. E is on $\overline{VG}$. *(Lessons 3-3, 3-2)*
   Given: $m\angle G = 30$, $m\angle GEO = 150$. Justify each conclusion.
   a. $m\angle VEO = 30$ **Linear Pair Theorem**
   b. $\overline{EO} \parallel \overline{GL}$ **corr. $\angle$s = $\Rightarrow \parallel$ lines**

23. In the figure below, $a \parallel b$. Find x. *(Lesson 3-4)* **25**

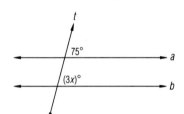

24. Draw three possible pictures of the antecedent in this sentence. (Make your pictures look different from each other.) Then write in as many consequents as you think are true. **See below.**

   If $r_\ell(A) = B$ and $r_\ell(C) = D$, then __?__ .

24.
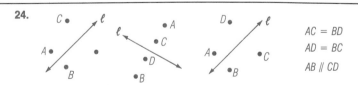

$AC = BD$
$AD = BC$
$AB \parallel CD$

Power-generating windmills reflected in a pond

LESSON 4-2

RESOURCES
■ Lesson Master 4-2
▯ Visual for Teaching Aid 20 displays the drawings for **Questions 8-11.**
▯ Visual for Teaching Aid 21 displays the drawings for **Questions 16** and **21-23.**
▯ Computer Master 5

In Lesson 4-1 each point in the image dog corresponds to a single point in the preimage dog. The reflection image of the dog is the set of all the individual image points. This is why tracing works. In general, the **reflection image of a figure** is the set of all the reflection images of points in the figure.

Below is $\angle AEH$ and its image, $\angle A'E'H'$. Individual points of $\angle AEH$ are black and their reflection images are shown in blue.

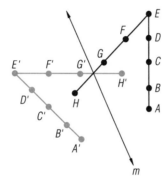

Several striking features of this figure are evident. Look at the *collinear* points E, D, and C. Their images E', D', and C' are also collinear. Also, D is *between* E and C, and its image, D', is between the images of E and C. This observation is true also for F, G, and H. Is it true for E, G, and A?

Look at $\overline{EA}$ and $\overline{E'A'}$. The unique *distance EA* is the same as the distance $E'A'$. Also, the measure of $\angle AEH$ is equal to the measure of its image angle, $\angle A'E'H'$. (You could measure the segments and angles to verify this.)

Each of these observations notes a property of the preimage that is also a property of the image. We say the property is **preserved** by reflections.

LESSON 4-2 Reflecting Figures **163**

measure (part **e**), B for betweenness (part **c**), C for collinearity (part **b**), and D for
distance (part **d**). Of course,
that the first letters of the
things preserved are the first
four letters of the alphabet is
only coincidence. You could
associate part **a** with the letter E: **E**ach point has exactly
one image.

The Figure Reflection Theorem is used often in later lessons. The converse of this
theorem is not true. Notation
affects how reflections are
described. If you say that $\overline{CD}$
is the image of $\overline{AB}$, the order
of vertices is not specified.
However, the notation $r(\overline{AB})$
$= \overline{CD}$ implies $r(A) = C$ and
$r(B) = D$. Note that with rays,
angles, or lines, this idea
does not work because they
can each be named in many
different ways.

We do not often ask students
to locate the reflection image
of an individual point. Students learn more from re-
flecting entire figures. This is
one of the unusual properties
of transformations; to a reasonable extent, the more
complicated the figure, the
easier it is to see what is going on. That is why the first
examples of reflections in this
chapter (on the first page of
the chapter and on the first
page of Lesson 4-1) were not
of segments, angles, or even
triangles.

Give several figures and ask
how many points are necessary to "determine" the figure
(triangle, segment, line, circle, the dogs in Lesson 4-1,
a polygon).

Note that a reflection over a
line transforms *every* point of
the plane, not just the points
of the figures we have used.
It can be compared to the
wind. The wind is not seen,
but is understood by observ-
ing its effect on various objects. Likewise, a reflection is
understood by seeing its
effect, for example, on a
triangle.

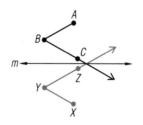

Reflection Postulate:

Under a reflection:

a. There is a 1-1 correspondence between points and their
images.

> This means that each preimage has exactly one image
> and each image comes from exactly one preimage.

b. If three points are collinear, then their images are collinear.

> Reflections preserve collinearity. The image of a line is a
> line.

c. If B is between A and C, then the image of B is between the
images of A and C.

> Reflections preserve betweenness. The image of a line
> segment is a line segment.

d. The distance between two preimages equals the distance
between their images.

> Reflections preserve distance.

e. The image of an angle is an angle of the same measure.

> Reflections preserve angle measure.

The order of the parts in the Reflection Postulate is a logical order.
Points must have images before there can be collinearity. Images
of collinear points must be collinear before betweenness can be
preserved. Betweenness precedes distance and the rays necessary
to have angles. But most people remember the entire postulate in
an alphabetical order, as follows:

Every reflection is a 1-1 correspondence that preserves angle
measure, betweenness, collinearity, and distance.

Since most figures in geometry are infinite sets of points, you cannot
construct their images by reflecting *every* point. Shortcuts are necessary. Suppose you want to reflect $\overline{AB}$ over m at the left. First note that
$\overline{AB}$ is completely determined by the two points A and B. Find the
images of A and B. Call them X and Y, so $r_m(A) = X$ and $r_m(B) = Y$
as shown. Every other point of $\overline{AB}$ is between A and B. Since reflections preserve betweenness, the images must lie between X and Y.
So, draw $\overline{XY}$, and you have the image of $\overline{AB}$. Using reflection notation, write $r_m(\overline{AB}) = \overline{XY}$.

The same idea holds for angles and rays. Angles can be determined
by a vertex and two points, one on each side. So, if $r(A) = X$,
$r(B) = Y$, and $r(C) = Z$, the reflection image of $\angle ABC$ is $\angle XYZ$.
Write $r(\angle ABC) = \angle XYZ$. Also, $r(\overrightarrow{BC}) = \overrightarrow{YZ}$.

Figure Reflection Theorem:

If a figure is determined by certain points, then its reflection image is the corresponding figure determined by the reflection images of those points.

Example 1   Draw the reflection image of △EFG over line m.

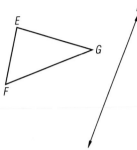

Solution   The three noncollinear points E, F, and G determine △EFG. Locate the images of E, F, and G. r(E) = E', r(F) = F', r(G) = G'. Draw △E'F'G'. r(△EFG) = △E'F'G'.

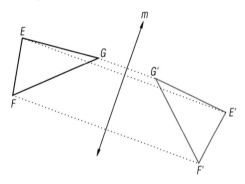

Check   Since reflections preserve distance, the corresponding sides should have the same length. Measuring shows EG = E'G', FG = F'G', and EF = E'F'. Another way of checking is by measuring the angles. Since reflections preserve angle measure, m∠E should equal m∠E', m∠G should equal m∠G', and m∠F should equal m∠F'.

When a figure intersects the reflecting line, the image must intersect the reflecting line in the *same* point or points. In Example 2, the preimage intersects the reflecting line at two points. This makes checking the image easier since the image of a point on the reflecting line is the point itself.

LESSON 4-2   Reflecting Figures   **165**

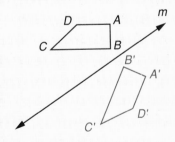

Example 2   Draw the reflection image of $\triangle PAW$ over line m.

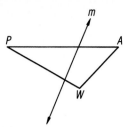

Solution   Find the images of A, P, and W. Connect them.

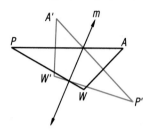

Check $\overline{AP}$ and $\overline{A'P'}$ should intersect m at the same point. So should $\overline{WP}$ and $\overline{W'P'}$

Questions

Covering the Reading

1. Name four properties that reflections preserve.
   collinearity, distance, betweenness, and angle measure
2. Can a point have two different reflection images over the same line?
   No
3. In the figure below, V is between A and Z. If the reflection images of these points are A', V', and Z', what is true?
   V′ will be between A′ and Z′.

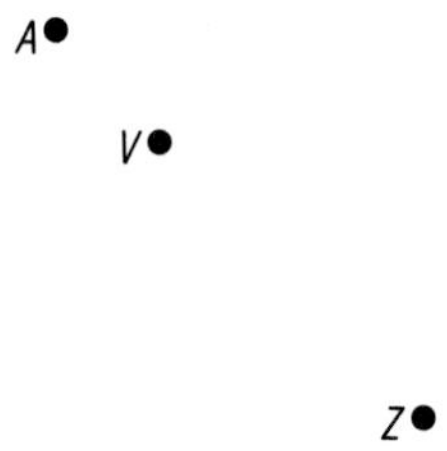

   $A\bullet$

   $V\bullet$

   $Z\bullet$

4. Since reflections preserve distance, if $D = r_\ell(C)$ and $B = r_\ell(A)$, then $AC = \underline{\ ?\ }$. BD

5. $m\angle ABC = 50$, $m\angle DEF = 100$.
   a. Can $\angle DEF$ be a reflection image of $\angle ABC$? No
   b. Why or why not? Reflections preserve angle measures, and these angles have different measures.
6. State the Figure Reflection Theorem. See margin.

7. If $r_m(X) = Z$, $r_m(T) = S$, then $r_m(\overline{XT}) = \underline{\ ?\ }$. $\overline{ZS}$

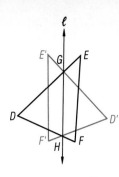

8. Trace the drawing at the left.
  a. Draw $r_\ell(\triangle DEF)$. **See answer on the drawing.**
  b. Check by measuring that the sides of $\triangle DEF$ and its image are of equal lengths. **See margin.**

9. a. In Question 8, which sides of the image $\triangle D'E'F'$ intersect the reflecting line? $\overline{D'E'}$ and $\overline{D'F'}$
  b. Where do they intersect the line? **at G and H**

10. Trace the drawing below.
  a. Draw $r_w(\angle ABC)$. **See below.**
  b. Check that $m\angle ABC = m\angle A'B'C'$ using a protractor.
  b) $m\angle ABC = m\angle A'B'C' \approx 60$

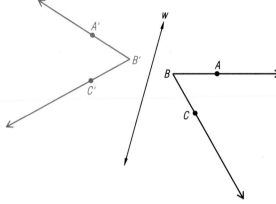

Applying the Mathematics

11. Trace the drawing below. Then reflect the figure over line w.
  See below.

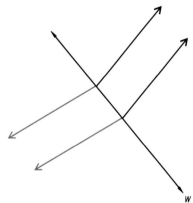

12. a. How many image points are needed to draw the image of pentagon *ABCDE* at the right over line *m*? **5**
  b. If $m\angle ABC = 130$, what is the measure of $\angle A'B'C'$ (its reflection image)? **130°**

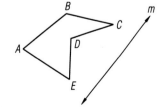

13. How many image points are needed to draw the image of an angle? **3**

LESSON 4-2 Reflecting Figures **167**

Question 11: After going over this question, elicit a conjecture about reflection images of parallel lines. (They are parallel.) Can it be proved? (Yes, parallel lines either do not intersect or are identical. If two lines do not intersect, neither can their images. If two lines are identical, so are their images. Thus, in either case, the images of parallel lines are parallel.)

Making Connections for Question 16: Students who have studied UCSMP *Transition Mathematics* have seen this kind of question but have not had reflection notation.

Questions 21-23: These questions are like those sometimes given to very young students. They tend to be quite easy.

Question 30: This question shows that the image of only one point needs to be given in order to determine the image of a figure. This is because the image of one point determines the reflecting line. By being asked to *construct* the image in this question, the idea is to try to find the image without picking any other arbitrary points on the angle.

ADDITIONAL ANSWERS
8.b. ED = E′D′ ≈ 24 mm;
DF = D′F′ ≈ 17 mm;
EF = E′F′ ≈ 26 mm
(measurements are based on student's edition.)

EXTENSION
An interesting way to demonstrate the notion of 1-1 correspondence is to study the
following *affine* transformation (a transformation that
preserves parallelism). Draw
a square grid on a small flat
piece of elastic. Then draw a
design on the grid like the
one shown below. If the elastic is stretched so that the
line segments of the grid remain parallel, the original design can be transformed into
many different shapes. The
transformations are all 1-1
(but they do not preserve distance).

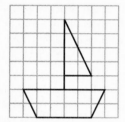

EVALUATION
Alternative Assessment
Oral activities can be used
to summarize and bring closure to the lesson. Have
small groups discuss the
following: (1) what a 1-1
transformation means; (2)
what properties are pre-
served by reflections; and (3)
how the various ways to reflect points are used.

In 14 and 15, what is the fewest number of points that must be reflected before you can draw the image of the entire figure over line *w*?

14. **one**

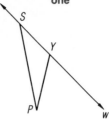

15. $\overline{GH}$ is a diameter of the circle.

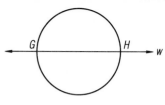

None are needed.

16. Copy the drawing below.
   a. Draw $r_x(\triangle ABC)$. **See below.**
   b. Give the coordinates of the images of the vertices.
   $A' = (-1, -3), B' = (5, -2), C' = (5, 1)$

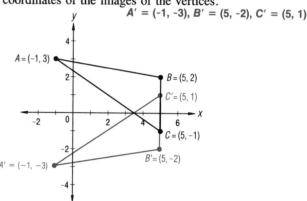

In 17–20, the reflection image of $\triangle MNO$ over line ℓ is $\triangle QRS$.
$r_\ell(M) = Q, r_\ell(N) = R, r_\ell(O) = S$. Choose the correct justification for the conclusion from the choices at the right.

17. $NO = RS$ **(d)**

18. $m\angle NMO = m\angle RQS$ **(a)**

19. $\ell \perp \overline{MQ}$ **(e)**

20. ℓ bisects $\overline{MQ}$. **(e)**

(a) Reflections preserve angle measure.

(b) Reflections preserve betweenness.

(c) Reflections preserve collinearity.

(d) Reflections preserve distance.

(e) definition of reflection image

In 21–23, copy the drawing. Then sketch where the reflecting line *m* should be so that *XYZ* is the reflection image of *ABC* over *m*.

21.

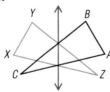

22.

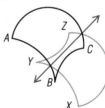

23.

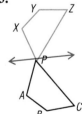

168

Review

In 24 and 25, trace the figure first.

24. Construct the reflecting line *m* for which the reflection image of *B*, at the left below, is *A*. *(Lessons 4-1, 3-6)* **See below.**

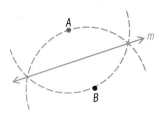
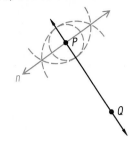

25. Trace the line $\overleftrightarrow{PQ}$ at the right above. Construct the line *n* perpendicular to $\overleftrightarrow{PQ}$ through *P*. *(Lesson 3-6)* **See above.**

26. Write the definition of perpendicular bisector as an if-and-only-if statement. *(Lessons 3-6, 2-5)* **See margin.**

27. If a line has slope -3, each line parallel to it has slope __?__ and each line perpendicular to it has slope __?__. *(Lessons 3-5, 3-4)* $-3, \frac{1}{3}$

28. If $p \Rightarrow q$ is true and *p* is false, what can be concluded? *(Lesson 2-3)* **Nothing more can be concluded.**

29. Write the Transitive Property of Equality. *(Lesson 1-7)* **If $a = b$ and $b = c$, then $a = c$.**

Exploration

30. Trace the drawing. Given that *A'* is the reflection image of *A* over a line *m*, construct the image of ∠1 over line *m*. **See below.**

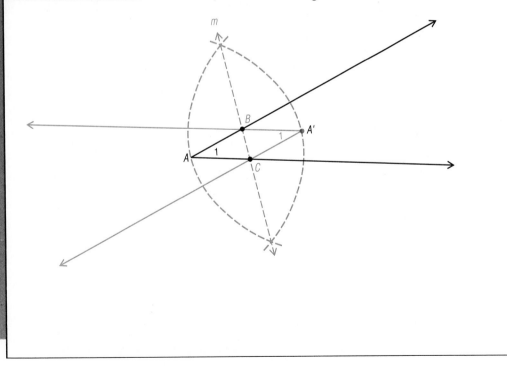

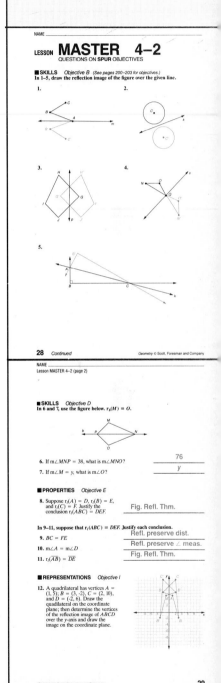
169

RESOURCES
■ Lesson Master 4-3
▣ Computer Master 6

OBJECTIVES

A Perform drawings and constructions applying the definition of reflection image.

B Draw reflection images of segments, angles, and polygons over a given line.

TEACHING NOTES

The term *automatic drawer* includes a variety of computer software which can be used to draw figures without the need to write programs. This would include the *Geometric Supposer,* available for IBM compatibles as well as the Apple II family and Macintosh; *Geodraw,* available only with IBM compatible machines; and Scott, Foresman's software package.

For general advice on using computers with UCSMP *Geometry,* see pages T42-T43 in the Teacher's Edition.

We suggest that this lesson be taught in a computer lab, if possible, and that you work through the examples one by one with students; then allow them to do **Questions 5-11** on their own. If this is impossible, we suggest that you bring a computer into the classroom and demonstrate the Examples. Then have the students simulate doing Questions 5-11.

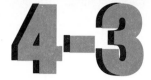

LESSON 4-3

Using an Automatic Drawer

Drawing or constructing figures can be time-consuming and difficult. If you do not have a good compass, your circles may start in one place and end in another. Pencil lines have thickness and if a ruler slips just a little, the entire drawing may be off.

Computers have changed the way many people draw. Nowadays, many of the Saturday morning television cartoons are drawn with the aid of a computer. Many commercials on TV use computer graphics. Manufacturers use computer drawings to help design new products.

Because a construction can be described by an algorithm, constructions are quite suited to computers. We call any computer software that enables figures to be constructed an **automatic drawing tool** or **automatic drawer.** Most automatic drawers enable you to construct, draw, or measure segments, angles, polygons, and circles of various sizes.

The area in which an automatic drawer can draw is called the **window.** Above the window is a **menu** bar of instructions and options. Below is pictured a screen from one such piece of software.

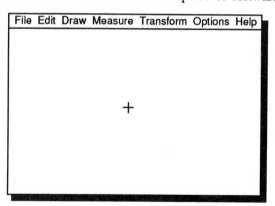

170

Example 1 Use an automatic drawer to create a picture of two parallel lines and a transversal.

Solution On many drawers, you can proceed as follows:
1. Choose two points. (Many automatic drawers label points in alphabetical order, so call them *A* and *B*.)
2. Draw the line through *A* and *B*.
3. Choose a third point not on $\overleftrightarrow{AB}$. (Call it *C*.)
4. Draw a line through *C* parallel to $\overleftrightarrow{AB}$.
5. Draw $\overleftrightarrow{AC}$.

Below we show how the window might look after each of the steps above.

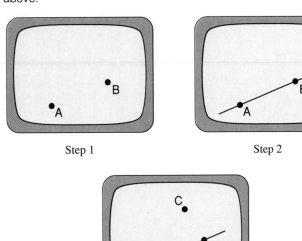

Step 1   Step 2

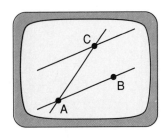

Step 3

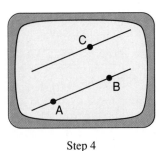

Step 4   Step 5

Most automatic drawers can draw reflection images. However, because the points are limited to the positions of the pixels on the computer screen, the images may not be drawn exactly. For instance, there might not be a pixel in the exact spot for a reflection image of a point over a given line. Still, the computer drawing will be very close.

LESSON 4-3 Using an Automatic Drawer **171**

3. Verify, using the image drawn in Additional Example 2, that reflections preserve distance.

Sample: Instruct the drawer to give the lengths of $\overline{AB}$, $\overline{AC}$, $\overline{BC}$, and their images $\overline{A'B'}$, $\overline{A'C'}$, $\overline{B'C'}$. Pairs of equal lengths should appear.

NOTES ON QUESTIONS

Questions 5-11: Involve automatic drawers with these questions. If students do not have access to computers with such software, they should simulate what they think the computer will do.

Making Connections for Questions 8-11: These questions preview Chapter 5 and should not be skipped. **Question 8** previews the proof of the Triangle-Sum Theorem to be found in Lesson 5-7. **Question 9** previews the theorem that if two lines are parallel, then alternate interior angles have the same measure. This theorem is given in Lesson 5-6. **Question 10** previews the Quadrilateral Sum Theorem in Lesson 5-7. **Question 11** shows how reflection preservation properties can help to deduce that lengths have the same measure and that angles have the same measure. This idea will be employed in Chapter 5 to deduce some of the properties of reflection-symmetric polygons.

Question 18: Encourage students to sketch the angles before trying to match them to the algebraic descriptions.

Question 22: Students who can do these questions will want to make more complicated designs. Encourage their creativity!

Example 2 Use an automatic drawer to draw the reflection image of a triangle over one of its sides.

Solution You can usually proceed as follows:
1. Draw a triangle, or choose three points and instruct the drawer to draw the segments connecting them. Call it △ABC.
2. Choose a side, say $\overline{AC}$, and instruct the drawer to reflect B, the vertex not on $\overline{AC}$, over that side.
3. Connect the images of the vertex points.

Depending on your choice of positions of the three points and line, you might have pictures that look like the following.

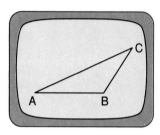 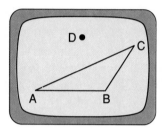 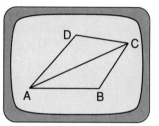

Because most automatic drawers allow you to measure segments and angles, they can be used to verify postulates or theorems.

Example 3 Use the drawing of Example 2 to verify that reflections preserve angle measure.

Solution Ask the automatic drawer to give you the measure of angle *BAC*. Then ask it for the measure of angle *DAC*. These should be equal. Do the same for the other corresponding angles, recording the measures. You should get three pairs of equal measures. Sample output from one automatic drawer is shown below.

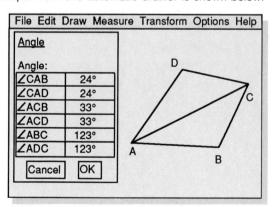

172

The freedom to choose the position of points and lines and the ease of erasing parts of drawings make automatic drawers a simple tool to use. They are particularly helpful for making complicated drawings, and for exploring. Below are two designs. The one on the left was made from reflecting $\triangle ABC$ from Example 2 over side $\overline{AB}$; the one on the right was made by reflecting the figure on the left over line $\overleftrightarrow{CD}$. The reflection can be done even though the line $\overleftrightarrow{CD}$ is not displayed.

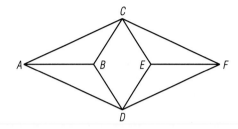

If your automatic drawer is connected to a printer, you may be able to get it to print out the drawings you create. This is called **hard copy.** Otherwise you should copy the drawings you get onto a sheet of paper.

Questions

Covering the Reading

1. What is an automatic drawer? any computer software that enables figures to be constructed

2. Why do many people like to use automatic drawers? See margin.

In 3 and 4, refer to Examples 2 and 3.

3. a. Measure $\overline{AB}$, $\overline{BC}$, $\overline{AD}$, and $\overline{DC}$ using a ruler. See margin.
   b. What part of the Reflection Postulate have you verified?
   Reflections preserve distance.

4. a. Trace $\triangle ABC$, and reflect it over $\overline{BC}$. Let $r_{\overline{BC}}(A) = D$.
   b. Draw $r_{\overline{DC}}(ABDC)$.
   See margin.

In 5–7, use your automatic drawer to draw a figure like the one at the left in which $D = r_{\overleftrightarrow{AB}}(C)$ and $E = r_{\overleftrightarrow{AB}}(F)$.

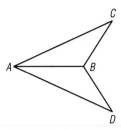

5. a. Measure $\overline{DE}$ and $\overline{CF}$. How do their lengths compare?
   b. Which part of the Reflection Postulate have you verified?
   a) They are equal. b) Reflections preserve distance.

6. a. Measure $\overline{AF}$ and $\overline{AE}$. How do their lengths compare?
   b. Which part of the Reflection Postulate have you verified?
   a) They are equal. b) Reflections preserve distance.

7. a. Measure $\angle EDB$ and $\angle FCB$. How do they compare?
   b. Which part of the Reflection Postulate have you verified?
   a) They are equal. b) Reflections preserve angle measure.

LESSON 4-3 Using an Automatic Drawer **173**

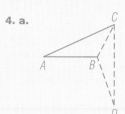
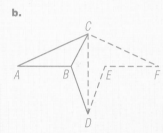
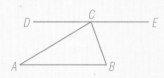
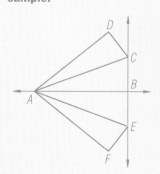
173

MORE PRACTICE
For more questions on SPUR
Objectives, use *Lesson Mas-
ter 4-3,* shown on page 175.

EXTENSION
Have students use an automatic drawer to draw the various types of polygons,
convex and nonconvex,
which they studied in Lesson
2-1 and 2-7. Also, have students use the drawer to perform steps of constructions.

ADDITIONAL ANSWERS
8., 11. a.-d. See the margin
on p. 173.

11.e. samples: m∠DAC =
m∠CAB = m∠BAE =
m∠FAE;
m∠ADC = m∠ABC =
m∠ABE = m∠AFE;
m∠DCA = m∠BCA =
m∠BEA = m∠FEA

14.

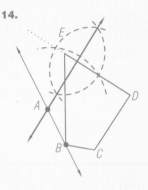

16. The slope of $\overleftrightarrow{PQ}$ is $-\frac{3}{2}$.
The slope of $\overleftrightarrow{QR}$ is $\frac{2}{3}$. Since
$\left(\frac{-3}{2}\right)\left(\frac{2}{3}\right) = -1$, the lines are
perpendicular by the
Perpendicular Lines and
Slopes Theorem. Thus, $\overleftrightarrow{PQ}$
⊥ $\overleftrightarrow{QR}$ and ∠PQR is a right
angle.

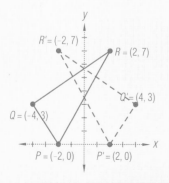

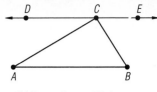

8. Use an automatic drawer to draw
a figure like the one at the right.
   a. Draw a triangle *ABC*. See margin.
   b. Draw a line $\overleftrightarrow{DE}$ through *C*
   parallel to $\overline{AB}$, with *C* between *D*
   and *E*. See margin.
   c. Find m∠DCA, m∠ACB, m∠BCE, m∠CAB, and m∠CBA.
   d. Name two pairs of angles in your figure that have equal measures.
   c) Answers may vary. d) m∠DCA = m∠CAB, m∠ECB = m∠ABC

In 9 and 10, use your automatic drawer to draw $\overleftrightarrow{AB} \parallel \overleftrightarrow{DC}$ and $\overleftrightarrow{AD} \parallel \overleftrightarrow{BC}$.
If possible, label angles 1 to 8 on the screen, as shown at the left.

9. a. Find the measure of each of angles 1 to 8. Answers may vary.
   b. Name all pairs among ∠1 to ∠8 that are corresponding
   angles. ∠1 and ∠3, ∠2 and ∠4, ∠8 and ∠6, ∠7 and ∠5
   c. What postulate do your responses to **a** and **b** verify?
   ∥ lines ⇒ corr. ∠s = (Parallel Lines Postulate)

10. a. Find m∠2 + m∠3 + m∠6 + m∠7. 360
   b. Compare your answer to part **a** to another student's answer. What
   might be true about m∠2 + m∠3 + m∠6 + m∠7 for any set of
   lines where $\overline{AB} \parallel \overline{DC}$ and $\overline{AD} \parallel \overline{BC}$? The sum is 360.

11. Use an automatic drawer. See margin.
   a. Draw line $\overleftrightarrow{AB}$. Draw a line through *B* perpendicular to $\overleftrightarrow{AB}$. Pick a
   point *C* on this perpendicular and draw $\overline{AC}$. You should see a right
   triangle (a triangle with one right angle).
   b. Draw the reflection image of △*ABC* over $\overline{AC}$. Label $r_{\overline{AC}}(B) = D$.
   c. Reflect the figure now on the screen over $\overline{AB}$. Label $r_{\overline{AB}}(C) = E$
   and $r_{\overline{AB}}(D) = F$.
   d. Measure $\overline{BC}$, $\overline{DC}$, $\overline{FE}$, and $\overline{EB}$. What property of reflections
   guarantees that they must be equal?
   e. Name at least three pairs of angles that are equal in measure.

12. According to the Reflection Postulate, what four properties are
preserved under reflections? (Hint: they start with the letters
a, b, c, and d.) *(Lesson 4-2)*
angie measure, betweenness, collinearity, and distance

In 13 and 14, trace the figure below.

13. Draw the reflection image of quadrilateral *BCDE* over $\overleftrightarrow{AB}$.
(Lesson 4-2) See below.

14. Construct the line containing point *A* perpendicular to $\overleftrightarrow{DE}$.
(Lesson 3-6) See margin.

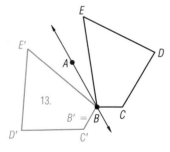

13.

In 15 and 16, $P = (-2, 0)$, $Q = (-4, 3)$, and $R = (2, 7)$.

15. Find the coordinates of the vertices of the image of $\triangle PQR$ when it is reflected over the *y*-axis. *(Lessons 4-2, 4-1)*
$P' = (2, 0)$, $Q' = (4, 3)$, $R' = (-2, 7)$.

16. Show that $\angle PQR$ is a right angle, by proving that $\overleftrightarrow{PQ} \perp \overleftrightarrow{QR}$. *(Lesson 3-5)* **See margin.**

17. Reflect the letter *R* over line ℓ at the left. *(Lesson 4-2)*

18. Match the following angle type with an algebraic description. *(Lesson 3-2)*

a. acute (vii)   (i) $m_1 + m_2 = 90$
b. complementary (i) (ii) $m_1 + m_2 = 180$
c. obtuse (vi)   (iii) $m = 0$
d. right (iv)   (iv) $m = 90$
e. straight (v)   (v) $m = 180$
f. supplementary (ii) (vi) $90 < m < 180$
g. zero (iii)   (vii) $0 < m < 90$

19. Name the angle shown in four different ways. *(Lesson 3-1)*
$\angle ABC, \angle CBA, \angle B, \angle 1$

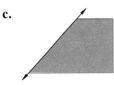

20. Characterize each region as convex or nonconvex. *(Lessons 2-7, 2-1)*

a.   b.   c.

convex   nonconvex   convex

21. Given A = {L, I, N, E, S} and B = {P, O, I, N, T, S}. Find A ∩ B. *(Lesson 2-6).* A ∩ B = {I, N, S}.

22. Using an automatic drawer, make the figures below. **Answers will vary.**

a.   b.

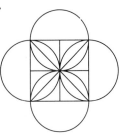

LESSON

The First Theorem in Euclid's *Elements*

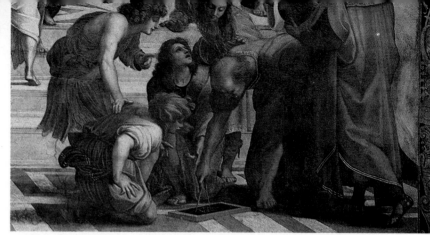

In this detail from Raphael's painting, School of Athens, *the artist has illustrated his concept of Euclid discussing geometry with a group of students.*

You have seen the proofs of a number of theorems. Books differ in the postulates they choose, in the order of theorems they prove, and even sometimes in the definitions of terms they use.

In Europe, it was not always this way. From 250 B.C. until the end of the 1700s, there was essentially only one geometry textbook, Euclid's *Elements.* Developments in geometry ultimately made the *Elements* out-of-date, but in some schools it was used even in the first part of this century. The *Elements* contains some of the greatest logical thinking of all time.

The first theorem in the *Elements* concerns the construction of an equilateral triangle. Recall that an equilateral triangle is defined as a triangle with all three sides having the same length. The task is to construct an equilateral triangle with one side the given segment $\overline{AB}$.

$$A\text{————}B$$

Here is an algorithm:
  Step 1. $\odot A$ containing B
  Step 2. $\odot B$ containing A
  Step 3. $\odot A$ and $\odot B$ intersect at C and D.
  Step 4. $\overline{AC}, \overline{BC}$

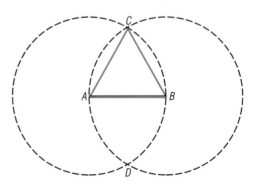

176

There is a natural question: How do you know that these steps construct an equilateral triangle? To answer this question, a proof is needed. Recall that a proof of $p \Rightarrow q$ is a sequence of justified statements beginning with p and ending with q. It is customary to call p the **given** and q **what is to be proved,** or just simply the **to prove** or **prove.** Here is a statement of Euclid's first theorem.

Theorem:

The triangle constructed in the above construction is an equilateral triangle.

Thus the given p is the segments and circles that are constructed, and q is the statement that $\triangle ABC$ is equilateral.

Here is Euclid's proof of this theorem. By the definition of circle (the meaning of $\odot A$), $AB = AC$. By the definition of circle (the meaning of $\odot B$), $AB = BC$. Thus, by the Transitive Property of Equality, all three sides are equal. And then, by the definition of equilateral triangle (sufficient condition), $\triangle ABC$ is equilateral.

Euclid wrote in paragraphs. Some teachers like to display proofs in *two-column form.* Here is Euclid's proof, rewritten in that form. The conclusions are in the left column and the justifications for them are in the right column. We write the given above the conclusions.

Given: the segments and angles in the above construction.

Conclusions	Justifications
1. $AB = AC$	definition of circle (meaning of $\odot A$)
2. $AB = BC$	definition of circle (meaning of $\odot B$)
3. $AB = AC = BC$	Transitive Property of Equality
4. $\triangle ABC$ is equilateral.	definition of equilateral triangle (sufficient condition)

Example 1 on the next page contains a proof. In it, p is the statement $m \parallel n$ and q is the statement $m\angle 1 = m\angle 7$. So we start with $m \parallel n$ and finish with the equality of angle measures $m\angle 1 = m\angle 7$. Example 1 illustrates a very common way of doing this. Each angle measure is shown equal to the same third measure. Then, as in Euclid's proof, the Transitive Property of Equality is used.

This thinking, which you do in your head, we show in a step called "Analyze." You do not have to write down this step. We put what you should write in **special bold type.** There are many ways of writing a proof; your teacher may prefer one way over another.

The second is the *transitivity proof.* This is found in the Examples and in **Questions 14-16.** It involves showing two things equal to a third and then deducing (using the Transitive Property of Equality) that they are equal to each other.

Example 1 can be done using $\angle 3$ instead of $\angle 5$. Ask students what would change if $\angle 3$ were used. (Change 5 to 3 wherever it appears in the proof and switch justifications for Steps 1 and 2.) Inform students that many of the proofs that they will do in this course can be done in more than one way, just as they found that equations in algebra could be solved in more than one way.

Making Connections   In the next lesson, the transitivity proofs used here are used to verify the construction of a circle through three points.

Error Analysis   Knowing what can be assumed from a picture can be confusing for students because there are built-in inconsistencies in geometry. For example, at times we want students to be able to judge figures by looking at them. At other times, we want students to make deductions only from information explicitly given. You might want to do an extra worksheet on what *can* be assumed from a figure. Draw various figures with all different combinations of intersecting or nonintersecting lines and angles and ask students to discuss them in **small groups.** Each group should be asked to come up with a summary list of what can be assumed, including betweenness, collinearity, which points are in the interior of an angle, and so on. Encourage them to look back in their textbooks.

Alternate Approach   A way of presenting a proof which some teachers prefer is a modified flowchart. It has two main advantages: (1) the antecedent of each statement is clear; and (2) the footnotes used for listing the justifications reduces the writing if a reason is used more than once.

Here is a flowchart proof of Euclid's First Theorem.

$$\left.\begin{array}{c} AB = AC^1 \\ AB = BC^1 \end{array}\right\} \Rightarrow$$

$AB = AC = BC^2 \Rightarrow$
$\triangle ABC$ is equilateral[3].

1. definition of circle
2. Transitive Property of Equality
3. definition of equilateral triangle

Computer Use an automatic drawer to construct an equilateral triangle and compare the algorithm the computer uses with the one given on page 176.

Example 1 **Given:** *(p): m ∥ n* and angles as numbered in the figure below.
Prove: *(q):* m∠1 = m∠7.

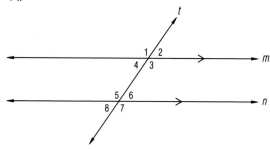

Analyze Angles 1 and 5 are corresponding angles formed by parallel lines. Angles 5 and 7 are vertical angles. That's enough.

Write **Given: *m ∥ n.***

Conclusions	Justifications
1. m∠1 = m∠5	∥ lines ⇒ corr. ∠s =
2. m∠5 = m∠7	**Vertical Angle Theorem**
3. m∠1 = m∠7	**Transitive Property of Equality (steps 1 and 2)**

Many teachers would say you do not have to rewrite the given above the conclusions if you have already written it once in introducing the problem.

In Example 1, you were given a figure. There are certain things you can assume from a figure. You can assume lines and angles intersect as shown, that points are in the order as shown, and that angles are marked as shown. For instance, in the figure below you can assume that ℓ, *m*, and *n* are all lines, that ℓ and *m* intersect at *B*, that *E*, *D*, *B*, and *C* all lie on *m*, that *A* and *B* lie on ℓ, and that *F* is not on ℓ, *m*, or *n*.

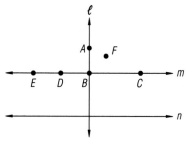

However, unless specifically given, you cannot assume lines are ∥ or ⊥, or that distances or angle measures are equal. For instance, you *cannot* assume from the figure above that ℓ is perpendicular to *m* or *n* or that *m* is parallel to *n*, even though they look it. You cannot tell the measure of ∠ABC. You cannot assume that *F* is between *A* and *C* or that $\overrightarrow{BF}$ bisects ∠ABC, or that *DE* = *DB*, even though all these may look true. Only if given, or after you have proved these things, can you take them as so.

178

Here is another proof which utilizes the Transitive Property of Equality.

Example 2

Given: *B* is the midpoint of $\overline{AC}$.
C is the midpoint of $\overline{BD}$.

Prove: *AB* = *CD*.

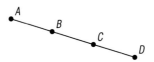

Analyze From midpoints come equal distances. *BC* is a distance equal to *AB* and *CD*.

Write Given: *B* is the midpoint of $\overline{AC}$, *C* is the midpoint of $\overline{BD}$.

Conclusions	Justifications
1. *AB* = *BC*	definition of midpoint (meaning)
2. *BC* = *CD*	definition of midpoint (meaning)
3. *AB* = *CD*	Transitive Property of Equality (steps 1 and 2)

Questions

Covering the Reading

1. Define: equilateral triangle.
   a triangle with all three sides having the same length

2. **a.** Trace $\overline{MT}$. Then construct an equilateral triangle with $\overline{MT}$ as one side.
   b. How many different triangles could you construct? 2

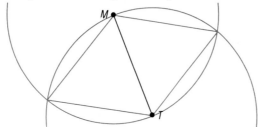

3. In circle *O* below, what is the justification for the conclusion *OA* = *OB*?   definition of ⊙ (meaning)

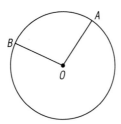

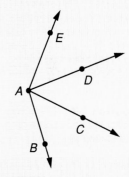
179

4. What caused people to stop using Euclid's *Elements* as a geometry text? **See margin.**

5. Use the drawing at the right.
   Given: *m* ∥ *n*.
   Justify each conclusion.
   a. m∠2 = m∠6 **∥ lines ⇒ corr. ∠s =**
   b. m∠6 = m∠8 **Vertical Angle Theorem**
   c. m∠2 = m∠8 **Transitive Property of Equality (steps a and b)**

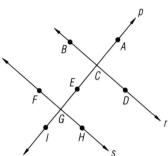

In 6–11, refer to the figure below at the right. Can you assume the listed information from the figure?

6. *r* intersects *p* at *C*. **Yes**

7. *r* ∥ *s* **No**

8. m∠*EGF* = 90 **No**

9. m∠*BCA* = m∠*FGA* **No**

10. *G* is the midpoint of $\overline{FH}$. **No**

11. *p* ⊥ *r* **No**

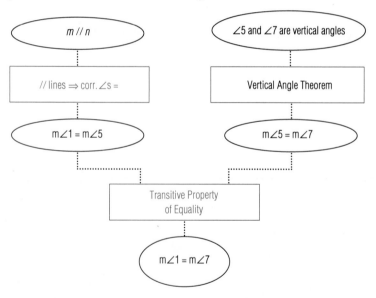

12. Here is a flowchart display of the proof of Example 1. One justification is already placed in a rectangle. Place the appropriate justifications in the other two rectangles.

13. In Question 12, which of the five statements (in the ovals) is given from the figure of Example 1? *m* ∥ *n* **and ∠5 and ∠7 are vertical angles.**

In 14–16, write proofs as in the Examples of this lesson.

14. Use the figure at the right.
Given: $\ell \parallel m$.
Prove: $m\angle 4 = m\angle 8$.
See margin.

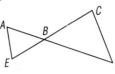

15. Use the figure at the right.
Given: $m\angle CBD = m\angle D$.
Prove: $m\angle ABE = m\angle D$.
See margin.

16. Given: $\triangle ABC$ is equilateral.
$\triangle BCD$ is equilateral.
Prove: $AB = DC$.
See margin.

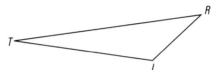

Review

17. a. Reflect $\triangle TRI$ below over line $\overleftrightarrow{RI}$. Let U be the image of T.
 b. Why does $TI = UI$? *(Lessons 4-3, 4-2)*
 a) See margin. b) Reflections preserve distance.

18. a. If two lines are perpendicular to the same line, then they are ___?___.
 (Lesson 3-5) parallel
 b. If two lines are parallel to the same line, then they are ___?___.
 (Lesson 3-4) parallel

19. The roof below is supported by $\overline{BE}$ and the top of the wall $\overline{CF}$. If $m\angle DCF = 145$ and $\overline{BE}$ is parallel to $\overline{CF}$, what must $m\angle ABE$ be?
(Lesson 3-4) 35°

LESSON 4-4   The First Theorem in Euclid's *Elements*   **181**

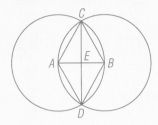
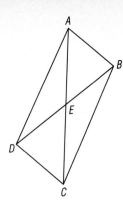

In 20–22, justify each conclusion. *(Lessons 3-3, 3-2, 2-7, 1-7)*

20. Given: The diagonals of quadrilateral *ABCD* at the left intersect at *E*. m∠*BEA* = 50.
Conclusion: m∠*AED* = 130. **Linear Pair Theorem**

21. Given: $3x - 4y = 5$.
Conclusion: $-4y = -3x + 5$. **Addition Property of Equality**

22. Given: $-4y = -3x + 5$.
Conclusion: $y = \dfrac{-3x + 5}{-4}$. **Multiplication Property of Equality**

23. Duplicate Euclid's construction (page 176) using an automatic drawer. Draw $\overline{AD}$ and $\overline{BD}$. Measure the angles and sides of the triangles formed. What can you conclude? See margin.

Exploration

24. Either by hand or with an automatic drawer, start with a triangle such as the one below and construct the perpendicular segment from *A* to $\overline{BC}$, the ⊥ segment from *B* to $\overline{AC}$, and the ⊥ segment from *C* to $\overline{AB}$. How are these constructed segments related? The three segments intersect at one point.

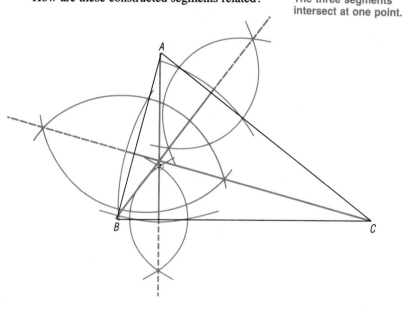

The Perpendicular Bisector Theorem

LESSON 4-5

RESOURCES
■ Lesson Master 4-5

Like any other definitions, postulates, or theorems, you can use properties of reflections as justifications in proofs.

Example 1   **Given:** P is on the perpendicular bisector m of segment $\overline{AB}$.
            Prove: $PA = PB$.

Analyze   Think of the perpendicular bisector m as a reflecting line. Then B is the image of A. P is on m, so P is the image of itself. Use the postulate that reflections preserve distance.

Write   **Given: m is the $\perp$ bisector of $\overline{AB}$. P is on m.**

Conclusions	Justifications
1. $r_m(P) = P$	definition of reflection (sufficient condition)
2. $r_m(A) = B$	definition of reflection (sufficient condition)
3. $PA = PB$	Reflections preserve distance.

The result proved in Example 1 can be written as an if-then statement. It is so important it is labeled as a theorem.

> **Perpendicular Bisector Theorem:**
>
> If a point is on the perpendicular bisector of a segment, then it is equidistant from the endpoints of the segment.

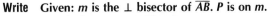

The Perpendicular Bisector Theorem has a surprising application. It can help locate the center of a circle.

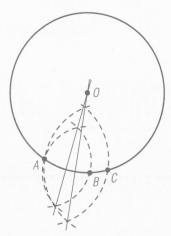

Example 2   Construct the circle through the three noncollinear points A, B, and C

Solution
Step 1.   Subroutine: m, the perpendicular bisector of $\overline{AB}$
Step 2.   Subroutine: n, the perpendicular bisector of $\overline{BC}$
Step 3. m and n intersect at O. (Point Rule)
Step 4.   ⊙O containing A (Compass rule)

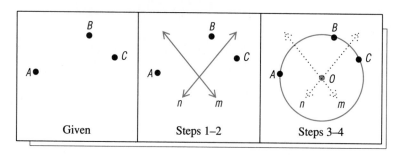

| Given | Steps 1–2 | Steps 3–4 |

If m and n intersect, it can be proven that this construction works. Because of the Perpendicular Bisector Theorem with line m, $OA = OB$. With line n, this theorem also justifies the conclusion $OB = OC$. By the Transitive Property of Equality, the three distances OA, OB, and OC are all equal. Thus ⊙O with radius OA contains points B and C also.

Questions

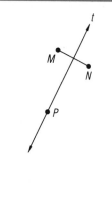

1. In the figure at the left, t is the ⊥ bisector of $\overline{MN}$. Justify each conclusion.
   a. P is the reflection image of P over t. **See margin.**
   b. $r_t(N) = M$ **def. of reflection (sufficient condition)**
   c. $PM = PN$ **Reflections preserve distance.**

2. What statement is proved by the reasoning of Question 1?
   the Perpendicular Bisector Theorem

3. Choose the correct words in parentheses. Any point on the (bisector, perpendicular bisector) of a segment is equidistant from the (endpoints, midpoint) of the segment. **⊥ bisector, endpoints**

4. Trace the three points A, B, and C below. Construct a circle containing points A, B, and C. **See margin.**

   A●

   ●C
   ●
   B

5. Trace the three points J, K, and L below. Construct a circle containing all three points. See margin.

●
J

●
K

●
L

Applying the Mathematics

6. Use the figure below.
Given: e is the $\perp$ bisector of $\overline{VW}$.
f is the $\perp$ bisector of $\overline{WX}$.
Prove: $VC = CX$. See margin.

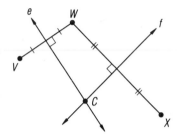

7. Use the figure below.
Given: $r_{\overleftrightarrow{QR}}(C) = D$.
Prove: $CQ = DQ$. See margin.

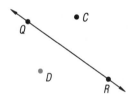

8. A tree stands midway between two stakes. Guy wires are attached from the stakes to the same point up the tree. Explain why the two guy wires must have the same length. See margin.

LESSON 4-5 The Perpendicular Bisector Theorem **185**

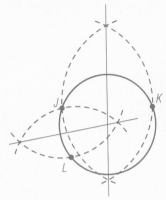

9. Use the figure at the right. **See margin.**
Given: △*ABC* is equilateral.
  C is the midpoint of $\overline{AD}$.
Prove: *BC* = *CD*. *(Lesson 4-4)*

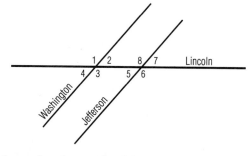

10. Draw a figure and state the justification for the conclusion.
Given: $r_\ell(\angle ABC) = \angle DEF$.
Conclusion: m∠*ABC* = m∠*DEF*. *(Lesson 4-2)* **See margin.**

K M
N
W X

11. Which of the letters at the left does *not* look the same as its reflection image over a vertical line? *(Lesson 4-2)* **K, N**

12. Write as an if-then statement: Reflections preserve betweenness. *(Lesson 4-2)* **See margin.**

13. Lincoln Avenue intersects the parallel streets Washington and Jefferson. Which of the eight angles at the corners have equal measures? *(Lesson 3-4)*
m∠1 = m∠3 = m∠8 = m∠6, m∠4 = m∠2 = m∠5 = m∠7

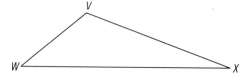

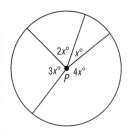

14. Suppose the angles about point *P* have measures as indicated in the drawing at the left.
  a. What is the measure of the largest angle? **4x° = 144°**
  b. Are any of the angles complementary? **No**
  c. Are any of the angles supplementary? *(Lesson 3-2)*
  Yes; the angles with measures x° and 4x°, 2x° and 3x° are supplementary pairs.

15. Trace the figure below.
  a. Draw the circle through the three vertices of △*VWX*.
  b. Is the center of the circle inside or outside the triangle?
  c. What determines whether the center will be inside or outside? (If you have an automatic drawer, experiment with triangles of different shapes.) **a) See margin. b) outside; c) See margin.**

186

LESSON

4-6

Reflecting Polygons

RESOURCES
■ Lesson Master 4-6

In Lesson 4-2, the shorthand r($\triangle ABC$) = $\triangle XYZ$ was introduced for the statement "The reflection image of $\triangle ABC$ is $\triangle XYZ$." This notation is used for polygons as well as triangles. As with triangles, when you use the r( ) notation for polygons, the order of the vertices is important.

r$_t$($ABCD$) = $MVWS$ is read "The reflection image of polygon $ABCD$ over line t is polygon $MVWS$."

From this it is understood that r$_t$(A) = M, r$_t$(B) = V, r$_t$(C) = W, and r$_t$(D) = S. The reasons for this are the Figure Reflection Theorem and the fact that a polygon is determined by its vertices.

OBJECTIVES

B Draw reflection images of segments, angles, and polygons over a given line.
D Determine measures of angles in figures and their reflection images.
E Apply properties of reflections to make conclusions, using one or more of the following justifications:
   definition of reflection
   Reflections preserve distance.
   Reflections preserve angle measure.
   Reflections switch orientation.
   Figure Reflection Theorem
   Flip-Flop Theorem

Example Draw r$_m$($ABCDE$).

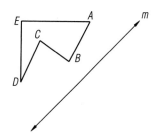

Solution Draw the images of A, B, C, D, and E. Call them A', B', C', D', and E'. Then draw $\overline{A'B'}$, $\overline{B'C'}$, $\overline{C'D'}$, $\overline{D'E'}$, and $\overline{E'A'}$.

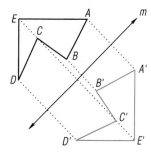

Because of the Figure Reflection Theorem, r$_m$($ABCDE$) = $A'B'C'D'E'$.

In the Example, r$_m$(A) = A'. Thus m is the perpendicular bisector of $\overline{AA'}$, by the definition of reflection. Since $\overline{AA'}$ and $\overline{A'A}$ are the same segment, m is the perpendicular bisector of $\overline{A'A}$. Thus r$_m$(A') = A. Similarly, r$_m$(B') = B, r$_m$(C') = C, r$_m$(D') = D, and r$_m$(E') = E. Putting this all together, r$_m$($A'B'C'D'E'$) = $ABCDE$. That is, if r$_m$(A) = A', then r$_m$(A') = A for points; and if r$_m$($ABCD...$) = $A'B'C'D'...$, then r$_m$($A'B'C'D'...$) = $ABCD...$ for polygons and other figures.

TEACHING NOTES

In some earlier work of the authors, students were asked to choose a name for the theorem on page 188, because it is used often in proofs. The name "Flip-Flop" usually was chosen. The theorem is important because it increases the number of conclusions that can be made about a figure since either point can be the preimage.

Making Connections
The shorthand r(ABC) = DEF, which forces points and their images to correspond, has a later payoff when discussing corresponding parts of congruent figures in Lesson 6-7.

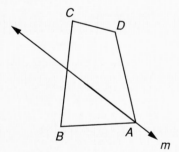
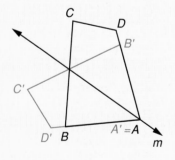
If F and F' are points or figures and $r(F) = F'$, then $r(F') = F$.

Look back at the above Example. Although reflections preserve angle measure, betweenness, collinearity, and distance, something is not preserved. The image $A'B'C'D'E'$ looks reversed from the preimage $ABCDE$. Now we explore that reversal.

Imagine that $ABCDE$ in the Example encloses a garden. Imagine further than you begin at A and walk around the garden to B, to C, to D, to E, and back to A. The garden is always on your *right* as you go around it. Do the same with the corresponding points on the image polygon. Begin at A' and go to B', C', D', and E'. This time the garden is always on your *left*.

When you think of the vertices of a polygon in order, as above, you have assigned an **orientation** to the polygon. Every polygon has two orientations. The orientation for which the interior is on the right is called **clockwise.** When the interior is on the left, the orientation is **counterclockwise.**

With convex polygons these names fit with intuition. Clockwise is the direction the hands move on nondigital clocks. However, for nonconvex polygons, the orientation names are not as descriptive.

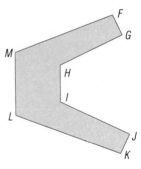

FGHIJKLM is clockwise but *GHIJ* seems to go in the wrong direction.

Orientation depends on the order in which the vertices are given. Back in the Example, when the orientation of $ABCDE$ was clockwise, the orientation of the image polygon, *taking the letters in the same order,* was counterclockwise. Had we chosen $EDCBA$ as the order of vertices in the first figure, then the orientation of the preimage would have been counterclockwise. The orientation of the image would have been the orientation of $E'D'C'B'A'$, clockwise.

In general, a figure and its reflection image always have opposite orientations. We take the word "orientation" as undefined, and add the following part to the Reflection Postulate of Lesson 4-2.

188

Reflection Postulate:

Under a reflection:

f. A polygon and its image, with vertices taken in corresponding order, have opposite orientations. Reflections switch orientation.

Questions

Covering the Reading

1. Trace the figure below.
   Draw $r_t(WXYZ)$.

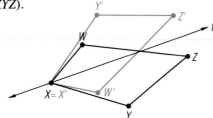

In 2 and 3, draw a picture of each situation.

2. $r_k(LOVE) = BATH$ See margin.

3. $r_\ell(\triangle ABC) = \triangle ADE$ See margin.

4. **a.** If $r_m(A) = C$, then $r_m(C) = \underline{\ ?\ }$. **A**
   b. What theorem justifies your answer to part **a**?
      Flip-Flop Theorem

5. **a.** Is *TXWA* below oriented clockwise or counterclockwise? clockwise
   b. What is the orientation of *XWAT*? clockwise
   c. Which way is *WXTA* oriented? counterclockwise

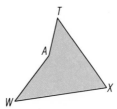

6. How are the orientations of a figure and its reflection image related?
   The two have opposite orientations.
7. *True* or *false*? Until you know the order of vertices, you cannot tell whether a polygon is oriented clockwise or counterclockwise.
   True
8. A triangle is drawn so that tracing its vertices *T, A, B* (in that order) yields a clockwise motion. What type of motion results if the vertices are traced in the following orders?
   a. *B, A, T* counterclockwise   **b.** *A, T, B,* counterclockwise
   c. *T, B, A* counterclockwise   **d.** *B, T, A* clockwise

LESSON 4-6 Reflecting Polygons   **189**

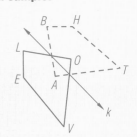
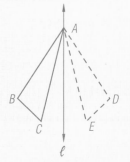
189

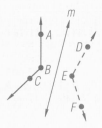
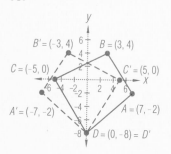

Applying the Mathematics

9. If r(*ONE*) = *SIX*, give:
   a. r(*N*) *I*
   b. r(∠*EON*) ∠*XSI*
   c. r($\overrightarrow{NO}$) $\overrightarrow{IS}$
   d. r($\overline{EO}$). $\overline{XS}$

10. Police Officer Hugh Hunter follows a clockwise path *ABCDXTZA* when he walks his beat. If Officer Marlene Snyder walks the same streets, beginning at *D*, but with a counterclockwise orientation, name the path she takes. **DCBAZTXD**

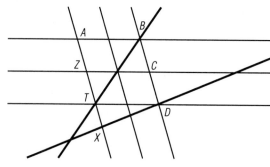

11. What is the orientation of the path run by a batter in baseball as he or she runs around the baseball diamond? **counterclockwise**

12. Given: r(*ABCD*) = *EFGH* and the length of $\overline{BD}$ is 12 cm. Make a conclusion. **FH = 12 cm**

13. r$_m$(∠*ABC*) = ∠*DEF*. r$_m$(*A*) = *D*, but r$_m$(*C*) ≠ *F*. Draw a figure.
   See margin.

14. Use the figure at the left.
   Given: ℓ is the ⊥ bisector of $\overline{AB}$.
   Fill in the blanks in the proof that r$_ℓ$($\overline{AB}$) = $\overline{BA}$.

Conclusions	Justifications
1. r$_ℓ$(*A*) = *B*	**a.** __?__ definition of reflection (meaning)
2. **b.** __?__ r$_ℓ$(*B*) = *A*	Flip-Flop Theorem
3. **c.** __?__ r$_ℓ$($\overline{AB}$) = $\overline{BA}$	Figure Reflection Theorem

Review

15. *Z* is the reflection image of *A* over line ℓ below. Match each conclusion with its justification. *(Lessons 4-2, 3-1)*

   a. $\overline{ZA}$ ⊥ ℓ (iii)
   b. ℓ bisects $\overline{ZA}$. (iii)
   c. *M* is the midpoint of $\overline{ZA}$. (i)
   d. *AM* = *MZ* (ii)

   (i) definition of bisector (meaning)
   (ii) definition of midpoint (meaning)
   (iii) definition of reflection (meaning)

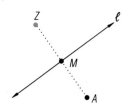

16. Given: *M* is the midpoint of $\overline{AB}$.
   AN = *AM*.
   Prove: *AN* = *MB*. *(Lesson 4-4)*
   See margin.

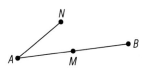

17. Use the figure below.

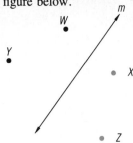

Given: $r_m(W) = X$, $r_m(Y) = Z$.
Fill in the justifications in this proof that $\overline{WX} \parallel \overline{YZ}$.
(Lessons 4-5, 4-1, 3-5)

Conclusions	Justifications
1. $\overline{WX} \perp m$	**a.** _?_ **definition of reflection (meaning)**
2. $\overline{YZ} \perp m$	**b.** _?_ **definition of reflection (meaning)**
3. $\overline{WX} \parallel \overline{YZ}$	**c.** _?_ **Two Perpendiculars Theorem**

In 18 and 19, let $A = (7, -2)$, $B = (3, 4)$, $C = (-5, 0)$, and $D = (0, -8)$.

18. Graph $ABCD$ and its reflection image over the y-axis.
(Lessons 4-2, 4-1) **See margin.**

19. a. Find the slope of $\overleftrightarrow{AB}$. $-\frac{3}{2}$
   b. Find the slope of a line perpendicular to $\overleftrightarrow{AB}$. $\frac{2}{3}$
   (Lessons 3-5, 3-4)

20. *True* or *false*? A supplement of an acute angle is always an obtuse angle. *(Lesson 3-2)* **True**

21. Give a counterexample to this statement: If $m\angle A = x$, then the measure of a complement to $\angle A$ cannot be x. *(Lessons 3-2, 2-2)*
Let x be 45.

Exploration

22. Many objects come in different orientations. For instance, there are right-handed golf clubs and left-handed golf clubs. Name at least three other objects that come in different orientations.
Samples: shoes, hands, scissors, desks

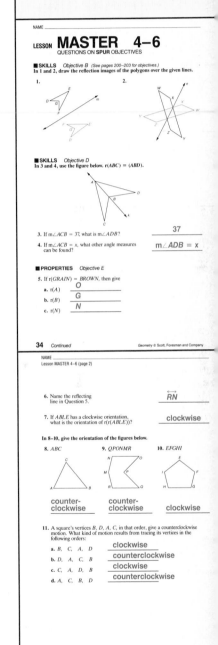

LESSON 4-7

Reflection-Symmetric Figures

When a figure is reflected over a line, either of two situations may arise. In the first case, as pictured below at the left, the preimage and image are *distinct*. This is the most common case.

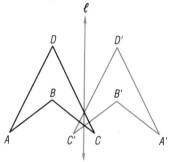

$$r_\ell(ABCD) = A'B'C'D'$$

$$r_m(ABCD) = A'B'C'D' = CBAD$$

In the second case, pictured at the right, the image of quadrilateral *ABCD* is itself. The preimage and image *coincide*. Note, however, that $r_m(A) = C$, $r_m(B) = B$, $r_m(C) = A$, and $r_m(D) = D$. Thus, $A'B'C'D' = CBAD$ and $r_m(ABCD) = CBAD$. The figure is called *reflection-symmetric,* and the reflecting line is called a *symmetry line* for the figure.

Definition:

A plane figure F is a **reflection-symmetric figure** if and only if there is a line *m* such that $r_m(F) = F$. The line *m* is a **symmetry line** for the figure.

With symmetric figures, it is absolutely necessary to name the images so that preimage and image points correspond. For example, in the figure above at the right, write $r_m(ABCD) = CBAD$, *not* $r_m(ABCD) = ABCD$. Although the quadrilateral and its image are the same set of points, their orientations are different. *ABCD* is oriented counterclockwise while *CBAD* is clockwise oriented.

The union of any figure and its reflection image is always a figure that is symmetric to the reflecting line. The ink blot in the opening to this chapter is an example of such reflection-symmetric figures.

192

Example Draw what appears to be a symmetry line for each capital letter shown below.

a. **A** b. **C** c. **X** d. **N**

Solutions In **a** and **b** there is one line of symmetry. In **c** there are two: one horizontal and one vertical. In **d** there are no symmetry lines.

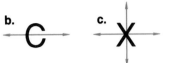

a. **A** b. **C** c. **X** d. **N**

Many simple figures are reflection-symmetric. Every segment is reflection-symmetric to its perpendicular bisector. Specifically, if ℓ is the $\perp$ bisector of $\overline{AB}$, $r_\ell(\overline{AB}) = \overline{BA}$. Every segment $\overline{AB}$ has a second symmetry line, namely $\overleftrightarrow{AB}$, the line containing it. Specifically, $r_{\overleftrightarrow{AB}}(A) = A$, $r_{\overleftrightarrow{AB}}(B) = B$, and so $r_{\overleftrightarrow{AB}}(\overline{AB}) = \overline{AB}$. No other symmetry lines are possible for a segment, since endpoints must have endpoints as reflection images.

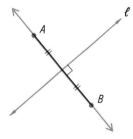

Segment Symmetry Theorem:

A segment has exactly two symmetry lines:
1. its perpendicular bisector, and
2. the line containing the segment.

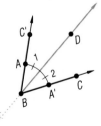

Angles also possess reflection symmetry. Consider $\angle ABC$ with its bisector $\overrightarrow{BD}$ so that $m\angle ABD = m\angle CBD$.

Imagine folding $\angle ABC$ along $\overrightarrow{BD}$. Since $m\angle 1 = m\angle 2$, $\overrightarrow{BC}$ will fold (reflect) onto $\overrightarrow{BA}$ even though C does not necessarily fold onto A.

Similarly $\overrightarrow{BA}$ reflects onto $\overrightarrow{BC}$ (but A does not necessarily reflect onto C). Thus the image of $\angle ABC$ is itself.

LESSON 4-7 Reflection-Symmetric Figures **193**

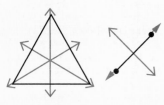
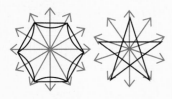
The following two theorems summarize this discussion.

Side-Switching Theorem:

> If one side of an angle is reflected over the line containing the angle bisector, its image is the other side of the angle.

Angle Symmetry Theorem:

> The line containing the bisector of an angle is a symmetry line of the angle.

In the next chapter, certain polygons are examined for symmetry. All of their symmetries can be traced back to symmetries of angles or segments.

Questions

Covering the Reading

1. Define: reflection-symmetric figure. **See margin.**

In 2–5, the figure has at least one symmetry line. Trace the figure and draw all symmetry lines.

2.

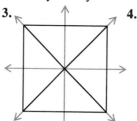

3.

4.

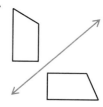

5.

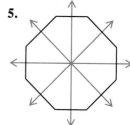

6. Alchemists used these symbols during the Middle Ages. How many symmetry lines does each have?

a. Copper 2   **b.** Tin 2   **c.** Lead 2

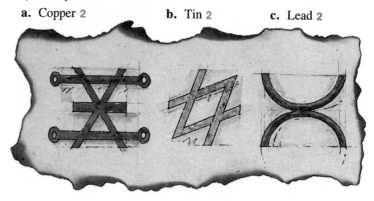

194

194

In 7 and 8, trace. Then draw all lines of symmetry for the given figure.

7. $\overline{AB}$

8. $\angle CDE$

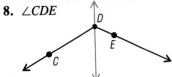

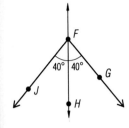

9. Use the drawing at the left. Give the reflection image of each figure over the line $\overleftrightarrow{FH}$.
   a. $\overrightarrow{FJ}$ $\overrightarrow{FG}$
   b. $\overrightarrow{FG}$ $\overrightarrow{FJ}$
   c. $\angle JFG$ $\angle GFJ$

10. Complete this statement of the Side-Switching Theorem. If m is the bisector of $\angle ABC$, then $r_m(\overrightarrow{BA}) = \underline{\ ?\ }$. $\overrightarrow{BC}$

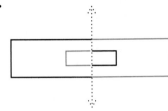

Applying the Mathematics

In 11–13, copy the figure and complete its shape so that the result is symmetric to the dotted line.

11.

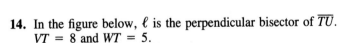

12.

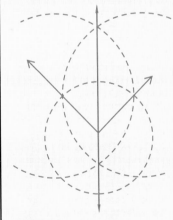

13.

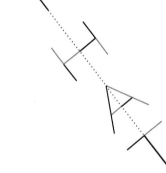

14. In the figure below, ℓ is the perpendicular bisector of $\overline{TU}$. $VT = 8$ and $WT = 5$.
   a. Find the length of $\overline{UV}$. 8
   b. $r_\ell(\triangle TUV) = \underline{\ ?\ }$ $\triangle UTV$

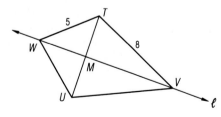

LESSON 4-7   *Reflection-Symmetric Figures*   **195**

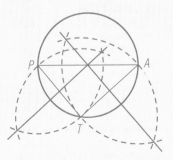

25. Yes; a straight angle, such as ∠AOB shown below, has symmetry lines $\overleftrightarrow{AB}$ and the perpendicular to $\overleftrightarrow{AB}$ through O.

FOLLOW-UP

MORE PRACTICE
For more questions on SPUR Objectives, use *Lesson Master 4-7*, shown on page 197.

EXTENSION
Reflection symmetry is not the only symmetry. A figure is symmetric with respect to the point *P* if and only if, for every point *A* on the figure, the point *B* is on the figure, such that *P* is the midpoint of *AB*. Point symmetry is the same as 180° rotation symmetry. You may wish to introduce point-symmetry here for two reasons:
(1) To explain why we refer to *reflection-symmetry* rather than just simply *symmetry*.
(2) To let students know their sense is correct that parallelograms and the letter N, for example, do have symmetry, namely point-symmetry, but not reflection-symmetry.

EVALUATION
Alternative Assessment
Have students do the following **writing activity:** (1) summarize the definition of a reflection-symmetric figure and the three theorems in this lesson; and (2) draw examples illustrating the theorems. You may wish to call upon individual students to present their work at the chalkboard.

---

15. **a.** Trace the figure at the right. Draw $r_{\overleftrightarrow{AC}}(ABCD)$.
    b. *True* or *false*? The figure at the right has no symmetry lines.
    True

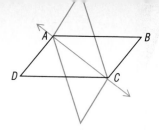

In 16 and 17, follow this algorithm for constructing the bisector of ∠AOB.

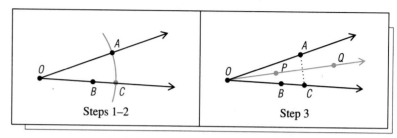

| Steps 1–2 | Step 3 |

Step 1. ⊙O containing A
Step 2. ⊙O intersects $\overrightarrow{OB}$ at C.
Step 3. Subroutine: $\overleftrightarrow{PQ}$, the ⊥ bisector of $\overline{AC}$

Trace the angle. Use the algorithm to construct its symmetry lines.

16.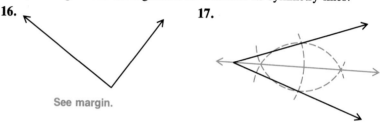

See margin.

17.

In 18 and 19, *multiple choice.* A, B, and C are noncollinear points, with m∠ABC = 40. Also, $D = r_{\overleftrightarrow{BA}}(C)$ and $E = r_{\overleftrightarrow{BD}}(C)$.

18. m∠EBC =
   (a) 40   (b) 80   (c) 120   (d) 160
   (e) can equal more than one number. (d)

19. m∠EBA =
   (a) 20   (b) 40   (c) 80   (d) 120
   (e) depends on the position of A. (d)

Review

20. If r(ABCD) = EFGH, find: *(Lesson 4-6)*
   a. r(EFGH)   **b.** r(C)   **c.** r(△ABD)   **d.** r(∠GCH).
   a) ABCD; b) G; c) △EFH; d) ∠CGD

21. Complete this proof. *(Lesson 4-4)*
Given: $\overrightarrow{OB}$ bisects $\angle AOC$.
$\overrightarrow{OC}$ bisects $\angle BOD$.
Prove: $m\angle AOB = m\angle COD$.

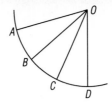

Conclusions	Justifications
1. **a.** __?__ $m\angle AOB = m\angle BOC$	1. def. of angle bisector (meaning)
2. $m\angle BOC = m\angle COD$	2. **b.** __?__ See below.
3. **c.** __?__ $m\angle AOB = m\angle COD$	3. Transitive Property of Equality (steps 1 and 2)

b) definition of angle bisector (meaning)

22. Construct a circle containing the three vertices of $\triangle PAT$ below. *(Lesson 4-2)* See margin.

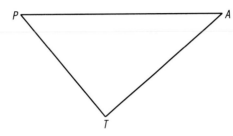

23. Line *m* goes through points (3, -1) and (-7, 4). Find the slope of line *n* if $m \perp n$. *(Lessons 3-5, 3-4)* 2

24. At the right, *ABCDEF* is a hexagon with diagonals $\overline{AD}$, $\overline{BF}$, and $\overline{CE}$. $m\angle 1 = 70$ and $m\angle 2 = 70$.

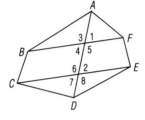

a. Which other numbered angles measure 70°? *(Lesson 3-4)* ∠4, ∠7
b. *True* or *false*? ∠4 and ∠6 are complementary angles. *(Lesson 3-2)* **False**

Exploration

25. Is there any angle which has more than one symmetry line? If so, draw such an angle. If not, why is there no such angle?
See margin.

26. a. Draw two non-perpendicular intersecting lines. The resulting figure has two symmetry lines. Draw these lines. a-b) See margin.
b. Repeat part **a** with two other lines.
c. How are these symmetry lines related to each other?
They are perpendicular.

NAME _____

■ **SKILLS** *Objective C (See pages 200–203 for objectives.)*
For 1–4, draw all symmetry lines of these figures.

1. *ABC* is equilateral.   2.

3.   4.

■ **PROPERTIES** *Objective E*
In 5 and 6, use the figure below. r⁻¹AC(∠BAC) = ∠DAC.

5. $\overrightarrow{AC}$ is the ____bisector____ of ∠*BAD*.
6. What theorem justifies this conclusion?
Side-Switching Theorem

36 *Continued*   *Geometry © Scott, Foresman and Company*

NAME _____
Lesson MASTER 4–7 (page 2)

■ **PROPERTIES** *Objective F*
In 7–9, $\overleftrightarrow{MN}$ is a symmetry line of polygon *NOPQRST*.

7. Which sides of the polygon have the same length?   RS and QP, ST and PO, TN and ON
8. Which angles of the polygon have the same measure?   ∠R and ∠Q, ∠S and ∠P, ∠T and ∠O
9. If m∠*ONM* = 45, which other angle or angles have measure 45°?   ∠TNM

■ **USES** *Objective H*

10. Draw all symmetry lines in each capital letter shown.

a. **B**   b. **H**

c. **L**   d. **I**

11. Draw all symmetry lines of the STOP sign.

Geometry © Scott, Foresman and Company   **37**

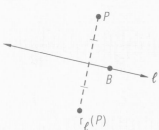

Summary

The reflection image of the point A over the line m is the point B if and only if m is the perpendicular bisector of $\overline{AB}$. In symbols, $r_m(A) = B$. If A is on line m, then $r_m(A) = A$.

The basic properties of reflections are assumed in the Reflection Postulate. Other important properties can be deduced:

Flip-Flop Theorem:
If $r(F) = F'$, then $r(F') = F$.

Figure Reflection Theorem:
If a figure is determined by certain points, its reflection image is determined by the images of those points.

Perpendicular Bisector Theorem:
If P is on the perpendicular bisector of $\overline{AB}$, then $PA = PB$.

Side-Switching Theorem:
If m is the bisector of $\angle ABC$, then $r_m(\overrightarrow{BA}) = \overrightarrow{BC}$.

Reflection images of points are easy to locate if the reflecting lines are the x-axis or the y-axis.

Sometimes a figure F and its reflection image $r_m(F)$ coincide. When this is the case, m is called a symmetry line for the figure. Every segment has two symmetry lines, its perpendicular bisector and itself. Every angle has one, the line containing its bisector.

Vocabulary

Below are the new terms and phrases for this chapter. You should be able to give a general description and specific example of each. For those terms that are starred, you should be able to give a precise definition. You should also be able to rewrite each named theorem or postulate in if-then or if-and-only-if form, as appropriate.

Lesson 4-1
preimage
reflecting line
line of reflection
*reflection image of a point
r, $r(P)$, $r_m(P)$

Lesson 4-2
reflection image of a figure
Reflection Postulate (a)–(e)
preserved property
Figure Reflection Theorem
$r_m(ABC)$

Lesson 4-3
automatic drawer
automatic drawing tool
window, menu, hard copy

Lesson 4-4
given
to prove, prove, what is
  to be proved
Proof Writing: Analyze, Write

Lesson 4-5
Perpendicular Bisector Theorem

Lesson 4-6
Flip-Flop Theorem
orientation
clockwise
counterclockwise
Reflection Postulate (f)

Lesson 4-7
*reflection-symmetric figure
*symmetry line
Segment Symmetry Theorem
Side-Switching Theorem
Angle Symmetry Theorem

Progress Self-Test

See margin for answers not shown below.

Directions: Take this test as you would take a test in class. Use a ruler, compass and a protractor. Then check your work with the solutions in the Selected Answers section in the back of the book.

In 1 and 2, given $r_m(A) = B$ and $r_m(C) = D$. Justify each conclusion.

1. $AC = BD$ **2.** $m \perp \overline{AB}$

In 3–5, polygon F′ below is the reflection image over line m of polygon F.

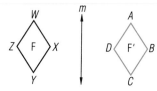

3. $r_m(X) = \underline{}$ **D**   **4.** $r_m(\angle ABC) = \underline{}$ **∠WZY**
5. What is the orientation of the image of WXYZ?
counterclockwise

In 6 and 7, polygon ABCD is symmetric to line n.

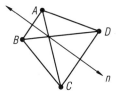

6. $r_n(ABCD) = \underline{}$ **BADC**
7. If $m\angle BDA = x$,
find $m\angle ACB$. **x**

8. Draw the reflecting line m such that $r_m(W) = V$.

9. $\triangle MNP$ below has vertices $M = (2, 0)$, $N = (5, -1)$, and $P = (-3, 4)$. Give the vertices of the reflection image of $\triangle MNP$ over the x-axis.

$M' = (2, 0)$
$N' = (5, 1)$
$P' = (-3, -4)$

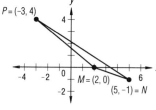

In 10 and 11, trace the figure first.
10. Draw $r_\ell(P)$.

11. Draw $r_m(\triangle CDE)$.

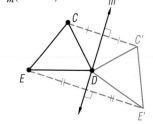

In 12 and 13, trace the figure. Then draw all lines that seem to be symmetry lines.

12. 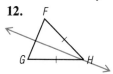   **13.**

14. Write the proof.
   Given: $m\angle 1 = m\angle 2$.
   Prove: $m\angle 3 = m\angle 2$.

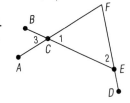

15. Fill in the blanks in this proof.
   Given: $r_\ell(W) = X$, $r_\ell(Y) = Z$.
   Prove: $\overline{WX} \parallel \overline{YZ}$.

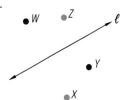

Conclusions	Justifications
1. $\ell \perp \overline{YZ}$	a. ?
2. $\ell \perp \overline{WX}$	b. ?
3. $\overline{WX} \parallel \overline{YZ}$	c. ?

Whereas end-of-chapter materials may be considered optional in some texts, they should not be considered optional in UCSMP *Geometry*. The Progress Self-Test provides the opportunity for feedback and correction; the Chapter Review provides additional opportunities for practice. It is at this point that the material "gels" for many students, allowing them to solidify skills and concepts before a test. In general, student performance is markedly improved after these pages.

USING THE PROGRESS SELF-TEST
Assign the Progress Self-Test as a one-night assignment. Worked-out *solutions* for all questions are in the Selected Answers section of the student text. Encourage students to take the Progress Self-Test honestly, grade themselves, and then be prepared to discuss the test in class.

Advise students to pay special attention to those Chapter Review questions (pages 200-203) which correspond to questions missed on the Progress Self-Test. A chart provided with the Selected Answers keys the Progress Self-Test questions to the lettered SPUR Objectives in the Chapter Review or to the Vocabulary. It also keys the questions to the corresponding lessons where the material is covered.

15. a. def. of reflection image (meaning)
b. def. of reflection image (meaning)
c. Two Perpendiculars Thm.

Chapter Review

Questions on **SPUR** Objectives

See margin for answers not shown below.

SPUR stands for **S**kills, **P**roperties, **U**ses, and **R**epresentations. The Chapter Review questions are grouped according to the SPUR Objectives for this chapter.

SKILLS deal with the procedures used to get answers.

■ **Objective A:** *Perform drawings and constructions applying the definition of reflection image.*
(Lessons 4-1, 4-3)

In 1–4, trace the figure first.

1. Draw $r_\ell(E)$.

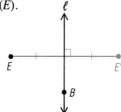

2. Construct $r_m(X)$.

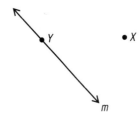

3. Construct the reflecting line ℓ for which $r_\ell(P) = Q$.

$\bullet$ P

$\circ$ Q

4. Draw the reflecting line m for which $r_m(\triangle ABC) = \triangle DEF$.

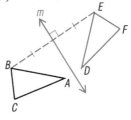

■ **Objective B:** *Draw reflection images of segments, angles, and polygons over a given line.*
(Lessons 4-2, 4-3, 4-6)

In 5–8, trace the figure first. Then draw the reflection image of the given figure over the given line.

5.

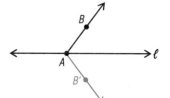

6.

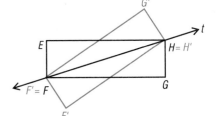

7.

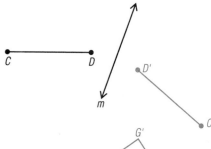

8.

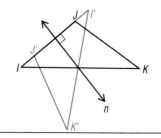

200

Objective C: *Draw all symmetry lines of segments and angles. (Lesson 4-7)*

9–11, draw all symmetry lines.

9.

10.

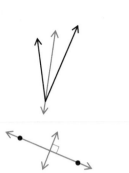

11.

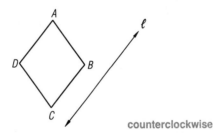

Objective D: *Determine measures of angles in figures and their reflection images. (Lessons 4-2, 4-6)*

In 12 and 13, use the figure below. $r_{\overleftrightarrow{AD}}(B) = C$.

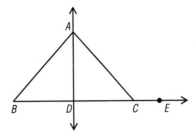

12. If $m\angle BAD = 42$, find $m\angle BAC$. 84
13. If $m\angle B = x$, find $m\angle ACE$. 180 − x

PROPERTIES deal with the principles behind the mathematics.

Objective E: *Apply properties of reflections to make conclusions, using one or more of the following justifications:*
   definition of reflection
   Reflections preserve distance.
   Reflections preserve angle measure.
   Reflections switch orientation.
   Figure Reflection Theorem
   Flip-Flop Theorem
   Side-Switching Theorem
(Lessons 4-1, 4-2, 4-6, 4-7)

14. If $r_m(A) = B$, then what conclusion follows due to the Flip-Flop Theorem? $r_m(B) = A$

15. If $r_\ell(A) = B$, what conclusion follows due to the definition of reflection?
ℓ is the ⊥ bisector of $\overline{AB}$.

In 16–19, suppose $r(CDEF) = GHIJ$. Justify each conclusion.

16. $r(E) = I$ Figure Reflection Theorem

17. $r(\angle EDF) = \angle IHJ$ Figure Reflection Thm.

18. $m\angle EDF = m\angle IHJ$ Reflections preserve ∠ measure.

19. $FC = JG$ Reflections preserve distance.

In 20 and 21, refer to the figure below.

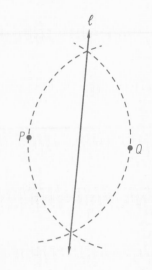

counterclockwise

20. What is the orientation of $ADCB$?

21. If $ADCB$ is reflected over line ℓ, what is the orientation of the image? clockwise

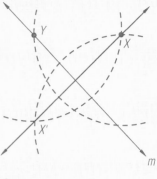

■ **Objective F:** *Apply properties of symmetry to make conclusions about symmetric figures.*
(Lesson 4-7)

In 22–24, $\overleftrightarrow{XZ}$ is a symmetry line of polygon *WXYZ* below.

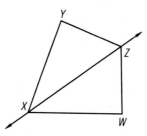

22. Which sides of the polygon have the same length? $\overline{XY}$ and $\overline{XW}$, $\overline{YZ}$ and $\overline{ZW}$
23. Which angles of the figure have the same measure?
24. If m∠*WXZ* = 35, which other angle or angles have measure 35°? ∠ZXY

In 25–27, polygon r(*FABCDE*) = *FEDCBA*.

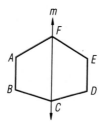

25. *True* or *false*? *FABCDE* is symmetric to line *m*. **True**
26. Name all angles with the same measure as ∠*D*. ∠B
27. *True* or *false*? *m* bisects ∠*AFE*. **True**
28. **a.** How many symmetry lines has a segment $\overline{PQ}$? **two**
   b. Name them. $\overleftrightarrow{PQ}$ **and the ⊥ bisector of** $\overline{PQ}$

■ **Objective G:** *Given appropriate information, write proofs, using theorems, postulates, or definitions you have studied in this book as justifications. (Lessons 4-4, 4-5)*

In 29 and 30, use the figure below. Justify the conclusion.

29. Given: $r_m(E) = F.$
   $r_m(G) = H.$
   Conclusion 1: $r_m(H) = G.$
   Conclusion 2: $EH = FG.$
30. Given: $r_m(E) = F.$
   $r_m(G) = H.$
   Conclusion 1: $r_m(I) = I.$
   Conclusion 2: m∠*EGI* = m∠*FHI*.

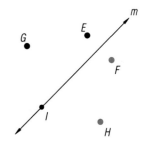

31. Use the figure below.
   Given: *m* ∥ *n*.
   Prove: m∠1 = m∠6.

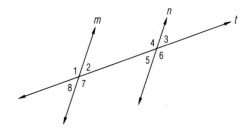

32. Given: △*MOP* in the figure below is equilateral.
   $MO = MN.$
   Prove: $MP = MN.$

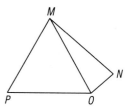

SES deal with applications of mathematics in real situations.

Objective H: *Locate and make symmetry lines designs.* *(Lesson 4-7)*

33–35, trace the figure. Then draw all lines that ~uld seem to be lines of reflection symmetry.

34. **35.**

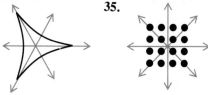

36. You see this writing in a mirror. What does the original say? MATH Я WE

ƎW R HTAM

EPRESENTATIONS deal with pictures, graphs, or objects that illustrate concepts.

Objective I: *Find coordinates of reflection images points over the coordinate axes.* *(Lessons 4-1, 4-2)*

. Find the reflection image of (3, 7) over the *x*-axis. **(3, -7)**

, A quadrilateral has vertices $A = (3, 7)$, $B = (3, 1)$, $C = (-2, 8)$, and $D = (0, 4)$. Find and graph the vertices of the reflection image of this quadrilateral over the *y*-axis.

▪. Give the image of (a, b) when reflected over the *y*-axis. **(-a, b)**

▪. Give the image of (c, d) when reflected over the *x*-axis. **(c, -d)**

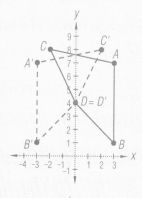

CHAPTER 5 ■ POLYGONS

DAILY PACING CHART ■ CHAPTER 5

Every chapter of UCSMP *Geometry* includes lessons, a Progress Self-Test, and a Chapter Review. For optimal student performance, the self-test and review should be covered. (See *General Teaching Suggestions: Mastery* on page T36 of this Teacher's Edition.) By following the pace of the Full Course given here, students can complete the entire text by the end of the year. Students following the pace of the Minimal Course spend more time when there are quizzes and on the Chapter Review and will generally not complete all of the chapters in this text.

When all lessons are covered from the beginning (the recommendation of the authors), then students in the Minimal Course can cover through Lesson 13-4 and will cover all they need for future courses. For more information on pacing, see *General Teaching Suggestions: Pace* on page T35 of the Teacher's Edition.

DAY	MINIMAL COURSE	FULL COURSE
1	5-1	5-1
2	5-2	5-2
3	5-3	5-3
4	5-4	5-4
5	Quiz (TRF); Start 5-5.	Quiz (TRF); 5-5
6	Finish 5-5.	5-6
7	5-6	5-7
8	5-7	Progress Self-Test
9	Progress Self-Test	Chapter Review
10	Chapter Review	Chapter Test (TRF)
11	Chapter Review	
12	Chapter Test (TRF)	

TESTING OPTIONS
■ Quiz for Lessons 5-1 Through 5-4   ■ Chapter 5 Test, Form A   ■ Chapter 5 Test, Cumulative Form
■ Chapter 5 Test, Form B

PROVIDING FOR INDIVIDUAL DIFFERENCES
The student text has been written for, and tested with, average students. It also has been used successfully with better and more poorly prepared students.

The Lesson Notes often include Error Analysis and Alternate Approach features to help you with those students who need more help. A blackline Lesson Master (in the Teacher's Resource File), keyed to the chapter objectives, is provided for each lesson to allow more practice. (However, since it is very important to keep up with the daily pace, you are not expected to use all of these masters. Again, refer to the suggestions for pacing on page T35.) Extension activities are provided in the Lesson Notes for those students who have completed the particular lesson in a shorter amount of time than is expected, even in the Full Course.

204A

OBJECTIVES ■ CHAPTER 5

The objectives listed here are the same as in the Chapter 5 Review on pages 249-251 of the student text. The Progress Self-Test on page 248 and the tests in the Teacher's Resource File cover these objectives. For recommendations regarding the handling of this end-of-chapter material, see the notes in the margin on the corresponding pages of the Teacher's Edition.

OBJECTIVES FOR CHAPTER 5 (Organized into the SPUR Categories—Skills, Properties, Uses, and Representations)	Progress Self-Test Questions	Chapter Review Questions	Lesson Master from Teacher's Resource File*
SKILLS			
A Draw polygons satisfying various conditions.	4a, 12	1 through 4	5-1, 5-3, 5-4, 5-5
B Apply the Trapezoid Angle Theorem and the theorems about alternate interior angles.	4b, 9, 11	5 through 12	5-5, 5-6
C Find unknown measures of angles using the Isosceles Triangle, Triangle-Sum, Quadrilateral-Sum, and Polygon-Sum Theorems.	3, 5, 6	13 through 20	5-1, 5-7
PROPERTIES			
D Classify special polygons by their properties.	1, 7	21 through 30	5-1, 5-2
E Identify properties of triangles and quadrilaterals.	2, 8	31 through 34	5-1, 5-4, 5-5
F Evaluate conjectures.	13	35 through 39	5-3
G Write proofs using the properties of triangles and quadrilaterals.	10	40 through 45	5-1, 5-2, 5-4, 5-5, 5-6
USES			
H Explain why everyday objects are shaped like certain polygons.	14	46 through 48	5-2
REPRESENTATIONS			
I Draw hierarchies of polygons.	15	49 through 50	5-2

*The masters are numbered to match the lessons.

OVERVIEW ■ CHAPTER 5

Ideas from Chapter 2 (good definitions), Chapter 3 (angles formed by parallel lines), and Chapter 4 (reflection symmetry) are applied in this chapter to help students learn the properties of polygons.

Lesson 5-1 uses the symmetry of an isosceles triangle to deduce the famous theorem that the base angles have equal measure.

The common types of quadrilaterals are defined in Lesson 5-2, where a classification process begins and continues through Lesson 5-6. During this process, Lesson 5-3 discusses conjectures, and pro-vides students with the means to check whether a property holds.

Properties of the more general types of quadrilaterals are deduced and then applied to more specific types. Lesson 5-4 applies the symmetry of the isosceles triangle to develop the properties of kites (a very useful figure too often ignored in school geometry), which also includes rhombuses and squares. Lesson 5-5 does the same for trapezoids, and thus gives properties of parallelograms and isosceles trapezoids.

Finally, the angle-sum properties of all polygons are presented. The alternate interior angle theorems are needed and therefore deduced in Lesson 5-6. This enables the sums of the measures of the angles in triangles and other polygons to be deduced in Lesson 5-7.

An important theme in this chapter is that of *classification*. Triangles, quadrilaterals, and polygons in general can be classified in various ways. One of the necessary prerequisites to understanding these figures is to know these classifications and the relationships among them.

PERSPECTIVES ■ CHAPTER 5

The Perspectives provide the rationale for the inclusion of topics or approaches, provide mathematical background, and make connections with other lessons and within UCSMP.

5-1

ISOSCELES TRIANGLES

This lesson contains a proof that isosceles triangles are symmetric. Once this is done, all corresponding angles, segments, and so on, have the same measures, and thus the base angles have the same measure. In this way, all of its properties can be deduced from the symmetry of the isosceles triangle without using congruent triangles. Included is a proof that the bisector of the vertex angle is also a perpendicular bisector, which makes it a median and altitude as well.

Proofs using symmetry are similar to proofs using coordinates. In coordinate proofs, the hard work is to deduce the coordinates of the vertices of the figure. In symmetry proofs, the hard work is to show a figure is symmetric. In both cases, once you have that property, other properties follow quickly, including properties of angle measure which are quite difficult with coordinates and usually require trigonometry. Both angle measure and segment length properties can be deduced using symmetry.

The emphasis in this lesson should be on the justifications, not on creating the proofs.

5-2

TYPES OF QUADRILATERALS

In this book, seven types of quadrilaterals are presented: trapezoids, isosceles trapezoids, parallelograms, rectangles, rhombuses, squares, and kites. Some are familiar to students; some not. All are defined in this lesson so that students can see the big picture and begin to understand how they are all related.

5-3

CONJECTURES

In earlier versions of the text, this lesson came earlier, but it was felt by teachers that students needed some experience with proof before they understood conjectures. Placing the lesson here not only fits

and helps to set up the other properties of quadrilaterals, but it also gives students a chance to have a second day to learn and discuss the seven types of quadrilaterals.

5-4

PROPERTIES OF KITES

The kite is the only special type of quadrilateral we present that is not standard in other texts. However, it is commonly studied in Europe due to the greater use of symmetry in European texts. Kites are related to rhombuses and to isosceles triangles, and kites appear wherever circles intersect. Kites also appear in other places. If tangents to a circle O from a point P intersect the circle at T and U, then $OTPU$ is a kite. If $\overline{OA}$ is a radius perpendicular to a chord $\overline{BC}$, then $OBAC$ is a kite. Also, if two points on the perpendicular bisector of a segment are connected to the endpoints of the segment, a kite is formed.

This lesson derives the symmetry of a kite, and from that the fact that each kite has a diagonal (its symmetry diagonal) which bisects two angles and is the perpendicular bisector of the other diagonal.

5-5

PROPERTIES OF TRAPEZOIDS

Due to its general nature, the trapezoid does not have many properties of its own. Other than the defining property (at least one pair of parallel sides), we discuss only two others in this book, the Trapezoid Angle Theorem (consecutive angles between a pair of parallel sides are supplementary) and the familiar area formula,

$A = \frac{1}{2}h(b_1 + b_2)$. These theorems justify the definition we choose for trapezoid; because parallelograms are trapezoids, the theorems automatically apply to parallelograms.

A further bonus from the definition of trapezoid we use is that all rectangles are isosceles trapezoids (in two ways), and so two symmetry lines for the rectangle comes from the symmetry line of the isosceles trapezoid.

5-6

ALTERNATE INTERIOR ANGLES

The two alternate interior angle theorems (if two lines are parallel, then alternate interior angles have equal measures and the converse) follow from the Parallel Lines and Corresponding Angles Postulates. We apply the theorem (not the converse) in this lesson to help prove that every rhombus is a parallelogram. That completes the quadrilateral hierarchy. In the next lesson, the converse is applied in the classic way to deduce the Triangle-Sum Theorem.

5-7

SUMS OF ANGLE MEASURES IN POLYGONS

In this lesson, the angle-sum theorems are proved for triangles and quadrilaterals. In the questions, students are asked to extend the formula to polygons of any number of sides.

Students who have taken previous UCSMP courses will be familiar with the Triangle-Sum Theorem; other students most likely will also know this theorem. The important points in the lesson are (1) the Triangle-Sum Theorem follows from other theorems and postulates, and (2) the Quadrilateral-Sum and Polygon-Sum Theorems follow from the Triangle-Sum Theorem.

This lesson also introduces extended ratios.

■ CHAPTER 5

This is a 10-to-12 day chapter: 7 to 8 days for the lessons and quiz; 1 day for the Progress Self-Test; 1 or 2 days for the Chapter Review; and 1 day for a Chapter Test. (See the Daily Pacing Chart on page 204A.)

The sets of questions at the end of each lesson are short, so you should be able to assign all of them.

CHAPTER 5

Polygons

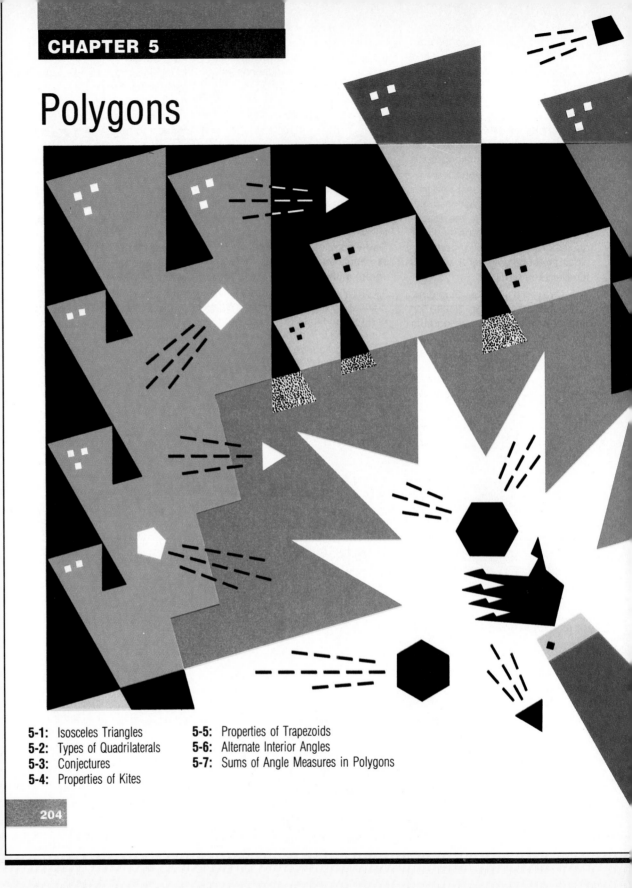

5-1: Isosceles Triangles
5-2: Types of Quadrilaterals
5-3: Conjectures
5-4: Properties of Kites
5-5: Properties of Trapezoids
5-6: Alternate Interior Angles
5-7: Sums of Angle Measures in Polygons

204

204

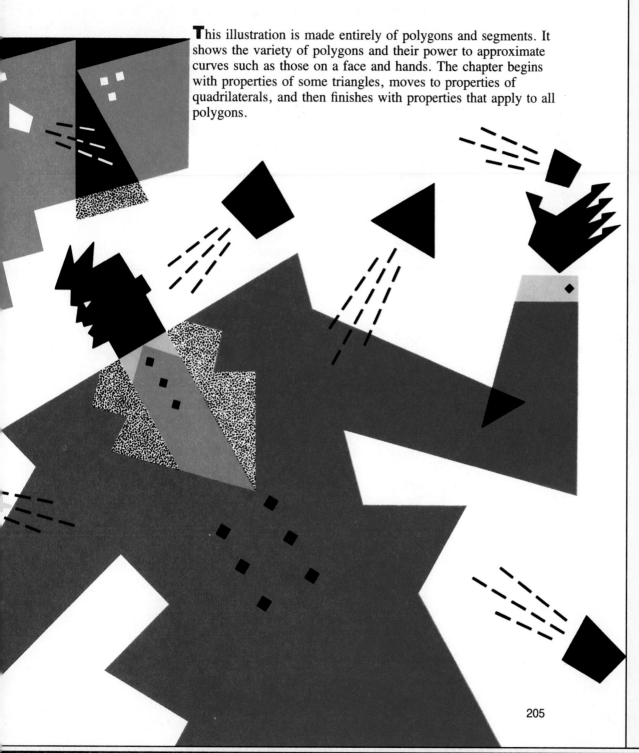

This illustration is made entirely of polygons and segments. It shows the variety of polygons and their power to approximate curves such as those on a face and hands. The chapter begins with properties of some triangles, moves to properties of quadrilaterals, and then finishes with properties that apply to all polygons.

USING PAGES 204-205
Notice the variety of visual effects that are created using only polygons and segments and the detail of the head and hands. Ask students to find a pentagon (sample: the tie), hexagon (sample: the lapels), an octagon (sample: the nonconvex polygon at the top in the middle). How many sides does the polygon that makes up the left hand have? (22)

Encourage students interested in drawing to create a simple picture using the same figures. Display the drawings in the classroom.

205

LESSON

Isosceles Triangles

In the last chapter, you were asked to draw symmetry lines of figures just by looking at them. Of course, that kind of exercise does not prove that a figure has symmetry. People make mistakes and draw symmetry lines where there aren't any. In this lesson is a proof that isosceles triangles are reflection-symmetric. This symmetry will enable you to deduce some other properties of isosceles triangles.

Recall that isosceles triangles have (at least) two sides of equal length. They are the outlines of rooftops, cones, and many other objects that taper to a point. They occur when the endpoints of two noncollinear radii of a circle are joined.

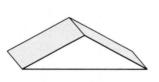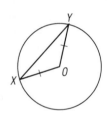

The angle determined by the equal sides in an isosceles triangle is called the **vertex angle** (∠*A* in the figure below). The other two angles are the **base angles** (∠*B* and ∠*C*). Each base angle is said to be *opposite* one of the equal sides. The side whose endpoints are the vertices of the base angles is called the **base** ($\overline{BC}$).

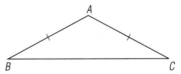

The proof of the next theorem is long. Long proofs are often easier to understand when they are written in paragraphs than when they are in the two-column format of Conclusions and Justifications. You should read the proof very slowly and refer to the drawing as figures are named.

206

Isosceles Triangle Symmetry Theorem:

The line containing the bisector of the vertex angle of an isosceles triangle is a symmetry line for the triangle.

Proof

First draw a figure and state the given and the conclusion in terms of that figure.

Given: Isosceles triangle ABC with vertex angle A bisected by m.

Prove: m is a symmetry line for $\triangle ABC$.

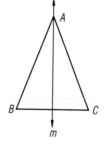

There are three things given. Each leads to conclusions that are used later in the proof. First, since m is an angle bisector, because of the Side-Switching Theorem, when $\overrightarrow{AB}$ is reflected over m, its image is $\overrightarrow{AC}$. Thus $r_m(B)$ is on $\overrightarrow{AC}$. Let $B' = r_m(B)$. Second, it is given that A is on the reflecting line, so $r_m(A) = A$. Hence, since reflections preserve distance, $AB' = AB$. Third, it is given that $\triangle ABC$ is isosceles with vertex angle A, so $AB = AC$. Now put all these conclusions together. By the Transitive Property of Equality, $AB' = AC$. So B' and C are points on ray $\overrightarrow{AC}$ at the same distance from A, and so $B' = C$. That is, $r_m(B) = C$. By the Flip-Flop Theorem, $r_m(C) = B$. So, by the Figure Reflection Theorem, $r_m(\triangle ABC) = \triangle ACB$, which is the sufficient condition for the symmetry of the triangle to line m.

In triangles that are not isosceles, no angle bisector is a symmetry line. Below, you can see that the reflection image of E over the bisector m is not F. ($r_m(E)$ is on $\overrightarrow{DF}$. You should estimate its location.)

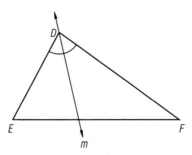

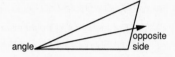

Given: The figure with
$AB = AC$.
Prove: $m\angle 3 = m\angle 4$.

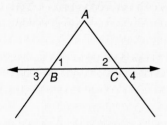

m∠3 = m∠1 **Vert. Angle Theorem**

m∠1 = m∠2 **Isosceles △ Theorem**

m∠2 = m∠4 **Vert. Angle Theorem**

m∠3 = m∠4 **Transitive Property of Equality**

A segment connecting a vertex of a triangle to the midpoint of the opposite side is called a **median** of the triangle. Drawn below are one median, one perpendicular bisector, and one angle bisector of △*DEF*.

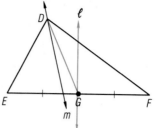

m is the bisector of ∠*EDF*.
ℓ is the ⊥ bisector of $\overline{EF}$.
$\overline{DG}$ is the median from vertex *D*.

For △*DEF*, the median, angle bisector, and ⊥ bisector are on different lines. But examine again isosceles triangle *ABC* with bisector *m* of ∠*A*. Since $r_m(B) = C$, *m* is the ⊥ bisector of $\overline{BC}$. And so *m* contains the midpoint of $\overline{BC}$. And so *m* contains the median from vertex *A*. This proves:

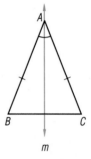

Theorem:

In an isosceles triangle, the bisector of the vertex angle, the perpendicular bisector of the base, and the median to the base determine the same line.

There's even more. In the proof of the Isosceles Triangle Symmetry Theorem, since $r_m(A) = A$, $r_m(B) = C$, and $r_m(C) = B$, then $r_m(\angle ABC) = \angle ACB$ by the Figure Reflection Theorem. Thus $m\angle ABC = m\angle ACB$ because reflections preserve angle measure. This conclusion is a very important theorem.

Isosceles Triangle Theorem:

If a triangle has two equal sides, then the angles opposite them are equal.

The Isosceles Triangle Theorem is useful in proofs in which you must go from equal sides to equal angles.

208

Example 1   Given: the figure at the right, with $PQ = QR$.
Prove: $m\angle 2 = m\angle 4$.

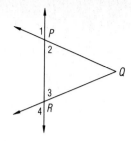

Analyze $PQ = QR$, and so, because of the Isosceles Triangle Theorem, $m\angle 2 = m\angle 3$. Angles 3 and 4 are vertical. Thus the Transitive Property strategy can be used.

Write

Conclusions	Justifications
1. m∠2 = m∠3	**Isosceles Triangle Theorem**
2. m∠3 = m∠4	**Vertical Angle Theorem**
3. m∠2 = m∠4	**Transitive Property of Equality (steps 1 and 2)**

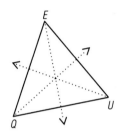

In an equilateral triangle all sides have the same length, so any side of an equilateral triangle may be considered as its base, and any angle its vertex angle. Thus, from the Isosceles Triangle Symmetry Theorem, an equilateral triangle has three symmetry lines. These lines can be thought of as the bisectors of its angles or the perpendicular bisectors of its sides. The lines contain its medians.

Example 2   Prove: If a triangle is equilateral, then it is equiangular (has three equal angles).

Draw   A figure is needed. Use equilateral $\triangle EQU$ at the left above and write a "given" and "prove" for that figure.
Given: Equilateral $\triangle QUE$.
Prove: $m\angle Q = m\angle U = m\angle E$.

Analyze   Take the equal sides two at a time. From each pair, get two equal angles.

Write

Conclusions	Justifications
1. QE = EU	**definition of equilateral $\triangle$ (meaning)**
2. m∠Q = m∠U	**Isosceles $\triangle$ Theorem**
3. EU = QU	**definition of equilateral $\triangle$ (meaning)**
4. m∠Q = m∠E	**Isosceles $\triangle$ Theorem**
5. m∠Q = m∠E = m∠U	**Transitive Property of Equality (steps 2 and 4)**

Questions

In Questions 1 and 2, refer to △*WIN* in which *IW* = *IN*.

1. Identify:
   a. the base $\overline{WN}$
   b. the vertex angle ∠*I*
   c. the base angles ∠*W* and ∠*N*
   d. the angles of equal measure. ∠*W* and ∠*N*

2. Describe the location of a symmetry line of △*WIN*. the bisector of ∠*I*

3. *Multiple choice.* When a triangle is isosceles, which of the following best describes the bisector of its vertex angle and the perpendicular bisector of its base?
   (a) They are the same line.
   (b) They are parallel.
   (c) They are both perpendicular to the base.
   (d) All of (a)-(c) are true. (d)

4. In △*DEF* at the right, *DE* = *EF* and *M* is the midpoint of $\overline{DF}$.
   a. $\overline{EM}$ is called a(n) ___?___. median
   b. What pairs of angles are equal? ∠*D* and ∠*F*

5. Use the figure below. (Hint: Use at least one theorem from this lesson as a justification.)
   Given: *XY* = *XZ*.
   Prove: m∠1 = m∠2. See margin.

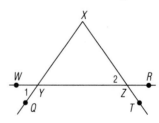

6. *True* or *false*?
   a. If a triangle is isosceles, then it is equilateral. False
   b. If a triangle is equilateral, then it is isosceles. True

7. Match the type of triangle with the number of symmetry lines.
   a. equilateral (iii)   (i)   1
   b. isosceles (i)   (ii) 2
   c. scalene (iv)   (iii) 3
                              (iv) 0

210

In 8 and 9, use the figure below. $\overleftrightarrow{OE}$ is a symmetry line for $\triangle HEP$.

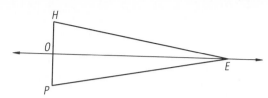

8. Name all pairs of segments with equal lengths.
   $\overline{HE}$ and $\overline{PE}$, $\overline{OH}$ and $\overline{OP}$

9. Name all pairs of angles with equal measures.
   $\angle P$ and $\angle H$, $\angle HOE$ and $\angle POE$, $\angle HEO$ and $\angle PEO$

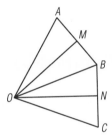

10. In the figure at the left, $\odot A$ and $\odot H$ each have radius AH and $\odot A \cap \odot H = \{M, T\}$.
    a. Is $\triangle AHM$ equilateral, isosceles but not equilateral, or neither isosceles nor equilateral? Justify your answer. **See margin.**
    b. Name all angles in the figure equal in measure to $\angle HMA$.
       $\angle MHA$, $\angle MAH$, $\angle AHT$, $\angle HAT$, $\angle ATH$

11. Given: In the figure at the right,
    $\overline{AD}$ and $\overline{BE}$ intersect at C,
    $AB = AC$, and $DC = DE$.
    Prove: $m\angle B = m\angle CED$.
    See margin.

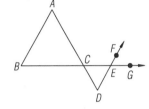

12. At the left, $\triangle AOB$ and $\triangle BOC$ are each isosceles. $\overrightarrow{OM}$ and $\overrightarrow{ON}$ are bisectors of the vertex angles AOB and BOC. If $m\angle AOC = 83$, what is $m\angle MON$? **41.5**

13. *Multiple choice.* The horizontal beam $\overline{RS}$ below helps to support other beams. To keep the top beams from collapsing, the vertical support $\overline{QT}$ is used. If the beams $\overline{RT}$ and $\overline{ST}$ are of equal length, which of (a)–(c) is not true?

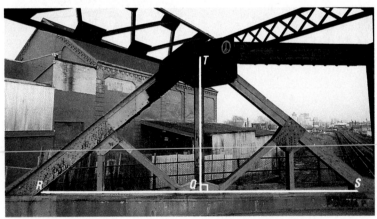

(a) $\overrightarrow{TQ}$ bisects $\angle RTS$.   (c) $\overrightarrow{TQ} \perp \overline{RS}$.
(b) Q is the midpoint of $\overline{RS}$.   (d) All of (a)-(c) are true. **(d)**

LESSON 5-1   Isosceles Triangles   **211**

FOLLOW-UP

MORE PRACTICE
For more questions on SPUR Objectives, use *Lesson Master 5-1*, shown below.

10. a. Equilateral; $AM = AH$ by being radii of $\odot A$. $MH = AH$ by being radii of $\odot H$. So $AM = AH = MH$ by the Transitive Prop. of Equality. Therefore, $\triangle AHM$ is equilateral by the definition of equilateral triangle (suff. cond.).

11.

Conclusions	Justifications
1. $m\angle B = m\angle ACB$	Isosceles $\triangle$ Thm.
2. $m\angle ACB = m\angle ECD$	Vertical Angle Thm.
3. $m\angle ECD = m\angle CED$	Isosceles $\triangle$ Thm.
4. $m\angle B = m\angle CED$	Trans. Prop. of Eq. (steps 1, 2, and 3)

17. sample:

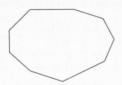

18. sample:

21. a. sample:

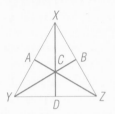

Median: AZ = YB = XD.
Distances from vertices to centroid: XC = YC = ZC.
XC = $\frac{2}{3}$AZ.
b. sample:

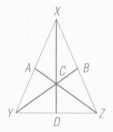

Medians: AZ and YB are equal, but different from XD. Distances from vertices to centroid are $\frac{2}{3}$ the lengths of the medians.
c. sample:

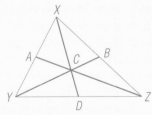

Medians: all have different lengths. Distances from vertices to centroid: all are different; they are $\frac{2}{3}$ the lengths of the medians.

---

14. $\overleftrightarrow{AD}$ is a symmetry line for polygon *ABCDEF* below.
   a. r(*ABCDEF*) = ___?___ AFEDCB
   b. Which sides of *ABCDEF* have the same length?
   c. Which angles in the figure have the same measure? *(Lesson 4-7)*

   b) $\overline{AB} \cong \overline{AF}$, $\overline{FE} \cong \overline{BC}$, $\overline{DE} \cong \overline{DC}$
   c) $\angle F \cong \angle B$, $\angle E \cong \angle C$, $\angle FAD \cong \angle BAD$, $\angle ADE \cong \angle ADC$

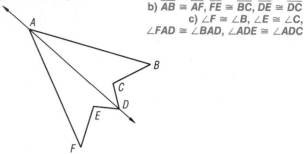

15. If F and G are figures and $r_m(F) = G$, then $r_m(G) = $ ___?___ . *(Lesson 4-6)* F

16. Give the reflection image of (*x*, *y*) over the y-axis. *(Lesson 4-1)* (-x, y)

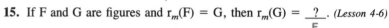

17. Draw a convex nonagon. *(Lesson 2-7)* See margin.

18. Draw an obtuse isosceles triangle. *(Lesson 2-7)* See margin.

19. Arrange from least to greatest number of sides: rectangle, octagon, pentagon, equilateral triangle, nonagon, 7-gon. *(Lesson 2-7)*
equilateral triangle, rectangle, pentagon, 7-gon, octagon, nonagon

20. Find three meanings of the word *median* other than the one in this lesson. See below.

21. Use a ruler, compass, and protractor or an automatic drawing tool.
   a. Draw an equilateral triangle. Draw all three medians. They should all intersect in a point called the **centroid** of the triangle. Measure the lengths of the medians and distances from the centroid to each of the vertices. What can you conclude?
   b. Draw an isosceles triangle that is not equilateral. Repeat the steps in part **a** for your triangle.
   c. Draw a scalene triangle. Repeat the steps in part **a** again.
   d. Summarize your work by writing a sentence or two that begins "In any triangle, the three medians... ." a–c) See margin.
   d) Sample: In any triangle, the three medians intersect at one point.

---

20. Sample: the middle number in an ordered sequence of numbers; the strip of land between highway lanes of traffic; (capitalized) relating to the Medes

5-2

Types of Quadrilaterals

RESOURCES
- Lesson Master 5-2
- Visual for Teaching Aid 23 shows the types of quadrilaterals in this lesson.
- Computer Master 7

The three-sided polygons, the triangles, were classified by the number of equal sides in Lesson 2-7. The four-sided polygons, the quadrilaterals, are more diverse and the classification is more complicated. There are seven major types: parallelogram, rhombus, rectangle, square, kite, trapezoid, and isosceles trapezoid. Here are definitions and examples for four of them. You should *memorize* these definitions.

OBJECTIVES

D Classify special polygons by their properties.

G Write proofs using the properties of triangles and quadrilaterals.

H Explain why everyday objects are shaped like certain polygons.

I Draw hierarchies of polygons.

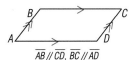

$AB \parallel CD, BC \parallel AD$

Definition:

A quadrilateral is a **parallelogram** if and only if both pairs of its opposite sides are parallel.

$EF = FG = GH = HE$

Definition:

A quadrilateral is a **rhombus** if and only if its four sides are equal in length.

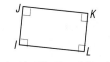

∠I, ∠J, ∠K, ∠L are right angles.

Definition:

A quadrilateral is a **rectangle** if and only if it has four right angles.

TEACHING NOTES

Classification is a task often taken for granted. But recent research by many people, sparked by the Dutch mathematics educators Pierre van Hiele and Dina van Hiele-Geldof, has alerted us to the fact that many students enter geometry thinking that squares are not rectangles, that rectangles are not parallelograms, and so forth. In fact, students are taught as early as pre-school or first grade to distinguish squares from rectangles. Given a picture of a square, if a student in the elementary grades says, "That is a rectangle," he or she is usually considered wrong. Thus, you may have to unteach, and this can be far more difficult than teaching something new.

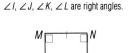

$MN = NO = OP = PM$
∠M, ∠N, ∠O, ∠P are right angles.

Definition:

A quadrilateral is a **square** if and only if it has four equal sides and four right angles.

From the definitions, you can see that every square is a rhombus since every square has four equal sides. You can also conclude that every square is a rectangle since every square has four right angles. This information is summarized in the network below. This network shows a part of a hierarchy of quadrilaterals.

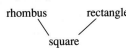

LESSON 5-2 Types of Quadrilaterals **213**

Notice that each special type of quadrilateral is defined distinctly. For instance, we do not define a rectangle as "a parallelogram with a right angle." This is not the way students perceive rectangles. Students perceive figures as being of different types and not categorized. To be able to categorize them is the subject of this lesson and of Lesson 5-4.

The definitions we use are chosen because of their simplicity and because of a desire to have as much nesting of figures as possible.

The definition of rectangle violates the stipulation that a good definition states no more than is necessary (it is sufficient to have three right angles—the fourth right angle can be deduced), but pedagogically it is satisfying to define it as having four right angles.

There is some controversy regarding the definition of "trapezoid," and it has generated occasional articles in the *Mathematics Teacher*. We favor the definition given on page 214 (at least one pair of parallel sides) rather than the alternative (exactly one pair of parallel sides) because, under the former definition, any statement true for all trapezoids is automatically true for all parallelograms. Also, all other classes of polygons are inclusive; for example, everyone defines an isosceles triangle as one with at least two equal sides; a rhombus is defined so that every rhombus is a parallelogram, and so on.

Students may not realize how important each word is in a good definition. To explain the significance of each word in the definition of *kite*, consider counterexamples for words which are omitted. For example,
(i) if *distinct* is omitted:

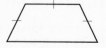

Because two perpendiculars to the same line are parallel, every rectangle is a parallelogram. So we can add "parallelogram" to the hierarchy.

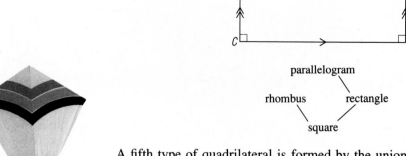

A fifth type of quadrilateral is formed by the union of two isosceles triangles having the same base, with the base removed. The result is a quadrilateral that resembles a *kite* or arrowhead. Pictured here are the convex kite *ABCD* and the nonconvex kite *FORM*.

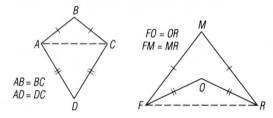

Definition:

A quadrilateral is a **kite** if and only if it has two distinct pairs of consecutive sides of the same length.

From the definitions of kite and rhombus, every rhombus is a kite. This information is added to the hierarchy. You can also now conclude that every square is a kite by reading up the hierarchy from square to rhombus to kite.

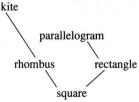

A figure more general than the parallelogram is the *trapezoid*.

Definition:

A quadrilateral is a **trapezoid** if and only if it has at least one pair of parallel sides.

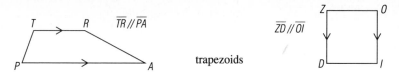

$\overline{TR} \parallel \overline{PA}$

$\overline{ZD} \parallel \overline{OI}$

trapezoids

Parallel sides of a trapezoid are called **bases.** In the figures above, $\overline{TR}$ and $\overline{PA}$ are bases and $\overline{ZD}$ and $\overline{OI}$ are bases. Two consecutive angles that share a base are called **base angles.** This terminology enables us to define a special type of trapezoid.

Definition:

A trapezoid is **isosceles** if and only if it has a pair of base angles equal in measure.

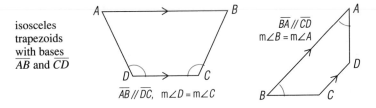

isosceles
trapezoids
with bases
$\overline{AB}$ and $\overline{CD}$

$\overline{AB} \parallel \overline{DC}, \ m\angle D = m\angle C$

$\overline{BA} \parallel \overline{CD}$
$m\angle B = m\angle A$

Because a rectangle has opposite sides parallel and all angles equal, every rectangle is an isosceles trapezoid. You can now relate all these seven types of quadrilaterals in the same hierarchy. This is shown by the dark lines below. One other hierarchy relationship can be deduced; every rhombus is a parallelogram. It will be deduced in Lesson 5-4. This is shown in the hierarchy now by a blue line.

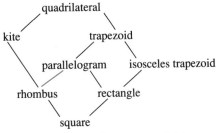

The hierarchy of quadrilaterals is very useful because it allows properties of some quadrilaterals to apply to other quadrilaterals. The general rule is:

ANY property held by a type of figure in the hierarchy is also held by *all* the types of figures below it to which it is connected.

For example, *square* is below *rhombus* in the hierarchy. Thus any square has all the properties of a rhombus. Squares and rhombuses are below *kite*. Thus they have all the properties of kites. In the next lessons this rule will be used to identify many properties of specific quadrilaterals.

(ii) if *consecutive* is omitted:

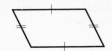

Traditionally, the isosceles trapezoid is defined as having equal legs. We define it with equal base angles for two important reasons: (a) the complication of stating an exception for parallelograms, if defined in terms of equal legs; and (b) the beauty of the proof of a symmetry line and consequent equal legs (see Lesson 5-5, page 230).

Using a hierarchy diagram to relate geometric figures is extremely useful. In addition to providing a clear visual diagram, it simplifies the work done in proving characteristics of the various types of quadrilaterals. For example, it is not necessary to prove that the diagonals of a square are perpendicular bisectors of each other, because this statement is true for a kite, and a square is a kite.

To formalize the use of the quadrilateral hierarchy in proofs, the Quadrilateral Hierarchy Theorem is done in Lesson 5-6.

ADDITIONAL EXAMPLES
In 1-4, fill in the blanks with one of the words *always, sometimes,* or *never.*

1. A parallelogram is __?__ an isosceles trapezoid.
sometimes (when it is a rectangle)

2. A rhombus is __?__ a kite.
always

3. A parallelogram is __?__ a square.
sometimes

4. A kite is __?__ a trapezoid.
sometimes (when it is a rhombus)

Questions

Covering the Reading

In 1–7, **a.** give a sufficient condition for each figure and **b.** draw an example. **See margin.**

1. parallelogram

2. rhombus

3. rectangle

4. square

5. kite

6. trapezoid

7. isosceles trapezoid

8. Draw a hierarchy of the following quadrilaterals: kite, square, rhombus, rectangle, parallelogram.

kite .... parallelogram
rhombus   rectangle
square

In 9–15, *true* or *false*?

9. Every square is a rhombus. **True**

10. Every rhombus is a square. **False**

11. Every square is a kite. **True**

12. Every kite is a rhombus. **False**

13. If a quadrilateral is a trapezoid, then it is a parallelogram. **False**

14. A property of a square is a property of a kite. **False**

15. A property of a trapezoid is a property of a parallelogram. **True**

Applying the Mathematics

In 16–19, write in symbols the information marked on the figure. Use this information to name the figure. Be as specific as you can, but do not be fooled by looks.

16.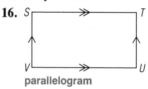
parallelogram

17.
rectangle

18.
rhombus

19.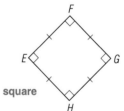
square

20. Let A = set of all rectangles and B = set of all rhombuses. Describe A ∩ B. **the set of all squares**

216

21. Circles O and Q intersect at N and P. Justify each conclusion in this proof that $NOPQ$ is a kite.

Conclusions	Justifications
1. $QN = QP$	**a.** __?__ Definition of circle (meaning)
2. $ON = OP$	**b.** __?__ Definition of circle (meaning)
3. $NOPQ$ is a kite.	**c.** __?__ Definition of kite (sufficient condition)

In 22–24, a real object is given. Name all of the types of quadrilaterals that describe each shape. **See margin.**

22. bedsheet   **23.** warning sign   **24.** trough

Review

25. In $\triangle ABC$, $AB = AC$.
If $m\angle B = 4x - 7$
and $m\angle C = 2x + 13$,
a. find x; **10**
b. find $m\angle B$. *(Lesson 4-2)* **33**

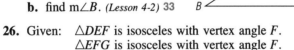

26. Given: $\triangle DEF$ is isosceles with vertex angle F.
$\triangle EFG$ is isosceles with vertex angle F.
Prove: $DF = FG$. *(Lesson 5-1)*

$EF = DF$	def. of isosceles triangle
$EF = FG$	def. of isosceles triangle
$DF = FG$	Trans. Prop. of Equality

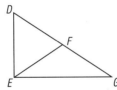

27. Draw a nonconvex hexagon. *(Lesson 2-7)* **Sample:**

Exploration

28. Which of the types of quadrilaterals on the hierarchy can be nonconvex? Support your answer with drawings. **See margin.**

29. Biologists place living things in a hierarchy. Show a hierarchy containing the following terms: man, cat, animal, mammal, primate, chimpanzee, lion, feline, plant. **See margin.**

30. Think of another hierarchy outside of mathematics different from that in Question 29. **See margin.**

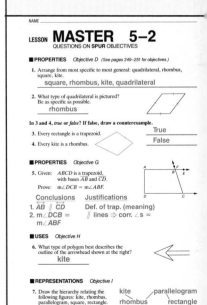

NAME _____

LESSON MASTER 5–2
QUESTIONS ON **SPUR** OBJECTIVES

■ **PROPERTIES**   *Objective D   (See pages 249–251 for objectives.)*

1. Arrange from most specific to most general: quadrilateral, rhombus, square, kite.
   square, rhombus, kite, quadrilateral

2. What type of quadrilateral is pictured? Be as specific as possible.
   rhombus

In 3 and 4, *true* or *false*? If false, draw a counterexample.

3. Every rectangle is a trapezoid.   True
4. Every kite is a rhombus.   False

■ **PROPERTIES**   *Objective G*

5. Given: $ABCD$ is a trapezoid, with bases $\overline{AB}$ and $\overline{CD}$.
   Prove: $m\angle DCB = m\angle ABF$.

Conclusions	Justifications
1. $\overline{AB} \parallel \overline{CD}$	Def. of trap. (meaning)
2. $m\angle DCB =$ $m\angle ABF$	$\parallel$ lines $\Rightarrow$ corr. $\angle$s =

■ **USES**   *Objective H*

6. What type of polygon best describes the outline of the arrowhead shown at the right?
   kite

■ **REPRESENTATIONS**   *Objective I*

7. Draw the hierarchy relating the following figures: kite, rhombus, parallelogram, square, rectangle.
   kite   parallelogram
   rhombus   rectangle
   square

39

RESOURCES
■ Lesson Master 5-3
🖳 Computer Master 8

OBJECTIVES

A Draw polygons satisfying various conditions.
F Evaluate conjectures.

TEACHING NOTES

In a study done by Z. Usiskin in 1976, the following statement was asked of juniors, all of whom had studied geometry and were now taking advanced algebra:

What kind of statement do mathematicians most often prove?
(a) A statement which is obvious without proof.
(b) A statement which seems to be true but the proof is necessary to convince everyone.
(c) A statement which does not seem to be true but the proof shows it to be true.
(d) A statement which is obviously not true.
(e) A statement which has a counterexample.

More students coming from traditional courses chose (c) than any other choice. Usiskin had thought most students in any course would choose (a), because they so often prove things that are visually obvious. This result suggests that many, if not most, students do not realize that proofs begin with a conjecture, a statement which is thought to be true.

Computer The major use of automatic drawers in geometry is to allow students to investigate hunches—to

---

Conjectures

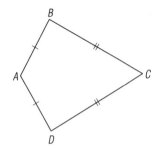

Pictured at the left is a kite, with two distinct pairs of equal sides. By measuring with a protractor, you can verify that m∠A = 122, m∠C = 60, and m∠B = m∠D = 89.

Does *every* kite have two angles of equal measure? Or is *ABCD* in some way an *unusual* kite? To answer this question, examine some other kites.

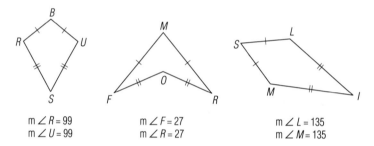

| m∠R = 99 | m∠F = 27 | m∠L = 135 |
| m∠U = 99 | m∠R = 27 | m∠M = 135 |

Each of the three kites above has two angles of equal measure.

A **conjecture** is an educated guess or opinion. The evidence above supports the conjecture "Every kite has at least two angles of equal measure."

To tell whether a conjecture is true or false, mathematicians usually start by examining instances. For conjectures about geometric figures, this means that drawings are made and explored. If even one counterexample is found, the conjecture is not true. If a counterexample is not found, there is evidence that the conjecture is true. Still, for a conjecture to be accepted as true for all cases, it must be proved.

The ancient Greeks tested conjectures with straightedge and compass constructions. Today we still have those tools, but increasingly people are using computers to explore conjectures. In this lesson, you may draw pictures using ruler, compass, and protractor, or you may use a computer with an automatic drawing tool.

218

To test a conjecture, it often helps to rewrite it in if-then form.

Example 1　**a.** Test this conjecture. "The diagonals of a kite are perpendicular."
b. Do you think the conjecture is true?

Solution

a. In if-then form the conjecture states that "if a figure is a kite, then its diagonals are perpendicular." Draw a variety of figures which satisfy the antecedent of the conjecture. That is, draw some kites. The more different they look, the better. We use the three kites from the previous page.

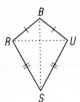 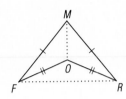 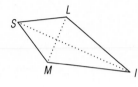

In each case drawn here, the diagonals do seem to form 90° angles at the point of intersection. (For kite *FORM,* the lines containing the diagonals seem to be perpendicular.)
b. You still could think the conjecture is false, but no counterexample is given here. The conjecture seems to be true.

Example 2　Show that the conjecture "The diagonals of a parallelogram have equal length" is false.

$AC = 3.1$ cm, $BD = 3.1$ cm

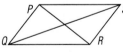

$PR = 1.8$ cm, $QS = 3.6$ cm

Solution　Restate the conjecture as an if-then statement: If a figure is a parallelogram, then its diagonals have equal length. To prove this statement is false you must find at least one figure satisfying the antecedent, but not the consequent. That is, you must find a parallelogram whose diagonals are not of equal length. At the left are two parallelograms. Notice that in *ABCD* the diagonals are equal; but in *PQRS* they are not. *ABCD* supports the conjecture. *PQRS* is a counterexample to the stated conjecture. It shows that the conjecture is false.

When a conjecture is not true, as in Example 2, you may try to **refine** it. This means to change the statement slightly so that the conjecture is true. In Example 2, the conjecture is true for some parallelograms, namely rectangles. Is it true for any other parallelograms? That conjecture is left for you in Question 7.

make and verify conjectures. You may wish to consider a lab day preceding Lesson 5-3 so that students may investigate the quadrilaterals. Students can work in **small groups** to make conjectures about properties in common. For example, have them draw a kite and measure the opposite pairs of angles. Repeat the construction and measurements on several kites. Draw a quadrilateral which is not a kite and repeat the measurements.

Alternate Approach:　If a computer is not available to test the conjectures about rhombuses, have students draw the rhombuses on grid paper, as shown below. As a group, they can summarize the properties they have discussed.

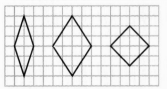

Reading　As students read through the examples in this lesson, they should ask: What are right and wrong ways to test a conjecture?

ADDITIONAL EXAMPLES
1. Test this conjecture: The diagonals of an isosceles trapezoid are equal in length. Methods:
(i) Use graph paper and a protractor to draw several isosceles trapezoids; measure the diagonals.
(ii) Use an automatic drawer and the Repeat feature to investigate several isosceles trapezoids.

2. Show that the conjecture "The diagonals of a rectangle are perpendicular" is false.
sample:

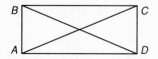

219　$\overline{AC}$ and $\overline{BD}$ are not ⊥.

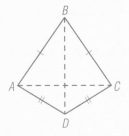
When you are asked to make a conjecture, it often helps to organize your work in a table.

Example 3 Make a conjecture about the diagonals of a rhombus.

Draw some rhombuses (the more different they look, the better), and draw their diagonals.

Because you are not asked to conjecture about any specific property of the diagonals, measure lengths of the diagonals and angles formed by the diagonals. For the rhombuses at the left, some measurements are organized in a table. Lengths are in millimeters.

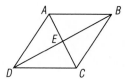

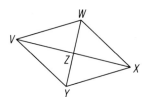

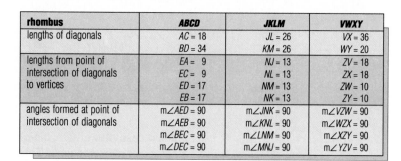

rhombus	ABCD	JKLM	VWXY
lengths of diagonals	AC = 18 BD = 34	JL = 26 KM = 26	VX = 36 WY = 20
lengths from point of intersection of diagonals to vertices	EA = 9 EC = 9 ED = 17 EB = 17	NJ = 13 NL = 13 NM = 13 NK = 13	ZV = 18 ZX = 18 ZW = 10 ZY = 10
angles formed at point of intersection of diagonals	m∠AED = 90 m∠AEB = 90 m∠BEC = 90 m∠DEC = 90	m∠JNK = 90 m∠KNL = 90 m∠LNM = 90 m∠MNJ = 90	m∠VZW = 90 m∠WZX = 90 m∠XZY = 90 m∠YZV = 90

Now look for patterns that hold for *all* the rhombuses. Here are two reasonable conjectures:
(1) The diagonals bisect each other; that is, they intersect at a point which is the midpoint of each segment.
(2) The diagonals are perpendicular.

Conjectures can be related to each other. If the conjecture of Example 1 is true, then so will be conjecture (2) of Example 3. Any property true of all kites is true of all rhombuses.

Questions

Covering the Reading

1. What is a conjecture? an educated guess or opinion

2. To show a conjecture is true, a(n) _?_ is needed. proof

3. To show a conjecture is not true, a(n) _?_ is enough. counterexample

4. Refer to Example 1. See margin.
 a. Draw another figure to test the conjecture.
 b. Does your figure support the conjecture?
 c. Do you think the conjecture is true?

5. Refer to Example 2.
 a. Which figure drawn supports the conjecture? ABCD
 b. Which figure shows that the conjecture is false? PQRS

220

6. What does *refining a conjecture* mean?
changing a statement slightly so that a conjecture is true

7. Refine the conjecture of Example 2.
The diagonals of a rectangle have equal length.

In 8 and 9, use the rhombuses drawn in Example 3.

8. Which rhombus provides a counterexample to the conjecture that "the diagonals of a rhombus are equal in length"?
ABCD and *VWXY*

9. Make a conjecture about the angles formed by the diagonals and the sides of a rhombus. Measure the angles first. Record your work in a chart like the one below. (You might want to number the angles to save writing.) See margin.

ABCD	*JKLM*	*VWXY*
m∠*DAE* =	m∠*MJN* =	m∠*ZVW* =
m∠*EAB* =	m∠*NJK* =	.
m∠*ABE* =	.	.
m∠*EBC* =	.	.
.	.	
.		
.		

Applying the Mathematics

In 10–13, a conjecture is made. Draw a counterexample to show that it is not true.

10. If $XM = MY$, then M is the midpoint of $\overline{XY}$. See margin.

11. If two angles are supplementary, then they have the same vertex.
See margin.

12. The square of any real number is positive. $0^2 = 0$

13. The three medians in an isosceles triangle are equal in length.
See margin.

14. a. Test this conjecture on at least three cases: The diagonals of an isosceles trapezoid are equal.
b. Do you think this conjecture is true?
See margin.

In 15–17, a conjecture is stated. If a figure is not drawn, you should draw one or more. Finally, choose the answer A, B, C, D, or E that best indicates your feeling about the statement.
(A) The conjecture is definitely true and in my mind needs no proof.
(B) The conjecture may be true, but I need a proof or a similar argument before I'd believe it.
(C) the conjecture doesn't seem true, but I am not sure. Some discussion would help.
(D) the conjecture is probably not true, but I'd be sure only if I had a counterexample.
(E) The conjecture is definitely false. No argument is needed to convince me that it is false.

15. If the midpoints of two sides of a triangle are joined, the segment is parallel to the third side. Opinions will vary.

16. If the midpoints of the four sides of a rectangle are connected, the resulting figure is a rectangle. Opinions will vary.

10. sample:

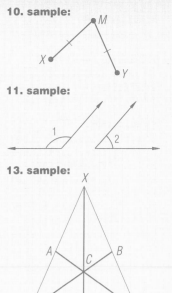

11. sample:

13. sample:

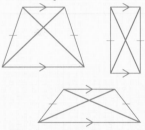

14. a. samples:

b. Yes (Opinions may vary.)

MORE PRACTICE
For more questions on SPUR Objectives, use *Lesson Master 5-3,* shown on page 221.

EXTENSION
Consider **Queston 26.** Suppose the closed curve is the portion of the parabola $y = 25 - x^2$ above the x-axis and the segment from (-5, 0) to (5, 0). Find a square with all four vertices on this curve. **Try to find a square with two vertices at (-b, 0) and (b, 0). Then its other vertices will be (-b, 25 - b²) and (b, 25 - b²). Since the sides must be the same length, 25 - b² = 2b. Solving the quadratic equation, since b > 0, b = 1 + √26.**

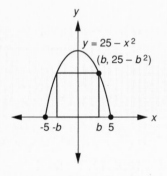

ADDITIONAL ANSWERS
18. A quadrilateral is a square if and only if it has four equal sides and four right angles.

19. A quadrilateral is a parallelogram if and only if both pairs of its opposite sides are parallel.

20. A quadrilateral is a rhombus if and only if its four sides are equal in length.

21. A triangle is isosceles if and only if it has two (or more) sides of equal length.

22., 24. See Additional Answers in the back of this book.

---

17. In the figure below, PQR is a semicircle with center S. Point O is the center of the larger circle. m∠$POR = 90$. Then the areas of the two shaded regions are equal. Opinions will vary.

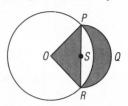

Review

In 18–21, define each term. *(Lessons 5-2, 2-7)*

18. square See margin.

19. parallelogram See margin.

20. rhombus See margin.

21. isosceles triangle See margin.

22. Given: In the figure at the left, $r_m(T) = U$
Prove: *RUST* is a kite. *(Lessons 5-2, 4-5)* See margin.

23. Arrange in order of most general to most specific: rhombus, polygon, square, quadrilateral, kite. *(Lesson 5-2)*
polygon, quadrilateral, kite, rhombus, square

24. Given: At the left, △ABC is isosceles with vertex angle C.
△BCD is isosceles with vertex angle C.
C is on $\overline{AD}$.
Prove: $\overline{BC}$ is a median in △ABD. *(Lesson 5-1)* See margin.

25. Given: ℓ and m are symmetry lines for quadrilateral $EFGH$. Simplify:
a. $r_\ell(F)$ E
b. $r_\ell(EFGH)$ FEHG
c. $r_m(∠GEF)$. *(Lesson 4-7)* ∠FHG

Exploration

26. A *simple closed curve* is a closed curve that does not intersect itself. Here are some examples.

a.   **b.**   **c.**

An unsolved conjecture (as of 1989) is that on every simple closed curve there are four points which are the vertices of a square. In curve **a** are four points which might be the vertices of a square. Trace and try to find the square for curves **b** and **c**.

Answers will vary.

5-4

Properties of Kites

LESSON 5-4

RESOURCES
■ Lesson Master 5-4
■ Quiz for Lessons 5-1
   Through 5-4
■ Computer Master 7

OBJECTIVES

A Draw polygons satisfying
various conditions.
E Identify properties of triangles and quadrilaterals.
G Write proofs using the
properties of triangles and
quadrilaterals.

TEACHING NOTES

Here again is the hierarchy of quadrilaterals. Remember that any property held by a type of figure in the hierarchy is held by all types below to which it is connected. Since all seven types of quadrilaterals are either kites or trapezoids or both, it is particularly useful to know the properties of these two types.

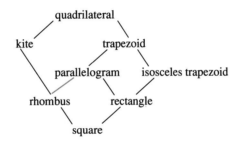

Properties held by all kites will also be properties of rhombuses and squares. These properties will be developed in this lesson. In the next lesson you will learn some properties of trapezoids.

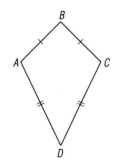

The common vertices of the equal sides of a kite are the **ends** of the kite. In the kite at the left, *B* and *D* are ends. All four of a rhombus' vertices are ends. Of all properties of kites, the most powerful is the kite's symmetry.

Kite Symmetry Theorem:

The line containing the ends of a kite is a symmetry line for the kite.

You might begin the lesson by asking students why a kite is an important figure. (The answer is given in the first paragraph of the lesson.) Then put the hierarchy of quadrilaterals on the chalk-board. As each property of the kite is derived, note that it gives a corresponding stron-ger property of rhombuses and squares (the property will be evident twice), because they can be considered kites in two ways. For example, every rhombus has two sym-metry diagonals.

The term *ends* may be new to you, but you will find it very convenient. Guard against the students tacitly defining the ends as being the endpoints of the longer diagonal. Draw flat-looking kites as well as the conven-tional kite found on page 223, and draw some noncon-vex kites as well. Nonconvex kites look like arrowheads.

Because of the time spent on the seven types of quadrilat-erals found in the hierarchy,

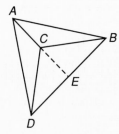
Proof

Draw   A figure is needed with the "given" and "prove" restated in terms of that figure.

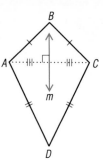

Given: ABCD is a kite with ends B and D.

Prove: $\overleftrightarrow{BD}$ is a symmetry line for ABCD.

Analyze   Use the symmetry lines of isosceles triangles ABC and ADC.

Write

Conclusions	Justifications
1. **AB = BC, AD = DC**	**def. of ends of kite (meaning)**
2. **△ABC and △ADC are isosceles.**	**def. of isosceles triangle (sufficient condition)**
3. **Let m be the ⊥ bisector of $\overline{AC}$.**	**A segment has exactly one ⊥ bisector.**
4. **$r_m(A) = C$, $r_m(C) = A$**	**definition of reflection (sufficient condition)**
5. **m contains B and D.**	**The ⊥ bisector of the base of an isosceles triangle is the angle bisector of the vertex angle (so it contains the vertex).**
6. **$r_m(B) = B$, $r_m(D) = D$**	**definition of reflection (sufficient condition)**
7. **$r_m(ABCD) = CBAD$**	**Figure Reflection Theorem**
8. **m (which is $\overleftrightarrow{BD}$) is a symmetry line for ABCD.**	**definition of symmetry line (sufficient condition)**

The diagonal determined by the ends ($\overline{BD}$ above) is called the **symmetry diagonal** of the kite. The line $\overleftrightarrow{BD}$ is the ⊥ bisector of the other diagonal of the kite. Notice that from conclusions 4 and 6 in the proof, $r_m(\angle ABD) = \angle CBD$ and $r_m(\angle ADB) = \angle CDB$ by the Figure Reflection Theorem. Thus $\overline{BD}$ bisects $\angle ABC$ and $\angle ADC$. This is summarized in the following theorem.

Kite Diagonal Theorem:

The symmetry diagonal of a kite is the perpendicular bisector of the other diagonal and bisects the two angles at the ends of the kite.

Example 1

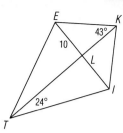

Given kite *KITE* with ends *K* and *T*. If *EL* = 10, m∠*EKT* = 43, and m∠*ITK* = 24, find as many other lengths and angle measures as you can.

Solution   Since $\overleftrightarrow{KT}$ is a symmetry line for the kite, r(∠*EKT*) = ∠*IKT* so m∠*IKT* = 43. Also r(∠*ITK*) = ∠*ETK* so m∠*ETK* = 24. By angle addition, m∠*ETI* = 48 and m∠*EKI* = 86. Since r(*E*) = *I*, $\overleftrightarrow{KT}$ is the ⊥ bisector of $\overline{EI}$, making *LI* = 10 and *EI* = 20. The four angles with vertex *L* have measure 90.

The Kite Diagonal Theorem applies to rhombuses and squares because of their positions in the hierarchy. Another important property of kites is that the two angles not bisected by the symmetry diagonal are equal in measure. You are asked to finish a proof of this in Question 9.

A rhombus is a kite, any of whose vertices can be ends. Thus a rhombus has two symmetry diagonals. In rhombus *RHOM* below, $\overline{RO}$ is the perpendicular bisector of $\overline{HM}$ and $\overline{HM}$ is the perpendicular bisector of $\overline{RO}$. Thus *X* is the midpoint of $\overline{HM}$ and $\overline{RO}$.

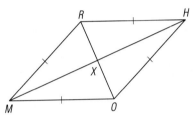

Rhombus Symmetry Theorem:

Every rhombus has two symmetry lines, its diagonals.

Example 2

In rhombus *RHOM* above, if m∠*RHM* = 23 and m∠*MRH* = 134, find as many other angle measures as you can.

Solution   Each diagonal bisects the angles at the vertices it connects. Thus m∠*ORH* = $\frac{1}{2}$ · 134 = 67. Opposite angles are equal in measure due to the rhombus' symmetry. All the angles surrounding *X* are right angles. All of the angle measures are given in the figure below.

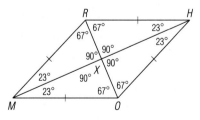

LESSON 5-4   *Properties of Kites*   **225**

NOTES ON QUESTIONS
Question 5:   Note that the kite has a symmetry line even though it is not drawn in the picture.

Question 7:   All angle measures in this figure can be determined if the Triangle-Sum Theorem is known, but that Theorem is not covered until Lesson 5-7. The answer lists only those measures found by symmetry and properties of kites.

Question 9:   Since the conclusions are given, you might use this problem to give students practice in writing paragraph proofs.

Computer and Small Group Work for Question 13:   This is an appropriate question for an automatic drawer. Draw both squares and thin rhombuses. Students may explore the result of joining in order the midpoints for a variety of quadrilaterals. This can lead to conjectures about the type of quadrilateral and the relationship between the angles of the quadrilateral and the angle formed by the diagonals.

Question 18:   To say *"LOVE* is a quadrilateral oriented clockwise"* means that the order of the points *L-O-V-E* is clockwise.

Question 19:   Check to see that students do not draw a vertical line.

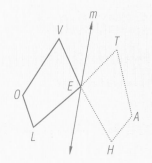
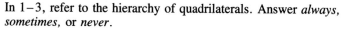

In 1–3, refer to the hierarchy of quadrilaterals. Answer *always*,
sometimes, or *never*.

1. A figure is a parallelogram if it is a rectangle. Always

2. Every square is a trapezoid. Always

3. If a figure is a rhombus, then it is a square. Sometimes

4. To which types of quadrilaterals on the hierarchy of quadrilaterals
does the Kite Symmetry Theorem apply?
kites; rhombuses, squares

5. Refer to kite *KITE* at the right.
$KI = IT$ and $KE = ET$.
  a. Name the ends of *KITE*. I and E
  b. Name the symmetry line. $\overleftrightarrow{EI}$
  c. $r_{\overleftrightarrow{IE}}(\angle IKE) =$ ___?___ ∠ITE

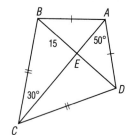

Associates Building
Chicago, Illinois

6. At the left, $RH = HO = OM = MR$.
  a. IS *RHOM* a kite?
  b. If so, name its ends. If not, why not?
  c. How many lines of symmetry has RHOM?
  a) Yes; b) Either R and O or H and M can be thought of as ends. c) 2

7. Use kite *ABCD* below. If $BE = 15$, m∠BCA = 30, and
m∠DAC = 50, find as many other angle measures and lengths as
you can.

ED = 15; BD = 30;
m∠BAC = 50;
m∠DCA = 30;
m∠BEA = m∠AED
= m∠DEC = m∠BEC
= 90;
m∠BCD = 60;
m∠BAD = 100

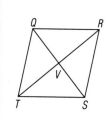

8. In rhombus *QRST* at the left, m∠SQR = 51 and m∠QRS = 78. Find
as many other angle measures as you can. See margin.

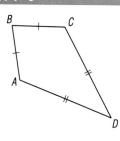

9. Complete the proof that non-end angles of a kite have equal measure.
  Given: Kite *ABCD* with ends *B* and *D*.
  Prove: m∠A = m∠C.

Conclusions	Justifications See margin.
1. $\overline{BD}$ is a symmetry diagonal of *ABCD*.	**a.** ___?___
2. $\overleftrightarrow{BD}$ is the ⊥ bisector of $\overline{AC}$.	**b.** ___?___
3. $r_{\overleftrightarrow{BD}}(A) = C$, $r_{\overleftrightarrow{BD}}(C) = A$	**c.** ___?___
4. $r_{\overleftrightarrow{BD}}(B) = B$, $r_{\overleftrightarrow{BD}}(D) = D$	**d.** ___?___
5. $r_{\overleftrightarrow{BD}}(\angle BAD) = \angle BCD$	**e.** ___?___
6. m∠BAD = m∠BCD	**f.** ___?___

226

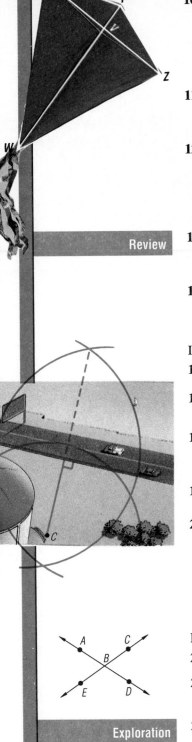

10. Complete the following paragraph proof that the opposite angles of a rhombus are equal. Use the diagram from Question 6.
    a. The reflection image of ∠M over $\overleftrightarrow{RO}$ is __?__, so m∠M = __?__ because reflections preserve __?__. ∠H, m∠H, angle measure
    b. Similarly, the reflection image of ∠R over __?__ is ∠O, so m∠O = m∠R. $\overleftrightarrow{MH}$

11. a. Draw a nonconvex kite *ABCD* with ends *B* and *D*. **See margin.**
    b. Does the proof of Question 9 work for this kite? **Yes**
    c. Is the Kite Diagonal Theorem true for nonconvex kites? **Yes**

12. Two sticks $\overline{XZ}$ and $\overline{WY}$ were lashed together to form the kite at the left. If *XZ* = 20″, *WY* = 30″, and *VY* = 7″, find
    a. *XV* 10″   b. *VZ* 10″
    c. *WV* 23″   d. m∠*YVZ*. 90

Review

13. Give a counterexample to show that the following conjecture is not true: If the midpoints of the sides of a rhombus are connected in order, the resulting figure is a square. *(Lesson 5-3)* **See margin.**

14. If the conjecture in Question 13 is refined by replacing the word "square" with "rectangle," do you think the conjecture is true? *(Lesson 5-3)* **Yes**

In 15 and 16, define the term. *(Lesson 5-2)*

15. trapezoid **See margin.**   16. isosceles trapezoid **See margin.**

17. Name all types of quadrilaterals which are isosceles trapezoids. *(Lesson 5-2)* **isosceles trapezoids, rectangles, squares**

18. Draw an example of this situation. *LOVE* is a quadrilateral oriented clockwise. r$_m$(*LOVE*) = *HATE*. (Caution: There can only be one point *E*.) *(Lesson 4-6)* **See margin.**

19. Trace the needed parts in the picture at the left. Construct the shortest path from *C* to the highway. *(Lesson 3-6)* **See the art at the left.**

20. In the figure below, *m* ∥ *n*. Find *x*. *(Lesson 3-4)* **21**

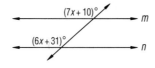

In 21 and 22, use the figure at the left. *(Lesson 3-2, Previous course)*

21. If m∠*ABC* = 8*x* − 7 and m∠*EBD* = 3*x* + 68, find *x*. **15**

22. If m∠*ABC* = 2*y* + 3 and m∠*CBD* = 4*y* + 9, find m∠*ABC*. **59**

Exploration

23. Design and build a "flat" kite that flies (not a box kite). Does your shape agree with the mathematical definition of kite?
    Answers may vary.

FOLLOW-UP

MORE PRACTICE
For more questions on SPUR Objectives, use *Lesson Master 5-4*, shown below.

EXTENSION
Have students interested in kites do research on how to build them and how they are used ceremoniously in certain cultures. They should note how close real-world examples are to textbook examples. Other students can look up "kite" in the dictionary to determine its several interesting usages (a kite is also a bird, a rogue, or the highest sail in a ship).

EVALUATION
A quiz covering Lesson 5-1 through 5-4 is provided in the Teacher's Resource File.

Alternative Assessment
Have students bring closure to the lesson by listing the properties of kites, rhombuses, rectangles, and squares. Ask students to relate the properties to the quadrilateral hierarchy orally.

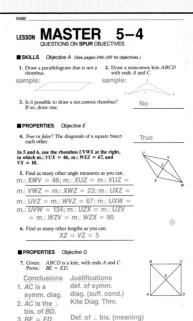

RESOURCES
■ Lesson Master 5-5
Computer Master 7

OBJECTIVES

A Draw polygons satisfying various conditions.
B Apply the Trapezoid Angle Theorem.
E Identify properties of triangles and quadrilaterals.
G Write proofs using the properties of triangles and quadrilaterals.

TEACHING NOTES

The Trapezoid Angle Theorem has a more general interpretation than the one given here. It says that "if two lines are parallel, then interior angles on the same side of the transversal are supplementary." While there is no formal definition of what is meant by "between a pair of parallel lines," it is easy visually for students to see and simple to say.

Point out that not all consecutive angles in a trapezoid are supplementary. All consecutive angles in a trapezoid are supplementary only if it is a parallelogram.

The drawings at the bottom of this page illustrate the wide applicability of the Trapezoid Angle Theorem. Students often make tacit definitions. For example, they may think that a trapezoid has "nonparallel sides that turn toward each other" because common usage often restricts trapezoids to such figures. However, it is important that students learn to accept any figure which satis-

Properties of Trapezoids

Because of the hierarchy of quadrilaterals, any property of a trapezoid holds for parallelograms, rhombuses, rectangles, squares, and isosceles trapezoids. In the trapezoid below, $\overline{AB} \parallel \overline{DC}$. $\overline{AD}$ has been extended beyond A to point E. This forms the linear pair $\angle 1$ and $\angle 2$. Now follow the reasoning.

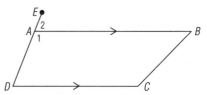

Conclusions	Justifications
1. $m\angle 1 + m\angle 2 = 180$	Linear Pair Theorem
2. $m\angle 2 = m\angle D$	$\parallel$ lines $\Rightarrow$ corr. $\angle$s =
3. $m\angle 1 + m\angle D = 180$	Substitution (step 2 into step 1)
4. $\angle 1$ and $\angle D$ are supplementary.	definition of supplementary (sufficient condition)

This argument could be repeated with $\angle B$ and $\angle C$ and with any trapezoid. The result is the following theorem:

> **Trapezoid Angle Theorem:**
>
> In a trapezoid, consecutive angles between a pair of parallel sides are supplementary.

Notice how the Trapezoid Angle Theorem is applied to other figures. A pair of the consecutive angles between parallel sides is marked in each figure below.

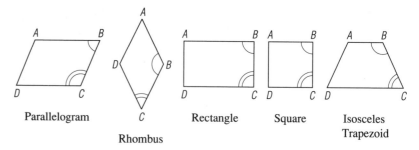

Parallelogram   Rhombus   Rectangle   Square   Isosceles Trapezoid

In all cases shown, angles B and C are supplementary.

228

Example 1 In trapezoid *TRAP* below, $\overline{TR} \parallel \overline{AP}$. If m∠*A* = 82, find the measures of as many other angles as you can.

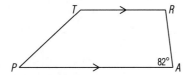

Solution From the Trapezoid Angle Theorem, angles *A* and *R* are supplementary. So 82 + m∠*R* = 180. So m∠*R* = 98. No other angle measures can be found. However, the Trapezoid Angle Theorem tells you that m∠*P* + m∠*T* = 180.

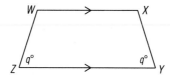

Recall that an isosceles trapezoid is defined to be a trapezoid with a pair of base angles of equal measure. Above is an isosceles trapezoid with bases $\overline{WX}$ and $\overline{YZ}$. Let m∠*Y* = m∠*Z* = *q*. According to the Trapezoid Angle Theorem, m∠*W* = 180 − *q* and m∠*X* = 180 − *q*. So m∠*W* = m∠*X*. This argument proves:

Theorem:

In an isosceles trapezoid, both pairs of base angles are equal in measure.

The isosceles trapezoid is also related to the isosceles triangle in a way that is shown below. Let △*ABC* be isosceles with vertex angle *A* and base $\overline{BC}$. Draw $\overleftrightarrow{DE} \parallel \overline{BC}$. Then you can prove that *DECB* is an isosceles trapezoid. (See Question 9.) Since an isosceles triangle is symmetric, you would expect that an isosceles trapezoid is symmetric as well.

fies the sufficient condition of the definition. Properties must hold for all figures of that type. Hence, the property "turn in toward each other" is not a property of all trapezoids.

The proof of the Isosceles Trapezoid Symmetry Theorem is the most difficult symmetry proof in the book. The idea is simple, however. A candidate for the symmetry line is the perpendicular bisector of one base. Most of the proof is involved with showing that that line is the perpendicular bisector of the other base. It is perpendicular to the other base because of the parallels; it bisects the other base because the equal base angles force *O* to be the reflection image of *Z*.

The Rectangle Symmetry Theorem, together with the symmetry of the rhombus (Lesson 5-4), guarantee that a square has four symmetry lines.

You might wish to tell students that the Incas built temples of granite high in the Andes during the 12th to 16th centuries. Only those torn down by people are not still standing today. All of the existing temples have walls in the shape of trapezoids. Why do you suppose they built trapezoidal walls which are much harder to carve from stone instead of rectangular ones? (The Andes experience major earthquakes every three hundred years, with many minor earthquakes in between. The trapezoidal design helps the walls to support each other as the vibrations travel through them.)

Making Connections
Already in this lesson there are quadrilaterals which are not rectangles that have the measures of all four angles known, and the sum of the measures is 360. This suggests that we already have enough information to prove theorems about the sum of the angles in a polygon.

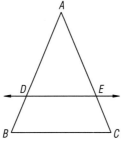

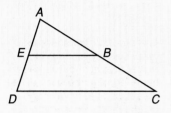
Isosceles Trapezoid Symmetry Theorem:

The perpendicular bisector of one base of an isosceles trapezoid is the perpendicular bisector of the other base and a symmetry line for the trapezoid.

Proof

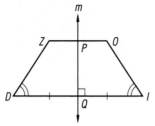

Use ZOID as marked at the left with $m\angle I = m\angle D$. Let m be the $\perp$ bisector of $\overline{ID}$. We need to show that m is also the $\perp$ bisector of $\overline{ZO}$. This will imply that m is a symmetry line for the trapezoid.

Since m is the $\perp$ bisector of $\overline{ID}$, $r_m(D) = I$ and $r_m(I) = D$. We want to show that $r_m(Z) = O$. Since reflections preserve angle measure, you know that $r_m(\overrightarrow{DZ}) = \overrightarrow{IO}$, so $r_m(Z)$ lies on $\overrightarrow{IO}$. Since ZOID is a trapezoid, $\overline{ZO} \parallel \overline{DI}$; thus $\overline{ZO} \perp m$ by the Perpendicular to Parallels Theorem. Thus by the definition of reflection, $r_m(Z)$ lies on $\overleftrightarrow{ZO}$. Since $r_m(Z)$ lies on $\overrightarrow{IO}$ and $\overleftrightarrow{ZO}$, and $\overrightarrow{IO}$ and $\overleftrightarrow{ZO}$ intersect at O, $r_m(Z)$ must be the point O. By the Flip-Flop Theorem, $r_m(O) = Z$. Thus by the Figure Reflection Theorem, $r_m(ZOID) = OZDI$, and m is a symmetry line of ZOID. Also, since $r_m(Z) = O$, m is the $\perp$ bisector of $\overline{OZ}$.

A **corollary** to a theorem is a theorem that is easily proved from the first theorem. The Isosceles Trapezoid Symmetry Theorem has a beautiful corollary. Since $r_m(Z) = O$, and $r_m(D) = I$, and reflections preserve distance, $ZD = OI$. This proves:

Isosceles Trapezoid Theorem:

In an isosceles trapezoid, the non-base sides are equal in measure.

■ ■ ■ ■ ■ ■ ■■■

Example 2   WXYZ at the left is an isosceles trapezoid with bases $\overline{WX}$ and $\overline{YZ}$. Fill in as many lengths and angle measures as you can.

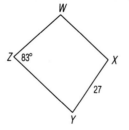

Solution   From the Isosceles Trapezoid Theorem, $WZ = XY$ so $WZ = 27$. From the Trapezoid Angle Theorem, $m\angle W = 180 - 83 = 97$. Since each pair of base angles has the same measure, $m\angle X = m\angle W = 97$ and $m\angle Y = m\angle Z = 83$.

A rectangle can be considered as an isosceles trapezoid in two ways. Either pair of parallel sides can be the bases. Thus another corollary of the Isosceles Trapezoid Symmetry Theorem is:

230

Questions

In 1–3, refer to the hierarchy of quadrilaterals. To which types of quadrilaterals does the theorem apply?

1. Trapezoid Angle Theorem **isosceles trapezoids, trapezoids, squares, rectangles, rhombuses, parallelograms**

2. Isosceles Trapezoid Symmetry Theorem **squares, rectangles, isosceles trapezoids**

3. Rectangle Symmetry Theorem **rectangles, squares**

4. In trapezoid *ZOID* below, $\overline{ZD} \parallel \overline{OI}$, m∠Z = 68, and m∠I = 95.
   a. Name the bases of *ZOID*. **ZD, OI**
   b. Name the two pairs of base angles. **∠Z and ∠D, or ∠O and ∠I**
   c. Find the measure of as many other angles as you can. **m∠O = 112, m∠D = 85**

The cane fields at a sugar mill in Kauai, Hawaii form trapezoids.

5. Use the figure above. Let *ZOID* be an isosceles trapezoid with bases $\overline{OI}$ and $\overline{ZD}$. If $\overline{OZ}$ = 12 cm and m∠O = 125, find as many other lengths and angle measures as you can.
m∠I = 125; m∠Z = m∠D = 55; DI = 12 cm

6. Isosceles trapezoid *ABCD* at the left has bases $\overline{AB}$ and $\overline{DC}$. Trace it and construct *m*, a symmetry line for the trapezoid.

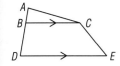

7. What is a corollary?
a theorem that is easily proved from another theorem

8. At the left, *B* is between *A* and *D*. *BCED* is a trapezoid with $\overline{BC} \parallel \overline{ED}$. Justify each statement in this proof of the Trapezoid Angle Theorem.
   a. m∠ABC = m∠D **∥ lines ⇒ corr. ∠s =**
   b. m∠ABC + m∠CBD = 180 **Linear Pair Theorem**
   c. m∠D + m∠CBD = 180 **substitution (part a into part b)**

LESSON 5-5 *Properties of Trapezoids* **231**

231

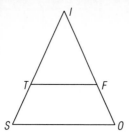

9. Given: △*ISO* at the left is isosceles with *IS* = *IO*. $\overline{TF} \parallel \overline{SO}$.

Justify each step in this proof that *SOFT* is an isosceles trapezoid.

Conclusions	Justifications See margin.
1. *SOFT* is a trapezoid.	**a.** ?
2. m∠*S* = m∠*O*	**b.** ?
3. *SOFT* is an isosceles trapezoid.	**c.** ?

10. Quadrilateral *PARL* at the right is a parallelogram. If m∠*R* = 27.3, find the measures of as many other angles as you can. m∠*L* = 152.7, m∠*P* = 27.3, m∠*A* = 152.7

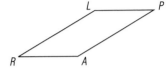

11. Trace rectangle *RECT* below, and draw all its symmetry lines.

12. Given: *ABCD* below is an isosceles trapezoid with bases $\overline{AB}$ and $\overline{DC}$.
a. Prove: *AC* = *BD*. (Hint: use symmetry and reflections.)
b. State the result in words as a theorem.
See margin.

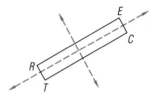

13. *True* or *false*?
a. The diagonals of an isosceles trapezoid are equal in measure. **True**
b. The diagonals of a rectangle are equal in measure. **True**
c. The diagonals of a square are equal in measure. **True**

14. a. What theorem of this lesson tells you that the top view of most beds has two symmetry lines? **Rectangle Symmetry Theorem**
b. Why do you think most beds are shaped this way? **Opinions may vary.**

Review

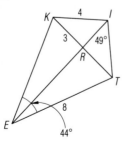

15. In the kite at the left, *I* and *E* are ends. If *KI* = 4, *KR* = 3, *ET* = 8, m∠*RIT* = 49, and m∠*KET* = 44, find as many other lengths and angle measures as you can. *(Lesson 5-4)* **See margin.**

16. In the kite at the left, justify the following conclusions:
(Lessons 5-4, 4-7, 4-1)
a. $\overleftrightarrow{IE}$ is a symmetry line for the kite. **Kite Symmetry Theorem**
b. $\overleftrightarrow{IE}$ is the ⊥ bisector of $\overline{KT}$. **Kite Diagonal Theorem**
c. $r_{\overleftrightarrow{IE}}(R) = R$ definition of reflection (sufficient condition)

17. At the left is a nonconvex kite.
   a. Name its ends. *B and D*
   b. Does it have a symmetry line? **Yes,** $\overleftrightarrow{BD}$.
   c. Does the Kite Diagonal Theorem hold for this kite? *(Lesson 5-2)* **Yes**

18. Given: Isosceles triangle *LOV*
               at the right with vertex angle *L*.
               $\overline{LE}$ is a median.
   Justify each conclusion.
   a. $LO = LV$ **def. of isosceles triangle (meaning)**
   b. $LE = LE$ **Reflexive Property of Equality**
   c. *E* is the midpoint of $\overline{OV}$.
   d. $EV = OE$ *(Lessons 5-1, 3-3, 2-7, 1-7)*
   c) def. of median (meaning); d) def. of midpoint (meaning)

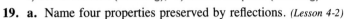

19. a. Name four properties preserved by reflections. *(Lesson 4-2)*
   b. Name one property not preserved by reflections. *(Lesson 4-6)*
      See margin.

In 20 and 21, use the figure at the right.

20. Trace the figure. Draw $r_{\overleftrightarrow{BD}} (\triangle ABC)$.
   (Lesson 4-2)

21. If $m\angle ADB = 3x - 2$ and
   $m\angle CDB = 9x - 10$, then
   a. find *x;* **16**
   b. find $m\angle CDB$. *(Lesson 3-2)* **134**

22. Refer to the figure below. (It is not drawn accurately.)
   a. Solve for *y.* **19**
   b. Is $m \parallel n$? Explain why or why not. *(Lessons 3-4, 3-2)*
      No; the corresponding angles
      do not have equal
      measure

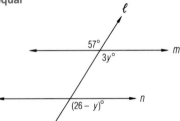

Exploration

23. Test this conjecture. If the midpoints of the sides of an isosceles trapezoid are connected in order, the resulting figure is a rhombus.
See below.

From the drawings, the conjecture appears to be true (and it is).

---

19. a. angle measure, betweenness, collinearity, distance
b. orientation

NAME _____

■ **SKILLS**   *Objective A (See pages 249–251 for objectives.)*

1. Draw a trapezoid that is not a parallelogram.

2. a. Draw a trapezoid with four sides of the same length that is not a square.

b. What kind of figure is this?
   rhombus

■ **SKILLS**   *Objective B*

3. Trapezoid *OMNI* at the right has bases $\overline{OI}$ and $\overline{MN}$. If $m\angle N = 3x - 15$ and $m\angle I = 4x + 41$, find $m\angle N$ and $m\angle I$.
   $m\angle N = 51; m\angle I = 129$

4. Use isosceles trapezoid *ABLE* at the right in which $\overline{AB} \parallel \overline{LE}$. $m\angle L = 4x + 20$ and $m\angle E = 10x - 28$. Find as many other angle measures as you can.
   $m\angle L = m\angle E = 52;$
   $m\angle B = m\angle A = 128$

For 5 and 6, use the parallelogram *ROTE* below.

5. If $m\angle O = 80$, find the measures of the other angles.
   $m\angle E = 80; m\angle R = m\angle T = 100$

6. If $3m\angle O = m\angle R$, find the measures of the two angles.
   $m\angle O = 45; m\angle R = 135$

42   *Continued*   *Geometry © Scott, Foresman and Company*

NAME _____
Lesson MASTER 5–5 (page 2)

■ **PROPERTIES**   *Objective E*
In 7 and 8, *true or false*?

7. The perpendicular bisector of one side of a rectangle is the perpendicular bisector of the opposite side.   **True**

8. In an isosceles trapezoid, two angles which share a common base are equal in measure.   **True**

■ **PROPERTIES**   *Objective G*

9. Given: *ABCD* is a trapezoid, with bases $\overline{AB}$ and $\overline{CD}$.
   Prove: $m\angle B + m\angle C = 180$.

Conclusions	Justifications
1. $\angle B$ and $\angle C$ are supplementary.	Trap. Angle Thm.
2. $m\angle B + m\angle C = 180$	def. of supplementary (meaning)

RESOURCES
■ Lesson Master 5-6

OBJECTIVES

B Apply the Trapezoid Angle Theorem and the theorems about alternate interior angles.

G Write proofs using the properties of triangles and quadrilaterals.

TEACHING NOTES

The length of the proof on page 236 may intimidate some students. Actually, the proof is rather easy, and the length follows only from rigor. The idea is that *RHOM* is symmetric to two lines. From the symmetry line $\overleftrightarrow{HM}$, m∠1 = m∠2. From the Isosceles Triangle Theorem, m∠2 = m∠4. Thus, m∠1 = m∠4, and applying the AIA = ⇒ ∥ Lines Theorem, two sides of the figure are parallel. Now the argument is repeated to get m∠2 = m∠3, so the other two sides of the figure are parallel.

The proof is a lot easier in paragraph form, as stated here, and you might indicate to students that when mathematicians write for each other, they almost always write proofs in paragraphs. Only short proofs of certain kinds are more easily done in two columns. The **Example** shows another proof written in paragraph form.

The Quadrilateral Hierarchy Theorem summarizes all of the connections between the seven special types of quadrilaterals.

Alternate Interior Angles

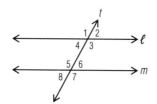

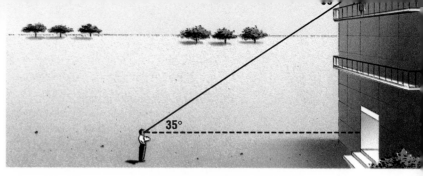

The angle at Gail is called an angle of depression. The angle at Jeff is called an angle of elevation. They are alternate interior angles and are equal in measure.

This lesson completes the hierarchy for quadrilaterals by proving that all rhombuses are parallelograms. To do so, it is first necessary to describe and justify some properties of parallel lines.

When two lines are cut by a transversal, the four angles between the lines (∠3, ∠4, ∠5, and ∠6 in the picture) are called **interior angles.** The other four angles are called **exterior angles.** Angles 4 and 6 are called **alternate interior angles** (they are on alternate sides of the transversal), as are angles 3 and 5.

The alternate interior angles are like the angles in the letter Z. If the top and bottom of the Z are parallel, the angles look equal in measure. The proof relies on the Parallel Lines Postulate. The proof is short and is one you should be able to do.

> **∥ Lines ⇒ AIA = Theorem:**
>
> If two parallel lines are cut by a transversal, then alternate interior angles are equal in measure.

Proof

Draw Two parallel lines cut by a transversal are needed. Number alternate interior angles as ∠1 and ∠2 and state the given and prove in terms of the figure.

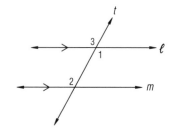

Given: ℓ ∥ m.
Prove: m∠1 = m∠2.
Analyze Both ∠1 and ∠2 equal ∠3 in measure. So the Transitive Property is used.

Write	**Conclusions**	**Justifications**
	1. m∠1 = m∠3	**Vertical Angle Theorem**
	2. m∠3 = m∠2	**∥ lines ⇒ corr. ∠s =**
	3. m∠1 = m∠2	**Transitive Property of Equality (steps 1 and 2)**

234

Example 1   In the figure below, $n \parallel p$. If $m\angle 3 = 43$ and $m\angle 4 = 57$, find the measures of angles 1 and 2.

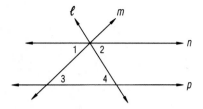

Solution   Angles 1 and 3 are alternate interior angles with m as a transversal. Thus, $m\angle 1 = m\angle 3 = 43$. Similarly, angles 2 and 4 are alternate interior angles with ℓ as a transversal and thus $m\angle 2 = m\angle 4 = 57$.

The converse of the $\parallel$ Lines $\Rightarrow$ AIA = Theorem is true also. You will prove it in Question 11.

AIA = $\Rightarrow$ $\parallel$ Lines Theorem:

If two lines are cut by a transversal and form alternate interior angles of equal measure, then the lines are parallel.

Example 2   Given the figure below (not drawn to scale) with angles as marked. *True* or *false*?

a. $\overline{AB} \parallel \overline{CD}$
b. $\overline{AD} \parallel \overline{BC}$

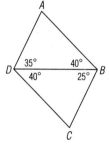

Solution   a. True. $\overline{BD}$ serves as a transversal for sides $\overline{AB}$ and $\overline{CD}$. (Note the Z formed by $\overline{AB}, \overline{BD}$, and $\overline{DC}$.) $\angle ABD$ and $\angle BDC$ are alternate interior angles with the same measure, so $\overline{AB} \parallel \overline{CD}$.
b. False. $\overline{BD}$ is a transversal, but alternate interior angles $\angle ADB$ and $\angle CBD$ have different measures, so $\overline{AD}$ is not parallel to $\overline{BC}$.

The AIA = $\Rightarrow$ $\parallel$ Lines Theorem enables you to finish the hierarchy of quadrilaterals. The proof of the next theorem is not short, but take your time and try to follow it.

Error Analysis   In Lesson 3-4, transversal and corresponding angles were introduced. Be careful that students do not make the tacit assumption that transversal $\Rightarrow$ parallel lines. For this reason, it is advisable not to abbreviate the first theorem by saying "alternate interior angles are equal." Always indicate that the antecedent includes that lines are parallel.

Making Connections
Students who have studied UCSMP *Transition Mathematics* have named and found the measures of angles in figures with parallel lines and transversals.

Alternate Approach
Use three sticks or straws and an overhead projector to demonstrate the measures of alternate interior angles (and other angles formed by parallel lines. Begin with two "lines" (sticks) that are not parallel and a third "line" (the transversal) which intersects them. Compose them on the overhead. Measure the alternate interior angles and then rotate the transversal until the lines look parallel. Measure the alternate interior angles again with a protractor.
   Using four sticks of equal length, have a student arrange them into a rhombus on the overhead projector. Ask why the quadrilateral made must be a rhombus? Ask if a different shaped rhombus can be made. Have another student arrange the sticks to show the rhombus. Ask how many different shapes can be made? Have students verify in each case that opposite sides are parallel. Challenge a student to arrange the four sticks in such a way that opposite sides are not parallel.

Computer   Use an automatic drawing program to verify the $\parallel$ Lines $\Rightarrow$ AIA = Theorem. Have students draw a figure similar to **Example 1.** They should identify and measure the alternate interior angles formed.

ADDITIONAL EXAMPLE
Given: *ABCD* is a square.
Prove: $\overline{AC} \perp \overline{BD}$.
Since *ABCD* is a square, it is a kite by the Quadrilateral Hierarchy Theorem. Since diagonals of a kite are perpendicular, $\overline{AC} \perp \overline{BD}$.

Theorem:

If a quadrilateral is a rhombus, then it is a parallelogram.

Proof

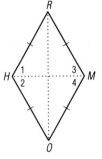

Draw   A rhombus is needed.
The figure is shown at the right.

Given: *RHOM* is a rhombus.
Prove: *RHOM* is a parallelogram.

Analyze   Since $RH = HO = OM = MR$, you need to show $\overline{RM} \parallel \overline{OH}$ and $\overline{RH} \parallel \overline{OM}$. A rhombus is a kite in two ways, so either diagonal is a symmetry line. This creates many equal angles, including alternate interior angles, which is enough to show that both pairs of opposite sides are parallel.

Write $\overleftrightarrow{HM}$ is a symmetry diagonal for kite *RHOM* with ends *H* and *M*. ∠1 and ∠3 are reflection images of ∠2 and ∠4. Thus m∠1 = m∠2 and m∠3 = m∠4. Also, since △*HRM* is isosceles, m∠1 = m∠3. Transitivity gives m∠1 = m∠4, where ∠1 and ∠4 are alternate interior angles for $\overleftrightarrow{HR}$ and $\overleftrightarrow{OM}$ formed by transversal $\overleftrightarrow{HM}$. By the AIA = ⇒ ∥ Lines Theorem, $\overleftrightarrow{HR} \parallel \overleftrightarrow{OM}$. In the same manner using isosceles triangle *HOM*, alternate interior angles 2 and 3 are equal and $\overline{RM} \parallel \overline{HO}$. Thus by the sufficient condition half of the definition of a parallelogram, *RHOM* is a parallelogram.

We call the connections between quadrilaterals the *Quadrilateral Hierarchy Theorem*.

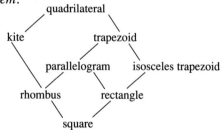

Quadrilateral Hierarchy Theorem:

If a figure is of any type on the hierarchy, it is also of all types connected above it.

236

236

The Quadrilateral Hierarchy Theorem is helpful in many proofs.

Example **Given:** *ABCD* is a square.
Prove: $\overline{AB} \parallel \overline{CD}$.

Solution 1 The proof is short. Here it is written in two columns.

Write **Conclusions**   **Justifications**
    1. *ABCD* is a parallelogram.   **Quadrilateral**
                                                       Hierarchy Theorem
    2. $\overline{AB} \parallel \overline{CD}$ **definition of parallelogram**
                                                       (meaning)

Solution 2 Here is a paragraph proof.

Since *ABCD* is a square, it is a parallelogram by the Quadrilateral Hierarchy Theorem. Because opposite sides of a parallelogram are parallel, $\overline{AB} \parallel \overline{CD}$.

Questions

Covering the Reading

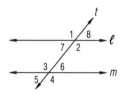

In 1–4, use the figure at the left.

1. a. Name the interior angles. ∠7, ∠2, ∠3, ∠6
   b. Name the alternate interior angles. ∠7 and ∠6, ∠2 and ∠3

2. If $\ell \parallel m$, which angles equal ∠7 in measure? ∠8, ∠6, ∠5

3. If $\ell \parallel m$, which angles are supplementary to ∠3? ∠5, ∠6, ∠7, ∠8

4. *True* or *false*? If m∠2 = m∠6, then $\ell \parallel m$. **False**

5. Write in words:
   a. AIA = ⇒ ∥ Lines Theorem **See margin.**
   b. ∥ Lines ⇒ AIA = Theorem **See margin.**
   c. Statement **a** is the __?__ of statement **b**. **converse**

In 6–8, *true* or *false*?

6. Every parallelogram is a kite. **False**

7. All rectangles are trapezoids. **True**

8. If a figure is an isosceles trapezoid, then it is a square. **False**

9. Given: *ABCD* is a rhombus.
   Prove: $\overline{AD} \parallel \overline{BC}$. **See margin.**

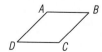

NOTES ON QUESTIONS
Questions 1-3: Ask students to name all the angles equal to ∠2 and all angles equal to ∠6. Point out that if $\ell \parallel m$, each angle is equal to one of two measurements.

Question 4: Although it is not necessary that ℓ and *m* be parallel, you might ask what would be the case if both m∠2 = m∠6 and $\ell \parallel m$. (Then the angles are right angles.)

Questions 6-8: Again, use the hierarchy diagram with these questions.

Question 9: Use this question to encourage paragraph proofs.

ADDITIONAL ANSWERS
5. a. If two lines are cut by a transversal and form equal alternate interior angles, then the lines are parallel.
b. If two parallel lines are cut by a transversal, then alternate interior angles are equal in measure.

9. *ABCD* **is a parallelogram, from the Quadrilateral Hierarchy Theorem. Therefore,** $\overline{AD} \parallel \overline{BC}$ **by the definition of parallelogram (meaning).**

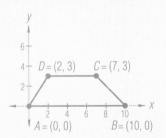
10. Refer to the figure for Questions 1–4.
    a. Which pairs of angles do you think are **alternate exterior** angles? ∠5 and ∠8, ∠1 and ∠4
    b. If ℓ ∥ m, are these pairs of angles equal in measure, supplementary, or complementary? equal in measure

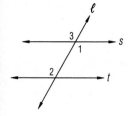

11. Complete this proof of the AIA = ⇒ ∥ Lines Theorem.
    Given: m∠1 = m∠2.
    Prove: s ∥ t.

Conclusions	Justifications
1. m∠3 = m∠1	**a.** _?_ Vertical Angle Theorem
2. m∠3 = m∠2	**b.** _?_ Transitive Property of Equality
3. s ∥ t	**c.** _?_ corr. ∠s = ⇒ ∥ lines

In 12–14, use the figure below where ℓ ∥ m.

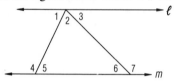

12. **a.** m∠1 + m∠2 + m∠3 = _?_ 180
    b. If m∠1 = 35, what is m∠5? 35
    c. If m∠1 + m∠2 = 145, what is m∠7? 145

13. If m∠5 = 45 and m∠6 = 40, find the measures of as many other numbered angles as you can.
    m∠4 = 135; m∠7 = 140; m∠2 = 95; m∠3 = 40; m∠1 = 45

14. *Multiple choice.* If m∠4 = x, then m∠2 + m∠3 =
    (a) x (b) $90 - x$ (c) $180 - x$ (d) $\dfrac{180 - x}{2}$. (a)

15. In the figure below, $\overleftrightarrow{BD} \parallel \overleftrightarrow{FI}$. If m∠EGH = 57 and m∠EHG = 43 find the measures of all other angles in the figure. See margin.

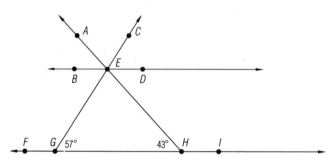

16. One angle of an isosceles trapezoid has measure 7 times another.
    a. Find the measures of all angles of the figure. 22.5°, 22.5°, 157.5°, 157.5°
    b. Draw an example. *(Lesson 5-5)* See margin.

17. Consider the lines with equations $y = 2x + 1$ and $y = 2x - 1$.
    a. Are these lines parallel? Yes
    b. Are these lines perpendicular? *(Lessons 3-5, 3-4)* No

238

238

18. Graph points $A = (0, 0)$, $B = (10, 0)$, $C = (7, 3)$, and $D = (2, 3)$. What kind of a figure is $ABCD$? *(Lessons 5-2, 3-4, 1-3)*
trapezoid; see margin.

19. If you take a square sheet of paper and fold it onto itself along a diagonal, what kind of figure is formed? *(Lesson 5-1)*
isosceles right triangle

20. $\overleftrightarrow{EF}$ and $\overleftrightarrow{GH}$ are symmetry lines for $ABCD$ at the right.
(Lessons 4-7, 4-2, 4-1)

a. $r_{\overleftrightarrow{GH}}(A) = \underline{\quad?\quad}$ B
b. $r_{\overleftrightarrow{EF}}(ABCD) = \underline{\quad?\quad}$ DCBA

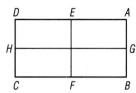

21. Below, $WXYZ$ is an isosceles trapezoid with base angles X and Y. If $m\angle X = -2q + 71$ and $m\angle Y = -5q + 32$, find $m\angle X$. *(Lesson 5-5)*
97

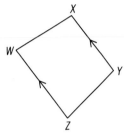

22. Measure the three angles of $\triangle TRI$ to the nearest degree.
(Lesson 3-1)
$m\angle T \approx 65$, $m\angle R \approx 55$,
$m\angle I \approx 60$

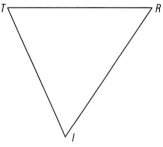

23. According to the Angle Measure Postulate, every angle has a unique measure between $\underline{\quad?\quad}$ and $\underline{\quad?\quad}$. *(Lesson 3-1)* 0°, 180°

24. State the Angle Addition Property. *(Lesson 3-1)*
If $\overrightarrow{VC}$ is in the interior of $\angle AVB$, then $m\angle AVC + m\angle CVB = m\angle AVB$.

25. Give a counterexample to this conditional: If a triangle is isosceles, then it is acute. *(Lessons 2-7, 2-2)* Sample:

> 115°

Exploration

26. a. Other than Z, which printed capital letters usually contain alternate interior angles? Print them. Samples: A, H, I, M, N, W
b. Which printed capital letters usually contain corresponding angles? Print them. Samples: E, F

MORE PRACTICE
For more questions on SPUR Objectives, use *Lesson Master 5-6*, shown below.

EXTENSION
Ask students to name the most general quadrilateral with the following diagonals:
(1) two equal diagonals that bisect each other
rectangle
(2) two unequal diagonals that bisect each other
parallelogram
(3) two unequal perpendicular diagonals with only one diagonal bisected
kite
(4) two equal diagonals
isosceles
trapezoid
(5) two diagonals that bisect each other and are perpendicular
rhombus
(6) two unequal diagonals
quadrilateral

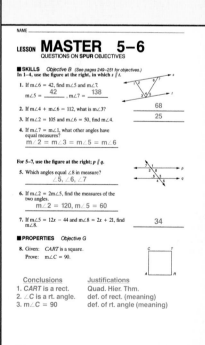

OBJECTIVE

C Find unknown measures of angles using the Isosceles Triangle, Triangle-Sum, Quadrilateral-Sum, and Polygon-Sum Theorems.

TEACHING NOTES

It is reasonable to ask: Didn't we already know that the sum of the angle measures in some quadrilaterals is 360° because a rectangle has four 90° angles? The answer is: Yes, if we know there are rectangles. We could be deducing theorems about figures that do not exist.

Students are certain there are rectangles. However, considering the surface of the earth as a perfect sphere, there are no rectangles on the surface. East-west streets and north-south streets seem to form rectangles, but the east-west streets are not parts of *great* circles (an idea to be examined in Chapter 9), and so they are not lines of the earth's surface. The sum of the measures of the angles of a quadrilateral on the earth's surface is greater than 360°, as the illustration below suggests.

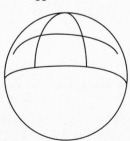

Sums of Angle Measures in Polygons

In the early 1800s, the great mathematician Karl Friedrich Gauss wondered whether the theorems of Euclidean geometry were true over long distances. And so he measured the angles between three mountaintops in Germany to see if they added to 180°. Gauss found that the sum of the angles in his measurements was very close to 180°, within the limits of the accuracy of his instruments. He was checking the truth of a theorem known to the ancient Greeks. It also probably has been known to you for some time. Here is a proof.

> **Triangle-Sum Theorem:**
>
> The sum of the measures of the angles of a triangle is 180°.

The statement of the Triangle-Sum Theorem can be rewritten as a conditional: If a figure is a triangle, then the sum of the measures of its angles is 180.

Proof

> **Draw** Draw a $\triangle ABC$ and restate the antecedent and consequent in terms of that triangle.
>
> **Given:** $\triangle ABC$.
>
> **Prove:** $m\angle A + m\angle B + m\angle C = 180$.

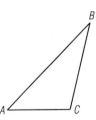

Analyze Much of what has been assumed and so far proved about angle measures relates to parallel lines. Use that knowledge by drawing a line parallel to a side through the third vertex. This creates alternate interior angles and it creates a straight angle which is 180°.

Write

Conclusions	Justifications
1. Draw $\overleftrightarrow{BD}$ with m∠1 = m∠A.	**Angle Measure Postulate**
2. $\overleftrightarrow{BD} \parallel \overleftrightarrow{AC}$	**AIA = ⇒ ∥ lines Theorem**
3. m∠3 = m∠C	**∥ lines ⇒ AIA = Theorem**
4. m∠1 + m∠2 = m∠DBC	**Angle Addition Postulate**
5. m∠DBC + m∠3 = 180	**Linear Pair Theorem**
6. m∠1 + m∠2 + m∠3 = 180	**Substitution** (step 4 into step 5)
7. m∠A + m∠ABC + m∠C = 180	**Substitution** (steps 1 and 3 into step 6)

■ ■ ■ ■ ■ ■ ■ ■ ■

Example In △ABC, the angles are in the *extended ratio* 1:2:3. This means they have measures 1x, 2x, and 3x. Find their measures.

Solution Draw a picture.

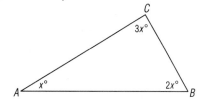

From the Triangle-Sum Theorem,
$$m\angle A + m\angle B + m\angle C = 180.$$
Substituting,
$$x + 2x + 3x = 180$$
$$6x = 180$$
$$x = 30.$$
So m∠A = 30, m∠B = 60, and m∠C = 90.

Check 30, 60, and 90 are in the extended ratio 30:60:90 or 1:2:3.

You might wonder why Gauss climbed the mountaintops in the first place. He was trying to imagine a geometry without the Corresponding Angle Postulate. Without that postulate, he could not prove the theorems about alternate interior angles, and so he would not have the Triangle-Sum Theorem. Within a generation, other mathematicians developed geometries like those Gauss imagined, so-called **non-Euclidean geometries.** In their geometries, the sum of the measures of the angles of a triangle is not 180°.

LESSON 5-7 Sums of Angle Measures in Polygons **241**

So you could say: The *definition* of rectangle does not assure us that there are rectangles in the plane. But the assumption of the Corresponding Angles Postulate does assure it, because it implies that a line perpendicular to one of two parallel lines is also perpendicular to the other.

We could define a fictangle as a quadrilateral whose four angles are each 45°. From this, students could prove that consecutive angles of a fictangle are complementary. The following theorem would then be true: If a quadrilateral is a fictangle, then its consecutive angles are complementary. But it would be like beginning with 2 = 1. Anything could be proved since the antecedent is never true.

Reading Students should not have any difficulty reading this lesson independently and doing all the questions. Encourage them to organize the information given on the sum of the measures of the angles of a convex polygon in chart form. They should study the pattern in the numbers to help them remember the Polygon-Sum Theorem.

Alternate Approach
The formula for the sum of the measures of the angles of a convex polygon also can be found recursively. Making a pentagon from a quadrilateral, as is done below, adds 180° to the angle sum, because all the angles of the triangle become parts of interior angles of the pentagon.

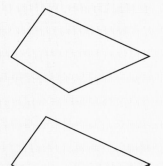

241

In a plane, two perpendiculars to the same line cannot intersect to form a triangle, but this can happen on a sphere. The surface of the earth can be approximated as a sphere. A triangle formed by two longitudes (north-south lines) and the equator is isosceles with two right base angles! Since there is a third angle at the North Pole, the measures add to more than 180°. Thus neither the Two Perpendiculars Theorem nor the Triangle-Sum Theorem works on the surface of the earth.

North Pole

Equator

In a plane, the Triangle-Sum Theorem enables the sum of the measures of the angles of any convex polygon to be calculated. Quadrilaterals are an obvious place to start.

Let $S =$ the sum of the measures of the angles of $QUAD$ below.
$$S = m\angle U + m\angle A + m\angle D + m\angle Q$$

Drawing $\overline{AQ}$ splits $\angle A$ and $\angle Q$ into four smaller angles. Now by the Angle Addition Postulate and substitution,
$$S = m\angle U + (m\angle 1 + m\angle 2) + m\angle D + (m\angle 3 + m\angle 4).$$

Rearrange the terms in this sum to put those in the same triangles together.
$$S = \underbrace{(m\angle U + m\angle 1 + m\angle 3)}_{180} + \underbrace{(m\angle 2 + m\angle 4 + m\angle D)}_{180}$$
$$= 360$$

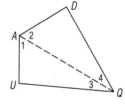

This argument proves:

Quadrilateral-Sum Theorem:

The sum of the measures of the angles of a convex quadrilateral is 360°.

242

The sum of the measures of the angles of a convex *n*-gon can be determined in a similar manner. Consider the polygons displayed below.

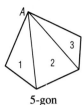

| 5-gon | 6-gon | 7-gon | *n*-gon |

Choose a vertex on each. Call it *A*. Draw the diagonals from *A*. For the 5-gon, the two diagonals form 3 triangles. The sum of the measures of the angles is 3 · 180° (180° in each triangle).

For the 6-gon, there are 4 triangles; for the 7-gon, 5 triangles; and for the *n*-gon, there are *n* − 2 triangles. The sums of the measures of the angles are thus

6-gon	4 · 180°
7-gon	5 · 180°
n-gon	(*n* − 2) · 180°

This argument can be formalized to prove the Polygon-Sum Theorem.

Polygon-Sum Theorem:

The sum of the measures of the angles of a convex polygon of *n* sides is (*n* − 2) · 180°.

Questions

Covering the Reading

1. Here is a slightly different drawing for a proof of the Triangle-Sum Theorem. ℓ ∥ $\overline{AB}$ below. Justify each statement.

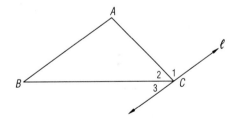

   a. m∠*A* = m∠1 ∥ Lines ⇒ AIA = Theorem
   b. m∠*B* = m∠3 ∥ Lines ⇒ AIA = Theorem
   c. Since m∠1 + m∠2 + m∠3 = 180, then
      m∠*A* + m∠2 + m∠*B* = 180. **substitution**

LESSON 5-7 Sums of Angle Measures in Polygons **243**

NOTES ON QUESTIONS
Question 3: Note that there are extended ratios which give nonintegral angle measures. For example, if angle measures are in the extended ratio 2:3:6, this would yield angle measures of $32\frac{8}{11}$, $49\frac{1}{11}$, and $98\frac{2}{11}$.

Question 13: Elicit other examples where measuring to the nearest minute may be required. Since some calculators give angle measures in degrees, minutes, and seconds, it may be appropriate at this time to discuss the use of the calculator to find angle measures.

Error Analysis for Question 17: Many students will think that the 39° angle must be a base angle. Others may think it must be the vertex angle.

Question 23: This question stumps many students at first, but it is fun to do.

ADDITIONAL ANSWERS
19. a.

Conclusions	Justifications
1. m∠*CBE* = m∠*E*	∥ Lines ⇒ AIA = Thm.
2. m∠*D* = m∠*E*	Transitive Prop. of Eq. (given & step 1)
3. *ABED* is a trapezoid.	def. of trapezoid (suff. cond.)
4. *ABED* is an isosceles trapezoid.	def. of isosceles trapezoid (suff. cond.)

b. 5. ∠*A* and ∠*D* are supplementary. | Trapezoid Angle Thm.

EXTENSION
Have students derive formulas relating the angle measures of nonconvex
polygons.
**Solution: For nonconvex
polygons with *n* > 3 and
one "turned in" angle, the
measure of that angle =
sum of the interior angles
− 180(*n* − 4).**

**For nonconvex polygons
with *n* > 4 and two "turned
in" angles, the sum of the
measures of the two
exterior angles = sum of
the interior angles
− 180(*n* − 6).**

**For nonconvex polygons
with *n* > 5 and three
"turned in" angles, the sum
of the measures of the
three exterior angles =
sum of the interior angles
− 180(*n* − 8).**

**In general, for nonconvex
polygons with *n* sides and
k "turned in" angles,
n ≥ *k* + 3, the sum of
the measures of the *k*
exterior angles = sum of
the interior angles
− 180(*n* − (2*k* + 2)).**

ADDITIONAL ANSWERS
**6. The sum of the
measures of the angles of
a convex polygon of *n*
sides is (*n* − 2) · 180°.**

In 2 and 3, refer to △*EFG* at the right.

2. If m∠*F* = 115 and m∠*G* = 40,
find m∠*E*. 25

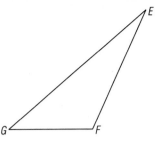

3. If the angles of a triangle are in the
extended ratio 1:3:5, find their
measures. 20°, 60°, 100°

4. Given: Rectangle *ABCD* at the right.
Fill in the blanks with numbers.
a. m∠1 = __?__ 90
b. m∠2 = m∠__?__ 5
c. m∠2 + m∠6 = __?__ 90
d. m∠3 + m∠5 = __?__ 90
e. m∠3 + m∠4 + m∠5 = __?__ 180
f. m∠1 + m∠2 + m∠3 + m∠4 + m∠5 + m∠6 = __?__ 360

5. In convex quadrilateral *HIJK*, m∠*H* + m∠*I* + m∠*J* + m∠*K* = __?__.
360

6. State the Polygon-Sum Theorem. See margin.

7. a. Give an example of a situation in which the measures of the angles
of a triangle do not add to 180°. See margin.
b. What are geometries called in which this happens?
non-Euclidean geometries

Applying the Mathematics

In 8–11, given is a type of figure.
a. Give the sum of the measures of the angles of that figure.
b. Identify the theorem in this lesson that justifies your answer.

8. convex kite a) 360°;
b) Quadrilateral-Sum Theorem

9. isosceles triangle a) 180°;
b) Triangle-Sum Theorem

10. 10-gon a) 1440°;
b) Polygon-Sum Theorem

11. 20-gon a) 3240°;
b) Polygon-Sum Theorem

12. Refer to the triangulated polygons pictured on the previous page.
a. *True* or *false*? Each side of the polygon which does not contain
vertex *A* is part of exactly one triangle. True
b. How many sides of the *n*-gon do not contain vertex *A*? *n* − 2
c. Into how many triangles does an *n*-gon triangulate? *n* − 2

13. A surveyor measures angles of a lot in degrees and minutes. There are
60 minutes in a degree. What should be the value of *x*? 82°26′

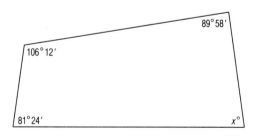

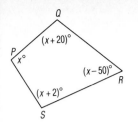

Q
(x + 20)°
P
x°
(x − 50)°
R
(x + 2)°
S

14. In the quadrilateral at the left:
   a. Find x. **97**
   b. Find the measures of the four angles.
   m∠P = 97, m∠Q = 117, m∠R = 47, m∠S = 99

15. a. Each angle of an equilateral triangle has what measure? **60°**
   b. Explain how you got your answer to part **a**. **See margin.**

16. One angle of a triangle is a right angle. The third angle is three times the smallest angle. What are their measures?
90°, 67.5°, 22.5°

17. One angle of an isosceles triangle has measure 39°. What are *all* the possible measures of the other angles?
39° and 102° or 70.5° and 70.5°

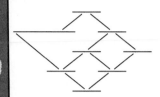

Review

18. Draw, from memory, the hierarchy of quadrilaterals. The diagram at the left below is a hint. *(Lesson 5-6)* **See margin.**

19. Given: m∠D = m∠CBE.
   $\overleftrightarrow{AB}$ ∥ $\overline{DE}$.
   Prove: **a.** *ABED* is an isosceles trapezoid.
   b. ∠A and ∠D are supplementary.
   (Lessons 5-6, 5-5, 5-2) **See margin.**

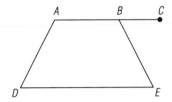

In 20 and 21, define the term. *(Lesson 5-2)*

20. rhombus **See margin.**   21. trapezoid **See margin.**

22. Write the Isosceles Triangle Theorem as an if-then statement.
(Lessons 5-1, 2-2) **If a triangle has two equal sides, then the angles opposite those sides are equal in measure.**

23. *P, Q,* and *R* below are ships. From ship *Q*, ship *P* is 30°N of E and ship *R* is 10°S of E. From ship *R*, ship *P* is 15°W of N. From the captain's viewpoint on ship *P*, what is the position of the other two ships? *(Lesson 3-1)* **R: 15° E of S; Q: 30° S of W**

Exploration

24. Find a globe. Estimate the sum of the measures of the angle of the triangle determined by Los Angeles, London, and Rio de Janiero.
Answers will vary. An approximation for the three vertices are Los Angeles: 80°; London: 75°; Rio de Janiero: 115°; that sum is 270°.

LESSON 5-7 Sums of Angle Measures in Polygons **245**

245

---

7. a. sample: a triangle formed by two north-south lines and the equator

15. b. The sum of the interior angles is 180°, and they are all of the same measure, so any one angle measures $\frac{180}{3}$ = 60°.

18.

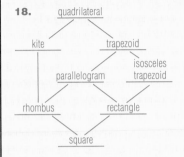

quadrilateral

kite   trapezoid

parallelogram   isosceles trapezoid

rhombus   rectangle

square

19. See the margin on p. 243.

20. A quadrilateral is a rhombus if and only if all four of its sides are equal in length.

21. A quadrilateral is a trapezoid if and only if it has at least one pair of parallel sides.

Summary

In this chapter you studied many polygons and their properties. The simplest polygon, with 3 sides, is the triangle.

Triangles can be classified by the number of equal sides (shown below on the left), or by the size of the largest angle (shown below on the right).

Every isosceles triangle has at least one line of symmetry. That line is the bisector of the vertex angle, is the perpendicular bisector of the base, and contains the median to the opposite side. An equilateral triangle has three lines of symmetry. A scalene triangle has no line of symmetry.

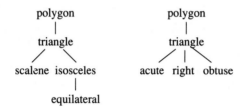

A hierarchy for common quadrilaterals is below.

The importance of this hierarchy is that any property true for all figures of some type is true for all figures of every type below it to which it is connected. Thus the Kite Symmetry Theorem applies to rhombuses and squares as well. The Trapezoid Angle Theorem can be applied to all special types of quadrilaterals except kites. Similarly, the Isosceles Triangle Symmetry Theorem applies to equilateral triangles as well.

From examining figures, if a property appears to be true, a conjecture is made. If a counterexample is then found, the conjecture is false. For a conjecture to be true and become a theorem, a proof of it must be found. Mathematicians, in their research, are constantly forming conjectures and searching for counterexamples or proofs.

In this chapter, two theorems about alternate interior angles are proved. They can be summarized in one if-and-only-if statement: Two lines cut by a transversal are parallel $\Leftrightarrow$ the alternate interior angles formed have the same measure. This theorem is applied to deduce the Triangle-Sum Theorem, which in turn is used to prove the Quadrilateral-Sum Theorem and to develop the formula that $S = (n - 2) \cdot 180°$ for the sum of the measures of the interior angles of any n-gon.

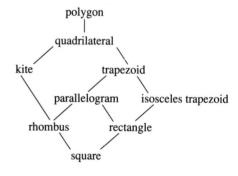

Vocabulary

Below are the new terms and phrases for this chapter.
(Some you have studied in previous years, but we repeat them here for reference.)
You should be able to give a general description and specific example of each.
For those terms that are starred (*), you should be able to give a precise definition.

Lesson 5-1
median of a triangle
vertex angle
base angles of an isosceles triangle
Isosceles Triangle Symmetry Theorem
Isosceles Triangle Theorem

Lesson 5-2
*parallelogram
*rhombus
*rectangle
*square
*kite
*trapezoid
bases, base angles
*isosceles trapezoid

Lesson 5-3
conjecture
refining a conjecture

Lesson 5-4
ends of a kite
symmetry diagonal
Kite Symmetry Theorem
Kite Diagonal Theorem

Lesson 5-5
corollary
Trapezoid Angle Theorem
Isosceles Trapezoid Symmetry Theorem
Isosceles Trapezoid Theorem
Rectangle Symmetry Theorem

Lesson 5-6
interior angles, exterior angles
alternate interior angles
// Lines $\Rightarrow$ AIA = Theorem
AIA = $\Rightarrow$ // Lines Theorem
Quadrilateral Hierarchy Theorem

Lesson 5-7
non-Euclidean geometries
Triangle-Sum Theorem
Quadrilateral-Sum Theorem
Polygon-Sum Theorem
extended ratio

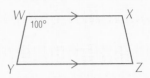
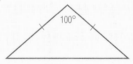
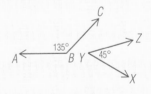
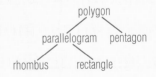
247

Progress Self-Test

See margin for answers not shown below.

Directions: Take this test as you would take a test in class. Use a ruler, compass, and protractor. Then check your work with the solutions in the Selected Answers section in the back of the book.

In 1 and 2, *true* or *false*?

1. Every square is a rectangle. **True**

2. Every kite has two lines of symmetry. **False**

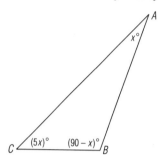

3. Use △ABC as drawn above.
   a. Find x. **18**
   b. Find the measures of the three angles. (Note: △ABC is not drawn accurately.)

4. Angle W of an isosceles trapezoid WXYZ with base $\overline{WX}$ has measure 100°.
   a. Draw such a trapezoid.
   b. Find the measure of as many other angles as you can.

5. Find the sum of the measures of the angles in a convex decagon. **1440°**

In 6–8, refer to the figure at the right. △MNP and △NOP are equilateral.

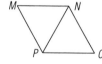

6. Find the measure of each angle.
   a. ∠M **60°**   b. ∠MNO **120°**

7. *True or false?* Quadrilateral MNOP is a rhombus. Justify your answer.

8. a. How many symmetry lines does MNOP have? **2**
   b. Name them. **$\overleftrightarrow{MO}$ and $\overleftrightarrow{NP}$**

9. ABCD below is a parallelogram. Justify each conclusion.   **Trapezoid Angle Theorem**
   a. m∠A + m∠B = 180
   b. m∠D = m∠DCE **|| Lines ⇒ AIA =**

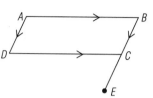

10. Given: AB = BC.
    Prove: m∠A = m∠ECD.

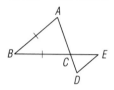

11. In the figure below, ℓ || m. If m∠5 = 9z − 52 and m∠3 = 2z + 45,
    a. find z; **17**   b. find m∠3. **79**

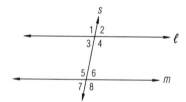

12. Draw an isosceles obtuse triangle.

In Question 13, a conjecture is made. **a.** Is it *true* or *false*? **b.** If it is false, draw a counterexample. If it is true, tell why it is true.

13. If two angles are supplementary, then they form a linear pair.

14. a. What polygon is the shape of the top of most briefcases? **rectangle**
    b. Why do you think it is this shape?

15. Draw the hierarchy relating the following: polygon, pentagon, parallelogram, rectangle, rhombus.

Chapter Review

Questions on SPUR Objectives

SPUR stands for **S**kills, **P**roperties, **U**ses, and **R**epresentations.
The Chapter Review questions are grouped according to the
SPUR Objectives for this chapter.

See margin for
answers not shown
below.

SKILLS deal with the procedures used to get answers.

■ **Objective A:** *Draw polygons satisfying various conditions.* (Lessons 5-1, 5-3, 5-4, 5-5)

In 1–4, draw an example of the figure using ruler, compass, or protractor.

1. a scalene right triangle
2. an isosceles acute triangle
3. a kite that is not a rhombus
4. a trapezoid that is not isosceles

■ **Objective B:** *Apply the Trapezoid Angle Theorem and the theorems about alternate interior angles.* (Lessons 5-5, 5-6)

In 5 and 6, use trapezoid *TRAP* below.

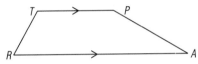

5. If m∠T = 2 · m∠R, find the measure of as many angles as you can.
6. If m∠A = 8x − 12 and m∠P = 15x − 15, find m∠A. **60**

7. Use isosceles trapezoid *NICE* at the right.
If m∠N = 5x − 7
and m∠E = 11x − 79,
   a. find m∠E; **53**
   b. find m∠C. **127**

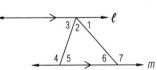

In 8–10, use the figure at the right where ℓ ∥ m.

8. If m∠1 + m∠5 = 140, find m∠2. **40**
9. If m∠7 = 117 and m∠3 = 60, find m∠2. **57**
10. If m∠5 = m∠6, what other pairs of angles have equal measures? **See margin.**

In 11 and 12, *s* ∥ *t* as pictured below at the right.

11. If m∠3 = 2x − 11
and m∠6 = -x + 46,
find m∠3. **27**
12. If m∠1 = 6x − 5
and m∠7 = 2x + 5,
find m∠1. **130**

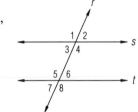

■ **Objective C:** *Find unknown measures of angles using the Isosceles Triangle, Triangle-Sum, Quadrilateral-Sum, and Polygon-Sum Theorems.* (Lessons 5-1, 5-7)

In 13 and 14 use the figure below in which AB = AC.

13. If m∠ABC = 42, find m∠GCF. **42**
14. If m∠DBE = x, find m∠ACG. **180 − x**

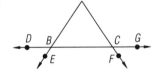

15. Two angles of a triangle have measures 43° and 91°. Find the measure of the third angle. **46°**
16. One angle in an isosceles triangle is 72°. What are the possible measures of the other angles?
17. In △DEF at the right:
   a. find x; **58**
   b. find the measures of the three angles of the triangle.
   m∠D = 59, m∠E = 60, and m∠F = 61

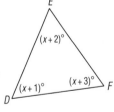

CHAPTER REVIEW

The main objectives for the chapter are organized here into sections corresponding to the four main types of understanding this book promotes: Skills, Properties, Uses, and Representations.

The four types of understanding are not in increasing order of difficulty. There may be hard skills and easy representations; some uses may be easier than anything else; and so on.

USING THE CHAPTER REVIEW
Students should be able to answer questions like these with about 85% accuracy by the end of the chapter.

You may assign these questions over a single night to help students prepare for a test the next day, or you may assign the questions over a two-day period.

If you assign the questions over two days, then we recommend assigning the *evens* for homework the first night so that students get feedback in class the next day. Then assign the *odds* for the second night (the night before the test) so that students can use the answers provided in the book as a study aid.

ADDITIONAL ANSWERS
1.-4., 5., 10., 16. See the margin on p. 250.

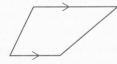

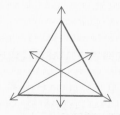
18. Find the measures of all four angles of quadrilateral *RSTU*.

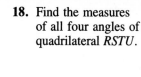

19. What is the sum of the measures of the interior angles of a convex octagon? **1080°**

20. A convex polygon has *n* sides. From one vertex all possible diagonals are drawn.
   a. How many diagonals are drawn? *n*−3
   b. Into how many triangular regions do the diagonals divide the *n*-gon? *n*−2
   c. What is the sum of the measures of the angles of the *n*-gon? (*n*−2)180°

PROPERTIES deal with the principles behind the mathematics.

■ **Objective D:** *Classify special polygons by their properties.* (Lessons 5-1, 5-2)

21. Arrange from general to specific: rhombus, quadrilateral, polygon, square, parallelogram.

22. Arrange from least to greatest number of sides: 6-gon, heptagon, kite, scalene triangle, octagon.
   scalene triangle, kite, 6-gon, heptagon, octagon

In 23 and 24, from the indications, what quadrilateral is pictured? Be as specific as possible.

23.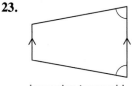
   isosceles trapezoid

24.
   rhombus

In 25 and 26, *true* or *false*?   If false, give a counterexample.

25. Every square is a parallelogram. **True**

26. Every parallelogram is a rectangle. **False**

In 27 and 28, refer to the quadrilateral at the right in which *AB* = *BC* and *DA* = *DC*.

27. Does the figure have any symmetry lines? **Yes**

28. Name two angles with equal measures.

29. *Multiple choice.* Suppose that in △*DEF* the bisector of ∠*D* coincides with the median to side $\overline{EF}$. What type of triangle is *DEF*?
   (a) acute   (b) right
   (c) isosceles   (d) obtuse **(c)**

30. Draw a triangle with 3 lines of symmetry.

■ **Objective E:** *Identify properties of triangles and quadrilaterals.* (Lessons 5-1, 5-4, 5-5)

In 31–34, *true* or *false*?

31. Every trapezoid has at least one line of symmetry. **False**

32. The diagonals of a rhombus bisect each other. **True**

33. The perpendicular bisector of one base of an isosceles trapezoid is the perpendicular bisector of the other. **True**

34. The perpendicular bisector of the base of an isosceles triangle contains the angle bisector of the vertex angle. **True**

■ **Objective F:** *Evaluate conjectures.* (Lesson 5-3)

In 35–37, a conjecture is stated. Explore it with drawings. Choose the answer A, B, C, D, or E below which best indicates your feeling about the statement.
   (A) The conjecture is definitely true and in my mind needs no proof.
   (B) The conjecture may be true, but I need a proof or a similar argument to believe it.
   (C) The conjecture doesn't seem true, but I am not sure. Discussion would help.
   (D) The conjecture is probably not true, but I'd be sure only if I had a counterexample.
   (E) The conjecture is definitely false. No argument is needed to convince me.

35. If two angles are vertical angles, then they are both acute. **Answers may vary.**

36. If two angles form a linear pair, then the bisectors of those angles form a right angle. **Answers may vary.**

37. It is possible for two squares to intersect in exactly five points. **Answers may vary.**

250

In 38 and 39, a conjecture is made. **a.** Is it *true* or *false*? **b.** If it is false, draw a counterexample.

38. If M is the midpoint of $\overline{AB}$, then $AM = MB$.

39. All adjacent angles are supplementary.

■ **Objective G:** *Write proofs using the properties of triangles and quadrilaterals.*
(Lessons 5-1, 5-2, 5-4, 5-5, 5-6)

40. Given: $ABCD$ is a square.
　　Prove: $\overline{BC} \parallel \overline{AD}$.

41. Given: $m\angle F = m\angle FHI$ in the figure below.
　　Prove: $EFHG$ is a trapezoid.

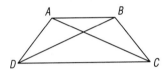

42. Given: Isosceles trapezoid $ABCD$ with bases $\overline{AB}$ and $\overline{CD}$.
　　Prove: $AC = BD$. (Hint: Use symmetry.)

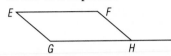

43. Given: $\triangle ABC$ is isosceles with vertex angle BAC.
　　　　$\triangle ACD$ is isosceles with vertex angle ACD.
　　Prove: $AB = CD$.

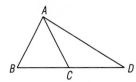

44. Complete the justifications in the following proof.
　　Given: kite $KITE$ with ends I and E.
　　Prove: $KX = TX$.

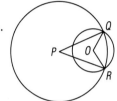

Conclusions	Justifications
1. $\overleftrightarrow{IE}$ is the $\perp$ bisector of $\overline{KT}$.	**a.** ?
2. X is the midpoint of $\overline{KT}$.	**b.** ?
3. $KX = TX$	**c.** ?

45. Given: $\odot O$ and $\odot P$.
　　Prove: $OQPR$ is a kite.

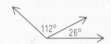

USES deal with applications of mathematics in real situations.

■ **Objective H:** *Explain why everyday objects are shaped like certain polygons. (Lesson 5-2)*

46. a. What polygon is the shape of most notebook paper? rectangle
b. Why do you think it is this shape?

47. The four bases on a baseball field are vertices of a polygon. **a.** What is the name of this polygon? **b.** What are its dimensions? **c.** Why are the bases placed this way?

48. Pictured below are several road signs.
a. Name the polygon that best describes each.
b. Why are road signs different shapes and colors? Answers may vary.

REPRESENTATIONS deal with pictures, graphs, or objects that illustrate concepts.

■ **Objective I:** *Draw hierarchies of polygons. (Lesson 5-2)*

49. Draw the hierarchy relating the following: rectangle, square, rhombus, parallelogram.

50. Draw the hierarchy relating the following: figure, quadrilateral, isosceles trapezoid, trapezoid, parallelogram, rectangle.

EVALUATION
Three tests are provided for this chapter in the Teacher's Resource File. Chapter 5 Test, Forms A and B cover just Chapter 5. The third test is Chapter 5 Test, Cumulative Form. About 50% covers Chapter 5, 25% covers Chapter 4, and 25% covers previous chapters. For information on grading, see *General Teaching Suggestions: Grading* on page T44 in the Teacher's Edition.

ASSIGNMENT RECOMMENDATION
We strongly recommend that you assign the reading and questions from Lesson 6-1 for homework the evening of the test. It gives students work to do if they complete the test before the end of the period and keeps the class moving.

If you do not give assignments on the days of tests, you may cover one less *chapter* over the course of the year.

38. True

39. a. False

b. sample counterexample:

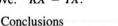

40. A square is a parallelogram due to the Quadrilateral Hierarchy Theorem. So, $\overline{BC} \parallel \overline{AD}$ by the definition of parallelogram.

41.

Conclusions	Justifications
1. $\overline{EF} \parallel \overline{GH}$	AIA = ⇒ $\parallel$ Lines Thm.
2. $EFHG$ is a trapezoid.	def. of trapezoid (suff. cond.)

42.-45., 47.-50.
See Additional Answers in the back of this book.
46. b. Answers may vary.

CHAPTER 6 ■ TRANSFORMATIONS AND CONGRUENCE

DAILY PACING CHART ■ CHAPTER 6

Every chapter of UCSMP *Geometry* includes lessons, a Progress Self-Test, and a Chapter Review. For optimal student performance, the self-test and review should be covered. (See *General Teaching Suggestions: Mastery* on page T36 of the Teacher's Edition.) By following the pace of the Full Course given here, students can complete the entire text by the end of the year. Students following the pace of the Minimal Course spend more time when there are quizzes and on the Chapter Review and will generally not complete all of the chapters in this text.

When all lessons are covered from the beginning (the recommendation of the authors), then students in the Minimal Course can cover through Lesson 13-4 and will cover all they need for future courses. For more information on pacing, see *General Teaching Suggestions: Pace* on page T35 of the Teacher's Edition.

DAY	MINIMAL COURSE	FULL COURSE
1	6-1	6-1
2	6-2	6-2
3	6-3	6-3
4	6-4	6-4
5	Quiz (TRF); Start 6-5.	Quiz (TRF); 6-5
6	Finish 6-5.	6-6
7	6-6	6-7
8	6-7	Progress Self-Test
9	Progress Self-Test	Chapter Review
10	Chapter Review	Chapter Test (TRF)
11	Chapter Review	Comprehensive Test (TRF)
12	Chapter Test (TRF)	
13	Comprehensive Test (TRF)	

TESTING OPTIONS

■ Quiz for Lessons 6-1 Through 6-4 ■ Chapter 6 Test, Form A ■ Chapter 6 Test, Cumulative Form
■ Chapter 6 Test, Form B ■ Comprehensive Test, Chapters 1-6

PROVIDING FOR INDIVIDUAL DIFFERENCES

The student text has been written for, and tested with, average students. It also has been used successfully with better and more poorly prepared students.

The Lesson Notes often include Error Analysis and Alternate Approach features to help you with those students who need more help. A blackline Lesson Master (in the Teacher's Resource File), keyed to the chapter objectives, is provided for each lesson to allow more practice. (However, since it is very important to keep up with the daily pace, you are not expected to use all of these masters. Again, refer to the suggestions for pacing on page T35.) Extension activities are provided in the Lesson Notes for those students who have completed the particular lesson in a shorter amount of time than is expected, even in the Full Course.

OBJECTIVES ■ CHAPTER 6

The objectives listed here are the same as in the Chapter 6 Review on pages 299-301 of the student text. The Progress Self-Test on pages 297-298 and the tests in the Teacher's Resource File cover these objectives. For recommendations regarding the handling of this end-of-chapter material, see the notes in the margin on the corresponding pages of the Teacher's Edition.

OBJECTIVES FOR CHAPTER 6 (Organized into the SPUR Categories—Skills, Properties, Uses, and Representations)	Progress Self-Test Questions	Chapter Review Questions	Lesson Master from Teacher's Resource File*
SKILLS			
A Draw or identify images of figures under composites of reflections.	1	1 through 5	6-2, 6-3, 6-6
PROPERTIES			
B Apply properties of reflections to obtain properties of translations and rotations.	3, 4, 7	6 through 9	6-2, 6-3
C Apply the Two Reflection Theorem for Translations and for Rotations.	2, 10, 11	10 through 13	6-2, 6-3, 6-6
D Determine properties of congruent figures.	5, 6, 8, 9	14 through 25	6-5, 6-6, 6-7
USES			
E Determine the isometry which maps one figure onto another.	16, 17	26 through 31	6-2, 6-3, 6-6
F Use reflections to find a path from an object to a particular point.	14, 15	32 through 35	6-4
REPRESENTATIONS			
G Apply a rule described using T( ) notation.	12, 13	36 through 42	6-1, 6-2, 6-3, 6-6

*The masters are numbered to match the lessons.

OVERVIEW ■ CHAPTER 6

This brief chapter, which should take about two and a half weeks of class time to complete, has two major goals. The first is to arrive at a definition of congruence general enough to apply to *all* figures. Needed for this definition are a general introduction to transformations (Lesson 6-1) and a specific discussion of two important kinds of transformations, namely, translations (Lesson 6-2) and rotations (Lesson 6-3). In these lessons, students learn that translations and rotations are composites of two reflections.

Lesson 6-4 is devoted to one of the nicest applications in elementary geometry, namely, the application of the composite of reflections to miniature golf and billiards.

The definition of congruence is presented in Lesson 6-5. In its shortest form, two figures are congruent if and only if one is the image of the other under a reflection or under a composite of reflections.

It is natural to ask if there are any composites of reflections other than rotations and translations. That question is answered in Lesson 6-6, where the only other composite, the glide reflection, is discussed.

The second goal of the chapter is to prepare students for the triangle congruence theorems and proofs they will study in Chapter 7. Lesson 6-7 deals with corresponding parts in congruent figures and is critical in the preparation for proofs. Since all the preceding lessons have dealt with correspondence and congruence, students should be able to recognize congruent figures quickly.

PERSPECTIVES ■ CHAPTER 6

The Perspectives provide the rationale for the inclusion of topics or approaches, provide mathematical background, and make connections with other lessons and within UCSMP.

6-1

TRANSFORMATIONS

A transformation is a special kind of function and is given its usual definition as a one-to-one function which maps points onto points. (Some mathematicians do not require that the function be one-to-one.) This lesson points out that a reflection is only one type of transformation, and also extends the notation of reflections to cover other transformations.

We also take this opportunity to review some function notation used in UCSMP *Algebra,* namely, the notation N(S) for the number of elements in a set and P(E) for the probability of an event. This notation is clear, and students who have not seen it before are often able to use it correctly.

The examples in this lesson demonstrate again that function notation is clearer in contexts where letters are abbreviations for ideas students understand rather than in contexts where the letters are variables.

6-2

TRANSLATIONS

Almost all students become proficient at drawing reflection images. A natural extension is to draw images of images. The surprise is that the transformations that result, the correspondences between the original preimage and the final image, are very simple and useful.

When the two reflecting lines are parallel, as in this lesson, the result, or *composite,* is a translation. When the two reflecting lines have a point in common (the case considered in the next lesson), the composite is a rotation. When the two reflecting lines are identical, then they are parallel and have a point in common, and the composite keeps each point where it is. The identity transformation keeps each point in place and is considered both a translation and a rotation.

6-3

ROTATIONS

For many students, the first experiences with congruence are in the primary grades and come from tracing a figure. (A figure is congruent to its traced image.) The tracer is allowed to slide, flip, or turn the tracing paper. This lesson discusses the "turns," or rotations of a figure.

Translations and rotations are quite similar mathematically, although they seem so different. A translation (rotation) is the composite of two reflections over parallel (intersecting) lines. The magnitude of a translation (rotation) is twice the distance (measure of the angle) between the reflecting lines in the direction from the first line to the second line.

6-4

MINIATURE GOLF AND BILLIARDS

This lesson, which is a favorite of students, begins with a discussion of the application of reflections to sound waves and objects which bounce off of surfaces. In miniature golf and billiards, two or more surfaces are involved. Although all situations in this lesson involve perpendicular sides of tables or golf holes, the principles apply to billiard tables or miniature golf holes of any shape.

6-5

CONGRUENT FIGURES

To Euclid, figures were congruent if they could be made to coincide, that is, if one could be "superimposed" on the other. Potentially, this enabled any kinds of figures to be congruent. Superposition, however, is not a rigorous idea. Mathematicians made Euclid's work more rigorous by substituting transformations for the idea of superposition.

The idea of describing Euclidean geometry in terms of transformations is due to Felix Klein. In a famous paper presented in 1872, he described all the known geometries of the time, Euclidean and non-Euclidean, in terms of groups of transformations. This paper is known as the "Erlanger program" because it was Klein's introductory paper as a faculty member at the University of Erlangen.

A transformation *definition* of congruence seems to have been used first by Mario Pieri in 1891.

In the new math curricula of the late 1950s and early 1960s, the idea of superposition was usually handled by separate definitions of congruence for segments, angles, and triangles. That is, segments were congruent if they had the same length, angles were congruent if they had the same measure, and triangles were congruent if a correspondence could be set up so that all six corresponding sides and angles had the same measure.

This was not a good approach because it lacked any connection to the early activities of children with congruent figures. It also lacked any connection to later work in geometry, and it forced one to invent a new definition of congruence for each new figure.

In the middle 1960s, a few books were published in the United States in which the general conception of congruence using transformations was presented. Most of these books, however, were written for capable students, and they left the impression that transformations are difficult. Our first work with transformations was done in the late 1960s and demonstrated conclusively that this approach is accessible to all geometry students.

6-6

ISOMETRIES

If two nonsymmetric figures have the same orientation and are congruent, then there is exactly one translation or rotation that maps one onto the other. (If there is symmetry, then there is more than one translation or rotation.) This is not obvious, but we have pointed out in previous lessons how to determine the translation or rotation.

If figures are congruent with a different orientation, then there is exactly one reflection or one glide reflection which maps one onto the other. Again, this is not obvious and this lesson explains, through the Glide Reflection Theorem, how to find the unique reflecting line.

With this lesson, all the transformations that yield congruent figures have been presented. These transformations are called isometries.

6-7

CORRESPONDING PARTS IN CONGRUENT FIGURES

The Corresponding Parts in Congruent Figures (CPCF) Theorem derives from the isometry definition. In fact, by "parts" we may mean

any corresponding subsets of points of the preimage and image figures. The primary use of the theorem will be with reference to angles and segments.

In some books, the CPCF Theorem is called the CPCTC Theorem (corresponding parts of congruent *triangles* are congruent). These books restrict the theorem to triangles and the term "corresponding parts" to segments and angles because they have only defined congruence for segments, angles, and triangles. The situation is different with transformations because transformations allow all figures to be considered. For instance, if two pentagons $ABCDE$ and $FGHIJ$ are congruent, then there is a composite of reflections T such that $T(ABCDE) = FGHIJ$.

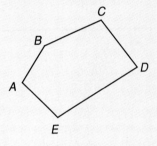
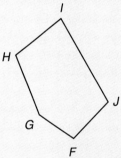

By the Polygon Reflection Theorem, $T(A) = F$, $T(B) = G$, and so on. Furthermore, by the same theorem, $T(BCDE) = GHIJ$. So the quadrilaterals $BCDE$ and $GHIJ$ are congruent. By a corresponding process, the diagonals $\overline{AD}$ and $\overline{FI}$ are congruent as are the angles ACE and FHJ (even though they are not angles of the original polygons). All other pairs of corresponding parts are congruent as well.

Transformations and Congruence

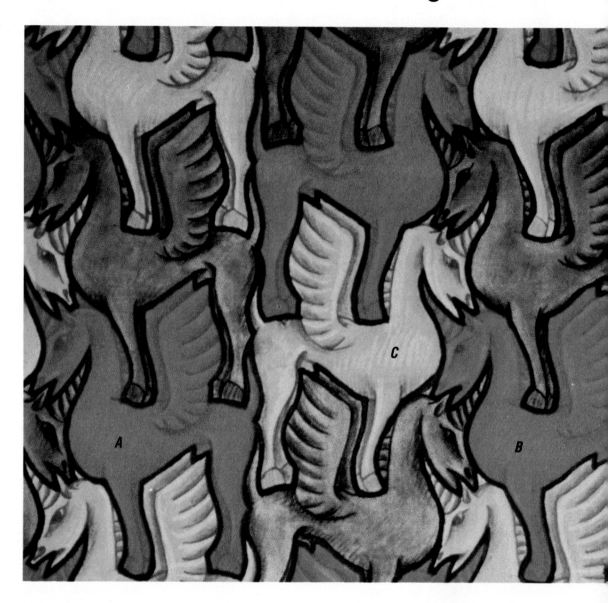

6-1: Transformations
6-2: Translations
6-3: Rotations

6-4: Miniature Golf and Billiards
6-5: Congruent Figures
6-6: Isometries
6-7: Corresponding Parts in Congruent Figures

The drawing at the left, called a *tessellation,* is one of the many tessellations drawn by the Dutch artist Maurits Escher (1898–1973). This tessellation was designed by piecing together unicorns of the same size and shape. We say that the unicorns are all *congruent* to each other.

Unicorns *A* and *B* are related to each other by a *slide* or *translation.* Each is a translation image of the other. (The translation is horizontal.) On the other hand, unicorns *A* and *C* have different orientations. But they are not related by a single reflection. They are related by another kind of transformation, a *walk* or *glide reflection.*

It is natural to ask for all the possible ways in which the various unicorns could be related to each other. In this chapter, you will learn that there are four types of transformations in the plane which yield congruent figures: reflections (flips), rotations (turns), translations (slides), and glide reflections (walks). These were first categorized in 1831 by the French mathematician Michel Chasles (1793–1880).

The first use of transformations dates back to the ancient Greeks about the time of Euclid. However, not until Euler (in 1776) did anyone identify all the kinds of transformations in space that could yield congruent figures. It is interesting that the three-dimensional analysis of congruence was accomplished before the two-dimensional. This is probably because the congruent objects seen daily are three-dimensional.

Studying these various transformations helps a person to become more aware of the movements of objects such as gears (which rotate), imprints (which flip), and conveyer belts (which slide). More complicated movements, such as those done by robots, can be taken apart into their component moves and analyzed.

Transformations

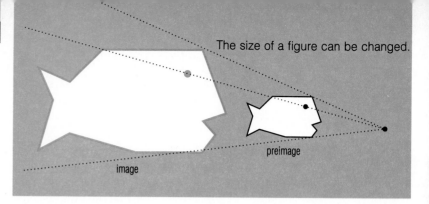

The size of a figure can be changed.

image   preimage

In Chapter 4 you studied reflections. Reflections are important because they describe how figures are related. But there are many things which can be done to figures other than reflecting them over lines. In the figures above and below, the dotted lines connect points in the preimages (black) to their images (blue) and are meant to suggest what is happening to specific points on the figure.

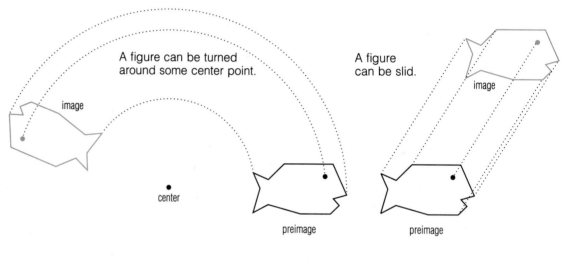

A figure can be turned around some center point.

image

center

preimage

A figure can be slid.

image

preimage

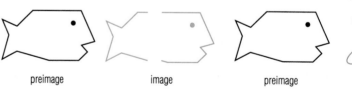

A figure can be split into parts.

preimage   image

A figure can be bent out of shape.

preimage   image

In each of these operations on figures, there is a preimage and an image. Sometimes the image looks identical to the preimage, at other times not. But in each case, the figure has been *transformed*. The operation applied to the figure is called a *transformation*.

254

Definition:

A **transformation** is a correspondence between two sets of points such that
(1) each point in the preimage set has a unique image, and
(2) each point in the image set has exactly one preimage.

The sufficient conditions for a transformation are satisfied by any reflection. Thus *every reflection is a transformation*.

A transformation is often called a **mapping;** a transformation *maps* a preimage onto an image. If the transformation is called T, then the image of a point P is written **T(P)**, which is read "T of P."

One way to describe a transformation is by a *rule* which tells how to locate the image of any point. For the reflection r_ℓ, the rule is rather long: If P is on ℓ, then $r_\ell(P) = P$. If P is not on ℓ, then $r_\ell(P)$ is the point such that ℓ is the ⊥ bisector of the segment connecting P and $r_\ell(P)$. In a coordinate plane, the rule for a transformation can be given by a formula.

Example A transformation T maps (x, y) onto $(x - 8, y - 12)$.

a. Find T(6, 11).

b. If $J = (6, 11)$, $K = (15, 15)$, and $L = (15, 9)$, graph T($\triangle JKL$).

c. Conjecture about the kind of transformation T is.

Solution

a. From the given, T(x, y) = $(x - 8, y - 12)$.
To find T(6, 11), substitute 6 for x, 11 for y.
$$T(6, 11) = (6 - 8, 11 - 12) = (-2, -1)$$

b. To find T($\triangle JKL$), find the images of J, K, and L. Call the images J', K', and L'. These are the vertices of the image, which is a triangle. J' was found in part **a**.
$$J' = T(J) = (-2, -1)$$
$$K' = T(K) = T(15, 15) = (15 - 8, 15 - 12) = (7, 3)$$
$$L' = T(L) = T(15, 9) = (15 - 8, 9 - 12) = (7, -3)$$

c. Graphing shows that $\triangle J'K'L'$ is the same size and shape as $\triangle JKL$. It appears to have been slid 8 units to the left and 12 units down.

students' experience is the transformation which maps the x-axis onto the parabola $f(x) = x^2$.

As with reflections studied in Lesson 4-1, students should realize that the entire plane is being transformed. We see the effect of the transformation by seeing what happens to a particular figure in the plane.

Students may understand transformations better if examples of transformations are used that do not preserve distance.

Stress that a transformation is the *correspondence* between points, not the physical act of moving points.

Making Connections
You might want to start a discussion about the identity transformation, the transformation in which the image coincides with the preimage. This will help when discussing composites in the next lesson and in future lessons. Include possible notation in the discussion.

ADDITIONAL EXAMPLE
The midpoint M of $\overline{JK}$ in the **Example** is (10.5, 13).
a. Find the image of M under the transformation T(x, y) = $(x - 8, y - 12)$.
(2.5, 1)
b. Does the image of the midpoint seem to be the midpoint of the image segment?
Yes
c. What point is the image of the origin under T?
(-8, -12)
d. What point has the origin as its image?
(8, 12)

Some transformations with simple rules give rise to distorted images. Drawn below is the front of a house and its image under the transformation S, where $S(x, y) = (2x, x + y)$. (To save space, only the outside vertices are named.) Although distorted, this image is not very different from a perspective view of the house and, in fact, some early work with transformations was done to understand artists' perspective drawings. Collinearity and betweenness are preserved, so you can still discern the house. But angle measures and distances are not preserved, so the image house is distorted.

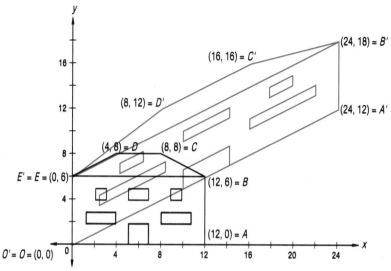

The T( ) notation for transformations is similar to notation used with other mathematics. For example, the number of elements of a set S is often written as N(S). The probability of an event E is often written as P(E).

Questions

Covering the Reading

1. Define: transformation. See margin.

2. A transformation can be described by giving a(n) __?__ which tells how to locate the image of any point. rule

In 3–8, *true* or *false*?

3. It is correct to say that a transformation *maps* a preimage onto an image. True

4. In any transformation, a preimage point has exactly one image. True

5. In any transformation, an image point has exactly one preimage. True

6. In any transformation, the image of a triangle is a triangle. False

256

7. Every transformation is a reflection. **False**

8. Every transformation preserves angle measure. **False**

9. Refer to the Example. The midpoint of $\overline{KL}$ is (15, 12). Call this point M.
   a. What are the coordinates of T(M)? **(7, 0)**
   b. Let $M' = $ T(M). Is M' the midpoint of $\overline{K'L'}$? **Yes**

10. Some of the early work with transformations was done to understand what kind of drawings of artists? **perspective drawings**

11. Suppose T(x, y) = ($x + 2$, $y - 3$). Let $N = $ (10, 7), $O = $ (0, 0), and $P = $ (-4, 3).
    a. Graph $\triangle NOP$ and its image under T. **See margin.**
    b. Which word(s) best describes the transformation T: reflection, slide, turn, or size change? **slide**

12. The door of the preimage house pictured on the previous page has vertices (5, 0), (5, 2), (7, 2), and (7, 0). Find the vertices of the image door under the transformation S. **(10, 5), (10, 7), (14, 9), (14, 7)**

Applying the Mathematics

13. Explain how you know that the transformation S on page 256 does not preserve angle measure. **See margin.**

14. A transformation T has the rule T(x, y) = ($10 - x$, y). This transformation preserves betweenness so you can find the image of segments using only their vertices. Let $A = $ (0, 0), $B = $ (3, 4), and $C = $ (-1, -6).
    a. Draw $\triangle ABC$ and its image under T. **See margin.**
    b. Describe the transformation T.
       reflection over the line x = 5

15. A transformation S maps (x, y) onto (-y, x).
    a. Draw the quadrilateral with vertices $Q = $ (2, 1), $U = $ (5, 1), $A = $ (5, 8), and $D = $ (2, 6). **See margin.**
    b. Draw S($QUAD$) and label it $Q'U'A'D'$. **See margin.**
    c. Which word best describes S: reflection, slide, or turn? **turn**

Review

16. Recall that, when outcomes occur randomly, the probability of an event is the number of successful outcomes divided by the number of possible outcomes. Let P(E) be the probability of an event E.
    a. What is P(heads in a toss of a fair coin)? $\frac{1}{2}$
    b. What is P(a randomly selected day falls on a weekend)?
       (Previous course) $\frac{2}{7}$

17. *Multiple choice.* The angles other than the right angle in a right triangle are
    (a) acute and supplementary
    (b) acute and complementary
    (c) obtuse and supplementary
    (d) obtuse and complementary
    (e) none of the above. *(Lessons 5-7, 3-2)* **(b)**

11. a.

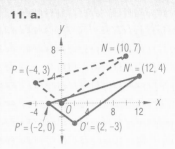

13. Sample: m∠$AOE \neq$ m∠$A'O'E'$.

14. a.

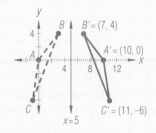

15. a. and b.

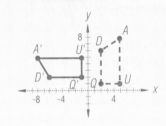

257

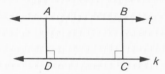
18. Let N(S) be the number of elements in a set S.
    a. Calculate N(set of even integers from 1 to 10). **5**
    b. Calculate N(set of even integers from 1 to 100).
       (Previous course) **50**

19. A right triangle is also isosceles. **a.** Is this possible? **b.** If not, why
    not? If so, what can be determined about the measures of the angles
    in this triangle? *(Lessons 5-7, 5-1)*
    a) Yes; b) The right angle has measure 90°; the other two have measure 45°.

20. One angle of a rhombus has measure 55°. Find the measures of as
    many other angles of the rhombus as you can. *(Lessons 5-5, 5-4)*
    125°, 55°, and 125°

21. Using ruler and protractor, draw a scalene acute triangle.
    (Lesson 5-1) **See margin.**

22. The **distance between two parallel lines** is the length of a
    perpendicular segment connecting two points on them.

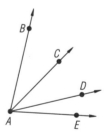

    Multiple choice. Which seems to be the distance between ℓ and m?
    (Lesson 3-6)
    (a) *PQ*   (b) *PR*   (c) *PS* **(b)**

23. Below, $\overrightarrow{AC}$ bisects $\angle BAD$, m$\angle DAE = \frac{1}{2} \cdot$ m$\angle CAD$, and
    m$\angle BAE = 80$. Find m$\angle DAE$. *(Lesson 3-1)* **16**

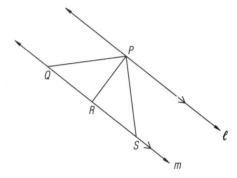

Exploration

24. Explore the transformation with rule T(x, y) = ($2x$, y) by finding
    images of common figures under T. (Hint: Use points in all
    quadrants.)
    It doubles the width of a figure while keeping its height constant.

258

6-2

Translations

In the figure below, $\triangle ABC$ has been slid about 7 cm up and to the right to produce the image $\triangle A''B''C''$ (read "A double prime, B double prime, C double prime"). This transformation is known as a *translation* or slide.

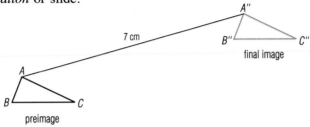

New transformations can result from successive applications of one type of transformation. The transformation from $\triangle ABC$ to $\triangle A''B''C''$ can be the result of two successive reflections over parallel lines. The drawing below shows $\triangle ABC$, its reflection image $\triangle A'B'C'$ over line ℓ, and a third triangle $A''B''C''$ which is the reflection image of $\triangle A'B'C'$ over a parallel line m.

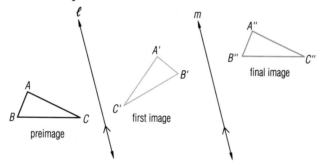

The relationships between these three triangles can be stated in symbols.

$$r_\ell(\triangle ABC) = \triangle A'B'C'$$
$$r_m(\triangle A'B'C') = \triangle A''B''C''$$

Substituting $r_\ell(\triangle ABC)$ in the second equation for $\triangle A'B'C'$ (they are equal in the first equation), you can write the result of first applying r_ℓ, then applying r_m.

$$r_m(r_\ell(\triangle ABC)) = \triangle A''B''C''.$$

When one reflection r_ℓ is followed by a second reflection r_m, the result of combining those reflections is called the *composite* of the reflections. Any transformations can follow each other.

LESSON 6-2 *Translations* **259**

RESOURCES
■ Lesson Master 6-2
⬚ Visual for Teaching Aid 25 provides the diagrams for **Questions 4, 5,** and **10.**
⬚ Visual for Teaching Aid 26 provides the drawings for **Questions 14** and **15.**
⬚ Computer Master 11

OBJECTIVES

A Draw or identify images of figures under composites of reflections.
B Apply properties of reflections to obtain properties of translations and rotations.
C Apply the Two Reflection Theorem for Translations.
E Determine the isometry which maps one figure onto another.
G Apply a rule described using T( ) notation.

TEACHING NOTES

Some students may have been introduced to slides, flips, and turns in elementary school or in junior high school. The words *translations, reflections,* and *rotations* are standard equivalents for work in high school.

We define translations as composites of reflections because that definition simplifies the mathematics of congruence. One difficulty with defining translations as composites of reflections is that students may think one cannot "do" a translation without doing reflections. Emphasize that a transformation is the correspondence between the preimage and image points, not the physical motion involved in locating the image points.

Making Connections In addition to studying translations in their own right, there are two important connections to earlier topics. First, composition of functions is demonstrated visually since a translation is the composite of two reflections. Second, the preservation properties of translations are very similar to those of reflections, with two exceptions: orientation is preserved and a line is parallel to its image.

The basis for studying vectors, direction and magnitude, is established in this lesson. Translations and vectors are intimately related. In a given translation, the set of directed segments connecting points to their images is the set of directed segments of a single vector. (See Lesson 14-5.)

Reading It is important for students to pay attention to the diagrams as they read and try to decide which points correspond. For coordinates, have students relate adding a positive number h to the x-coordinate to moving h units to the right. Then adding a negative number h to the x-coordinate is moving h units to the "negative right," or left. Adding a positive number k to the y-coordinate is moving k units up, and adding a negative number k to the y-coordinate is moving k units "negative up," or down.

Alternate Approach Ask students to try to think of other ways to find the reflecting lines for the translation shown in the **Example.** (For example, find the perpendicular bisector of $\overline{AA'}$ at P. Then find the perpendicular bisector of $\overline{AP}$ and $\overline{PA'}$. These lines are parallel reflecting lines.)

260

Definition:

The **composite** of a first transformation S and a second transformation T is the transformation mapping a point P onto $T(S(P))$.

The composite of S and T may be thought of as "apply transformation S, then apply transformation T to the image you found under S"; it is written $T \circ S$ and is read "T following S." In the drawing on page 259, r_ℓ is the first transformation, r_m the second. You can write either $r_m(r_\ell(\triangle ABC)) = \triangle A''B''C''$ or $r_m \circ r_\ell(\triangle ABC) = \triangle A''B''C''$.

Notice that the transformation applied first is written *on the right*. The reason for this is that with transformations, as in algebra, you must work inside parentheses first. Thus in $r_m(r_\ell(A))$, the transformation r_ℓ should be applied before r_m, and r_ℓ is on the right.

Above, it seems that the composite of the two reflections has the effect of sliding $\triangle ABC$. This can be verified. Have you ever been in a room with two mirrors on opposite walls? (Barber shops and beauty salons often have such rooms.)

If you look in one of the mirrors, you see not only the usual reflection image but also many images of images. Some of these look like slide images. This is why, by using two parallel mirrors, you can see the back of your head.

$r_m \circ r_\ell (F)$ $r_m(F)$ m F ℓ $r_\ell (F)$

Below is still another example of a composite of two reflections over parallel lines. Again, the preimage looks like it could have been slid onto the image.

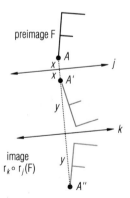

preimage F

x •A

x •A' j

y

k

image
$r_k \circ r_j(F)$ y

•A''

Definition:

A **translation** (or **slide**) is the composite of two reflections over parallel lines.

That is, when $m \parallel n$, the transformation $T = r_m \circ r_n$ is a translation.

Since each reflection in a translation preserves angles, betweenness, collinearity, and distance, so does the translation. Also, the translation preserves orientation, because the first reflection switches orientation, and the second switches it back.

A translation is often called a slide because the preimage looks as if it could have been slid onto the image. Thus you can describe a slide by telling how far a preimage is slid and in what direction. The **direction** of a translation is given by any ray from a preimage point through its image point. The **magnitude** of a translation is the distance between any point and its image.

For the transformation on the previous page, $\overrightarrow{AA''}$ is the direction and AA'' is the magnitude. The direction and magnitude of a translation are related to the reflecting lines in a surprisingly simple way.

Two Reflection Theorem for Translations:

If $m \parallel \ell$, the translation $r_m \circ r_\ell$ slides figures two times the distance between ℓ and m, in the direction from ℓ to m perpendicular to those lines.

Proof

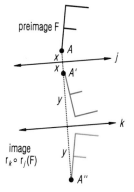

preimage F

image $r_k \circ r_j(F)$

Use the figure at the left, concentrating on points A, A', and A''. By the definition of reflection, $\overline{AA'} \perp j$ and $\overline{A'A''} \perp k$. So, by the Two Perpendiculars Theorem, $\overleftrightarrow{AA'} \parallel \overleftrightarrow{A'A''}$. But A' is on each line. So $\overleftrightarrow{AA'} = \overleftrightarrow{A'A''}$ and the three points are collinear. This means $\overleftrightarrow{AA''}$ is perpendicular to both reflecting lines. Notice that the distance between the parallel lines is $x + y$. Thus $AA'' = 2x + 2y$, which is double $x + y$. The proof is similar if A is located in a different position relative to j and k.

Since a translation is defined by reflections, the Figure Reflection Theorem holds for translations. Thus to translate a figure, you only have to translate the points which determine the figure. You can translate a preimage in either of two ways: (1) slide each preimage point the proper distance in the proper direction, or (2) reflect over two parallel lines which are perpendicular to the direction and exactly half the distance apart.

LESSON 6-2 Translations   261

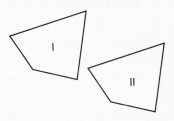

Example   Draw possible reflecting lines for the translation mapping △ABC onto △$A'B'C'$.

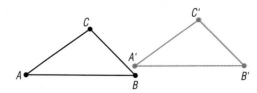

Solution   The reflecting lines are perpendicular to the translation's direction. So first draw *any* line m perpendicular to $\overleftrightarrow{AA'}$. Let $AA' = d$. The magnitude d of the translation is 2 times the distance between ℓ and m. So draw a second line n parallel to m in the same direction as the translation such that the perpendicular distance between m and n is $\frac{d}{2}$.

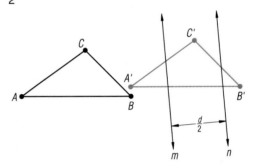

Check   If you do the reflections over the lines m and n, will it work? That is, does $r_n \circ r_m(\triangle ABC) = \triangle A'B'C'$?
Draw $r_m(\triangle ABC)$. Call it $\triangle XYZ$. Now reflect $\triangle XYZ$ over n. The image of $\triangle XYZ$ should coincide with $\triangle A'B'C'$, which is the case.

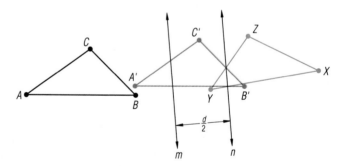

A surprising thing about the solution to the Example is that line m could be anywhere in the plane so long as it is perpendicular to $\overleftrightarrow{AA'}$. It does not have to be close to the preimage.

262

Questions

1. A translation is the __?__ of two reflections over parallel lines.
   composite
2. Where might you see parallel mirrors in a room? Why are they there?
   See margin.
3. *Multiple choice.* Which of the following symbols stands for the transformation which results from first applying f, then applying s?
   (a) f(s)　　　　(b) s(f)　　　　(c) f ∘ s　　　　(d) s ∘ f **(d)**

In 4 and 5, use the diagram at the left. Fill in the blank with a named point.

4. **a.** $r_m(F) =$ __?__ **C**
   b. $r_\ell(r_m(F)) =$ __?__ **B**
   c. $r_\ell \circ r_m(F) =$ __?__ **B**

5. **a.** $r_\ell(A) =$ __?__ **D**
   b. $r_m \circ r_\ell(A) =$ __?__ **E**

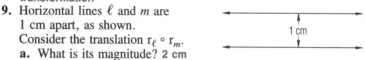

6. If $\ell \parallel m$, what kind of transformation is $r_\ell \circ r_m$? **translation**

7. Name five properties preserved under translations.
   angle measure, betweenness, collinearity, distance, orientation
8. Which is the more general term: translation or transformation?
   transformation
9. Horizontal lines ℓ and m are 1 cm apart, as shown. Consider the translation $r_\ell \circ r_m$.
   a. What is its magnitude? **2 cm**
   b. What is its direction? **vertically up**

10. **a.** Trace this drawing on a sheet of paper. Leave a lot of room at the right and above. **See margin for a.–d.**

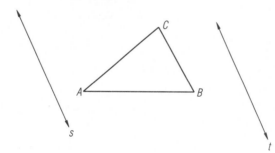

   b. Draw $r_s(\triangle ABC)$. Call it $\triangle A^*B^*C^*$.
   c. Draw $r_t \circ r_s(\triangle ABC)$. Call it $\triangle A'B'C'$.
   d. Verify in your drawing that $\overline{AA'}$, $\overline{BB'}$, and $\overline{CC'}$ are parallel segments of the same length.
   e. *Multiple choice.* How does the length of $\overline{AA'}$ compare with the distance between s and t?
   (i)　It is the same.
   (ii)　It is twice as much.
   (iii)　It is half as much. **(ii)**

LESSON 6-2 *Translations* **263**

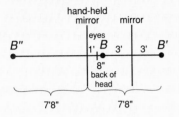

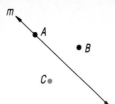

11. At the left, $r_m(B) = C$. What is $r_m \circ r_m(\overline{AB})$? $\overline{AB}$

12. Generalize the result of Question 11. The composite of a reflection with itself results in mapping a figure onto itself.

13. Describe two methods for translating an image 6 inches to the left. See margin.

14. When the letter R is reflected over line ℓ, and then line m, its final image is as shown. But someone erased line m. Trace the figure and put line m back.

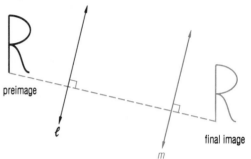

15. Carla has just had her hair cut. With her back to a mirror on the wall, she holds a hand mirror in front of her face.

If Carla's eyes are 1 ft from the hand mirror, her head is 8″ thick, and the back of her head is 3′ from the wall mirror, about how far from her eyes will the image of the back of Carla's head appear in her mirror? about 8′8″

16. The transformation with rule $T(x, y) = (x + 2, y + 6)$ is a translation.
  a. Graph (7, 3) and T(7, 3). See margin.
  b. Find the slope of the line through (7, 3) and its image. (The slope helps to indicate the direction of the translation.) 3
  c. Describe in words the effect of T on a figure.
     It slides a figure up 6 units and over to the right 2 units.

17. **a.** Suppose the point (2, 5) is translated 4 units to the right and 6 units down. What is its image? (6, -1)
  b. Suppose (x, y) is translated 4 units to the right and 6 units down. What is its image? (x + 4, y − 6)

264

264

18. a. If S is the set of vertices of an octagon, what is N(S)? 8
   b. If S is the set of diagonals of an octagon, what is N(S)?
      (Lesson 6-1) 20

19. If T(*x, y*) = (*x* − 8, 3*y*), what is T(-4, 5)? *(Lesson 6-1)* (-12, 15)

20. Given: ℓ ∥ *m* as shown below.
   Prove: m∠1 = m∠8. *(Lessons 4-4, 3-4)*   See margin.

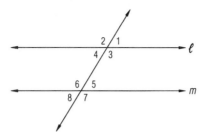

21. *True* or *false?*   *(Lesson 5-5)*
   a. If a figure is a rhombus, then it is a trapezoid. **True**
   b. If a figure is a trapezoid, then it is a rhombus. **False**

22. Trace the diagram below. Draw two different 49° angles with one side
   $\overrightarrow{PQ}$. *(Lesson 3-2)*

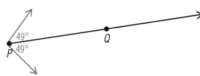

23. Give a good definition for *circle*. *(Lesson 2-5)* **A circle is a set of points
   in a plane a certain distance (its radius) from a certain point (its center.)**

24. If a room has parallel mirrors on opposite walls and you view your
   image, what happens?

One sees the image
of one mirror
reflected in the other,
reflected in the other,
reflected in the other
. . ., and the result is
many translation
images of the room in
both directions.

Portrait of Mr. Edward James by the
Belgian surrealist René Magritte
Magritte is famous for his
paintings of impossible situations.

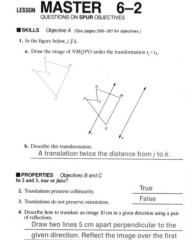

Rotations

Sir David Brewster (1781-1868) invented the first kaleidoscope.

In Lesson 6-2, a composite of reflections was done over parallel
lines. Kaleidoscopes like the one shown above result from reflections over intersecting lines. In the situation below, the preimage
flag is reflected over intersecting lines. The transformation can be
described as $r_m \circ r_\ell$ (r_ℓ is done before r_m).

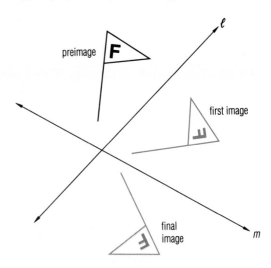

Because each reflection switches orientation, the preimage and final
image have the same orientation. Though the final image is almost
upside down, it is not backwards. (Turn the page upside down to
check.)

The preimage and the final image are related in an astounding way.
Cover up the first image. You can *turn* the preimage onto the second
image! Moreover, the center of the turn is the intersection of the
lines, because that point coincides with its image under each
reflection.

266

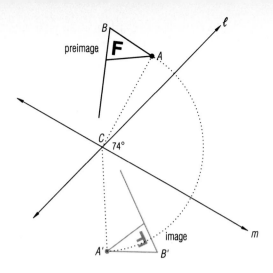

preimage

74°

image

This composite is called a *rotation*.

Definition:

A **rotation** is the composite of two reflections over intersecting lines.

If the reflecting lines are ℓ and m, the **center** of the rotation $r_m \circ r_\ell$ is the point of intersection of the lines. Now measure (with a protractor) $\angle ACA'$ or $\angle BCB'$ in the figure above. The measure of these angles is about 148°. We say that the flag has been rotated 148° **clockwise.** Clockwise is the negative direction; **counterclockwise** is positive. The rotation of the flag has **magnitude** -148°. Magnitudes range from -180° to 180°. (There can be magnitudes outside this range, such as a rotation of 720°. This can always be converted to a rotation in the given range by adding or subtracting a multiple of 360°.)

Now measure the angle between the lines ℓ and m in the figure above. It is 74°, half of 148°. In general, the magnitude of a rotation is easily found from the angle between the reflecting lines. The following theorem illustrates the power of proof to establish results that are not obvious at first glance.

Two Reflection Theorem for Rotations:

The rotation $r_m \circ r_\ell$, where m intersects ℓ, "turns" figures twice the non-obtuse angle between ℓ and m, measured from ℓ to m, about the point of intersection of the lines.

There is another unmentioned surprise in this lesson. If two triangles are congruent and oriented in the same direction, then one is a rotation or translation image of the other. To find the center of the rotation, connect corresponding points with segments and draw the perpendicular bisectors of these segments. The perpendicular bisectors will either be parallel (in which case one is a translation image of the other) or concurrent (in which case the point of concurrency is the center of rotation).

As with translations, students may have difficulty understanding rotations as single transformations; they should not think that reflecting lines are required to accomplish a rotation.

Reading When students read this lesson, expect questions on the proof of the Two Reflection Theorem. Encourage students to draw the flag diagram and to reflect the points themselves as you go through the proof.

Making Connections By allowing both clockwise and counterclockwise rotations (and their corresponding negative and positive magnitudes), the way is being prepared for students to understand circular functions. In later UCSMP courses, the cosine and sine functions are defined in terms of rotations.

ADDITIONAL EXAMPLES

1. Using the **Example** on page 269, what reflecting lines could you use if you wished to draw the image of *ABCD* under a rotation with center *P* and magnitude -48°? **Use the same lines but reverse the order of the reflections.**

2. Describe the composite of reflections over the *x*-axis and *y*-axis (in that order). **A rotation of 180° (or -180°) with center at the origin; the order makes no difference.**

The proof that follows is lengthy. Be sure to go on to read the Example even if you have difficulty following the proof.

Proof

Draw   Use the diagram with the flags. But instead of considering the entire flag, consider a single point *A* at the tip of the flag. $r_\ell(A) = A^*$ and $r_m(A^*) = A'$. Below, the given and prove is written in terms of this diagram.

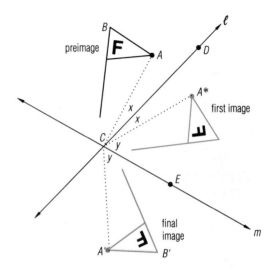

Given: $r_m \circ r_\ell (A) = A'$
   $\ell \cap m = C.$

Prove: (1) $r_m \circ r_\ell (C) = C$
   (2) $m\angle ACA' = 2 \cdot m\angle DCE$
   (3) $AC = A'C.$

Write

(1) **C is on both reflecting lines.**
So $r_m \circ r_\ell(C) = r_m (r_\ell(C)) = r_m(C) = C.$
(2) **By the Figure Reflection Theorem, $r_\ell (\angle ACD) = \angle A^*CD$ and $r_m(\angle A^*CE) = \angle A'CE$. Since reflections preserve angle measure, $m\angle ACD = m\angle A^*CD$ (call it x) and $m\angle A^*CE = m\angle A'CE$ (call it y). From the Angle Addition Property, $m\angle DCE = x + y$ and $m\angle ACA' = 2(x + y)$. By substitution, $m\angle ACA' = 2(m\angle DCE).$**
(3) **Since $AC = A^*C$ and $A^*C = A'C$ (reflections preserve distance), $AC = A'C.$**

If *A* were located on one of the lines, or on the other side of ℓ or *m*, the steps would be a little different, but the result would still hold.

268

Example   Use two reflections to draw the image of *ABCD* under a rotation with center *P* and magnitude of 48°.

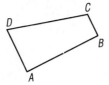

P●

Solution   The angle between reflecting lines must be $\frac{1}{2}$ the magnitude. Since the magnitude is 48°, the angle between the reflecting lines must be 24°.

Step 1.   Draw any line $\overleftrightarrow{PO}$ through *P*.
Step 2.   Draw $\overleftrightarrow{PQ}$ such that m∠*OPQ* = 24 (counterclockwise).
Step 3.   Reflect *ABCD* over $\overleftrightarrow{PO}$. Call the image *A*B*C*D**.
Step 4.   Reflect *A*B*C*D** over $\overleftrightarrow{PQ}$. This is the final image *A'B'C'D'*.

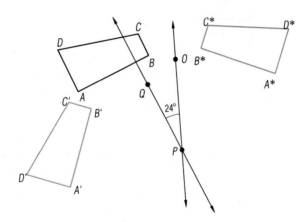

Check 1   Measure ∠*BPB'* and ∠*APA'* to see that each is a 48° angle. Check also that *BP* = *B'P*, *AP* = *A'P*, *CP* = *C'P*, and *DP* = *D'P*.

Check 2   Trace *ABCD*. Turn your tracing 48° counterclockwise about point *P*. It should coincide with *A'B'C'D'*.

In clothing stores you often find intersecting mirrors. These mirrors allow a shopper to see how clothes look from the front, side, and back. The shopper can see the reflection image of a reflection image in the mirrors. In the figure, the shopper is using the left and middle mirrors. This, in effect, turns the shopper twice the angle between

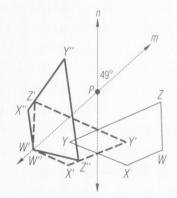
the mirrors. Below, the acute angle between the mirrors is 55°, and as a result, the final image of the shopper is rotated 110°. This is enough of a turn to show the shopper what the back of the clothing looks like.

Questions

Covering the Reading

1. The composite of two reflections over two intersecting lines is a(n) __?__. rotation

2. The center of the rotation in Question 1 is the __?__ of the reflecting lines. point of intersection

3. *Multiple choice.* If a magnitude of a rotation is negative, then the direction of the rotation is
   (a) clockwise   (b) counterclockwise. (a)

In 4–6, use the figure below. Given $r_\ell(P) = Q$ and $r_m(Q) = P'$. The angle between the lines has measure 37°.

4. What is $m\angle POP'$? 74

5. Justify each conclusion.
   a. $OP = OQ$
   b. $OQ = OP'$
   c. $OP = OP'$
   See margin.

6. Justify each conclusion.
   a. $r_\ell(\angle POD) = \angle QOD$ Figure Reflection Theorem
   b. $m\angle POD = m\angle QOD$ Reflections preserve angle measure.

7. To rotate a figure -160°, you could reflect the figure over two lines where the acute angle between the lines has measure __?__. 80°

8. Name two places in the real world where you can find intersecting mirrors.
   samples: clothing store, kaleidoscopes, exercise or dance rooms

9. Trace the figure at the left. Leave a lot of room. Rotate *WXYZ* -98° about *P* by using two reflections. See margin.

270

10. Trace the figure below.
  a. Draw $r_m \circ r_\ell (\triangle ABC)$. See below.
  b. Use a protractor to determine the magnitude of this rotation.
    about −65°

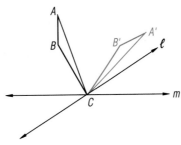

11. Reflect (4, 2) over the *x*-axis. Reflect its image over the *y*-axis.
  a. What is the final image? (-4, -2)
  b. What rotation has taken place? 180° with center at origin

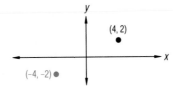

12. Identify the properties that rotations preserve from this list:
  angle measure, betweenness, collinearity, distance, orientation.
  all of them

In 13–15 below, $r_\ell(\triangle LMN) = \triangle OPQ$ and $r_m(\triangle OPQ) = \triangle RST$. Prove:
13. $MN = ST$. See margin.   **14.** $m\angle N = m\angle T$. See margin.

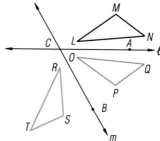

15. Suppose $m\angle NCT = 172$.
  a. What is the magnitude of the rotation with center *C* under which $\triangle RST$ is the image of $\triangle LMN$? -172°
  b. What is the magnitude of the rotation with center *C* under which $\triangle LMN$ is the image of $\triangle RST$? 172°
  c. What is $m\angle ACB$? 86

16. A view through a kaleidoscope is pictured at the beginning of this lesson. What is the magnitude of the rotation R with center *O* if $R(B) = C$? -120°

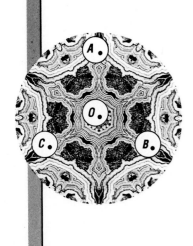

13.

Conclusions	Justifications
1. *MN* = *PQ*; *PQ* = *ST*	Reflections preserve distance.
2. *MN* = *ST*	Transitive Prop. of Eq.

14.

Conclusions	Justifications
1. m∠*N* = m∠*Q*; m∠*Q* = m∠*T*	Reflections preserve angle measure.
2. m∠*N* = m∠*T*	Transitive Prop. of Eq.

NAME _____

■ **SKILLS**   *Objective A (See pages 299–301 for objectives.)*

1. Use the drawing below.
  a. Draw $r_p(\overline{MN})$. Let $r_p(\overline{MN}) = \overline{M'N'}$.
  b. Draw $r_s \circ r_p(\overline{MN})$. Let $r_s \circ r_p(\overline{MN}) = \overline{M''N''}$.
  c. Measure ∠*M''LM* and ∠*KLJ*. How are these angle measures related?
    m∠*M''LM* = 58, m∠*KLJ* = 29;
    ─────────────────────────────
    m∠*M''LM* = 2 · m∠*KLJ*

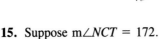

■ **PROPERTIES**   *Objectives B and C*

2. a. Explain why rotations preserve betweenness.
  A rotation is a composite of 2 reflections.
  Since reflections preserve betweenness,
  so do rotations.
  b. Explain why rotations preserve orientation.
  A rotation is a composite of 2 reflections. The
  first reflection reverses orientation; the second
  reverses it back to the original orientation.

3. To rotate a figure 150° you could reflect the figure over two lines. What would the acute angle between the two lines have to be?   75°

■ **USES**   *Objective E*

4. A person standing in front of a dressing room mirror sees his image rotated by 100°. What is the acute angle made by the two mirrors?   50°

17. *Multiple choice.* Translations do *not* preserve
    (a) angle measure
    (b) collinearity
    (c) orientation
    (d) All are preserved. *(Lesson 6-2)* (d)

18. In the drawing at the right, *s* ∥ *t*. Trace the drawing and draw $r_t \circ r_s(ABCD)$. *(Lesson 6-2)*

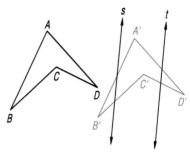

19. If T(x, y) = (x + 43, y − 210), what is T(-30, -2)? *(Lesson 6-1)*
    (13, −212)

20. One angle of an isosceles triangle measures 50°.
    a. If this angle is a base angle, what are the measures of the two other angles? 50° and 80°
    b. If this angle is the vertex angle, what are the measures of the two other angles? *(Lessons 5-7, 5-1)* 65° and 65°

21. In rhombus *ABCD* at the left, m∠A = x and m∠B = 3x + 3. Find the measure of ∠D. *(Lesson 5-5)* 135.75°

22. Below, *n*-gon *ABCD...L* is pictured.
    a. What is *n*? 12
    b. Is *ABCD...L* clockwise or counterclockwise oriented? *(Lesson 4-6)*
    counterclockwise

23. In 4 minutes, through how many degrees turns:
    a. the minute hand of a clock? 24°
    b. the hour hand of a clock? *(Lesson 3-1)* 2°

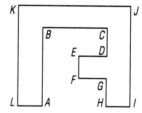

24. Point *B* is the image of *A* under a rotation.
    a. Identify a point which could be the center of the rotation.
    b. Identify another point which could be the center.
    c. Identify a third point which could be the center.
    d. Generalize parts **a, b,** and **c.**

    A•

    a) sample: the midpoint of $\overline{AB}$;
    b-d) *Any point on the perpendicular bisector of $\overline{AB}$ will work.*

    •B

Miniature Golf and Billiards

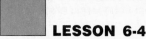

© John Margolies/Esto

When a ball is rolled without spin against a wall, it bounces off the wall as if it had gone through the wall and its path were reflected over the wall. The ball takes the shortest path to its destination. The marked angles are always of equal measure.

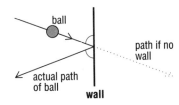

ball

path if no wall

actual path of ball

wall

This property is not limited to bouncing balls. It is true of any object traveling without spin which hits a surface. It holds for sound, light, and radio waves which bounce off surfaces. For example, when you look in a mirror to see a person, your eye receives as images only those light waves which bounce off the mirror in your direction. This is shown in the diagram below. You see the person's image in the mirror as if the person were reflected to the other side of the mirror. The image appears to be as far "behind" the mirror as the person is in front of it, and the orientation of the image is reversed.

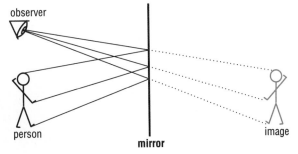

observer

person

mirror

image

LESSON 6-4 Miniature Golf and Billiards   **273**

LESSON 6-4

RESOURCES
■ Lesson Master 6-4
■ Quiz for Lessons 6-1 Through 6-4
▣ Visual for Teaching Aid 28 displays the miniature golf diagrams on page 274 and can be used with **Question 8**.
▣ Visual for Teaching Aid 29 displays the billiards diagrams on pages 274-275.
▣ Visual for Teaching Aid 30 displays the diagrams for **Questions 3, 4, 5**, and **9**.
▣ Visual for Teaching Aid 31 displays the diagrams for **Questions 7, 11**, and **12**.
▪ Computer Master 12

OBJECTIVE

F Use reflections to find a path from an object to a particular point.

TEACHING NOTES

Some students may not grasp that this lesson is using some of the same ideas as previous lessons. Point out that there is a reflection over one line, and then a reflection of the first *image* over the second line. To demonstrate this, name the points B', B'', and B''' on page 275 as $r_z(B)$, $r_y(r_z(B))$, and $r_x(r_y(r_z(B)))$. You may wish to consider different sequences of walls so students do not think that alphabetical order is important.

The movie *Donald Duck in Mathemagic Land* is appropriate with this lesson, for there is a section on billiards. There are dots on sides of billiard tables to allow players to employ reflection ideas.

Head toward the reflection of the wagon over the river.

The simple idea of bouncing off a wall has applications also in many sports, including miniature golf and billiards. In miniature golf, the object of the game is to hit a golf ball into a hole. The hole is often placed so that a direct shot into it is impossible. Below is a picture of a miniature golf hole with a golf ball at G and the hole at H.

In this situation, a good strategy is to bounce (carom) the ball off a board, as shown below. To find where to aim the ball, reflect the hole H over line $\overleftrightarrow{AB}$. If you shoot for image H', the ball will bounce off $\overline{AB}$ at P and go toward the hole. If its path intersects wall $\overline{CD}$, then another strategy, using at least two caroms, is needed.

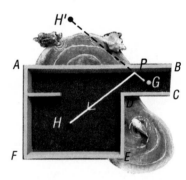

The following discussion of billiards shows how to aim when two or more caroms are needed. Billiards is a game played on a table with rubber cushions on its sides and no holes. In 3-cushion billiards the goal is to hit the cue ball so that it bounces off three cushions and then hits another ball. Pictured below is a table with cushions w, x, y, and z, the cue ball C, and another ball B.

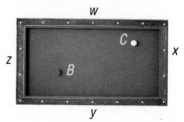

274

Suppose you want to shoot C off x, then y, then z, and finally hit B. Reflect the target B successively over the sides in *reverse* order: first z, then y, then x. Shoot in the direction of $B''' = r_x \circ r_y \circ r_z (B)$.

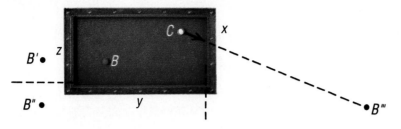

Notice what happens with the shot. (Observe the diagram below.) On the way toward B''', it bounces off side x in the direction of B''. On the way toward B'', it bounces off y in the direction of B'. Finally it hits z, and is reflected to B.

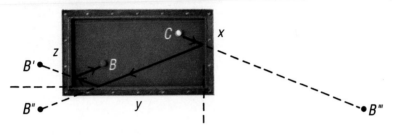

In general, to shoot an object J off wall 1 and then wall 2 and into a second object K, aim at $r_1 \circ r_2 (K)$.

Questions

Covering the Reading

1. A ball B is rolling toward the wall without spin. Trace the figure and draw the rest of the path showing how the ball will bounce off the wall.

2. Trace this figure. To shoot a ball from A to B off the wall w, where should you aim? **at the reflection image of B over w**

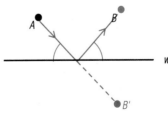

4.

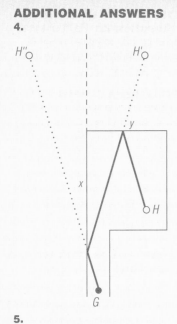

5.

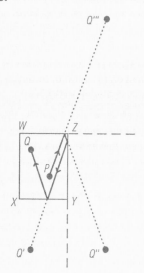

7. See Additional Answers in the back of this book.

8. samples:

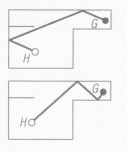

3. Trace the diagram of Hole 3 in the miniature golf course below. Where can you shoot in order to get the ball *G* into the hole *H*?

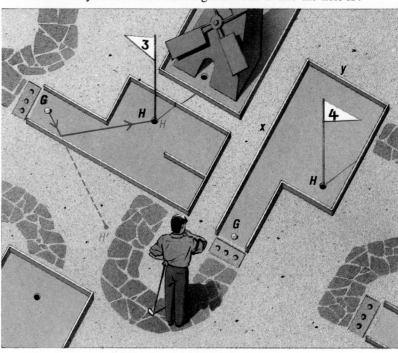

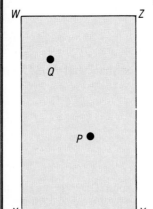

Applying the Mathematics

4. Trace Hole 4 above. Where should you aim on wall *x* to shoot a golf ball off sides *x* and *y* and into the hole at *H*? **See margin.**

5. Trace the picture of the billiards table at the left. If you wish to bounce *P* off the top, right, and bottom sides, and then hit *Q*, in what direction should you shoot *P*? **See margin.**

6. A billiard ball travels along the path shown below. Trace the figure and mark all angles that are equal in measure.

7. A laser beam sent from point *S* is to be reflected off two lines ℓ and *m* in such a way that it finally passes through point *D*. Trace the figure below. Then construct the path of the laser beam. **See margin.**

8. Find two other paths for getting from the golf ball *G* to the hole *H* in one shot in the first miniature golf picture on page 274. **See margin.**

276

In 9 and 10, pocket billiards is played on a table with rubber cushions on its sides and 6 holes called *pockets*. The goal is to hit the cue ball so it hits an object ball into a pocket. Trace the figure below.

9., 10., 11., 12. See Additional Answers in the back of this book.

9. If you want to bounce the object ball *B* off wall *y* to go into the upper right corner pocket, where on *y* should the ball bounce? See margin.

10. If you want to hit the cue ball *C* off side *x* before hitting object ball *B*, where should you aim? See margin.

11. Trace the diagram of the miniature golf hole below. Where should you shoot in order to get the ball *G* into the hole *H*? See margin.

12. A billiards table with sides *w*, *x*, *y*, and *z* is diagrammed at the left on a coordinate plane. A player wants to hit a cue ball at $C = (3, 2)$ into a second ball at $B = (1, 6)$. At what point should the player aim in order to bounce the cue ball off sides *W*, *Z*, and *Y*, in that order? See margin.

13. Below is Captain Natalie looking through a periscope at a ship. The line of sight through the periscope from Captain Natalie's eye to the ship is given. What are the measures of angles 1 and 2 at which the mirrors are slanted? $m\angle 1 = m\angle 2 = 45$

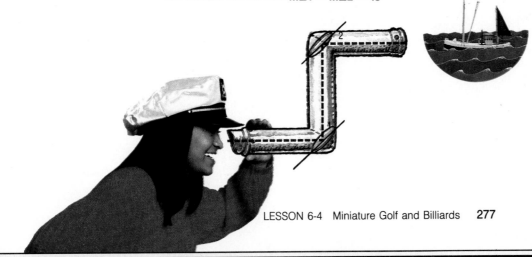

LESSON 6-4   Miniature Golf and Billiards   **277**

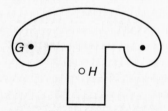
Review

14. *Multiple choice.* Which parallelogram below is not a rotation image of one of the other two? *(Lesson 6-3)* **(a)**

(a)   (b)   (c)

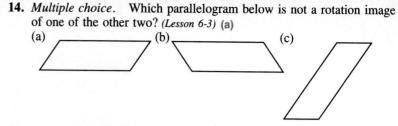

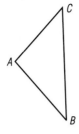

15. Trace the figure at the left. Rotate $\triangle ABC$ 100° about point P by using two reflections. *(Lesson 6-3)* **See margin.**

16. Let P(E) be the probability of an event E. If a number x is randomly picked from {2, 3, 4, 5, 6, 7, 8}, what is P(x is even)? *(Lesson 6-1)* $\frac{4}{7}$

In 17 and 18, refer to the figure below.

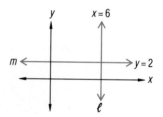

17. Let ℓ be the line with equation $x = 6$. Let m be the line with equation $y = 2$. Give the center and magnitude of the rotation $r_\ell \circ r_m$. *(Lesson 6-3)* **center: (6, 2); magnitude: 180°**

18. Let m be the line with equation $y = 2$. Let n be the x-axis. Give the direction and magnitude of the translation $r_n \circ r_m$. *(Lesson 6-2)* **direction is down or in the negative y direction; magnitude is 4**

19. In $\triangle ABC$, the angles are in the extended ratio 2:3:4.
  a. Find the measure of the largest angle. **80°**
  b. Is $\triangle ABC$ acute, right, or obtuse? *(Lesson 5-7)* **acute**

Exploration

20. Design a miniature golf hole in which smart golfers, but not those who don't apply reflections, could make a hole-in-one. **See margin.**

Congruent Figures

Figures are copied everywhere. Teachers photocopy pages for students. Tool and die makers create devices (the "dies") for cutting and forging metal so that manufacturers can make identical parts. Artists use copies of figures to create designs or patterns. Children draw copies of figures by tracing. People look at copies of themselves every time they look in mirrors.

The idea of "copy" is found everywhere in geometry also, and geometers have a special word to describe figures which are copies of each other: *congruent*. To be used in reasoning, like any other idea in mathematics, the word "congruent" needs a careful definition. But recall that good definitions can only use undefined terms or terms previously defined. We cannot define "congruent" as "exact copy" because "copy" has never been defined nor is "copy" an undefined term.

The key to the definition of congruence comes from the idea of tracing. When you make a tracing, you get a copy of an original figure. You can slide (translate) or turn (rotate) the tracing and your copy remains. You can even turn the paper over, reflecting the tracing image. You can do these movements and reflections again and again—what we call *composing* them. Thus we say that two figures are congruent if and only if one can be gotten from the other by these transformations.

> **Definition (longer form):**
>
> Two figures, F and G, are **congruent figures,** written **F ≅ G,** if and only if G is the image of F under a translation, a reflection, a rotation, or any composite of these.

But you have learned that rotations and translations are each composites of two reflections. This enables a shorter definition to be used.

> **Definition (shorter form):**
>
> Two figures F and G are **congruent figures,** written **F ≅ G,** if and only if G is the image of F under a reflection or composite of reflections.

LESSON 6-5 Congruent Figures **279**

LESSON 6-5

RESOURCES
■ Lesson Master 6-5
▐▟ Visual for Teaching Aid 32 provides the drawings on page 280 and can be used with **Questions 7** and **8**. It also displays the hierarchy of isometries on page 280.

OBJECTIVE

D Determine properties of congruent figures.

TEACHING NOTES

One advantage of the transformation conception of congruence is that it applies to all figures, not merely to triangles or angles or segments. Another advantage is that this approach is more intuitive, being based upon students' previous experiences with drawings.

Making Connections
Congruent figures are described in previous UCSMP textbooks as figures with the same size and shape. Point out that the formal definition given in this lesson is made so that it can be used in reasoning. The definition is used in all proofs of the triangle congruence theorems (SAS, SSS, etc.) so it is important that students know it. The same size and shape is a consequence of the preservation properties of isometries.

Ask students to look around the classroom for instances of congruence. There are many such instances, and most have nothing to do with segments, angles, or triangles. Examples include congruence of student chairs, of window panes, of the parts of grates in a heating unit, of tiles on the floor, of new pieces of chalk, of the various pages of this book, and so on.

The properties of congruence on page 280 are like those of equality, and therefore congruence is called an *equivalence relation*. In discussing these properties, relate them to equality.

The Segment Congruence Theorem and the Angle Congruence Theorem are often seen as definitions of congruence for segments and angles. The proofs are similar to the proofs of the triangle congruence theorems, which are discussed in Lesson 7-2. You should go through the proof immediately preceding the statement of the Segment Congruence Theorem.

Alternate Approach

You might need to demonstrate how figures can be congruent by showing students the composite of reflections which is used to "get" from one figure to its congruent image figure. An effective way to do this is to use large paper congruent figures, tape, and the chalkboard. Cut out various sets of congruent figures and tape them in pairs on the chalkboard. Then show the reflecting lines that allow you to go from preimage figure to image figure. The preimage figure can be physically moved until it coincides with the image figure.

Below are six figures. Each is a reflection image of another. Since $r_\ell \circ r_k$ maps Figure 1 onto Figure 3, Figures 1 and 3 are congruent (sufficient condition). Conversely, since Figure 4 and Figure 6 are congruent, then they can be mapped one onto the other by a reflection or composite of reflections. In this case $r_p \circ r_n$ does the job.

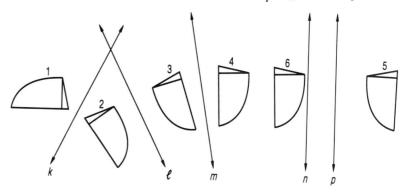

Use the same reflecting line twice and a figure is reflected back onto itself. Thus any figure is congruent to itself. If $F \cong G$, then use the reflecting lines in reverse order and you see that $G \cong F$. When $F \cong G$ and $G \cong H$, use all the reflecting lines of both these congruences to get $F \cong H$. Thus $\cong$ satisfies three properties also satisfied by $=$, called the *equivalence properties*.

Equivalence Properties of $\cong$ Theorem:

For any figures F, G, and H:
Reflexive Property of Congruence: $F \cong F$.
Symmetric Property of Congruence: If $F \cong G$, then $G \cong F$.
Transitive Property of Congruence: If $F \cong G$ and $G \cong H$, then $F \cong H$.

A transformation that is a reflection or composite of reflections is called a **congruence transformation** or **isometry.** "Isometry" comes from the Greek *isos* meaning "equal" and *metron* meaning "measure." Below is a hierarchy of the transformations you have studied so far.

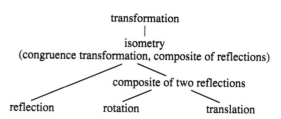

Every reflection preserves angle measure, betweenness, collinearity, and distance. So these properties are preserved by any isometry. The names of these four properties happen to begin with the first four letters of the alphabet.

A-B-C-D Theorem:

Every isometry preserves Angle measure, Betweenness, Collinearity (lines), and Distance (lengths of segments).

When figures are congruent, corresponding parts are images of each other under an isometry. Since every isometry has the A-B-C-D preservation properties, corresponding parts have equal measures. In general:

If two segments are congruent, they have equal lengths.
If two angles are congruent, they have equal measures.

Are the converses of these statements true as well? If segments have equal lengths, then are they congruent? Yes, here is a proof. At the left below, $WX = YZ$.

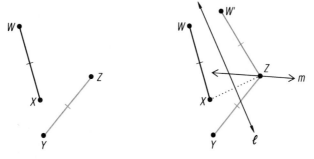

Reflect $\overline{WX}$ over ℓ, the $\perp$ bisector of $\overline{XZ}$, as shown above at the right. Now $WX = W'Z = YZ$. So $\triangle W'ZY$ (not drawn) is isosceles. Now reflect $\overline{W'Z}$ over m, the bisector of $\angle W'ZY$. By the Isosceles Triangle Symmetry Theorem, $r_m(\overline{W'Z}) = \overline{YZ}$. So $r_m \circ r_\ell(\overline{WX}) = \overline{YZ}$ and the segments are congruent by the definition of congruence (sufficient condition).

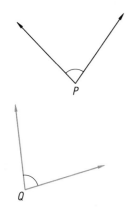

Similarly, if $\angle P$ and $\angle Q$ at the left have the same measure, you can map one onto the other by a composite of reflections. (The first reflecting line can be the $\perp$ bisector of $\overline{PQ}$.) The results of these arguments are two quite useful theorems.

Segment Congruence Theorem:

Two segments are congruent if and only if they have the same length.

LESSON 6-5 Congruent Figures   **281**

NOTES ON QUESTIONS
Question 20: There are many other possible transformations mapping G onto F, but the given answer is the only one that can be described using the information stated in the question.

Question 21: Discuss this question because it is important for students to realize that there is a transformation that maps each point onto itself (the identity transformation). One way of describing the identity transformation is as the composite of two reflections over the same line. This shows that the identity transformation is a special kind of translation or rotation, but not a special kind of reflection. Students may be puzzled that there is something called a transformation which does not change the position of the figure. Remind them that when studying changes, such as changes in cost, changes in temperature, or changes in grades, the presence of no change from one time to the next cannot be ignored.

Question 23: This figure purposely has triangles that look equilateral to force students to work from what is given. Warn students about assuming measures from a figure. You might have them draw a diagram satisfying the condition in which ∠B is not congruent to ∠D.

Making Connections for Question 24: The triangles are related by a glide reflection. Use this question to connect to the next lesson, in which glide reflections are presented.

Angle Congruence Theorem:

Two angles are congruent if and only if they have the same measure.

Because of these theorems, in this book the phrase *congruent segments* can be substituted for the phrase *segments of equal length,* and *congruent angles* for *angles with the same measure.* For instance, the definition of a square could be restated as: A quadrilateral is a square if and only if it has four congruent sides and four right angles.

Questions

Covering the Reading

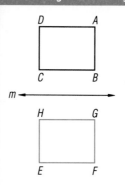

1. Define: congruent figures. See margin.

2. *Multiple choice.* Suppose ∠A is congruent to ∠B. Which is true?
   (a) m∠A + m∠B = 90
   (b) m∠A + m∠B = 180
   (c) m∠A = m∠B
   (d) none of these (c)

3. In the figure at the left, $r_m(ABCD) = FGHE$. Assume nothing else about this figure.
   a. $\overline{BC} \cong$ __?__ GH
   b. ∠CAB ≅ __?__ ∠HFG
   c. △BCD ≅ __?__ △GHE

In 4–6, which equivalence property justifies each statement?

4. If $\overline{AB} \cong \overline{CD}$ and $\overline{CD} \cong \overline{GF}$, then $\overline{AB} \cong \overline{GF}$.
   Transitive Property of Congruence

5. If △MPQ ≅ △ABC, then △ABC ≅ △MPQ.
   Symmetric Property of Congruence

6. ∠QAM ≅ ∠QAM **Reflexive Property of Congruence**

In 7 and 8, refer to the drawing of the six congruent figures on page 280.

7. a. Which transformation maps figure 6 onto figure 4? $r_n \circ r_p$
   b. Which transformation maps figure 4 onto figure 6? $r_p \circ r_n$

8. Which transformation maps figure 1 onto figure 5? $r_n \circ r_m \circ r_\ell \circ r_k$

9. Give two synonyms for "isometry."
   congruence transformation, composite of reflections

10. Name four properties preserved by isometries.
    angle measure, betweenness, collinearity, distance

11. Name three places outside of mathematics where congruent figures may be found.
    samples: tool and die making, teacher photocopies, art

12. According to the Segment Congruence Theorem, if $AX = BY$, then __?__. $\overline{AX} \cong \overline{BY}$

13. According to the Angle Congruence Theorem, if ∠C ≅ ∠T, then __?__. m∠C = m∠T

282

14. *Multiple choice.* If r(△ABC) = △DEF, then according to the definition of congruence,

(a) $\overline{AB} \cong \overline{DE}$ (b) m∠C = m∠F   (c) △ABC ≅ △DEF.   (c)

In 15 and 16, reword the statement using the word *congruent*.

15. An isosceles triangle has two sides of the same length.
An isosceles triangle has two congruent sides.

16. If two lines are cut by a transversal and alternate interior angles have the same measure, then the lines are parallel. See margin.

17. Draw two congruent nonsymmetric pentagons with the same orientation. See margin.

18. Draw a figure congruent to the stick figure at the left and with different orientation.

19. Can two circles not be congruent? Yes

20. If $r_\ell \circ r_m(F) = G$, what transformation maps G onto F? $r_m \circ r_\ell$

21. What does the transformation $r_\ell \circ r_\ell$ do to a figure? maps it onto itself

22. Explain why any two positions of the minute hand of a clock are congruent to each other. One position is a rotation image of another.

23. △ABC is isosceles with vertex angle A.
△CAD is isosceles with vertex angle A.
   a. Which segments in the figure are congruent to $\overline{AB}$? $\overline{AC}$ and $\overline{AD}$
   b. Which angles are congruent to ∠B?
   ∠ACB

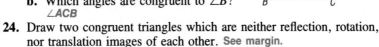

24. Draw two congruent triangles which are neither reflection, rotation, nor translation images of each other. See margin.

25. If you want to hit the cue ball C off side x before C hits object ball B, where should you aim? *(Lesson 6-4)* See margin.

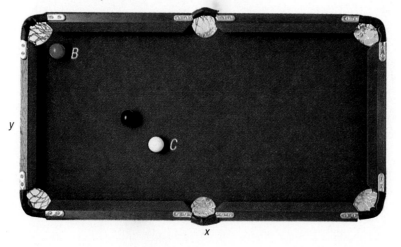

LESSON 6-5   Congruent Figures   **283**

---

16. If two lines are cut by a transversal and alternate interior angles are congruent, then the lines are parallel.

17. sample:

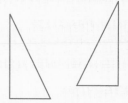

24. sample:

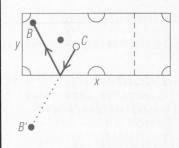

25.

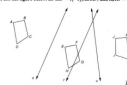

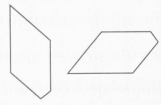

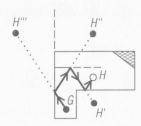
26. Trace the picture of the miniature golf hole below. Where can you shoot in order to get the ball *G* into the hole *H*? *(Lesson 6-4)*
See margin.

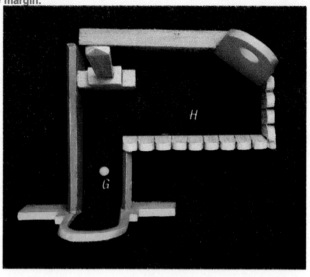

In 27 and 28, use the figure at the left. All triangles in the figure are equilateral.

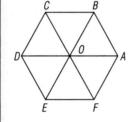

27. Suppose a rotation R has center *O*.
   a. What is its magnitude if R(*B*) = *C*? 60°
   b. What is its magnitude if R(*A*) = *E*? *(Lesson 6-3)* -120°

28. Justify the steps in this proof that *OAFE* is a parallelogram.
   (Lessons 5-6, 5-1, 4-5)

Conclusions	Justifications
1. *OA* = *AF* = *OF*	**a.** __?__ def. of equilat. △ (meaning)
2. *OF* = *FE* = *OE*	**b.** __?__ def. of equilat. △ (meaning)
3. *OA* = *AF* = *FE* = *OE*	**c.** __?__ Transitive Prop. of Equality
4. *OAFE* is a rhombus.	**d.** __?__ def. of rhombus (suff. cond.)
5. *OAFE* is parallelogram.	**e.** __?__ Quadrilateral Hierarchy Theorem

29. Seven angles of an octagon each has measure 150°.
   a. Is this possible? Yes
   b. If so, what is the measure of the eighth angle? If not, why is it not possible? *(Lesson 5-7)* 30°

Exploration

30. Let G be clockwise oriented. F is the image of G under a composite of *n* reflections.
   a. What is the orientation of F when *n* = 3? counterclockwise
   b. What is the orientation of F when *n* = 10? clockwise
   c. For what values of *n* will F and G have the same orientation?
   d. For what values of *n* will F and G have opposite orientations?
   c) even; d) odd

284

284

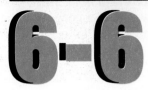

Isometries

By the definition of congruence you know that for any pair of congruent figures, such as the letter *R*s drawn below, there exists a composite of reflections which maps one image onto the other. But what is the least number of reflections needed? And how can you find the reflecting lines?

Figure I   Figure II

The answer may be surprising. If two figures are oriented the same way, as these are, only two reflections are needed! We do not prove this theorem in this book, but you can verify it with drawings.

Example 1 Draw reflecting lines ℓ and m for a composite of reflections $r_m \circ r_\ell$ which maps Figure I onto Figure II above.

Solution

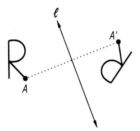

Since the two figures are of the same orientation, it will take two reflections. Select two corresponding points, such as A and A' above, and let ℓ be the perpendicular bisector of $\overline{AA'}$. Then reflect Figure I over ℓ.

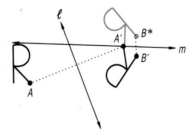

Pick a point from that image (in blue above) and its corresponding point in Figure II. We have labeled these points B^* and B'. Let m be the perpendicular bisector of $\overline{B^*B'}$. Then $r_m \circ r_\ell$ (Figure I) = Figure II.

LESSON 6-6

RESOURCES
■ Lesson Master 6-6
⊿ Visual for Teaching Aid 33 displays the tessellations of **Example 3** and **Questions 4-6**.
⊿ Visual for Teaching Aid 34 displays the drawings for **Questions 7, 8, 16,** and **25**.

OBJECTIVES

A Draw or identify images of figures under composites of reflections.
C Apply the Two Reflection Theorem for Translations and for Rotations.
D Determine properties of congruent figures.
E Determine the isometry which maps one figure onto another.
G Apply a rule described using T( ) notation.

TEACHING NOTES

There are many ways to represent the number 6 (for example, 2 + 4, 1 · 6, 18 ÷ 3, 3 + 2 + 1, and so on), but there is only one number 6. Similarly, there are many ways of representing a transformation that maps one figure onto another (for example, a translation might be represented by a formula for the image of (*x, y*) by an arrow, by a composite of two reflections, or by a composite of four reflections). Continue to stress that two transformations are different only if they give different images. Thus, for instance, a composite of two reflections *equals* a translation or rotation.

The procedure outlined works whether the original figures are rotation or translation images. In Example 1, since ℓ and m intersect, the original figures were rotation images. Now consider congruent figures of different orientations such as Figures III and IV below.

Figure III   Figure IV

There is no single reflection that will map Figure III onto Figure IV. But reflect Figure III over *any* line and its image (Figure III* in blue below) has the same orientation as Figure IV. Now, as was shown on the previous page for letter R, the image, Figure III*, can be mapped onto Figure IV in two reflections. In all, then, Figure III can be mapped onto Figure IV in three reflections.

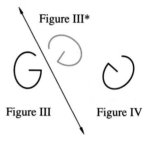

Figure III*

Figure III   Figure IV

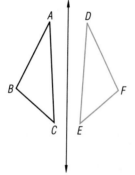

If you reflect over the same line twice, the final image is the same as the original preimage. At the left, $r_\ell(\triangle ABC) = \triangle DFE$ and $r_\ell \circ r_\ell(\triangle ABC) = \triangle ABC$.

If you reflect over ℓ three times, the final image equals the first image.

$$r_\ell \circ r_\ell \circ r_\ell(\triangle ABC) = r_\ell \circ r_\ell(\triangle DFE)$$
$$= \triangle DFE$$

Thus, sometimes the composite of three reflections equals a single reflection.

When the composite of three reflections is not equal to one reflection, an isometry called a **glide reflection** occurs. A glide reflection is the composite of a translation (the "glide" part) and a reflection over a line parallel to the direction of the translation. Informally this is called a *walk* as you can see from the picture below.

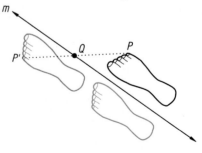

Definition:

Let r_m be a reflection and T be a translation with nonzero magnitude and direction parallel to m. Then $G = T \circ r_m$ is a **glide reflection**.

Successive footprints are very close to being glide reflection images of one another, because each can be mapped onto the other by reflecting over a line and then translating in a direction parallel to that line.

A glide reflection is clearly determined by giving the reflecting line and the magnitude and direction of the translation. The reflecting line has an interesting property. We will give a proof of this property in a later lesson.

Glide Reflection Theorem:

Let $G = T \circ r_m$ be a glide reflection, and let $G(P) = P'$. Then the midpoint of $\overline{PP'}$ is on m.

According to the theorem, in the figure on the bottom of the previous page, since P' is the glide reflection image of P, the intersection of $\overline{PP'}$ and m is Q, the midpoint of $\overline{PP'}$.

The Glide Reflection Theorem suggests a way to find the reflecting line for the reflection or glide reflection that maps one congruent figure onto another. Just connect corresponding points. Since the midpoints of these segments lie on the reflecting line, they determine it.

Example 2 Find the reflecting line ℓ of the glide reflection mapping Figure III onto Figure IV on the previous page.

Solution

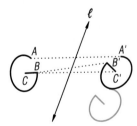

Connect at least two pairs of corresponding points. ℓ is determined by the midpoints of $\overline{AA'}$, $\overline{BB'}$, and $\overline{CC'}$. The image in blue shows the initial reflection of Figure III over ℓ.

LESSON 6-6 Isometries **287**

ADDITIONAL EXAMPLES
1. Give each student a sheet of paper showing a triangle and 6 reflecting lines, with reflection images of the triangle over the lines in a given order. The final triangle should be the image of the first under a composite of 6 reflections.
a. Find two reflections which map the original triangle to the final image.
Answer depends on triangle chosen.
b. Would it be possible to find two reflections if the isometry had been the composite of some other number of reflections?
Yes, if even
c. What is the fewest number of reflections necessary to duplicate the effect of a composite of an odd number of reflections?
3

2. Trace a scalene triangle twice on a sheet of paper but with different orientation. Find the reflection line of the glide reflection which maps one triangle onto the other.
The line goes through the midpoints of the segments connecting corresponding vertices of the triangles.

All congruent figures can be mapped onto each other by a single reflection, rotation, translation, or glide reflection. These four transformations are all the isometries. The transformation hierarchy from Lesson 6-5 can be extended to include all the isometries.

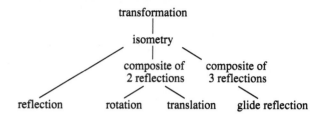

Reflection and glide reflection images have opposite orientation; rotation and translation images the same orientation.

Example 3 Examine the tessellation below.
   a. Which type of isometry maps figure A onto figure B?
   b. Which type of isometry maps figure A onto figure C?

Solution

a. Since A and B have the same orientation, they are related either by a rotation or a translation. A and B can't be related by a translation because they are tilted differently. So B is a rotation image of A. (Can you determine the center of the rotation?)

b. Since A and C have opposite orientations, they are related by a reflection or glide reflection. They are not reflection images of each other, so C must be a glide reflection image of A. The glide reflection line contains the midpoints of segments connecting corresponding points on A and C.

288

Questions

1. When two congruent figures have the same orientation, at most how many reflections are needed to map one onto the other? 2

2. When two congruent figures have different orientations, at most how many reflections are needed to map one onto the other? 3

3. Define: glide reflection. **See margin.**

In 4–6, use the tessellation below.

4. Which type of isometry maps figure A onto figure B? **translation**

5. Which type of isometry maps figure A onto figure C?
glide reflection

6. Which type of isometry maps figure C onto figure D?
glide reflection

In 7 and 8, trace the figures. Figure I ≅ Figure II. Find the reflecting line ℓ of the glide reflection mapping Figure I onto Figure II.

7.

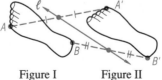

Figure I   Figure II

8.

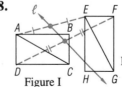

Figure I   Figure II

LESSON 6-6   Isometries   **289**

9. sample:

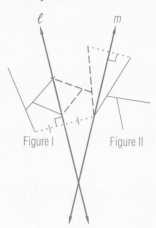

Figure I   Figure II

13. a. angle measure, betweenness, collinearity, distance

14. a. T(A) = (6, -6); T(B) = (1, -6); T(C) = (1, 2)
b.

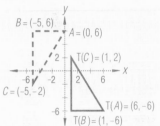

c. x-axis
d. magnitude: 6
direction: horizontal from left to right

15. a. (art is reduced in size.)

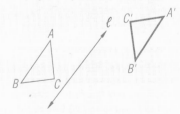

20. See Additional Answers in the back of this book.

22.

Conclusions	Justifications
1. m∠CDG = m∠CEH	∥ lines ⇒ corr. ∠s =
2. m∠CEH = m∠BEF	Vertical Angle Thm.
3. m∠CDG = m∠BEF	Transitive Prop. of Eq.

25. One isometry is the glide reflection shown below. The reflecting line is determined by the common bisector of the segments connecting corresponding points.

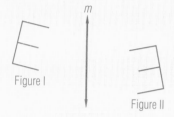

The second isometry shown below is a rotation through point *P*, which is the intersection of ⊥ bisectors of $\overline{AA'}$ and $\overline{BB'}$.

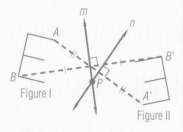

FOLLOW-UP

MORE PRACTICE
For more questions on SPUR Objectives, use *Lesson Master 6-6,* shown on page 291.

EXTENSION
Investigate the figures formed by the midpoints of segments joining any figure to its image under various isometries. For example,
(i)The midpoints of segments joining preimage points to reflection images all lie on the reflecting line.
(ii) The midpoints of segments joining preimage points to translation images form a figure congruent to the preimage.
(iii)The midpoints of segments joining preimage points to glide reflection im-

---

In 9 and 10, trace the figures. Figure I ≅ Figure II. Find a composite of reflections $r_m \circ r_\ell$ which maps Figure I onto Figure II. **See margin.**

9.

Figure II

Figure I

10.

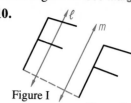

Figure I

Figure II

11. Name the four types of isometries.
reflection, rotation, translation, glide reflection
12. *True* or *false*?
For any two figures, there is an isometry mapping one onto the other.
False

Applying the Mathematics

13. a. Name four properties preserved by glide reflections.
b. Name a property that glide reflections do not preserve.
a) See margin. b) orientation
14. Use the transformation T(*x, y*) = (*x* + 6, -*y*).
a. Find T(△*ABC*) where *A* = (0, 6), *B* = (-5, 6), and *C* = (-5, -2).
b. Graph △*ABC* and T(△*ABC*) on the same axes.
c. T is a glide reflection. What is the reflecting line?
d. What are the magnitude and direction of the translation?
See margin.
15. a. Trace the figure at the left. Perform a glide reflection by reflecting △*ABC* over line ℓ and then translating the image 4 cm parallel to ℓ. See margin.
b. Is your answer to part **a** unique? No

16. Trace the figure below. Let ℓ ∥ *m*, *m* ⊥ *n*, and
$r_\ell \circ r_m \circ r_n(ABCDE) = (FGHIJ)$. Draw ℓ, *m*, and *n*. See margin.

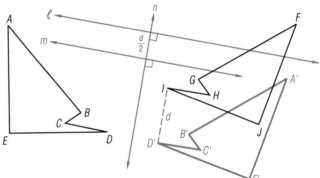

Review

In 17 and 18, justify each conclusion. *(Lesson 6-5)*
17. Given: *AB* = *CD*.
Conclusion: $\overline{AB} \cong \overline{CD}$. Segment Congruence Theorem

18. Given: ∠*EFG* ≅ ∠*HIJ*.
Conclusion: m∠*EFG* = m∠*HIJ*. Angle Congruence Theorem

19. Rewrite this statement using the word *congruent:* The bisector of an angle splits it into two angles of the same measure. *(Lesson 6-5)*
The bisector of an angle splits it into two congruent angles.

290

20. Trace the diagram of this billiards table. If you wish to have *P* bounce off the top, right, and bottom sides, and then hit *Q,* in what direction should you shoot *P*? *(Lesson 6-4)* **See margin.**

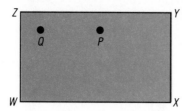

21. Refer to kite *CHIP* at the left. *(Lessons 6-5, 5-4)*

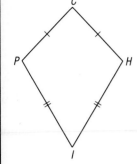

  a. Name its ends. **C and I**
  b. Name its symmetry line. **$\overleftrightarrow{CI}$**
  c. $r_{\overleftrightarrow{CI}}(\triangle CIP) = \underline{\ ?\ }$ **△CIH**
  d. $\triangle CIP \cong \underline{\ ?\ }$ **△CIH**

22. Use the figure below.
  Given: $\overleftrightarrow{AG} \parallel \overleftrightarrow{BH}$.
  Prove: $m\angle CDG = m\angle BEF$. *(Lessons 4-4, 3-4)* **See margin.**

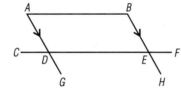

23. Nine times the measure of angle *T* is greater than 801.
  a. Give the possible values of $m\angle T$. **89 < m∠T ≤ 180**
  b. Can $\angle T$ be an acute angle? *(Lesson 3-2, Previous course)* **Yes**

24. A lot has 50′ of frontage and is *x* feet deep. If the area of the lot is less than 1000 square feet, what is *x*? *(Previous course)* **0 < x < 20**

50′

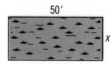

X

Exploration

25. Below are two congruent reflection-symmetric figures. Find and describe two isometries of different types which will map Figure I onto Figure II. **See margin.**

Figure I

Figure II

LESSON 6-6   Isometries   **291**

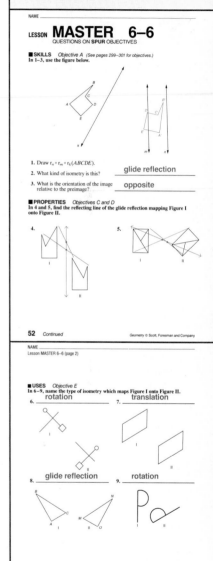

OBJECTIVE

D Determine properties of congruent figures.

TEACHING NOTES

This lesson is easy for most students and should allow some time to review questions from previous lessons that you may still wish to discuss.

In order to check that students understand the idea of corresponding parts, give some questions where the triangles are drawn close to equilateral; doing this will force students to look at the given information independently of the figure to get the corresponding parts.

Emphasize the idea of marking figures to show the corresponding parts. Also, stress that students copy the figures onto their own papers before marking them.

Alternative Approach
Students who cannot list the corresponding parts of two congruent figures can be given labeled paper models of congruent figures. If they make the figures "coincide," the correspondences between vertices become quite easy to determine and list.
    If students cannot match up corresponding vertices of

Corresponding Parts in Congruent Figures

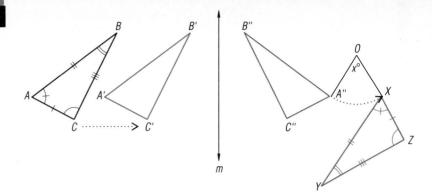

In the figure above, $\triangle ABC$ was translated onto $\triangle A'B'C'$. Then $\triangle A'B'C'$ was reflected over m onto $\triangle A''B''C''$. Lastly, $\triangle A''B''C''$ was rotated about O onto $\triangle XYZ$. Under this composite of transformations, call it T, $\triangle XYZ$ is the image of $\triangle ABC$. So by the definition of congruence, $\triangle ABC \cong \triangle XYZ$.

Specifically, T(A) = X, T(B) = Y, and T(C) = Z. Angles and sides that are images of each other are called *corresponding parts*. Since T can also be described as a composite of reflections (in this case, three reflections), and every composite of reflections preserves distance and angle measure, all the corresponding parts are congruent.

$$\angle A \cong \angle X \qquad \angle B \cong \angle Y \qquad \angle C \cong \angle Z$$

$$\overline{AB} \cong \overline{XY} \qquad \overline{BC} \cong \overline{YZ} \qquad \overline{AC} \cong \overline{XZ}$$

In general, when two figures are congruent, all corresponding angles and sides and other parts of the figures are congruent. This is a *widely used* theorem, and we give it an abbreviated name.

Corresponding Parts in Congruent Figures (CPCF) Theorem:

If two figures are congruent, then any pair of corresponding parts is congruent.

Unless stated otherwise, corresponding parts of a figure refer to sides and angles. With a pair of congruent triangles, there are six pairs of corresponding parts, three pairs of sides and three pairs of angles. However, other corresponding parts in a figure that may exist are bisectors, diagonals, other segments, polygons, or other figures.

Remember that the order of vertices tells you which points are images of which points and, therefore, which parts correspond.

292

Example 1 △TOP ≅ △JKL. List the six pairs of congruent parts. Sketch this situation and mark the congruent parts.

Solution ∠T ≅ ∠J, ∠O ≅ ∠K, and ∠P ≅ ∠L.
$\overline{TO} ≅ \overline{JK}$, $\overline{OP} ≅ \overline{KL}$, and $\overline{TP} ≅ \overline{JL}$.

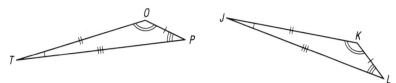

Sometimes it is not so easy to determine corresponding parts from a picture. Then the order of vertices is very helpful. Example 2 demonstrates this.

. . . .

Example 2 A student was able to prove ABCD ≅ FGAE. Using the CPCF Theorem, which angle is congruent to ∠BAD? Which segment is congruent to $\overline{DB}$ (not drawn)?

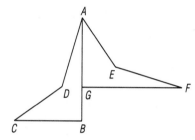

Solution Read the corresponding vertices from the congruence statement, ABCD ≅ FGAE. ∠BAD ≅ ∠GFE and $\overline{DB} ≅ \overline{EG}$.

Check The two angles look like the smallest angles in their respective quadrilaterals, and the segments are the shortest diagonals.

Questions

1. By the definition of congruence, when are triangles congruent?
   See margin.
2. Unless otherwise stated, corresponding parts refer to __?__.
   sides and angles
3. For congruent triangles, there are __?__ pairs of corresponding parts. **6**
4. State the CPCF Theorem. **If two figures are congruent, then any pair of corresponding parts is congruent.**
5. △ATV ≅ △MCI. What part is congruent to the part named?
   a. ∠T **∠C** **b.** ∠VAT **∠IMC** **c.** $\overline{IC}$ **$\overline{VT}$**

LESSON 6-7 Corresponding Parts in Congruent Figures **293**

---

figures, suggest that they use their visual skills to match up respective sides and angles. That is, the smallest side (or angle) of a polygon *must* match the smallest side (or angle) of its image polygon, and so forth.

ADDITIONAL EXAMPLES
1. ABCD shown below is a parallelogram.

a. State a congruence between the two triangles shown.
sample: △ABC ≅ △CDA
b. Describe the isometry which maps one triangle to the other.
rotation of 180° whose center is the midpoint of $\overline{AC}$

2. In the figure below, ABCD ≅ AEDC.

a. Using the CPCF Theorem, which angle is congruent to ∠ADC
b. Which angle is congruent to ∠BDC?
∠ECD
c. Which segment is congruent to $\overline{BC}$?
$\overline{ED}$
d. Name two triangles which are isosceles.
△ACD and △AEB
e. Describe the isometry which yields the given congruences.
reflection over the perpendicular bisector of $\overline{CD}$

ADDITIONAL ANSWERS
1. Two triangles are congruent when one is the image of the other under a reflection or composite of reflections.

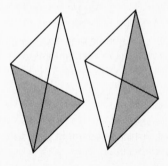

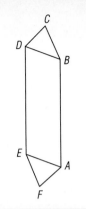

6. Suppose $\triangle ADE \cong \triangle BNO$.
   a. Which sides are congruent? $\overline{AD} \cong \overline{BN}$, $\overline{AE} \cong \overline{BO}$, $\overline{DE} \cong \overline{NO}$
   b. Which angles are congruent? $\angle A \cong \angle B$, $\angle D \cong \angle N$, $\angle E \cong \angle O$

7. For the figure at the left, a student was able to prove $ABCDEF \cong DEFABC$. What segment is congruent to $\overline{CD}$? $\overline{FA}$

8. Suppose $\triangle ATV \cong \triangle MCI$ and $AT = 5$ cm. What other distance can be found? $MC = 5$ cm

9. Suppose $\triangle MCI \cong \triangle GTE$ and $m\angle ICM = 94$. What other angle measures $94°$? $\angle ETG$

In 10–13, assume the two triangles in each figure that appear to be congruent are congruent. **a.** Write a congruence statement for each with the vertices in *correct* order. **b.** List, in pairs, all corresponding congruent parts. **See margin.**

10. 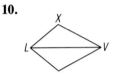   11.   12.   13.

14. Tell whether or not the task uses the idea of congruence.
   a. sorting records into 33 and 45 rpms **Yes**
   b. making sure that the rear window of a car fits snugly into the window frame **Yes**
   c. constructing a circle with diameter equal to the length of $\overline{FY}$ **Yes**
   d. demonstrating that a tall thin glass and a short fat glass can hold the same amount of water **No**
   e. explaining to a Martian that M and *M* are two ways to represent the same letter **Yes**
   f. figuring out that two jigsaw puzzle pieces fit together **Yes**

15. Draw two triangles which have the same shape but are not congruent. **See margin.**
16. Draw two triangles which have the same area but are not congruent. **See margin.**

17. Name four kinds of isometries. *(Lesson 6-6)*
   translation, rotation, reflection, glide reflection
18. Name four properties preserved by isometries. *(Lessons 6-6, 6-5)*
   angle measure, betweenness, collinearity, distance
19. Consider the line with equation $y = 3x$. *(Lessons 6-3, 6-2, 3-5, 3-4)*
   a. What is the slope of this line under a -90° rotation with center $(0, 0)$? $-\frac{1}{3}$
   b. What is the slope of this line under a translation? **3**

294

In 20–22, Figure I ≅ Figure II. Which type of isometry maps Figure I onto Figure II? *(Lesson 6-6)*

20.

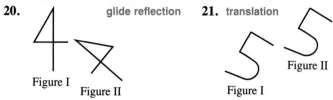

glide reflection

Figure I

Figure II

21. translation

Figure II

Figure I

22.

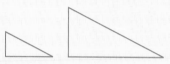

Figure I   Figure II

rotation

23. Rewrite the Isosceles Triangle Theorem using the word *congruent*. *(Lessons 6-5, 5-1)* If a triangle has two congruent sides, then the angles opposite them are congruent.

24. Let the image of △DEF under a translation be △D'E'F'. What property of translations is exemplified by each statement? *(Lessons 6-5, 6-2)*

a. ∠FED ≅ ∠F'E'D' Translations preserve angle measure.
b. $\overline{E'D'} \cong \overline{ED}$ Translations preserve distance.
c. If B is between E and D, then the image of B under this translation is between E' and D'. Translations preserve betweenness.

25. If T(a, b) = (2a, 3b), find T(x, y). *(Lesson 6-1)* (2x, 3y)

26. The measure of an angle is greater than three times the measure of a supplement to it. Is this possible? If so, what is the measure of the angle? *(Lesson 3-2, Previous course)* Yes; greater than 135° and less than 180°

Exploration

27. a. Find three characteristics that make Figure I not congruent to Figure II. See margin.

Figure I

Figure II

b. Make up a puzzle like the one in part **a**, or find such a puzzle in a newspaper or magazine. Answers will vary.

MORE PRACTICE
For more questions on SPUR Objectives, use *Lesson Master 6-7*, shown below.

13. a. △MNO ≅ △PON
b. $\overline{MN} \cong \overline{PO}$, $\overline{MO} \cong \overline{PN}$, $\overline{ON} \cong \overline{NO}$; ∠M ≅ ∠P, ∠PNO ≅ ∠MON, ∠PON ≅ ∠MNO

15. sample:

16. sample:

27. a. Differences are in the length of the painter's brush, the angle at the elbow of the arm holding the palate, and the length of the back right leg of the easel.

Summary

This chapter starts with transformations. Two special ones, rotations and translations, are related to reflections in an extraordinary way. A composite of two reflections over parallel lines is a translation. Do the composite over two intersecting lines, and the result is a rotation. The reflecting lines completely determine the magnitude and direction of the translation, or the center and magnitude of the rotation.

Two figures are congruent if and only if one is the image of the other under a reflection or composite of reflections. A transformation which preserves congruence is called an isometry. There are four types of isometries: reflections, rotations, translations, and glide reflections. All isometries preserve angle measure, betweenness, collinearity, and distance. Single rotations and translations preserve orientation, while single reflections and glide reflections reverse orientation.

If two figures are congruent, then all pairs of corresponding parts are congruent. If the parts are segments, then they have the same length. If they are angles, then they have the same measure.

The transformations which underlie the theory of congruence have many applications. In billiards and miniature golf, using reflections and composites of reflections can help a player succeed. The same principles apply to light, sound, and radio waves bouncing off surfaces. Combinations of mirrors are used in kaleidoscopes, periscopes, and other optical instruments, as well as in stores and in the home.

Vocabulary

Below are the new terms and phrases for this chapter. For the starred terms (*) below, you should be able to produce a *good* definition. For the other terms, you should be able to give a general description and specific example of each.

Lesson 6-1
*transformation, mapping
maps, T(*P*)

Lesson 6-2
*translation, slide
composite of two
   transformations
$T_2 \circ T_1$, $T_2(T_1(P))$, $T_2 \circ T_1(P)$
direction of translation
magnitude of translation
Two Reflection Theorem
   for Translations

Lesson 6-3
*rotation
center of rotation
magnitude of rotation
clockwise, counterclockwise
direction of rotation
Two Reflection Theorem for
   Rotations

Lesson 6-5
*congruent figures, ≅
*congruence transformation
isometry
Equivalence Properties of
   ≅ Theorem

Reflexive Property, Symmetric
   Property, and Transitive
   Property of Congruence
transformation hierarchy
A-B-C-D Theorem
Segment Congruence Theorem
Angle Congruence Theorem

Lesson 6-6
glide reflection, walk
Glide Reflection Theorem

Lesson 6-7
corresponding parts
Corresponding Parts in
   Congruent Figures (CPCF)
   Theorem

Progress Self-Test

See margin for answers not shown below.

Directions: Take this test as you would take a test in class. Use a ruler and a protractor. Then check your work with the solutions in the Selected Answers section in the back of the book.

1. Trace this drawing. $\ell \parallel m$.
   a. Draw $r_\ell \circ r_m (\triangle ABC)$.
   b. Describe this transformation.

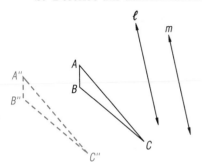

2. *Multiple choice.* In the figure below, $r_\ell \circ r_m (\triangle ABC)$ is which one of these?
   (a) reflection
   (b) rotation
   (c) translation **(b)**

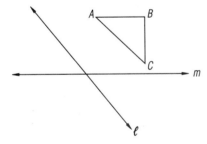

In 3 and 4, in the figure below, $\ell \parallel m$ and $\ell \perp n$.

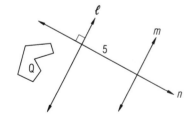

3. Describe the transformation $r_\ell \circ r_m$.

4. Describe the transformation $r_n \circ r_m \circ r_\ell$.

In 5 and 6, $\triangle ABC$ below has been reflected over line m, then its image was reflected over line n.

5. What angle of $\triangle JKL$ has the same measure as $\angle C$? **∠L**

6. Name all segments whose length is equal to FG. **$\overline{AB}$ and $\overline{KJ}$**

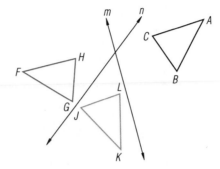

7. Below, $\triangle ABC$ has been reflected over line m. Then its image has been reflected over line ℓ. Fill in the blanks.
   $\triangle ABC \cong \underline{\ ?\ } \cong \underline{\ ?\ }$ **△FED, △HGI**

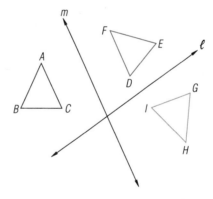

8. According to the CPCF Theorem, what happens if $\triangle ABC \cong \triangle DEF$?

9. Name five properties preserved by translations.

10. Name four kinds of isometries.

11. *True* or *false*? If one figure can be mapped onto another by a series of reflections, then the figures are congruent. **True**

PROGRESS SELF-TEST

Whereas end-of-chapter materials may be considered optional in some texts, they should not be considered optional in UCSMP *Geometry*. The Progress Self-Test provides the opportunity for feedback and correction; the Chapter Review provides additional opportunities for practice. It is at this point that the material "gels" for many students, allows them to solidify skills and concepts before a test. In general, student performance is markedly improved after these pages.

USING THE PROGRESS SELF-TEST
Assign the Progress Self-Test as a one-night assignment. Worked-out *solutions* for all questions are in the Selected Answers section of the student text. Encourage students to take the Progress Self-Test honestly, grade themselves, and then be prepared to discuss the test in class.

Advise students to pay special attention to those Chapter Review questions (pages 299-301) which correspond to questions missed on the Progress Self-Test. A chart provided with the Selected Answers keys the Progress Self-Test questions to the lettered SPUR Objectives in the Chapter Review or to the Vocabulary. It also keys the questions to the corresponding lessons where the material is covered.

10. reflection, rotation, translation, glide reflection

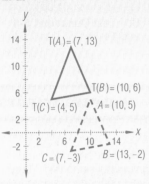
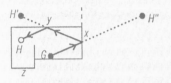
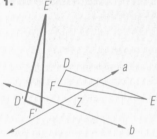
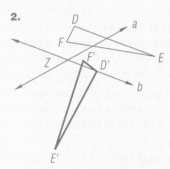
12. Let T be a transformation with the rule
   T(x, y) = (x − 3, y + 8). Let A = (10, 5),
   B = (13, -2), and C = (7, -3).
   a. Graph △ABC and T(△ABC) on the
   same axes.
   b. Describe this transformation.

13. Suppose V(x) is the number of vertices of a
   figure x. What is V(hexagon)? 6

In 14 and 15, use the miniature golf hole
diagrammed below. The piano keys are part
of the floor.

14. Give the path a ball at G must take to carom
   off y and go into the hole at H. See above.

15. Give the path a ball at G must take to bounce
   off x and then y and go into the hole at H.

In 16 and 17, Figure I ≅ Figure II. Trace the
figures, then find and describe an isometry that w
map Figure I onto Figure II.

16.

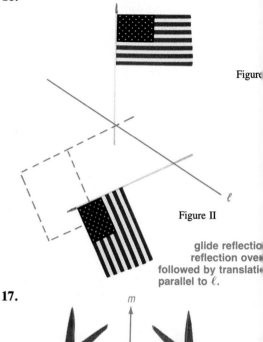

Figure

Figure II

glide reflectio
reflection ove
followed by translati
parallel to ℓ.

17.

Figure I   Figure II

reflection over line m.

298

298

Chapter Review

Questions on **SPUR** Objectives

SPUR stands for **S**kills, **P**roperties, **U**ses, and **R**epresentations.
The Chapter Review questions are grouped according to the
SPUR Objectives for this chapter.

See margin
for answers
not shown below.

SKILLS deal with the procedures used to get answers.

■ **Objective A:** *Draw or identify images of figures under composites of reflections. (Lessons 6-2, 6-3, 6-6)*

In 1 and 2, draw and describe each transformation.

1. $r_a(r_b(\triangle DEF))$.   **2.** $r_b \circ r_a (\triangle DEF)$

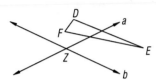

In 3 and 4, use this drawing. $n \parallel m$.

3. a. Draw the image
of *ABCDE* under
the transformation
$r_n \circ r_m$.
b. Describe this
transformation.

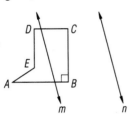

4. a. Draw $r_m \circ r_n (ABCDE)$.
b. Describe this transformation.

5. Trace the figure below. Perform a glide
reflection by reflecting *PQRS* over line ℓ and
then translating the image $1\frac{1}{2}$ inches parallel
to ℓ.

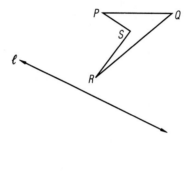

PROPERTIES deal with the principles behind the mathematics.

■ **Objective B:** *Apply properties of reflections to obtain properties of translations and rotations. (Lessons 6-2, 6-3)*

6. Multiple choice.   Rotations do *not* preserve
(a) betweenness   (b) distance
(c) orientation.   (d) All are preserved. **(d)**

7. Multiple choice.   A composite of two
reflections
(a) can never be a reflection
(b) can never be a rotation
(c) can never be a translation
(d) can be any of the tranformations
mentioned in (a), (b), and (c). **(a)**

In 8 and 9, use the figure below.
$r_m(\triangle ABC) = \triangle FED$;
$r_\ell(\triangle DEF) = \triangle IGH$.

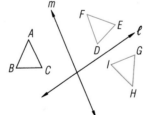

8. What side of $\triangle GHI$ has the same length
as $\overline{BC}$? **GI**

9. What angle of $\triangle ABC$ has the same measure
as $\angle G$? **∠B**

RESOURCES
■ Chapter 6 Test, Form A
■ Chapter 6 Test, Form B
■ Chapter 6 Test, Cumulative
Form
■ Comprehensive Test,
Chapters 1-6
▣ Visual for Teaching Aid 37
provides the drawings for
Review **Questions 8-9,
20-25,** and **32-35.**

CHAPTER REVIEW

The main objectives for the
chapter are organized here
into sections corresponding
to the four main types of understanding this book promotes: Skills, Properties,
Uses, and Representations.
We call these the SPUR objectives.

The four types of understanding are not in increasing order of difficulty. There may
be hard skills and easy representations; some uses may
be easier than anything else;
and so on.

**USING THE CHAPTER
REVIEW**
Students should be able to
answer questions like these
with about 85% accuracy by
the end of the chapter.
You may assign these questions over a single night to
help students prepare for a
test the next day, or you may
assign the questions over a
two-day period.

If you assign the questions
over two days, then we recommend assigning the *evens*
for homework the first night
so that students get feedback
in class the next day. Then
assign the *odds* for the second night (the night before
the test) so that students can
use the answers provided in
the book as a study aid.

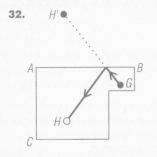
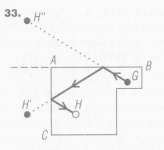
Objective C: *Apply the Two Reflection Theorem for Translations and for Rotations.*
(Lessons 6-2, 6-3, 6-6)

In 10–12, $\ell \parallel m$
and $\ell \perp n$.
Describe the
transformation.

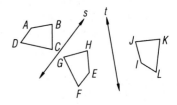

10. $r_\ell \circ r_m$

11. $r_m \circ r_n$

12. $r_m \circ r_\ell \circ r_n$

13. To rotate $\triangle MNO$ 30° about a point *C*, you can reflect successively over two lines that form an angle of measure __?__ whose vertex is __?__.
15°, C

Objective D: *Determine properties of congruent figures. (Lessons 6-5, 6-6, 6-7)*

In 14 and 15, use the given and figure of Questions 8 and 9.

14. Name all segments congruent to $\overline{FE}$. $\overline{AB}$, $\overline{HG}$

15. Name all angles congruent to $\angle A$. $\angle F$, $\angle H$

16. *True* or *false*?   Congruent figures must have the same orientation. **False**

17. *True* or *false*?   A figure and its glide reflection image are always congruent. **True**

18. Define: congruence.

19. Name the four types of isometries.

In 20–22, use the figure below.
$r_s(ABCD) = EHGF$; $r_t(EHGF) = IJKL$.

20. $ABCD \cong$ __?__ $\cong$ __?__ **EHGF, IJKL**

21. $GFEH \cong$ __?__ $\cong$ __?__ **CDAB, KLIJ**

22. $ABCD \cong EHGF$ and
$EHGF \cong IJKL \Rightarrow ABCD \cong$ __?__. **IJKL**

In 23–25, use the figure above. Justify each conclusion.

23. $\overline{AB} \cong \overline{IJ}$ See below.

24. $m\angle C = m\angle K$
Reflections preserve angle measure.

25. $ABCD \cong ABCD$
Reflexive Property of Congruence

23) definition of congruence (sufficient condition)

USES deal with applications of mathematics in real situations.

Objective E: *Determine the isometry which maps one figure onto another. (Lessons 6-2, 6-3, 6-6)*

In 26–29, name the type of isometry which maps Figure I onto Figure II.

26. **rotation**

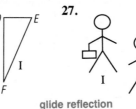

27.

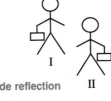

glide reflection

28.

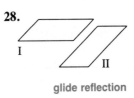

glide reflection

29.

translation

In 30 and 31, use the tessellation below.

30. Which type of isometry maps figure A onto figure B? **translation**

31. Which type of isometry maps figure B onto figure C? **glide reflection**

Objective F: *Use reflections to find a path from an object to a particular point. (Lesson 6-4)*

In 32 and 33, use the drawing below. Find a path to shoot a ball at G into the hole at H after bouncing off the named sides.

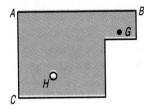

32. $\overline{AB}$

33. $\overline{AB}$ and then $\overline{AC}$

In 34 and 35, use the drawing below.

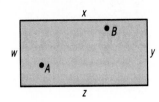

34. Draw the path of a ball that starts at B and bounces off x, y, and z in that order, and then hits A.

35. Draw a path from B that bounces off x and z in that order, then hits A.

REPRESENTATIONS deal with pictures, graphs, or objects that illustrate concepts.

Objective G: *Apply a rule described using T( ) notation. (Lessons 6-1, 6-2, 6-3, 6-6)*

36. A transformation T has the rule
$T(x, y) = (x + 4, y - 2)$. Let $P = (7, 3)$, $Q = (4, 0)$, and $R = (-2, 2)$.
  a. Graph $\triangle PQR$ and its image under T.
  b. What isometry is T? **translation**

37. A transformation S has the rule
$S(x, y) = (y, 2x)$.
  a. Graph the quadrilateral with vertices
  $A = (5, 2)$, $B = (5, -2)$, $C = (-5, -2)$, and $D = (-5, 2)$.
  b. Graph $S(ABCD)$ on the same axes and label it $A'B'C'D'$.
  c. Describe the transformation S.

38. Use the transformation $T(x, y) = (-x, y - 4)$.
  a. Find $T(\triangle DEF)$ where $D = (-2, -1)$, $E = (5, 0)$, and $F = (0, 8)$.
  b. Graph $\triangle DEF$ and $T(\triangle DEF)$ on the same axes.
  c. Describe this transformation.

39. Let N(S) be the number of elements in set S. What is N({2, 3, 4, 5})? **4**

40. Let P(E) be the probability of an event E. If a number x is randomly picked from {1, 2, 4, 5, 7, 8}, what is P(x is divisible by 4)? $\frac{1}{3}$

In 41 and 42, *multiple choice*.

41. At the right, Figure B is the image of Figure A under transformation S. What could be the rule?
  (a) $S(x, y) = (-x, -y)$
  (b) $S(x, y) = (-y, -x)$
  (c) $S(x, y) = (x, -y)$
  (d) $S(x, y) = (-y, x)$ **(a)**

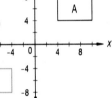

42. Figure D is the image of Figure C under transformation T. What could be the rule?

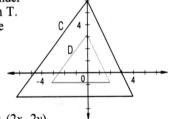

  (a) $T(x, y) = (2x, 2y)$
  (b) $T(x, y) = (x + 2, y + 2)$
  (c) $T(x, y) = (x - 2, y - 2)$
  (d) $T(x, y) = \left(\dfrac{x}{2}, \dfrac{y}{2}\right)$ **(d)**

CHAPTER 6 Chapter Review **301**

37. c. The transformation stretches the figure by a factor of 2 in the horizontal direction only and then reflects it about the line $x = y$.

38. a. T(D) = (2, -5), T(E) = (-5, -4), T(F) = (0, 4)
b.

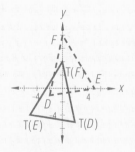

c. The transformation is a glide reflection which reflects the figure over the y-axis and then translates it down 4 units.

CHAPTER 7 ■ TRIANGLE CONGRUENCE

DAILY PACING CHART ■ CHAPTER 7

Every chapter of UCSMP *Geometry* includes lessons, a Progress Self-Test, and a Chapter Review. For optimal student performance, the self-test and review should be covered. (See *General Teaching Suggestions: Mastery* on page T36 of the Teacher's Edition.) By following the pace of the Full Course given here, students can complete the entire text by the end of the year. Students following the pace of the Minimal Course spend more time when there are quizzes and on the Chapter Review and will generally not complete all of the chapters in this text.

When all lessons are covered from the beginning (the recommendation of the authors), then students in the Minimal Course can cover through Lesson 13-4 and will cover all they need for future courses. For more information on pacing, see *General Teaching Suggestions: Pace* on page T35 of the Teacher's Edition.

DAY	MINIMAL COURSE	FULL COURSE
1	7-1	7-1
2	7-2	7-2
3	7-3	7-3
4	Quiz (TRF); Start 7-4.	Quiz (TRF); 7-4
5	Finish 7-4.	7-5
6	7-5	7-6
7	7-6	Quiz (TRF); 7-7
8	Quiz (TRF); Start 7-7.	7-8
9	Finish 7-7.	Writing Proofs
10	7-8	Progress Self-Test
11	Writing Proofs	Chapter Review
12	Progress Self-Test	Chapter Test (TRF)
13	Chapter Review	
14	Chapter Review	
15	Chapter Test (TRF)	

TESTING OPTIONS

■ Quiz for Lessons 7-1 Through 7-3   ■ Chapter 7 Test, Form A   ■ Chapter 7 Test, Cumulative Form
■ Quiz for Lessons 7-4 Through 7-6   ■ Chapter 7 Test, Form B

PROVIDING FOR INDIVIDUAL DIFFERENCES

The student text has been written for, and tested with, average students. It also has been used successfully with better and more poorly prepared students.

The Lesson Notes often include Error Analysis and Alternate Approach features to help you with those students who need more help. A blackline Lesson Master (in the Teacher's Resource File), keyed to the chapter objectives, is provided for each lesson to allow more practice. (However, since it is very important to keep up with the daily pace, you are not expected to use all of these masters. Again, refer to the suggestions for pacing on page T35.) Extension activities are provided in the Lesson Notes for those students who have completed the particular lesson in a shorter amount of time than is expected, even in the Full Course.

OBJECTIVES ■ CHAPTER 7

The objectives listed here are the same as in the Chapter 7 Review on pages 350-353 of the student text. The Progress Self-Test on page 349 and the tests in the Teacher's Resource File cover these objectives. For recommendations regarding the handling of this end-of-chapter material, see the notes in the margin on the corresponding pages of the Teacher's Edition.

OBJECTIVES FOR CHAPTER 7 (Organized into the SPUR Categories—Skills, Properties, Uses, and Representations)	Progress Self-Test Questions	Chapter Review Questions	Lesson Master from Teacher's Resource File*
SKILLS			
A Draw triangles satisfying given conditions and determine whether all such triangles are congruent.	3, 4	1 through 9	7-1, 7-2, 7-5
PROPERTIES			
B Determine whether figures are congruent from information given in drawings.	1	10 through 15	7-2
C Write proofs that triangles are congruent.	2	16 through 20	7-3, 7-4, 7-5
D Apply the triangle congruence and CPCF theorems to prove that segments or angles are congruent.	7, 9, 10	21 through 25	7-3, 7-4, 7-5, 7-6
E Determine whether conditions are properties of or sufficient conditions for parallelograms.	5, 8	26 through 31	7-6, 7-7
USES			
F Use theorems about triangles and parallelograms to explain real situations.	11	32 through 38	7-2, 7-7, 7-8
REPRESENTATIONS (There are no objectives for Representations in this chapter.)			

*The masters are numbered to match the lessons.

OVERVIEW ■ CHAPTER 7

The content of this chapter is traditional, but some aspects of it are different. All the standard triangle congruence statements can be proved using transformations; there is no need to assume any of them (see the Perspective for Lesson 7-2). There is also a theorem called SsA included (see the Perspective for Lesson 7-5).

The first lesson of the chapter is exploratory; the goal is to consider various *conditions* which might determine congruent triangles. In Lesson 7-2, four conditions (SAS, SSS, ASA, and AAS) are given which determine congruent trian-

gles, and students are expected to be able to choose the appropriate theorem that justifies the triangle congruence.

The one-step proofs of Lesson 7-2 (the application of a triangle congruence theorem, given appropriate information) are extended in two ways in Lesson 7-3. Given information may lead to congruent sides or angles, such as a midpoint or a particular kind of polygon. The congruence of some corresponding parts of the triangles requiring the CPCF Theorem are to be proved. The ideas are applied immediately

to prove the converse of the Isosceles Triangle Theorem.

Lesson 7-4 has no new ideas, but the triangles overlap. In Lesson 7-5, the HL Theorem is deduced, and the more general condition, SSA, is considered.

All the triangle congruence theorems are applied in Lessons 7-6 and 7-7 to deduce properties of regular polygons and parallelograms. Lesson 7-8 is an easy lesson that considers a related idea, the SAS Inequality, and gives a day to assimilate the ideas of the preceding lessons.

PERSPECTIVES ■ CHAPTER 7

The Perspectives provide the rationale for the inclusion of topics or approaches, provide mathematical background, and make connections with other lessons and within UCSMP.

7-1

DRAWING TRIANGLES

There is the SSS *condition* and the SSS Congruence *Theorem*. Anything can be a condition; the question is whether the condition guarantees that triangles are congruent. Of course, SSS does. (In contrast, AAA does not.)

Many people think of the triangle congruence theorems (SAS, ASA, and so on) as only relating two triangles. This lesson covers a different aspect of the triangle congruence theorems, namely that each theorem states the sufficient information about a triangle so that all triangles drawn using that information will be congruent. Thus, the SAS Theorem states that all triangles drawn with two sides of given lengths and an included angle of a given measure will be congruent.

Lesson 7-1 is informal. It helps make more intuitive the triangle congruence theorems, which are proved in subsequent lessons.

7-2

TRIANGLE CONGRUENCE THEOREMS

Euclid did not assume any of the congruence theorems. He proved them all from his postulates by using the idea of superposition, that is, moving a figure and placing it on top of another figure. In the 1700s it was recognized that these proofs might be faulty, and in the 1800s it was shown that they were. Thus, when Hilbert wrote down his set of postulates, he assumed SAS Congruence. In the 1930s, George David Birkhoff and Ralph Beatley wrote a high school geometry textbook which included SAS Similarity as a postulate. In a rigorous treatment of Euclidean geometry, there has to be an assumption that leads to the SAS Congruence Theorem or some other triangle congruence theorem.

The assumption made in this book in place of a congruence assumption is the property that reflec-

tions preserve distance. Using this property and other properties of reflections, the three main congruence theorems, SSS, SAS, and ASA, are proved in this lesson.

7-3

TRIANGLE CONGRUENCE PROOFS

Nationwide, only about one-third of the students enrolled in a proof-oriented geometry course can do nontrivial proofs at the end of the year, and about 28% cannot do even the most simple triangle congruence proofs.

Proof-writing in high school geometry is burdened with tradition. It is typical for a student to begin every proof in the following way: (1) copy the given, (2) copy the statement to be proved, (3) copy (or draw) the figure and set up two columns on the page, (4) label the left column "statements," (5) label the right column "reasons," (6) rewrite the statement(s) of the given as the first statement(s) of the proof, and (7) put down the word "given" on the right side. During this seven-step ritual, no thinking is going on. Every effort should be made to get students working on the proof itself as quickly as possible.

One way the proofs in this book cut down on the ritual is to not always repeat the given(s) in the proof itself. To emphasize this approach, deduced statements are labeled *Conclusions*. A second way is to sometimes use paragraph proofs. In a paragraph proof, one might write *from the given . . ., you get* (conclusion) *because of* (justification).

7-4

OVERLAPPING TRIANGLES

Students who have studied transformations are generally a little better prepared when it comes to overlapping triangles than those who have not.

7-5

THE SSA CONDITION AND HL CONGRUENCE

Some textbooks assert "there is no SSA condition" or "SSA never works." This view is not correct mathematically. The HL condition is a special case of the SSA condition. And there *is* an SSA Congruence Theorem. There are two forms in which the theorem is stated. The less general of the two forms is: If two sides and a non-included *nonacute* angle of one triangle are congruent to two sides and the corresponding non-included angle of the other triangle, then the triangles are congruent. That is, the SSA condition guarantees congruence if the angles are right or obtuse.

The second more general form is the one used in this lesson: the larger of the two sides is opposite the non-included angle. That is, the SSA condition guarantees congruence if the sides indicated by the first S are larger than the sides indicated by the second S. Thus, we call it "SsA." The HL Congruence Theorem is still a special case; with HL, the hypotenuse is the first S and the right angle is the A. The hypotenuse is always the larger side.

In trigonometry, the SSA condition has been traditionally called the *ambiguous* condition or case, although it is no more ambiguous than solving an equation of the form $x^2 = k$. That is, there may be 0, 1, or 2 solutions, and it can be determined when each situation happens. The SsA Congruence Theorem tells when there is exactly one solution.

7-6

PROPERTIES OF SPECIAL FIGURES

In order for students to be familiar with synthetic, transformation, and coordinate proofs, all three types are presented rather than an in-depth study of only one type. The special polygons of this lesson are all rotation-symmetric. If transformations were the emphasis, properties of rotations could have been used to deduce all the properties deduced here, but we choose to use synthetic proofs instead.

The parallelogram is special because any of its properties apply to rhombuses, rectangles, and squares. The last two of these are fundamental in the study of area and thus are needed for Chapter 8. The properties of the parallelogram are useful in developing the properties of vectors in Chapter 14.

The regular polygons are special

because of their symmetry and their relationship to the circle, which can be viewed as the limit of a regular *n*-gon as *n* approaches infinity.

7-7

SUFFICIENT CONDITIONS FOR PARALLELOGRAMS

As early as Lesson 2-5, it was noted that one sufficient condition for a figure to be a parallelogram comes from the definition. For instance, for a parallelogram, two pairs of parallel sides is a sufficient condition. In this lesson, other conditions that determine parallelograms are presented.

Properties are if-then statements: If a figure is a ____, then. . . . Since converses may not be true, they need to be proved. Sufficient conditions are also if-then statements: If . . ., then a figure is a ____. These statements look like converses of properties, but they may be true without the corresponding converse (which would be a property) being true.

7-8

THE SAS INEQUALITY

An effort is made throughout this book to include inequalities alongside equalities. This is done with the Triangle Inequality when discussing betweenness, with the solving of inequalities, and with equations when reviewing algebra skills.

The SAS Inequality Theorem is easy to understand and has intuitive applications, such as the cat shown in the lesson, but its proof is quite difficult. All students are not expected to follow the proof, but it illustrates that sometimes even common-sense theorems have difficult proofs.

302D

We recommend 12 to 15 days for this chapter: 8 to 10 on the lessons and quizzes; 1 for the Progress Self-Test; 1 or 2 for the Chapter Review; and 1 for a Chapter test. Also, one additional day should be spent on writing proofs after completing Lesson 7-8. Proof ideas will be reviewed and extended in the succeeding chapters.

Triangle Congruence

7-1: Drawing Triangles
7-2: Triangle Congruence Theorems
7-3: Triangle Congruence Proofs
7-4: Overlapping Triangles
7-5: The SSA Condition and HL Congruence
7-6: Properties of Special Figures
7-7: Sufficient Conditions for Parallelograms
7-8: The SAS Inequality

302

Triangles are said to be rigid
and quadrilaterals not rigid
because all tringles with
sides of three given lengths
are congruent, but all quadrilaterals of four given lengths
are not. However, in practice,
rigidity has to do with the
strength of what is bolted and
what is not. The bridge has
triangular supports in most
places, but near each end
there are two quadrilaterals
supported by a more significant framework. Rigidity is a
very difficult topic to treat
mathematically in a rigorous
manner. The theory of rigidity
still has not been completely
developed for three-
dimensional figures. That is,
there is not a general procedure to determine which
three-dimensional networks
would collapse and which are
rigid.
    Triangulation to draw accu-
rate maps was for centuries
an important application of
trigonometry. Today, triangulation still is used in surveying and locating the position
of objects. For instance, triangulation can determine the
location of a batted ball in
space and thus can help to
determine its path and how
far it can travel.

Triangles, the simplest of all polygons, have many uses. The supporting structures for many bridges utilize triangles because triangles are rigid. The bridge pictured at the left splits in the middle into two parts which are raised to let tall boats through. The mechanism which raises and lowers the bridge has triangles in its design. Notice that many of the triangles of the bridge are congruent, a feature which ensures the smoothness of the bridge and a pleasant design.

If a person at a point *A* sights an airplane or other object in the sky, that person can only determine the direction of the plane, not how far it is away. But if a person at a second point *B* sights the airplane simultaneously, then the airplane is at the intersection *C* of the two rays and can be located precisely. This method is called *triangulation*, because *A, B,* and *C* are vertices of a triangle. For hundreds of years, until satellites gave us accurate maps of the earth with cameras, triangulation was the best way to determine the precise locations of mountain peaks, harbors, and other places not easily reached.

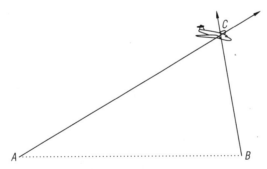

*The Lake Street bridge in
Chicago provides support for
commuter trains.*

In this chapter, you will draw or construct triangles given lengths of their sides and measures of their angles. This activity will help you learn the conditions that are sufficient to make pairs of triangles congruent. These conditions, which are formulated as the triangle congruence theorems, have been utilized from the time of the ancient Greeks to deduce properties of polygons. And so, in this chapter, you are studying an old subject with many modern applications.

CHAPTER 7 Triangle Congruence **303**

OBJECTIVE

A Draw triangles satisfying given conditions and determine whether all such triangles are congruent.

TEACHING NOTES

Reading Students can read this lesson independently. If you assigned the reading and questions for the night of the Chapter 6 Test, you may wish to begin the lesson with a discussion of **Questions 11-19**, which summarize and are critical to the lesson. If you did not already assign the reading, you might want to discuss the paragraph at the top of page 307 first and then have students read the lesson independently. Ask students to take notes about the methods of drawing triangles and to be prepared to summarize the methods presented in the Examples.

Drawing Triangles

Before Ramon built a shed for firewood, he constructed a scale model of the lean-to.

A lean-to roof has only one slanted side. To make such a roof, triangular supports (shown in orange) are often used. In order for the lean-to roof to be a plane, and to fit snugly with the walls, the triangular supports must be congruent. Since roofs and their supports are often made of wood, these triangles cannot be made by machine; they have to be measured and cut.

Ramon was building a lean-to to serve as a shed for firewood on his farm. He cut long pieces of wood into lengths of 2, 4, and 5 feet. Using one piece of each length, he made triangles out of them. He did this by cutting and nailing the ends together. He made four triangular frames for his shed.

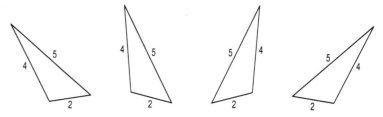

Ramon's frames

Ramon was uncertain as to whether his frames would be congruent, as required by the plan for the shed. Was it possible the angles might have different measures in these triangles? This is a question to be answered in Lesson 7-2, but we explore it here.

Drawing a triangle with sides 2 cm, 4 cm, and 5 cm on a sheet of paper is different than constructing one out of wood. You can't pick up, cut, or nail the sides when they are on paper! Some automatic drawers enable you to enter side lengths and angle measures in a triangle and they then draw a triangle. If you do not have such software, here is an algorithm for constructing a triangle with three sides of given lengths that satisfy the Triangle Inequality.

304

Example 1 Construct a triangle given sides of lengths 2, 4, and 5.

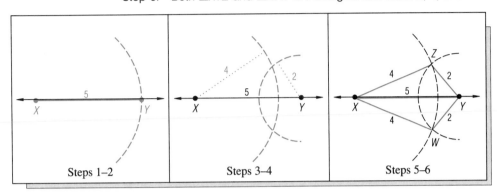

Step 1. Construct any line. Choose point *X* on the line.
Step 2. Construct $\odot X_1$ with radius $XY = 5$.
Step 3. Construct $\odot X_2$ with radius 4.
Step 4. Construct $\odot Y$ with radius 2.
Step 5. $\odot X_2 \cap \odot Y = \{Z, W\}$. (The circles will not intersect if the Triangle Inequality is violated.)
Step 6. Both $\triangle XYZ$ and $\triangle XYW$ are triangles with sides 2, 4, and 5.

Steps 1–2   Steps 3–4   Steps 5–6

Check   Measure to see if the sides of the constructed triangle have the required lengths.

Now consider a situation where you are asked to draw a triangle given measures of its three angles. First, check that the angle measures add to 180°. If they do, you can draw an appropriate triangle.

Example 2 Draw a triangle *ABC* in which $m\angle A = 80$, $m\angle B = 45$, and $m\angle C = 55$.

Solution   First, check that $m\angle A + m\angle B + m\angle C = 180$. Then, to start, draw a line containing one of the sides. We draw $\overleftrightarrow{AB}$. Now draw a 45° angle at *B* open to the right and an 80° angle at *A* open to the left. The result is the desired triangle.

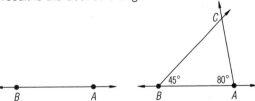

Check   Does $m\angle C = 55$? It does, so the triangle satisfies the given conditions.

Notice that only two angles were needed in Example 2. The third angle is the check. This is because all triangles with two given angles have congruent third angles.

LESSON 7-1 Drawing Triangles   **305**

The rigidity of a triangle is so obvious that it is useful to mention something that is not rigid. For example, suppose a gate was made with a quadrilateral having opposite sides congruent by putting one bolt at each corner. Is the gate rigid?

(No, the gate could sag over time, as shown below.)

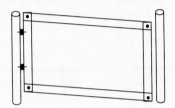

In short, there is rigidity for triangles because the SSS condition guarantees congruence (as is proved in the next lesson), but there is no SSSS theorem for quadrilaterals. (This is the Exploration question for Lesson 7-3, so do not say more now.)

To prevent the gate from sagging, either more fixed lengths are needed, or some angles need to be fixed.

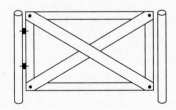

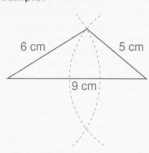

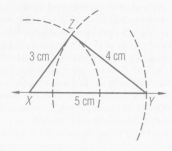
306

Proof

Draw a picture and restate the given in terms of the picture.

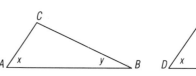

Given: $\angle A \cong \angle D$, $\angle B \cong \angle E$.
Prove: $\angle C \cong \angle F$.

The proof uses algebra. Since the pairs of angles are congruent, they have the same measures.
Let $m\angle A = m\angle D = x$, and let $m\angle B = m\angle E = y$.
Now, because of the Triangle-Sum Theorem in $\triangle ABC$,
$$x + y + m\angle C = 180,$$
so $$m\angle C = 180 - x - y.$$
Similarly, in $\triangle DEF$,
$$x + y + m\angle F = 180$$
$$m\angle F = 180 - x - y.$$
Using the Transitive Property of Equality, $m\angle C = m\angle F$.
So they are congruent.

In the following situation, you are asked to draw a triangle given some angles and some sides.

■ ■ ■ ■ ■ ■ ■ ■ ■

Example 3

In a triangular sail ABC, $m\angle A = 70$, $AB = 5$ meters, and $AC = 3.5$ meters. Make a scale drawing using centimeters instead of meters as the unit.

Solution First draw the 70° angle. Call it $\angle A$. Let 1 cm in the drawing equal 1 meter of the actual sail. Then, mark off 5 cm on one side and 3.5 cm on the other. Connect the points.

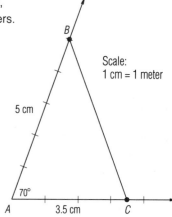

B

Scale:
1 cm = 1 meter

5 cm

70°

A   3.5 cm   C

Examples 1–3 in this lesson showed how to draw a triangle given measures of some of its sides or angles.

Example	Given	Name for given condition
1	three sides	SSS
2	three angles	AAA
3	two sides and included angle	SAS

In Questions 11–19, you are asked to draw triangles given AA, SSA, SA, SS, ASA, and AAS. Part **b** of these questions introduces an important idea: will everyone else's drawings be congruent to yours? In other words, is enough given to determine the size and shape of the triangle?

Questions

Covering the Reading

1. What is a lean-to roof? one that has only one slanted side

2. State the Triangle Inequality. The sum of the lengths of two sides of any triangle is greater than the length of the third side.

3. Construct a triangle with sides of the lengths given here. See margin.

   ——— 3 cm ———

   ——————— 4 cm ———————

   ————— 5 cm —————

4. Construct a triangle with sides having the lengths given at the left. See margin.

5. If two angles of a triangle have measures $x°$ and $y°$, what is the measure of the third angle? $(180 - x - y)°$

6. In quadrilateral *ABCD*, $\overline{AC}$ bisects ∠*DAB* and ∠*DCB*. Why are angles *B* and *D* congruent? If two triangles have two pairs of congruent angles, then their third pair of angles is congruent.

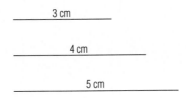

7. Draw a triangle with angles of measures 110° and 30°. See margin.

8. Suppose in a triangular sail *ABC*, m∠*A* = 80, *AB* = 4.5 meters, and *AC* = 2 meters. Make a scale drawing using centimeters instead of meters as the unit. See margin.

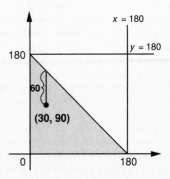

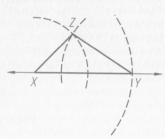
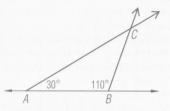

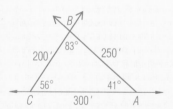

9. A triangular plot of land is bounded by side lengths $AB = 250$ feet, $BC = 200$ feet, and $AC = 300$ feet. A surveyor has found that m∠A ≈ 41, m∠B ≈ 83, and m∠C ≈ 56. Draw an accurate picture of this plot of land with 1 inch = 100 feet. **See margin.**

10. Try the construction of Example 1 with these segments. Explain what happens. **See margin.**

_____   _____   _____

In 11–19, you may use an automatic drawer or any other drawing tools.

  a. Accurately draw a triangle ABC with the given information.
  b. Conjecture whether all other accurately drawn triangles will be congruent to yours. **See margin.**

11. SS condition: $AB = 2''$, $BC = 1\frac{3}{4}''$.

12. AA condition: m∠$A = 70$, m∠$B = 38$.

13. SA condition: $AB = 4$ cm, m∠$A = 60$.

14. SSS condition: $AB = 4$ cm, $BC = 5$ cm, $AC = 6$ cm.

15. AAA condition: m∠$A = 41$, m∠$B = 100$, m∠$C = 39$.

16. SSA condition: $AB = 2''$, $BC = 1''$, m∠$A = 20$.

17. SAS condition: $AB = 2''$, $BC = 1''$, m∠$B = 20$.

18. ASA condition: m∠$A = 55$, $AB = 3''$, m∠$B = 90$.

19. AAS condition: m∠$A = 40$, m∠$B = 60$, $BC = 3$ cm.

20. △QZP ≅ △KRA. List six pairs of corresponding parts.
(Lesson 6-7) $\overline{QZ}$ ≅ $\overline{KR}$, $\overline{ZP}$ ≅ $\overline{RA}$, $\overline{PQ}$ ≅ $\overline{AK}$, ∠Q ≅ ∠K, ∠Z ≅ ∠R, ∠P ≅ ∠A

21. The composite of two reflections over parallel lines is a(n) __?__ .
(Lesson 6-2) **translation**

22. Find the measures of angles D and F in △DEF. *(Lesson 5-7)*
m∠$F = 21.6$; m∠$D = 86.4$

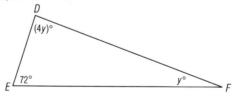

23. State the Kite Symmetry Theorem. *(Lesson 5-4)* **The line containing the ends of a kite is a symmetry line for the kite.**

24. The measure of an angle is greater than the measure of a complement to it. What can be deduced about this measure? *(Lesson 3-2)*
It is between 45° and 90°.

25. Two sides of a triangle are 91 cm and 38 cm. Give the possible lengths of the third side. *(Lesson 1-9)*
greater than 53 cm but less than 129 cm

26. Find the congruent copy of each figure at the left in the picture at the right.

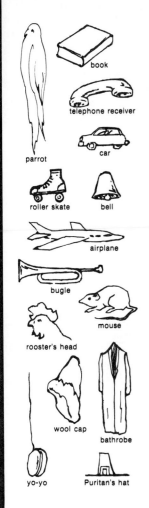

book

telephone receiver

parrot

car

roller skate

bell

airplane

bugle

mouse

rooster's head

wool cap

bathrobe

yo-yo

Puritan's hat

"Hidden Pictures" puzzle by Christopher Wray from *Highlights for Children,* July-August, 1986.

NOTES ON QUESTIONS
Question 26: This picture is from the magazine *Highlights for Children,* which has a similar puzzle each month. It is good practice for developing students' ability to see embedded figures.

FOLLOW-UP

MORE PRACTICE
For more questions on SPUR Objectives, use *Lesson Master 7-1,* shown below.

EXTENSION
You might encourage students to look up topics like aviation, architecture, construction, and so forth, in order to explore the modern real-world applications of triangles or triangulation. Ask each student to find a book or article that he or she can share with the class.

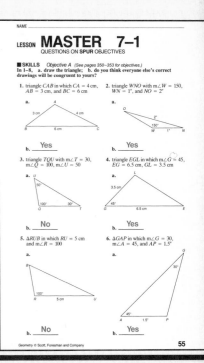

RESOURCES
■ Lesson Master 7-2
◢ Visual for Teaching Aid 39
displays the drawings for
Questions 10-15.

OBJECTIVES

A Draw triangles satisfying given conditions and determine whether all such triangles are congruent.
B Determine whether figures are congruent from information given in drawings.
F Use theorems about triangles to explain real situations.

TEACHING NOTES

Like Euclid, we believe these theorems are not self-evident and therefore should not be taken as postulates. The key to the proofs of the SSS, SAS, and ASA Congruence Theorems is found in the paragraph following the SSS proof. Emphasize that properties of reflections and kites (which are self-evident) are being used to deduce these theorems.

Many books begin with SAS. SSS is presented first in this book because it is easier to follow; you can concentrate on sides alone. The corresponding angles are also easy to find; they are opposite the corresponding sides. You should discuss one of these proofs in detail, but it is not necessary to discuss all of them.

7-2

Triangle Congruence Theorems

In Lesson 7-1, you drew or constructed a triangle given some lengths of sides or measures of angles. After drawing each triangle, you were asked if everyone else's triangle would be congruent to yours. This is an important question. Stated differently, it is: What is enough about the measures of a triangle's sides and angles so that all triangles drawn with those measures are congruent?

Consider the SSS condition. This means two triangles have three pairs of congruent sides. It can be proved that these triangles are congruent.

SSS Congruence Theorem:

> If, in two triangles, three sides of one are congruent to three sides of the other, then the triangles are congruent.

Proof

Given $\overline{AB} \cong \overline{DE}$, $\overline{BC} \cong \overline{EF}$, and $\overline{AC} \cong \overline{DF}$. Here is a possible figure.

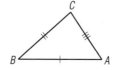 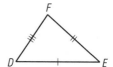

The proof uses the idea of transitivity of congruence. That is, to prove $\triangle ABC \cong \triangle DEF$, we prove that each triangle is congruent to a third triangle. An appropriate third triangle for this task is a nicely located image of $\triangle ABC$ under an isometry.

Since $\overline{AB} \cong \overline{DE}$, there is an isometry which maps $\overline{AB}$ onto $\overline{DE}$. So there is a congruent image $\triangle A'B'C'$ of $\triangle ABC$ which shares a side with $\triangle DEF$. Now $\overline{AC} \cong \overline{A'C'}$ and $\overline{BC} \cong \overline{B'C'}$, so by the Transitive Property of Congruence $\overline{A'C'} \cong \overline{DF}$ and $\overline{B'C'} \cong \overline{EF}$. Thus $\triangle A'B'C'$ and $\triangle DEF$ form a kite. The common side $\overline{DE}$ is the symmetry diagonal of that kite.

310

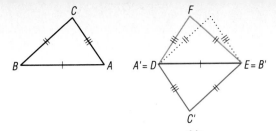

Since this kite is reflection-symmetric to $\overleftrightarrow{DE}$, $\triangle DEF$ is a reflection image of $\triangle A'B'C'$. So, if all three pairs of sides of $\triangle ABC$ and $\triangle DEF$ are congruent, then $\triangle ABC$ can be mapped onto $\triangle DEF$ by an isometry. (First map $\overline{AB}$ onto $\overline{DE}$ as we did, then reflect $\triangle A'B'C'$, the image of $\triangle ABC$, over $\overleftrightarrow{DE}$.) So, by the definition of congruence, $\triangle ABC \cong \triangle DEF$.

For instance, if two triangles have sides with lengths 6.5, 2.8, and 7.0, the triangles are congruent.

Now consider the SAS condition. This refers to two sides and the angle they include (the **included angle**). This information also is enough to make triangles congruent.

SAS Congruence Theorem:

If, in two triangles, two sides and the included angle of one are congruent to two sides and the included angle of the other, then the triangles are congruent.

Proof

The given here is that $\overline{AB} \cong \overline{DE}$, $\overline{AC} \cong \overline{DF}$, and $\angle A \cong \angle FDE$. (Look carefully at the tick and angle marks. They are the only things making this drawing different from the previous drawing.)

Since $\overline{AB} \cong \overline{DE}$, we can, as in the SSS proof, map $\overline{AB}$ onto $\overline{DE}$. In this case, the defining conditions for a kite do not appear. However, $\triangle C'DF$ (not drawn) is isosceles and $\overline{DE}$ bisects its vertex angle. Because of the Isosceles Triangle Symmetry Theorem, the reflection image of C' over $\overleftrightarrow{DE}$ is F. So the reflection image of $\triangle A'B'C'$ is $\triangle DEF$. This implies $\triangle A'B'C' \cong \triangle DEF$. But because $\triangle A'B'C'$ is the image of $\triangle ABC$ under some isometry, $\triangle ABC \cong \triangle A'B'C'$. So by the transitivity of congruence, $\triangle ABC \cong \triangle DEF$. This proves that the SAS condition guarantees congruence.

For instance, if two triangles have sides of lengths $4''$ and $6''$ including an angle of $50°$, then the triangles are congruent.

A note on the proofs: There are actually two different isometries which map A to D and B to E and thus $\overline{AB}$ to $\overline{DE}$; the other maps C to the same side of $\overline{DE}$ as F. We chose to use the isometry discussed because a kite's symmetry has been established.

In the SSS proof, it is possible that C', D, and F could be collinear. Then a kite is not formed, but the figure is still reflection-symmetric.

Stress that the reason for proving these theorems is to use them to deduce other facts. Students usually are relieved to know they do not have to write proofs as complicated as the ones in this lesson.

With CPCF and SSS and many more acronyms to follow, teachers often worry that students are only memorizing the acronyms and do not know the theorems they represent. To avoid the problem of students memorizing names without knowing what they represent, there are questions in the lessons asking students to write out the statements of the theorems. Also, tell students that there may be such questions on the Chapter Test.

Do not allow students to write just "SSS." The word "congruence" must be included. There are SAS and SSS *Similarity* Theorems coming up in the next chapter.

Making Connections
Only certain conditions *necessarily* lead to triangle congruence, and not all of them are discussed in this lesson. You might want to mention the SsA and HL conditions covered in Lesson 7-5.

1.

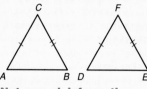

Not enough information given

2.

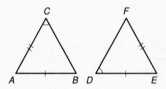

No, the angles do not correspond.

3.

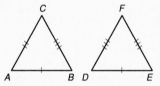

No, there are only two sides congruent.

The ASA condition refers to two angles and the side which they include (called the **included side**). This condition also yields congruent triangles.

ASA Congruence Theorem:

If, in two triangles, two angles and the included side of one are congruent to two angles and the included side of the other, then the triangles are congruent.

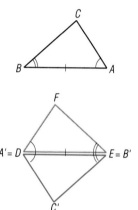

Proof

Given $\overline{AB} \cong \overline{DE}$, $\angle A \cong \angle FDE$, and $\angle B \cong \angle FED$, as shown at the left. Again consider the image $\triangle A'B'C'$ of $\triangle ABC$ under an isometry mapping $\overline{AB}$ onto $\overline{DE}$. $\triangle A'B'C'$ and $\triangle DEF$ form a figure much like that in the other two congruence theorems, but with two pairs of congruent angles.

Again, think of reflecting $\triangle A'B'C'$ over line $\overleftrightarrow{DE}$. Applying the Side-Switching Theorem to $\angle C'DF$, the image of $\overrightarrow{A'C'}$ is $\overrightarrow{DF}$. Applying the Side-Switching Theorem to $\angle C'EF$, the image of $\overrightarrow{B'C'}$ is $\overrightarrow{EF}$. This forces the image of C' to be on both $\overrightarrow{DF}$ and $\overrightarrow{EF}$, and so the image of C' is F. Therefore the image of $\triangle A'B'C'$ is $\triangle DEF$.

So if originally two angles and the included side are congruent ($\overline{AB} \cong \overline{DE}$, $\angle A \cong \angle D$, $\angle B \cong \angle E$) then $\triangle ABC$ can be mapped onto $\triangle DEF$ by an isometry exactly as before. (First map $\overline{AB}$ onto $\overline{DE}$ as we did, then reflect the image of $\triangle ABC$ over the line $\overleftrightarrow{DE}$.) Thus, by the definition of congruence, $\triangle ABC \cong \triangle DEF$.

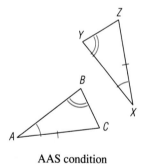

AAS condition

There is another condition to consider: AAS. This means two angles and one pair of *corresponding non-included* sides of two triangles are congruent. The AAS condition leads to congruent triangles because if two pairs of angles are congruent, the third pair is also congruent. For instance, in the diagram at the left, $\angle C \cong \angle Z$. So ASA can be applied to make them congruent. This can always be done.

AAS Congruence Theorem:

If, in two triangles, two angles and a non-included side of one are congruent respectively to two angles and the corresponding non-included side of the other, then the triangles are congruent.

312

The situation below is not AAS because the congruent sides are not corresponding sides. They are not opposite corresponding angles. Even though the third pair of angles are congruent, you can see that the triangles are not congruent.

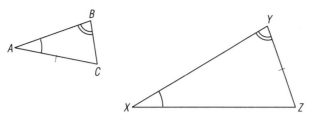

This is not the AAS condition.
(In △ABC and △XYZ, side $\overline{AC}$ does not correspond to side $\overline{YZ}$.)

■ ■ ■ ■ ■ ■ ■ ■

Example Using only the information marked, is the pair of triangles congruent? Justify each pair of congruent triangles with a triangle congruence theorem.

a.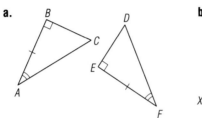

b.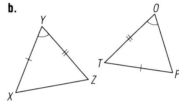

c.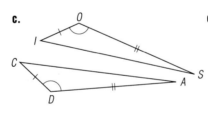

d.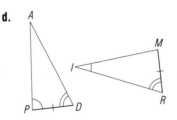

Solution

a. △ABC ≅ △FED by the ASA Congruence Theorem.
b. You cannot conclude that the triangles are congruent. The congruent angles are not included by the corresponding sides in both triangles.
c. △CAD ≅ △ISO by the SAS Congruence Theorem.
d. You cannot conclude that the triangles are congruent. The congruent angles are not in the same relative positions in the triangles.

Small Group Work for Question 6: This is a good question for students to discuss in groups. You can make up a worksheet with triangle pairs that have corresponding parts "missing." Have students discuss which additional parts should be congruent to apply the SSS, SAS, ASA, or AAS Congruence Theorems.

Questions 10-15: You may want to anticipate the next lesson by writing these as simple proofs; for example, writing down the following for Question 10 and similar information for others in which sufficient information is given.

10. Given $\overline{AB} \cong \overline{CE}$, $\overline{BF} \cong \overline{ED}$, and ∠B ≅ ∠E. Thus, by the SAS Congruence Theorem, △ABF ≅ △CED.

Error Analysis for Question 11: Students who answer "congruent" are either (1) misusing SAS by not realizing that the angle must be included, or (2) assuming too much from the figure. Remind them that in such questions only the information specifically given or marked on the figure can be used. Even in Lesson 7-5, where the SsA Theorem is discussed, there is still not sufficient information for congruence.

Computer for Questions 17-19: These may be done with an automatic drawer.

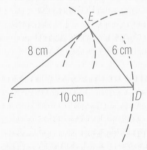
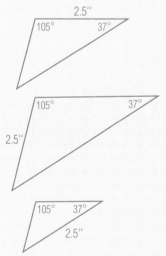
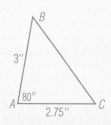
Questions

1. List four conditions that lead to triangle congruence. SSS, SAS, ASA, AAS

2. **a.** *Multiple choice.* The triangle congruence theorems have the same
   (a) antecedent
   (b) consequent
   (c) proof
   (d) conditional (b)

   b. What words are the same in all the triangle congruence theorems? then the triangles are congruent

3. △ABC has sides of 2, 8, and 7 centimeters. △DOT has sides of 7, 2, and 8 centimeters. What can you conclude about the triangles? They are congruent.

4. In the proof of the SSS Congruence Theorem, the symmetry of what figure is used? kite

5. In the proof of the SAS Congruence Theorem, the symmetry of what figure is used? isosceles triangle

6. *Multiple choice.* What additional information is needed to have the SAS condition in the triangles below?
   (a) $\overline{BC} \cong \overline{DE}$
   (b) $\overline{AC} \cong \overline{DE}$
   (c) $\overline{BC} \cong \overline{EF}$
   (d) $\overline{AC} \cong \overline{EF}$ (a)

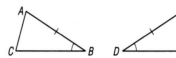

7. State the ASA Congruence Theorem. See margin.

8. Use the figure below. In △ACD, what side is included by ∠A and ∠ADC? $\overline{AD}$

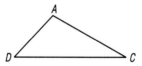

9. Give reasons as found in the proof of the ASA Congruence Theorem. In quadrilateral *EFGH* below, $\overleftrightarrow{FH}$ bisects angles *F* and *H*. Consider $\overrightarrow{FH}$ as the reflecting line.

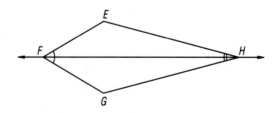

   a. Why is the image of *E* on $\overleftrightarrow{HG}$? Side-Switching Theorem
   b. Why is the image of *E* on $\overrightarrow{FG}$? Side-Switching Theorem
   c. Because of the definition of congruence, △EFH ≅ _?_. △GFH

In 10–15, if the given triangles are congruent, explain why they are congruent, and indicate corresponding vertices.

10.

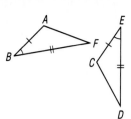

See margin.

11.

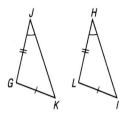

not necessarily congruent

12.

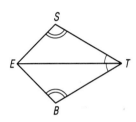

not necessarily congruent

13.

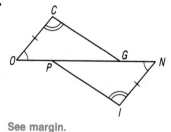

See margin.

14.

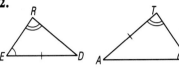

See margin.

15.

See margin.

Applying the Mathematics

16. Given $\overline{DP} \cong \overline{JK}$, $\overline{DO} \cong \overline{JL}$, $\overline{OP} \cong \overline{LK}$.
   a. $\triangle DPO \cong \underline{\ ?\ }$ $\triangle JKL$
   b. If $OD = 5$ yards, then $\underline{\ ?\ }$ is 5 yards. *LJ*
   c. $\angle O \cong \angle \underline{\ ?\ }$ *L*
   d. If $m\angle P = 73$, then $\underline{\ ?\ } = 73$. $m \angle K$

17. a. Construct a triangle DEF with $DE = 6$ cm, $EF = 8$ cm, and $DF = 10$ cm. See margin.
   b. Will everyone else's correct drawings be congruent to yours?
   Yes, because of the SSS Congruence Theorem.

18. a. Draw a triangle satisfying the following information. One side has length 2.5″. Two angles have measures 37° and 105°. See margin.
   b. Will everyone else's triangles (if correctly drawn) look congruent to yours? Why or why not?
   No, because the side can be opposite any angle.

19. a. Draw a triangle with $AB = 3″$, $CA = 2.75″$, and $m\angle CAB = 80$. See margin.
   b. Will everyone else's correctly done drawings be congruent to yours? Why or why not?
   Yes, because of the SAS Congruence Theorem.

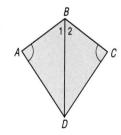

20. In this sail for a hang glider, seam $\overline{BD}$ bisects $\angle ABC$, and $\angle A \cong \angle C$. Why can you be sure that the cloth used for the left side can be cut from the same pattern outline as the right side?
$\triangle ABD \cong \triangle CBD$ by the AAS Congruence Theorem

LESSON 7-2 Triangle Congruence Theorems   **315**

21. Sally attached three sticks together as shown. She rotated stick A until
it made an angle of 23° with the meter stick, and stick B so that it
made an angle of 49° with the meter stick. She secured where A and
B crossed to make a triangle. Why will anyone get a triangle
congruent to hers if they repeat the procedure?
because of the ASA Congruence Theorem

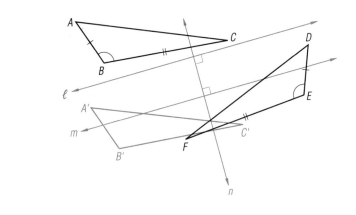

Review

22. $\triangle ABC \cong \triangle DEF$. If $m\angle A = 32$ and $m\angle B = 64$, what is $m\angle F$?
(Lessons 7-1, 6-7) 84

23. Arrange in order from most general to most specific:
rhombus, figure, square, quadrilateral, kite. *(Lesson 5-2)*
figure, quadrilateral, kite, rhombus, square

24. Suppose x is the measure of an angle and $360 - 3x < 90$. Is the
angle acute, obtuse, or right? *(Lesson 3-2, Previous course)* obtuse

Exploration

25. Below, $\triangle ABC \cong \triangle DEF$. Trace this figure. Locate lines ℓ, m, and n
so that $r_n \circ r_m \circ r_\ell(\triangle ABC) = \triangle DEF$.

316

7-3

Triangle Congruence Proofs

To use any triangle congruence theorem, you need to know that three parts (SSS, SAS, ASA, or AAS) of one triangle are congruent to the corresponding three parts of another. The particular theorem then enables you to conclude that the triangles are congruent. Because the triangles are congruent, all their corresponding parts are congruent due to the CPCF Theorem. Thus the SSS, SAS, ASA, and AAS theorems enable you to get six pairs of parts congruent where you only had three. That makes them quite powerful.

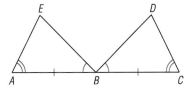

Example 1 **Given:** $\angle EBA \cong \angle CBD$
$\overline{AB} \cong \overline{BC}$
$\angle A \cong \angle C.$

Prove: $\overline{EB} \cong \overline{DB}.$

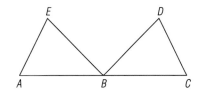

Draw Copy the figure and mark it with the given information.

Analyze Two pairs of angles and their included sides are congruent. This is the ASA condition. To get corresponding parts, the correct order for the vertices of the triangles must be used.

Write **Given:** $\overline{AB} \cong \overline{BC}$, $\angle EBA \cong \angle CBD$, $\angle A \cong \angle C.$

Conclusions	Justifications
1. $\triangle ABE \cong \triangle CBD$	ASA Congruence Theorem (from the given)
2. $\overline{EB} \cong \overline{DB}$	CPCF Theorem

Often information is not given in as nice a way as in Example 1. Even so, from given information you can deduce enough to get congruent triangles.

LESSON 7-3

RESOURCES
■ Lesson Master 7-3
■ Quiz for Lessons 7-1 Through 7-3
▬ Visual for Teaching Aid 40 can be used with **Questions 2** and **8**.
■ Computer Master 14

OBJECTIVES

C Write proofs that triangles are congruent.
D Apply the triangle congruence and CPCF theorems to prove that segments or angles are congruent.

TEACHING NOTES

Although much has been said about students' difficulty with proof, little has been said about the fact that being able to *follow* a proof is different from being able to *write* one. Proof-writing is essentially a writing task, and there are many students who are poor at writing a logical argument of any kind in any subject area. One of the major reasons students should write proofs is that it gives them practice in writing logical arguments. It is for this reason that all students should have some experience with proof.

All the proofs in this lesson are shown in two columns. Although few people other than teachers and students in geometry classes write proofs in two columns, this form is instructive and tailormade for short proofs involving congruent triangles.

You may want to demonstrate the Examples with an overhead projector to show

how important it is to draw the figure, label it with the congruent parts, and analyze how to do the proof.

The converse of the Isosceles Triangle Theorem, proved on page 319, shows how elegant triangle congruence proofs can be in deducing useful theorems.

There is an interesting proof of this theorem which uses the fact that an isosceles triangle has a nontrivial congruence with itself. Since $\angle B \cong \angle C$, then $\angle C \cong \angle B$ by the Symmetric Property of Congruence. Segment $\overline{BC} \cong \overline{CB}$ by the Reflexive Property of Congruence. Therefore, $\triangle BAC \cong \triangle CAB$ by the ASA Congruence Theorem, and hence, $\overline{BA} \cong \overline{CA}$ by the CPCF Theorem.

Questions 2 and **8** are the first of a number of questions in this chapter in which students are asked to give justifications. Do not waste time writing all of the conclusions during class. Use *Visual for Teaching Aid 40* that is provided for the lesson.

ADDITIONAL EXAMPLES

1. Given: $\overrightarrow{AE}$ bisects $\angle BAD$.
$\qquad \angle B \cong \angle D$.
Prove: $\triangle ABC \cong \triangle ADC$.

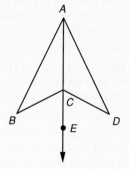

∠**BAC** ≅ ∠**DAC** by the definition of angle bisector (meaning).
$\overline{AC} \cong \overline{AC}$ by the Reflexive Property of Congruence and with the given, △**ABC** ≅ △**ADC** by the AAS Congruence Theorem.

Example 2 **Given:** M is the midpoint of $\overline{CD}$ and $\overline{EF}$.
$\qquad\qquad$ **Prove:** $\triangle CME \cong \triangle DMF$.

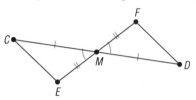

Draw and Analyze   Because M is a midpoint of two segments, there are two pairs of equal sides. The intersecting lines form vertical angles which are congruent. Marked in the figure below are two sides and the included angle of each triangle. This is the SAS condition.

Write **Given:** **M is the midpoint of $\overline{CD}$.**
$\qquad\qquad\qquad$ **M is the midpoint of $\overline{EF}$.**

Conclusions	Justifications
1. $MC = MD$, $ME = MF$	definition of midpoint (meaning)
2. $\angle CME \cong \angle DMF$	Vertical Angle Theorem
3. $\triangle CME \cong \triangle DMF$	SAS Congruence Theorem (steps 1 and 2)

There are two things to notice in this proof. First, we use equality of length (or measures) and congruence interchangeably. Second, in the justification for step 3, the part in parentheses refers to the steps in which the corresponding parts were explicitly stated as congruent. You must state these parts either in the given or in the proof before applying a triangle congruence theorem.

In Example 2, you could conclude $\angle E \cong \angle F$ by the CPCF Theorem. This in turn enables you to conclude that lines $\overleftrightarrow{EC}$ and $\overleftrightarrow{FD}$ are parallel by the AIA = ⇒ // Lines Theorem. Angles often lead to deductions about parallel lines. This is one of the important features of congruent triangles; they allow deductions to be made about angles and lines.

318

Example 3 **Given:** $AB = CD$
$BC = AD$.
Prove: $\overline{AB} \parallel \overline{CD}$.

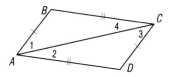

Draw Copy the figure and mark it with the given information.
Label the angles which might help get parallel lines for convenience.

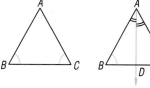

Analyze The triangles have the side $\overline{AC}$ in common. With the given, this is enough for SSS.

Write **Given:** $AB = CD, BC = AD$.

Conclusions	Justifications
1. $\overline{AC} \cong \overline{AC}$	Reflexive Property of Congruence
2. $\triangle ABC \cong \triangle CDA$	SSS Congruence Theorem (step 1 and given)
3. $\angle 1 \cong \angle 3$	CPCF Theorem
4. $\overline{AB} \parallel \overline{CD}$	AIA = $\Rightarrow \parallel$ Lines Theorem

Important theorems can be proved using the triangle congruence theorems. The AAS Congruence Theorem helps to prove the converse of the Isosceles Triangle Theorem.

Theorem:

If two angles of a triangle are congruent, then the sides opposite them are congruent.

Proof

Draw a figure and write the given and prove in terms of that figure.

Given: $\angle B \cong \angle C$.
Prove: $\overline{AB} \cong \overline{AC}$.

Triangles are needed. By drawing $\overrightarrow{AD}$, the bisector of $\angle A$, there is enough to deduce $\triangle ABD \cong \triangle ACD$.

Conclusions	Justifications
1. $\angle BAD \cong CAD$	def. of angle bisector (meaning)
2. $\overline{AD} \cong \overline{AD}$	?
3. $\triangle ABD \cong \triangle ACD$	AAS Congruence Theorem (steps 1, 2, and given)
4. $\overline{AB} \cong \overline{AC}$	?

You are asked to fill in the missing justifications as Question 5.

2. Given: $\overleftrightarrow{KJ} \parallel \overleftrightarrow{ML}$ and
$\overline{KJ} \cong \overline{LM}$.
Prove: $\triangle KJL \cong \triangle LMK$.

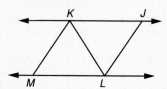

$\angle LKJ \cong \angle KLM$ **because if two lines are parallel, alternate interior angles are congruent.**
$\overline{KL} \cong \overline{KL}$ **by the Reflexive Property of Congruence. Thus, $\triangle KJL \cong \triangle LMK$ by the SAS Congruence Theorem.**

NOTES ON QUESTIONS
Small Group Work for Questions 2, 7, 8, and 9: Groups may be used to discuss and correct these proofs.

Questions 7 and 9: These two proofs are very similar to the Examples. Confidence is an important factor in having the patience to search for the appropriate reasons in proofs. You may wish to tell students in advance that they are expected to follow the reasoning in the Examples.

Making Connections for Question 10: Students will study overlapping triangles in Lesson 7-4. Ask them to draw the triangles separately if they have trouble naming the congruent triangles.

Question 20: The Exploration question in the next lesson is a companion question; it deals with the SSASS condition for quadrilaterals.

These kinds of proofs are helpful in deducing properties of many figures, as you will see. Writing triangle congruence proofs takes some practice; it often takes a while to become proficient.

Questions

Covering the Reading

1. Given: ∠1 ≅ ∠2
$\overline{AC} \cong \overline{AE}$
$\overline{AB} \cong \overline{AD}$.
a. Copy the figure and mark the given on it.
b. What theorem justifies the congruence of the triangles?
c. Prove: ∠B ≅ ∠D.
b) SAS Congruence Theorem; c) See margin.

2. Using the figure and given of Example 2, complete this proof that $\overline{EC} \cong \overline{FD}$. See margin.

Conclusions	Justifications
1. MC = MD, ME = MF	a. _?_
2. ∠CME ≅ ∠DMF	b. _?_
3. △CME ≅ △DMF	c. _?_
4. $\overline{EC} \cong \overline{FD}$	d. _?_

3. Using the figure and given of Example 3, prove $\overleftrightarrow{BC}$ ∥ $\overleftrightarrow{AD}$. See margin.

4. Finish this statement of the converse of the Isosceles Triangle Theorem: If two angles of a triangle are congruent, then _?_ . the sides opposite them are congruent

5. In the proof of the converse of the Isosceles Triangle Theorem, give a justification for
a. conclusion 2;　　　　b. conclusion 4.
a) Reflexive Property of Congruence; b) CPCF Theorem

Applying the Mathematics

6. a. With angle measures as given below, which sides of △ABC are congruent? $\overline{AB}$ and $\overline{BC}$
b. What is the justification for your answer to a? the converse of the Isosceles Triangle Theorem

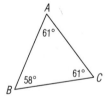

7. Given: AB = CD
BC = AD.
Prove: △ABC ≅ △CDA.
See margin.

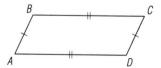

8. Use the figure at the right. Supply the missing justifications.

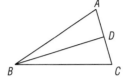

Given: $\overrightarrow{CA}$ bisects $\angle XCY$.
$XC = YC$.
Prove: $\angle X \cong \angle Y$.

Conclusions	Justifications
1. $\overline{AC} \cong \overline{AC}$	**a.** _?_ Reflexive Prop. of Congruence
2. $\angle XCA \cong \angle YCA$	**b.** _?_ def. of $\angle$ bisector (meaning)
3. $\triangle ACX \cong \triangle ACY$	**c.** _?_ SAS Congruence Theorem
4. $\angle X \cong \angle Y$	**d.** _?_ CPCF Theorem

9. Use the figure at the right.

Given: $\triangle ABC$ is isosceles with
vertex angle B. D is the
midpoint of $\overline{AC}$.
Prove: $\triangle ABD \cong \triangle CBD$. **See margin.**

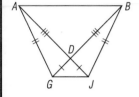

10. a. List all eight triangles in the figure at the left.
b. From the marked information, there are three pairs of triangles which can be proved congruent. Name them, with vertices in corresponding order. **See margin.**

Review

11. Tony and Trisha each made a triangle out of straws with lengths 3 cm, 4 cm, and 6 cm. *True* or *false*?
a. The two triangles must be congruent. **True**
b. The two triangles must have the same orientation. **False**
(Lessons 7-2, 7-1)

12. Explain why the SAS Congruence Theorem cannot be used to prove $\triangle ADC$ congruent to $\triangle ABC$ in the figure below. *(Lesson 7-2)*

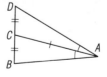

The marked angles are not included between the congruent sides.

LESSON 7-3   Triangle Congruence Proofs   **321**

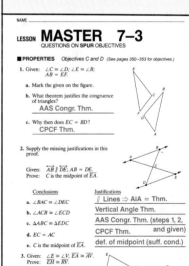

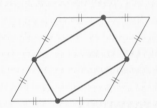
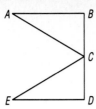

13. Given: *C* is the midpoint of $\overline{BD}$. $AC = EC$.
   $\angle ACB \cong \angle DCE$.
   Why are the triangles congruent? *(Lesson 7-2)* See margin.

14. Electric wires run from post to post over the buildings shown below. We can't measure the length of wire needed because the buildings are in the way. Place a stake at *H*. Then mark off *J* on $\overleftrightarrow{FH}$ so that $FH = HJ$. Now mark off *I* on $\overleftrightarrow{GH}$ so that $GH = HI$. What triangle congruence theorem indicates that $\triangle FGH \cong \triangle JIH$ so that the distance from *I* to *J* is equal to the distance between the posts? *(Lessons 7-2, 6-7)* See margin.

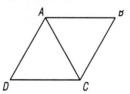

15. Draw a triangle with sides 3 cm, 11 cm, and 6 cm. *(Lesson 7-1)*
   Not possible; it violates the Triangle Inequality.

In 16 and 17, all five segments in the figure below are congruent.

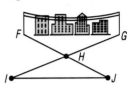

16. Make and justify at least two conclusions from this given information. *(Lessons 5-4, 5-3, 4-2)* See margin.

17. If the perimeter of *ABCD* is *x*, what is the length of $\overline{AC}$?
   (Previous course) $\frac{x}{4}$

18. The sum of the measures of the acute angles in a right triangle is __?__.
   (Lesson 5-7) 90°

19. a. Draw a figure to test this conjecture: If the midpoints of the sides of a rhombus are connected in order, the resulting figure is a square. See margin.
   b. Do you think the conjecture is true? *(Lesson 5-3)*
   Opinions will vary.

20. a. What would be an SSSS condition for two quadrilaterals to be congruent? See below.
   b. Show by drawing a counterexample that there is no SSSS Congruence Theorem for quadrilaterals. See below.
   a) If, in two quadrilaterals, four sides of one are congruent respectively to four sides of the other, then the quadrilaterals are congruent.

   b) sample:

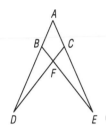
7-4

Overlapping Triangles

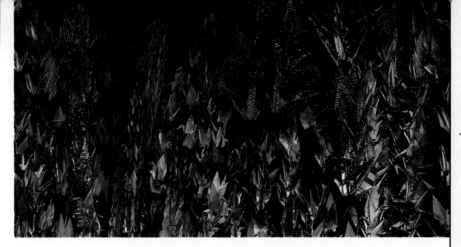

LESSON 7-4

RESOURCES
■ Lesson Master 7-4
▱ Visual for Teaching Aid 41
   can be used with
   Questions 2 and **8**.
▪ Computer Master 14

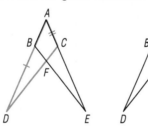

How many triangles do you see in the figure at the left? At first, many people see only the small triangles *BFD* and *CFE*. But there are **overlapping triangles** *ACD* and *ABE*. Given appropriate information, these triangles can be proved congruent just as other triangles can.

Example 1

In the figure at the left above, if *AC* = *AB* and *AD* = *AE,* prove ∠*D* ≅ ∠*E*.

Analyze   It may seem that the triangles to use are the small triangles *BFD* and *CFE*. But no sides or angles of these triangles are given as congruent. So try the overlapping triangles, △*ACD* and △*ABE*. At the beginning you may have to draw the figure twice to see the triangles. Mark the figure with the given information.

Notice that although only two sides are given congruent, there is a common angle, ∠*A*.

Write   Given: *AC* = *AB* and *AD* = *AE*.

Conclusions	Justifications
1. ∠*A* ≅ ∠*A*	**Reflexive Property of Congruence**
2. △*ADC* ≅ △*AEB*	**SAS Congruence Theorem (step 1 and given)**
3. ∠*D* ≅ ∠*E*	**CPCF Theorem**

OBJECTIVES

C Write proofs that triangles are congruent.
D Apply the triangle congruence and CPCF theorems to prove that segments or angles are congruent.

TEACHING NOTES

As there are no new theorems in this lesson, you can take advantage of this day to review questions from previous lessons which you may not have had time to discuss.

To aid students' visualization of the overlapping triangles, you may wish to prepare three transparencies for a situation like that in **Example 1:** (1) the given figure, (2) △*ACD* in a color, and (3) △*ABE* in a different color.

In **Example 2,** students need to discern two kinds of triangles. One kind is the two noncongruent isosceles triangles. The second kind is the pair of congruent triangles.

Reading   The proof analysis is an important paragraph students should focus on as they are reading.

Error Analysis   Keeping track of vertices, angles, and sides which correspond can be difficult for overlapping triangles. Encourage students to redraw the figures with the triangles separated.

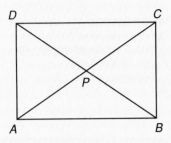
With overlapping triangles, keeping track of corresponding vertices can be tricky. As you deduce congruent sides or angles, mark the figure.

Example 2   **Given:** $\overline{GH} \cong \overline{GK}$
$\overline{GJ} \cong \overline{GI}$.

Prove: $\overline{HJ} \cong \overline{KI}$.

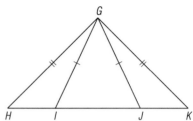

Analyze $\overline{HJ}$ and $\overline{KI}$ are sides of the overlapping triangles *GHJ* and *GKI*. So it is natural to try to prove these triangles congruent. Also, the marked congruent sides mean that △*GIJ* and △*GHK* are isosceles, so their base angles are congruent. This is enough.

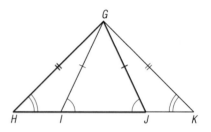

Write

Conclusions	Justifications
1. ∠H ≅ ∠K	Isosceles Triangle Thoerem (with △GHK)
2. ∠GJI ≅ ∠GIJ	Isosceles Triangle Theorem (with △GIJ)
3. △GHJ ≅ △GKI	AAS Congruence Theorem (steps 1, 2, and given)
4. $\overline{HJ} \cong \overline{KI}$	CPCF Theorem

Notice that the proof in Example 2 uses the AAS Congruence Theorem, not SAS or SSS, even though two pairs of congruent segments are given. When you analyze a problem, don't be limited by the most obvious clues. Also notice that in Step 3, it does not matter whether the proof used $\overline{GH} \cong \overline{GK}$ or $\overline{GJ} \cong \overline{GI}$.

Covering the Reading

1. Use the figure below.
  a. How many triangles are in the figure? **8**
  b. It looks like △QUA is congruent to what other triangle? **△DAU**
  c. Find a second pair of overlapping triangles that seem congruent.
       △QUD, △DAQ

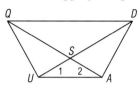

2. Using the diagram and given of Example 1, fill in justifications in the proof that ∠DCA ≅ ∠EBA.

Conclusions	Justifications
1. ∠A ≅ ∠A	**a.** __?__ Reflexive Property of Congruence
2. △ADC ≅ △AEB	**b.** __?__ SAS Congruence Theorem
3. ∠DCA ≅ ∠EBA	**c.** __?__ CPCF Theorem

3. Using the figure and given of Example 2, prove that ∠HGJ ≅ ∠KGI. **See margin.**

4. In the figure of Question 1, suppose $\overline{QU} \cong \overline{AD}$ and $\overline{QA} \cong \overline{UD}$.
  Prove: ∠1 ≅ ∠2. **See margin.**

Applying the Mathematics

5. Given: AD = AE
         m∠D = m∠E.
  Prove: EB = CD. **See margin.**

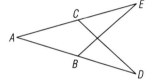

6. In pentagon ALIVE at the left, $\overline{AE} \cong \overline{IV}$ and ∠AEV ≅ ∠EVI. Prove that $\overline{AV} \cong \overline{IE}$. **See margin.**

7. Given: PR = QS
         PS = QR.
  Prove: m∠P = m∠Q. **See margin.**

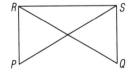

Review

8. Given: G, J, K, and H are collinear.
         $\overline{GJ} \cong \overline{HK}$ and $\overline{GI} \cong \overline{HI}$.
  Prove: $\overline{JI} \cong \overline{KI}$. *(Lesson 7-3)* **See margin.**

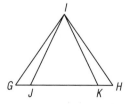

6.

Conclusions	Justifications
1. $\overline{EV} \cong \overline{EV}$	Reflexive Prop. of Congruence
2. △AEV ≅ △IVE	SAS Congruence Thm. (step 1 and given)
3. $\overline{AV} \cong \overline{IE}$	CPCF Thm.

7.

Conclusions	Justifications
1. RS = RS	Reflexive Prop. of Equality
2. △PRS ≅ △QSR	SSS Congruence Thm. (given and step 1)
3. m∠P = m∠Q	CPCF Thm.

8.

Conclusions	Justifications
1. m∠G = m∠H	Isosceles △ Thm.
2. △JGI ≅ △KHI	SAS Congruence Thm. (step 1 and given)
3. $\overline{JI} \cong \overline{KI}$	CPCF Thm.

FOLLOW-UP

MORE PRACTICE

For more questions on SPUR
Objectives, use *Lesson Master 7-4,* shown on page 325.

ADDITIONAL ANSWERS

9. a. Vertical Angle Thm.
   b. SAS Congruence Thm. (step 1 and given)
   c. CPCF Thm.
   d. Vertical Angle Thm.
   e. Transitive Prop. of Eq.

10.

Conclusions	Justifications
1. QS = SU	def. of midpoint (meaning)
2. m∠QSR = m∠UST	Vertical Angle Thm.
3. m∠SQR = m∠SUT	∥ Lines ⇒ AIA ≅ Thm.
4. △QSR ≅ △UST	ASA Congruence Thm. (steps 1, 2, and 3)
5. ST = SR	CPCF Thm.
6. S is the midpoint of $\overline{RT}$.	def. of midpoint (suff. cond.)

11. △PCA ≅ PCB by the SAS Congruence Theorem. So, PA = PB by the CPCF Theorem.

12. a.

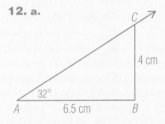

or

9. Given that $\overline{DF}$ and $\overline{AG}$ intersect at E with segments equal as marked, justify each conclusion in this proof that ∠FGE ≅ ∠DBC.
   (Lessons 7-3, 6-7, 4-4)
   Given: AE = EF; EG = EB.   **See margin.**

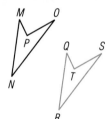

Conclusions	Justifications
1. ∠AEB ≅ ∠FEG	a. ?
2. △ABE ≅ △FGE	b. ?
3. ∠FGE ≅ ∠ABE	c. ?
4. ∠ABE ≅ ∠DBC	d. ?
5. ∠FGE ≅ ∠DBC	e. ?

10. Given: $\overline{QR} \parallel \overline{TU}$
    S is the midpoint of $\overline{QU}$.
    Prove: S is the midpoint of $\overline{RT}$. *(Lesson 7-3)* **See margin.**

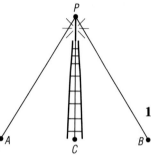

11. $\overline{PC}$ is a vertical radio tower supported by the taut guy wires $\overline{PA}$ and $\overline{PB}$. Explain why the guy wires will have the same length if they are attached to level ground at the same distance from C. *(Lessons 7-3, 7-2)*
    See margin.

12. a. Draw a triangle with AB = 6.5 cm, BC = 4 cm, and m∠A = 32.
    b. Will everyone else's correct drawing be congruent to yours?
    (Lessons 7-2, 7-1)
    a) See margin. b) No, because two triangles are possible.

In 13 and 14, QRST at the right is the translation image of MNOP. *True* or *false*? *(Lessons 6-7, 6-6)*

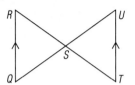

13. MNOP ≅ QRST **True**

14. MQ = OS **True**

15. If y is the measure of an angle and 0 < 180 − 2y, is the angle acute, obtuse, or right? *(Lesson 3-2)* **acute**

16. Below, WY = 13, WZ = 25, and XZ = 17. Find WX. *(Lesson 10-8)* **8**

Exploration

17. Is there an SSASS Congruence Theorem for quadrilaterals?
    No, as shown by these figures.

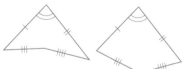

The distance of the children from the maypole is determined by the height of the pole and the length of the streamer. See Question 13.

Since there are AAS and ASA Congruence Theorems and there is a congruence theorem with 2 sides and an included angle (SAS), it is natural to ask what happens if the angle is not included. We call this the **SSA condition.**

Examine △*ABC* and △*XYZ* below. There are two pairs of congruent sides, $\overline{AB} \cong \overline{XY}$ and $\overline{BC} \cong \overline{YZ}$. Also, there is a pair of corresponding non-included angles, $\angle A \cong \angle X$.

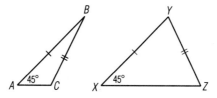

But clearly the triangles are not congruent. In fact, a translation image of △*ABC* fits nicely into △*XYZ*.

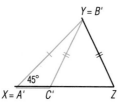

Thus, in general, the SSA condition does not guarantee the congruence of triangles. However, when the corresponding non-included angles are right angles, the situation is different. Recall that in a right triangle, the **legs** are the sides that include the right angle while the **hypotenuse** is the side opposite the right angle. Suppose

$BC = YZ$, $AB = XY$, and $\angle C$ and $\angle Z$ are right angles as shown in the triangles below. This is the **hypotenuse-leg** or **HL condition.** This is enough to guarantee congruence.

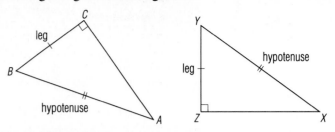

HL Congruence Theorem:

If, in two right triangles, the hypotenuse and a leg of one are congruent to the hypotenuse and a leg of the other, then the two triangles are congruent.

Proof

Given: $\overline{BC} \cong \overline{YZ}$; $\overline{AB} \cong \overline{XY}$.
$\angle C$ and $\angle Z$ are both right angles.

Prove: $\triangle ABC \cong \triangle XYZ$.

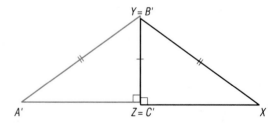

Since $\overline{BC} \cong \overline{YZ}$, there is a composite of reflections that maps $\overline{BC}$ onto $\overline{YZ}$, with the image of A on the other side of $\overline{YZ}$ from X. This gives the figure below, in which $\triangle ABC \cong \triangle A'B'C'$.

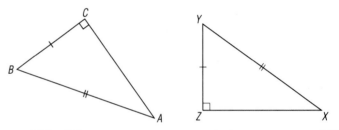

By Angle Addition, $m\angle A'ZX = 180$, so A', Z, and X are collinear. Since $\overline{AB} \cong \overline{XY}$ and $\overline{AB} \cong \overline{A'B'}$, by the Transitive Property of Congruence, $\overline{A'B'} \cong \overline{XY}$. This makes $\triangle A'YX$ a big isosceles triangle. Applying the Isosceles Triangle Theorem, $\angle A' \cong \angle X$. Thus by the AAS Congruence Theorem, $\triangle A'B'C' \cong \triangle XYZ$, making $\triangle ABC \cong \triangle XYZ$, again by the Transitive Property of Congruence.

Example 1 The triangles in the figure below are congruent. For each pair of triangles, indicate the corresponding vertices and the theorem that justifies the congruence.

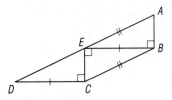

Solution
1. △ABE ≅ △CEB by HL Congruence.
2. △CEB ≅ △ECD by SAS Congruence.
3. △ABE ≅ △ECD by the Transitive of Property of Congruence.

Example 2 Given △ABC and △POT with the congruent parts marked, make and justify at least three conclusions.

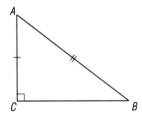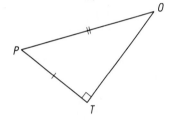

Solution Here are two conclusions you could have made before studying this chapter.

Conclusion	Justification
1. △ABC is a right triangle.	definition of right △ (suff. cond.)
2. m∠B + m∠A = 90	Triangle-Sum Theorem

Here are four conclusions possible because of triangle congruence ideas.

3. △ABC ≅ △POT	HL Congruence Theorem (step 1 and given)
4. ∠A ≅ ∠P	CPCF Theorem
5. $\overline{BC}$ ≅ $\overline{OT}$	CPCF Theorem
6. ∠O ≅ ∠B	CPCF Theorem

The HL condition is the special case of SSA when the congruent angles are right angles. Because we could deduce an HL Congruence Theorem, the SSA condition works sometimes. A natural question is: Does the SSA condition give congruent triangles at

LESSON 7-5 The SSA Condition and HL Congruence **329**

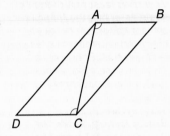
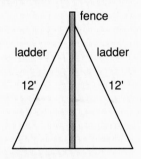

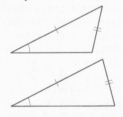
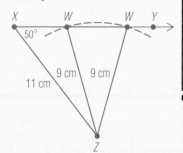
any other time? The answer is "Yes." It is written as the *SsA Congruence Theorem* since, for it to work, the sides opposite the congruent angles in each triangle must be longer than the other congruent sides. It is presented here without a proof because the proof is quite difficult.

SsA Congruence Theorem:

> If, in two triangles, two sides and the angle opposite the longer of the two sides in one are congruent respectively to two sides and the angle opposite the corresponding side in the other, then the triangles are congruent.

If $\overline{AB} \cong \overline{XY}$, $\overline{AC} \cong \overline{XZ}$, $\angle C \cong \angle Z$, and $AB > AC$ (so $XY > XZ$ by substitution), then $\triangle ABC \cong \triangle XYZ$.

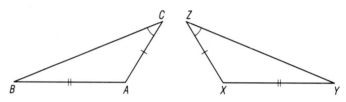

Questions

Covering the Reading

1. Draw two noncongruent triangles satisfying the SSA condition.
   See margin.
2. **a.** What kind of triangle has sides represented by H and L?
   b. What does H stand for? What does L stand for?
   a) a right triangle; b) hypotenuse, leg
3. *Multiple choice.* Which of these justifications is not used in the proof of the HL Congruence Theorem?
   (a) AAS Congruence Theorem
   (b) Isosceles Triangle Theorem
   (c) Triangle-Sum Theorem
   (d) Angle Addition Property (c)

4. When does the SSA condition lead to congruence?
   See margin.

In 5–7, use the information given in the figure. **a.** What triangle congruence theorem tells you that the pair of triangles is congruent?
b. Write the congruent triangles with vertices correctly corresponding.

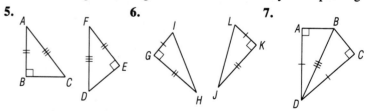

5.
a) HL Congruence Thm.
b) △ABC ≅ △FED

6.
a) SAS Congruence Thm.
b) △GHI ≅ △KJL

7.
a) HL Congruence Thm.
b) △ABD ≅ △CBD

8. Follow the steps to make a single drawing of a triangle given the SSA condition.
   a. Draw a ray $\overrightarrow{XY}$.
   b. Draw an $\angle ZXY$ with measure 50° and with $XZ = 11$ cm.
   c. Draw circle Z with radius 9 cm. Let W be a point of intersection of $\odot Z$ and $\overrightarrow{XY}$.
   d. Consider $\triangle XZW$. Will everyone else who does this correctly have a triangle XZW congruent to yours?
   a–c) See margin. d) No, there are two possible triangles XZW.

9. Use the figure at the left.

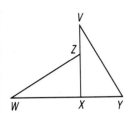

   Given: $\overrightarrow{VX} \perp \overrightarrow{WY}$
   $WZ = VY$
   $XZ = XY$.
   Prove: $\angle W \cong \angle V$. See margin.

10. Use the figure at the right.

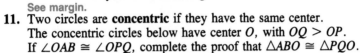

   Given: $AP = AR$,
   $\angle P$ and $\angle R$ are right angles.
   Prove: a. $\triangle PBA \cong \triangle RBA$
   b. $PBRA$ is a kite.
   c. a different conclusion of your own choosing

   See margin.

11. Two circles are **concentric** if they have the same center. The concentric circles below have center O, with $OQ > OP$. If $\angle OAB \cong \angle OPQ$, complete the proof that $\triangle ABO \cong \triangle PQO$.

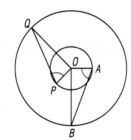

   Given: $OQ > OP$, $\angle OAB \cong \angle OPQ$

Conclusions	Justifications
1. $OP = OA$	a. __?__ definition of a circle (meaning)
2. $OQ = OB$	b. __?__ definition of a circle (meaning)
3. $\triangle ABO \cong \triangle PQO$	c. __?__ SsA Congruence Theorem (steps 1, 2, 3, and given)

12. Use the figure at the right.

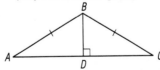

   Given: $\overline{BD} \perp \overline{AC}$
   $AB = BC$.
   Prove: $\triangle ABD \cong \triangle CBD$.
   See margin.

FOLLOW-UP

MORE PRACTICE
For more questions on SPUR Objectives, use *Lesson Master 7-5*, shown below.

9.

Conclusions	Justifications
1. $\triangle WXZ \cong$ $\triangle VXY$	HL Congr. Thm. (given)
2. $\angle W \cong \angle V$	CPCF Thm.

10. a.

Conclusions	Justifications
1. $\overline{AB} \cong \overline{AB}$	Reflexive Prop. of Congruence
2. $\triangle PBA \cong$ $\triangle RBA$	HL Congr. Thm. (step 1 and given)

b.

3. $\overline{PB} \cong \overline{RB}$	CPCF Thm.
4. $PBRA$ is a kite.	def. of kite (suff. cond.)

c. Sample: $\angle PAB \cong \angle RAB$ by the CPCF Theorem.

12.

Conclusions	Justifications
1. $\overline{BD} \cong \overline{BD}$	Reflexive Prop. of Congruence
2. $\triangle ABD \cong$ $\triangle CBD$	HL Congr. Thm. (step 1 and given)

331

NOTES ON QUESTIONS
Question 19: It may be difficult for students to draw a nonrectangular quadrilateral with a pair of opposite right angles. This can be corrected by drawing a rectangle, then cutting it along a diagonal, then turning one of the right angles to form a quadrilateral. In Chapter 15, students will learn that an inscribed angle of a circle which contains the endpoints of a diameter is a right angle. This enables such quadrilaterals to be drawn easily.

ADDITIONAL ANSWERS
13. Let *T* be the top of the maypole, *M* the point on the maypole that is the same height as June and April's hands, *J* the position of June's hand, and *A* the position of April's hand. $\overline{JA}$ is parallel to the ground, since *J* and *A* are equal in height (given). So, $\overline{JA} \perp \overline{TM}$ by the Perpendicular to Parallels Theorem. Since $\overline{TM} \cong \overline{TM}$ and $\overline{TJ} \cong \overline{TA}$, $\triangle TJM \cong \triangle TAM$ by the HL Congruence Theorem. Thus, $\overline{JM} = \overline{AM}$ by the CPCF Theorem.

15. a.

Conclusions	Justifications
1. m∠B = m∠C	Isosceles △ Thm.
2. △ABD ≅ △ACE	SAS Congruence Thm. (step 1 and given)
3. $\overline{AD} \cong \overline{AE}$	CPCF Thm.
4. ∠ADE ≅ ∠AED	Isosceles △ Thm.

b.

5. △ADE is isosceles.	def. of isosceles △ (suff. cond.; step 3)

17. a. (Art is reduced in size.)

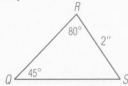

b. The drawings will be congruent because of the AAS Congruence Theorem

332

---

13. June and April are dancing around the maypole. The streamers they are holding are the same length. If June's and April's hands are the same height, explain why their hands are also the same distance from the maypole. **See margin.**

Review

14. Fill in the justifications in this proof that the diagonals of an isosceles trapezoid are congruent. *(Lessons 7-4, 5-5)*

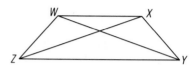

Given: *WXYZ* is an isosceles trapezoid with bases $\overline{WX}$ and $\overline{ZY}$.
Prove: $\overline{XZ} \cong \overline{WY}$.

Conclusions		Justifications
1. ∠WZY ≅ ∠XYZ	**a.** _?_	def. of isos. trap. (meaning)
2. $\overline{WZ} \cong \overline{XY}$	**b.** _?_	Isosceles Trapezoid Theorem
3. $\overline{ZY} \cong \overline{ZY}$	**c.** _?_	Reflexive Prop. of Congruence
4. △WZY ≅ △XYZ	**d.** _?_	SAS ≅ Theorem (steps 1–3)
5. $\overline{XZ} \cong \overline{WY}$	**e.** _?_	CPCF Theorem

15. Use the figure at the right.
Given: $AB = AC$, $BD = CE$.
Prove:
a. ∠ADE ≅ ∠AED
b. △ADE is isosceles. *(Lessons 7-4, 7-3)*
See margin.

16. Find all triangles congruent to △AGX, given $\overline{AB} \perp \overline{XY}$ and the figure at the left as marked. *(Lesson 7-2)* △AGY, △DEX, △DEY

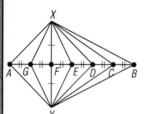

17. a. Draw △QRS with m∠Q = 45, m∠R = 80, and RS = 2″.
b. Will everyone else's correct drawing be congruent to yours? Explain why or why not. *(Lessons 7-2, 7-1)* **See margin.**

18. Suppose r(△ABC) = △DEF. State a conclusion which follows due to each justification. *(Lessons 6-5, 4-5, 4-2)*
a. definition of congruence △ABC ≅ △DEF
b. Flip-Flop Theorem r(△DEF) = △ABC
c. Figure Reflection Theorem sample: r($\overline{AB}$) = $\overline{DE}$

Exploration

19. Explore this conjecture. If, in quadrilaterals *ABCD* and *EFGH*, angles *A, C, E,* and *G* are right angles, $AB = EF$, and $BC = FG$, then the quadrilaterals are congruent. counterexample:

LESSON 7-6

Soccer balls are constructed from regular pentagons and regular hexagons.

Properties of Special Figures

An important use of the triangle congruence theorems is to deduce properties of special figures. *PARL* below is a parallelogram. Its diagonals, $\overline{PR}$ and $\overline{AL}$, form 4 nonoverlapping triangles and four overlapping triangles. (Do you see these eight triangles?) Pairs of these triangles can be proved congruent and, from the congruences, many properties of *PARL* can be deduced. Because *PARL* is not otherwise special in any way, these properties are true in any parallelogram.

■ ■ ■ ■ ■ ■ ■ ■ ■

RESOURCES
■ Lesson Master 7-6
■ Quiz for Lessons 7-4 Through 7-6
▶ Visual for Teaching Aid 43 can be used with the **Example.**

OBJECTIVES

D Apply the triangle congruence and CPCF theorems to prove that segments or angles are congruent.
E Determine whether conditions are properties of or sufficient conditions for parallelograms.

TEACHING NOTES

Making Connections
The three theorems on pages 334 and 335 are applied in Chapter 8. Part **a** of the Properties of a Parallelogram Theorem helps to calculate the area of a triangle from the area of a rectangle in Lesson 8-5. The theorem about the distance between parallel lines allows us to speak of the height of a trapezoid in the formula for its area derived in Lesson 8-6. The Center of a Regular Polygon Theorem is used to find the area of a circle in Lesson 8-9.

You might wish to anticipate these applications by noting that congruence is basic to area—the area of a region is the number of nonoverlapping congruent copies of a region that fit inside that region. This is the reason that a chapter on congruence comes before a chapter on area.

Example

Given: Parallelogram *PARL*.

Prove:
1. $\triangle RPL \cong \triangle PRA$
2. $\overline{PA} \cong \overline{RL}, \overline{PL} \cong \overline{RA}$
3. $EP = ER$.

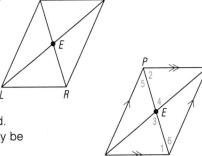

Draw The figure is marked. Some of the angles which may be used are numbered.

Analyze
1. There is a common side to $\triangle RPL$ and $\triangle PRA$. Each pair of parallel sides makes a pair of congruent alternate interior angles. This is sufficient for congruence of the triangles.
2. These are corresponding parts of $\triangle RPL$ and $\triangle PRA$.
3. Show $\triangle ERL \cong \triangle EPA$ to get $EP = ER$ by corresponding parts.

Write	**Conclusions**	**Justifications**
	1. $\overline{PA} \parallel \overline{LR}$	def. of parallelogram (meaning)
	2. $\angle 1 \cong \angle 2$	$\parallel$ Lines $\Rightarrow$ AIA = Theorem
	3. $\overline{PL} \parallel \overline{AR}$	_____?_____
	4. $\angle 5 \cong \angle 6$	_____?_____
	5. $\overline{PR} \cong \overline{RP}$	_____?_____
	6. $\triangle RPL \cong \triangle PRA$	_____?_____ (This proves 1.)
	7. $\overline{PA} \cong \overline{RL}, \overline{PL} \cong \overline{RA}$	CPCF Theorem (This proves 2.)
	8. $\angle 3 \cong \angle 4$	Vertical Angle Theorem
	9. $\triangle ERL \cong \triangle EPA$	AAS Congruence Theorem (Steps 2, 7, 8)
	10. $EP = ER$	CPCF Theorem (This proves 3.)

You are asked to fill in the missing justifications in Question 1.

LESSON 7-6 *Properties of Special Figures* **333**

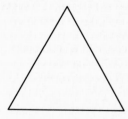

equilateral
triangle
n = 3

square
n = 4

regular
pentagon
n = 5

regular
hexagon
n = 6

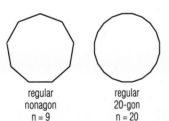

regular
heptagon
n = 7

regular
octagon
n = 8

regular
nonagon
n = 9

regular
20-gon
n = 20

Regular *n*-gons

Another type of figure which lends itself to congruent triangles is the *regular polygon*.

Definition:

A **regular polygon** is a convex polygon whose angles are all congruent and whose sides are all congruent.

The regular polygons with 3 sides are the equilateral triangles. Those with 4 sides are squares. Otherwise they are simply called regular pentagons, regular hexagons, and so on.

In the Example, the given was simply a parallelogram, yet many properties were deduced. The final conclusion $EP = ER$ implies E is the midpoint of $\overline{PR}$. Since we could have substituted diagonal $\overline{LA}$ for $\overline{PR}$, E is also the midpoint of $\overline{LA}$. Thus, this one proof has proved the following properties of parallelograms.

Properties of a Parallelogram Theorem:

In any parallelogram:
a. each diagonal forms two congruent triangles;
b. opposite sides are congruent;
c. the diagonals intersect at their midpoints.

Because of the Quadrilateral Hierarchy Theorem, you can further conclude that the properties of parallelograms apply to all rhombuses, rectangles, and squares.

A corollary of the Properties of a Parallelogram Theorem involves the distance between parallel lines. This result is important for deducing area formulas, as you will see in the next chapter.

Theorem:

The distance between parallel lines is constant.

Proof

Given: $\ell \parallel m$, $\overline{AB} \perp \ell$, $\overline{XY} \perp \ell$.
Prove: $\overline{AB} \cong \overline{XY}$.

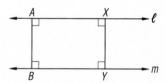

We know that $\overline{AB} \perp m$ and $\overline{XY} \perp m$ by the Perpendicular to Parallels Theorem. So AB and XY are distances between ℓ and m.

334

Also, *ABYX* satisfies the sufficient condition for a rectangle. Since opposite sides of any parallelogram are congruent, opposite sides of this rectangle are congruent. So $\overline{AB} \cong \overline{XY}$.

In Lesson 4-5, you learned how to construct the circle through three non-collinear points. Thus there is a circle which contains all the vertices of an equilateral triangle. Now think of squares. Because the diagonals of a square bisect each other (part **c** of the Properties of a Parallelogram Theorem) and because the diagonals have equal length (a square is a rectangle), the intersection of the diagonals of a square is the center of a circle which contains all the vertices of the square.

Using congruent triangles, this result can be extended to apply to all regular polygons.

Center of a Regular Polygon Theorem:

In any regular polygon there is a point (its center) which is equidistant from all its vertices.

Proof

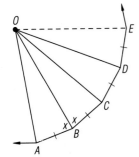

Analyze   Since the theorem is known to be true for regular polygons of 3 and 4 sides, the cases that need to be dealt with have 5 or more sides. What is done is to show that the circle through three consecutive vertices of the regular polygon contains the next vertex. Then that fourth vertex can be used with two others to obtain the fifth, and so on, as many times as needed.

Given: regular polygon *ABCD*...
Prove: There is a point *O* equidistant from *A*, *B*, *C*, *D*, ...

Draw   *ABCD*... at the left.

Write   Let *O* be the center of the circle containing *A*, *B*, and *C*. Then $OA = OB = OC$. Since $AB = BC$ by the definition of regular polygon, *OABC* is a kite with symmetry diagonal $\overline{OB}$. Thus $\overrightarrow{BO}$ bisects $\angle ABC$. Let $x = m\angle ABO = m\angle OBC$. Since $\triangle OBC$ is isosceles, $m\angle OBC = m\angle OCB = x$. Now the measures of the angles of the regular polygon are equal to $2x$, so $m\angle OCD = x$ also. Then $\triangle OCB \cong \triangle OCD$ by the SAS Congruence Theorem, and so by the CPCT Theorem, $OC = OD$.

The Center of a Regular Polygon Theorem implies that there is a circle which contains all the vertices of a regular polygon. This enables regular polygons to be drawn quite easily. Draw the circle first and equally space the vertices of the polygon around the circle.

LESSON 7-6   Properties of Special Figures   **335**

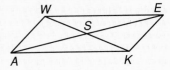

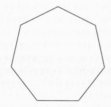
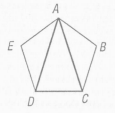
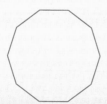
Questions

1. Fill in the missing justifications in the proof in the Example.
   See margin.
2. Consider parallelogram *ABDC*.
   a. Which sides are congruent?
   b. Which angles are congruent?
   c. The midpoints of __?__ and __?__ are the same. $\overline{AD}$, $\overline{BC}$
   a) $\overline{AC} ≅ \overline{BD}$, $\overline{AB} ≅ \overline{CD}$; b) ∠A ≅ ∠D, ∠B ≅ ∠C

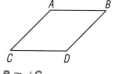

3. Repeat Question 2, but suppose *ABDC* is a rhombus.
   See margin.
4. *ZQID* below is a trapezoid with bases $\overline{ZO}$ and $\overline{ID}$. $\overleftrightarrow{ZO} ⊥ \overline{DR}$. $\overleftrightarrow{ID} ⊥ \overline{PO}$.
   a. Which two segments are congruent? $\overline{RD}$ and $\overline{OP}$
   b. What theorem justifies your answer to part **a**?
   The distance between parallel lines is constant.

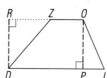

5. A regular polygon with four sides is usually called a(n) __?__. square

6. a. Draw a regular hexagon.
   b. Draw a regular heptagon.
      See margin.

7. Prove: If *ABCDE* is a regular pentagon, then $\overline{AC} ≅ \overline{AD}$.
   See margin.
8. a. In rectangle *RIGH* with diagonals intersecting at *T*, how many triangles are formed? 8
   b. Arrange them in sets of congruent triangles.
      {△IRH, △HGI, △GHR, △RIG}
      {△TRH, △TGI}
      {△THG, △TIR}

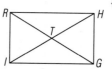

In 9 and 10, *OPQR* at the left is a parallelogram.
9. If *OQ* = *PR* = *x*, find as many lengths in terms of *x* as you can.
   OS = *SQ* = *RS* = *SP* = $\frac{x}{2}$
10. If m∠*POR* = 102, find as many other angle measures as you can.
    m∠*RQP* = 102, m∠*ORQ* = m∠*OPQ* = 78
11. a. Draw a regular decagon. See margin.
    b. What is the sum of the measures of the angles of a regular decagon? 1440°
    c. What is the measure of each angle of a regular decagon? 144°
12. Construct equilateral triangles *AOB, BOC, COD, DOE, EOF*, and *FOA* where points *A, B, C, D, E,* and *F* are distinct, coplanar points.
    a. What kind of figure is *ABCDEF*? regular hexagon
    b. Justify your answer to part **a**. See margin.

336

13. In quadrilateral *ABCF* below, $\overline{AE} \perp \overline{CF}$ and $\overline{BD} \perp \overline{CF}$. Also, *AE = BD* and *AF = BC*. Prove that $\angle F \cong \angle C$. *(Lesson 7-5)*
See margin.

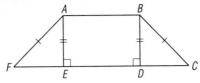

14. In right triangles *ABC* and *XYZ* below, two sides and an angle of one are congruent to two sides and an angle of the other. Why aren't the triangles congruent? *(Lesson 7-5)*
The congruent sides are not corresponding parts.

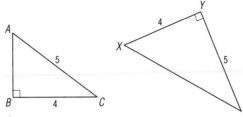

15. Use the figure at the left.
Given: *X* is the midpoint of $\overline{MN}$.
$\angle M \cong \angle N$
$\angle MXZ \cong \angle NXY$.
Prove: $\angle Y \cong \angle Z$. *(Lesson 7-4)* **See margin.**

16. Use the figure below.
Given: $\triangle PTS$ is isosceles with vertex angle *T,* and
m$\angle PTQ$ = m$\angle STR$.
Prove: **a.** $\triangle TPQ \cong \triangle TSR$; **b.** $\triangle TQR$ is isosceles. *(Lesson 7-3)*
See margin.

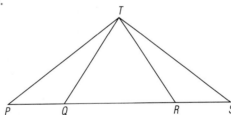

17. a. Draw a triangle with sides of length 2″, 3.5″, and a 90° angle included by them. **See margin.**
b. Will everyone's correct drawing of this triangle be congruent to yours? Explain your answer. *(Lessons 7-2, 7-1)*
Yes, by the SAS Congruence Theorem.

18. Justify the conclusion. *(Lessons 3-5, 3-3)*
Given: $\overline{AB} \perp m$, $\overline{CD} \perp m$.
Conclusion: $\overline{AB} \parallel \overline{CD}$. **Two Perpendiculars Theorem**

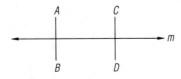

LESSON 7-6   Properties of Special Figures   **337**

12. a. sample:

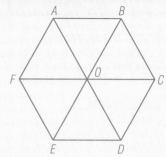

b. All the sides are congruent since they are formed by equilateral triangles with common sides, and all the vertex angles are congruent since each is 120°.

13.

Conclusions	Justifications
1. $\triangle AEF \cong$ $\triangle BDC$	HL Congr. Thm. (given)
2. $\angle F \cong \angle C$	CPCF Thm.

15.

Conclusions	Justifications
1. $\overline{MX} = \overline{NX}$	def. of midpoint (meaning)
2. $\triangle MXZ \cong$ $\triangle NXY$	ASA Congr. Thm. (step 1 and given)
3. $\angle Y \cong \angle Z$	CPCF Thm.

16.a., 17.a. See the margin on p. 338.

EXTENSION
Generalize the idea of the
distance between two lines.
The distance between two
figures is sometimes defined
as the length of the shortest
segment connecting a point
on one figure to a point on
the other. Discuss how to
find the distance between
two circular regions which
have no points in common.
(Draw the segment connecting their centers. Subtract the
lengths of the radii of the circles from the length of this
segment.) Give examples of
the distance between irregular regions. What is the distance between the United
States and the Soviet Union?
(Only a few miles; there are
islands in Alaska that are
very close to islands belong-
ing to the Soviet Union.)

EVALUATION
A quiz covering Lessons 7-4
through 7-6 is provided in the
Teacher's Resource File.

ADDITIONAL ANSWERS
16. a.

Conclusions	Justifications
1. *PT = TS*	def. of isosceles △ (meaning)
2. ∠*P* ≅ ∠*S*	Isosceles △ Thm.
3. △*TPQ* ≅ △*TSR*	ASA Congruence Thm. (steps 1, 2, and given)

b.

4. $\overline{QT} \cong \overline{RT}$	CPCF Thm.
5. △*TQR* is isosceles.	def. of isosceles △ (suff. cond.)

17. a. (Art is reduced in size.)

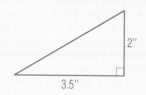

3.5"
2"

19. Below, $\overline{AB} \cong \overline{XY}$ and ∠*A* ≅ ∠*Y*. Name three additional pieces of information each of which is enough to guarantee congruence of the triangles and name the appropriate congruence theorem to justify. *(Lesson 7-2)* ∠*B* ≅ ∠*X* for ASA; $\overline{AC} \cong \overline{YZ}$ for SAS; ∠*C* ≅ ∠*Z* for AAS

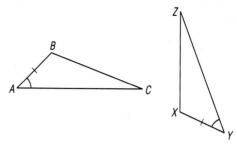

20. Write a true if-then statement whose converse is false. *(Lesson 2-4)*
Sample: If *M* is the midpoint of $\overline{AB}$, then *AM = BM*.

Exploration

21. Regular pentagon *ABCDE* and its diagonals are drawn.
    a. How many triangles are in the drawing? 3 5
    b. Sort the triangles into sets of congruent triangles.

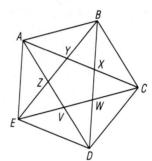

{△*AZY*, △*BXY*, △*CXW*, △*DVW*, △*EVZ*}
{△*AZB*, △*AYE*, △*BYC*, △*BXA*, △*CXD*, △*CWB*, △*DVC*, △*DWE*, △*EZD*, △*EVA*}
{△*AVC*, △*AXD*, △*BWE*, △*BZD*, △*CYE*}
{△*ADC*, △*BEC*, △*ADB*, △*DEB*, △*ECA*}
{△*ADE*, △*ACB*, △*BCD*, △*BEA*, △*CDE*}
{△*AYB*, △*BXC*, △*CWD*, △*DVE*, △*EZA*}

338

LESSON 7-7

Sufficient Conditions for Parallelograms

Pictured above is a rectangular box with its top and bottom removed, so it is no longer rigid. If you are careful not to bend the sides, then the colored edge always seems to be a parallelogram. This can be proved with the help of the triangle congruence theorems.

To determine what is given in this proof, note that the box once was rectangular, so opposite sides are known to be of the same length. But the angles can now change; they no longer must be right angles. Using only the fact that opposite sides have the same length, you can prove that the quadrilateral is a parallelogram. This is done in Example 1.

Example 1 **Prove:** If both pairs of opposite sides of a quadrilateral are congruent, the quadrilateral is a parallelogram.

Draw Use a representative figure and restate the theorem in terms of the figure.

Given: Quadrilateral *ABCD*.
$\overline{AB} \cong \overline{CD}$; $\overline{AD} \cong \overline{BC}$.
Prove: *ABCD* is a parallelogram.

Analyze If a diagonal is drawn, then the triangles formed are congruent. This gives enough to deduce that opposite sides are parallel.

Write

Conclusions	Justifications
1. Draw $\overline{BD}$.	Two points determine a line. (Point-Line Postulate)
2. $\overline{BD} \cong \overline{DB}$	Reflexive Property of $\cong$
3. $\triangle ABD \cong \triangle CDB$	SSS Congruence Theorem (Step 2 and given)
4. $\angle ABD \cong \angle CDB$	CPCF Theorem
5. $\overline{AB} \parallel \overline{CD}$	AIA $= \Rightarrow \parallel$ Lines Theorem
6. $\angle ADB \cong \angle CBD$	___?___
7. $\overline{AD} \parallel \overline{BC}$	___?___
8. *ABCD* is a parallelogram.	definition of parallelogram (sufficient condition)

Question 5 asks you to fill in the missing justifications.

LESSON 7-7 *Sufficient Conditions for Parallelograms* **339**

LESSON 7-7

RESOURCES
■ Lesson Master 7-7
◨ Visual for Teaching Aid 44 can be used with **Example 2**.
◨ Visual for Teaching Aid 45 can be used with **Question 10** and **12**.

OBJECTIVES

E Determine whether conditions are properties of or sufficient conditions for parallelograms.
F Use theorems about triangles and parellelograms to explain real situations.

TEACHING NOTES

There are two important reasons for doing proofs involving sufficient conditions. First, the sufficient conditions for figures are not always obvious. The picture which begins the lesson and **Example 1** are illustrative. Second, there are so many sufficient conditions that most people do not memorize them all; instead they test a possible set of sufficient conditions by drawing a figure and quickly thinking through a proof.

You might want to go through **Example 1** very quickly, indicating what is meant by "thinking through a proof." It means first drawing a figure and marking all the congruent sides or angles given, as done on this page. Then, instead of writing the proof, one just does the deductions, marking more and more congruent angles and sides as they are found. For instance, in **Example 1**, one would see SSS satisfied and therefore mark the angles *ABD* and

339

You should verify the result of Example 1 by trying to draw a plane figure with opposite sides congruent that is not a parallelogram. It can't be done.

Example 1 shows that both pairs of opposite sides being congruent is a *sufficient condition* for a quadrilateral to be a parallelogram. In general, *p* is a **sufficient condition** for *q* means *if p, then q* or *p implies q.* Sufficient conditions for parallelograms are any conditions that imply a figure is a parallelogram.

Pictured below are three quadrilaterals having *one pair of sides both parallel and congruent.* In each, $\overline{WX} \parallel \overline{YZ}$ and $WX = YZ$.

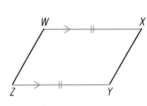 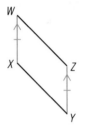 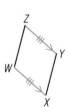

These quadrilaterals appear to be parallelograms. Thus this condition *may* be a sufficient condition. In Example 2, it is proved to be so.

Example 2   **Prove:**   If a quadrilateral has a pair of sides both parallel and congruent, the quadrilateral is a parallelogram.

Draw   Draw a figure and restate the given in terms of the figure.

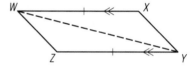

Given: WXYZ is a quadrilateral with $\overline{WX} \parallel \overline{YZ}$ and $WX = YZ$.
Prove: WXYZ is a parallelogram.
Analyze   Again, a diagonal forms triangles that are congruent. The proof is similar to that in Example 1 and you are asked to fill in the justifications in Question 7.

Write

Conclusions	Justifications
1. Draw $\overline{WY}$.	?
2. $WY = WY$	?
3. $m\angle XWY = m\angle ZYW$	?
4. $\triangle WZY \cong \triangle YXW$	?
5. $m\angle ZWY = m\angle XYW$	?
6. $\overline{WZ} \parallel \overline{XY}$	?
7. WXYZ is a parallelogram.	?

340

Examples 1 and 2 have proved parts **(a)** and **(d)** of the following theorem. Parts **(b)** and **(c)** are left for you to do in Questions 10 and 11.

Sufficient Conditions for a Parallelogram Theorem:

If, in a quadrilateral,
- **(a)** both pairs of opposite sides are congruent, or
- **(b)** both pairs of opposite angles are congruent, or
- **(c)** the diagonals bisect each other, or
- **(d)** one pair of sides is parallel and congruent,

then the quadrilateral is a parallelogram.

Notice that all four parts **(a)**–**(d)** are converses of properties of parallelograms. But beware. Not all converses of properties are true. Consider this property of rectangles.

If a quadrilateral is a rectangle, its diagonals are congruent.

The converse of this theorem is

If the diagonals of a quadrilateral are congruent, then it is a rectangle.

To prove this converse is *not* true, a counterexample is all that is needed. Recall that a counterexample to an if-then statement is a situation in which the antecedent is true and the consequent is false. Here are two counterexamples to the above converse.

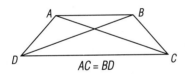 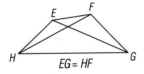

quadrilaterals with congruent diagonals that are not rectangles

---

Questions

Covering the Reading

1. Give three properties of parallelograms. See margin.

2. According to its definition, what is a sufficient condition for a figure to be a parallelogram?
   both pairs of opposite sides are parallel

3. Give four sufficient conditions for parallelograms. See margin.

4. Name a property of a rectangle whose converse is not a sufficient condition for a rectangle.
   If a quadrilateral is a rectangle, its diagonals are congruent.

LESSON 7-7 Sufficient Conditions for Parallelograms **341**

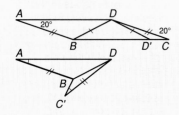
In 5 and 6, consider the proof of Example 1.

5. Write the justifications for Steps 6 and 7.
   Step 6: CPCF Theorem; Step 7: AIA $= \Rightarrow \parallel$ Lines Theorem

6. Suppose auxiliary segment $\overline{AC}$ was drawn instead of $\overline{BD}$. Prove the theorem using $\overline{AC}$ instead of $\overline{BD}$. See margin.

7. Finish the proof of Example 2. See margin.

8. Prove or disprove: If quadrilateral *ABCD* has $\overline{AB} \parallel \overline{CD}$ and $\angle A \cong \angle C$, then *ABCD* is a parallelogram. See margin.

9. Two yardsticks and two meter sticks are joined end to end to form a quadrilateral. What possible quadrilaterals can be formed?
   kite, parallelogram

10. Finish the proof of part (b) of the Sufficient Conditions for a Parallelogram Theorem.

    Part (b): If opposite angles of a quadrilateral are congruent, then the quadrilateral is a parallelogram.
    Given: Quadrilateral *WXYZ*
    $$m\angle W = m\angle Y$$
    $$m\angle WXY = m\angle Z.$$
    Prove: *WXYZ* is a parallelogram.

    Let $m\angle WXY = m\angle Z = a$ and $m\angle Y = m\angle W = b$.
    Now $a + b + a + b = 360$ so $2a + 2b = 360$ or $a + b = 180$. Thus $b = 180 - a$. The rest of the proof is in column format.

Conclusions	Justifications
1. $m\angle W = m\angle Y = 180 - a$	Substitution
2. $m\angle WXV + a = 180$	**a.** __?__ Linear Pair Theorem
3. $m\angle WXV = 180 - a$	Addition Property of Equality
4. $m\angle WXV = m\angle W$	Substitution (Step 1 into 3)
5. $\overline{WZ} \parallel \overline{XY}$	**b.** __?__ AIA $= \Rightarrow \parallel$ Lines Theorem
6. $m\angle WXV = m\angle Y$	Substitution (Step 1 into 3)
7. $\overline{WX} \parallel \overline{ZY}$	**c.** __?__ corr. $\angle$ s $= \Rightarrow \parallel$ lines Postulate
8. *WXYZ* is a parallelogram.	**d.** __?__ Definition of parallelogram (sufficient condition)

11. The quadrilaterals V, W, X, and Y which form the sides of this hatbox are parallelograms. Why must the quadrilateral Z also be a parallelogram?
    See margin.

12. If the diagonals of a quadrilateral bisect each other, then the quadrilateral is a parallelogram.

Given: Quadrilateral *ABCD*.
  O is the midpoint of $\overline{AC}$ and $\overline{BD}$.

Prove: *ABCD* is a parallelogram.

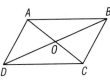

Conclusions

1. $\overline{AO} \cong \overline{OC}; \overline{DO} \cong \overline{OB}$
2. $\angle AOD \cong \angle COB$
3. $\triangle AOD \cong \triangle COB$
4. $\overline{AD} \cong \overline{BC}$
5. $\angle ADO \cong \angle CBO$
6. $\overline{AD} \parallel \overline{BC}$
7. *ABCD* is a parallelogram.

Justifications

a. __?__ def. of midpoint (meaning)
b. __?__ Vertical Angle Theorem
c. __?__ SAS ≅ Thm. (1, 2)
d. __?__ CPCF Theorem
e. __?__ CPCF Theorem
f. __?__ AIA = ⇒ ∥ Lines Theorem
Sufficient Conditions of a
Parallelogram Theorem, part (d)

13. Prove in two steps without drawing a figure: If both pairs of opposite sides of a quadrilateral are congruent, then both pairs of opposite angles are congruent. (Hint: Use logical principles.) See margin.

Review

14. a. What is the sum of the measures of the angles of an octagon?
  b. What is the sum of the measures of the angles of a regular octagon?
  c. What is the measure of each interior angle of a regular octagon? *(Lessons 7-6, 5-7)*
    a) 1080°; b) 1080°; c) 135°

15. Prove that the diagonals of a rectangle are congruent.
  (Lesson 7-6) See margin.

16. State the HL Congruence Theorem. *(Lesson 7-5)* See margin.

In 17–19, **a.** draw the triangle. **b.** Will everyone else's correct drawings be congruent to yours? **c.** Explain why or why not. *(Lessons 7-2, 7-1)*

17. triangle *ABC* where *AB* = 5 cm, *BC* = 7 cm, and m∠*B* = 110

18. triangle *DEF* where *DE* = 2″, m∠*E* = 90, and m∠*F* = 60

19. triangle *GHI* where m∠*G* = 60, m∠*H* = 35, and m∠*I* = 85

  See margin for 17–19.

Exploration

20. Given: Quadrilateral *ABCD* with *AB* = *CD* and ∠*A* ≅ ∠*C*. Is *ABCD* a parallelogram or not? Prove it or produce a counterexample.

Sample counterexample:

A ———————————————————— D
      H   H
                B
                 C

FOLLOW-UP

MORE PRACTICE
For more questions on SPUR Objectives, use *Lesson Master 7-7*, shown below.

7. Justifications
1. **Point-Line-Plane Postulate**
2. **Reflexive Prop. of Eq.**
3. **∥ Lines ⇒ AIA = Thm.**
4. **SAS Congruence Thm. (steps 2, 3, and given)**
5. **CPCF Thm.**
6. **AIA = ⇒ ∥ Lines Thm.**
7. **def. of parallelogram (suff. cond.)**

8., 11., 13., 15.-19. See **Additional Answers in the back of this book.**

NAME _____

LESSON **MASTER 7-7**
QUESTIONS ON **SPUR** OBJECTIVES

■**PROPERTIES** *Objective E (See pages 350–353 for objectives.)*

1. Give four sufficient conditions for parallelograms.
  Any four of the following:
  1) Both pairs of opp. sides are parallel.
  2) Both pairs of opp. sides are congruent.
  3) Both pairs of opp. angles are congruent.
  4) The diagonals bisect each other.
  5) One pr. of sides is parallel and congruent.

2. Fill in justifications in the following proof of this statement:
  If the diagonals of a parallelogram are perpendicular, then the parallelogram is a rhombus.

Given: *OPQR* is a parallelogram.
  $\overline{OQ} \perp \overline{PR}$.
Prove: *OPQR* is a rhombus.

Conclusions

a. *PQ* = *OR*, *QR* = *OP*
b. *PT* = *TR*
c. ∠*PTQ* ≅ ∠*QTR*
d. *QT* = *QT*
e. △*PQT* ≅ △*RQT*
f. *PQ* = *QR*
g. *PQ* = *QR* = *OR* = *OP*
h. *OPQR* is a rhombus.

Justifications

Prop. of a Parallelogram Thm.
Prop. of a Parallelogram Thm.
def. of ⊥ (meaning)
Reflex. Prop. of Eq.
SAS Congr. Thm. (steps b, c, and d)
CPCF Thm.
Trans. Prop. of Eq.
def. of rhombus (suff. cond.)

■**USES** *Objective F*

3. A piece of land is shaped like a quadrilateral. Two of its sides face parallel streets. What would be a fast way to determine if the property is parallelogram-shaped?
  Measure the sides to see if they are of equal length.

 Geometry © Scott, Foresman and Company

RESOURCES
■ Lesson Master 7-8
◗ Visual for Teaching Aid 46 can be used when discussing the SAS Inequality Theorem.
▣ Computer Master 15

OBJECTIVE

F Use theorems about triangles and parallelograms to explain real situations.

TEACHING NOTES

Students have liked the cat example quite a bit, and it is most instructive.

The proof of the SAS Inequality Theorem is very different from previous proofs. Students have become accustomed to looking for "sameness." Because of that, the method of proof often seems obvious. A clue here is to recall any previous experience with inequalities in triangles, but there is only the Triangle Inequality. So we try to create a triangle with one side equal in length to *AC* and the other two sides adding in length to *XZ*.

You may want to point out the equivalent form of the SAS Inequality Theorem, namely that if the measure of the included angle of the first triangle is greater than the measure of the included angle of the second triangle, then the third side of the first triangle must be greater than the third side of the second triangle.

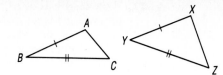

LESSON

7-8

The SAS Inequality

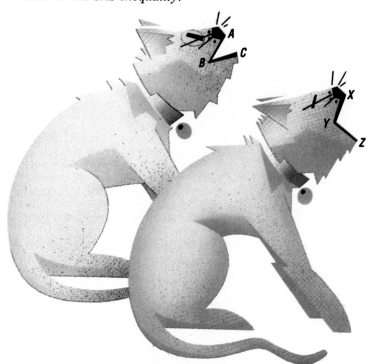

The SAS Congruence Theorem states that when two sides and the included angle of a triangle are congruent to corresponding parts of a second triangle, the triangles will be congruent. But what happens if the included angles are not congruent?

Percy, a sleepy Persian cat, is having a big yawn as shown below. As he starts his yawn, his mouth is not opened wide, but in the second picture his mouth is opened very wide. A geometric view of this everyday occurrence is as follows. The top and bottom of his jaw are the same in both pictures; thus $AB = XY$ and $BC = YZ$. But since m$\angle XYZ$ is greater than m$\angle ABC$, $XZ > AC$. This result generalizes as the *SAS Inequality*.

SAS Inequality Theorem:

If two sides of a triangle are congruent to two sides of a second triangle, and the measure of the included angle of the first triangle is less than the measure of the included angle of the second, then the third side of the first triangle is shorter than the third side of the second.

344

Proof

A figure is drawn. Below it is stated the given and what is to prove in terms of the figure.

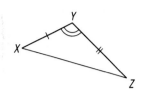
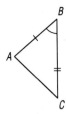

Given: $AB = XY$, $BC = YZ$, and $m\angle B < m\angle Y$.
Prove: $AC < XZ$.

The method to use is not obvious. Since $AB = XY$, there is an isometry T with $T(\overline{AB}) = \overline{XY}$. $\triangle A'B'C'$ (in blue) is $T(\triangle ABC)$. T is chosen so that C', the image of C, is on the same side of $\overline{XY}$ as Z. The result is shown below. Note that $\triangle C'YZ$ (not drawn) is isosceles since $C'Y = ZY$.

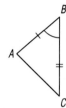
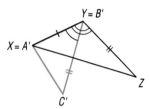

Since $m\angle A'B'C' < m\angle XYZ$, $\overrightarrow{YC}$ lies in the interior of $\angle XYZ$. Below, the symmetry line m of isosceles $\triangle C'YZ$ is drawn, intersecting $\overline{XZ}$ at Q. m is the $\perp$ bisector of $\overline{C'Z}$, so Q is equidistant from C' and Z, making $QC' = QZ$.

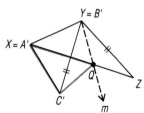

Now focus on $\triangle A'C'Q$ (in orange). From the Triangle Inequality,
$$A'C' < A'Q + QC'.$$
But $A'C' = AC$, $A'Q$ is XQ, and $QC' = QZ$. Substituting,
$$AC < XQ + QZ.$$
$XQ + QZ = XZ$ by the Betweenness Theorem.
So $\qquad\qquad\qquad\qquad AC < XZ \qquad$ by substitution.

Alternate Approach
Students can investigate and verify the SAS Inequality Theorem by using straws or sticks for sides and their measuring tools. Some students may be interested in demonstrating their findings to the class.

Making Connections
Students have already seen the Triangle Inequality. In Lesson 13-7, still other inequalities in triangles will be discussed. Students will learn that larger sides are opposite larger angles, and conversely.

ADDITIONAL EXAMPLE
Is there an ASA Inequality Theorem? That is, if two angles of a triangle are congruent to two angles of a second triangle, and the length of the included side of the first triangle is less than the length of the included side of the second triangle, then must the measure of the third angle of the first triangle be smaller than the measure of the third angle of the second triangle?

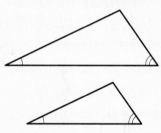

No; the third angles of the triangles have the same measure; a theorem studied in Lesson 7-1.

NOTES ON QUESTIONS
Question 2: If you can bring a tension spring used for muscle toning to class, you can invite those willing to participate to see how long they can stretch it with their arms fully extended. Of course, the greater the angle between their arms, the greater the length of the spring.

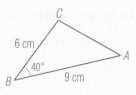
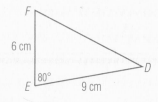
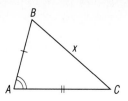

You now know many things about triangles and SAS. From the lengths AB and AC of two sides of a triangle, you can compute a range of possible lengths for the third side $\overline{BC}$ using the Triangle Inequality. The larger m$\angle A$ is, the larger BC is. If you know m$\angle A$, the length of the third side is determined. This length can be found using trigonometry, a branch of mathematics that we introduce later in this course.

Questions

Covering the Reading

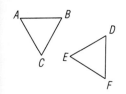

1. If $AB = DF$, $AC = DE$, and m$\angle A >$ m$\angle D$ in the figure at the left, then BC is (greater than, less than, equal to) EF. **greater than**

2. State an application of the SAS Inequality Theorem.
   See margin.

3. *Multiple choice.* Which of the following is *not* used in the proof of the SAS Inequality?
   (a) Betweenness Theorem
   (b) Isosceles Triangle Symmetry Theorem
   (c) Isosceles Triangle Theorem **(c)**

4. The Triangle Inequality is applied to which triangle in the proof of the SAS Inequality Theorem? $\triangle A'C'Q$

5. Suppose in $\triangle ABC$ that $AB = 6''$, $BC = 3''$, and m$\angle B = 62$.
   a. Is AC uniquely determined? **Yes**
   b. What branch of mathematics studies the calculation of AC from this given information? **trigonometry**

Applying the Mathematics

6. **a.** Draw $\triangle ABC$ with $AB = 9$ cm, $BC = 6$ cm, and m$\angle B = 40$.
   b. Draw $\triangle DEF$ with $DE = 9$ cm, $EF = 6$ cm, and m$\angle E = 80$.
   c. Measure AC and DF. $AC \approx 5.9$ cm; $DF \approx 9.9$ cm
   d. Which is longer? DF
   e. Why? **because of the SAS Inequality Theorem**
       See margin.

7. Use the figure at the right as marked. Explain why $RS > QR$.
   See margin.

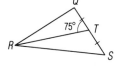

In 8 and 9, suppose Percy the cat's jaws $\overline{BA}$ and $\overline{BC}$ are the same length, 5 cm.

8. What are the largest and smallest possible lengths for $\overline{AC}$, the opening of his mouth? **0 cm and 10 cm**

9. What will be the length of $\overline{AC}$ when m$\angle ABC = 60$? **5 cm**

10. What theorem explains the fact that as a lunchbox is opened, the distance between the front of the top and the handle increases?
    SAS Inequality Theorem

346

11. Prove or produce a counterexample: If one angle of a quadrilateral is bisected by a diagonal and the angles not cut by the diagonal are congruent, then the quadrilateral is a kite. *(Lesson 7-7)* See margin.

12. Use the figure at the right.
Given: $QT = RS$
$TS = QR$.
Prove: **a.** $\triangle QTS \cong \triangle SRQ$
b. $\overline{QT} \parallel \overline{RS}$ *(Lesson 7-6)*
See margin.

In 13 and 14, tell whether the triangles as marked are congruent. If so, what triangle congruence theorem justifies the congruence? *(Lesson 7-2)*

13.

14.

not congruent   Yes; ASA Congruence Theorem

15. a. Draw a triangle with sides of length 3, 7, and 8 cm.
b. Draw a triangle with sides of length 3, 5, and 7 cm.
c. Measure the angles of these triangles to verify that two of the angles are congruent and two are supplementary. *(Lesson 7-1)*
See margin.

In 16 and 17, $\triangle GHI$ has been reflected over line ℓ, and then its image has been reflected over line m.

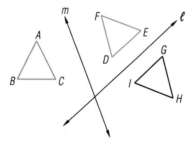

16. $\triangle GHI \cong \underline{\ ?\ } \cong \underline{\ ?\ }$ *(Lesson 6-5)* $\triangle EFD$, $\triangle BAC$

17. $\triangle BAC$ is a (reflection, rotation, translation) image of $\triangle GHI$. *(Lesson 6-3)* rotation

18. One side of a triangle is double the length of a second side. The third side is triple the length of the second side. Explain why this is impossible. *(Lesson 1-9)*
The length of the third side would be equal to the sum of the lengths of the other two sides, which violates the Triangle Inequality Postulate.

19. The SAS Inequality Theorem is sometimes called the Hinge Theorem. Explain the reasoning behind this nickname. A hinge is formed by two sides. When the included angle is greater, so is the distance between the ends of the hinge.

LESSON 7-8 The SAS Inequality **347**

FOLLOW-UP

MORE PRACTICE
For more questions on SPUR Objectives, use *Lesson Master 7-8,* shown below.

EXTENSION
What might be an SSS Inequality? Have students explore. One possibility is: If in $\triangle ABC$ and $\triangle DEF$, $\overline{AB} \cong \overline{DE}$, $\overline{BC} \cong \overline{EF}$, and $AC > DF$, then $m\angle B > m\angle E$.

EVALUATION
Alternative Assessment
Have students summarize all the properties they know so far about inequalities in one triangle or two triangles. Include a discussion of exterior angles and the Triangle Inequality.

7. $QT = TS$ and $RT = RT$, but $m\angle QTR = 75$ while $m\angle STR = 105$. So, applying the SAS Inequality Theorem in $\triangle QTR$ and $\triangle STR$, $RS > QR$.

11., 12a., 15. See Additional Answers in the back of this book.

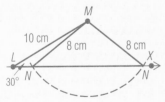
Summary

In this and previous chapters, you have learned many ways of deducing that segments are congruent. Segments are congruent in situations involving regular polygons, midpoints, radii of the same circle, isosceles triangles, and kites, because of the definitions of these terms. And segments are also congruent when they are corresponding parts of congruent figures.

You have also learned many ways of deducing that angles are congruent. Angles are congruent when there are angle bisectors, isosceles trapezoids, or regular polygons, because of the definitions of those terms. When parallel lines are cut by transversals, corresponding angles and alternate interior angles are congruent. Two intersecting lines form congruent vertical angles, and base angles of isosceles triangles are congruent. Angles are congruent also when they are corresponding parts of congruent figures.

Using properties of isometries, we deduced five conditions that force triangles to be congruent. Four sets of conditions always work: SSS, SAS, ASA, and AAS. A fifth condition we call SsA works when the pair of congruent sides opposite the congruent angles is known to be longer than the other pair. A special case of SsA for right triangles is called HL.

From congruent segments and angles, you can get congruent triangles. Congruent triangles enable many properties of figures to be deduced. Some properties of parallelograms, isosceles trapezoids, rectangles, and regular polygons were deduced, as were some sufficient conditions for parallelograms.

Vocabulary

Below are the most important terms and phrases for this chapter.
For the starred(*) terms you should be able to give a definition of the term.
For the other terms you should be able to give a general description and a specific example of each.
You should be able to state any theorem in if-then form and draw a picture.

Lesson 7-2
SSS Congruence Theorem
included angle
SAS Congruence Theorem
included side; non-included side
ASA Congruence Theorem
AAS Congruence Theorem

Lesson 7-3
converse of the Isosceles
    Triangle Theorem

Lesson 7-4
overlapping triangles

Lesson 7-5
legs, hypotenuse of a right
    triangle
concentric circles
HL Congruence Theorem
SsA Congruence Theorem

Lesson 7-6
Properties of a Parallelogram
    Theorem
* regular polygon

Lesson 7-7
sufficient condition
Sufficient Conditions for a
    Parallelogram Theorem

Lesson 7-8
SAS Inequality Theorem

348

Progress Self-Test

See margin for answers not shown below.

Directions: Take this test as you would take a test in class. You will need a ruler, compass, and protractor. Then check your work with the solutions in the Selected Answers section in the back of the book.

1. Use the figure below. $\angle 1 \cong \angle 3$ and $\angle 2 \cong \angle 4$.
   a. Name the congruent triangles with vertices in correct order. $\triangle ABC \cong \triangle CDA$
   b. What theorem guarantees that the triangles are congruent? ASA Congruence Theorem

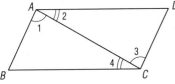

2. $\overleftrightarrow{AC}$ and $\overleftrightarrow{BD}$ below intersect at M. M is the midpoint of $\overline{AC}$ and $\overleftrightarrow{AB} \parallel \overleftrightarrow{CD}$. Justify each conclusion.
   a. $\overline{AM} \cong \overline{MC}$
   b. $\angle AMB \cong \angle CMD$
   c. $\angle MBA \cong \angle MDC$
   d. $\triangle MBA \cong \triangle MDC$

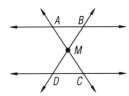

3. a. Draw a triangle LMN with $LM = 10$ cm, $MN = 8$ cm, and m$\angle L = 30$.
   b. Will everyone else's correct drawing be congruent to yours? not necessarily
   c. Explain why or why not.

4. a. Draw a triangle ABC with $AB = 2.5''$, $BC = 4.5''$ and $AC = 3.5''$.
   b. Will everyone else's correct drawing be congruent to yours? Yes
   c. Explain why or why not.

5. State three sufficient conditions for a quadrilateral to be a parallelogram.

6. State the SAS Inequality Theorem in your own words.

7. Use the figure below.
   Given: $PS = PT$
   Angles S and T are right angles.
   Prove: a. $QS = QT$
   b. $\overrightarrow{QP}$ is the angle bisector of $\angle SQT$.

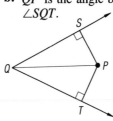

8. Walt bought Kelly a pogo stick for her birthday. The handle $\overline{AB}$ is parallel to and congruent to the foothold $\overline{CD}$. Prove that $ABDC$ is a parallelogram.

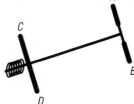

9. Given: $ABCDEFGHIJ$ is a regular decagon.
   Prove: $AC = FH$.

10. Use the figure at the right.
    Given: $WX = WY$;
    $\angle WUY \cong \angle WVX$.
    Prove: $\triangle WUV$ is isosceles.

11. $\overline{AB}$ and $\overline{AC}$ are ropes that attach a tarpaulin over a picnic table. $\overline{AD}$ is perpendicular to the ground, which is level. If B and C are each the same distance from D, explain why the ropes have the same length.

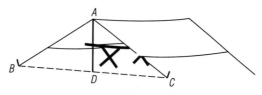

Whereas end-of-chapter materials may be considered optional in some texts, they should not be considered optional in UCSMP *Geometry*. The Progress Self-Test provides the opportunity for feedback and correction; the Chapter Review provides additional opportunities for practice. It is at this point that the material "gels" for many students, allowing them to solidify skills and concepts before a test. In general, student performance is markedly improved after these pages.

USING THE PROGRESS SELF-TEST
Assign the Progress Self-Test as a one-night assignment. Worked-out solutions for all questions are in the Selected Answers section of the student text. Encourage students to take the Progress Self-Test honestly, grade themselves, and then be prepared to discuss the test in class.

Advise students to pay special attention to those Chapter Review questions (pages 350-353) which correspond to questions missed on the Progress Self-Test. A chart provided with the Selected Answers keys the Progress Self-Test questions to the lettered SPUR Objectives in the Chapter Review or to the Vocabulary. It also keys the questions to the corresponding lessons where the material is covered.

4. a. (Art is reduced in size.)

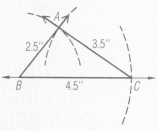

4.c.-11. See Additional Answers in the back of this book.

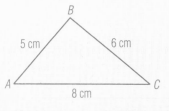
Chapter Review

Questions on **SPUR** Objectives

See margin for answers not shown below.

SPUR stands for **S**kills, **P**roperties, **U**ses, and **R**epresentations. The Chapter Review questions are grouped according to the SPUR Objectives for this chapter.

SKILLS deal with the procedures used to get answers.

■ **Objective A:** *Draw triangles satisfying given conditions and determine whether all such triangles are congruent. (Lessons 7-1, 7-2, 7-5)*

In 1–9, **a.** draw the triangle. **b.** Will everyone else's correct drawings be congruent to yours? **c.** Explain why or why not.

1. triangle *ABC* in which *AB* = 5 cm, *BC* = 6 cm, and *AC* = 8 cm

2. triangle *DEF* in which *DE* = 3″, *EF* = 2″, and *DF* = 2.5″

3. triangle *GHI* in which *GH* = 6 cm, m∠*G* = 60, and m∠*H* = 70

4. triangle *JKL* in which *JK* = 2.75″, m∠*K* = 40, and m∠*L* = 100

5. right triangle *MNO* with hypotenuse *MN* = 7.5 cm and leg *MO* = 4.5 cm

6. a right triangle with legs having lengths 1″ and 1.25″

7. triangle *STU* with m∠*S* = 30, *ST* = 6 cm, and *TU* = 4 cm

8. triangle *VWX* with *VW* = 4″, m∠*W* = 55, and *WX* = 2″

9. triangle *YZA* with m∠*Y* = 60, *YZ* = 2 cm, and *ZA* = 5 cm

PROPERTIES deal with the principles behind the mathematics.

■ **Objective B:** *Determine whether figures are congruent from information given in drawings.* (Lesson 7-2)

10. **a.** The triangles at the right are congruent by what theorem?
    b. $\overline{AB} \cong$? *FD*
    c. ∠*A* ≅ ? ∠*F*
    d. ∠*B* ≅ ? ∠*D*
    a) SAS Congruence

11. Refer to the figure below.
    a. Which triangle congruence theorem guarantees that the two triangles are congruent?
    b. Name the congruent triangles with vertices in correct order.

In 12–15, **a.** explain why the given triangles are congruent and **b.** indicate corresponding vertices.

12.

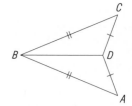

a) SSS Congruence Theorem;
b) △*BDA* ≅ △*BDC*

13.

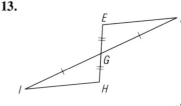

a) SAS Congruence Theorem;
b) △*GFE* ≅ △*GIH*

14.

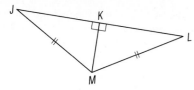

a) HL Congruence Theorem; b) △KLM ≅ △KJM

15.

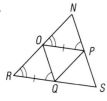

a) ASA Congruence Theorem; b) △NOP ≅ △ORQ

■ **Objective C:** *Write proofs that triangles are congruent. (Lessons 7-3, 7-4, 7-5)*

16. Fill in the blanks to complete this proof.
Given: ∠DAC ≅ ∠BAC
∠DCA ≅ ∠BCA.
Prove: △ADC ≅ △ABC.

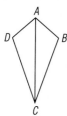

Conclusions		Justifications
1. $\overline{AC} \cong \overline{AC}$	**a.**	?
2. △ADC ≅ △ABC	**b.**	?

17. Use the figure of Question 16.
Given: $\overline{AD} \perp \overline{DC}$, $\overline{AB} \perp \overline{BC}$,
AD = AB.
Prove: △ADC ≅ △ABC.

18. Circles P and Q intersect
at A and B.
Prove: △APQ ≅ △BPQ.

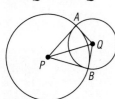

19. Refer to the figure below.
Given: $\overrightarrow{UW}$ bisects ∠YUV.
$\overline{UW} \cong \overline{UY}$; ∠V ≅ ∠UXY.
Prove: △UVW ≅ △UXY.

20. Refer to the figure below.
Given: $\overline{AB} \cong \overline{DC}$; ∠ABC ≅ ∠DCB.
Prove: △ACB ≅ △DBC.

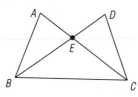

■ **Objective D:** *Apply the triangle congruence and CPCF theorems to prove that segments or angles are congruent. (Lessons 7-3, 7-4, 7-5, 7-6)*

21. Refer to the figure below. Fill in the blanks to complete this proof.
Given: $\overline{AB} \cong \overline{AC}$
$\overline{BD} \cong \overline{DC}$.
Prove: ∠BAD ≅ ∠CAD.

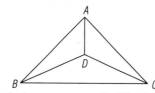

Conclusions		Justifications
1. $\overline{AD} \cong \overline{AD}$	**a.**	?
2. △ABD ≅ △ACD	**b.**	?
3. ∠BAD ≅ ∠CAD	**c.**	?

22. Refer to the figure at the right.
Given: ABCDEFGH
is a regular
octagon.
Prove: $\overline{AC} \cong \overline{BD}$.

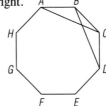

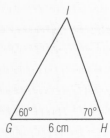
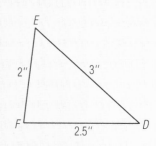
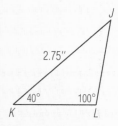

Conclusions	Justifications
1. ∠KJM ≅ ∠KJL	def. of angle bis. (meaning)
2. JK ≅ JK	Reflexive Prop. of Congruence
3. ΔKJM ≅ ΔKJL	SAS Congruence Thm. (steps 1, 2, and given)
4. ∠M ≅ ∠L	CPCF Thm.

24.

Conclusions	Justifications
1. NE ≅ NO	def. of midpoint (meaning)
2. ∠NUO ≅ ∠NAE; ∠NOU ≅ ∠NEA	∥ Lines ⇒ AIA ≅ Thm.
3. ΔNUO ≅ ΔNAE	AAS Congruence Thm. (steps 1 and 2)
4. AE ≅ UO	CPCF Thm.

25.

Conclusions	Justifications
1. BC ≅ BC	Reflexive Prop. of Congruence
2. ΔABC ≅ ΔDCB	AAS Congruence Thm. (step 1 and given)
3. AC ≅ DB	CPCF Thm.

31.

Conclusions	Justifications
1. BD = BD	Reflexive Prop. of Eq.
2. m∠ABD = m∠CDB	∥ Lines ⇒ AIA ≅ Thm.
3. ΔABD ≅ ΔCDB	AAS Congruence Thm. (steps 1, 2, and given)
4. AB = DC	CPCF Thm.
5. ABCD is a parallelogram.	Suff. Cond. for a Parallelogram Thm.

---

23. Refer to the figure below.

Given: $\overleftrightarrow{JK}$ bisects ∠MJL.
$\overline{MJ} \cong \overline{LJ}$

Prove: ∠M ≅ ∠L.

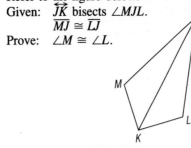

24. Refer to the figure below.

Given: N is the midpoint of $\overline{OE}$.
$\ell \parallel m$.

Prove: $\overline{AE} \cong \overline{UO}$.

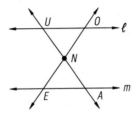

25. Refer to the figure below.

Given: ∠ABC ≅ ∠DCB
∠A ≅ ∠D.

Prove: $\overline{AC} \cong \overline{DB}$.

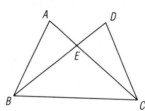

USES deal with applications of mathematics in real situations.

■ **Objective F:** *Use theorems about triangles and parallelograms to explain real situations.*
(Lessons 7-2, 7-7, 7-8)

32. $\overline{RA}$ and $\overline{AB}$ are beams of the same length at the end of a roof. $\overline{AP}$ is perpendicular to $\overline{RB}$. Explain why $\overline{RP}$ and $\overline{PB}$ have the same length.
ΔARP ≅ ΔABP by the HL Congruence Theorem. So, by the CPCF Theorem, RP = PB.

■ **Objective E:** *Determine whether conditions are properties of or sufficient conditions for parallelograms.* *(Lessons 7-6, 7-7)*

In 26–30, complete each statement with the most specific correct answer.

26. The diagonals of a parallelogram __?__ . intersect at their midpoints

27. Opposite angles of a parallelogram are __?__ . congruent

28. If all pairs of consecutive angles in a trapezoid are supplementary, then the trapezoid is a(n) __?__ . parallelogram

29. A quadrilateral is a parallelogram if its diagonals __?__ . bisect each other

30. A quadrilateral is a parallelogram if one pair of opposite sides is both __?__ and __?__ . parallel, congruent

31. Complete the proof of this statement: If one pair of opposite angles of a trapezoid is congruent, then the trapezoid is a parallelogram.

Given: *ABCD* below is a trapezoid with bases $\overline{AB}$ and $\overline{DC}$.
∠A ≅ ∠C.

Prove: *ABCD* is a parallelogram.

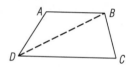

33. A radio tower is supported by guy wires that hit the level ground at points *A, C,* and *D*. Explain why, if the angles at *A, C,* and *D* have the same measure, then these points are the same distance from *B*, the bottom of the tower. (Assume the tower is perpendicular to the ground.)

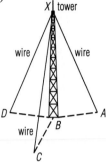

34. Tony and Maria each made pieces of triangular jewelry with sides 21 mm, 18 mm, and 26 mm. Explain why the pieces must have the same shape.

35. What theorem explains this fact: the more you open a door, the wider the opening is.

SAS Inequality Theorem

36. A scout used the following process to estimate the width of a river. Standing directly across from the tree at point *P*, the scout walked 10 paces to *X*, placed a stick at *X*, then continued on $\overrightarrow{PX}$ 10 paces to *Q*. The scout then turned 90° and walked until point *R*, where the scout, stick, and tree were lined up.
   a. Which line segments have lengths equal to the width of the river? $\overline{QR}$ and $\overline{ZP}$
   b. Why does this method work?

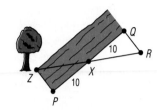

37. The sides of a corral *ABCD* are measured. *AB* is found to be 123′ 4″ long, *BC* = 73′ 6″, *CD* = 124′ 1″, and *AD* = 73′ 11″. Then *ABCD* is approximately in the shape of a(n) __?__. **parallelogram**

38. See the figure below. You have two equally long diagonal supports, $\overline{MN}$ and $\overline{PQ}$, for a bed. How should they be attached so that you can be certain *MPNQ* is a parallelogram?

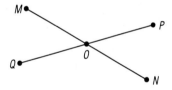

Let *O* be the midpoint of both $\overline{PQ}$ and $\overline{MN}$.

REPRESENTATIONS deal with pictures, graphs, or objects that illustrate concepts.

There are no objectives for Representations in this chapter.

CHAPTER 8 ■ MEASUREMENT FORMULAS

DAILY PACING CHART ■ CHAPTER 8

Every chapter of UCSMP *Geometry* includes lessons, a Progress Self-Test, and a Chapter Review. For optimal student performance, the self-test and review should be covered. (See *General Teaching Suggestions: Mastery* on page T36 of the Teacher's Edition.) By following the pace of the Full Course given here, students can complete the entire text by the end of the year. Students following the pace of the Minimal Course spend more time when there are quizzes and on the Chapter Review and will generally not complete all of the chapters in this text.

When all lessons are covered from the beginning (the recommendation of the authors), then students in the Minimal Course can cover through Lesson 13-4 and will cover all they need for future courses. For more information on pacing, see *General Teaching Suggestions: Pace* on page T35 of the Teacher's Edition.

DAY	MINIMAL COURSE	FULL COURSE
1	8-1	8-1
2	8-2	8-2
3	8-3	8-3
4	Quiz (TRF); Start 8-4.	Quiz (TRF); 8-4
5	Finish 8-4.	8-5
6	8-5	8-6
7	8-6	Quiz (TRF); 8-7
8	Quiz (TRF); Start 8-7.	8-8
9	Finish 8-7.	8-9
10	8-8	Progress Self-Test
11	8-9	Chapter Review
12	Progress Self-Test	Chapter Test (TRF)
13	Chapter Review	
14	Chapter Review	
15	Chapter Test (TRF)	

TESTING OPTIONS

■ Quiz for Lessons 8-1 Through 8-3   ■ Chapter 8 Test, Form A   ■ Chapter 8 Test, Cumulative Form
■ Quiz for Lessons 8-4 Through 8-6   ■ Chapter 8 Test, Form B

PROVIDING FOR INDIVIDUAL DIFFERENCES

The student text has been written for, and tested with, average students. It also has been used successfully with better and more poorly prepared students.

The Lesson Notes often include Error Analysis and Alternate Approach features to help you with those students who need more help. A blackline Lesson Master (in the Teacher's Resource File), keyed to the chapter objectives, is provided for each lesson to allow more practice. (However, since it is very important to keep up with the daily pace, you are not expected to use all of these masters. Again, refer to the suggestions for pacing on page T35.) Extension activities are provided in the Lesson Notes for those students who have completed the particular lesson in a shorter amount of time than is expected, even in the Full Course.

OBJECTIVES ■ CHAPTER 8

The objectives listed here are the same as in the Chapter 8 Review on pages 410-413 of the student text. The Progress Self-Test on pages 408-409 and the tests in the Teacher's Resource File cover these objectives. For recommendations regarding the handling of this end-of-chapter material, see the notes in the margin on the corresponding pages of the Teacher's Edition.

OBJECTIVES FOR CHAPTER 8 (Organized into the SPUR Categories—Skills, Properties, Uses, and Representations)	Progress Self-Test Questions	Chapter Review Questions	Lesson Master from Teacher's Resource File*
SKILLS			
A Draw a tessellation using a given figure as a fundamental region.	1	1 through 3	8-2
B Describe or apply a method for determining the area of an irregular-shaped region.	13	4 through 6	8-4
C Calculate perimeters of parallelograms, kites, and equilateral polygons from lengths of sides, and vice versa.	3	7 through 14	8-1
D Calculate areas of squares, rectangles, parallelograms, trapezoids, and triangles from relevant lengths.	4-6	15 through 20	8-3, 8-5, 8-6
E Given areas of figures, determine relevant lengths.	2	21 through 24	8-3, 8-5, 8-6
F Calculate lengths and measures of arcs, the circumference, and the area of a circle from relevant lengths, and vice versa.	9, 11, 12	25 through 30	8-8, 8-9
G Apply the Pythagorean Theorem to calculate lengths of sides in right triangles and other figures.	7	31 through 35	8-7
H Apply the Pythagorean Converse.	19	36 through 39	8-7
PROPERTIES			
I Tell how to derive formulas for area.	18	40 through 46	8-3, 8-5, 8-6, 8-9
USES			
J Apply perimeter formulas for parallelograms, kites, and regular polygons to real situations.	8	47 through 50	8-1, 8-7
K Apply the Pythagorean Theorem in real situations.	14	51 through 52	8-7
L Apply formulas for areas of squares, rectangles, parallelograms, trapezoids, and triangles to real situations.	16, 17	53 through 57	8-3, 8-5, 8-6
M Apply formulas for the area and circumference of a circle to real situations.	10, 15	58 through 62	8-8, 8-9
REPRESENTATIONS			
N Determine the areas of polygons on a coordinate plane.	20, 21	63 through 66	8-3, 8-5, 8-6

*The masters are numbered to match the lessons.

OVERVIEW ■ CHAPTER 8

The measurement formulas discussed in this chapter involve length, angle measure, and area. The content covers some of the most famous and familiar theorems in all of geometry, the familiar formulas for area and perimeter, and the Pythagorean Theorem.

Much of the content of this chapter may have been studied by students in previous years. In fact, most students coming into geometry are familiar with the formulas for area and perimeter of a rectangle and with the Pythagorean Theorem. It is unlikely, however, that they have seen any logical development of these ideas.

Familiarity with the area and perimeter formulas often causes problems for students when they are expected to follow proofs of these formulas. Proof may seem unnecessary because they learned these results earlier, but the use of formulas for one shape to justify formulas for another shape should put proof into perspective.

One purpose of this chapter is for students to become more competent with all sorts of problems involving measure relationships. Another purpose is for students to see how the different formulas are related and how they follow from each other and from relationships among figures.

The chapter begins with the concept of perimeter, then moves on to area by discussing tessellations in general, and then tessellations of squares in particular. Lessons 8-1 through 8-4 should be viewed as concept-building lessons. Lessons 8-5 and 8-6 develop area formulas by beginning with the area of a rectangle. Lesson 8-7 develops the Pythagorean Theorem by using what is known about the area of a square. The last two lessons, Lessons 8-8 and 8-9, cover the circumference and area of a circle.

Students will need calculators for each lesson in the chapter.

PERSPECTIVES ■ CHAPTER 8

The Perspectives provide the rationale for the inclusion of topics or approaches, provide mathematical background, and make connections with other lessons and within UCSMP.

8-1

PERIMETER FORMULAS

This lesson has many goals, one of which is to review the familiar formula for the perimeter of a rectangle. Students learn that the formula $p = 2(l + w)$ is a special case of the formula $p = 2(a + b)$, which holds for any quadrilateral with two distinct pairs of equal sides.

A second goal is to have students become more intuitive about perimeter in order that they understand how area and perimeter are different. One way this is done is by showing that different figures can have the same perimeter. Another way is through examples, such as the museum situation that opens the chapter.

Other goals are to make use of algebra in solving certain problems and to review units of length.

8-2

TILING THE PLANE

Tiling is to finding area (how much space is inside a figure) as counting is to determining "how many." There are shortcut formulas for finding counts and areas, but they are based upon the fundamental idea of breaking up a quantity into its units.

The mathematics of tiling patterns ranges from drawing such patterns to analyzing them using group theory. Applications range from putting down square tiles on a bathroom floor to classifying crystals in chemistry.

There are four goals in this lesson. The first goal is for students to recognize and draw tessellations; the second is to have students learn that tessellations occur in many places in mathematics and

the real world; the third is to relate this work to congruence and transformations; and the fourth is to give students an example of some "new" mathematics.

8-3

FUNDAMENTAL PROPERTIES OF AREA

The special tessellation of squares customarily is used to measure area. This lesson introduces the properties of area that are applied in the remainder of the chapter to determine or estimate areas for any plane regions and to deduce area formulas for the common plane figures. It also asks students to find areas of unions of rectangles on a coordinate grid.

8-4

AREAS OF IRREGULAR REGIONS

One aspect of mathematics is its use of simple ideas to develop powerful techniques. This lesson may be simple in that it uses only counting, but its idea is basic to all considerations of area and is fundamental in calculus.

The vast majority of students' experiences with areas will have been with polygons and circles. In real life, many figures have these shapes, but many do not. This lesson is an eye opener for many students; it shows them how to calculate areas of regions that they may have never thought possible to calculate. The lesson also points out and stresses that the concept of area is separate from its calculation.

8-5

AREAS OF TRIANGLES

This is a standard lesson. From the formula for the area of a rectangle, the formula for the right triangle is derived; combining right triangles gives the formula for any triangle. The Example includes triangles on coordinate grids to continue to reinforce the notion of square units in area.

8-6

AREAS OF TRAPEZOIDS

There is a difference between a formula and an algorithm. You can have an algorithm without having a formula. For example, there is an algorithm for finding the area of any polygon: triangulate, find the areas of each triangle, and then add them. There is no formula, however, for finding the area of any polygon.

If a polygon is constructed so that its triangles have the same altitudes (as in a trapezoid) or have the same length bases (as in a regular polygon), then the distributive property can be employed to derive a rather simple formula. In this lesson, the formula for the area of any trapezoid is derived.

8-7

THE PYTHAGOREAN THEOREM

Students who have studied from UCSMP texts have seen the Pythagorean Theorem twice before. Other students also may have seen this theorem once or twice. Thus, the purpose of this lesson is to discuss the proof of the theorem, not just to calculate lengths. Also, the Pythagorean Theorem, together with the SSS Congruence Theo-

rem, enables the converse of the Pythagorean Theorem to be deduced, giving a condition that determines right triangles.

8-8

ARC MEASURE AND ARC LENGTH

This lesson introduces some of the terminology associated with circles, including central angles, major and minor arcs, arc measure, and arc length. The degree measure of an arc arises naturally from previous work with angle measure and rotations.

The length of an arc is the limit of the sums of the lengths of inscribed segments. *Circumference* is just another word for perimeter. The famous number π is defined as the ratio of the circumference of a circle to its diameter.

8-9

THE AREA OF A CIRCLE

The proof of the area formula for a circle, $A = \pi r^2$, uses the idea of a limit for the third time in this chapter. Limits are unavoidable since the area of a curved region is found by using properties based on rectangles.

RESOURCES
Visual for Teaching Aid 47 displays the museum diagrams on page 355.

We recommend 12 to 15 days for this chapter: 9 to 11 on the lessons and quizzes; 1 for the Progress Self-Test; 1 or 2 for the Chapter Review; and 1 for a Chapter test. (See the Daily Pacing Chart on page 354A.) If you spend more than 15 days on this chapter, you are moving too slowly. Keep in mind that each lesson includes Review questions to help students firm up content studied previously.

CHAPTER 8

Measurement Formulas

8-1: Perimeter Formulas

8-2: Tiling the Plane

8-3: Fundamental Properties of Area

8-4: Areas of Irregular Regions

8-5: Areas of Triangles

8-6: Areas of Trapezoids

8-7: The Pythagorean Theorem

8-8: Arc Measure and Arc Length

8-9: The Area of a Circle

354

Diagramed below is a museum surrounded by an elliptical walkway. The museum and walkway both lie inside a large rectangle that is 2 blocks long and 1 block wide.

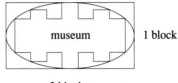

1 block

2 blocks

Area measures the space occupied by a two-dimensional region. The area of the rectangle is clearly 2 square blocks. The museum occupies a space inside that. So the area of the museum is less than 2 square blocks. The area of the elliptical region is larger than the area of the museum but smaller than the area of the rectangle. All of this can be seen by separating out the three regions.

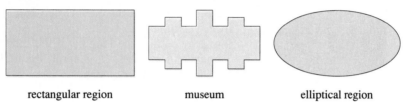

rectangular region   museum   elliptical region

Perimeter is different. The **perimeter** of a region is the length of its boundary. It tells you how far it would be to walk around it. The perimeter of the rectangle above is 6 blocks. It is harder to calculate the perimeter of the museum because the museum is a nonconvex 28-gon. But you can see that it would take longer to walk around all the walls of the museum than to walk around either the rectangle or the ellipse. The perimeter of the museum is longer than the perimeter of either the rectangle or the ellipse.

Thus the museum has the smallest area but the longest perimeter. So, though area and perimeter both measure how big something is, they are quite different.

You probably already know how to calculate the area and perimeter of squares, rectangles, and circles. In this chapter, you will learn formulas for the areas of many of the figures you have studied so far in this book. You will learn how these formulas are related to each other, so that if you forget one of them, you may be able to derive it.

Formulas for perimeter are the simplest, so this chapter begins with them.

CHAPTER 8   Measurement Formulas   **355**

USING PAGES 354-355
Although perimeter and area are both measures of a figure, they measure different things. Use the museum idea to point out the difference; the perimeter measures the distance around the museum, and the area measures how much ground the museum covers. The capacity of the museum is determined more by its floor area than its perimeter.

A person's height and weight can be used as an example to illustrate the difference between perimeter and area. Height and weight are both measures that describe the size of a person, but they measure different things. A person can be tall but not heavy, and vice versa.

355

RESOURCES
■ Lesson Master 8-1

OBJECTIVES

C Calculate perimeters of parallelograms, kites, and equilateral polygons from lengths of sides, and vice versa.

J Apply perimeter formulas for parallelograms, kites, and regular polygons to real situations.

TEACHING NOTES

Students may notice that the distance between Chicago and Peoria is greater than the distance between Peoria and Hannibal, but the time is less. Discuss situations for which the distance in miles is important, and other situations for which the distance in time is important.

Making Connections
Those who have taken previous UCSMP courses will be familiar with the concept of perimeter but will not have seen the formulas for the perimeter of a kite or of an equilateral polygon.

Error Analysis After a long study of triangles, students sometimes confuse "equilateral," "equiangular," and "regular." Make sure you discuss the differences between the terms and give labeled examples so that students can visualize the differences from the way the parts are labeled.

LESSON

8-1

Perimeter Formulas

Reproduced below is a portion of a United States mileage and driving-time map from the *1989 Rand McNally Road Atlas*. It is a network whose nodes are towns or cities. The lengths of arcs in this network are given in miles and in minutes. For instance, the length of the arc from Hannibal to Jefferson City is 108 miles or 2 hours, 23 minutes.

There are many paths on this network. For instance, there is a path from Springfield to Dallas through Atoka. The length of that path is found by adding the lengths of the individual arcs. It is 424 miles or 7 hours, 58 minutes. In general, the length of a path is the sum of the lengths of its segments.

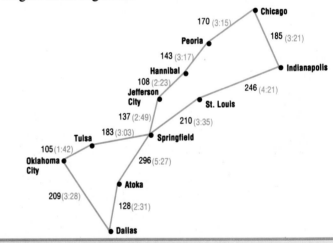

Definition:

The **perimeter of a polygon** is the sum of the lengths of its sides.

There are two polygons in this network. There is a heptagon *CPHJSStI* and a pentagon *STODA*. Think of traveling along the sides of one of these polygons, say *STODA*. You will have taken a

356

tour through five cities (the vertices), ending where you started. According to this map, you will have traveled about 921 miles and it would take you a little over 16 hours. In calculating these totals, you have calculated the *perimeter* of *STODA*.

The above situation illustrates that the length of a side of a polygon may be measured in various units. Usually the units are those of length in the metric system (meters, centimeters, etc.) or in the customary system (inches, miles, etc.). To help you convert from one unit to another in either system or between systems, use the conversion formulas at the back of this book. When calculating perimeter, the important thing is that the units for all sides be the same.

If all the sides of a polygon have different lengths, there is no special formula for its perimeter. A formula for the perimeter p of a triangle with sides x, y, and z is just $p = x + y + z$.

$$p = x + y + z$$

But if a polygon has some sides equal, then the calculations of the perimeter can be shortened. For instance, we know that a kite has two pairs of equal sides. If the lengths of these sides are a and b, then its perimeter p can be given by the formula
$$p = a + a + b + b$$
or, using simple algebra, $\quad p = 2a + 2b$
or, factoring, $\qquad\qquad p = 2(a + b)$.

■ ■ ■ ■ ■ ■ ■ ■ ■

Example 1 Kite *ABCD* with ends *B* and *D* has side lengths as shown. Find its perimeter.

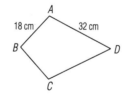

Solution 1 Use the definition of perimeter.
$$\text{Perimeter of } ABCD = AB + BC + CD + AD$$
Since *B* and *D* are ends of the kite, $AB = BC$ and $CD = AD$.
Substituting,
$$\text{perimeter of } ABCD = 18 \text{ cm} + 18 \text{ cm} + 32 \text{ cm} + 32 \text{ cm}$$
$$= 100 \text{ cm}.$$

Solution 2 Use a formula. If a and b are the lengths of the sides, then the perimeter
$$p = 2(a + b)$$
$$= 2(18 \text{ cm} + 32 \text{ cm})$$
$$= 2(50 \text{ cm})$$
$$= 100 \text{ cm}.$$

LESSON 8-1 Perimeter Formulas **357**

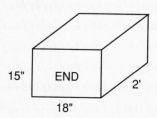

a. Can a box 15 in. × 18 in. × 2 ft be mailed?
Yes

b. What is the longest box that can be mailed if the end is 1 ft × 1 ft?
5 ft

3. Material for framing paintings and large photographs comes in long segments which must be cut to make a frame. Will a piece of framing material 1 yard long be enough to make a 8″ × 10″ picture frame?
Yes, barely. Don't make any mistakes in cutting the frame!

4. If the perimeter of a square is 14 meters, how long is each side?
3.5 meters

5. A carpenter needs to put duct tape around a heating duct which is rectangular. Its dimensions are $15\frac{3}{8}$ inches by $8\frac{5}{16}$ inches. How much tape is needed?
just over $47\frac{3}{8}$ inches

6. If a person who wanted to make a square flower box 1 foot on a side bought 4 boards that were 1′ long, why wouldn't it work?
The thickness of the boards adds to the perimeter, which will be greater than 4′ unless something is cut off.

Recall that the opposite sides of a rectangle are congruent. So the perimeter of the rectangle in Example 2 below is $\ell + w + \ell + w$, or $2\ell + 2w$, or $2(\ell + w)$. In general, the formulas at the back of the book have an advantage in that they allow you to apply what you know about algebra to geometry, and thus shorten calculations.

■ ■ ■ ■ ■ ■ ■ ■ ■

Example 2   Most flags are rectangles about 1.6 times as long as they are wide. If you have 10 meters of material for the edges, about how big a flag can you make?

Solution   First draw a picture. The edges are the length ℓ and width w of the rectangle. The perimeter
$$p = 2(\ell + w).$$
Here, $\ell = 1.6w$ and $p = 10$.
Substitute for p and ℓ.
$$10 = 2(1.6w + w)$$
$$10 = 2(2.6w)$$
$$10 = 5.2w$$

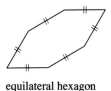

The Gadsden Flag of South Carolina, which was used around 1776, was one of many flags used by the American colonies to rally public support against the British.

DON'T TREAD ON ME

Solving the equation, $w = \frac{10}{5.2} \approx 1.923$ meters. Since $\ell = 1.6w$, $\ell \approx 3.077$ meters. Knowing that 1 meter = 100 centimeters, you can make a flag about 192 centimeters wide and 308 centimeters long.

If all sides of a polygon have the same length, the polygon is called **equilateral.** Rhombuses and squares are equilateral quadrilaterals. There are equilateral polygons with any number of sides. A formula for the perimeter of an equilateral polygon follows directly from the definition of perimeter.

equilateral pentagon

equilateral hexagon

Equilateral Polygon Perimeter Formula:

In an equilateral polygon with n sides of length s, the perimeter $p = ns$.

Since all regular polygons are equilateral, this formula applies to regular polygons. For instance, in an equilateral triangle, $p = 3s$. In a square, $p = 4s$. In a regular octagon, $p = 8s$.

358

Questions

Covering the Reading

In 1–3, use the map pictured in this lesson.

1. What does the number 3:28 on the segment from Oklahoma City to Dallas mean?
   It takes 3 hours, 28 minutes to drive from Oklahoma City to Dallas.

2. A trucker with a perishable load should choose which route from Chicago to Dallas? **the route passing through Indianapolis, St. Louis, Springfield, and Atoka**

3. Give the perimeter of the polygon *StICPHJS:*
   a. in miles; **1199 miles**
   b. in hours. **23 hours, 1 minute**

4. Give three different expressions for the perimeter of the polygon pictured below. **$a + b + a + b$, $2a + 2b$, $2(a + b)$**

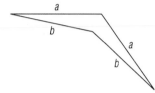

In 5–9, give the perimeter of each figure.

5. A rectangular shaped piece of land $3\frac{1}{2}$ miles long and $\frac{1}{2}$ mile wide
   8 miles

6. an equilateral hexagon with one side of length 14 mm **84 mm**

7. a square with side t **4t**

8. an equilateral triangle with side s **3s**

9. a regular heptagon with side $(x + 1)$ **$7(x + 1)$, or $7x + 7$**

10. The perimeter of a rectangle is 70. One side of the rectangle is 3 times the length of the other. What are the lengths of the sides?
    8.75 and 26.25

11. A poster is to be 1.5 times as wide as it is high. If its edges total 3 meters in length, how wide will the poster be? **0.9 meters**

Applying the Mathematics

12. The perimeter of a rhombus is 12 feet.
    a. Is this enough information to find the length of a side of the rhombus? **Yes**
    b. If so, find that length. If not, why not? **3 ft**

13. A stop sign is a regular octagon. If its edges total 10′ in length, what is the length of each side? **1.25 ft**

14. The perimeter of an equilateral triangle is p. What is the length of each side? **$\frac{p}{3}$**

LESSON 8-1 Perimeter Formulas **359**

NOTES ON QUESTIONS
Question 2: You might ask if the trucker's decision is based on time or distance. (Time, no doubt; the answer in the text is based on time.)

Questions 5-9: Point out that these are the same kinds of questions; if a student cannot answer Questions 7-9, go back to a special case like those in Questions 5 and 6.

Question 10: Encourage students to solve the problem in various ways. Here are three possibilities. In (i) and (ii), let s be the shorter side. (i) Substitute in the formula $p = 2\ell + 2w$ to get $70 = 2(3s + s)$ and solve for s. (ii) One length + one width equals half the perimeter; thus, $3s + s = 35$. (iii) Let x and y be the dimensions and solve a system: $x + y = 35$ and $y = 3x$.

Question 14: Most students need practice solving for variables in formulas. Here, $p = 3s$, so $s = \frac{p}{3}$. In conversion formulas, 1 in. = 2.54 cm (exactly), and so 1 cm = .3937 in. Also, 1 square mile = 640 acres and so 1 acre = .0015625 square mile. The coefficients are reciprocals; this is one reason for having the $1/x$ key on scientific calculators. Point out that **Question 13** is the same kind of question.

Question 15: Parts **b** and **c** of this question use the formula found in part **a**.

Making Connections for Question 17: This question can help prepare students for the study of area. To show the connection to area, choose a point on the graph, for example (3, 5). (This is not easy for some students.) Draw the rectangle with vertices (0, 0), (3, 0), (3, 5), and (0, 5). This rectangle has perimeter 16 and area 15. Do the same with other points on the graph.

NOTES ON QUESTIONS
Question 18: Emphasize that only in the case of $n = 3$ does equiangular ⇔ equilateral. You might restate the definition of a regular polygon as one which is equilateral and equiangular.

Question 19: As a review, note that (c) is the sum of the measures of the angles of an n-gon; (b) is the number of its diagonals (ignoring the degree sign).

Questions 22-24: These questions cover units of length, and may be a review or new material for students. A table of conversions is on page 858.

Question 28: The algebra in this question is needed later in the chapter in the proof of the Pythagorean Theorem.

ADDITIONAL ANSWERS
17.

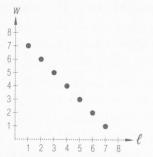

26. b. Substitute a number for y in $5(3 + 2y)$ and $15 + 10y$. See if the values of the expressions are the same.

27. Sample counterexample: If $x = -1$, $(x + 1)(2x - 3) = 0$, but $2x^2 - 3 = -1$.

30. Sample: The distance was measured from different points in the cities or remeasured more accurately. The change in time results from a lowering of speed limits. In 1989, the number of miles became 296, the time 5:27!

15. The boundary of the museum on the first page of the chapter has sides of three different lengths. Let the smallest sides have length s, the middle sides have length m, and the largest sides have length ℓ.
    a. What is the perimeter of the museum? $8s + 18m + 2\ell$
    b. If $s = 25$ meters, $m = 50$ meters, and $\ell = 100$ meters, what is the perimeter of the museum? 1300 meters
    c. If $s = 25$ meters, $m = 50$ meters, and $\ell = 100$ meters, estimate the perimeter of the surrounding rectangle. 1200 meters

16. a. On the map drawn in this lesson, distance is measured in hours and minutes. Name some place whose distance from where you live you know in minutes, but not in miles or kilometers. sample: school or a friend's house
    b. Give an example of a situation in which the time to get from A to B is more important than is the distance in miles or kilometers. sample: routes for emergency vehicles

17. A rectangle has perimeter 16. Suppose the sides are integers. Graph all pairs of possible lengths ℓ and widths w. See margin.

18. If all angles of a polygon have the same measure, the polygon is **equiangular.**
    a. What is the sum of the measures of the angles in an equiangular decagon? 1440
    b. What is the measure of each angle in an equiangular decagon? 144
    c. What is the measure of each angle in an equilateral decagon? not enough information to determine

Review

19. *Multiple choice.* The measure of each angle of a regular n-gon is
    (a) $\dfrac{360}{n}$
    (b) $\dfrac{n(n - 3)}{2}$
    (c) $(n - 2) \cdot 180$
    (d) $\dfrac{(n - 2) \cdot 180}{n}$. *(Lesson 7-6)* (d)

20. In the figure below, find $m\angle BDC$. *(Lesson 3-1)* 161

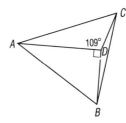

21. Is the network shown in this lesson traversable? *(Lesson 1-4)* Yes

22. Fill in the blanks of these conversion formulas. *(Previous course)*
    a. 1 yard = __?__ feet 3
    b. 1 kilometer = __?__ meters 1000
    c. 1 mile = __?__ feet 5280

23. One inch is about 2.54 centimeters. About what part of an inch is two centimeters? *(Previous course)* $\dfrac{2}{2.54} \approx .79$ inch

24. Do these calculations, which are like those often found when adding lengths. *(Previous course)*
   a. 3 feet 6 inches + 8 feet 11 inches **12 feet, 5 inches**
   b. 8 · (2 feet, 3 inches) **18 feet**
   c. 2.4 meters + 62 centimeters **3.02 meters or 302 centimeters**

25. If $p = 2\ell + 2w$, $\ell = 11$, and $p = 25$, find w. *(Previous course)* **1.5**

26. a. Multiply 5 by $3 + 2y$. **15 + 10y**
   b. How can you check your answer to part **a**? *(Previous course)*
   See margin.

27. Show that $(x + 1)(2x - 3)$ is not equal to $2x^2 - 3$. *(Previous course)*
   See margin.

28. *Multiple choice.* $(r + s)^2 =$
   (a) $r^2 + s^2$
   (b) $r^2 + rs + r^2$
   (c) $r^2 + 2rs + s^2$
   (d) none of these. *(Previous course)* **(c)**

29. Refer to the map in this lesson.
   a. What average speed did the map makers assume in a trip from Dallas to Oklahoma City? **≈60 mph**
   b. What average speed is assumed in a trip from Dallas to Atoka? **≈51 mph**
   c. What conditions could account for the different rates?
   (Previous course) **Sample: the route from Dallas to Atoka has more stops or slower speed limits.**

Exploration

30. In the *1973 Rand McNally Road Atlas,* the path from Springfield to Atoka was labeled 289 (5:15). In the *1988 Rand McNally Road Atlas,* the same path was labeled 294 (6:45). What might account for the difference between these numbers and those given in the *1989 Rand McNally Road Atlas*? **See margin.**

LESSON 8-1   Perimeter Formulas   **361**

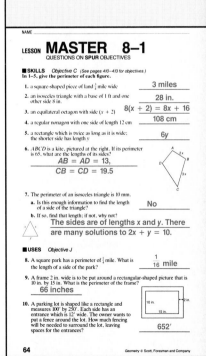

RESOURCES
■ Lesson Master 8-2
↪ Visual for Teaching Aid 48
  shows the two tiling
  patterns on page 362.
▣ Computer Master 16

OBJECTIVE

A Draw a tessellation using a
given figure as a funda-
mental region.

TEACHING NOTES

There are many applications
of tessellations: brick walls,
tile floors, ceilings, wallpaper
designs, graph paper, side-
walks, and grate patterns are
just a few. For many applications of tessellations, it is
easy, convenient, and efficient to manufacture congruent copies of the same figure
or object for use as a cover
on a flat surface.

The history of tessellations
demonstrates that new mathematics is not necessarily
more difficult mathematics.
Thus, there are simple geometry problems for which discoveries still can be made.
Marjorie Rice had no more
mathematical training than a
high school geometry course
before her discovery of a
new type of pentagon that
tessellates the plane. Many
mathematicians have worked
on the problem of determining which pentagons tessellate. The problem is still
unsolved.
  The problem is made more
complicated by the recent
discovery (within the past 20
years) of tessellations which
have no translation symmetry
and thus cannot be slid onto
themselves. These are called
nonperiodic tessellations.

Floors and walls are often covered with copies of the same polygon.
A rectangular tile pattern may cover a floor, as pictured above.
Square glass blocks in outside walls are often used.

Other regions can be used to cover the plane. Here are two tiling
patterns using copies of △*ABC*. Notice that the patterns are different. Pattern II contains kites whereas Pattern I does not.

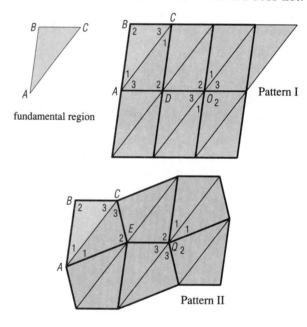

A covering of a plane with congruent copies of the same region,
with no holes and no overlaps, is called a **tessellation.** The region is
called a **fundamental region** for the tiling. △*ABC* is a fundamental
region for each tessellation shown above. We say that △*ABC*
tessellates the plane.

Look at the points *O* and *Q* in the patterns above. Six regions meet
at these points. Each angle in the fundamental region is represented
twice at *O*. Thus the 360° around a point is completely accounted

362

for by the six angles—twice the sum of the angles of the fundamental region. In general, in any tessellation of a region, where the regions meet at a point, the sum of the angle measures must be 360. If this does not occur, a tessellation is not possible.

The idea of a tessellation is an old one. The word "tessellate" comes from a Latin word meaning "small stone." Small stones, put together into mosaics, covered the floors of many Roman buildings. The Moors, whose religion (Islam) still does not allow any pictures in their places of worship, used all kinds of tessellations in decorating their mosques. Below is a photograph of tessellations in the Alhambra, a museum in Grenada, Spain, that was built in the 1300s as a mosque.

In studying tessellations one key question is whether a given shape can cover the plane. It is easy to see that any triangular region can tessellate the plane.

Algorithm for tessellating part of a plane with any triangular region *ABC*:

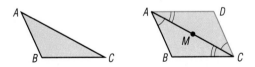

Step 1. Rotate $\triangle ABC$ 180° about *M*, the midpoint of $\overline{AC}$. The image of $\triangle ABC$ is the congruent triangle *CDA*. Since the triangles are congruent, $\angle BAC \cong \angle ACD$ and $\angle DAC \cong \angle ACB$. Because of the AIA = ⟹ ∥ Lines Theorem, $\overleftrightarrow{CD} \parallel \overleftrightarrow{AB}$ and $\overline{AD} \parallel \overline{BC}$. So *ABCD* is a parallelogram.

LESSON 8-2 Tiling the Plane **363**

Making Connections
Students who have studied UCSMP *Transition Mathematics* have seen and made tessellations. This is not an uncommon activity in middle school grades, so ask your students if they have ever done such designs.

ADDITIONAL EXAMPLE
Tessellate the plane with this triangular region as the fundamental region.

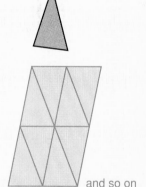

and so on

NOTES ON QUESTIONS
Small Group Work for Question 9: You may wish to ask groups of students to discuss why kites will always tessellate and then make some conjectures (They are made up of congruent triangles.)

Question 12: Ask students to use squares to make up other polygonal shapes that tessellate.

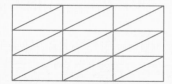

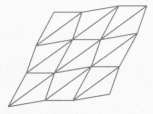
Step 2. Repeatedly translate the region *ABCD* (and $\overline{AC}$) along $\overleftrightarrow{BC}$ in both directions with magnitude *BC*.

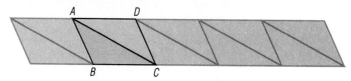

Step 3. Translate the entire figure along $\overleftrightarrow{AB}$ in both directions with magnitude *AB*. The result covers the plane.

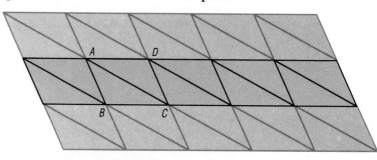

It is not as easy to see that any quadrilateral region will tessellate. (You are asked to explore this in the Questions.) Beyond this there are still unsolved problems. In 1975, Marjorie Rice, a homemaker from California, discovered a new type of pentagon that tessellates the plane. As recently as 1985, Rolf Stein of the University of Dortmund in West Germany found still another new type of tessellating pentagon. So an old application of geometry is still yielding new mathematics.

Questions

Covering the Reading

1. What is a tessellation? a covering of a plane with congruent copies of the same region with no holes and no overlaps

In 2–4, trace the figure repeatedly to show a tessellation using the figure as a fundamental region. See margin.

2.

3.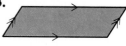

4.

5. A museum where many tessellations can be found is the __?__. Alhambra

6. What is the key question concerning tessellation mentioned in this lesson? whether a given shape can cover the plane

7. A new type of tessellating pentagon was discovered as recently as __?__. 1985

364

8. Give two examples of tessellations seen where you live.
Samples: brickwork, floor or wall tiles, wallpaper patterns

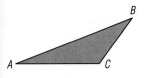

In 9 and 10, use △*ABC* at the left as the fundamental region.

9. Make a tessellation in which kites occur. See margin.

10. Make a tessellation in which no kites occur. See margin.

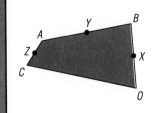

Applying the Mathematics

11. The tessellation below is from the work of the artist Maurits Escher. Trace a possible fundamental region.

12. At the left is an octagon made of 5 squares. Trace it and show that it will tessellate the plane. See margin.

13. *Multiple choice.* Pictured here are regular polygons with 3, 4, 5, and 6 sides. Three of these polygons can be fundamental regions for a tessellation. Which one cannot? (c)

(a)   (b)   (c)   (d)

equilateral triangle   square   regular pentagon   regular hexagon

14. a. Follow this algorithm to tessellate with quadrilateral *ABOC* at the left, where *X*, *Y*, and *Z* are the midpoints of $\overline{BO}$, $\overline{AB}$, and $\overline{AC}$. See margin.

Step 1.   Trace quadrilateral *ABOC*.
Step 2.   Rotate *ABOC* 180° about *X*.
              (image *A'OBC'*).
Step 3.   Rotate *A'OBC'* 180° about *Y'*, the image of *Y*
              (image *OA'B*C**).
Step 4.   Rotate *OA'B*C** 180° about *Z**, the image of *Z'*
              (image *C*A"CO*).

b. There are now 4 angles with vertex *O*. How do you know that these angles fit around *O* exactly? See margin.
c. What needs to be done to complete the tessellation?
Translate the figure repeatedly in all directions.

LESSON 8-2   Tiling the Plane   **365**

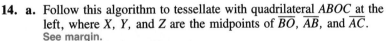

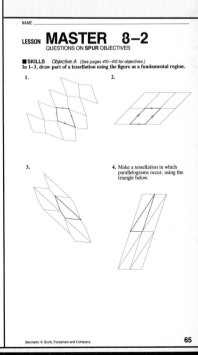

FOLLOW-UP

MORE PRACTICE
For more questions on SPUR Objectives, use *Lesson Master 8-2,* shown below.

EXTENSION
Some teachers like to have students draw Escher-type tessellations. There is not time in this course to do this as an in-class activity, but it is appropriate if you like to give it as extra credit. A book that instructs students how to do this is *Creating Escher-Style Drawings,* published by Creative Publications.

EVALUATION
Alternative Assessment
Designing tessellations of the plane using triangles, kites, or parallelograms can be fun in a **small group** environment. Have the groups discuss the specific algorithms presented in the lesson and then work together to design figures that will tessellate.

10., 11., 12., 14. See the margin on p. 366.

NAME _____

LESSON **MASTER 8-2**
QUESTIONS ON **SPUR** OBJECTIVES

■ SKILLS *Objective A (See pages 410–413 for objectives.)*
In 1–3, draw part of a tessellation using the figure as a fundamental region.

1.   2.

3.   4. Make a tessellation in which parallelograms occur, using the triangle below.

Geometry © Scott, Foresman and Company   **65**

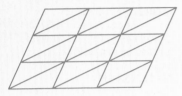

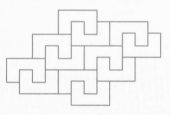

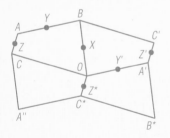

15. A regular pentagon has perimeter 13. What is the length of a side? *(Lesson 8-1)* 2.6

16. A parallelogram has perimeter 462 cm. One side is 185 cm. Find the lengths of the other three sides. *(Lessons 8-1, 7-7)*
46 cm, 185 cm, 46 cm

17. What is the measure of each angle of a regular pentagon? *(Lesson 5-7)* 108

18. A rectangle has vertices at (-2, 5), (-2, -1), (3, -1), and (3, 5). Find its perimeter. (Hint: A drawing may help.) *(Lessons 8-1, 1-3)* 22

19. Refer to the figure at the left.
Given: m∠ABD = m∠BDC
m∠ADB = m∠DBC.
Prove: AB = CD. *(Lessons 7-4, 6-7)* See margin.

20. Expand: $(a + 5)^2$. *(Previous course)* $a^2 + 10a + 25$

21. Solve: $2x^2 = 54$. *(Previous course)* $\sqrt{27} \approx 5.2, -\sqrt{27} \approx -5.2$

22. *Multiple choice.* $\sqrt{27} =$
(a) $9\sqrt{3}$ (b) $3\sqrt{9}$ (c) $9\sqrt{9}$ (d) $3\sqrt{3}$. *(Previous course)* (d)

23. a. Who were the Moors? a North African people of Berber and Arab descent who invaded and conquered Spain in the eighth century
  b. What happened to them? They were expelled back to Africa during wars and inquisitions.

24. The artist Maurits Escher was famous for his tessellations.
  a. When did he live? 1898–1971
  b. Look in a library for books containing pictures of his work.
  sample: *The Intimate World of M. C. Escher*

25. Below is part of a tessellation using the pentagon discovered by Rolf Stein. Trace the part below and continue it to fill a sheet of paper.

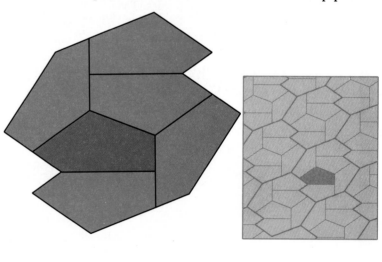

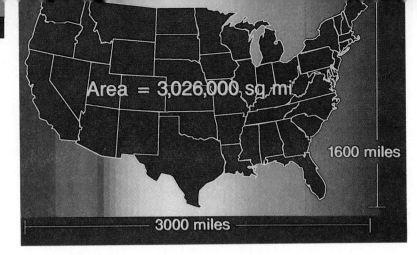

Area = 3,026,000 sq mi

1600 miles

3000 miles

Fundamental Properties of Area

LESSON 8-3

RESOURCES
- Lesson Master 8-3
- Quiz for Lessons 8-1 Through 8-3
- Visual for Teaching Aid 49 can be used with **Example 1**.
- Computer Master 17

OBJECTIVES

D Calculate areas of squares, rectangles, and parallelograms from relevant lengths.

E Given areas of figures, determine relevant lengths.

I Tell how to derive formulas for area.

L Apply formulas for areas of squares, rectangles, and parallelograms to real situations.

N Determine the areas of polygons on a coordinate plane.

An almanac gives the area of the 48 contiguous United States as about 3,026,000 square miles. (The other two states, Alaska and Hawaii, add about 593,000 square miles to the area.) The contiguous United States is about 3000 miles from east to west and 1600 miles from north to south. In this and the next lesson, you will see how this area can be calculated.

$w = 8$

$\ell = 4$

1 unit

1 unit

1 unit square

To find the area of a region, cover it with congruent copies of a fundamental region. The area is the number of copies that are needed. For instance, the rectangle with length $\ell = 4$ and width $w = 8$ can be covered with 32 unit squares. So we say that the area is 32 square units or 32 units^2. There are 4 rows and 8 columns. These numbers are the **dimensions** of the rectangle. The number of squares in the rectangle is the product of its dimensions.

Whenever the dimensions of the rectangle are integers, the unit squares will fit exactly. But suppose a farm is shaped like a rectangle, 1.5 kilometers by 2.5 kilometers, as shown here.

2.5 km

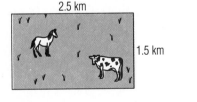

1.5 km

1 square kilometer

One way to find the farm's area is shown by the figures on the next page. First a unit is picked. Here the natural unit is 1 square kilometer. Then the farm region is split into square kilometers.

TEACHING NOTES

The previous lesson suggests a method of measuring a region. For example, suppose a wall is to be covered with a mosaic of congruent tiles. A measure of the wall is the number of tiles required to cover the wall. A measure of the floor can then be the number of tiles needed to cover the floor. A measure of a sports field can be the number of pieces of sod needed to cover it.

Discuss the need to establish an easy-to-use unit for measuring area, one that does not overlap and which will fill the region. The square meets these criteria.

LESSON 8-3 Fundamental Properties of Area   **367**

There are two whole-square kilometers, three half-square kilometers, and one quarter-square kilometer. Think of putting them end to end. The result is 3.75 square kilometers. This is exactly what you could get by multiplying 1.5 kilometers by 2.5 kilometers.

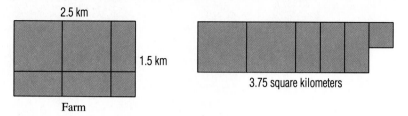

Farm

3.75 square kilometers

This one situation illustrates the four fundamental properties of area which we assume.

Area Postulate:

   a. Uniqueness Property Given a unit region, every polygonal region has a unique area.

   b. Rectangle Formula The area of a rectangle with dimensions ℓ and w is ℓw.

   c. Congruence Property Congruent figures have the same area.

   d. Additive Property The area of the union of two nonoverlapping regions is the sum of the areas of the regions.

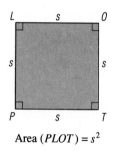

Area $(PLOT) = s^2$

A special case of the Rectangle Formula is that the area of any square with side s is s^2. This is pictured at the left.

Sometimes we write **Area(F)** for the *area of a figure F*. With this notation, the Congruence Property of Area becomes: If $F \cong G$, then Area(F) = Area(G). **Nonoverlapping** regions means regions that do not share interior points. They may share boundaries, as in the drawing below. The Additive Property of Area becomes: If F and G do not overlap, the Area(F $\cup$ G) = Area(F) + Area(G).

Area (F $\cup$ G) = Area (F) + Area (G)

Notice that the perimeter of F $\cup$ G does not equal the sum of the perimeters of F and G. (The common border is counted twice.)

All of the fundamental properties of area are used in Example 1.

368

Example 1 The floor plan of a ranch house is drawn on a coordinate system.

a. Find the dimensions of rooms I, II, and III if the unit is 1 foot.

b. Find the floor area of the house.

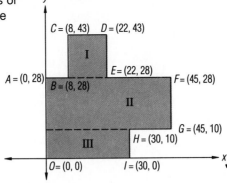

Solution

a. I, II, and III are rectangles. The horizontal dimensions are found by subtracting an appropriate pair of x-coordinates of the vertices. For example, $CD = |22 - 8| = 14$. Similarly, the vertical dimensions are found by subtracting the y-coordinates of the vertices. For example, $BC = |28 - 43| = 15$.

Dimensions of room I: $CD = 14$ and $BC = 15$
Dimensions of room II: $AF = 45$ and $FG = 18$
Dimensions of room III: $IO = 30$ and $HI = 10$

b. By the Additive Property of Area, the area of the house is the sum of the areas of I, II, and III. By the Rectangle Formula:

Area(I) = 15 ft · 14 ft = 210 sq ft
Area (II) = 18 ft · 45 ft = 810 sq ft
Area (III) = 10 ft · 30 ft = 300 sq ft.

Now apply the Additive Property of Area.

Area(floor plan) = 210 + 810 + 300
= 1320 sq ft

Check   One way to check is to consider the rectangle with vertices (0, 0), (45, 0), (45, 43), and (0, 43). This rectangle has area 43 · 45, or 1935 sq ft. It includes the entire floor plan plus rectangles in three corners. The sum of the areas of those corner rectangles, added to the floor plan's area, should be 1935 sq ft. You are asked to verify this in the Questions.

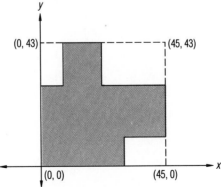

1. Find the area of the region shown below.

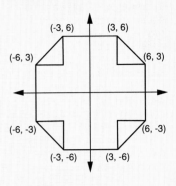

108 square units

2. A playground is 50 yards by 100 yards. Sod costs $1.59 per roll, which is 18 inches by 54 inches. How much will it cost to sod the field?
$10,600

Example 2 provides a common use of area.

■ ■ ■ ■ ■ ■ ■ ■ ■

Example 2   A carpet dealer advertises a particular carpet for $18.95 a square yard. How much will it cost to carpet a room that is 9 feet by 12 feet?

Solution   Since the price of carpeting is in square yards, the dimensions of the room must be converted from feet to yards: 9 feet = 3 yards and 12 feet = 4 yards. Thus, in square yards, the area of the room is 3 yards · 4 yards = 12 yards². The cost of the carpeting is 12 · $18.95 = $227.40. This is before tax and any other charges such as installation or padding.

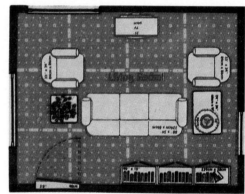

9 feet = 3 yards

12 feet = 4 yards

Questions

1. Below, two different unit squares are used to determine the area of the large congruent rectangles.

   unit A 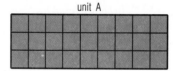   unit B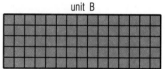

   a. What is the area using unit A? **27 units²**
   b. What is the area using unit B? **75 units²**

2. Rectangle $ABCD$ has dimensions 8.3 cm and 11.4 cm.
   a. What is an appropriate unit of area in this situation?
   b. Find Area $(ABCD)$. **a) square centimeter; b) 94.62 cm²**

3. Suppose the United States were a rectangle 3000 miles from east to west and 1600 miles from north to south.
   a. What would be the perimeter of the United States?
   b. What would be its area?
      a) 9200 miles; b) 4,800,000 sq miles

370

4. Find the area of each polygonal region.
   a. *ABFG* 35 units²
   b. *CDEF* 16 units²
   c. *ABCDEG* 51 units²

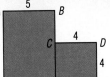

5. What properties of area are used in answering Question 4? See margin.

6. A floor plan of a house is given below. Each unit of length is one meter. Find the area of the floor. 315 m²

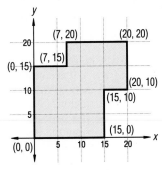

7. Verify the check in Example 1 in this lesson. See margin.

8. A carpet dealer advertises a particular carpet for $11.95 a square yard. How much will it cost to carpet a room that is 15 feet by 12 feet (before tax or any other charges)? $239

Applying the Mathematics

9. Find the area of the polygon whose vertices are given.
   a. (0, 0), (0, 10), (10, 10), (10, 0) 100 units²
   b. (0, 0), (0, *k*), (*k*, *k*), (*k*, 0) *k*² units²

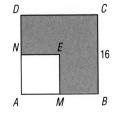

10. At the left, *ABCD* and *AMEN* are squares, *M* is the midpoint of $\overline{AB}$, and *BC* = 16. Find Area(*BCDNEM*). 192 units²

11. The area of a rectangle is 50 square yards. The length of the rectangle is 100 yards. What is the width of the rectangle? ½ yard

12. To the nearest whole unit, find the side of a square with the given area.
   a. 49 square units 7 units
   b. ¾ square unit $\sqrt{\frac{3}{4}} \approx 1$ unit
   c. 200 square units
   $\sqrt{200} \approx 14$ units
   d. 3141 square units
   $\sqrt{3141} \approx 56$ units

13. a. A desk is 24″ by 12″. What is its area in square inches? 288 sq in.
   b. The same desk is 2′ by 1′. What is its area in square feet? 2 sq ft
   c. How many square inches are in a square foot? 144

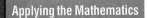

14. At the left, all the angles are right angles.
   a. *MO* = __?__ *x* + 5
   b. *MR* = __?__ *x* + 3
   c. Area (*MOQR*) = __?__ (*x* + 5)(*x* + 3) = *x*² + 8*x* + 15

15. The length of a rectangle is 3 times its width *w*. Find its area in terms of *w*. 3*w*² square units

LESSON 8-3 *Fundamental Properties of Area* **371**

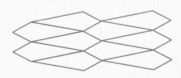
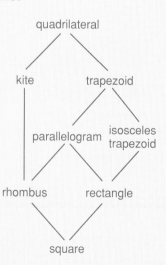
16. Find the number of 3 ft by 1 ft pieces of sod needed to cover a normal 120 yd by 160 ft football field (end zones are included in these dimensions). **19,200**

17. Using a tracing of kite *ABCD* below as a fundamental region, draw a part of a tessellation of a plane. *(Lesson 8-2)* **See margin.**

18. A pool is 50 m long and 25 m wide.
    a. A fence around the pool is built parallel to the sides of the pool and 10 m from each side. What is the perimeter of the fenced region? **230 m**
    b. If a park district has money for 200 meters of fencing, how far from the pool (equally on all sides) can they put the fence? *(Lesson 8-1)* **6.25 m**

In 19 and 20, find all solutions. *(Previous course)*

19. $x^2 = 16$ **4, -4**

20. $5y^2 = 240$
    $\sqrt{48} \approx 6.93, -\sqrt{48} \approx -6.93$

21. *Multiple choice.* Which is equal to $\sqrt{75}$? *(Previous course)*
    (a) $3\sqrt{5}$ (b) $5\sqrt{3}$ (c) $5\sqrt{15}$ (d) $25\sqrt{3}$ **(b)**

22. Calculate to the nearest hundredth. *(Previous course)*
    a. $\sqrt{2}$ b. $\sqrt{3}$ c. $\sqrt{4^2 + 3^2}$ d. $\sqrt{\frac{25}{4}}$
    1.41   **1.73**   **5.00**   **2.50**

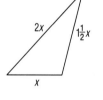

23. The longest side of the triangle at the left is twice as long as the shortest side. The third side is $1\frac{1}{2}$ times as long as the shortest side. If the perimeter of the triangle is 45, how long are its three sides? *(Lesson 8-1)* **10, 15, 20 units**

24. Factor: $\frac{1}{2}ha + \frac{1}{2}hb$. *(Previous course)* $\frac{1}{2}h(a + b)$

25. Draw a hierarchy for quadrilaterals. *(Lesson 5-6)* **See margin.**

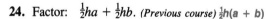
26. Find a rectangular room where you live. Calculate its area **a.** to the nearest square foot; **b.** to the nearest square meter.
    Answers will vary.

27. In 1860, the area of the United States was 3,021,295 square miles. By 1870, the area had become 3,612,299 square miles. What caused such a large change? **The region that later became the state of Alaska was purchased from Russia.**

8-4

Areas of Irregular Regions

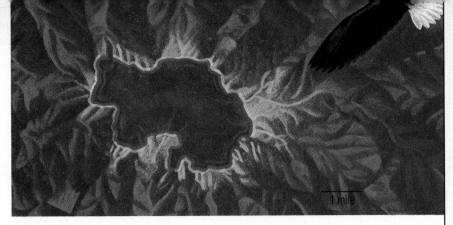

RESOURCES
■ Lesson Master 8-4
▨ Visual for Teaching Aid 50 shows how to estimate the area of a lake.
▨ Visual for Teaching Aid 51 can be used with **Questions 8** and **9**.

Here is a picture of a lake.

Like many shapes, its boundary is not the union of circular arcs or segments. The shape is *irregular*. Still it has an area; it takes up space. For all sorts of reasons, such as zoning or for planning to stock the lake with fish, people might want to know its area.

To get a first approximation, you can draw a rectangle around the lake.

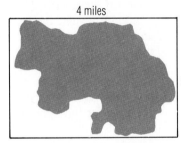

4 miles

2.75 miles

The area of the lake is less than the area of the rectangle, which is 4 miles · 2.75 miles. That is, the area of the lake is less than 11 square miles.

To get a better estimate, you might cover the lake with part of a tessellation of congruent squares. Here the squares are 1 mile on a side.

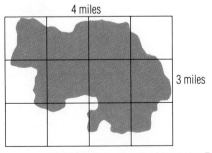

4 miles

3 miles

LESSON 8-4   Areas of Irregular Regions   **373**

OBJECTIVE

B Describe or apply a method for determining the area of an irregular-shaped region.

TEACHING NOTES

It may seem unusual to take up the study of areas of irregular regions immediately after the introduction of the area concept, but, in fact, this lesson provides a better context for the Area Postulate because formulas do not interfere with the ideas. Also, this approach supports the student's sense that many real-world shapes are not polygonal, yet it is important to know their areas.

Students hear of the areas of geographical regions but they do not know how they are found. Point out that the process is easy and natural. Cover the region with smaller and smaller squares. Count the squares inside the region and half of those on the boundary. The reason for adding half of the boundary squares is the assumption that, on the average, about half of the boundary squares are inside the region.

Many students will want exactness even when the situation does not call for it. They

The squares above are too big to accurately estimate the lake's area. Within every square you would have to estimate how much of the square is covered by the lake. Smaller squares are needed. Below, the squares are $\frac{1}{2}$ mile on a side.

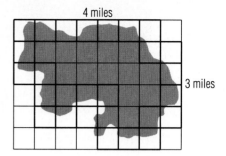

4 miles

3 miles

The idea now is to count the number of small squares entirely inside the lake. (There are 13.) Then count the number of squares partially covering the lake. (These are the boundary squares. You should get 26. They are drawn with bold edges.) A useful approximation is that, on average, each boundary square is half covered. So add the first number to *half* the second: $13 + \frac{26}{2} = 13 + 13 = 26$. An estimate for the area is 26 of these squares. Since each small square is $\frac{1}{2}$ mile on a side, the area of each small square is $\frac{1}{4}$ square mile, so an estimated area of the lake is $26 \cdot \frac{1}{4}$ square mile, or 6.5 square miles.

In general, if I is the number of inside squares, B is the number of boundary squares, and U is the area of a single square, then an estimate for the total area is $(I + \frac{1}{2}B) \cdot U$.

To get still a better estimate, use a grid with smaller squares. Below, the sides of the squares are $\frac{1}{4}$ mile, so $U = \frac{1}{16}$ square mile. We have identified those squares that lie on the boundary. In Question 4, you are asked to use this grid to estimate the area of the lake.

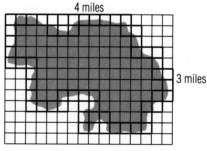

4 miles

3 miles

77 squares entirely inside lake
59 squares on boundary
56 squares entirely outside lake

When calculating area this way, do not spend too much time deciding whether a square is entirely inside or on the boundary. You only get an estimate anyway, so do not search for an exact answer.

The above procedure can be continued using finer and finer grids. The estimates can be made to differ from the actual area by no more than .1 square mile, or .01 square mile, or even closer. When smaller and smaller squares are used, we say that the estimates approach the actual area as a *limit*.

The biggest advantage of this method is that it works for any reasonably smooth curve. This same idea is used in calculus to calculate areas bounded by curves. Although it takes a long time to figure out areas in this way by hand, the method can be programmed to be done by a computer, and, when the curve can be described by an equation, there may exist a simple formula for its area.

Questions

Covering the Reading

1. Three tessellations of squares are used in this lesson to estimate the area of a lake. What is the area of a square: **a.** in the first grid; **b.** in the second grid; **c.** in the finest grid?
   a) 1 sq mile; b) $\frac{1}{4}$ sq mile; c) $\frac{1}{16}$ sq mile

2. Give two reasons people might have for estimating the area of a lake. sample: for zoning, for stocking with fish

3. *Multiple choice.* Using a grid, suppose E is the number of squares entirely inside a region and P is the number of squares partially inside the region. If each square has area Q square units, which is an estimate for the region's area (in square units)?

   (a) $(E + 2P) \cdot Q$

   (b) $\left(E + \dfrac{P}{2}\right) \cdot Q$

   (c) $(2E + P) \cdot Q$

   (d) $\left(\dfrac{E}{2} + P\right) \cdot Q$ (b)

4. Using the finest grid, estimate the area of the lake in this lesson.
   6.656 square miles

5. **a.** What is an advantage of the method of using grids to estimate area? See margin.
   b. What is a disadvantage? See margin.

6. The area of a region is the __?__ of the estimates made using finer and finer grids. limit

Applying the Mathematics

7. Recall that the resolution of TV screens or computer monitors of different sizes can be compared by calculating the number of dots (pixels) per square inch. A Macintosh computer screen is about 5.5″ by 7.5″. There are 512 rows and 342 columns of dots. About how many dots per square inch is this? 4245 dots/in.²

Question 4: The change in the estimate from the grid at the top of page 374 to the grid at the bottom of that page is from 6.5 square miles to 6.656 square miles. If the latter value is correct, then the previous estimate is off by only about 2%. That shows the power of this method. If the purpose of estimation is to determine how much water is available for migrating ducks, would the first estimate be adequate? (Yes) If the estimate is to be used to purchase land around the lake at $25,000 an acre, by how much would the estimates differ in the value of land available? (0.156 square miles = 99.8 acres, and the first estimate would be $2,496,000 higher.)

Question 8: Many students may remember a formula for finding the area of a triangle. If so, they may be amazed that the approximation method gives the exact value with both grids. Use the fact that the nonhorizontal sides are diagonals of rectangles of which the triangle has half the area. That will help verify the method of the approximation of adding half the number of squares on the boundary.
   You might note that the triangle can be split into two right triangles and that each is half a rectangle. This will prepare students for Lesson 8-5.

ADDITIONAL ANSWERS
5. a. Sample: It works for any reasonably smooth curve.
b. Sample: It takes a long time to figure out areas by hand.

8. Estimate the area of the triangle below **a.** using the grid at the left, then **b.** using the grid at the right. The small squares at the left are $\frac{1}{4}''$ on a side. See margin.

a. 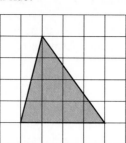   b.

9. At the left is a scale drawing of a lake covered with a grid of squares each 0.5 km on a side. Estimate the area of the lake. ≈ 14.25 km²

In 10–12, use this information. An *acre* is a unit of area often used to measure plots of land. Originally an acre was about the amount of land a farmer could plow in a day. Today an acre has an exact measure: 640 acres = 1 square mile.

10. There are 5280 feet in a mile. **a.** How many square feet are in a square mile? **b.** How many square feet are in an acre? a) 27,878,400 ft²; b) 43,560 ft²

11. Lake Dumont in the state of Michigan has an area of 215 acres. About what part of a square mile is this? about $\frac{1}{3}$ or about .34 sq mile

12. A house is built on a rectangular half-acre lot. What might be the dimensions (in feet) of the lot? sample: 242 ft by 90 ft

13. A farm in Europe has an area of 30 square kilometers. A farm in the United States has an area of 20 square miles. Using 1 mile ≈ 1.6 km, which farm is bigger? farm in U.S.

Review

14. A tilted square of side y is placed inside a square with side x. What is the area of the shaded region? *(Lesson 8-3)* $x^2 - y^2$

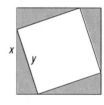

15. Factor: $x^2 - y^2$. *(Previous course)* $(x - y)(x + y)$

16. A person wishes to tile the kitchen floor with square tiles 8 inches on a side. If the kitchen measures 10 feet by 12 feet, how many tiles are needed? *(Lesson 8-3)* 270

17. A rectangle has an area of 96 square units. If its width is 4 units, what is its perimeter? *(Lessons 8-3, 8-1)* 56 units

18. If the unit of area of a figure is square kilometers, what is the natural unit for the perimeter of the figure? *(Lesson 8-1)* kilometers

376

In 19 and 20, use the figure at the right.

19. Given: $\angle PAQ \cong \angle DAR$
$\angle PQA \cong \angle DRA$
$PQ = RD$.
Prove: $\triangle PAD$ is isosceles.
(Lessons 7-4, 5-1) **See margin.**

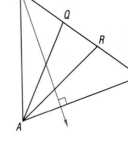

20. Accurately draw or construct the line perpendicular to $\overline{AD}$ containing P. *(Lesson 3-6)*

In 21 and 22, solve. *(Previous course)*

21. $x^2 + 9 = 25$ **x = -4 or 4**

22. $y^2 + 10 = 90$
$y = \sqrt{80} \approx 8.94$ or $-\sqrt{80} \approx -8.94$

23. *Multiple choice.* If $\sqrt{48} = k\sqrt{3}$, what is k? *(Previous course)*
(a) 4
(b) 16
(c) $\sqrt{45}$
(d) cannot be determined **(a)**

Exploration

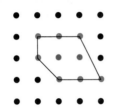

24. *Multiple choice.* When the vertices of a polygon are on a lattice, there is a formula for its area. The formula is known as Pick's Theorem. Use the polygon at the left and test with other polygons, to answer this question. Let P be the number of lattice points *on* the polygon. Let I be the number of lattice points *inside* the polygon. Which is the polygon's area (in square units)?
(a) $\frac{1}{2}P + I - 1$
(b) $\frac{1}{2}P + I$
(c) $\frac{1}{2}P + I + 1$
(d) $\frac{1}{2}(P + I)$ **(a)**

25. Below is a pentagon that tessellates, of a type discovered by Marjorie Rice in 1975. Draw enough of a tessellation to show the pattern.
See margin.

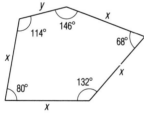

MORE PRACTICE
For more questions on SPUR Objectives, use *Lesson Master 8-4,* shown below.

25. See Additional Answers in the back of this book.

NAME _____

LESSON **MASTER 8–4**
QUESTIONS ON **SPUR** OBJECTIVES

■**SKILLS** *Objective B (See pages 410–413 for objectives.)*
In 1–3, use the grid to estimate the area of the island.

1. side of small square: 1 mile
2. side of small square: 4 km

Area ≈ _____**31.5 sq mi**_____   Area ≈ _____**736 km²**_____

3. side of small square: $\frac{1}{4}$ mile

4. Estimate the area of the trapezoid below **a.** using the grid at the left; **b.** using the grid at the right. The small squares at the left are 10 mm on a side.

Area ≈ _____**47.5 sq mi**_____
a. _____**600 mm²**_____
b. _____**600 mm²**_____

67

OBJECTIVES

D Calculate areas of squares, rectangles, parallelograms, and triangles from relevant lengths.

E Given areas of figures, determine relevant lengths.

I Tell how to derive formulas for area.

L Apply formulas for areas of squares, rectangles, parallelograms, and triangles to real situations.

N Determine the areas of polygons on a coordinate plane.

TEACHING NOTES

Most students will have seen the formulas for the areas of right triangles and triangles previously. If they have not, this lesson may take longer than a day.

Error Analysis Although most students have seen a formula for the area of a triangle, they may make tacit assumptions which hinder their application of it. Often the area formula is memorized as "one-half of the product of base and height." Tacitly, *base* becomes the "longest side" or "the bottom side." Students may have

Areas of Triangles

This photograph of a diamond shows triangular pock marks left in the outermost layers when crystal growth stopped.

Most of the shapes you have studied so far have not been irregular, but are special types of polygons. These shapes are so common that formulas have been developed to give their areas in terms of lengths of segments. One such formula is assumed in the Area Postulate: The area of a rectangle equals the product of its dimensions.

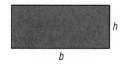

Area = hb

All of the other area formulas for polygons can be derived from that postulate. To start, it is easy to find the area of any right triangle ABC. Just rotate $\triangle ABC$ 180° about M, the midpoint of $\overline{AC}$, as you did in making a tessellation. The image is $\triangle CDA$. Quadrilateral $ABCD$ is a parallelogram with a right angle, so $ABCD$ is a rectangle. By the Congruence and Additive Properties of the Area Postulate, the area of each triangle is half the rectangle.

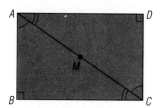

Area($ABCD$) = $AB \cdot BC$
So Area($\triangle ABC$) = $\frac{1}{2}(AB \cdot BC)$.

This argument shows:

Right Triangle Area Formula:

The area of a right triangle is half the product of the lengths of its legs.

$A = \frac{1}{2}hb$

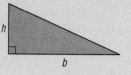

378

From the area of a right triangle, a formula for the area of *any* triangle can be derived. The idea of *altitude* is needed. In a triangle, an **altitude** is the perpendicular segment from a vertex to the line containing the opposite side. In each drawing below, $\overline{AD}$ is the altitude to side $\overline{BC}$ of $\triangle ABC$.

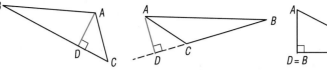

altitude $\overline{AD}$ inside $\triangle ABC$
D between B and C

altitude $\overline{AD}$ outside $\triangle ABC$
D not between B and C

altitude $\overline{AD}$ on $\triangle ABC$
$D = B$

Suppose $\triangle ABC$ is given and you don't know its shape. As shown above, there are only three possibilities for the altitude from A to side $\overline{BC}$. Either the altitude is inside the triangle, outside the triangle, or is a side of the triangle. In all cases, the same simple formula for the area of the triangle can be deduced.

Triangle Area Formula:

The area of a triangle is half the product of a side and the altitude to that side.

$$A = \tfrac{1}{2} hb$$

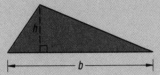

Proof

We want the area of $\triangle ABC$, which could be any triangle. In each case below, b is a side of the triangle and h is an altitude to that side. We want to show in all cases that
Area($\triangle ABC$) = $\tfrac{1}{2} hb$.

Case I: The altitude is inside the triangle. The altitude splits $\triangle ABC$ into two right triangles. Let $BD = x$ and $DC = y$. Then $x + y = b$.

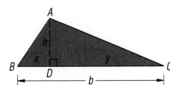

Area($\triangle ABC$) = Area($\triangle ABD$) + Area($\triangle ADC$)	Additive Property of Area
$= \tfrac{1}{2} hx + \tfrac{1}{2} hy$	Right Triangle Area Formula
$= \tfrac{1}{2} h(x + y)$	Distributive Property
$= \tfrac{1}{2} hb$	Substitution

LESSON 8-5 Areas of Triangles   **379**

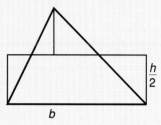

Questions 6b, 7, and 14:
These questions have more
than enough information.
This bothers some students,
who view such problems as
ones containing tricks. This is
not the case at all. In the real
world, you can sometimes
get any dimension you wish
by measuring. A basic task in
calculating area is to first determine which lengths are
needed.

**Small Group Work for
Questions 13-16:** Ask
students to discuss their answers. Have them (1) identify
which number is the altitude
and which is the base (any
side can be a base); (2) give
the area. Other members of
the group should respond
with corrections or assis-
tance.

Question 13: This is an
important question. Students
need the experience of actually doing measurements.
Consider dividing students
into **small groups,** with students in each group measuring a different side and the
altitude to that side. Due to a
variation in skill of measurement, answers will vary
slightly. Students will learn to
discern when an answer is
acceptable.

Question 16: The area
formula has three variables.
Given any two, the third is
determined. So far, area has
been calculated from the two
lengths. In this question, the
area and one length are
known, from which the other
length can be calculated.

Question 17: There are
at least five ways to ap-
proach this problem:
(i) Pick's Theorem;
(ii) interior squares + half of
boundary squares;
(iii) squares pieced together
from congruent triangles;
(iv) large square with four
triangular corners;
(v) triangles determined by
horizontal and vertical lines
through vertices.

Case II: The altitude is outside the triangle. The area of $\triangle ABC$ is found by subtracting.

$$\text{Area}(\triangle ABC) = \text{Area}(\triangle ADC) - \text{Area}(\triangle ADB)$$
$$= \tfrac{1}{2} h(x + b) - \tfrac{1}{2} hx$$
$$= \tfrac{1}{2} hx + \tfrac{1}{2} hb - \tfrac{1}{2} hx$$
$$= \tfrac{1}{2} hb$$

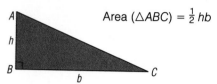

Case III: The altitude is a side of the triangle. In this case, the triangle is a right triangle, so the formula works.

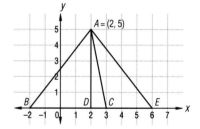

Area $(\triangle ABC) = \tfrac{1}{2} hb$

In the Example, the unit is not given; therefore, the answer is given using a general term of square units, or units^2.

Example Given coordinates as shown, find the area of:

a. $\triangle ABC$
b. $\triangle ADE$
c. $\triangle ACE$.

Solution $\overline{AD}$ is the altitude of each triangle and $AD = 5$ units.

a. Area$(\triangle ABC) = \tfrac{1}{2} \cdot BC \cdot AD$
$= \tfrac{1}{2} \cdot |3 - \text{-}2| \cdot 5$
$= \tfrac{1}{2} \cdot 5 \text{ units} \cdot 5 \text{ units}$
$= 12.5 \text{ units}^2$

b. Area$(\triangle ADE) = \tfrac{1}{2} \cdot DE \cdot AD$
$= \tfrac{1}{2} \cdot |6 - 2| \cdot 5$
$= \tfrac{1}{2} \cdot 4 \text{ units} \cdot 5 \text{ units}$
$= 10 \text{ units}^2$

c. Area$(\triangle ACE) = \tfrac{1}{2} \cdot CE \cdot AD$
$= \tfrac{1}{2} \cdot |6 - 3| \cdot 5$
$= \tfrac{1}{2} \cdot 3 \text{ units} \cdot 5 \text{ units}$
$= 7.5 \text{ units}^2$

380

Questions

Covering the Reading

1. Define: altitude of a triangle. **the perpendicular segment from a vertex to the line containing the opposite side**

2. Sketch a triangle and an altitude: **See margin.**
   a. with the altitude outside the triangle;
   b. with the altitude coinciding with a side;
   c. with the altitude interior to the triangle.

In 3–5, give an area formula for the figure.

3. rectangle
   $A = \ell w$

4. right triangle
   $A = \frac{1}{2} hb$

5. triangle
   $A = \frac{1}{2} hb$

6. a. How is Area($\triangle ABC$) related to the area of the two right triangles in the figure below?

   Area($\triangle ABC$) = Area($\triangle ABD$) − Area($\triangle CBD$)

   b. If $BD = 7$ mm, $AC = 15$ mm, and $CD = 5$ mm, what is Area($\triangle ABC$)? **52.5 mm²**

7. Give the area of
   a. $\triangle EFH$; **24 units²**
   b. $\triangle FGH$; **60 units²**
   c. $\triangle EGH$. **84 units²**

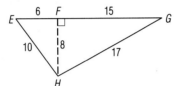

In 8–10, find the area of the triangle.

8.

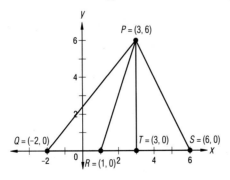

10.5 units²

9.

12 units²

10.

1 sq unit

11. Find the area of: **a.** $\triangle PQR$; **b.** $\triangle PRS$; **c.** $\triangle PQS$.

   a) 9 units²;
   b) 15 units²;
   c) 24 units²

Question 18: This result is quite useful. In some books, it is applied only to rhombuses. Encourage students to remember it in its full generality, as applying to all quadrilaterals with perpendicular diagonals, and also as a kite area formula.

Questions 22 and 23: While this is a review of simplifying radical expressions, consider having students check their answers to Questions 22 and 23 by using their calculators. For Question 22, find the square root of 2, multiply it by 3, and then square the result. They should get 18. For Question 23, find the square root of 5, multiply it by 3, and then square the result.

Question 24: Teachers identified this question as particularly well liked by students.

ADDITIONAL ANSWERS
2. samples:
a.

b.

c.

13. a. (Art is reduced in size.)

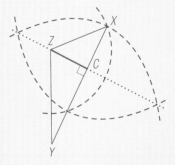

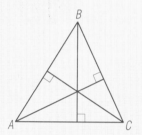
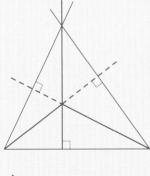
12. Main, First, and Elm streets border the triangular lot with dimensions (in feet) as given below. If Main is an east-west street and First a north-south street, what is the area of the lot? **21,000 ft²**

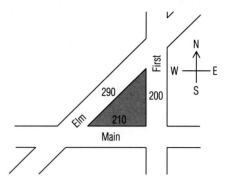

13. Trace $\triangle XYZ$ at the left.
  a. Construct one of its altitudes. See margin.
  b. Estimate its area in square centimeters by measuring an altitude and appropriate side and using the Triangle Area Formula.
  Sample: $XY \approx 7.9$ cm; $CZ \approx 2.3$ cm; area ≈ 9.1 cm²

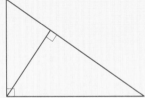

14. Approximate dimensions (in meters) of ABC, a part of a roof, are given at the right.
  a. What is the perimeter of this part of the roof? **32 m**
  b. What is its area? **48 m²**

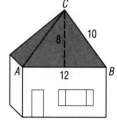

15. Given $\triangle ABC$ with altitudes $\overline{AW}$ and $\overline{CF}$. If $AB = 8$, $CF = 6$, and $AW = 7$, find CB.
  $\frac{48}{7} \approx 6.86$ units

16. Find the length of a side of a triangle whose area is 18 square inches and altitude is 1 foot in length. **3 in.**

17. The grid at the right is a tessellation of unit squares. Find the exact area of quadrilateral $ABCD$.
  23 units²

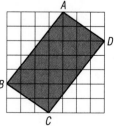

382

382

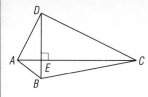

18. A quadrilateral with perpendicular diagonals is drawn at the left.
   a. Prove that the area of this quadrilateral is $\frac{1}{2} AC \cdot BD$, half the product of the lengths of its diagonals.
   b. To which of the following types of quadrilaterals does the result of part **a** apply: isosceles trapezoids, kites, parallelograms, rectangles, rhombuses, squares, or trapezoids?

Review

19. Estimate the area of Texas **a.** first using the grid below at the left, then **b.** using the grid at the right. Each little square at the left is 96 miles on a side. *(Lesson 8-4)* **See margin.**

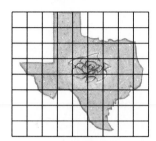
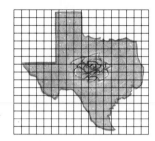

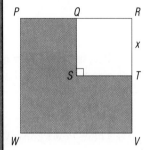

20. At the left, *PRVW* is a square. *Q* and *T* are midpoints. *RT = x*. Find the area of the green section. *(Lesson 8-3)* $3x^2$

21. Hexagon *ABCDEF* has vertices at points $A = (0,12)$, $B = (11, 12)$, $C = (11, 4)$, $D = (9, 4)$, $E = (9, 0)$, and $F = (0, 0)$. Find Area(*ABCDEF*). *(Lesson 8-3)* **124 units²**

In 22 and 23, rewrite with a smaller integer under the radical sign.
(Previous course)

22. $\sqrt{18}$ $3\sqrt{2}$

23. $\sqrt{45}$ $3\sqrt{5}$

Exploration

24. Below, the named points are equally spaced along the path *AEHLA*. Each point *A, B, C, D, E* is connected to each point *H, I, J, K, L*. How many triangles in the drawing have the same area as △*CLH*?
9 (not counting △CLH)

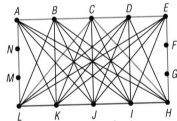

25. Use a ruler, compass, or automatic drawer.
   a. Draw a triangle △*ABC*, the altitudes to $\overline{AB}$, $\overline{BC}$, and $\overline{AC}$, and extend the altitudes so they intersect.
   b. Repeat part **a** with triangles of various shapes.
   c. Conjecture when the altitudes intersect inside a triangle, when outside the triangle, and when at a point on the triangle.
   See margin.

LESSON 8-5 Areas of Triangles **383**

FOLLOW-UP

MORE PRACTICE
For more questions on SPUR Objectives, use *Lesson Master 8-5,* shown below.

NAME _____

LESSON **MASTER 8-5**
QUESTIONS ON **SPUR** OBJECTIVES

■ **SKILLS** *Objectives D and E (See pages 410–413 for objectives.)*
In 1–4, find the areas of the triangles given the relevant lengths.

1. Area(△*ABC*) = _____ **84 units²**   2. Area(△*BCE*) = _____ **32 units²**

3. Area(△*LMN*) = $\dfrac{648x^2}{\text{units}^2}$ 4. *DF* = 4 cm, *DH* = 3.8 cm, *EF* = 6 cm.
   Area(△*DEF*) = _____ **11.4 cm²**

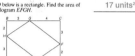

5. *ABCD* below is a rectangle. Find the area of parallelogram *EFGH*. **17 units²**

6. △*LPO* has an area of 48 square in. One base measures 16 in. What is the measure of the altitude to the base? **6 in.**

7. An equilateral triangle has an approximate area of 73 square inches and a perimeter of 39 inches. What is the length of the altitude of the triangle? $\dfrac{146}{13} \approx 11.23$ in.

68 *Continued* Geometry © Scott, Foresman and Company

NAME _____
Lesson MASTER 8–5 (page 2)

■ **PROPERTIES** *Objective I*

8. Name the figure that is used to derive the formula for the area of a right triangle. **rectangle**

9. What idea is needed to derive the formula for the area of any triangle? **altitude**

■ **USES** *Objective L*

10. In the town plan below, Broadway is parallel to Lincoln St. and perpendicular to 5th Ave. The town decides to fertilize the grass in the triangular park surrounded by Broadway, Washington, and Jackson. Each bag of fertilizer will cover about 400 square feet of grass. How many bags will be needed? $156\frac{1}{4}$
(or 157)

■ **REPRESENTATIONS** *Objective N*

11. A triangle has vertices (-4, 6), (5, 6), and (2, 8).
   a. Draw the triangle on the coordinate plane at the right.
   b. Find the area of the triangle **9 units²**

Geometry © Scott, Foresman and Company **69**

RESOURCES
■ Lesson Master 8-6
■ Quiz for Lessons 8-4
  Through 8-6

OBJECTIVES

D Calculate areas of squares, rectangles, parallelograms, trapezoids, and triangles from relevant lengths.
E Given areas of figures, determine relevant lengths.
I Tell how to derive formulas for area.
L Apply formulas for areas of squares, rectangles, parallelograms, trapezoids, and triangles to real situations.
N Determine the areas of polygons on a coordinate plane.

TEACHING NOTES

The word *algorithm* was introduced in Lesson 3-6. Most students should be familiar with it by now; if not, provide some examples: the long division algorithm; the algorithm for constructing a perpendicular bisector with a ruler and compass; the algorithm for approximating the area of an irregular region.

Note that Step 2 of the algorithm (page 384) is easier said than done. Students should see that much work is necessary to find the areas. If there are two measurements for each triangle, then there are $2(n - 2)$ measurements for an n-gon. Point out that to reduce the number of measurements use sides shared by triangles.

Areas of Trapezoids

Knowing a formula for the area of a triangle is useful because any polygon can be split into triangles. When this occurs, it is said that the polygon has been **triangulated.** Below, pentagon *ABCDE* at the left has been copied and triangulated at the right.

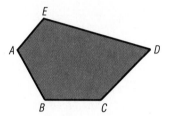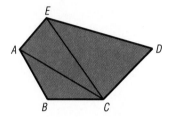

This idea provides an algorithm for getting the area of *any* polygon. Step 1: Triangulate the polygon. Step 2: Get the area of each triangle (by measuring lengths of sides and altitudes). Step 3: Add the areas to get the area of the polygon.

But an algorithm is not the same as a formula. There is no known general formula for the area of a polygon even if you know all the lengths of its sides and the measures of its angles. But if a polygon can be split into triangles with altitudes or sides of the same length, then there can be a formula. One kind of polygon that can be split in this way is the trapezoid. A bonus is that a trapezoid area formula will apply to all of the special kinds of quadrilaterals which are below the trapezoid in the hierarchy of quadrilaterals.

Here is an example of how to get the area of a trapezoid. In trapezoid *CDEF* below, given are the lengths of the bases (10 and 5) and its *altitude* $\overline{CP}$ (14). The **altitude of a trapezoid** is the distance between its bases. This is enough to find the area.

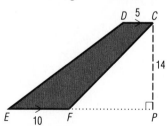

384

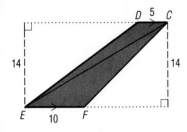

First, split the trapezoid into triangles *CDE* and *CEF*. Do you see that in each triangle, one side and the altitude to that side is known? Furthermore, in each case the altitude is 14. So the area can be found.

$$Area(CDEF) = Area(\triangle CDE) + Area(\triangle CEF)$$
$$= \tfrac{1}{2}(14 \cdot 5) + \tfrac{1}{2}(14 \cdot 10)$$
$$= 35 + 70$$
$$= 105 \text{ square units}$$

The idea of this example can be used to deduce a formula for the area of a trapezoid.

Trapezoid Area Formula:

The area of a trapezoid equals half the product of its altitude and the sum of the lengths of its bases.

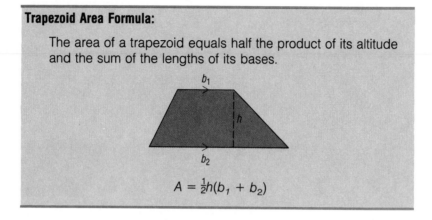

$$A = \tfrac{1}{2}h(b_1 + b_2)$$

Proof

Draw a figure. *CPIO* is a trapezoid with altitude h and bases b_1 and b_2. The proof is just a generalization of the example that preceded the theorem.

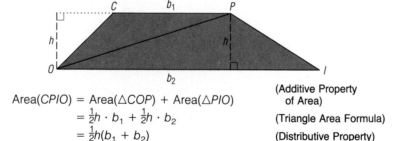

$Area(CPIO) = Area(\triangle COP) + Area(\triangle PIO)$	(Additive Property of Area)
$= \tfrac{1}{2}h \cdot b_1 + \tfrac{1}{2}h \cdot b_2$	(Triangle Area Formula)
$= \tfrac{1}{2}h(b_1 + b_2)$	(Distributive Property)

In symbols, if A is the area of a trapezoid with bases b_1 and b_2 and altitude h, then $A = \tfrac{1}{2}h(b_1 + b_2)$. Because of the Commutative Property of Multiplication, $\tfrac{1}{2}h(b_1 + b_2) = h \cdot \tfrac{1}{2}(b_1 + b_2)$. Remember that $\tfrac{1}{2}(b_1 + b_2)$ is the mean or average of b_1 and b_2. So the area of a trapezoid equals the product of its altitude and the average of its bases.

Students often have been asked to "show work" to get full credit or to use a particular procedure to arrive at an answer to a question that they could obtain more easily some other way. For this reason, some students will not use the Trapezoid Area Formula, but will split up every trapezoid into two triangles (as is done on page 385) to find the area. When asked why they don't use the formula, they will point to page 385 and say, "That's the way it was done in the book."

Point out that the book goes through one example this way for two reasons. First, the example is generalized to get the formula. Thus, on page 385 at the bottom, students will see exactly the same idea as on page 385 in the middle, but using variables instead of quantities. Second, if students forget the formula, they can go through the process that was used to arrive at the formula.

Some students and teachers prefer the following form of the Trapezoid Area Formula: The area of a trapezoid equals the product of its altitude and the average of its bases.

Error Analysis   To avoid the tacit assumption that an altitude of a trapezoid is "vertical," place a trapezoid on an overhead projector in a variety of positions. Recall that in Lesson 7-6 the fact that parallel lines are equidistant was proved. Therefore, it is appropriate to speak of the altitude as the distance between the parallel lines.

Making Connections
You might want to mention that the areas of trapezoids (and rectangles) are important in calculus to help approximate the area of a nonpolygonal region.

Example 1   Compute the area of polygon $ABCD$ below.

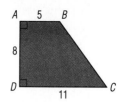

Solution   From the markings, you can deduce that $\overline{AB} \parallel \overline{CD}$, making $ABCD$ a trapezoid with $b_1 = 5$, $b_2 = 11$, and $h = 8$. Apply the Trapezoid Area Formula.

$$\begin{aligned}\text{Area}(ABCD) &= \tfrac{1}{2}h(b_1 + b_2) \\ &= \tfrac{1}{2} \cdot 8(5 + 11) \\ &= 4 \cdot 16 \\ &= 64 \text{ units}^2\end{aligned}$$

Since a parallelogram is a special trapezoid, the trapezoid formula applies to parallelograms as well. For example, $SPOT$ is a parallelogram with altitude h. In a parallelogram, opposite sides are equal, so $b_1 = b_2 = b$.

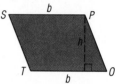

$$\begin{aligned}\text{Area}(SPOT) &= \tfrac{1}{2}h(b_1 + b_2) \\ &= \tfrac{1}{2}h(b + b) \\ &= \tfrac{1}{2}h(2b) \\ &= hb\end{aligned}$$

Since either pair of parallel sides can be considered as its bases, a parallelogram has two altitudes.

Parallelogram Area Formula:

The area of a parallelogram is the product of one of its bases and the altitude for that base.

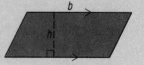

$A = hb$

In Example 2, lengths of sides and altitudes are given. You must be careful to sort out which lengths to use.

Example 2 Find the area of the parallelogram *ABCD* at the right.

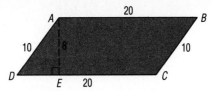

Solution

$$Area = hb$$
$$= 8 \cdot 20$$
$$= 160 \text{ units}^2$$

(Notice that the side with length 10 is not used.)

Another way of justifying the Parallelogram Area Formula is as follows. In Example 2, think of translating △*ADE* to the right of the parallelogram. A rectangle *ABFE* is formed. Its area is the same as that of the parallelogram. So the area of the parallelogram is 160 units².

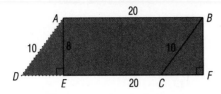

Questions

Covering the Reading

1. Trace trapezoid *ABCD* below and triangulate it.

 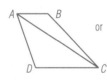 or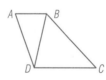

2. Describe an algorithm for obtaining the area of any polygon.
   See margin.

In 3 and 4, use the figure at the right.

3. **a.** Name the bases and altitude of trapezoid *EFGH*.
   b. Find Area(*EFGH*). **6720 units²**
   a) bases: $\overline{EF}$ **and** $\overline{GH}$, **altitude:** $\overline{IF}$

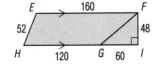

4. Find Area(*EFIH*). **8160 units²**

5. Give the area formula for any trapezoid. $A = \frac{1}{2}h(b_1 + b_2)$

6. *Multiple choice.* To find the area of a trapezoid,
   (a) you must triangulate;
   (b) you must use the Trapezoid Area Formula;
   (c) you can either triangulate or use the Trapezoid Area Formula. **(c)**

7. $\frac{1}{2}(b_1 + b_2)$ is the __?__ or __?__ of b_1 and b_2. **mean, average**

LESSON 8-6 Areas of Trapezoids **387**

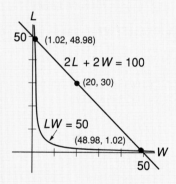

NOTES ON QUESTIONS
Question 25: You might remind students that the two north-south borders of Nevada intersect even though they are perpendicular to the same line. The lines (great circles) containing these borders intersect at the North Pole. Even so, the calculations are very close to the actual area of the state. Ask: What other states have shapes which allow their areas to be rather easily approximated? (Colorado and Wyoming, rectangles; Utah and New Mexico, union of rectangles; North Dakota and Connecticut, trapezoids)

FOLLOW-UP

MORE PRACTICE
For more questions on SPUR Objectives, use *Lesson Master 8-6,* shown on page 389.

EXTENSION
You may wish to have students explain why the four regions made by intersecting diagonals in a parallelogram have the same area.

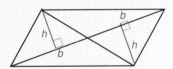

All four triangles have height *h* and base *b.*
Similarly, you might also have students prove that a median divides a triangle into two triangles of equal area. **Again, the triangles have the same height and equal bases.**

EVALUATION
A quiz covering Lessons 8-4 through 8-6 is provided in the Teacher's Resource File.

In 8–10, find the area of the largest trapezoid in the drawing.

8.
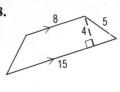

46 units²

9.

57 units²

10. 87.5 units²
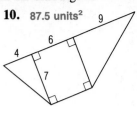

11. Give an area formula for any parallelogram. $A = hb$

In 12 and 13, find the area of the parallelogram.

12.

36 units²

13.

16,800 units²

Applying the Mathematics

In 14 and 15, find the area of the trapezoid with the given vertices.

14.

31.5 units²

15.

$\frac{1}{2}bc$ units²

16. A trapezoid has one base 20, a second base 15, and an area of 60. What is the altitude of the trapezoid? ≈ **3.43 units**

Review

In 17 and 18, use the figure below. *(Lesson 8-5)*

17. *Multiple choice.*
The area of $\triangle ABC$ is
(a) $h + x + g$ units²
(b) hx units²
(c) $\frac{1}{2}hxg$ units²
(d) $\frac{1}{2}hx$ units². **(d)**

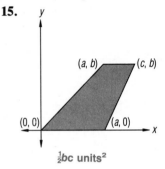

18. *Multiple choice.*
The area of $\triangle ABE$ is
(a) $h(x + y + z)$ units²
(b) $\frac{1}{2}h(x + y + z)$ units²
(c) $g + x + y + z + j$ units²
(d) $\frac{1}{2}(g + j)(x + y + z)$ units² **(b)**

388

19. A piece of fabric is made in the shape at the left. Explain how the amount of fabric needed for that piece could be estimated. *(Lesson 8-4)* **See margin.**

20. Draw a rectangle with perimeter 100 mm and area less than 50 square mm. *(Lessons 8-3, 8-1)* 1 mm
49 mm

21. If the length of a radius of $\odot O$ is $6x$, what is the length of a diameter? *(Lesson 2-5)* **12x**

22. Find the area of $\triangle KLM$ below. *(Lesson 8-5)* **21 units²**

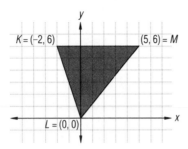

$K = (-2, 6)$ $(5, 6) = M$

$L = (0, 0)$

In 23 and 24, expand. *(Previous course)*

23. $(a + b)(c + d)$
$ac + ad + bc + bd$

24. $(e + f)^2$
$e^2 + 2ef + f^2$

Hoover Dam in Lake Mead, Nevada

25. The state of Nevada is roughly shaped like a trapezoid.
  a. Use the dimensions given below to estimate the area of the trapezoid that includes Nevada. **113,150 sq miles**
  b. The Colorado River cuts a region off southeast Nevada that is almost a trapezoid with north-south bases 80 and 120 miles long and an east-west length of 30 miles. Approximate the area of this region, shaded in the drawing. **3000 sq miles**
  c. From your calculations in **a** and **b,** estimate the area of Nevada. **110,150 sq miles**
  d. From a map or almanac, find the area of Nevada in square miles. How close is your estimate from part **c**? **From the** *1987 Information Please Almanac,* **the area is 109,893 mi². The estimate is off by 257 mi², or about 0.2%. (Other sources may have different areas.)**

310 miles

210 miles

520 miles

LESSON 8-6 Areas of Trapezoids   **389**

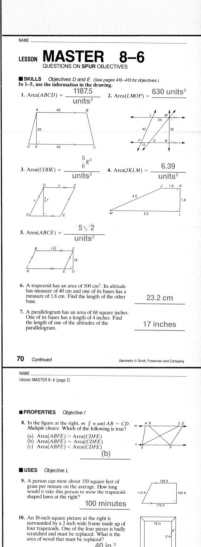

The Pythagorean Theorem

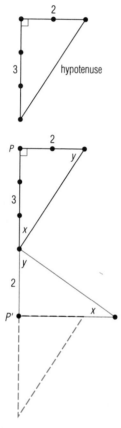

hypotenuse

390

area = A | side = $\sqrt{A}$

From the area of a square you can determine the length of any of its sides. If the area is A, the length of the side is $\sqrt{A}$. That is why $\sqrt{A}$ is called the **square root** of A. Just as a plant rests on its roots, a square can rest on its (positive) square root.

Thus if the area of a square is 400 square centimeters, its side has length 20 cm. If the area is 13 square feet, its side has length $\sqrt{13}$ feet. You can verify the latter of these with a calculator:
$\sqrt{13} \cdot \sqrt{13} \approx 3.6055513 \cdot 3.6055513 \approx 13$.

This idea, that area can tell you something about length, was used by the Greek mathematician Pythagoras in the 6th century B.C. to obtain the theorem that is named after him. The *Pythagorean Theorem* enables you to find the length of the hypotenuse of a right triangle if you know the lengths of its legs. It is a famous theorem and most students have seen it before taking a geometry course.

But first imagine that you do not know this theorem. (This will be easy if in fact you don't!) Suppose you were given a right triangle with legs of 2 and 3 units. There are a couple of ways you could find the length of the hypotenuse. You could draw the right triangle and estimate the hypotenuse by measuring. At the left is a right triangle with legs of length 2 cm and 3 cm. You can measure the hypotenuse. You should get about 3.6 cm.

An exact answer can be found by the procedure illustrated at the left. Translate the triangle 5 cm along its 3 cm side. Under this translation, the image of P is P'. Then rotate the image triangle 90° about P'. Do this process twice more and you get a figure like that below. The angle measures x and y add to 90°, so the angles of the middle figure (shaded) are right angles. All sides of the shaded region are congruent, so they have the same length. So the shaded region is a square.

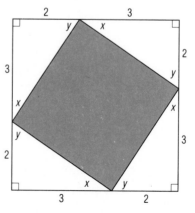

Of course, the large, outlining figure is also a square. Its area is $5 \cdot 5$ or 25. Each corner triangle has area $\frac{1}{2} \cdot 2 \cdot 3$, or 3, so the four corners have a total area of 12. This leaves 13 for the area of the shaded square. So its side is $\sqrt{13}$. This agrees with the estimate found by measuring.

The sides of the right triangle are thus 2, 3, and $\sqrt{13}$. Notice that $2^2 + 3^2 = (\sqrt{13})^2$. The general relationship is the Pythagorean Theorem, and its proof involves the same procedure as above, except with a and b instead of 2 and 3.

Pythagoras (6th century B.C.) imagined to have the appearance and stature of a Biblical figure, by an unknown artist in an 18th century copper engraving book (no drawing of the actual Pythagoras exists)

Pythagorean Theorem:

In any right triangle with legs a and b and hypotenuse c,
$$a^2 + b^2 = c^2.$$

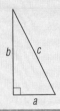

Proof

The original triangle with its translation and rotation images is below. Its legs are a and b and the hypotenuse is c. The area of the shaded square is thus c^2. Now we find the shaded area in a second way.

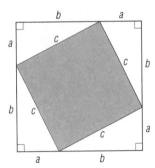

Side of big square $= a + b$.
Area of big square $= (a + b)^2$.
Each of the four corner right triangles has area $\frac{1}{2} ab$.
So the shaded square has area
$(a + b)^2 - 4 \cdot \frac{1}{2} ab = a^2 + 2ab + b^2 - 2ab$
$\qquad\qquad\qquad = a^2 + b^2$.
But the area of the shaded square is c^2. So $c^2 = a^2 + b^2$.

Computer If your students have not seen the Pythagorean Theorem before, consider having them explore it with an automatic drawer before reading this lesson. Students should be asked to draw a variety of triangles, including right triangles, measure the sides, add the squares of the two shorter sides, and compare the sum with the square of the longest side. Encourage students to make conjectures about their observations.

Remind students that a calculator approximates square roots to the number of digits it can display, unless x is a perfect square.

Alternate Approach
Students are often intrigued by the Egyptian method for constructing a right triangle, as described on page 393. For the best effect, you must actually do the technique. Using a rope, chalk, and a ruler, mark off equal consecutive lengths from one end of the rope (12 lengths). Then bend the rope at the third mark and the seventh mark and stretch to make a triangle. Note that the lengths 3, 4, and 5 satisfy the Pythagorean relationship and the triangle is a right triangle. Repeat by bending at other points as counterexamples, or splitting into other lengths, such as 5, 12, and 13.

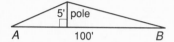
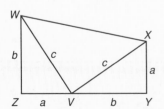
The Pythagorean Theorem is useful in many kinds of problems.

Example 1 Find YZ in the picture below.

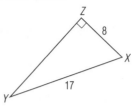

Solution From the Pythagorean Theorem,
$$XZ^2 + YZ^2 = XY^2.$$
So
$$8^2 + YZ^2 = 17^2$$
$$64 + YZ^2 = 289$$
$$YZ^2 = 225$$
$$YZ = 15 \text{ units.}$$

Check Does $8^2 + 15^2 = 17^2$? Yes, $64 + 225 = 289$.

Materials tend to expand when heated. Roads and railroad tracks must be built with some "give" to allow for expansion in hot weather. The expansion is more than most people think, as the Pythagorean Theorem can show.

Example 2 Suppose a 200-foot long rail ($\overline{AB}$ in the drawing) is solidly anchored at both ends. On a hot day, such a rail could expand 1 inch in length, causing it to buckle. Though it might curve, as shown below in an exaggerated picture, use a right triangle ($\triangle AMC$) to estimate the distance h it curves out from the straight track.

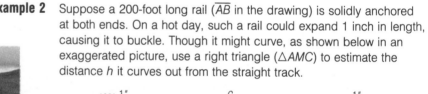

Solution First make the units consistent. Inches are easier. $100' = 1200''$ and so $100'\frac{1}{2}'' = 1200.5''$. Using the Pythagorean Theorem in $\triangle AMC$,
$$AM^2 + MC^2 = AC^2$$
$$1200^2 + h^2 = 1200.5^2$$
$$1,440,000 + h^2 = 1,441,200.25$$
$$h^2 \approx 1200.25$$
$$h \approx \sqrt{1200.25} \text{ or about 35 inches.}$$
The track will buckle almost 3 feet! For this reason, expansion joints are put on tracks. They give room for the rail to expand.

392

To make a right triangle, the ancient Egyptians took a rope with 12 equally spaced knots in it, and then bent it in two places to form a triangle with sides of lengths 3, 4, and 5.

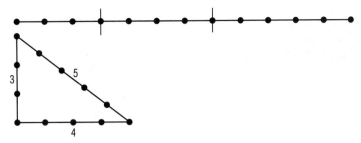

Does this work, or is it just close? Here we know $3^2 + 4^2 = 5^2$, and wonder if the triangle is a right triangle. This is an instance of the converse of the Pythagorean Theorem. Since the converse of a theorem is not necessarily true, its truth needs to be checked. As it happens, this converse is true. The proof is subtle; it uses the Pythagorean Theorem itself and the SSS Congruence Theorem.

Pythagorean Converse Theorem:

If a triangle has sides of lengths a, b, and c, and $a^2 + b^2 = c^2$, then the triangle is a right triangle.

Proof

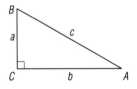

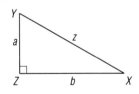

At the left is the given triangle ABC with sides of length a, b, and c and with $c^2 = a^2 + b^2$. The goal is to prove that $\triangle ABC$ is a right triangle. Consider right $\triangle XYZ$ with legs of lengths a and b.

By the Pythagorean Theorem, in $\triangle XYZ$, $a^2 + b^2 = z^2$.
But it is given that $a^2 + b^2 = c^2$.
By substitution, $z^2 = c^2$.
Taking positive square roots of each side, $z = c$.

Thus, by SSS Congruence, $\triangle ABC \cong \triangle XYZ$. So, by the CPCF Theorem, $\angle C$ is a right angle and thus $\triangle ABC$ is a right triangle.

Questions

Covering the Reading

1. Babylonian manuscripts indicate knowledge of the Pythagorean Theorem a thousand years before Pythagoras. About how many years ago were the Babylonian manuscripts created?
about 3600 years

2. If a square has area 225 square meters, how long is a side?
15 meters

LESSON 8-7 The Pythagorean Theorem   **393**

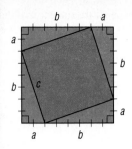

3. Use the figure at the left.
   a. What is the area of each corner triangle? $\frac{1}{2}ab$
   b. What is the area of the large square? $(a + b)^2$ or $a^2 + 2ab + b^2$
   c. What is the area of the tilted square in terms of a and b? $a^2 + b^2$
   d. What is c in terms of a and b? $\sqrt{a^2 + b^2}$

4. To find the length of the hypotenuse of a right triangle, which is shorter, the method of Question 3 or the Pythagorean Theorem? **Pythagorean Theorem**

5. *Multiple choice*. In this lesson, the Pythagorean Theorem is proved by (a) triangulation
   (b) estimating square roots
   (c) the method of Question 3. (c)

6. State the Pythagorean Theorem.
   In any right triangle with legs a and b and hypotenuse c, $a^2 + b^2 = c^2$.

In 7 and 8, find the length of the hypotenuse in each right triangle.

7.

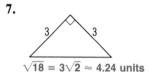

$\sqrt{18} = 3\sqrt{2} \approx 4.24$ units

8.

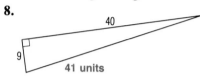

41 units

In 9 and 10, find the length of the third side of each right triangle.

9.

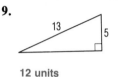

12 units

10.

$\sqrt{1599} \approx 39.99$ units

11. Suppose that the track in Example 2 expanded only 1/2″ instead of 1″. To the nearest inch, by how much would the track buckle? **24″**

In 12–20, a set of three numbers that can be sides of a right triangle is called a **Pythagorean Triple.** Determine if the set is a Pythagorean Triple.

12. 3, 4, 5 **Yes**

13. 70, 24, 74 **Yes**

14. 10, 24, 26 **Yes**

15. 14, 8, 17 **No**

16. 25, 24, 7 **Yes**

17. 40, 9, 41 **Yes**

18. 1.67, 2.67, 3.33 **No**

19. 1.5, 3.6, 3.9 **Yes**

20. 2, $2\frac{2}{3}$, $3\frac{1}{3}$ **Yes**

Applying the Mathematics

21. If a square room has an area of 20 square feet, to the nearest inch what is the length of a wall of the room? **54″**

In 22–24, it helps to draw a picture.

22. Felice walked from her home due north 10 miles, then due east 3 miles. How far, to the nearest tenth of a mile, is she from home? **10.4 miles**

23. Find the length of a diagonal of a rectangular field with sides 24 meters and 70 meters. **74 meters**

24. The base of a 10-foot ladder is placed 2 feet away from a wall. How high up the wall will the ladder reach? ≈ **9.8 feet**

394

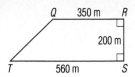

25. How long would it take a person to walk around the trapezoidal field pictured here, at a rate of 90 meters per minute? (Hint: Find QT by drawing a perpendicular from Q to $\overline{TS}$.) $\frac{1400}{90} \approx$ **15.56 minutes**

26. One leg of a right triangle is twice the length of the other. How many times larger than the smaller leg is the hypotenuse? (That is, find the value of k in the drawing below.) $k = \sqrt{5} \approx$ **2.2**

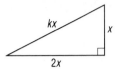

Review

27. Surveyors were hired to find the area of the empty lot $\triangle DNF$. First, they laid off an east-west line $\overleftrightarrow{EW}$. Then they measured segments and recorded distances.

segment	$\overline{DC}$	$\overline{NB}$	$\overline{FG}$	$\overline{CB}$	$\overline{BG}$
distance (in feet)	80	200	160	66	250

What is the area of the lot? (Hint: Find the area of $FNDCG$ and subtract the area of $FDCG$.) *(Lesson 8-6)* **16,320 sq ft**

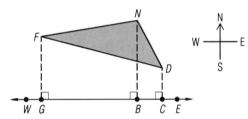

28. Explain how the area formula for a parallelogram is deduced from the formula for the area of a trapezoid. *(Lesson 8-6)* **See margin.**

29. Find the area of the triangle of Question 7. *(Lesson 8-5)*
4.5 units²

30. Drawn at the left is a pond in Wilson Park. If 1 cm on this drawing corresponds to 100 m on the pond, estimate the area of the pond by tracing it on a grid. A good estimate here is within 10,000 square meters of the actual area. *(Lesson 8-4)* $\approx$ **70,000 sq meters**

31. A rectangle has area 12 and perimeter 26. By trial and error, find the dimensions of the rectangle. *(Lessons 8-3, 8-1)* **1 and 12 units**

Exploration

32. For any positive numbers x and y with $x > y$, the three numbers
$$x^2 - y^2, \quad 2xy, \quad x^2 + y^2$$
will be a Pythagorean triple. For instance, if $x = 3$ and $y = 2$, then $x^2 - y^2 = 5$, $2xy = 12$, and $x^2 + y^2 = 13$. Since $5^2 + 12^2 = 13^2$, the set $\{5, 12, 13\}$ is a Pythagorean triple. Some Pythagorean triples are the correct answers in Questions 12–20. By substitution, find some other Pythagorean triples not listed there.
samples: $x = 3$, $y = 1$: $\{6, 8, 10\}$; $x = 10$, $y = 1$: $\{20, 99, 101\}$

LESSON 8-7 The Pythagorean Theorem **395**

FOLLOW-UP

MORE PRACTICE
For more questions on SPUR Objectives, use *Lesson Master 8-7*, shown below.

EXTENSION
There are a number of topics in this lesson that students may be interested in investigating. Some students may want to give a report on Pythagoras. Others may want to research the Egyptian method of using knotted cords to help them form right angles. Others may be interested in finding other proofs of the Pythagorean Theorem in the library. Encourage students to find a topic that interests them and to pursue it. Extra credit may motivate them.

ADDITIONAL ANSWERS
28. By the Quadrilateral Hierarchy Theorem, a parallelogram is a special trapezoid where $b_1 = b_2$, so $\frac{1}{2}h(b_1 + b_2) = \frac{1}{2} \cdot h \cdot 2b = hb$.

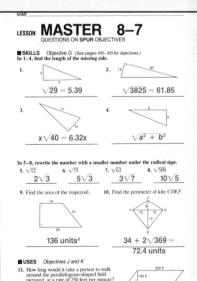

NAME _____

LESSON MASTER 8–7
QUESTIONS ON **SPUR** OBJECTIVES

■**SKILLS** *Objective G (See pages 410–413 for objectives.)*
In 1–4, find the length of the missing side.

1. $\sqrt{29} \approx 5.39$ 2. $\sqrt{3825} \approx 61.85$

3. $x\sqrt{40} \approx 6.32x$ 4. $\sqrt{a^2 + b^2}$

In 5–8, rewrite the number with a smaller number under the radical sign.

5. $\sqrt{12}$ $2\sqrt{3}$ 6. $\sqrt{75}$ $5\sqrt{3}$ 7. $\sqrt{63}$ $3\sqrt{7}$ 8. $\sqrt{500}$ $10\sqrt{5}$

9. Find the area of the trapezoid.
136 units²

10. Find the perimeter of kite *CDEF*.
$34 + 2\sqrt{369} \approx$ **72.4 units**

■**USES** *Objectives J and K*
11. How long would it take a person to walk around the parallelogram-shaped field pictured, at a rate of 250 feet per minute?
$\approx$ **5.29 min**

12. A ten-foot ladder has a warning on it not to place the bottom of the ladder closer than 2 feet to the base of a wall that it is leaning against. If you followed this restriction, how high could the ladder reach up a vertical wall?
$\sqrt{96} \approx$ **9.8 ft**

72   Geometry © Scott, Foresman and Company

LESSON 8-8

RESOURCES
■ Lesson Master 8-8
▣ Computer Master 19

TEACHING NOTES

Emphasize that arc measure involves the amount of rotation, whereas circumference is associated with arc length. Every circle contains 360° of arc, but circles may have quite different circumferences. These are difficult ideas for some students, and you may need to go carefully through the questions.

The term *circumference* is used to denote the perimeter of any simple closed curve, but it is not used for other figures. Thus, one speaks of the *circumference* of an ellipse, but the *perimeter* of a regular 32-gon.

To create a sense of need for two different types of measure for arcs, a bicycle race track with several lanes and turns of different degrees may be useful. Students would agree that all 90° turns are the same and are different from a sharp 60° turn. Yet, they would also see that a bike in the outer lane on the 90° turn travels farther than a bike on the inner lane.

LESSON

8-8

Arc Measure and Arc Length

Arcs of circles are formed by the streets in a planned community in Sun City, Arizona.

A circle with center O is drawn at the left. Suppose you walk along the circle counterclockwise from A to B. The part of the circle you have walked is **arc** AB, written $\overset{\frown}{AB}$.

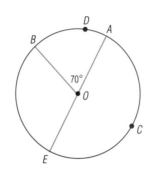

The measure of arc $\overset{\frown}{AB}$ is given in degrees, and is the same as the measure of the *central angle AOB*. Thus, the *measure of the arc AB* is 70°. That is, from A to B you have walked 70° around the circle. This tells how much you have turned and what part of the 360° circle you have traversed. If you walked the other way (clockwise) from A to C to B, you would have gone 290° around the circle.

Now we define these terms more precisely. A **central angle of a circle** is an angle whose vertex is the center of the circle. So, when A and B are points on a circle O, then $\angle AOB$ is a central angle. When $\angle AOB$ is not a straight angle, the points of $\odot O$ that are on or interior to $\angle AOB$ constitute the **minor arc** $\overset{\frown}{AB}$. The points A and B are the **endpoints** of the arc.

The points of $\odot O$ which are on or exterior to $\angle AOB$ constitute a **major arc** of circle O. Above at the left, this arc is named $\overset{\frown}{ACB}$. The third point C is included to distinguish the major arc ($\overset{\frown}{ACB}$) from the minor arc ($\overset{\frown}{AB}$). For extra clarity, the minor arc above can also be described as $\overset{\frown}{ADB}$.

When a central angle is a straight angle, then the arcs are called **semicircles.** Above, $\angle AOE$ is a straight angle, and both $\overset{\frown}{ACE}$ and $\overset{\frown}{ABE}$ are semicircles.

> **Definitions:**
>
> The **degree measure of a minor arc** or **semicircle** $\overset{\frown}{AB}$ of circle O, written **m$\overset{\frown}{AB}$,** is the measure of central angle AOB.
> The **degree measure of a major arc** $\overset{\frown}{ACB}$ of circle O, written **m$\overset{\frown}{ACB}$,** is 360° − m$\overset{\frown}{AB}$.

396

Example 1 In ⊙*O* at the right, find **a.** m$\widehat{RS}$; **b.** m$\widehat{RTS}$.

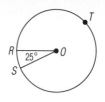

Solution

a. m$\widehat{RS}$ = m∠*ROS* = 25°
b. m$\widehat{RTS}$ = 360° − m$\widehat{RS}$ = 360° − 25° = 335°

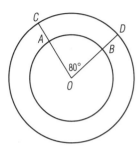

At the left, in the two concentric circles with center *O*, arcs $\widehat{AB}$ and $\widehat{CD}$ have the same degree measure as m∠*O*: m$\widehat{AB}$ = m$\widehat{CD}$ = 80°. Yet if you walked from *C* to *D*, you would walk a longer distance than if you walked from *A* to *B*. The arcs $\widehat{AB}$ and $\widehat{CD}$ have different lengths. **Arc length** *is not the same* as arc measure. Arc length indicates a distance; arc measure indicates an amount of a turn.

In the larger circle at the left, the length of $\widehat{CD}$ is a distance measured in linear units such as centimeters or inches, but m$\widehat{CD}$ is measured in degrees. The units of measure are different. To avoid confusion, in this book we always put the degree ° sign by an arc measure.

The *length* of an arc can be estimated by drawing chords. A **chord** is a segment whose endpoints are on a given circle. Below, the length of $\widehat{MN}$ is approximated by *MP* + *PQ* + *QR* + *RN*. By drawing more and more chords, their total length approaches the length of the arc as a limit. If this is done with an entire circle, the limit is the **circumference of a circle.** The term *circumference* is a synonym for perimeter. It is how far you would go if you walked around the circle. The ratio of the circumference *C* to the diameter *d* is equal in all circles. It is denoted by the famous number π, the Greek letter *pi*.

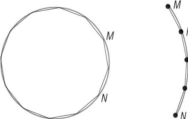

Definition:

π = $\frac{C}{d}$, where *C* is the circumference and *d* the diameter of a circle.

The number π is irrational; π cannot be written either as a finite or repeating decimal or as a simple fraction. The decimal for π is infinite. Here are the first 50 decimal places.

3.14159 26535 89793 23846 26433 83279 50288 41971 69399 37510

LESSON 8-8 Arc Measure and Arc Length **397**

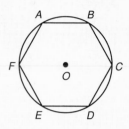
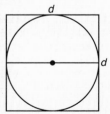

Alternate Approach

You might perform the following experiment. Hand students a sheet of paper with a circle of radius ≈ 4 inches. Have half of the class inscribe a polygon with sides of 1 inch (except for the last one) by starting at a point and carefully drawing chords 1 inch long. Have the other half of the class circumscribe the circle with a polygon of sides 1 inch. Arrive at the idea that the circumference of the circle is a number between the perimeters of the two polygons. Compare the average of the two perimeters with the number 8π.

Making Connections

Students have seen the approximation of area by smaller and smaller grids of squares superimposed on the region in question. To find arc length, the lengths of segments are added together. The smaller the lengths, the more accurate the approximation. These two geometric examples are a good foundation for the notion of limit.

A good preparation for size transformations (in Chapter 12) is to draw concentric circles and an angle from the center. Students should see that each arc in the interior of the angle is the same fraction of each circle. Hence, an arc could be measured by indicating what fraction of the circle it is. Conventionally, this is done by taking that fraction of 360°. For example, an arc which is one-fifth of the circle has measure 72°. The remaining four-fifths of the circle form an arc whose measure is 288°.

ADDITIONAL EXAMPLES

1. The two points A and B on circle O separate it into two arcs. If one arc is twice the measure of the other, what are their measures?
120° and 240°

2. A new truck tire has a radius of about 24 inches. A worn tire has a radius of 23 inches. How many more times will a worn tire turn in

Most scientific calculators have a key for π which gives the first 6 or 8 places in its decimal approximation. π is about 3.14159 or about $\frac{22}{7}$.

Solving the defining equation $\pi = \dfrac{C}{d}$ for C gives a formula for the circumference of any circle.

Circle Circumference Formula:

If a circle has circumference C and diameter d, then $C = \pi d$.

$$C = \pi d$$

Substituting $2r$ for d in the formula gives another version of it.
$$C = 2\pi r$$

Substituting 3.14 for π in the circumference formula gives an estimate for C.
$$C \approx 3.14d$$

In real situations, the estimate you use for π depends on the accuracy of the data. In Example 2, the given information does not warrant a closer approximation than 3.14.

Example 2 A mountain bicycle wheel has a diameter of 22 inches. If a rider can get it to go 300 revolutions in a minute, how far will the bike have traveled?

Solution   One revolution moves the bike the length of the circumference.
$$C \approx 3.14 \cdot 22$$
$$= 69.08 \text{ inches each revolution}$$
In 300 revolutions, the distance traveled is
$$300 \cdot 69.08 = 20{,}724 \text{ inches.}$$
Dividing by 12 gives the answer in feet, about 1727 feet.

Check   Is 1727 feet about what should be expected? 22″ is a little less than 2 feet. π is a little more than 3. So the circumference of the wheel is about 6 feet. In 300 revolutions, the bike should go about 1800 feet. The answer seems reasonable.

398

You can compute the length of an arc if you know its radius and the degree measure of the arc.

Example 3 In ⊙O, OB = 1.3 cm and m∠AOB = 80. Find the length of $\overarc{AB}$.

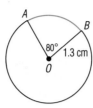

Solution m∠AOB = 80, so m$\overarc{AB}$ = 80°. Thus $\overarc{AB}$ covers $\frac{80}{360}$ of the entire circumference of ⊙O. So:

$AB = \frac{80}{360} \cdot C$

$\quad = \frac{80}{360} \cdot (2\pi r)$

$\quad = \frac{80}{360} \cdot 2 \cdot \pi \cdot 1.3$

$\quad = \frac{208\pi}{360}$ cm

$\quad \approx 1.8$ cm.

Questions

Covering the Reading

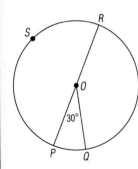

In 1–6, $\overline{PR}$ is a diameter of ⊙O at the left below.

1. Name the minor arcs in the drawing. $\overarc{RS}$, $\overarc{SP}$, $\overarc{PQ}$, $\overarc{QR}$, $\overarc{QS}$

2. **a.** m$\overarc{PQ}$ = __?__ 30°
   b. m$\overarc{PSQ}$ = __?__ 330°

3. **a.** m$\overarc{PSR}$ = __?__ 180°
   b. m$\overarc{PQR}$ = __?__ 180°
   c. m$\overarc{QR}$ = __?__ 150°

4. P and Q are the __?__ of $\overarc{PQ}$. endpoints

5. ∠ROQ is a(n) __?__ angle of ⊙O. central

6. $\overarc{PSR}$ is a(n) __?__. semicircle

7. What is the difference between arc length and arc measure?
   See margin.

8. Circumference is a synonym for __?__. perimeter

9. Is circumference an arc length or an arc measure? arc length

10. Define: π. **π is $\frac{C}{d}$, where**
    C is the circumference and d the diameter of a circle.

11. π is often approximated by the fraction __?__ or the decimal __?__.
    $\frac{22}{7}$, 3.14

---

a mile than a new tire?
About 18 more turns, since a 24-in. tire turns about 420 times in a mile, while a 23-in. tire turns 438 times.

3. The minute hand on a clock is 20 cm long. A fly has been sitting on the tip of the minute hand. How far has it traveled between 11 am and 3:45 pm?
The arc traveled is 4.75 × 360° = 1710°. The distance = $\frac{1710}{360}$ × 2 × 20 × π ≈ 597 cm.

4. What is the degree measure of an arc 10 inches long on a circle of radius 10 inches?
$\frac{180°}{\pi}$ ≈ 57°. This is exactly equal to one radian.

5. Two pulleys have a belt around them. The smaller pulley is attached to the power source, the larger to a machine. If the diameter of the larger pulley is three times that of the smaller pulley, and the smaller pulley is turning at a rate of 1200 rpm, what is the turning rate of the larger pulley?
Since the diameter is three times as large, its circumference is also three times as much. Thus, the smaller pulley must turn three times for one turn of the larger pulley. Its rate is 400 rpm.

NOTES ON QUESTIONS
Question 10: Students may find defining a number as a ratio of lengths as unusual. However, they have seen it before. The number "half" can be thought of as a ratio of lengths, as can any fraction.

Question 11: Another ratio of integers which approximates π well is $\frac{355}{113}$, which was used by the Chinese. It differs from π by less than .00000027.

ADDITIONAL ANSWERS
7. Arc length indicates a distance, while arc measure indicates the amount of a turn.

In 12 and 13, use ⊙*F* at the left.

12. a. Name all radii shown. $\overline{FA}, \overline{FC}, \overline{FD}$
  b. Name all diameters shown. $\overline{CA}$
  c. If $CF = 7$, then $FD = \underline{\ ?\ }$. 7
  d. If $CA = 28$, then $FD = \underline{\ ?\ }$. 14
  e. If $CA = 6x$, then $FC = \underline{\ ?\ }$. 3x

13. If $CA = 8$, find the circumference of the circle: **a.** exactly; **b.** to the nearest tenth. a) 8π units; b) 25.1 units

14. In Example 2 of this lesson, how far will the bike travel in five minutes if the wheel turns 210 revolutions per minute?
about 72,534 inches = 6044.5 ft. ≈ 1.14 miles

15. In ⊙*O* below, m$\widehat{AB}$ = 30°. Find the length of $\widehat{AB}$:
  a. exactly; $\frac{5\pi}{6}$ units
  b. to the nearest hundredth.
    2.62 units

Allen-Bradley clock,
Milwaukee, Wisconsin

16. A square wall ten meters on a side contains a circular pond. How long is it around the pond? 10π ≈ 31.4 m

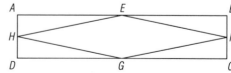

17. On the Allen-Bradley Company building in Milwaukee, Wisconsin, are four clocks facing in four different directions. The minute hand on each clock is 20′ long. How far does the tip of the minute hand travel in a day
  a. measured in degrees; 8640°
  b. measured in feet? 960π or about 3016 feet

18. Suppose it takes you 110 seconds to walk around a circular garden. At this rate, about how long would it take you to walk straight through the garden along a diameter? $\frac{110}{\pi}$ or about 35 seconds

Review

19. *E, F, G,* and *H* are midpoints of the sides of rectangle *ABCD*. If $AB = 8$ and $BC = 6$, find the perimeter of *EFGH*. *(Lessons 8-7, 8-1)*
20 units

400

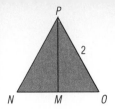

20. △PON is equilateral. M is the midpoint of $\overline{NO}$.
   a. Give the length of $\overline{PM}$. $\sqrt{3} \approx$ **1.7 units**
   b. Give the area of △PON. *(Lessons 8-7, 8-5)* $\sqrt{3} \approx$ **1.7 square units**

In 21–26, give a formula for the indicated quantity.
(Lessons 8-6, 8-5, 8-3, 8-1)

21. area of a trapezoid
   $A = \frac{1}{2}h(b_1 + b_2)$

22. area of a rectangle
   $A = \ell w$

23. perimeter of a square
   $p = 4s$

24. perimeter of a kite
   $p = 2a + 2b$

25. the measure of an angle in a regular n-gon $\dfrac{(n-2) \cdot 180}{n}$

26. area of a triangle $A = \frac{1}{2}hb$

In 27 and 28, $\ell \parallel m$ below. Assume the figure is drawn accurately.

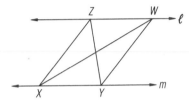

27. *Multiple choice.* *(Lesson 8-5)*
   (a) Area(△XYZ) > Area(△XYW)
   (b) Area(△XYZ) = Area(△XYW)
   (c) Area(△XYZ) < Area(△XYW) (b)

28. *Multiple choice.*
   If q is the perimeter of △XYZ and r is the perimeter of △XYW, then
   (a) $q > r$ (b) $q = r$ (c) $q < r$. *(Lesson 8-1)* (c)

29. Refer to Example 2. How fast is the rider going in miles per hour?
   (Previous course) ≈ **20 mph**

30. a. Measure the circumference of your neck with a tape measure to the nearest half inch or centimeter. **sample: $14\frac{1}{2}$ inches**
   b. Assuming your neck is circular, use your measurement to estimate your neck's radius. **sample: $\frac{14.5}{2\pi} \approx$ 2.3 inches**
   c. What would be another way to get its radius? (Cutting is not allowed, of course!)
   Estimate the diameter by measuring the distance between straightedges on either side of your neck. Half the diameter is its radius.

FOLLOW-UP

MORE PRACTICE
For more questions on SPUR Objectives, use *Lesson Master 8-8*, shown below.

EXTENSION
There are a number of topics related to circles that students may be interested in investigating. Some students may want to give a report on π and computer approximations to π. Some students may wish to discuss in groups why objects are made round and how that relates to the lesson. Some students may look for examples of circular structures in magazines that show arcs, as shown in the art on page 396.

EVALUATION
Alternative Assessment
It might be appropriate at this point to summarize all the formulas presented thus far. Include examples of finding the original dimensions from the formula as well as just applying the formulas to figures with known dimensions.

NAME _____

LESSON **MASTER 8–8**
QUESTIONS ON **SPUR** OBJECTIVES

■**SKILLS**   *Objective F (See pages 410–413 for objectives.)*

1. Give the circumference of a circle with a radius of 15
   a. exactly ___ 30π
   b. estimated to the nearest thousandth. ___ 94.248

2. Give the circumference of a circle with a diameter of 20 m
   a. exactly ___ 20π m
   b. estimated to the nearest meter. ___ 63 m

In 3 and 4, find the radius, to the nearest millimeter, of a circle whose circumference is given.
3. 0.5 cm ___ 1 mm   4. 12 cm ___ 19 mm

5. What is the length of an arc, with a measure of 120°, on a circle whose radius is 10? $\frac{20\pi}{3} \approx$ 20.94 units

6. In the figure at the right, $OB = 12$, m$\widehat{AB} =$ 50°. Find $\widehat{AB}$ to the nearest tenth. 10.5 units

■**USES**   *Objective M*

7. To contain oil spills, circular booms which trap the oil are put in the water. One oil slick is measured to be 150 meters across in diameter. How much boom material will be needed to surround it? $50\pi \approx$ 471.2 m

8. While the earth's orbit is actually shaped like an ellipse, it can be closely approximated by a circle with a radius of about 93,000,000 miles.
   a. What is the circumference of the earth's orbit? ≈186,000,000π mi
   b. About how fast is the earth traveling in its orbit in miles per hour? (Note: 1 year ≈ 8760 hours.) 66,705 mph

9. A dolphin can swim around the edge of a circular pool in 12 seconds. How long would it take the dolphin to swim straight across the pool along a diameter? $\frac{12}{\pi} \approx$ 3.82 sec

RESOURCES
■ Lesson Master 8-9
▤ Visual for Teaching Aid 53
can be used with
Questions 11 and **19**.
▤ Computer Master 20

OBJECTIVES

F Calculate lengths and
measures of arcs, the circumference, and the area
of a circle from relevant
lengths, and vice versa.
I Tell how to derive formulas
for area.
M Apply formulas for the area
and circumference of a
circle to real situations.

TEACHING NOTES

Students should be familiar
with the formula for the area
of a circle from previous
mathematics courses. This
lesson thus provides a good
opportunity to start the review
of the chapter.

It is important for students to
be able to go back and forth
from radius to diameter to
circumference to area. It
might be worth the class time
to show students how to calculate the other three quantities, given any one of them.
Stress that if the circumference is given, the radius
should be calculated first because it is the quantity
needed for substituting into
the area formula.

In explaining the proof of the
Circle Area Formula, stress
the idea that by increasing
the number of sectors, the
region formed by rearranging
the sectors is more closely

LESSON

8-9

The Area of a Circle

*These rocks, grouped to form a circle, can be found at a lookout point where the Gulf of
Mexico and the Carribean Sea meet. The design is based on an old Mayan style.*

A circle is not a polygon. But it can be approximated as closely as
you want by a polygon. We could try to get its area by finer and
finer grids, using the method in Lesson 8-4. However, it is easier to
use three-sided *wedges* (or *sectors*) and put them together to form a
figure like a parallelogram.

Circle *A* at the left below has radius *r*. It is split into 16 sectors.
Each sector is close to a triangle with altitude *r* and a curved base.
At the right the sectors are rearranged to form something like a
parallelogram. The height of the "parallelogram" is *r*. Each base is a
union of 8 arcs. So each base is half the circumference.

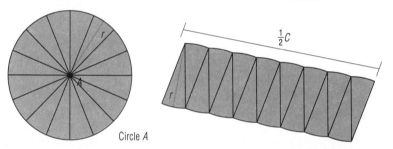

Circle *A*

As the number of wedges increases, the wedges more closely form a
parallelogram, and the area of the parallelogram becomes a better
approximation to the area of the circle. We say that the limit of the
area of the parallelogram is the area of the circle. This argument
yields a famous formula.

Circle Area Formula:

The area *A* of a circle with radius *r* is $A = \pi r^2$.

$A = \pi r^2$

402

Proof

Use the drawing on page 402 of a circle split into wedges and reformed to approximate a parallelogram.

Conclusions | Justifications
Area(circle A) = limit of | Congruence and Additive
    Area(parallelogram) | Properties of Area
    $= h \cdot b$ | Parallelogram Area Formula
    $= r \cdot \frac{1}{2}C$ | Substitution
    $= r \cdot \frac{1}{2} \cdot 2\pi r$ | definition of circumference
    $= r \cdot \pi r$ | Assoc. Prop. of Multiplication
    $= \pi r^2$ | definition of exponent

Example 1 Find the area of the top of a manhole cover with diameter 22″.

Solution Since $d = 22″$, $r = 11″$.
$$\text{Area(circle)} = \pi r^2$$
$$= 121\pi$$
$$\approx 121 \cdot 3.14$$
$$\approx 380 \text{ square inches}$$

Recall that the probability of an event is the ratio
$$\frac{\text{measure of event}}{\text{measure of all possibilities}}.$$

Example 2 A circle is drawn through the four vertices of a square with side 7 cm.
a. If a dart is thrown at random into the circle, what is the probability that it lands in the square?
b. Approximate the area of the shaded region between the square and the circle.

Solution **a.** The event is landing in the square. The probability equals
$$\frac{\text{area of square}}{\text{area of circle}}.$$
The area of the square is 7^2 cm^2, or 49 cm^2. For the area of the circle, find its radius first. $r^2 + r^2 = 7^2$, so $2r^2 = 49$, so $r^2 = \frac{49}{2}$ cm. The area of the circle is πr^2, or $\frac{49\pi}{2}$ cm^2. Thus the probability is
$$\frac{49 \text{ cm}^2}{\frac{49\pi}{2} \text{ cm}^2} = \frac{1}{\frac{\pi}{2}} = \frac{2}{\pi}.$$
With a calculator, $\frac{2}{\pi} \approx 0.64$, so the probability is about 64%. About 64% of the area of the circle is within the square.
b. Area(shaded region) = Area(circle) − Area(square)
$$= \frac{49\pi}{2} - 49$$
$$\approx 77 - 49$$
$$\approx 28 \text{ cm}^2$$

approximated by a parallelogram. These experiences build the notion of limit. Stress that the idea of limit is very important in higher mathematics.

Alternate Approach To give students a concrete view of the area formula, you might give them scissors, a circle, and several squares with sides equal to the radius of the circle. Have them cut the squares to cover the circle without overlapping as best they can. (Sample: Using three squares, cut out a 90° sector as shown below. One of the three cutoffs fits in the fourth quadrant of the circle.)

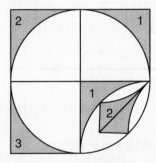

Students will have to decide if the football-shaped region remaining can be covered with the two remaining cutoffs. One of them fits easily as shown. By cutting and placing the pieces of the third cutoff, students will see that the circle has an area a little more than three squares of sides equal to the radius. The fact that $3\frac{1}{7}$ squares are approximately enough will have meaning for students.

Making Connections
The use of area formulas to calculate geometric probabilities may be new for students. Most students do not have a natural sense for guessing the amount of shaded area outside an inscribed square. They usually guess too low.

ADDITIONAL EXAMPLES

1. A rotating lawn sprinkler shoots water a distance of 30 feet. What is the area of the region where it waters?
about 900π ≈ 2827 sq ft

2. Mr. Perez has a box of grass seed which will cover 5000 square feet. He plans to have a square garden with a circular lawn centered in the square and to have flowers in the corners as shown.

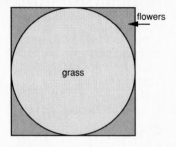

flowers

grass

If he makes the square 75 feet on a side, will there be enough seed for the circular lawn?
Yes, 5000 sq ft will cover a circle of diameter 79.79 ft.

NOTES ON QUESTIONS
Questions 2-4: Answers must be expressed in terms of π because the exact answer is required. **Question 5** asks for an estimate, so an approximation to π is fine.

Question 7: Real-life applications like this are important for students to know and should be discussed in detail.

Question 8: To express the area of a circle in terms of π is common. However, students should not expect that the expression must be in terms of π. For instance, if we ask for a circle with the same area as a square 10 cm on a side, then the area of the circle is 100 cm².

Question 9: Point out that the perimeter includes half the circumference of the circle. While circumference is reserved for simple closed (usually convex) curves, perimeter is used for the distance around any shape.

Covering the Reading

1. A circle with radius 10 below is split into 16 sectors. The 16 sectors can be put together (as in the lesson) into a "parallelogram."
  a. What is the height of the parallelogram? **10 units**
  b. What is the base of the parallelogram? **10π ≈ 31.42 units**
  c. What is the area of the parallelogram? **100π ≈ 314.2 units²**

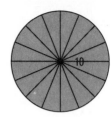

In 2–4, give the exact area.

2. a circle with radius r **πr^2**

3. a circle with radius 70″ **4900π sq inches**

4. a circle with diameter 10 inches **25 π sq inches**

5. Estimate the area of the circle in Question 3 to the nearest square inch. **15,394 in.²**

6. In Example 2, suppose that the side of the square was 9 cm.
  a. If a dart is thrown at random into the circle, what is the probability that it lands in the square? **$\frac{2}{\pi} \approx$ 64%**
  b. Approximate the area of the shaded region between the square and the circle (to the nearest tenth of a cm²). **≈ 46.2 cm²**

Applying the Mathematics

7. a. Give the area of a field that can be irrigated by a circular sprinkler 60 meters long rotating around a fixed point.
  b. Give the circumference of this field, to the nearest meter.
  a) 3600π ≈ 11,300 sq meters; b) 377 meters

8. A circle has area 144π. Find:
  a. its radius; **b.** its diameter; **c.** its circumference.
  12 units   **24 units**   **24π units**

9. *ABCD* below is a square with side 8 and $\overline{AB}$ is a diameter of the circle.
  a. Find the area of the shaded region. **64 − 8π ≈ 38.87 units²**
  b. Find the perimeter of the shaded region. **24 + 4π ≈ 36.57 units**

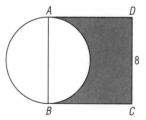

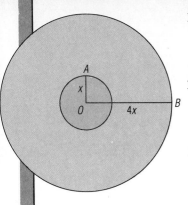

10. a. On a 10″ pizza, what measures 10″: the radius, diameter, or circumference? **diameter**
b. How many times more ingredients are in an 18″ pizza than in a 10″ pizza with the same thickness? **3.24**

11. Use the concentric circles at the left. $OA = x$, $OB = 4x$. The small circle is a bull's eye on a dart board. If a dart lands randomly in the large circle, what is the probability it will land: **a.** in the bull's eye; **b.** outside the bull's eye? **a) $\frac{1}{16}$; b) $\frac{15}{16}$**

12. Eight circular metal disks are to be cut out of a 12 cm by 24 cm piece of metal. The rest is wasted.
a. How much of the metal is wasted? **$288 - 72\pi \approx 61.8$ cm²**
b. What percent of the metal is wasted? **$\approx 21.5\%$**

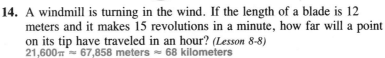

12 cm

24 cm

13. In $\odot O$ below, $OA = 15$ and $m\angle AOB = 72$.
a. Find $m\widehat{AB}$. **72°**
b. Find the length of $\widehat{AB}$. *(Lesson 8-8)* **$6\pi \approx 18.8$ units**

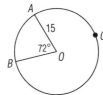

14. A windmill is turning in the wind. If the length of a blade is 12 meters and it makes 15 revolutions in a minute, how far will a point on its tip have traveled in an hour? *(Lesson 8-8)*
$21,600\pi \approx 67,858$ meters ≈ 68 kilometers

15. $\odot C$ below is contained by a square with sides of length 90. What is the circumference of $\odot C$? *(Lesson 8-8)* **$90\pi \approx 282.74$ units**

windmill in Consuegra, Spain

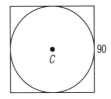

90

C

16. A rectangle has dimensions 16″ by 22″.
a. Find the lengths of its diagonals. *(Lesson 8-7)* **$\sqrt{740} \approx 27.2″$**
b. Find its perimeter. *(Lessons 8-7, 8-1)* **76″**

17. The two legs of a right triangle have lengths $4x$ and $9x$.
a. What is the area of the triangle? **$18x^2$ units²**
b. What is the perimeter of the triangle? *(Lesson 8-7, 8-5, 8-1)*
$(13 + \sqrt{97})x \approx 22.8x$ units

LESSON 8-9 The Area of a Circle **405**

Question 11: Some students may not see that the region is formed by removing a smaller circle from a larger one. The results are the same no matter where the smaller circle is removed from the larger one.

Question 12: Use the problem-solving strategy of *solving a simpler equivalent problem*. Split the piece into the 8 squares circumscribing the given circles. The ratio of metal wasted is the same for a single part as for the entire piece.

Many students have difficulty with part **b** and some students will be quite surprised with the result. Some will guess as low as 1/8 wasted. Ask students to conjecture whether more or less space is wasted if the diameter of metal disks is doubled? Only two can be cut out. (the same amount)

Question 19: The drawing is very rough; in one almanac, the area of Lake Michigan is given as 22,400 square miles.

NAME

LESSON **MASTER 8–9**
QUESTIONS ON **SPUR** OBJECTIVES

■**SKILLS** *Objective F (See pages 410–413 for objectives.)*
In 1–4, find the area of the circles with the given property:
a. exactly; b. estimating to the nearest tenth of a unit.

1. radius of 10 inches
   a. exactly **100π in.²**
   b. about **314.2 in.²**
2. diameter of 36 meters
   a. exactly **324π m²**
   b. about **1017.9 m²**
3. a circumference of 12π centimeters
   a. exactly **36π cm²**
   b. about **113.1 cm²**
4. radius of π units
   a. exactly **π^3 units²**
   b. about **31.0 units²**

5. Find the area of the shaded region between the concentric circles.
   $75\pi \approx 235.6$ units²

■**PROPERTIES** *Objective I*

6. Name the figure that is used to approximate the area of a circle in deriving the Circle Area Formula. **parallelogram**

■**USES** *Objective M*

7. A gardener needs to know the area of a circular flowerbed in order to know how much topsoil to lay. She measures the edge of the garden and finds that it is about 31.4 meters around. What is the area of the plot to the nearest tenth of a square meter? **78.5 m²**

8. A certain radio signal can be heard clearly up to 35 miles from the transmitter.
   a. How much area will the signal cover? **$1225\pi \approx 3848$ mi²**
   b. If the station can increase its range by 5 miles, how much more area will it cover? **$375\pi \approx 1178$ mi²**

9. You are offered two 8-inch pizzas or a 12-inch pizza for the same price. Which should you choose and why?
   12-in. pizza; area of 8-in. $= 4^2 \cdot \pi = 16\pi$,
   area of 12-in. $= 6^2 \cdot \pi = 36\pi$, $16\pi + 16\pi < 36\pi$.

74   Geometry © Scott, Foresman and Company

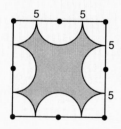
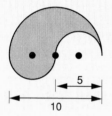
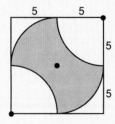
18. Can 13, 84, and 85 be the lengths of sides of a right triangle?
(Lesson 8-7) **Yes**

19. Estimate the area of Lake Michigan **a.** using the grid at the left, then
b. using the grid at the right. *(Lesson 8-4)* **See margin.**

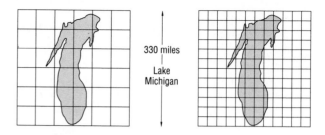

20. Find the area of the polygon with vertices (4, 3), (4, -3), (-4, -3), and
(-4, 3). *(Lesson 8-3)* **48 units²**

In 21 and 22, use parallelogram *DEFG* below.

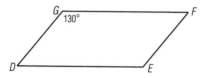

21. Find the measures of angles *D, E,* and *F. (Lesson 5-5)*
m∠E = 130, m∠D = m∠F = 50

22. Trace and draw a part of a tessellation with *DEFG* as the fundamental
region. *(Lesson 8-2)* **See margin.**

23. Fill in the blanks in these conversion formulas. *(Previous course)*
   a. 1 centimeter = ___?___ meter **.01**
   b. 1 yard = ___?___ inches **36**
   c. 1 mile = ___?___ yards **1760**

Exploration

24. Find a soft drink or other can with a circular base.
   a. Measure the diameter *d* with a ruler as accurately as you can.
   b. Measure the circumference *C* by rolling it, again as accurately as
   you can.
   c. Calculate $\frac{C}{d}$ to the nearest hundredth.
   d. What number should $\frac{C}{d}$ approximate?
   e. Why isn't $\frac{C}{d}$ exactly that number?

   For a 12-oz soft drink can,
   a) $d \approx 2\frac{9}{16}$ inches;
   b) $C \approx 8\frac{1}{4}$ inches;
   c) 3.22; d) π;
   e) Samples: measurements
   are approximate; base of
   can may not be
   an exact circle

Summary

This chapter is devoted to deriving and applying formulas for area, perimeter, and circumference. Perimeter measures the boundary of a figure. An equilateral n-gon with sides of length s has perimeter ns. A circle with diameter d has circumference πd. The length of an arc is a fraction of that circumference.

In contrast to perimeter, area measures the space enclosed by a figure. This space can be estimated by using congruent squares. With finer and finer grids, even the areas of irregular shapes can be estimated. Grids are examples of tessellations, patterns in which congruent copies of a single region cover the plane. Tessellations are based on rotation, translation, and reflection images of a fundamental region.

Mathematics captivates the imagination of many people because so many things can be derived from just a few simple statements. In this chapter, that idea is exemplified by the derivation of many area formulas from just a few basic properties.

A rectangle with dimensions h and b has area hb. Splitting it with a diagonal, two congruent right triangles are formed. Each has area $\frac{1}{2}hb$. By splitting into right triangles, the area of any triangle can be shown to be $\frac{1}{2}hb$. Putting two triangles together, the area of any trapezoid is $\frac{1}{2}h(b_1 + b_2)$. A special case of a trapezoid is a parallelogram, whose area is hb. (See the List of Formulas at the back of the book for a summary of these and other formulas.)

This chapter contains some of the most important formulas in all geometry. Areas of right triangles and squares help to develop the Pythagorean Theorem: In a right triangle with legs a and b and hypotenuse c, $c^2 = a^2 + b^2$. The area of triangles can be put together to derive the formula $A = \pi r^2$ for the area of a circle.

Vocabulary

Below are the most important terms and phrases for this chapter.
For the starred (*) terms you should be able to give a definition of the term. For the other terms you should be able to give a general description and a specific example of each.

Lesson 8-1
*perimeter
equilateral polygon
equiangular polygon
Equilateral Polygon Perimeter
 Formula: $p = ns$

Lesson 8-2
tessellation, tessellate
fundamental region

Lesson 8-3
dimensions
Area Postulate:
 Uniqueness Property of Area
 Rectangle Formula: $A = \ell w$
 Congruence Property of Area
 Additive Property of Area
Area(F)
nonoverlapping regions

Lesson 8-4
irregular region
grid, limit

Lesson 8-5
*altitude of a triangle
Right Triangle Area Formula:
 $A = \frac{1}{2}hb$
Triangle Area Formula:
 $A = \frac{1}{2}hb$

Lesson 8-6
triangulate
*altitude of a trapezoid
Trapezoid Area Formula:
 $A = \frac{1}{2}h(b_1 + b_2)$
Parallelogram Area Formula:
 $A = hb$

Lesson 8-7
square root
Pythagorean Theorem:
 $c^2 = a^2 + b^2$
Pythagorean Converse Theorem
Pythagorean triple

Lesson 8-8
*central angle of a circle
arc, minor arc, $\overparen{AB}$,
major arc, $\overparen{ADB}$
semicircle, endpoints of an arc
*degree measure of an arc
circumference, arc length,
chord, *π (pi)
Circle Circumference Formula:
 $C = \pi d$

Lesson 8-9
wedge, sector
Circle Area Formula: $A = \pi r^2$

CHAPTER 8 Summary and Vocabulary **407**

Progress Self-Test

See margin for answers not shown below.

Directions: Take this test as you would take a test
in class. Then check your work with the solutions
in the Selected Answers section in the back of this
book. You will need graph paper and a calculator
in addition to pencil and paper.

1. Draw part of a tessellation with trapezoid
PQRS as a fundamental region.

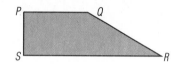

2. A rectangle has area 200 m² and length 25 m.
What is its width? **8m**

3. The perimeter of a regular hexagon is *q*. What
is the length of a side? $\frac{q}{6}$

In 4–6, give the area of the figure.

4.   5.

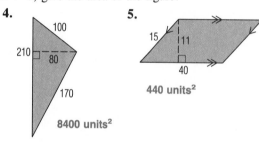

8400 units²   **440 units²**

6.

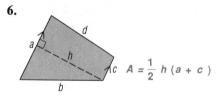

$A = \frac{1}{2} h (a + c)$

7. The two legs of a right triangle have lengths
11 and 60. What is the perimeter of the
triangle? **132 units**

8. A frame 2″ wide is put around a rectangular
painting that is 12″ by 17″. What is the outside
perimeter of the frame? **74″**

In 9 and 10, Circle *A* with radius 5 is contained in
square *WXYZ*.

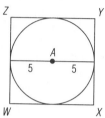

9. How much longer is it to go around the square
than to go around the circle?

10. If a point is chosen at random inside the
square, what is the probability that it is in the
circle? $\frac{\pi}{4} \approx$ **0.79, or 79%**

In 11 and 12, $\overrightarrow{OC}$ bisects right angle *DOB* in
⊙*O* below. *OB* = 20.

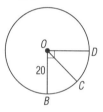

11. What is the length of arc $\overarc{CD}$? **5π ≈ 15.7 units**

12. What is m$\overarc{CBD}$? **315°**

13. In the map and grid shown below, each small
square of the grid has side length 10 miles.
Use the method of this chapter to determine
the area of Hawaii. **≈ 4800 sq miles (Answers
may vary.)**

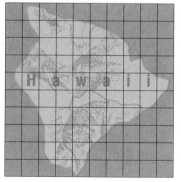

14. A 5-meter ladder is resting against a wall. Its base is 1.8 meters away from the wall. How high up the wall will it reach? Answer to the nearest tenth of a meter. **4.7 meters**

15. In October, 1989, an earthquake measuring 7.1 on the Richter scale caused substantial damage in San Francisco, 80 miles from the epicenter in Santa Cruz, California. To the nearest hundred square miles, how much area was within 80 miles of the epicenter? **20,100 square miles**

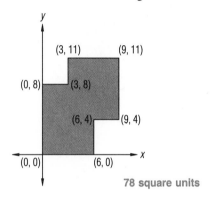

16. A room measures 9 ft by 15 ft. How many square yards of carpeting are needed to cover the floor? **15 sq yds**

17. A park is shaped like a square and has a perimeter of 2640 ft. What is its area? **435,600 sq ft**

18. Explain how the area formula for a right triangle is deduced from the formula for the area of a rectangle.

19. a. Could 11, 60, and 61 be lengths of sides of a right triangle? **Yes**
   b. Why or why not? **Pythagorean Conv. Thm.**

20. A triangle has vertices (8, 0), (-1, 0), and (0, 1). Find its area. **4.5 units²**

21. Find the area of the octagon below.

y

(3, 11)   (9, 11)

(0, 8) (3, 8)

(6, 4) (9, 4)

(0, 0)   (6, 0)   *x*

78 square units

ADDITIONAL ANSWERS
1. See Additional Answers in the back of this book.

9. $40 - 10\pi \approx 8.6$ units

18. A right triangle is tessellated to form a rectangle whose sides are the legs of the triangle. So the area of the triangle is one-half the area of the rectangle, which is one-half the product of the lengths of its legs.

CHAPTER REVIEW

The main objectives for the chapter are organized here into sections corresponding to the four main types of understanding this book promotes: Skills, Properties, Uses, and Representations. We call these the SPUR objectives.

The four types of understanding are not in increasing order of difficulty. There may be hard skills and easy representations; some uses may be easier than anything else; and so on.

USING THE CHAPTER REVIEW

Students should be able to answer questions like these with about 85% accuracy by the end of the chapter.

You may assign these questions over a single night to help students prepare for a test the next day, or you may assign the questions over a two-day period.

If you assign the questions over two days, then we recommend assigning the *evens* for homework the first night so that students get feedback in class the next day. Then assign the *odds* for the second night (the night before the test) so that students can use the answers provided in the book as a study aid.

Chapter Review

Questions on **SPUR** Objectives

See margin for answers not shown below.

SPUR stands for **S**kills, **P**roperties, **U**ses, and **R**epresentations. These Chapter Review questions are grouped according to the SPUR Objectives for this chapter.

SKILLS deal with the procedures used to get answers.

■ **Objective A:** *Draw a tessellation using a given figure as a fundamental region. (Lesson 8-2)*

In 1–3, trace the figure and draw part of a tessellation using the figure as a fundamental region.

1.

2.

3.

■ **Objective B:** *Describe or apply a method for determining the area of an irregular-shaped region. (Lesson 8-4)*

In 4 and 5, two grids cover the same island. Each small square at the left below is 100 feet on a side. Estimate the area of the island (in square feet).

4.

5.

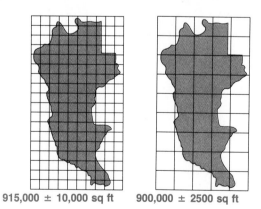

915,000 ± 10,000 sq ft   900,000 ± 2500 sq ft

410

6. A metal piece is to be made in the shape shown below. Explain how the amount of metal needed for that piece could be estimated.

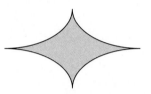

■ **Objective C:** *Calculate perimeters of parallelograms, kites, and equilateral polygons from lengths of sides, and vice-versa. (Lesson 8-1)*

In 7–10, give the perimeter of the figure.

7. a kite in which one side has length 10 and another side has length 6 **32 units**

8. a rhombus in which one side has length t **4t units**

9. a regular pentagon in which one side has length 47 meters **235 meters**

10. a square whose area is 324 square feet **72 ft**

11. The perimeter of a rectangle is 28 cm. One side has length 4 cm. What is the length of the other side? **10 cm**

12. If the perimeter of an equilateral triangle is P, what is the length of a side of the triangle? $\frac{P}{3}$

13. *ABCD* is a parallelogram pictured below. If its perimeter is 75, what are the lengths of its sides? **12.5 units and 25 units**

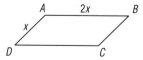

14. An equilateral hexagon has perimeter 1. What is the length of each side? $\frac{1}{6}$ **unit**

■ **Objective D:** *Calculate areas of squares, rectangles, parallelograms, trapezoids, and triangles from relevant lengths.* (Lessons 8-3, 8-5, 8-6)

In 15–19, calculate the area of the figure.

15. a square whose perimeter is 100 feet **625 sq ft**

16. the rectangle *MOST* drawn below **4.55 sq cm**

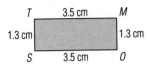

17. $\triangle EFG$ at the right in which $GE = 36x$ **$288x^2$ units^2**

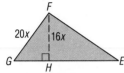

18. a trapezoid with bases 11 and 13 and altitude 6 **72 units^2**

19. the triangle with sides of lengths 13, 14, and 15 drawn here **84 units^2**

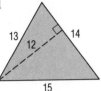

20. Find the area of the isosceles trapezoid below. **≈ 153.2 units^2**

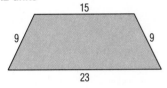

■ **Objective E:** *Given areas of figures, determine relevant lengths.* (Lessons 8-3, 8-5, 8-6)

21. A right triangle has area 60 square millimeters and one leg has length 6 millimeters. What is the length of the other leg? **20 mm**

22. The bases of a trapezoid have lengths 20 feet and 30 feet and the trapezoid has area 800 square feet. What is the length of the altitude of the trapezoid? **32 ft**

23. A square has area $12.25s^2$. What is the length of a side of this square? **3.5s units**

24. Can a rectangle with area 20 have one side of length 21? If so, draw such a rectangle. If not, tell why not.

■ **Objective F:** *Calculate lengths and measures of arcs, the circumference, and the area of a circle from relevant lengths, and vice-versa.* (Lesson 8-8, 8-9)

25. Give the circumference and area of a circle with radius 10: **a.** exactly; **b.** estimated to the nearest hundredth.

26. Give the circumference and area of a circle with diameter 6 cm: **a.** exactly; **b.** estimated to the nearest cm or sq cm.

27. A circle has area 144π. What is its diameter? **24 units**

28. A circle has circumference $40x$ meters. What is its radius? $\frac{40x}{2\pi} \approx$ **6.4x meters**

29. $\overline{BD}$ is a diameter of $\odot O$. $m\angle AOD = 20$.
  a. Find $m\widehat{AD}$. **20°**
  b. Find $m\widehat{AB}$. **160°**
  c. Find $m\widehat{ADB}$. **200°**

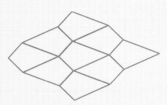

30. What is the length of a 60° arc of a circle with radius 9? $3\pi \approx$ **9.42 units**

■ **Objective G:** *Apply the Pythagorean Theorem to calculate lengths of sides in right triangles and other figures.* (Lesson 8-7)

In 31 and 32, find the length of the missing side.

31.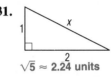
$\sqrt{5} \approx$ **2.24 units**

32.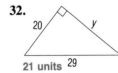
21 units

33. The two legs of a right triangle have lengths $6x$ and $7x$. What is the perimeter of the triangle? $13x + x\sqrt{85} \approx$ **22.2x units**

34. The hypotenuse of a right triangle is 50 and one leg is 40. What is the area of the triangle? **600 units^2**

35. A rectangle has dimensions 60 cm by 45 cm. What is the length of a diagonal? **75 cm**

■ **Objective H:** *Apply the Pythagorean Converse.* (Lesson 8-7)

In 36–39, could the numbers be lengths of sides of a right triangle?

36. 8, 31, 32 **No**   **37.** 16, 30, 34 **Yes**

38. 1, 2, $\sqrt{3}$ **Yes**   **39.** 2, 4, 20 **No**

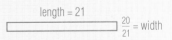

PROPERTIES deal with the principles behind the mathematics.

■ **Objective I:** *Tell how to derive formulas for area.* (*Lessons 8-3, 8-5, 8-6, 8-9*)

40. Explain how the area formula for a trapezoid is derived from the formula for the area of a triangle.

41. Explain how the area formula for a parallelogram is derived from the formula for the area of a trapezoid.

42. Give dimensions of a rectangle with perimeter 200 ft and area less than 100 ft². **sample: 99 ft by 1 ft**

43. In the figure below, $\ell \parallel m$.
Multiple choice.
(a) Area ($\triangle ABC$) < Area ($\triangle ABD$)
(b) Area ($\triangle ABC$) = Area ($\triangle ABD$)
(c) Area ($\triangle ABC$) > Area ($\triangle ABD$) **(b)**

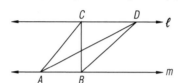

44. $\overline{AB}$ is a diameter of $\odot O$, $\overline{AO}$ is a diameter of $\odot P$. $AP = x$. Find the area of the shaded region. **$3\pi x^2$ units²**

45. *WXYZ* is a square, with segments as marked. Find the area of the shaded region. **$8s^2$ units²**

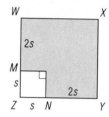

46. If the unit of the perimeter of a figure is millimeters, what is a natural unit for the area of the figure? **square millimeters**

USES deal with applications of mathematics in real situations.

■ **Objective J:** *Apply perimeter formulas for parallelograms, kites, and regular polygons to real situations.* (*Lessons 8-1, 8-7*)

47. A frame 3 cm wide is put around a rectangular-shaped painting that is 8 cm by 20 cm. What is the outside perimeter of the frame? **80 cm**

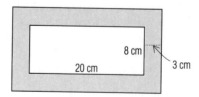

48. A stop sign is a regular octagon. Since it is metal, it could be sharp. Consequently, the manufacturer of the sign wishes to dull its edges by wrapping them with tape. If one edge of the sign has length *k,* what is the total length of tape needed? **8k**

49. A rectangular room is 9′ by 11′. Baseboard is to be put around the room in all places except the 3′ wide door. How many feet of baseboard are needed? **37′**

50. How long would it take for a person to walk around the trapezoidal field pictured here at a rate of 300 feet per minute? **14 minutes**

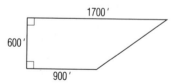

■ **Objective K:** *Apply the Pythagorean Theorem in real situations.* (*Lesson 8-7*)

51. If a 20-foot ladder reaches 18 feet high on a wall, how far away from the wall is the bottom of the ladder? **≈ 8.7 ft**

52. A rectangular field is 100 meters by 200 meters. To the nearest meter, how long is it diagonally across the field? **224 m**

412

Objective L: *Apply formulas for areas of squares, rectangles, parallelograms, trapezoids, and triangles to real situations.* (*Lessons 8-3, 8-5, 8-6*)

53. What is the area of a square park that is 210 meters on a side? **44,100 m²**

54. A person wishes to tile a bathroom floor with 1″ square tiles. How many tiles will be needed if the floor is 6′ long and 4′ wide? **3456**

55. What is the area of the field pictured in Question 50? **780,000 sq ft**

56. A triangular piece of fabric is needed for a sail. If the sail is to be 14′ high and is 15′ long at the base, about how much fabric will be used? **105 sq ft**

57. The larger square in Question 45 represents a farm, and the smaller square has been planted with corn. If a skydiver falls onto the farm, what is the probability he will fall on the part planted with corn? $\frac{1}{9}$ **or 11.1%**

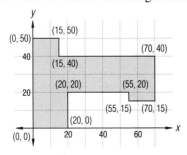

Objective M: *Apply formulas for the area and circumference of a circle to real situations.* (*Lessons 8-8, 8-9*)

58. Due to a chemical spill, the authorities had to evacuate all people within 3 km of the spill. To the nearest tenth of a square kilometer, how much area had to be evacuated? **28.3 km²**

59. A park 600 feet square contains a circular path, as pictured at the right. To the nearest foot, how long is it once around the path? **1885′**

600′

60. A car's tire has a radius of 1 foot. How many revolutions does the tire make while the car goes 1 mile? (1 mile = 5280 feet) ≈ **840**

61. For her dog, Betsy wants to make a circular play area surrounded by a fence. She has 100 feet of fence. What is the diameter of the largest play area she can make? $\frac{100}{\pi}$ ≈ **32 ft**

62. Use the figure for Question 44. If a dart lands at random in the larger circle, what is the probability that it will land in the smaller circle? $\frac{1}{4}$ **or 25%**

EVALUATION
Three tests are provided for this chapter in the Teacher's Resource File. Chapter 8 Test, Forms A and B cover just Chapter 8. The third test is Chapter 8 Test, Cumulative Form. About 50% of this test covers Chapter 8, 25% covers Chapter 7, and 25% covers previous chapters. For information on grading, see *General Teaching Suggestions: Grading* on page T44 in the Teacher's Edition.

ASSIGNMENT RECOMMENDATION
We strongly recommend that you assign the reading and questions from Lesson 9-1 for homework the evening of the test. It gives students work to do if they complete the test before the end of the period and keeps the class moving.

If you have not been giving assignments on the days of tests, a change now may allow you to cover half a chapter more over the course of the remainder of the year.

REPRESENTATIONS deal with pictures, graphs, or objects that illustrate concepts.

Objective N: *Determine the areas of polygons on a coordinate plane.* (*Lessons 8-3, 8-5, 8-6*)

63. Find the area of the decagon below. **2025 units²**

64. A triangle has vertices (7, -4), (-3, -4), and (-1, 11). Find its area. **75 units²**

65. The grid is in unit squares. Find the area of quadrilateral *ABCD*. **32 units²**

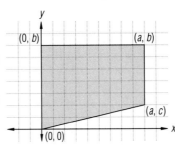

66. Find the area of the quadrilateral with the given vertices. Assume *a*, *b*, and *c* are positive, with $b > c$. $\frac{1}{2}a(2b - c)$ or $ab - \frac{1}{2}ac$

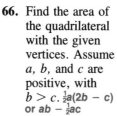

CHAPTER 9 THREE-DIMENSIONAL FIGURES

DAILY PACING CHART ■ CHAPTER 9

Every chapter of UCSMP *Geometry* includes lessons, a Progress Self-Test, and a Chapter Review. For optimal student performance, the self-test and review should be covered. (See *General Teaching Suggestions: Mastery* on page T36 of the Teacher's Edition.) By following the pace of the Full Course given here, students can complete the entire text by the end of the year. Students following the pace of the Minimal Course spend more time when there are quizzes and on the Chapter Review and will generally not complete all of the chapters in this text.

When all lessons are covered from the beginning (the recommendation of the authors), then students in the Minimal Course can cover through Lesson 13-4 and will cover all they need for future courses. For more information on pacing, see *General Teaching Suggestions: Pace* on page T35 of the Teacher's Edition.

DAY	MINIMAL COURSE	FULL COURSE
1	9-1	9-1
2	9-2	9-2
3	9-3	9-3
4	Quiz (TRF); Start 9-4.	Quiz (TRF); 9-4
5	Finish 9-4.	9-5
6	9-5	9-6
7	9-6	Quiz (TRF); 9-7
8	Quiz (TRF); Start 9-7.	9-8
9	Finish 9-7.	Progress Self-Test
10	9-8	Chapter Review
11	Progress Self-Test	Chapter Test (TRF)
12	Chapter Review	Comprehensive Test (TRF)
13	Chapter Review	
14	Chapter Test (TRF)	
15	Comprehensive Test (TRF)	

TESTING OPTIONS

■ Quiz for Lessons 9-1 Through 9-3   ■ Chapter 9 Test, Form A   ■ Chapter 9 Test, Cumulative Form
■ Quiz for Lessons 9-4 Through 9-6   ■ Chapter 9 Test, Form B   ■ Comprehensive Test, Chapters 1-9

PROVIDING FOR INDIVIDUAL DIFFERENCES

The student text has been written for, and tested with, average students. It also has been used successfully with better and more poorly prepared students.

The Lesson Notes often include Error Analysis and Alternate Approach features to help you with those students who need more help. A blackline Lesson Master (in the Teacher's Resource File), keyed to the chapter objectives, is provided for each lesson to allow more practice. (However, since it is very important to keep up with the daily pace, you are not expected to use all of these masters. Again, refer to the suggestions for pacing on page T35.) Extension activities are provided in the Lesson Notes for those students who have completed the particular lesson in a shorter amount of time than is expected, even in the Full Course.

OBJECTIVES ■ CHAPTER 9

The objectives listed here are the same as in the Chapter 9 Review on pages 462-465 of the student text. The Progress Self-Test on page 461 and the tests in the Teacher's Resource File cover these objectives. For recommendations regarding the handling of this end-of-chapter material, see the notes in the margin on the corresponding pages of the Teacher's Edition.

OBJECTIVES FOR CHAPTER 9 (Organized into the SPUR Categories—Skills, Properties, Uses, and Representations)	Progress Self-Test Questions	Chapter Review Questions	Lesson Master from Teacher's Resource File*
SKILLS			
A Draw common 3-dimensional shapes.	6-8	1 through 6	9-1, 9-2, 9-3, 9-4
B Draw plane sections of common 3-dimensional shapes.	9, 15	7 through 10	9-4
C Give views of a figure from the top, sides, or bottom.	14	11 through 14	9-6
D From a net, make a surface, and vice versa.	13, 16	15 through 18	9-7
E Give appropriate lengths, calculate areas and lengths in 3-dimensional figures.	17, 18	19 through 23	9-2, 9-3, 9-4
F From 2-dimensional views of a figure, determine properties of the 3-dimensional figure.	22	24 through 26	9-6
PROPERTIES			
G Identify parts of common 3-dimensional figures.	1-5, 11, 12	27 through 29	9-2, 9-3, 9-7
H Distinguish 3-dimensional figures by their defining properties.	19	30 through 33	9-2, 9-3, 9-7
USES			
I Recognize 3-dimensional figures in the real world.	20	34 through 37	9-2, 9-4
J Determine and draw symmetry planes in 3-dimensional figures.	10	38 through 41	9-5
REPRESENTATIONS			
K Factor algebraic expressions using common monomial factoring.	21	42 through 45	previous course
HISTORY			
L Relate the history of the Four-Color Problem.	23	46 through 50	9-8

*The masters are numbered to match the lessons.

414B

OVERVIEW ☐ CHAPTER 9

This chapter is a noncomputational chapter dealing with the common 3-dimensional shapes: prisms, cylinders, pyramids, cones, and spheres. A hierarchy relating the major types of surfaces covered in the chapter is in the Summary on page 460.

The main goals of the chapter are drawing and visualization of the common figures, and learning their vocabulary and basic properties. The lack of algebra and formulas in the chapter contrasts with the computational chapters that precede and follow it. For most students, this is an easy chapter.

In the real world, virtually all students can visualize well enough to drive a car and to recognize details in drawing. Visualization in life, however, is not the same as visualization in geometry; there are many skills associated with geometric visualization. Some practice is needed by students, particularly in determining the cues that help to distinguish one figure from another.

Drawing is much more a learned skill than visualization and you may have students with learning disabilities that prevent them even from copying drawings, even with practice. However, the authors believe strongly that drawing skills can be learned. Students usually improve in their drawing skills as they become more experienced.

There are review exercises throughout this chapter on factoring common factors. The reason is to prepare students for the algebra they will need in the next chapter to use formulas for surface area and volume. The reviews also apply the formulas of Chapter 8 in 3-dimensional figures.

Many visual teaching aids are provided to support the teaching of this chapter. Still, when possible, it is recommended that physical models of 3-dimensional shapes be used also, both for this chapter and Chapter 10.

PERSPECTIVES ☐ CHAPTER 9

The Perspectives provide the rationale for the inclusion of topics or approaches, provide mathematical background, and make connections with other lessons and within UCSMP.

9-1

POINTS, LINES, AND PLANES IN SPACE

This lesson introduces three additional parts of the Point-Line-Plane Postulate. These three parts complete the constraints on the undefined terms, and form the basis for making deductions in Euclidean geometry of three dimensions.

The major ideas of this lesson are: (1) planes customarily are drawn as parallelograms, and (2) certain combinations of points or lines determine a plane.

9-2

PRISMS AND CYLINDERS

This is a drawing and vocabulary lesson. The important idea introduced in this lesson is that with 3-dimensional figures, major types of surfaces include both curved and rectilinear (with straight edges) surfaces. This does not happen in two dimensions; polygons are separated in most classifications from circles or ellipses. In three dimensions, however, prisms and cylinders are classified as cylindric surfaces, and pyramids and cones are classified together as conic surfaces.

Another important idea in the lesson is that a given type of figure covers objects from big to small, as exemplified by the different types of boxes described in the second paragraph on page 422.

9-3

PYRAMIDS AND CONES

The goal of this lesson is to continue the development of vocabulary and drawing skills. A drawing quiz is appropriate after the lesson. Simply give names of figures (two intersecting planes, hexagonal prism, and so on) and ask students to make reasonable drawings. Ask students also to identify parts of these figures: the vertex of a pyramid; the line of intersection of two planes; and so on. Some students may have difficulty doing this because of perceptual disabilities that may or may not have been diagnosed.

In this book, all cones and cylinders have circular bases. In some books, the figure in the middle of page 428 would be called a right *circular* cone, but our definition of a cone makes this terminology redundant.

With pyramids, the word *vertex* has a dual meaning. *A vertex* of a pyramid can mean either endpoint of any edge. *The vertex* of a pyramid, however, always means the one vertex which is not a vertex of the base.

9-4

PLANE SECTIONS

This lesson contains a great deal of content, beginning with the sections of spheres (great circles and small circles), continuing with the sections of prisms, cylinders, and pyramids, and ending with the famous conic sections.

In this lesson, students need to be able to conceptualize plane sections for many calculations dealing with surface area and volume. However, drawing plane sections is quite difficult for many students. Though drawing should be covered, it should not be overemphasized.

9-5

REFLECTIONS IN SPACE

The purpose of this lesson is to introduce the idea of reflections in space. It is important for students to realize that the reflection images they see in mirrors can be described mathematically; that is, there are reflections over planes just as there are reflections over lines.

The definition of a reflection-symmetric figure for a space figure is a natural extension of the corresponding definition in the plane and is introduced in this lesson.

9-6

VIEWS OF SOLIDS AND SURFACES

The content of this lesson usually is not found in geometry courses, but is taught in drafting or mechanical drawing courses. The primary goal of the lesson is to teach visualization and drawing skills. Students are asked to draw a solid given various views of it, and to draw various views given a solid.

For many students, the questions that involve viewing a figure from different positions are quite difficult. This is not because they are inherently difficult, but rather that students have never been asked to do this kind of viewing before. Yet the ability to visualize is important in reading architect's plans and directions for building models, as well as maps, blueprints, and many other designs and diagrams.

9-7

MAKING SURFACES

The ideas of this lesson are applied at the beginning of the next chapter to the concept of surface area. If a net exists for a surface (as for any conic or cylindric surface), then the surface area of the surface equals the area of the net. So, the word *net,* not always found in geometry books, has a nice application.

In this lesson, the concept of a net is used for a simpler reason, namely, the surface itself can be constructed using a net.

9-8

THE FOUR-COLOR PROBLEM

This lesson is devoted to coloring problems. The Four-Color Conjec-

ture had a life of 124 years, before it was finally proved in 1976. Before 1976, mathematicians developed many new theorems trying to prove the conjecture.

The proof of the Four-Color Theorem demonstrated the power of computers in proving theorems. Haken and Appel first proved a number of reduction theorems. (Here they relied heavily on the earlier work of others.) A key step in their work was to correct some arguments in an earlier flawed proof. They then reduced the problem to 1,952 different types of configurations in maps. Each configuration type had as many as 500,000 different cases. The computer was then employed to go through all the cases of each type and show that they could be colored with four colors.

The entire proof of the Four-Color Theorem has never been written down on paper. The proof is partially a usual paper-and-pencil demonstration and partially a computer program. To write down the steps the computer has taken would take hundreds of thousands of pages and many lifetimes. For this reason, there are still some mathematicians who would say that the conjecture has not been proved; however, most mathematicians today accept the computer-assisted proof.

CHAPTER 9

We recommend 12 to 15 days for this chapter: 8 to 10 for the lessons and quizzes; 1 for the Progress Self-Test; 1 or 2 for the Chapter Review; 1 for a Chapter test. There is also a Comprehensive Test, which can serve as a quarterly exam. (See the Daily Pacing Chart on page 414A.) If you spend more than 15 days on this chapter, you are moving too slowly. Much of the vocabulary properties, and visualization are reviewed in the next chapter.

USING PAGES 414-415

Analogy is a powerful tool for understanding the concept of different dimensions. The classic book *Flatland,* by Edwin A. Abbott, is highly recommended for student reading as a study in understanding different dimensions.

Some students have heard of the fourth dimension. The following analogy can help them with one conceptualization of the fourth dimension.

A point is the 0-dimensional figure. It is fixed, a location. Suppose it could suddenly "break out" and move along a line, tracing out a segment. The segment is a 1-dimensional figure which is bounded by 2 points. The segment may travel back and forth along the line in its 1-dimensional world.

Suppose the segment could suddenly "break out" and move in a different direction, tracing out a square. The square is a 2-dimensional figure which is bounded by 4 segments and has 4 points at the corners. At each vertex, there are 2 perpendicular edges. The square may move about in its 2-dimensional world, a plane.

Suppose the square could suddenly "break out" and move in a different direction,

Three-Dimensional Figures

9-1: Points, Lines, and Planes in Space
9-2: Prisms and Cylinders
9-3: Pyramids and Cones
9-4: Plane Sections
9-5: Reflections in Space
9-6: Views of Solids and Surfaces
9-7: Making Surfaces
9-8: The Four-Color Problem

414

The world is not flat. Everything you touch or see, from paper to pencil, from house to car, from city to planet, is not in a single plane. The world is three-dimensional. This is why it was necessary for artists, if they wanted to convey reality, to develop the techniques of perspective.

Every figure has counterparts in a higher dimension.

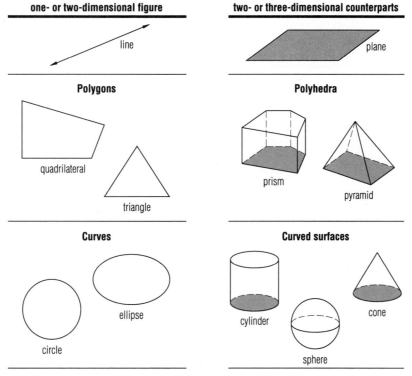

In this chapter, you will learn the important properties of the above basic three-dimensional shapes, how to draw them, and how they are used. You will also see how they are related to the two-dimensional figures you already know.

tracing out a cube. The cube is a 3-dimensional figure which is bounded by 6 squares and has 12 segments for edges and 8 points for corners. At each vertex, there are 3 edges, each perpendicular to the other two. Each edge is the intersection of perpendicular faces. The cube may move about in its 3-dimensional world or space.

Suppose the cube could suddenly 'break out" and move in a different direction, tracing out a hypercube. The hypercube is a 4-dimensional figure. By analogy, it is bounded by 8 cubes, has 24 squares for faces, has 32 segments for edges, and 16 points at corners. At each vertex, there are 4 edges, each perpendicular to the other three. Each edge is the intersection of 3 faces, each perpendicular to the other two. Each face is the intersection of 2 cubes; by analogy, it might be said that the cubes are perpendicular to each other.

Note that each figure is bounded by the figure of the previous dimension (segments bounded by points, squares by segments, cubes by squares, thus hypercubes by cubes).

OBJECTIVE

A Draw common 3-dimensional shapes.

TEACHING NOTES

Reading You might want students to take notes as they read this lesson. They should list the different meanings that point and line can have, and the conditions that determine a plane. Students should pay careful attention to how familiar terminology is used with respect to planes.

Only parts **e, f,** and **g** of the Point-Line-Plane Postulate are new in this lesson. You can motivate part **e** by using an example and counterexample. Place two tacks on a flat surface and tie a taut string around them. The string, representing a line, lies flat on the surface. For the same two tacks on a flexible surface, which may be bent into a nonplanar shape, the taut string will not lie on the surface. Note that the postulate determines the property we refer to as *flatness*.

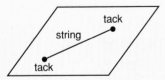

LESSON

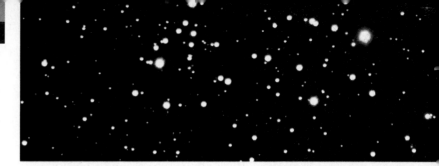

Points, Lines, and Planes in Space

Recall from Chapter 1 that the three terms "point," "line," and "plane" are undefined because we cannnot define every word and because, in different situations, they may have different meanings. A point could be an ordered pair, a location, a node of a network, or a dot. A line might be an arc connecting two nodes in a network, a set of ordered pairs described by an equation like $y = 2x + 5$, or a line of sight. In order to reason precisely with points and lines, it is necessary to make assumptions about them. Our assumptions were summarized in the Point-Line-Plane Postulate, repeated here.

Point-Line-Plane Postulate (Lesson 1-7):

a. Given a line in a plane, there exists a point in the plane not on the line. Given a plane in space, there exists a point in space not on the plane.

b. Every line is a set of points that can be put into a one-to-one correspondence with the real numbers, with any point on it corresponding to 0 and any other point corresponding to 1.

c. Through any two points, there is exactly one line.

d. On a number line, there is a unique distance between two points.

Just as you have an idea about what points and lines should be, you may have ideas about planes. Most of the figures you have seen in the previous chapters are coplanar. Think of a plane as being flat and having no thickness, like a tabletop that goes on forever. In fact, mathematicians draw a plane in three dimensions like they would draw a tabletop.

table	plane (as seen slightly from above)	line ℓ intersecting plane X at point P

416

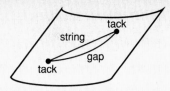

To convey these ideas precisely, three new parts—**e**, **f**, and **g**—are added to the Point-Line-Plane Postulate. The remainder of this lesson discusses these three new parts and presents other information about planes.

> **e.** If two points lie in a plane, the line containing them lies in the plane.

This guarantees that segments connecting points do not jump out of planes. It implies that planes are flat and go on forever.

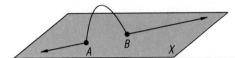

impossible because of **e**

> **f.** Through three noncollinear points, there is exactly one plane.

Part **f** is sometimes restated: Three noncollinear points determine a plane.

A tripod works on the principle of part **f**. It balances on the plane containing the tips of its three legs even when on the side of a hill (as long as its center of gravity is above the triangular region determined by the points). But a chair with four legs will not balance on a floor unless the tips of the legs are coplanar.

The tripod balances on the plane containing *A*, *B*, and *C*.

The chair is sturdy only if *E*, *F*, *G*, and *H* lie in the same plane.

Three noncollinear points *A*, *B*, and *C* also determine other figures. They can determine a triangle *ABC* or ∠*ABC*; a line $\overleftrightarrow{AB}$ and a point *C* not on it; two intersecting lines $\overleftrightarrow{AC}$ and $\overleftrightarrow{BC}$; and so on. Through any of these there is exactly one plane.

To motivate part **f**, you might hand a student a piece of plywood and three dowels of the same length. Ask what can be done to ensure that the plywood is in a plane parallel to the desk top. Is one dowel sufficient, excluding the idea of finding the center of gravity of the piece of plywood? Are two sufficient to determine the tilt of the plane? If three dowels are placed in a line, will that determine the tilt of the plane? Clearly, three noncollinear positions are sufficient to determine the tilt of the plane.

Because of the models used to demonstrate planes, students may tacitly assume properties for planes that are not true. For example, one sheet of paper may be positioned to touch another in only one point. Part **g** ensures that planes *do not have edges*. Another misconception is that planes have thickness; two intersecting planes, like two pieces of cardboard, may have a long rectangular solid in common. Part **g** also ensures that the planes *do not have thickness*.

Even copying a simple figure is difficult for some students, and almost everyone can benefit by some practice. If students have difficulty drawing planes and 3-dimensional figures, a transparent plastic ruler with lines on it can assist in drawing parallel lines. Emphasize that to make drawings of horizontal planes, draw a parallelogram with a pair of horizontal sides; to draw a vertical plane, use a pair of vertical sides.

417

However, there are many planes through a single line. Think of an open door in various positions. At each position a broad side of the door determines a plane through an imaginary line determined by the hinges. The planes are called **intersecting planes.**

Intersecting planes *P* and *Q*
$P \cap Q = \overleftrightarrow{AB}$

g. If two different planes have a point in common, then their intersection is a line.

Part **g** implies that planes, like lines, have no thickness. This part also implies that it is impossible for two different planes to intersect in just a single point. Even though planes cannot be drawn as if they go on forever, they do.

A sewing needle piercing fabric is like a line intersecting a plane.

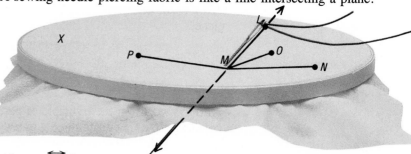

Above, $\overleftrightarrow{LM}$ intersects plane *X* at *M*, forming many angles with lines in the plane through *M*. Three of the angles are $\angle LMO$, $\angle LMN$, and $\angle LMP$. The measure of the smallest of all the possible angles defines the angle measure between the line and the plane. This cannot be greater than 90°. In a three-dimensional drawing like the one above, it is difficult to tell if the smallest angle has been drawn.

If the measure of an angle between a line and a plane is 90°, then the line is *perpendicular* to the plane. Think of a flagpole. The pole is perpendicular to any line on the ground through the pole. This makes the pole perpendicular to the ground.

Definition:

A **line ℓ is perpendicular to a plane X** if and only if it is perpendicular to every line in X through their intersection.

418

The ideas of parallel and perpendicular lines have counterparts with planes. Two planes are **parallel planes** if and only if they have no points in common, or they are identical. As with parallel lines, the distance between parallel planes is measured along any perpendicular segment connecting the planes. The distance to a plane from a point not on it is measured along the perpendicular segment to the plane from the point.

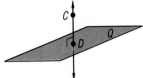

parallel planes M and N
distance AB between them

$\overleftrightarrow{CD}$ perpendicular to plane Q
distance CD from point C to plane Q

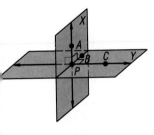

Suppose planes X and Y intersect in $\overleftrightarrow{PB}$, as shown at the left. Then the planes are **perpendicular planes** if and only if, when $\overline{PA} \perp \overline{PB}$ in X and $\overline{PC} \perp \overline{PB}$ in Y, then $\overline{PA} \perp \overline{PC}$ in the plane determined by A, P, and C.

Questions

Covering the Reading

In 1–6, name a higher dimensional counterpart for the one- or two-dimensional idea.

1. line plane

2. polygons polyhedra

3. circle
sphere, cylinder, or cone

4. collinear coplanar

5. perpendicular lines
perpendicular planes

6. If two lines in a plane are perpendicular to the same line, then they are parallel.
See margin.

In 7–10, draw the figure. See margin.

7. two parallel planes

8. a plane as seen slightly from above

9. two intersecting planes

10. a line perpendicular to a plane

11. a. When will a three-legged stool rest solidly on rough ground?
b. When will a four-legged stool rest solidly?
c. To what part of the Point-Line-Plane Postulate are the answers to **a** and **b** related? See margin.

12. Can the figure be contained by exactly one plane?
a. a line and a point not on the line Yes
b. two intersecting lines Yes
c. three non-collinear points Yes
d. a triangle Yes

LESSON 9-1 Points, Lines, and Planes in Space **419**

8.

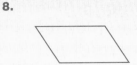

9.

10.

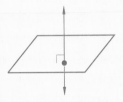

11. a. always (unless the center of gravity is not above the triangular region determined by the legs)
b. when the ends of the legs are coplanar
c. Through three noncollinear points, there is exactly one plane. (part f)

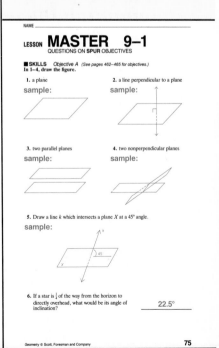

EXTENSION
What are the possible intersections of three different
planes?
**If all three are parallel,
there are no points in
common.
If exactly two are parallel,
then there are no points in
common; however, the
third intersects both and
the lines of intersection
are parallel.
If no two are parallel, then
either (a) the intersection
is a single point, or (b) the
intersection is a line.**

ADDITIONAL ANSWERS
**13. by measuring the
length of a segment
perpendicular to both walls
with one endpoint on each
wall**

**14. by measuring the
length of the segment from
the corner of the page
perpendicular to the floor**

**18., 19. See Additional
Answers in the back of this
book.**

**22. The segment with
endpoints A and B is the
set consisting of the
distinct points A and B and
all points between A and B.**

**23. A polygon is the union
of three or more segments
in the same plane such
that each segment
intersects exactly two
others, one at each of its
endpoints.**

**24. A quadrilateral is a
four-sided polygon.**

**25. A quadrilateral is a
rectangle if and only if it
has four right angles.**

**26. See Additional
Answers in the back of this
book.**

13. The front and back walls of most classrooms are like parts of parallel planes. How is the distance between them measured? See margin.

14. How would you measure the distance from the upper right hand corner of this page to the floor? See margin.

Applying the Mathematics

In 15–17, think of a classroom having west, east, north, and south walls, a floor, and a ceiling. What in the classroom illustrates each idea?

15. two perpendicular planes sample: the floor and a wall

16. three planes each perpendicular to the other two
sample: the corner of the floor, north wall, and east wall

17. a line perpendicular to a plane sample: the ceiling and the intersecting line of the south and west walls

18. Draw a plane intersecting two parallel planes. See margin.

19. Draw a line that intersects a plane at a 30° angle. See margin.

20. A 180-foot tall pine tree is chopped down in a forest. When "timber" is yelled, what is the approximate measure of the angle through which the tree falls? 90°

21. The *angle of inclination* of an object S in the sky is the measure of the angle formed by S, the observer, and the plane of the earth. For instance, a star halfway up to overhead has an angle of inclination of 45°.
    a. What is the largest possible angle of inclination? 90°
    b. What is the angle of inclination of a star that is $\frac{1}{3}$ the way from the horizon to directly overhead? 30°

Review

In 22–25, give a precise definition. See margin.

22. segment *(Lesson 1-8)*   23. polygon *(Lesson 2-7)*

24. quadrilateral *(Lesson 2-7)*   25. rectangle *(Lesson 5-2)*

26. Given: M is the midpoint of $\overline{BC}$ and $\overline{AD}$ in the figure at the left.
    Prove: $ABDC$ is a parallelogram. *(Lesson 7-7)* See margin.

27. Two lines intersect with angle measures as pictured at the left. Find x and y. *(Lesson 3-2)* $x = 67.5$, $y = 112.5$

28. Three identical cubes are pictured below. What symbol is on the face opposite the black disc? *(Lesson 1-5)*   plus sign

Exploration

29. Examine the legs of a chair at home or in school.
    a. Measure the angle between each leg and the plane of the floor.
    b. Are most of the chair legs you see perpendicular to the floor?

a) Answers may vary. b) Most are not exactly perpendicular to the floor.

LESSON
9-2

Prisms and Cylinders

polygon

polygonal region

A carton is a surface.   *A brick is a solid.*

Recall that polygons and polygonal regions are different. A polygon refers to the boundary, whereas a polygonal region is the union of the boundary and the interior.

Similarly, a distinction is made with three-dimensional figures. A **surface** is the boundary of the three-dimensional figure. A **solid** is the union of the boundary and the region of space enclosed by the surface. The earth is a solid; a soap bubble is not, it is a surface. A brick is a solid; a carton is a surface. A solid is distinguished from a surface by shading and showing none of the hidden edges.

The carton pictured below exemplifies a surface called a **box.** The union of a box and its interior is called a **rectangular solid.** Boxes are as important in three dimensions as rectangles are in two, so it is useful to have names for their parts. In the next two paragraphs, we refer to the box drawn below.

A box has six **faces.** Each face is a rectangular region. The faces are drawn as parallelograms to give the appearance of three dimensions. When two of the faces are horizontal, all faces can be identified by their locations: top *(AEFD)*, bottom *(BHGC)*, right *(EFGH)*, left *(ADCB)*, front *(DFGC)*, and back *(AEHB)*. The **opposite faces** lie in parallel planes. The plane of the front face is perpendicular to the planes of the top, bottom, and sides. At each corner of the box, three planes meet and each of these planes is perpendicular to the other two.

The 12 segments, $\overline{AB}$, $\overline{AE}$, $\overline{AD}$, $\overline{BH}$, etc., are the **edges** of the box. Each edge is perpendicular to two faces. For example, edge $\overline{CG}$ is perpendicular to the left face *ABCD* and the right face *EFGH*. The endpoints of the edges are the 8 **vertices** of the box, *A, B, C, D, E, F, G,* and *H*. Consider the lines $\overleftrightarrow{AD}$ and $\overleftrightarrow{CG}$. These lines are not coplanar. They are called **skew lines.**

LESSON 9-2 Prisms and Cylinders **421**

LESSON 9-2

RESOURCES
■ Lesson Master 9-2

OBJECTIVES

A Draw common 3-dimensional shapes.
E Given appropriate lengths, calculate areas and lengths in 3-dimensional figures.
G Identify parts of common 3-dimensional figures.
H Distinguish 3-dimensional figures by their defining properties.
I Recognize 3-dimensional figures in the real world.

TEACHING NOTES

The definitions of prism and cylinder given in this lesson are analogous. A cylinder and prism are surfaces, not solids, yet the common use of the terms often refers to solids; for example, a roller for a conveyor belt or a glass which reflects light are solid. The definitions are traditional, and analogous to those of polygons and curves by including the boundaries but not the interior points.

Students need practice in drawing figures and should be expected to make drawings that are good enough to be used for reasoning.

The sketch in the **Example** on page 423 is done without using perspective. The method used in the Example

421

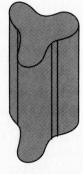
Most classrooms are very much like big boxes. The floor and two adjacent walls meet in a bottom corner of the room just as the bottom, front, and left side of the box on the previous page meet. The plane of the floor is perpendicular to the plane of each wall.

Classrooms and cartons exemplify the same kind of geometric figure. Even a piece of notebook paper can be thought of as a three-dimensional figure, for it has thickness (about 0.002 inch or 0.05 mm). Thus, the geometric figure that best describes the *surface* of a piece of notebook paper is a box. Part of the power of geometry is that the same ideas may apply to things as small as parts of atoms or as large as galaxies, as wide as classrooms or as thin as paper.

A rectangular solid is a special type of *cylindric solid*. In general, to form a cylindric solid, begin with a two-dimensional region. Think of translating the region out of its plane into space in a fixed direction. Below, a circular region and a pentagonal region have been translated in the direction indicated by the arrow. Their translation images lie in a plane parallel to the original plane. Note that circles are represented by ovals to appear three-dimensional.

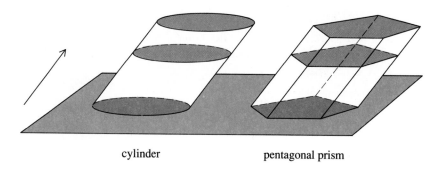

cylinder   pentagonal prism

Definition:

A **cylindric solid** is the set of points between a region and its translation image in space, including the region and its image.

The original region and its translation image are the **bases** of the cylindric solid. Bases are always congruent and always in parallel planes. The **height** or **altitude** of the solid is the distance between the planes of the bases. The rest of the surface of the solid is the **lateral surface.** The union of the bases and the lateral surface is the **cylindric surface.**

422

Two cylindric surfaces have special names.

Definitions:

A **cylinder** is the surface of a cylindric solid whose base is a circle.

A **prism** is the surface of a cylindric solid whose base is a polygon.

When the direction of sliding is perpendicular to the plane of a base, a **right prism** or **right cylinder** is formed. A non-right prism or cylinder is called **oblique.** The cylinder drawn on the previous page is oblique; a can is a right cylinder.

Prisms are named by their bases. On page 422 a pentagonal prism is shown. A triangular prism has a triangle for its bases; a regular hexagonal prism has bases that are regular hexagons; and so on. The faces of the lateral surface of a prism are called **lateral faces** and are always parallelograms.

Tin cans, rolls of paper as shown in the adjacent photograph, rolls of steel, and new pencils (without erasers) are a few of the physical objects that illustrate cylindric solids or surfaces. You should be able to sketch any type of cylindric surface.

Example   Sketch a right hexagonal prism.

Solution

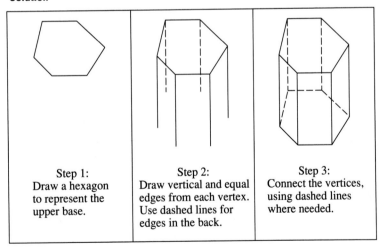

| Step 1: Draw a hexagon to represent the upper base. | Step 2: Draw vertical and equal edges from each vertex. Use dashed lines for edges in the back. | Step 3: Connect the vertices, using dashed lines where needed. |

To sketch an oblique prism, in Step 2 you would draw parallel, nonvertical, and equal edges.

LESSON 9-2 Prisms and Cylinders   **423**

If the base of a prism is a parallelogram, then the prism is a **parallelepiped.** All the faces of a parallelepiped are parallelograms, and opposite faces are congruent.

parallelepiped

A box is a right parallelepiped whose base is a rectangle. Thus its fancy name is **rectangular parallelepiped.** In this book the simpler name, *box,* is usually used.

From their definitions, the various types of cylindric surfaces fit nicely into a hierarchy.

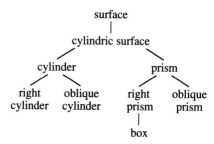

Questions

Covering the Reading

1. What is the difference between a solid and a surface? See margin.

2. Sketch: **a.** the surface of a brick; **b.** a solid brick. See margin.

3. Use the box drawn below.
   a. A segment connecting two vertices is a(n) __?__ . edge
   b. How many faces does the box have? six
   c. Name faces in two parallel planes. See margin.
   d. How many edges does the box have? 12
   e. Name two parallel edges not on the same face.
   samples: $\overline{AD}$ and $\overline{HE}$, $\overline{AG}$ and $\overline{CE}$

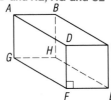

4. Give the special name for the surface of a cylindric solid:
  a. if its base is a hexagon; hexagonal prism
  b. if its base is a circle. cylinder

In 5–8, sketch a figure of the given type. See margin.

  5. triangular right prism

  6. oblique regular octagonal prism

  7. right cylinder

  8. an oblique cylindrical solid

  9. Another name for *rectangular parallelepiped* is __?__ . box

Applying the Mathematics

In 10 and 11, tell which three-dimensional figure most resembles the real world object. Give as specific a name as you can, distinguishing solids from surfaces.

  10. phonograph record (ignoring the hole in the middle)
  solid right cylinder

  11. unsharpened pencil without an eraser solid right prism (often hexagonal)

In 12 and 13, use the fact that the edges of an oblique prism are not perpendicular to the plane of the base. Such prisms seem to lean as does the famous Leaning Tower of Pisa. The amount of lean is measured from the perpendicular as shown at the left.

  12. Sketch a triangular prism with a 30° lean. See margin.

  13. Sketch a pentagonal prism with a 60° lean. See margin.

In 14 and 15, apply what you know about two-dimensional figures.

  14. A box is drawn below. $BC = 4$, $HG = 12$, and $CG = 3$.
  a. Find the length of $\overline{FH}$. $\sqrt{160} \approx 12.65$ units
  b. Find the length of $\overline{BH}$. (Hint: There are right triangles in this drawing.) 13 units
  c. Find the area of $\triangle BFH$. $\dfrac{3\sqrt{160}}{2} \approx 18.97$ units²

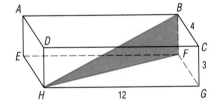

  15. Refer to the oblique cylinder below.
  a. What is the height of the cylinder? 15 units
  b. What is the area of the lower base? $36\pi \approx 113.1$ square units

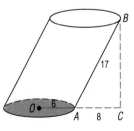

LESSON 9-2 Prisms and Cylinders **425**

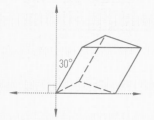
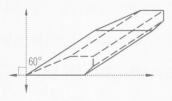
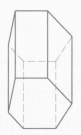
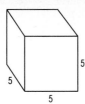

16. A cube is made of sticks, so it is hollow and you can stick a hand through it.
    a. If one edge has length 5, what is the total length of the sticks needed to make the cube? **60 units**
    b. Generalize part **a** for edges of any length. **See margin.**

17. By changing the dotting of segments, a surface can be made to appear to be viewed from a different direction. Change the dashed lines in Figure 3 of the Example to cause the surface to appear to be viewed from underneath. **See margin.**

18. A computer artist wants to show a box on a computer screen. For this the artist has to think of the drawing as two-dimensional, even though it looks three-dimensional. Given the coordinates of A, B, C, and D as shown below, what are the coordinates of E, F, G, and H?
    E = (25, 70), F = (85, 70), G = (60, 50), H = (25, 20)

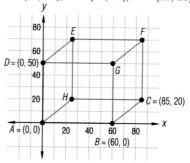

Review

19. Name a three-dimensional counterpart of intersecting lines. *(Lesson 9-1)* **intersecting planes**

20. Draw two perpendicular planes. *(Lesson 9-1)* **See margin.**

21. How many planes contain two given points A and B? *(Lesson 9-1)* **an infinite number of planes**

22. Circle O has radius 2 cm. What is the area of the shaded region between the circle and the hypotenuse of right triangle AOB? *(Lessons 8-9, 8-5)* $\pi - 2 \approx 1.14$ cm²

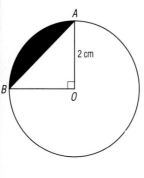

23. Draw a tessellation of the plane using equilateral triangles. *(Lesson 8-2)* **See margin.**

24. Define: **a.** coplanar; **b.** collinear. *(Lessons 1-2, 1-1)* a) two or more figures that lie in the same plane; b) points that are part of one line

In 25–27, factor. *(Previous course)*

25. $2\ell w + 2wh$
    $2w(\ell + h)$

26. $\pi r^2 + \pi h^2$
    $\pi(r^2 + h^2)$

27. $\pi r^2 + 2\pi rh$
    $\pi r(r + 2h)$

Exploration

28. Some prisms have a special property relative to light. What is this property?
    A prism separates a beam of white light into the spectrum of colors.

29. The cells in honeycombs of bees are in the shapes of hexagonal prisms. Why do bees use this shape? **See margin.**

426

426

Pyramids and Cones

Transamerica Building,
San Francisco, California

The pyramids of Giza, Egypt: Mycerinus, Chephren, and Cheops

One of the wonders of the world is the collection of pyramids of the ancient Egyptians. The first Egyptian pyramid built seems to have been designed by Imhotep for the pharaoh Zoser around 2600 or 2800 B.C. Pyramids were built in many places in the ancient world for temples and burial sites. The Transamerica building in San Francisco is a recent building shaped like a pyramid.

A *solid pyramid* is a set of points on and between a polygonal region (its *base*) and a point (its *vertex*) not in the plane of the region. Like prisms, pyramids are classified by the shape of the base. The Egyptian pyramids are square. Pictured below is a pentagonal pyramid.

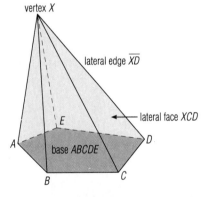

The parts of a pyramid are named in the figure. Segments connecting the vertex of the pyramid to the vertices of the base are **lateral edges.** The sides of the base are edges but not lateral edges. The polygonal regions formed by the edges are the **faces** of the pyramid. All faces, other than the base, are triangular regions, and are the **lateral faces** of the pyramid.

In a **regular pyramid,** the base must be a regular polygon and the segment connecting the vertex to the center of this polygon must be perpendicular to the plane of the base.

LESSON 9-3 Pyramids and Cones   **427**

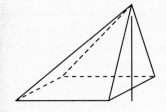
Example 1 Sketch a regular square pyramid.

Solution

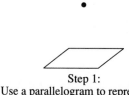

Step 1:
Use a parallelogram to represent a square not in the plane of the paper, and put a point above its center.

Step 2:
Sketch the lateral edges, using dashed lines for the unseen edges.

A *cone* is like a pyramid in that it has one base and a vertex. But the base of a cone is a circle. The line through the vertex and the center of the circle is the **axis** of the cone. When the axis is perpendicular to the plane of the circle, the cone is called a **right cone.** The surface of a cone other than the base is the **lateral surface** of the cone. A **lateral edge** of a cone is any segment connecting its vertex to a point on the circle.

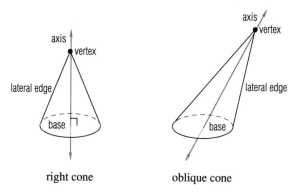

right cone   oblique cone

Pyramids and cones are two types of **conic surfaces.**

Definitions:

Given a region (the **base**) and a point (the **vertex**) not in the plane of the region, a **conic solid** is the set of points between the vertex and all points of the base, together with the vertex and the base.

A **cone** is the surface of a conic solid whose base is a circle.

A **pyramid** is the surface of a conic solid whose base is a polygon.

428

The **height** or **altitude** of a pyramid or cone is the length of a segment from the vertex perpendicular to the plane of the base. In a regular pyramid or right cone, that segment contains the center of the base.

height h
slant height ℓ

regular pyramid   right cone

Each lateral face of a regular pyramid is an isosceles triangle congruent to all the other lateral faces. The altitude from the vertex on any one of the lateral faces of a regular pyramid (ℓ in the drawing above at the left) is called the **slant height** of the pyramid. The slant height is greater than the height but less than the length of a lateral edge. In a right cone, the slant height equals the length of a lateral edge.

■ ■ ■ ■ ■ ■ ■ ■ ■ ■

Example 2 Find the slant height VT of the regular hexagonal pyramid shown at the left below.

Solution To find VT, create the right triangle VXT, where VX is the height. By the Pythagorean Theorem,

$$VT^2 = TX^2 + VX^2$$
$$= 7^2 + 12^2$$
$$= 193.$$
$$VT = \sqrt{193} \approx 14 \text{ units}$$

Notice the similarities between the definitions of cones and pyramids, and how they are related to cylinders and prisms. In the next chapter, you will see similarities in the formulas for the volumes and surface areas of these figures.

Below is a hierarchy of conic surfaces. Compare this hierarchy with the hierarchy of cylindric surfaces. They are very much alike.

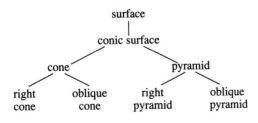

surface
|
conic surface
/   \
cone   pyramid
/   \   /   \
right   oblique   right   oblique
cone   cone   pyramid   pyramid

 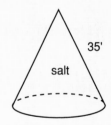
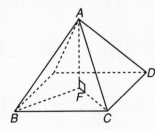

NOTES ON QUESTIONS
Question 1: You might
ask if it can be determined
from the drawing whether or
not the pyramid drawn is a
regular square pyramid. (No)

Question 2: This drawing
is harder for some students
than the square pyramid,
since drawing squares in perspective has been learned.
Have students practice drawing triangular pyramids with
(a) all three lateral edges
showing; (b) only two lateral
edges showing. One method
is to draw a square pyramid,
then separate it as shown
below into two triangular pyramids.

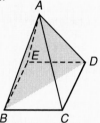

ADDITIONAL ANSWERS
2. sample:

7. sample:

8. a. and b. sample:

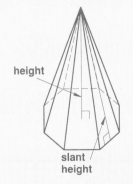

Covering the Reading

1. A square pyramid is sketched below. Name:
   a. its base; *ABDE*
   b. its vertex; *C*
   c. a lateral edge;
      $\overline{BC}$ or $\overline{AC}$ or
      $\overline{DC}$ or $\overline{EC}$
   d. a lateral face. △*BCD* or △*ACB* or
      △*ACE* or △*DCE*

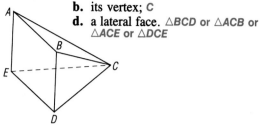

2. Draw a triangular pyramid. **See margin.**

3. *O* is the center of the circle drawn at the left, and $\overline{MO}$ is
   perpendicular to the plane of the circle.
   a. What is the name of the surface? **right cone**
   b. Name its axis. $\overrightarrow{MO}$
   c. Name a lateral edge. $\overline{MN}$ or $\overline{ML}$
   d. Name its vertex *M*
   e. Name the base. ⊙*O*
   f. What is its height? *MO*
   g. What is its slant height? *ML* or *MN*

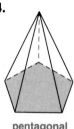

In 4–6, name each three-dimensional surface.

4.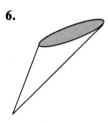

   pentagonal
   pyramid

5. hexagonal
   pyramid

6. oblique cone

7. Sketch a cone with a base having radius 2 cm. **See margin.**

8. a. Sketch a regular octagonal pyramid.
   b. On your sketch, identify the height and the slant height.
   See margin.

9. In the regular pentagonal pyramid below, *RQ* = 4 and *PQ* = 10.
   a. Find the height. **10 units**
   b. Find the slant height.
      $\sqrt{116} \approx$ **10.77 units**

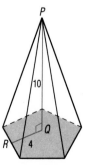

10. Suppose the base of a pyramid is an *n*-gon.
    a. How many faces has the pyramid? n + 1
    b. How many edges has the pyramid? 2n

11. The base of a right cone has radius 3 cm. The height of the cone is 11 cm.
    a. Make a sketch of this cone. See margin.
    b. Find the slant height. √130 ≈ 11.4 cm
    c. Find the area of its base. 9π ≈ 28.3 cm²

In 12 and 13, when a conic surface is cut by a plane parallel to its base, the part of the conic surface between and including the two parallel planes is called a **truncated cone** or **truncated pyramid.**

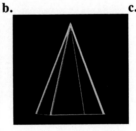

truncated
cone

truncated
pentagonal
pyramid

12. Where in a circus might you find a truncated cone?
    sample: a platform that elephants stand on
13. Draw a truncated hexagonal pyramid. (Hint: Think of the original vertex as a vanishing point.) See margin.

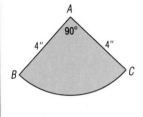

14. Cut a quarter of a disk out of a piece of paper with dimensions as shown. Bend the paper so that $\overline{AB}$ and $\overline{AC}$ coincide and a cone is formed.
    a. What is the circumference of the base of this cone? 2π″ ≈ 6.28″
    b. What is the radius of the base of the cone (to the nearest tenth of an inch)? 1.0″ exactly

15. Suppose you can only see the edges of a regular square pyramid and they glow in the dark. From where are you looking if you see it as shown?

a.   b.   c.

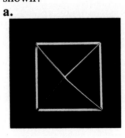   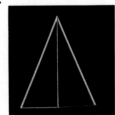   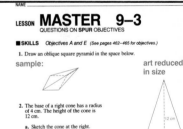

above the vertex   left of front in   in front of corner
                        plane of base   in plane of base

16. Define: cylindric solid. *(Lesson 9-2)* See margin.

17. What is the difference between a right cylinder and an oblique cylinder? *(Lesson 9-2)* See margin.

18. Tell how many different planes contain:
    a. three given noncollinear points; one
    b. a given △ABC; one
    c. a given line. *(Lesson 9-1)* infinitely many

LESSON 9-3   Pyramids and Cones   **431**

Questions 12 and 13:   A truncated conic solid is also called a *frustum*. To draw the truncated surface, suggest to students that they first draw the entire cone or pyramid, next draw a cross-section, and then erase the top part.

11. a. (Art is reduced in size.)

13. sample:

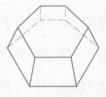

16., 17. See the margin on p. 432.

ADDITIONAL ANSWERS
16. A cylindric solid is the set of points between a region and its translation image in space, including the region and its image.

17. In a right cylinder, the direction of the translation is perpendicular to the base; in an oblique cylinder, it is not.

FOLLOW-UP

MORE PRACTICE
For more questions on SPUR Objectives, use *Lesson Master 9-3,* shown on page 431.

EXTENSION
Students may enjoy extending **Question 15** by trying to draw "top views" on projections of the conic solids shown in this lesson.

EVALUATION
A quiz covering Lessons 9-1 through 9-3 is provided in the Teacher's Resource File.

Alternative Assessment
You might want students to do the following *writing activities:* (1) make a list of all the physical objects they can think of that illustrate conic solids or surfaces; (2) try to categorize their lists according to the hierarchy; (3) give common or special names for the items on their lists; and (4) list and compare the properties of cylindric solids and conic solids.

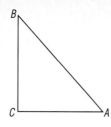

19. Given $\triangle ABC$ with $m\angle A = 50$, $m\angle B = 40$. What definition or theorem justifies each statement?
  a. $m\angle C = 90$ Triangle-Sum Theorem
  b. $\overline{BC} \perp \overline{CA}$ definition of perpendicular (suff. cond.)
  c. $\triangle ABC$ is a right triangle. definition of right triangle (suff. cond.)
  d. $AC^2 + BC^2 = AB^2$ *(Lessons 8-7, 3-5, 3-2)* Pythagorean Theorem

20. Refer to the cube drawn below, in which $AT = 5$. Find:
  a. AB; **b.** EA; **c.** ET. *(Lessons 5-2, 8-7)*
     a) 5 units; b) $\sqrt{50} \approx 7.07$ units; c) $\sqrt{75} \approx 8.66$ units

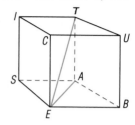

21. Of two rectangles, one has double the length and triple the width of the other. How do their areas compare? *(Lesson 8-3)*
The larger has six times the area of the smaller.

In 22 and 23, factor. *(Previous course)*

22. $\pi r \ell + 2\pi r$ $\pi r(\ell + 2)$ **23.** $\ell h + wh$ $h(\ell + w)$

Exploration

24. The pyramids of Egypt have been called one of the seven "wonders of the ancient world."
  a. Name one of the other wonders of the ancient world. See below.
  b. Look in an almanac to find the name of a structure that has been called one of the wonders of today's world.

a) The other six are the Hanging Gardens of Babylon, the statue of Zeus at Olympia, the Temple of Artemis at Ephesus, the Mausoleum at Halicarnassus, the Colossus at Rhodes, and the Pharos of Alexandria. b) sample: the Brooklyn Bridge, Hoover Dam

432

LESSON 9-4

Plane Sections

A 3-dimensional counterpart of the circle is the *sphere*.

> **Definition:**
>
> A **sphere** is the set of points in space at a fixed distance (its radius) from a point (its center).

To draw a solid sphere (such as an orange or a baseball), shade the drawing as below at the left. To draw the surface (a basketball or a tennis ball), normally only an outline is drawn. Then arcs are added to give the illusion of depth.

solid sphere

sphere

The terminology of a circle extends to spheres. Above at the right is a sphere with center O and radius OA. We also call the segment $\overline{OA}$ a **radius.** Similarly, the **diameter** of a sphere is a number that is twice the radius, while any segment connecting two points of the sphere and containing the center of the sphere is *a* diameter.

Think of slicing a melon. The boundary of the slice is like the intersection of a plane and a sphere. The intersection is a point if the plane just touches the sphere, and a circle otherwise. (This can be proved; see Question 20.) If the plane contains the center of the sphere, the intersection is called a **great circle** of the sphere. A great circle (shown in orange below) splits the sphere into two **hemispheres.** Otherwise the intersection is called a **small circle** (in blue below).

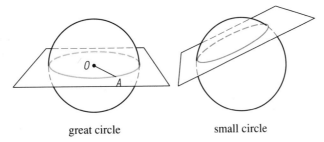

great circle   small circle

RESOURCES
■ Lesson Master 9-4
▫ Visual for Teaching Aid 56 displays sections of solids.
▫ Visual for Teaching Aid 57 displays conic sections.

OBJECTIVES

A Draw common 3-dimensional shapes.
B Draw plane sections of common 3-dimensional shapes.
E Given appropriate lengths, calculate areas and lengths in 3-dimensional figures.
I Recognize 3-dimensional figures in the real world.

TEACHING NOTES

Students may be studying biology simultaneously with this course; if so, they may have seen cross-sections of leaves or of animals. The drawings in this lesson provide good intuition for plane sections.

This is an appropriate time to bring in a globe and talk about the great circles of longitude and the small circles of latitude, and to discuss the latitude and longitude of various places.

Many students are surprised to learn that Europe is quite a bit north of the United States. For example, Chicago is at the same latitude as Rome; Anchorage, Alaska is about the same latitude as Stockholm, Sweden. But to fly from Anchorage to Stockholm you would not fly due east (or due west) even though these cities are on the same circle of latitude.

The earth is almost a solid sphere. One of its great circles is the equator. Points on the equator are about 6378 km (or 3963 miles) from the center of the earth. However, the earth has been slightly flattened by its rotation. The North and South poles are about 6357 km (or 3950 miles) from the center of the earth.

Below are two sketches of the earth. The sketch at the left is of the earth as seen from slightly north of the equator, so the equator is tilted. Notice how the oval representing the circle of the equator is widened to give the illusion of looking at it from above. Then the South Pole cannot be seen. The sketch at the right is as seen from the plane of the equator.

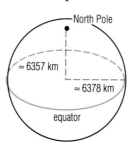

Earth as seen from above equator and North Pole

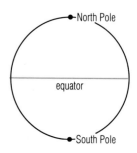

Earth as seen from plane of equator

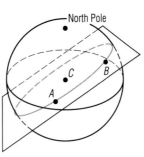

There are many planes through two points. So if points A and B are on a sphere, there are many planes that contain them. However, in Lesson 9-1, you learned there is only one plane that contains three noncollinear points. So if A and B are not endpoints of a diameter, there is only one plane containing A, B, and the sphere's center C. The intersection of that plane with the sphere is a great circle. To get from point A to point B on the earth, aircraft and ocean liners often travel along an arc of that great circle because it is the shortest way to get from A to B. The path they take is called a **great circle route.** Both great circles and small circles are examples of *plane sections* of a sphere.

> **Definition:**
>
> A **plane section** of a three-dimensional figure is the intersection of that figure with a plane.

Biologists use plane sections of tissue to study a tissue's cell structure. These sections are thin enough so that light from a microscope will shine through them. A floor plan is an intersection of a building with the plane of a floor. Concerning these and other plane sections, two questions arise. What are the plane sections of a figure? How can plane sections be sketched?

434

Prisms and cylinders: If the intersecting plane is parallel to the bases, then the section is a region congruent to the bases. Sketch it by drawing edges parallel to the edges of the bases. This is pictured below.

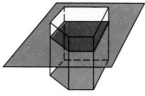

plane section // to bases

Suppose the intersecting plane is not parallel to the bases and does not intersect them. For a prism, the section is a polygon with the same number of sides but not congruent to the bases. Sketch it by identifying the intersections of the plane and the lateral edges and joining the appropriate vertices (as shown below, at the left). For a cylinder, the plane section is an ellipse (as shown below, at the right).

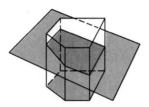

plane section not // to bases

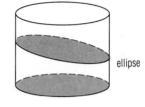

ellipse

plane section not // to bases

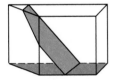

Plane sections may have quite different shapes if the plane intersects a base as well as lateral faces. An example of a plane intersecting a solid quadrangular prism is shown at the left; the plane section is a pentagonal region.

Pyramids and cones: Sections parallel to the base have shapes similar to the base, but they are smaller. Sketch them by drawing segments or arcs parallel to the base.

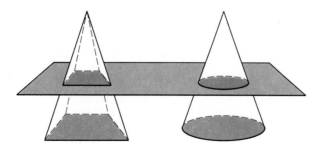

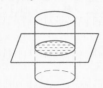
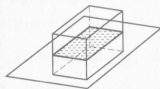
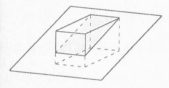

Below at the far left are two right conical surfaces with the same axis, formed by rotating a line intersecting the axis about that axis. The plane sections formed are called the **conic sections.** The conic sections describe orbits of planets and paths of balls and rockets. They are used in radar, telescopes, headlights, and TV receivers, and you are certain to study them in other mathematics courses.

The thrown basketball follows the path of a parabola.

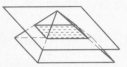
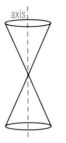

circle (plane ⊥ to axis)

ellipse (plane not ⊥ to axis, intersecting only one cone)

parabola (plane // to edge)

hyperbola (plane intersecting both cones)

Questions

1. Define: sphere.
A sphere is the set of points in space at a fixed distance from a point.
2. How does the definition of *sphere* differ from the definition of *circle*? A circle is the set of points in a plane (not space) at a fixed distance from a point.
3. The intersection of a plane and a sphere is either a single point or a(n) __?__ . circle
4. Define: great circle. the intersection of a sphere and a plane containing the center of the sphere
5. Define: small circle. the intersection of a sphere and a plane not containing the center of the sphere
6. What is a plane section?
the intersection of a 3-dimensional figure with a plane
7. a. Draw a cylinder and a plane section parallel to its bases.
b. How do the section and the bases compare?
a) See margin. b) They are congruent.
8. a. Draw a right square pyramid and a plane section parallel to its base. See margin.
b. How do the section and the base compare?
The plane section is also a square, but smaller.
9. What are the conic sections? See margin.

10. *Multiple choice.* Thinking of the earth as a sphere, the equator is
(a) a diameter
(b) a small circle
(c) a great circle
(d) a chord. (c)

11. Name two fields in which you would often see plane sections of objects. sample: biology and architecture

436

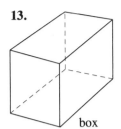

Applying the Mathematics

12. What is the length of a diameter of the earth: **a.** at the equator; **b.** connecting the poles?
a) 12,756 km or 7926 miles; b) 12,714 km or 7900 miles

In 13–15, copy the figure shown. See margin.

a. Sketch a plane section parallel to the base.
b. Sketch a plane section not parallel to and not intersecting the base(s).
c. Name the shape of each section.

13.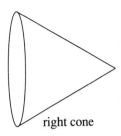

box

14.

regular
hexagonal
pyramid

15.

right cone

In 16 and 17, plane sections of an object are shown, as seen in a microscope focused at different levels of the object. Scientists use these plane sections to approximate its shape. Sketch a shape that yields the given sequence of plane sections.

16.

17.

In 18 and 19, tell which three-dimensional figure most resembles the real world object. Distinguish solids from surfaces.

18. blown-up balloon sphere   **19.** golf ball solid sphere

20. Here is a proof that the intersection of a sphere and a plane not through its center is a circle. Given is sphere O and plane M, intersecting in the curve as shown at the right. Fill in the justifications.

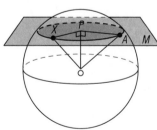

Proof
Let P be the foot of the $\perp$ from point O to plane M. Let A be a fixed point and X be any other point on the intersection. Then $\overline{OP} \perp \overline{PA}$ and $\overline{OP} \perp \overline{PX}$, because **a.** _?_. $\overline{OP} \cong \overline{OP}$, because of the **b.** _?_ and $\overline{OA} \cong \overline{OX}$ because **c.** _?_. So $\triangle OPX \cong \triangle OPA$ by **d.** _?_. Thus, due to **e.** _?_, $PX = PA$. Thus any point X on the intersection lies at the same distance from P as A does. So by the definition of circle (sufficient condition), the intersection of sphere O and plane M is the circle with center P and radius PA. See margin.

LESSON 9-4 Plane Sections **437**

---

15. See Additional Answers in the back of this book.

20. a. def. of line $\perp$ to a plane (meaning)
b. Reflexive Prop. of Congruence
c. def. of a sphere (meaning)
d. the HL Congruence Thm.
e. the CPCF Thm.

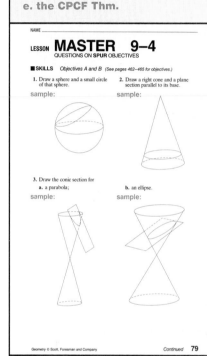

NAME _____

LESSON **MASTER   9–4**
QUESTIONS ON SPUR OBJECTIVES

■SKILLS   Objectives A and B (See pages 462–465 for objectives.)

1. Draw a sphere and a small circle of that sphere.
sample:

2. Draw a right cone and a plane section parallel to its base.
sample:

3. Draw the conic section for
a. a parabola;   **b.** an ellipse.
sample: sample:

NAME _____
Lesson MASTER 9–4 (page 2)

For 4 and 5, **a.** draw a plane section which is parallel to the base; **b.** draw a plane section which is not parallel to the base but does not intersect it; **c.** draw a plane section which is not parallel to the base and intersects the base; **d.** name the shape of each section.

4. parallelepiped (with base of a rhombus)
a.   **b.**   **c.**
d. rhombus   **d.** parallelogram   **d.** parallelogram

5. regular square pyramid
a.   **b.**   **c.**
d. square   **d.** isosceles trapezoid   **d.** triangle

■SKILLS   Objective E

6. A grapefruit 4 inches in diameter is sliced in half for breakfast.
a. Find the area of its plane section.   12.56 in.²
b. Find the circumference of its plane section.   12.56 in.

■USES   Objective I

7. Below are the plane sections of an object. Use them to draw the shape of the object and to suggest what it might be.

• ○ ○ ○ ○ ○

sample: pencil

21. A *quadrangular pyramid* has a quadrilateral as its base. Draw a quadrangular pyramid. *(Lesson 9-3)* See margin.

22. Draw a right cylinder whose lateral edges are congruent to a diameter of the base. *(Lesson 9-2)* See margin.

23. In the box below, $AB = 10$, $AE = 6$, and $AD = 8$. Find each length. (Some segments are not drawn.) *(Lesson 9-2)*
   a. *CD* 10   **b.** *DE* 10   **c.** *CE* $\sqrt{200} \approx 14.14$

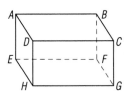

24. Using the information in this lesson, give the circumference of the equator: **a.** to the nearest 100 miles; **b.** to the nearest 100 km. *(Lesson 8-8)* a) 24,900 mi; b) 40,100 km

25. Give the definition. *(Lessons 4-7, 4-1)*
   a. reflection image of a point *P* over a line ℓ when *P* is not on ℓ
   b. reflection-symmetric figure a) the point Q where ℓ is the perpendicular bisector of $\overline{PQ}$ b) See margin.

26. From the information in this lesson, about how many km are in 1 mile? *(Previous course)* $\approx$ 1.6 km

27. On the earth, the union of the prime meridian and international date line approximates a great circle containing the North and South poles.
   a. Name a country through which the prime meridian goes.
   b. Name the ocean that contains the international date line.
   c. What is the purpose of this circle?
   a) sample: England; b) Pacific; c) See below.

28. **a.** It is possible for a plane section of a cube to be a hexagon. Draw a cube or make a model to demonstrate how this happens.
   b. Is it possible for a plane section of a cube to be a pentagon?
   c. Is it possible for a plane section of a cube to be a triangle?
   d. Is it possible for a plane section of a cube to be a quadrilateral that is not a parallelogram? b) Yes; c) Yes; d) Yes

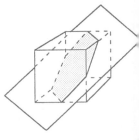

27c) It divides the earth into east and west hemispheres for date and time purposes.

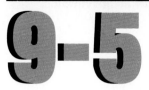

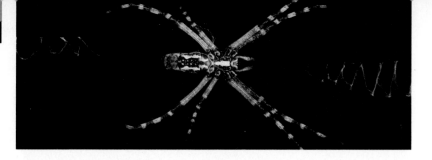

Reflections in Space

Many of the properties of reflections in two dimensions carry over to three dimensions. For example, when you look in a mirror, the mirror appears to lie halfway between you and your image. It contains the midpoint of the segment connecting a point to its image. That is, the mirror *bisects* the segment. Also, an imaginary line from the tip of your nose to its image will always be perpendicular to the mirror.

In general, a plane M is the **perpendicular bisector** of a segment $\overline{AB}$ if and only if $M \perp \overline{AB}$ and M contains the midpoint of $\overline{AB}$. This enables three-dimensional reflections (over planes) to have the same defining condition as their two-dimensional counterparts (over lines).

Definition:

For a point A which is not on a plane M, the **reflection image of A over M** is the point B if and only if M is the perpendicular bisector of $\overline{AB}$. For a point A on a plane M, the **reflection image of A over M** is A itself.

reflecting plane M

B is the reflection image of A over M.

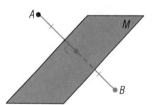

Reflections over planes preserve the same properties as their two-dimensional counterparts. That is, reflections in space preserve angle measure, betweenness, collinearity, and distance. So the definition of congruence in the plane can be extended to three dimensions.

Definition:

Two figures F and G in space are **congruent figures** if and only if G is the image of F under a reflection or composite of reflections.

You are congruent to your mirror image.

LESSON 9-5

RESOURCES
■ Lesson Master 9-5
▲ Visual for Teaching Aid 58 displays symmetric surfaces.
▲ Visual for Teaching Aid 59 can be used with **Questions 10, 15** and **16.**

OBJECTIVE

J Determine and draw symmetry planes in 3-dimensional figures.

TEACHING NOTES

In this chapter, the definitions of three-dimensional ideas are analogous to those in two dimensions. It is not surprising, therefore, that three-dimensional reflections and congruence possess many of the same properties as their two-dimensional counterparts. For instance, reflections in space have the A-B-C-D properties, the Flip-Flop Theorem holds, congruence is transitive, and the CPCF Theorem is true.

Other properties have analogs also. For instance, if F is a figure and M is a plane, and $r_M(F) = F$, then the points of F which are their own images are exactly the points of intersection with the plane M.

Alternate Approach
This lesson can be used to review all the space figures studied so far. They are listed below with the minimum number of symmetry planes in parentheses: prism (0), right prism (1), cylinder (1), right cylinder (1 parallel to bases, infinitely many perpendicular), pyramid (0),

regular pyramid with *n* lateral
faces (*n*), right cone (infinitely
many, all containing the
axis), sphere (infinitely many,
all containing the center). A
good beginning exercise in
finding symmetry planes is to
have students try to draw the
nine symmetry planes for a
box with congruent faces (a
cube).

Drawing symmetry planes
is not easy for students who
have never drawn anything
like this before.

Reading Because so
many of the properties in two
dimensions carry over into
three dimensions, this is an
appropriate time to review
the properties of reflections
and the definition of congruent figures. Suggest that students think of the properties
in two dimensions along with
their analogues in three dimensions as they are reading
the lesson.

ADDITIONAL EXAMPLE
Suppose two congruent
square pyramids are placed
so their square bases coincide (forming an octahedron).
Determine the number of
symmetry planes for the octahedron.
**5, the planes perpendicular
to the base through the
symmetry lines of the
square and the plane
containing the coinciding
bases**

NOTES ON QUESTIONS
Questions 1-6: Point out
to students that if a figure
has no symmetry lines in two
dimensions, then solids with
plane sections of those
shapes will not have symmetry planes. For instance, the
parallelepiped seems to students to be symmetric, but
just as with the parallelogram, it has point symmetry,
not reflection symmetry.
These are good questions to
discuss in **small groups.**

Question 6: The vertical
symmetry plane is difficult for
many students to visualize.

A two-dimensional figure has been defined to be reflection-symmetric
if and only if it coincides with its image under some reflection.
There is a corresponding definition for three dimensions.

> **Definition:**
>
> A space figure F is a **reflection-symmetric figure** if and only if
> there is a plane *M* such that $r_M(F) = F$.

The plane *M* is called a **symmetry plane.** The presence or absence
of symmetry planes is used to help rock collectors, chemists, and
geologists identify types of crystals. In some applications, reflection
symmetry is called **bilateral symmetry.** Many animals have
bilateral symmetry.

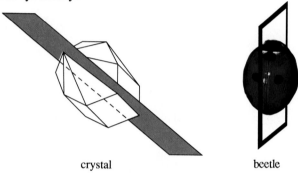

crystal   beetle

The body surfaces of most people have approximate bilateral symmetry. The right side and left side are reflection images of each
other over the plane that goes through the middle of the body from
head to toe. Note that you cannot slide or turn a right hand onto a
left hand, because they have different orientation. Like reflections
over a line, reflections over a plane reverse orientation.

Space figures may have any number of symmetry planes, from zero
to infinitely many. The right cylinder below at the left has infinitely
many vertical symmetry planes (any plane through $\overline{PQ}$) and one
horizontal symmetry plane. The regular triangular pyramid at the
right has exactly 3 symmetry planes, one of which is drawn.

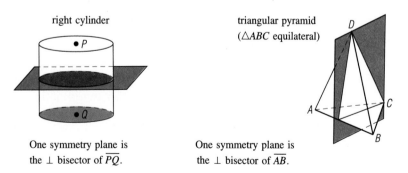

right cylinder

triangular pyramid
($\triangle ABC$ equilateral)

One symmetry plane is
the ⊥ bisector of $\overline{PQ}$.

One symmetry plane is
the ⊥ bisector of $\overline{AB}$.

440

Example Determine the number of symmetry planes for a common cardboard box, like that shown here. Sketch each symmetry plane.

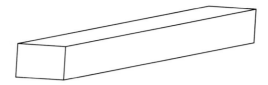

Solution A box is a right rectangular prism. Planes parallel to the opposite faces which intersect four edges at their midpoints are symmetry planes. There are thus three symmetry planes. The sketch below shows these planes, one parallel to each pair of parallel faces.

Question 9: This might be a good point to review the properties that are preserved by reflections and discuss their analogues for space.

Question 10: This is a difficult question for many students. They probably have never drawn something like this before.

Question 11: The difference between the cube and the box of the **Example** in the lesson is that the cube has symmetry planes through the parallel diagonals of opposite faces. Since there are three pairs of opposite faces with two diagonals in each, there are six additional symmetry planes.

Question 14: If a prism has more than one symmetry plane, then its base must have reflection symmetry.

Question 25: Almost every one is surprised by the result of this Exploration. Most people have the misconception that if they cannot see their feet in a mirror, by moving farther away, they will be able to see their feet because the image is smaller. On the contrary, the mirror always allows you to see the same amount of your body exactly twice the vertical height of the mirror (unless you bend your head forward or backward).

Question 26: Students may find it interesting that many people have facial expressions that are not symmetric. For example, some faces seem to smile on the left and be somber on the right. Have students examine their own faces.

Questions

Covering the Reading

In 1–6, **a.** tell if the figure has bilateral symmetry; **b.** give the number of symmetry planes.

1.

right circular cylinder

a) Yes; b) infinitely many

2.

regular square pyramid

a) Yes; b) 4

3.

top

a) Yes; b) infinitely many

4.

parallelepiped

a) No; b) none

5.

right cone

a) Yes; b) infinitely many

6.

oblique circular cylinder

a) Yes; b) 1

7. How many symmetry planes does a box have? 3

8. *Multiple choice.* If a human stands upright, the symmetry plane is:
(a) Parallel to the ground about waist high.
(b) ⊥ to the ground, halfway between the front and back.
(c) ⊥ to the ground, halfway between right and left sides. (c)

9. Name a property of a figure not preserved by reflections in space. **orientation**

LESSON 9-5 Reflections in Space   **441**

12.

13.

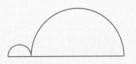

14. A right prism with a base that is not reflection-symmetric has exactly one plane of symmetry. sample:

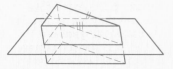

15. a. sample:

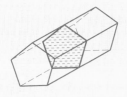

b. sample:

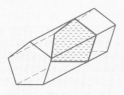

c. Part (a) is a pentagon congruent to the base. Part (b) is a pentagon.

16. See Additional Answers in the back of this book.

Applying the Mathematics

10. Trace the diagram below and sketch the reflection image of the surface over the shaded plane.

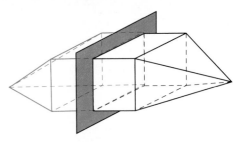

11. How many symmetry planes does a cube have? 9

12. A symmetry plane of a triangular pyramid is drawn in this lesson. Draw and label the plane section of the pyramid formed by the symmetry plane. See margin.

13. Repeat Question 12 for the beetle in this lesson. See margin.

14. Is it possible for a prism to have only one plane of symmetry? Explain why or why not, and sketch one if it is possible. See margin.

Review

In 15 and 16, copy the figure shown.
  a. Sketch a plane section parallel to the bases.
  b. Sketch a plane section not parallel to and not intersecting the bases.
  c. Name the shape of each section. *(Lesson 9-4)*

15. See margin.

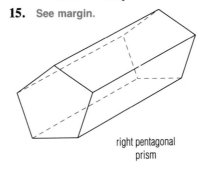

right pentagonal prism

16. See margin.

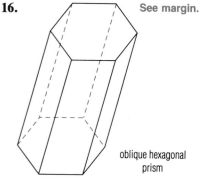

oblique hexagonal prism

In 17 and 18, tell which figure most resembles the real world object. Give as specific a name as you can, distinguishing solids from surfaces. *(Lessons 9-4, 9-2)*

17. a penny   solid right cylinder

18. a desk drawer   box, without its top

442

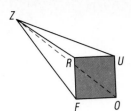

19. In the figure at the left, *FOUR* is a square. *Z* is not in the plane of *FOUR*.
  a. Identify the figure. **a square pyramid**
  b. Name its base. **FOUR**
  c. Name its vertex. **Z**
  d. Name all the lateral edges. $\overline{ZF}, \overline{ZO}, \overline{ZU}, \overline{ZR}$
  e. Name all faces. *(Lesson 9-3)* △ZRF, △ZRU, △ZUO, △ZOF, FOUR

20. Refer to the parallelepiped with bases *DEFG* and *HIJK* pictured below.
  a. What is the area of a base? **39 square units**
  b. What is the perimeter of a base? **36 units**
  c. What is the height of the parallelepiped? *(Lessons 9-2, 8-6, 8-1)* **9 units**

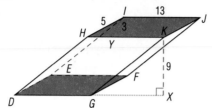

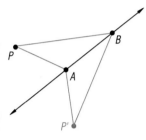

21. Suppose *P* is not on $\overleftrightarrow{AB}$ at the left.
  a. Draw $r_{\overleftrightarrow{AB}}(P)$. Call this point *P'*. *(Lesson 4-1)* **See drawing.**
  b. What kind of figure is *PBP'A*? *(Lesson 5-2)* **kite**

22. Fill in the blanks. *(Previous course)*
  a. 1 square yard = __?__ square feet **9**
  b. 1 square mile = __?__ square yards **3,097,600**
  c. 1 square mile = __?__ acres **640**

In 23 and 24, factor. *(Previous course)*

23. $x^2y - 4x$ **x(xy − 4)**   **24.** $2\ell h + 2\ell w + 2wh$ **2(ℓh + ℓw + wh)**

25. Standing upright and still, you want to see your entire body, head to toe, in a mirror. How far up and down the wall does the mirror have to go? (Hint: try with an actual mirror. Block out parts of the mirror that are not needed.) **See below.**

Exploration

26. Find a picture of your face, taken from the front. Except for scars, is the surface of your face *exactly* symmetric to a vertical plane down the middle? **No**

---

25. The top of the mirror has to be at half the distance between your eyes and the top of your head; the bottom of the mirror has to be at half the distance between your eyes and the bottoms of your feet.

LESSON 9-5 Reflections in Space   **443**

MORE PRACTICE
For more questions on SPUR Objectives, use *Lesson Master 9-5*, shown below.

EXTENSION
An interesting project for students is to make a collage of objects which have bilateral symmetry. The collage could have a theme like insects, shellfish, nature in general, geometric objects, people, or animals.

EVALUATION
Alternative Assessment
A good way to review the cylindric and conic surfaces hierarchies is to have students write them out, tell whether each figure has bilateral symmetry, and give the number of symmetry planes for each figure.

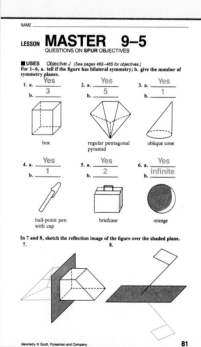

LESSON 9-6

RESOURCES
- Lesson Master 9-6
- Quiz for Lessons 9-4 Through 9-6
- Visual for Teaching Aid 60 displays **Examples 1** and **2**.

OBJECTIVES

C Give views of a figure from the top, sides, or bottom.

F From 2-dimensional views of a figure, determine properties of the 3-dimensional figure.

TEACHING NOTES

This lesson may help students develop their visualization abilities more than any other in the chapter. It has been both engaging and frustrating to students, who find the questions easy to understand, think they should be easy to answer, yet have difficulty even with the easiest drawings.

The content of this lesson enhances skills important to the consumer. Most students will encounter situations in their lives in which diagrams of projected views are used, for example, houses and their furnishings.

You might want to use various objects around the room or have students bring in various objects for use in drawing different views. Students could work in **small groups** of three to make the drawings, with each student taking either the top, side, or front view to draw, then rotating.

LESSON

9-6

Views of Solids and Surfaces

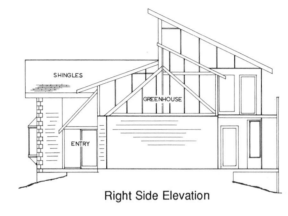

Right Side Elevation

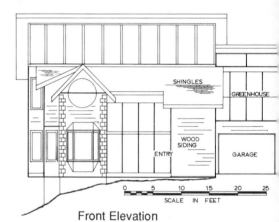

Front Elevation

The house pictured above was built in Ames, Iowa. Like most houses today, it was designed by an architect. Underneath the picture of the house are **views** from the front and right sides. These views are called **elevations.** Architects draw views of a planned building from the top, bottom, and sides to give a client a picture of the finished product. These elevations give accurate scale-model measurements, while most photographs and perspective-type drawings do not.

In geometry, views of three-dimensional figures are drawn without perspective as if the figures are solid but with all visible edges shown. (You were shown two views of the earth in Lesson 9-4.) From the views you can determine a possible shape of the original figure. The abbreviations L (left), R (right), F (front), and B (back) give guidance.

444

Example 1 Given the rectangular pyramid at the right, draw views from the front, right side, and top.

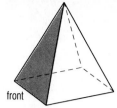

front

Solution The bottoms of the front and side views are the width and length of the base. The views are triangles, the same height as the pyramid. The top view shows the vertex with edges going towards the vertices of the base.

L — R

F — B

L R

F

front view   right side view   top view

Few people can determine shapes just from views without experience. In this book, unless told otherwise, assume that the solids and surfaces viewed are those we have already discussed—prisms, cylinders, pyramids, or cones—or combinations of them, as in Example 2.

Example 2 Here are three views of a prefabricated building made up of sections in the shape of congruent boxes.

a. How tall in stories is the building?
b. How long in sections is the building from front to back?
c. Where is the tallest part of the building located?

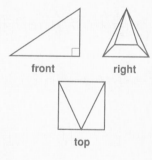

L R

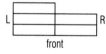

L — R

front

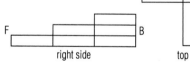

F — B

right side   top

Solution

a. The top view tells you nothing about the height of the building. The front view tells you it is 3 stories high on the left. The right side view confirms that the height, in the back, is 3 stories.
b. The top view tells you it is 3 sections long, the right side view confirms this.
c. The front view tells you that the tallest point is somewhere on the left side. The right side view tells you that the tallest point is at the back. Combining this, you can conclude that the tallest point of the building is at the back left corner.

LESSON 9-6 Views of Solids and Surfaces **445**

The reverse process, deducing the figure from its views (as in **Examples 1** and **2**) is more difficult and provides good practice in deduction.

Reading You might want to read this lesson aloud with students, especially the Examples. Make sure students understand how to interpret the solutions given in the Examples, and encourage them to make sketches if needed.

ADDITIONAL EXAMPLES
1. A square pyramid has one lateral face which is an isosceles triangle perpendicular to the base of the pyramid, as shown below.

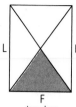

Draw views from the front, the right side (facing the isosceles face), and the top.

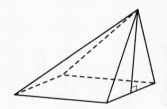

front   right

top

2. A child has stacked up building blocks. Three views of the stack are shown.

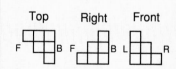

Top   Right   Front

F ⬚ B F ⬚ B L ⬚ R

Draw one possible shape.
sample:

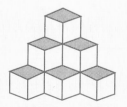

445

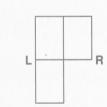

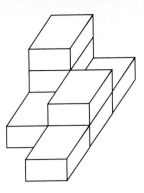

Here is a drawing of a possible shape for the building whose views are given in Example 2. There are other possible shapes. In the middle row either the left or the right side or both sides could be two stories high.

It helps to make sketches to understand views. In making your sketches, you may want to put the hidden lines in at first and erase them as the shape nears completion. Sometimes, in picturing these solids and surfaces, the hidden lines are omitted so that the final shape is more easily viewed.

Questions

Covering the Reading

1. To an architect, what are elevations?
   different views of a building
2. A building is pictured at the right. **See margin.**
   a. Draw a top view.
   b. Draw a view from the right side.
   c. Draw a front view.

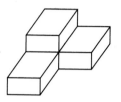

In 3–7, sketch the **a.** top, **b.** front, and **c.** right side views of each shape. **See margin.**

3. a cube

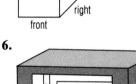

4. a sphere

5. a triangular prism

6.

7.

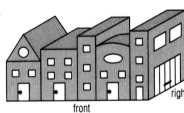

8. A building has the views shown below.
   a. How tall in stories is the building? 2
   b. How long in sections is the building from front to back? 3
   c. Where is the tallest part of the building located?
      on the left side,
      the two back sections

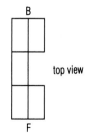

front view   side view   top view

446

446

9. Sketch a possible shape, different from the solution given, for the building with the views given in Example 2. **See margin.**

3., 4., 5., 6., 7., 9., 14.b.-c. See Additional Answers in the back of this book.

Applying the Mathematics

In 10 and 11, refer to the elevations at the beginning of this lesson.

10. How wide (in feet) is the house? (Include the garage.)
≈ 46 ft

11. How high is it (in feet) from the ground to the top of the upper roof?
≈ 28 ft

12. Which solid studied in this chapter has these views?
a solid right cylinder

F B
top view

L R
front view

F B
side view

Review

13. Give the number of symmetry planes of the cube in Question 3. *(Lesson 9-5)* 9

In 14 and 15, use the right circular cone shown below.

14. a. How many symmetry planes are there? infinitely many
  b. Sketch a plane section parallel to the base. **See margin.**
  c. Sketch a plane section parallel to an edge. **See margin.**
  d. Name the sections in parts **b** and **c**. *(Lessons 9-5, 9-4)*
    circle, parabola

15. If the base of the cone has radius 8 and its slant height is 10, what is its height? *(Lessons 9-3, 8-7)* 6 units

16. How many great circles on the earth contain a given point in New York and a given point in Tokyo? *(Lesson 9-4)* one

Akihabara District in Tokyo, Japan

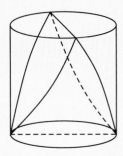
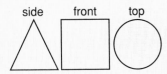
17. A regular heptagonal region is translated into a congruent region in a parallel plane. What solid figure is formed by connecting all points of the original region and its image? *(Lesson 9-2)*
regular heptagonal prism

18. Here is a view of the moon and its equator as seen from the earth. The distance from L to R (through the center of the moon) is approximately 2160 miles.
    a. What is the approximate radius of the moon? **1080 miles**
    b. How far is it from L to R along the surface of the moon?
       (Lesson 8-8) **$1080\pi \approx 3400$ miles**

19. The area of a square is 11 square units.
    a. What is the length of a side? $\sqrt{11} \approx$ **3.32 units**
    b. What is the length of a diagonal? *(Lesson 8-7)*
       $\sqrt{22} \approx$ 4.69 units

20. Given: $\overline{AD}$ is an altitude in $\triangle ABC$.
    a. Find Area($\triangle ABC$). **1599 units²**
    b. Find AC. *(Lessons 8-7, 8-5)* $\sqrt{2421} \approx$ **49.20 units**

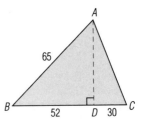

21. Given: $ABCD$ is a parallelogram with diagonals $\overline{AC}$ and $\overline{BD}$.
    Prove: $\triangle AQB \cong \triangle CQD$. *(Lesson 7-7)* **See margin.**

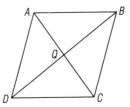

In 22 and 23, factor. *(Previous course)*

22. $x^2y^2 + 4x^2y + 6xy$ **xy(xy + 4x + 6)**

23. $\pi r^2 + 2\pi rh - \pi h$ **$\pi(r^2 + 2rh - h)$**

Exploration

24. Draw a front, side, and top elevation of the building in which you live. **Answers will vary.**

9-7

Making Surfaces

A 3-dimensional surface which is the union of polygonal regions and which has no holes is called a **polyhedron**. The plural of polyhedron is either **polyhedrons** or **polyhedra.** Prisms and pyramids are special kinds of polyhedra. Each polygonal region is a **face** of the polyhedron. Each vertex of the region is a **vertex** of the polyhedron. Each side of the region is an **edge** of the polyhedron. Polyhedra can be classified by the number of faces. Below are pictured a tetrahedron (4 faces) and a hexahedron (6 faces). The tetrahedron has 4 vertices and 6 edges. A cube and a box are both special types of hexahedra.

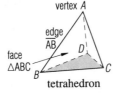
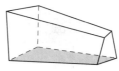

tetrahedron   hexahedron

In previous lessons you have used perspective and nonperspective drawings, plane sections, and views to describe 3-dimensional figures in 2-dimensional drawings. You can also go the other way and use 2-dimensional drawings that can make polyhedra and other 3-dimensional surfaces.

A **net** is a 2-dimensional figure that can be folded on its segments or curved on its boundaries into a 3-dimensional surface. To find the net for a particular surface, you can cut along the edges of the surface until it is flat. Suppose cuts are made along some of the edges of a cube. Then the cube can be flattened out.

Below is drawn a net for a cube. The six faces are identified by the first letters of the words up, down, left, right, back, and front. If you cut around the outside boundary and then fold these squares along their common edges so as to make perpendicular faces, a cube will be formed.

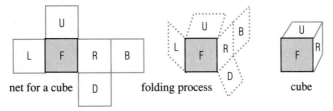

net for a cube   folding process   cube

LESSON 9-7

RESOURCES
■ Lesson Master 9-7
▣ Visual for Teaching Aid 61 shows a net for a cube, pyramid, prism, and cylinder.
▣ Visual for Teaching Aid 62 can be used with **Questions 5, 10,** and **17**.
▣ Visual for Teaching Aid 63 can be used with **Questions 26, 28, 29, and 30.**

OBJECTIVES

D From a net, make a surface, and vice versa.
G Identify parts of common 3-dimensional figures.
H Distinguish 3-dimensional figures by their defining properties.

TEACHING NOTES

You might wish to have students bring in cereal boxes that can be unfolded and cut into their nets. A display may be made of different nets of rectangular prisms and other figures.

Some teachers like to have classes spend a day making models of the polyhedra. This is an appropriate activity. Posters of the regular polyhedra as well as models of polyhedra are available commercially and make attractive displays in the classroom as well as being excellent teaching tools.

You might recall that a polygon was defined as a union of three or more coplanar segments such that each intersected exactly two others, one at each endpoint. By analogy, we could define a *polyhedron* as a union of four of more polygonal regions such that each edge is the intersection of two of the regions. However, that definition would allow polyhedra with holes.

This lesson presents another opportunity for extending ideas by analogy. In one-dimensional space (a line), "regions" are bound by zero-dimensional figures, that is, by points, and the minimum number of points needed to bound a region of space is 2 (the endpoints of a segment). In two-dimensional space, regions may be bounded by one-dimensional figures, that is, by segments, and the minimum number of segments needed to bound a region of space is 3 (a triangle). In three-dimensional space, regions may be bound by two-dimensional figures, that is, by polygonal regions, and the minimum number of polygonal regions needed to bound a region of space is 4 (a tetrahedron). In general, in dimension *n*, the minimum number of bounding figures is *n* + 1.

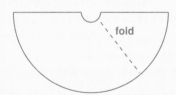
Not all networks of six squares fold to make a cube. The 2 by 3 network drawn below at the left is not a net for a cube. It can be folded into a prism with no bases, as shown below at the right, but this is not a polyhedron.

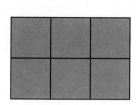

Prisms and pyramids often have relatively simple nets.

Example 1 Draw a net for a regular square pyramid like the one shown here.

Solution The base is a square, and the faces are triangles with one side on the square. It is easiest to draw the square base first, and then make all the faces congruent and attached to a side of the square. The altitude of each triangular face must be greater than one half that side. Do you see why? The finished net is shown below at the right.

Example 2 Draw a net for the right triangular prism shown here.

Solution The bases are congruent triangles. The other faces are rectangles with one pair of sides the same length as the corresponding sides of the base. A net is shown here.

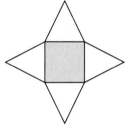

450

In both Examples 1 and 2, the nets were drawn. You may be able to improve accuracy by constructing the bases and faces using a straightedge and compass, or by very careful tracing and measuring with ruler and protractor. Printout from an automatic drawer can also be useful.

Cones and cylinders have simple nets.

Example 3   Draw a net for a right cylinder *h* units high with base diameter *d*.

Solution   First draw the circle that will be one base. The lateral surface of a cylinder is a rectangle. Since the diameter of the circle is *d*, the rectangle will have one side of length πd, to match the circumference of the base. The other side is the height *h* of the cylinder.

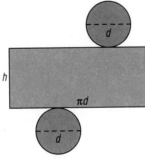

A net for a cone is given in Question 9.

Questions

Covering the Reading

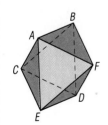

1. Define: polyhedron. a 3-dimensional surface which is a union of polygonal regions and which has no holes

2. Is the surface a polyhedron?
   a. cone No
   b. cube Yes
   c. cylinder No
   d. prism Yes
   e. pyramid Yes
   f. sphere No

3. Pictured at the left is an octahedron.
   a. Name its vertices. A, B, C, D, E, F
   b. Name its edges. See margin.
   c. Name its faces. △ABF, △ABC, △BCD, △BDF, △EFD, △AEF, △ACE, △CDE

LESSON 9-7   Making Surfaces   **451**

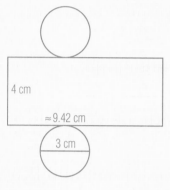
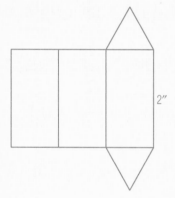

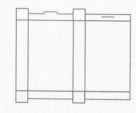
4. A hexahedron is pictured in this lesson. Give the number of:
   a. vertices; **b.** edges; and **c.** faces. a) 8; b) 12; c) 6

5. Here is a net for a cube. Identified are the locations of three faces. Where will the other squares of the net wind up on the cube?
   a) back; b) up; c) left

6. Draw a net for a pyramid whose base is a pentagon. Make each side of the pentagon 2 inches or 5 cm. Cut out the net and fold it to make a pyramid. See margin.

7. Suppose you wanted to make the cylinder pictured at the left out of cardboard. Draw a net you could use. Make the net actual size. Cut it out to make the cylinder. See margin.

8. Draw a net for a regular triangular prism with a height of 2″. Make the net actual size. See margin.

9. **a.** If the partial disk below is cut out of cardboard and $\overline{AB}$ is moved to coincide with $\overline{AC}$, what 3-dimensional figure will be formed?
   cone without a base

   b. Let $AB = 4$ in. and m$\angle BAC = 100$. Cut out the shape and make the surface. Answers may vary slightly.

Applying the Mathematics

10. *Multiple choice.* Which is not a net for a cube? (d)

    (a) (b) (c) (d)

11. A polyhedron is **convex** if the segment connecting any two points of it is contained within the corresponding solid. Draw a nonconvex polyhedron. See margin.

12. Order from most general to most specific: polyhedron, surface, pentagonal pyramid, regular pentagonal pyramid, pyramid, figure. See margin.

In 13 and 14, give the number of: **a.** vertices; **b.** edges; and **c.** faces.

13. a pyramid whose base is an octagon a) 9; b) 16; c) 9

14. a prism whose base is an *n*-gon a) 2n; b) 3n; c) n + 2

452

15. Draw a net for a cereal box. *See margin.*

16. *Multiple choice.* Descartes discovered and Euler proved a simple relationship between the numbers of vertices V, edges E, and faces F of any polyhedron. By examining polyhedra, determine which of the following is the relationship.
(a) $V + E - F = 2$
(b) $F + E - V = 2$
(c) $F + V - E = 2$
(d) $E + F - V = 2$ (c)

Review

17. Here are three views of a building. *(Lesson 9-6)*
a. How tall in stories is the building? 3
b. How long in sections is the building from front to back? 3
c. Where is the tallest part of the building located?
middle, left section

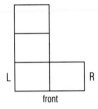
top

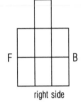
front

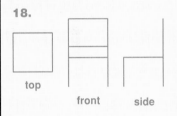
right side

18. Draw top, front, and side views of the chair pictured at the left. (Assume the seat is horizontal.) *(Lesson 9-6)* See margin.

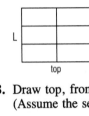

19. Refer to the right triangular prism of Example 2 in this lesson.
a. Is the figure reflection-symmetric? Yes
b. If so, give the number of symmetry planes. *(Lesson 9-5)* one

20. *Multiple choice.* A bass drum is best described as
(a) a cylindric solid
(b) a cylindric surface
(c) a spherical solid
(d) a spherical surface. (b)
(Lessons 9-4, 9-2)

21. Use the figure below. R is the midpoint of $\overline{QS}$. The figure is not drawn to scale.

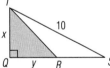

a. If $x = 6$, find y. 4 units
b. If $x = 8$, find y. 3 units
c. If $x = 8$, find Area($\triangle TQR$). *(Lessons 8-7, 8-5)* 12 units²

22. $\triangle CAE$ and $\triangle CDB$ are right triangles, as pictured at the left. *True* or *false*? $m\angle CBD - m\angle E = 0$ *(Lesson 5-7)* True

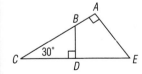

23. Suppose, in a quadrilateral $ABCD$, that $AB = BC = CD = DA$. Why can you conclude that $ABCD$ is a rhombus? *(Lessons 5-2, 3-3)* definition of a rhombus (sufficient condition)

24. $m\angle 1 = t$ and $m\angle 2 = t - 10$. Find t if angles 1 and 2 are supplementary. *(Lesson 3-2)* 95

LESSON 9-7 Making Surfaces **453**

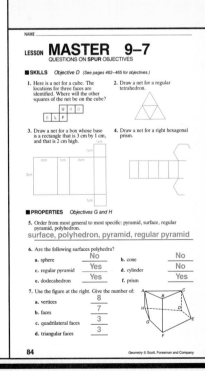

NOTES ON QUESTIONS
Questions 26-30: These questions are appropriate to assign for extra credit. You may wish to give special credit based on size, neatness, creativity in color or decoration, or presentation. Some students may wish to make a mobile.

25. A **regular polyhedron** is a convex polyhedron in which all faces are congruent regular polygons and the same number of edges intersect at each of its vertices. There are only five regular polyhedra; they are pictured here.

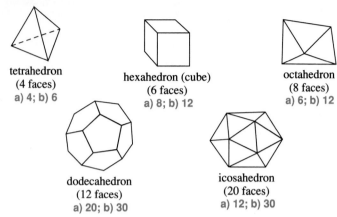

tetrahedron
(4 faces)
a) 4; b) 6

hexahedron (cube)
(6 faces)
a) 8; b) 12

octahedron
(8 faces)
a) 6; b) 12

dodecahedron
(12 faces)
a) 20; b) 30

icosahedron
(20 faces)
a) 12; b) 30

a. Determine the number of vertices of each regular polyhedron.
b. Determine the number of edges of each regular polyhedron.

In 26–30, use cardboard and tape to construct a model of the regular polyhedron from the net provided. The patterns shown below should be enlarged. Cut on solid lines, fold on dotted lines. Answers will vary in size.

26. tetrahedron

27. cube

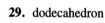
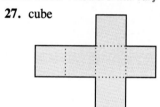

28. octahedron

29. dodecahedron

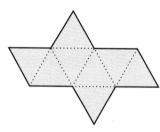
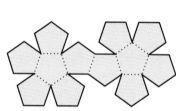

30. icosahedron

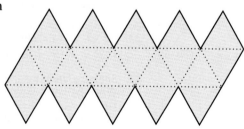

The Four-Color Problem

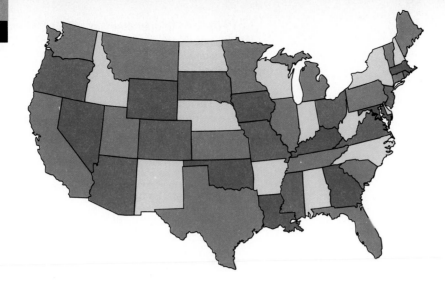

RESOURCES
- Lesson Master 9-8
- Visual for Teaching Aid 64 can be used with **Questions 4** and **10**.
- Visual for Teaching Aid 65 can be used with **Question 9**.

OBJECTIVE

L Relate the history of the Four-Color Problem.

TEACHING NOTES

The Four-Color Theorem can be stated as a theorem about networks. To do this, represent the capital of each state by a point. Connect two capitals if the states are adjacent. Color the capitals with the color you give the states. Then the four-color problem essentially says that, in certain networks, the nodes can be colored with four colors such that no arc connects two nodes of the same color.

The partial map on page 456 can be colored with three colors, but if you add Oregon and California to it, a fourth color is needed.

Most students are intrigued by the four-color problem. The fact that it is a theorem will not deter students from attempting to draw a configuration that contradicts the theorem. This provides a good opportunity to once again explain the finality of proof in mathematics.

Here is a map of the 48 states of the continental United States. To distinguish the states, each state has been colored differently than any of its neighbors. If two states only share a corner, as is the case with Colorado and Arizona, then they can have the same color. Notice that only four colors are needed for this map.

In 1852, after studying many maps, Thomas Guthrie, a British mathematician, conjectured that *any* regions of a map on a sphere or a plane could be so distinguished if four colors were used. For Guthrie, regions could have any shape as long as they were connected. (The two unconnected parts of the state of Michigan could have different colors.)

The Four-Color Conjecture (1852-1976):

> Suppose regions which share a border of some length must have different colors. Then any map of regions on a plane or a sphere can be colored in such a way that only four colors are needed.

Guthrie was not able to prove his conjecture. In fact, many mathematicians tried to prove the conjecture but failed. For almost 125 years, this conjecture, the "four-color problem," was one of the most famous undecided questions in mathematics. By 1975, mathematicians had proved that any map with fewer than 40 states could be colored with four colors or less, but they had not proved that *any* map could be so colored.

By working on this problem, mathematicians discovered much new mathematics. Much of the mathematics of complicated networks, called *graph theory*, was discovered in the search for a proof to the Four-Color Conjecture.

In 1976, two mathematicians at the University of Illinois, Wolfgang Haken and Kenneth Appel, *proved* that Guthrie's Four-Color conjecture was correct. They could not prove this just by drawing maps and coloring, for there are infinitely many maps. First they showed that any map they needed to consider was one of 1,952 types of maps. Then they used a computer to help prove that for each type, no more than four colors would be needed to color it. Because of their proof, the Four-Color Conjecture became the Four-Color *Theorem*.

The Four-Color Theorem (1976):

Suppose regions which share a border of some length must have different colors. Then any map of regions on a plane or a sphere can be colored in such a way that only four colors are needed.

While working on the four-color problem, mathematicians examined many other surfaces, particularly surfaces with holes. One of these surfaces is called a **torus.** A torus is formed by bending a cylinder until its bases coincide. The result looks like a doughnut. It has been proved that no more than seven colors are needed to color any map drawn on a torus. Below is a way to make a torus with a map needing seven colors.

To make a torus:
1. Begin with a rectangle.

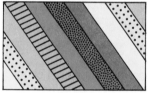

2. Roll it into a cylinder.

3. Bend the cylinder until the bases coincide.

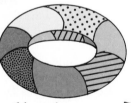

Work is still being done on this topic. In 1987, Elizabeth Wilmer, a student at Stuyvesant High School in New York City, won second prize in the nation in the Westinghouse Science Talent Search for her work on a *three*-color problem. She analyzed maps which could be colored with three colors. Here is an example of such a map with 19 regions.

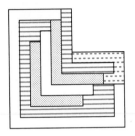

Covering the Reading

1. Who first stated the Four-Color Conjecture, and when?
   Thomas Guthrie, in 1852
2. **a.** State the Four-Color Theorem. See margin.
   b. Who proved this theorem, and when?
   Wolfgang Haken and Kenneth Appel, in 1976
3. How many years elapsed between the statement and proof of the Four-Color Conjecture? 124

4. Trace the map at the left. Show that it can be colored with no more than four colors. See map.

5. Draw a map with 15 states or regions that can be colored with three colors. (Do not use part of the U.S. map). See margin.

6. Who is Elizabeth Wilmer? a student at Stuyvesant High School who worked on a three-color problem
7. Any map on a torus can be colored with no more than __?__ colors. 7

8. Make a torus. Answers may vary.

Applying the Mathematics

9. Below is a map of Europe. Trace the map and color it using the least number of colors. (Hint: Start where the countries are most densely packed, and end up on the outside countries.) Sample: see map.

Have them color the maps themselves and then discuss their results with the other members of their groups.

Question 4: You might use transparencies to show that the coloring is not unique. (By unique we mean that one coloring cannot be derived from another coloring by exchanging colors; that is, a permutation of the assignment of colors does not produce a different coloring scheme.)

Question 10: This map, requiring only two colors, will surprise many students.

Question 11: Point out that a map does not have to contain many states to require four colors.

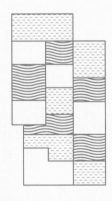

9. and 22. See the margin on p. 458.

457

10. In the map below, the borders of states are circular arcs. What is the least number of colors needed to color this map? 2

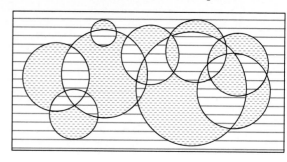

11. Draw a map with only four regions that needs four colors to color it. See margin.

Review

12. Draw a net for a pentagonal pyramid. *(Lesson 9-7)* See margin.

13. Order from most general to most specific: box, surface, polyhedron, prism, right prism. *(Lesson 9-7)*
surface, polyhedron, prism, right prism, box

14. Give a view of the triangular right prism below as seen from
   a. the top   b. the front   c. the right side. *(Lesson 9-6)*
   See margin.

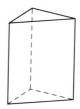

In 15–18, draw the figure. *(Lessons 9-4, 9-3, 9-2, 9-1)* See margin.

15. an oblique cone

16. a right prism with a nonconvex kite as a base

17. a solid sphere

18. two intersecting planes

19. *A-BCDE* below is a regular pyramid. *AO* is the height.
   Let $DE = 12$ and $AO = 10$.
   a. Find the slant height. $\sqrt{136} \approx 11.7$ units
   b. Find the area of $\triangle AOD$. *(Lessons 9-3, 8-7)*
   $\sqrt{1800} \approx 42.4$ square units

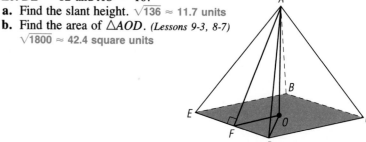

20. Consider $\odot Q$ below with sector RSQ. Suppose $QR = 30$ cm.
  a. Find the length of $\overset{\frown}{RTS}$. $\frac{17,400\pi}{360} \approx$ **151.8 cm**
  b. Find the area of the circle. **$900\pi \approx 2827$ cm²**
  c. What percent of the interior of the circle lies in the sector? (Answer to the nearest percent.) *(Lesson 8-8)* **19%**

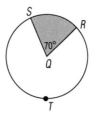

21. If $x = 4$, what is the value of $2x^3 - 7x^2 - x + 11$? *(Previous course)* **23**

Exploration

22. Name all the countries in the map of Question 9. **See Question 9.**

23. Name all the states in the United States map at the beginning of this lesson that are: **See margin.**
  a. colored in red
  b. colored in blue
  c. colored in yellow
  d. colored in green
  e. missing.

24. Find a globe in a library, study, or store.
  a. How many colors are used to color the countries and the oceans?
  b. What conventions are used in coloring the regions?
  See below.

24 a) Sample: Some Rand McNally globes use six colors.
  b) Sample: the areas are colored according to elevation or features such as mountains and bodies of water.

FOLLOW-UP

MORE PRACTICE
For more questions on SPUR Objectives, use *Lesson Master 9-8,* shown below.

EXTENSION
Have students cut out a long strip of paper. Put one twist in it and tape the ends together. Then, choose a point *A* on the strip, place a pencil on it, and begin drawing a line down the middle of the strip. Continue until you have returned to A. There will be one continuous "line" which shows on both sides of the paper, showing that the shape has only one surface. It is called a Mobiüs strip.

15.-18., 23. See Additional Answers in the back of this book.

NAME _____

LESSON **MASTER   9–8**
QUESTIONS ON **SPUR** OBJECTIVES

■**HISTORY**   *Objective L (See pages 462–465 for objectives.)*

1. In what year was the Four-Color Theorem proved?   **1976**

2. Why was a computer necessary to prove the Four-Color Theorem?   **There were too many types of maps to check by hand.**

3. What type of mathematics was discovered and developed as mathematicians searched for a proof of the Four-Color Theorem?   **graph theory**

4. Below is a map of eleven eastern states. Color it using no more than three colors.

sample:

5. What high school student analyzed maps that could be done with three colors?   **Elizabeth Wilmer**

6. Draw a map with ten regions that requires four colors to be colored.

sample:

Geometry © Scott, Foresman and Company   **85**

Summary

The purpose of this chapter is to familiarize you with the common three-dimensional figures, the figures of solid geometry. To accomplish this, you should know their definitions and how they are related, be able to sketch them, identify plane sections, draw views from different positions, and be able to make some of them from two-dimensional nets. Below is a hierarchy relating many of these surfaces.

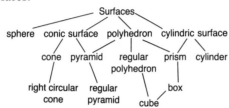

Many ideas from two dimensions extend to three. The basic properties of planes are given in the Point-Line-Plane Postulate. Like lines, planes may be perpendicular or parallel. Circles and spheres have the same defining property except spheres are in 3 dimensions. Reflections and reflection-symmetry are defined the same way in 2 and 3 dimensions except that the reflecting line is replaced by a reflecting plane.

The Four-Color Theorem deals with maps drawn on planes and spheres. In the 124 years it took to discover a proof, much new mathematics about surfaces and networks was discovered.

Vocabulary

Below are the most important terms and phrases for this chapter.
For the starred (*) terms you should be able to give a definition of the term.
For the other terms you should be able to give a general description and a specific example of each.

Lesson 9-1
Point-Line-Plane Postulate,
    parts **e**, **f**, and **g**
intersecting planes
angle measure between
    a line and a plane
*line perpendicular to a plane,
    parallel planes
distance between parallel planes
distance to a plane from a point

Lesson 9-2
surface, solid
box, rectangular solid
faces, edges, vertices of a box
skew lines
*cylindric solid, cylindric surface
*cylinder,
*prism
bases, height, altitude
lateral surface of a cylindric
    surface, lateral face
right prism, oblique prism
right cylinder, oblique cylinder
parallelepiped,
    rectangular parallelepiped

Lesson 9-3
*conic solid, conic surface
*cone, *pyramid
base, vertex, lateral edge,
    lateral face of a conic surface
regular pyramid
axis of a cone, lateral edge of a cone
right cone, oblique cone
right pyramid, oblique pyramid
height, altitude, slant height
truncated cone, truncated pyramid

Lesson 9-4
*sphere, *center of sphere
*the radius of a sphere,
    a radius of a sphere
the diameter of a sphere,
    a diameter of a sphere
*great circle of sphere
*small circle of sphere
hemisphere
*plane section, conic section

Lesson 9-5
perpendicular bisector of a segment
    (in space)
*reflection image of a point
    over a plane
reflecting plane
congruence (in space)
*reflection-symmetric space figure
bilateral symmetry
symmetry (in space)
symmetry plane

Lesson 9-6
view, elevation

Lesson 9-7
*polyhedron, polyhedra, polyhedrons
face, vertex, edge of polyhedron
tetrahedron, hexahedron, octahedron
net, regular polyhedron

Lesson 9-8
The Four-Color Theorem
torus

460

Progress Self-Test

See margin for answers not shown below.

Directions: Take this test as you would take a test in class. Then check your work with the solutions in the Selected Answers section in the back of the book. You will need graph paper and a calculator.

In 1–4, use this figure.

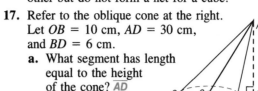

1. Name the figure. Be as specific as possible.
2. Give the number of edges. 9
3. Give the number of faces. 5
4. Give the number of vertices. 6

5. What is the difference between a solid and a surface?

In 6–8, draw each figure.

6. two intersecting planes
7. oblique square prism
8. oblique cylinder

In 9 and 10, use the truncated regular square pyramid drawn here.

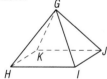

9. Sketch a plane section parallel to the base.
10. How many symmetry planes does this figure have? 4

In 11–14, use the regular square pyramid pictured here.

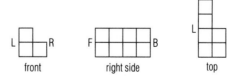

11. **a.** Name a lateral edge. sample: $\overline{GI}$
    b. Name the vertex. G
12. Copy the drawing and identify the height and slant height of the pyramid.
13. Draw a net to make this pyramid.
14. Draw top, front, and right side views of this pyramid.

15. The intersection of the surface of the earth with a plane containing the center of the earth is called a(n) __?__. great circle

16. Draw six squares that are adjacent to each other but do not form a net for a cube.

17. Refer to the oblique cone at the right. Let $OB = 10$ cm, $AD = 30$ cm, and $BD = 6$ cm.

    a. What segment has length equal to the height of the cone? $\overline{AD}$
    b. Find the area of the base of the cone. $100\pi \approx 314.16$ cm²

18. In the right triangular prism below, $\overline{EF} \perp \overline{FG}$, $EF = 4''$, and $EG = 9''$. If the height of the pyramid is 22'',
    a. find Area(*FIHG*);
    b. find Area($\triangle EFG$).
    a) ≈ 177.4 sq. in.
    b) ≈ 16.12 sq. in.

19. *Multiple choice.* A box is *not* a special type of: (a) hexahedron
    (b) pyramid
    (c) prism
    (d) polyhedron. (b)

20. Name the three-dimensional figure which most resembles a slice of American cheese. Give as specific a name as you can, distinguishing whether it is a solid or a surface.

21. Factor: $\pi r^2 + 2\pi rh$. $\pi r(r + 2h)$

22. Here are front, side, and top views of a building.
    a. How tall in stories is the building? 2
    b. How long in sections is the building from front to back? 4
    c. Where is the tallest part of the building located? all sections of the left side

    front   right side   top

23. Draw a map with five regions that requires four colors to be colored.

CHAPTER REVIEW

The main objectives for the chapter are organized here into sections corresponding to the four main types of understanding this book promotes: Skills, Properties, Uses, and Representations. We call these the SPUR objectives. In this chapter, we have included another category, History.

The five types of understanding are not in increasing order of difficulty. There may be hard skills and easy representations; some uses may be easier than anything else; and so on.

USING THE CHAPTER REVIEW
Students should be able to answer questions like these with about 85% accuracy by the end of the chapter.

You may assign these questions over a single night to help students prepare for a test the next day, or you may assign the questions over a two-day period.

If you assign the questions over two days, then we recommend assigning the *evens* for homework the first night so that students get feedback in class the next day. Then assign the *odds* for the second night (the night before the test) so that students can use the answers provided in the book as a study aid.

Chapter Review

Questions on **SPUR** Objectives

See margin for answers not shown below.

SPUR stands for **S**kills, **P**roperties, **U**ses, and **R**epresentations. The Chapter Review questions are grouped according to the SPUR Objectives for this chapter.

SKILLS deal with the procedures used to get answers.

■ **Objective A:** *Draw common 3-dimensional shapes. (Lessons 9-1, 9-2, 9-3, 9-4)*

In 1–6, draw each figure.
1. two perpendicular planes
2. an oblique cylinder
3. a regular hexagonal prism
4. a sphere
5. a square pyramid
6. a right cone

■ **Objective B:** *Draw plane sections of common 3-dimensional shapes. (Lesson 9-4)*

In 7–9, copy the figure shown.
   a. Sketch a plane section parallel to the base.
   b. Sketch a plane section not parallel to and not intersecting the base(s).
   c. Name the shape of each section.

7.

8.
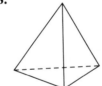

9.
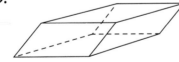

10. a. Draw a sphere and a plane section not containing the center.
    b. Name the plane section. Be as specific as possible.

■ **Objective C:** *Give views of a figure from the top, sides, or bottom. (Lesson 9-6)*

11. Give a view of this oblique circular cylinder as seen from
    a. the top;
    b. the front;
    c. the right side.

In 12 and 13, sketch the **a.** top, **b.** front, and **c.** right side view of the object.

12.
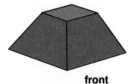
front

13.

front

14. Draw a picture of the earth with its equator as seen from directly above the North Pole.

■ **Objective D:** *From a net, make a surface, and vice-versa. (Lesson 9-7)*

15. Which are nets for cubes? c and d only
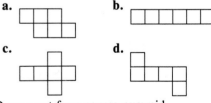
   a.
   b.
   c.
   d.

16. Draw a net for a square pyramid.
17. Draw a net for a rectangular parallelepiped.
18. Draw a net for a cylinder.

462

Objective E: *Given appropriate lengths, calculate areas and lengths in three-dimensional figures.* (Lessons 9-2, 9-3, 9-4)

19. In the regular triangular pyramid shown, $AC = 12$ and $AD = 10$.
   a. Find the area of the base. **≈ 62.4 units²**
   b. Find the slant height. **8 units**

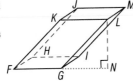

20. In the oblique square prism below, $GN = 15$ and $LN = 40$.
   a. What segment's length equals the height of the prism? **$\overline{LN}$**
   b. What is the length of $\overline{LG}$? **$\sqrt{1825} \approx 42.7$ units**

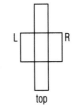

   c. If the perimeter of the base is 52, what is the area of *KLGF*? **520 square units**

21. In the oblique cylinder below, $AC = 9$ cm, $BD = 10$ cm, and $CD = 3$ cm.
   a. Find the area of the base of the cylinder.
   b. Find the height of the cylinder. **$\sqrt{32} \approx 5.66$**

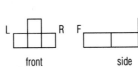

22. A sphere has radius of 12″. What is the area of a great circle of that sphere?
$144\pi \approx 452.4$ square inches

23. A right circular cone has a height of 24 mm and a slant height of 25 mm.
   a. Draw such a cone.
   b. Find the area of the base. **$49\pi \approx 153.9$ mm²**

Objective F: *From 2-dimensional views of a figure, determine properties of the 3-dimensional figure.* (Lesson 9-6)

In 24 and 25, use the given views of buildings.
   a. How tall in stories is the building?
   b. How long in sections is the building from front to back?
   c. Where is the tallest part of the building located?

24. a) 2; b) 2; c) back right-hand side

front   side   top

25. a) 2; b) 3; c) back section

front   side   top

26. Which solid studied in this chapter has these views? **solid right cone**

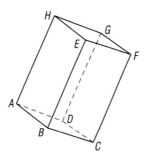

top   front   side

PROPERTIES deal with the principles behind the mathematics.

Objective G: *Identify parts of common three-dimensional figures.* (Lessons 9-2, 9-3, 9-7)

27. Use the figure at the right. In this figure, all opposite faces are parallel, and all adjacent faces are perpendicular.
   a. Give two different names for this figure.
   b. How many edges does the figure have?
   c. Name two edges that are not coplanar.
   a) sample: box, rectangular parallelepiped, rectangular hexahedron; b) 12; c) sample: $\overline{BC}$ and $\overline{HE}$

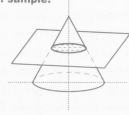

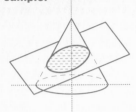

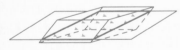

28. *P* is the center of the circle at the right below. *Q* is not in the plane of circle *P*.

a. Name the figure drawn. Be as specific as possible. oblique cone

b. Name a lateral edge. $\overline{RQ}$ or $\overline{SQ}$

c. Name the vertex. Q

d. Name the base. $\odot P$

e. Name the axis. $\overleftrightarrow{QP}$

29. Use the figure at the right.

a. How many vertices does this figure have?

b. How many edges does this figure have?

c. How many faces of this figure are quadrilaterals?

d. Give a technical name for this figure.

a) 7; b) 13; c) 2; d) octahedron

■ **Objective H:** *Distinguish three-dimensional figures by their defining properties.* (Lessons 9-2, 9-3, 9-7)

30. What is the difference between a right cylinder and an oblique cylinder?

31. A pyramid has a triangular base. Could any other face of this pyramid be its base?

32. Order from most general to most specific: prism, cube, square prism, polyhedron.

33. A pentagonal region is translated into a congruent region in a parallel plane. What solid figure is formed by connecting all points of the original region and its image?

30. In a right cylinder, the lateral surface forms a right angle with the base.

31. Yes; any face could be the base.

32. polyhedron, prism, square prism, cube

33. solid pentagonal prism

USES deal with applications of mathematics in real situations.

■ **Objective I:** *Recognize three-dimensional figures in the real world.* (Lessons 9-2, 9-4)

In 34–37, tell which three-dimensional figure most resembles the real world object. Give as specific a name as you can, distinguishing solids from surfaces.

34. a phonograph record with the middle hole filled in solid right cylinder

35. a bubble sphere

36. the moon solid sphere

37. a sheet of notebook paper rectangular solid

■ **Objective J:** *Determine and draw symmetry planes in 3-dimensional figures.* (Lesson 9-5)

In 38 and 39,

a. tell if the figure has bilateral symmetry;

b. give the number of symmetry planes.

38. a) Yes; b) 5

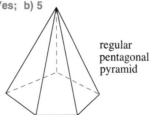

regular pentagonal pyramid

39.

a) Yes;
b) infinitely many

40. How many symmetry planes does a box have? 3

41. Sketch the reflection image of the comb over the shaded reflection mirror below.

REPRESENTATIONS deal with pictures, graphs, or objects that illustrate concepts.

■ **Objective K:** *Factor algebraic expressions using common monomial factoring.* (*Previous course*)

In 42–45, factor.

42. $ph - \frac{1}{2}\ell p$
$p(h - \frac{1}{2}\ell)$

43. $\ell wh + 2\ell w$
$\ell w(h + 2)$

44. $x^2y + 2xy + xy^2$
$xy(x + 2 + y)$

45. $4\pi r^2 + \pi r^3$
$\pi r^2(4 + r)$

HISTORY deals with the development of mathematics.

■ **Objective L:** *Relate the history of the Four-Color Problem.* (*Lesson 9-8*)

46. Who stated the Four-Color Conjecture?

47. The Four-Color Conjecture dealt with maps on what surfaces? **in a plane or on a sphere**

46. **Thomas Guthrie**

48. When was a proof found for the Four-Color Theorem? **1976**

49. Draw a map with nine regions that needs four colors in order to be colored.

50. Trace this map of the continent of Africa and color it with at most four colors.

EVALUATION
Three forms of a Chapter Test are provided in the Teacher's Resource File. Chapter 9 Test, Forms A and B cover just Chapter 9. The third test is Chapter 9 Test, Cumulative Form. About 50% of this test covers Chapter 9, 25% covers Chapter 8, and 25% covers previous chapters. A fourth test, Comprehensive Test, Chapters 1-9, that is primarily multiple choice in format, is also provided. For information on grading, see *General Teaching Suggestions: Grading* on page T44 in the Teacher's Edition.

ASSIGNMENT RECOMMENDATION
We strongly recommend that you assign the reading and questions from Lesson 10-1 for homework the evening of the test. It gives students work to do if they complete the test before the end of the period and keeps the class moving.

11. b.

front

c.

right

12. a.

top

b.

front

46., 49. See Additional Answers in the back of this book.

DAILY PACING CHART ■ CHAPTER 10

Every chapter of UCSMP *Geometry* includes lessons, a Progress Self-Test, and a Chapter Review. For optimal student performance, the self-test and review should be covered. (See *General Teaching Suggestions: Mastery* on page T36 of the Teacher's Edition.) By following the pace of the Full Course given here, students can complete the entire text by the end of the year. Students following the pace of the Minimal Course spend more time when there are quizzes and on the Chapter Review and will generally not complete all of the chapters in this text.

When all lessons are covered from the beginning (the recommendation of the authors), then students in the Minimal Course can cover through Lesson 13-4 and will cover all they need for future courses. For more information on pacing, see *General Teaching Suggestions: Pace* on page T35 of the Teacher's Edition.

DAY	MINIMAL COURSE	FULL COURSE
1	10-1	10-1
2	10-2	10-2
3	10-3	10-3
4	Quiz (TRF); Start 10-4.	Quiz (TRF); 10-4
5	Finish 10-4.	10-5
6	10-5	10-6
7	10-6	Quiz (TRF); 10-7
8	Quiz (TRF); Start 10-7.	10-8
9	Finish 10-7.	10-9
10	10-8	Progress Self-Test
11	10-9	Chapter Review
12	Progress Self-Test	Chapter Test (TRF)
13	Chapter Review	
14	Chapter Review	
15	Chapter Test (TRF)	

TESTING OPTIONS

■ Quiz for Lessons 10-1 Through 10-3   ■ Chapter 10 Test, Form A   ■ Chapter 10 Test, Cumulative Form
■ Quiz for Lessons 10-4 Through 10-6   ■ Chapter 10 Test, Form B

PROVIDING FOR INDIVIDUAL DIFFERENCES

The student text has been written for, and tested with, average students. It also has been used successfully with better and more poorly prepared students.

The Lesson Notes often include Error Analysis and Alternate Approach features to help you with those students who need more help. A blackline Lesson Master (in the Teacher's Resource File), keyed to the chapter objectives, is provided for each lesson to allow more practice. (However, since it is very important to keep up with the daily pace, you are not expected to use all of these masters. Again, refer to the suggestions for pacing on page T35.) Extension activities are provided in the Lesson Notes for those students who have completed the particular lesson in a shorter amount of time than is expected, even in the Full Course.

OBJECTIVES ■ CHAPTER 10

The objectives listed here are the same as in the Chapter 10 Review on pages 516-519 of the student text. The Progress Self-Test on page 515 and the tests in the Teacher's Resource File cover these objectives. For recommendations regarding the handling of this end-of-chapter material, see the notes in the margin on the corresponding pages of the Teacher's Edition.

OBJECTIVES FOR CHAPTER 10 (Organized into the SPUR Categories—Skills, Properties, Uses, and Representations)	Progress Self-Test Questions	Chapter Review Questions	Lesson Master from Teacher's Resource File*
SKILLS			
A Draw 3-dimensional figures, given their dimensions.	1a, 2a	1 through 4	10-1, 10-2, 10-8
B Calculate surface areas and volumes of cylinders and prisms from appropriate lengths, and vice versa.	1b, 7-10	5 through 10	10-1, 10-3, 10-5
C Calculate surface areas and volumes of pyramids and cones from appropriate lengths, and vice versa.	2b, 6	11 through 16	10-2, 10-7
D Calculate the surface area and volume of a sphere from appropriate lengths, and vice versa.	11	17 through 20	10-8, 10-9
E Calculate cube roots.	12	21 through 24	10-3
PROPERTIES			
F Develop formulas for specific figures from more general formulas.	16, 17	25 through 26	10-2, 10-3, 10-6, 10-7, 10-8
G Determine what happens to the surface area and volume of a figure when its dimensions are multiplied by some number.	15	27 through 30	10-4
H Know the conditions under which Cavalieri's Principle can be applied.	13, 14	31 through 33	10-5, 10-7, 10-8
USES			
I Apply formulas for surface area to real situations.	4	34 through 37	10-1, 10-2, 10-9
J Apply formulas for volume to real situations.	3, 5	38 through 42	10-3, 10-5, 10-7, 10-8
REPRESENTATIONS			
K Represent products of two (or three) expressions as areas of rectangles (or volumes of boxes), and vice versa.	18	43 through 46	10-4

*The masters are numbered to match the lessons.

466B

OVERVIEW ■ CHAPTER 10

This chapter develops and discusses the formulas for the surface area and the volume of common 3-dimensional shapes: prisms, cylinders, pyramids, cones, and spheres. The major goals of the chapter are for students to know and to be able to apply these formulas in both theoretical and real situations.

Lessons 10-1 and 10-2 cover surface area by using the concept of a net, introduced at the end of Chapter 9. Lesson 10-3 introduces the basic properties of volume. Lesson 10-4 reminds students of the algebraic relationship between multiplication of polynomials, area, and volume. Lessons 10-5 and 10-7 discuss the volume formulas for prisms and cylinders, and pyramids and cones, again treating these as pairs of related figures.

Lessons 10-8 and 10-9 discuss the volume and surface area of a sphere.

The content of this chapter is difficult for some students. Unlike formulas for area, which they have probably seen before, many of the formulas in this chapter will be encountered by students for the first time. Thus, it is important that connections are made between formulas and that their derivations be discussed. Lesson 10-6 points out how the hierarchies of three-dimensional figures can help students remember the formulas.

The following are some helpful teaching hints for this chapter.
(1) Use concrete materials when possible. For instance, unroll a cylinder to find its lateral surface area. Use an open pyramid and prism with the same base and height and show that one has three times the volume of the other.
(2) Focus students' attention on units. Surface area is area, so it is measured in square units. Volume is measured in cubic units. Thus, surface-area formulas always multiply two variables; in volume formulas, three variables are multiplied.
(3) Formulas must be memorized. Students should begin to memorize new formulas the day they are presented and not wait until the night before a test.

The formulas for surface area and volume are summarized in four places in the book: Lesson 10-6 (p. 495), Lesson 10-9 (p. 511), the chapter Summary (p. 514), and at the end of the book (p. 809).

Students will need calculators for every lesson in this chapter.

PERSPECTIVES ■ CHAPTER 10

The Perspectives provide the rationale for the inclusion of topics or approaches, provide mathematical background, and make connections with other lessons and within UCSMP.

10-1

SURFACE AREAS OF PRISMS AND CYLINDERS

This lesson illustrates the way formulas are presented in this book. Formulas for all figures are not given. Rather formulas are given that apply to most figures and students are expected to derive more specific formulas. The basic formula derived in this lesson is L.A. = ph for the lateral area of a right prism or cylinder. It is a simple formula, but together with the formulas for the perimeter (or circumference) of a figure (from Chapter 8), it enables students to calculate lateral area. Thus, a formula for the lateral area of a cylinder (L.A. = $2\pi rh$) is a special case of L.A. = ph, and the formula for the surface area of a cylinder is

found by adding the lateral area to the area of the bases. Do not require that students memorize these special formulas.

10-2

SURFACE AREAS OF PYRAMIDS AND CONES

Generally, all formulas for pyramids and cones are more complicated than those for prisms and cylinders. Simple formulas only exist for the lateral areas of right cones and regular pyramids.

There is one basic formula in this lesson: the lateral area of a regular pyramid or right cone is $\frac{1}{2}\ell p$. Usually, ℓ is found by using the Pythagorean Theorem. To find p, either use ns (for a regular polygon) or $2\pi r$ (for a circle).

10-3

FUNDAMENTAL PROPERTIES OF VOLUME

The fundamental properties of volume are analogous to the fundamental properties of area. There is a uniqueness property (to ensure that there are not two different values for the volume of a figure); there is a formula for a simple figure (in area, it is a rectangle, in volume, a box); there is a congruence property (this enables the use of a unit again and again without its measure changing); and there is an additive property (this enables taking figures apart and putting them together again without changing the total measure).

10-4
MULTIPLICATION, AREA, AND VOLUME

This lesson uses algebra. In algebra, students are usually introduced to a distributive property by using examples involving area. The multiplication of three polynomials, however, generally is not related to the study of volume. In this lesson, the multiplication of two and three polynomials is reviewed.

10-5
VOLUMES OF PRISMS AND CYLINDERS

There is only one formula discussed in this lesson, $V = Bh$. The importance of this formula is that it applies to *all* prisms and cylinders. The postulate known as Cavalieri's Principle is required for its proof.

Cavalieri's Principle was stated before calculus was invented, and its idea is important in calculus. In using Cavalieri's Principle, one sums an infinite number of areas of infinitely small thickness to find the volume. In calculus, one takes the limit of the sums of many thin volumes to find the total volume. Each section in Cavalieri's Principle is called a *lamina,* the base of the word "laminate," as a credit card is covered or laminated with a very thin layer of plastic.

10-6
REMEMBERING FORMULAS

This lesson serves two purposes, one of which is to provide an extra day to work on surface area. This is an easier lesson than the two lessons preceding it and should help students master the ideas of those lessons. The other, more important purpose, is to serve as an organizer for the formulas in the chapter and thus help students to memorize them.

10-7
VOLUMES OF PYRAMIDS AND CONES

There is no known simple derivation of the volume formula $V = \frac{1}{3}Bh$ for any pyramid or cone. The derivation is to dissect a prism into three pyramids of equal volume to find the volume of each pyramid; then Cavalieri's Principle is used to show that the volume of a cone has the same formula.

Not all things in two dimensions generalize so easily to three dimensions. In two dimensions, any two polygons with the same area can be dissected and rearranged into congruent pieces. In 1902, Max Dehn proved that in three dimensions there can exist two triangular pyramids with equal altitudes and with bases of equal area that cannot be dissected and rearranged into congruent solids.

10-8
THE VOLUME OF A SPHERE

In this lesson and the next, the formulas for the volume and surface area of a sphere are derived. Both derivations are ingenious. The ingenuity is required because no part of the surface of a sphere contains a planar region. The volume of a sphere is shown (by using Cavalieri's principle) to be equal to the difference in volume between a cylinder and two cones, and thus is found by subtraction.

10-9
THE SURFACE AREA OF A SPHERE

To derive the formula for the area of a circle, we split it into sections (almost triangles) and then added their areas. Analogously, to derive the formula for the surface area of a sphere, we begin by splitting it up into "almost pyramids" and then add their volumes to find the volume of the sphere. Knowing the volume, the surface area of the sphere can now be found because the sum of the bases of the "almost pyramids" is the surface area of the sphere; that is, $\frac{4}{3}\pi r^3 = \frac{1}{3}r \cdot$ S.A., or $4\pi r^2 =$ S.A.

CHAPTER 10

We recommend 12 to 15 days for this chapter: 9 to 11 on the lessons and quizzes; 1 for the Progress Self-Test; 1 or 2 for the Chapter Review; and 1 for a Chapter test. (See the Daily Pacing Chart on page 466A). If you spend more than 15 days on this chapter, you are moving too slowly. Keep in mind that each lesson includes Review questions to help students firm up content studied previously.

Surface Areas and Volumes

10-1: Surface Areas of Prisms and Cylinders

10-2: Surface Areas of Pyramids and Cones

10-3: Fundamental Properties of Volume

10-4: Multiplication, Area, and Volume

10-5: Volumes of Prisms and Cylinders

10-6: Remembering Formulas

10-7: Volumes of Pyramids and Cones

10-8: The Volume of a Sphere

10-9: The Surface Area of a Sphere

466

The two most important measures of 3-dimensional figures are **surface area** and **volume.** They are the counterparts of perimeter and area in 2-dimensional figures. Like perimeter, surface area measures a boundary, the surface of a 3-dimensional figure. Volume, like area, measures the space enclosed by the figure.

Surface Area helps in determining:	Volume helps in determining:
how much paper is needed to make the bag	how much the bag can hold
how much land there is to explore	how much material makes up the moon
how much heat a bird loses through its skin	how much the bird weighs
how much fabric is needed to cover the toy.	how much stuffing is needed to make the toy.

Surface area and volume are quite different, as the above examples show. In this chapter, you will learn how to calculate the surface area and volume of the 3-dimensional figures introduced in the last chapter. You will also learn how these measures are related to each other, and the general properties underlying them.

OBJECTIVES

A Draw prisms and cylinders, given their dimensions.
B Calculate surface areas of cylinders and prisms from appropriate lengths, and vice versa.
I Apply formulas for surface area to real situations.

TEACHING NOTES

There are two things you may wish to emphasize in this lesson. First is the relationship between nets and formulas. A net is an aid in calculating and understanding surface area, but it is not a necessity. Formulas exist so that the derivation is not necessary each time.

Second is the way formulas are organized in the book. The first formula given in this lesson is a general Right Prism-Cylinder Lateral Area Formula; from this, if one knows a formula for the circumference of a circle, a specific formula for a right cylinder can be found.

The second formula in the lesson, S.A. = L.A. + 2B, for the surface area of a prism or cylinder, requires only an understanding of surface area and what the figures are.

LESSON

Surface Areas of Prisms and Cylinders

The cost of any container, from a suitcase to a new house, from a paper bag to an open air balloon, depends on the amount of material used to make it. The amount of material on the outside of the container is its **surface area (S.A.)**.

Consider a paper bag. It is approximately a box, a type of prism, with the top base missing. Since each face of a box is a rectangular region, the surface area of the bag is the sum of the areas of 5 rectangles. The areas are easily seen by examining the net for the bag.

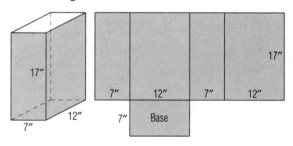

Example 1 A paper grocery bag has a base 7″ by 12″ and a height of 17″. At least how much paper is needed to make it?

Solution Draw the bag and a net for it.

Surface area = area of base + sum of areas of lateral faces
= 7 · 12 + (17 · 7 + 17 · 12 + 17 · 7 + 17 · 12)
Use the Distributive Property for the lateral surface.
= 7 · 12 + 17(7 + 12 + 7 + 12)
= 84 + 17 · 38
= 730 square inches

So at least 730 sq in. of paper is needed. Overlapping parts at the bottom (for strength) and by the seams increase this amount somewhat.

468

The area of the lateral surface of a solid is its **lateral area (L.A.)**. In Example 1, the lateral area was calculated by finding the sum of the areas of the four lateral faces. Since the base rectangle had perimeter $7'' + 12'' + 7'' + 12'' = 38''$ and the height of the bag was $17''$, the calculation could be reduced to

$$\text{L.A.} = 38 \cdot 17 = \text{perimeter of base} \cdot \text{height of prism.}$$

This idea works with any right prism (or cylinder) because the length of any lateral edge equals the height of the prism (or cylinder).

Right Prism-Cylinder Lateral Area Formula:

The lateral area L.A. of a right prism (or cylinder) is the product of its height h and the perimeter (circumference) p of its base.

$$\text{L.A.} = ph$$

Proof

Here are a representative right prism and right cylinder, each with height h. For the prism, the perimeter of a base is $a + b + c + d + e$. For the cylinder, the perimeter of a base is $2\pi r$.

$$p = a + b + c + d + e \qquad\qquad p = 2\pi r$$

Here are their nets.

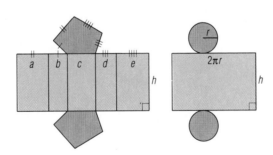

Now we obtain the lateral areas. That is the area of everything but the bases.

For the prism,   For the cylinder,
L.A. $= (a + b + c + d + e)h$ L.A. $= 2\pi r \cdot h$
     $= ph.$ $= ph.$

Every prism or cylinder has two congruent bases. The bases have the same area. So the next theorem holds even for oblique prisms and cylinders.

LESSON 10-1   Surface Areas of Prisms and Cylinders   **469**

Prism-Cylinder Surface Area Formula:

The total surface area S.A. of any prism or cylinder is the sum of its lateral area L.A. and twice the area B of a base.
$$\text{S.A.} = \text{L.A.} + 2B$$

Notice that the formulas for the lateral and surface areas of right prisms are identical to those for cylinders. But the formulas for cylinders can be rewritten in terms of h and r by applying the formulas for the area and circumference (perimeter) of a circle.

In a right cylinder,

$$
\begin{aligned}
\text{L.A.} &= ph & \text{S.A.} &= 2B + ph \\
&= (2\pi r)h & &= 2 \cdot \pi r^2 + 2\pi r \cdot h \quad \text{(substituting the formulas)} \\
&= 2\pi rh & &= 2\pi r(r + h) \quad \text{(factoring out } 2\pi\text{)}.
\end{aligned}
$$

Some people like to memorize many formulas. We advise you to learn at least those formulas highlighted in boxes. Of course, you must know what each letter in the formula represents. As shown in Example 2, always begin a problem by writing an appropriate formula. Substitute for the area and perimeter only when needed.

■ ■ ■ ■ ■ ■ ■ ■ ■ ■

Example 2 For the right cylinder shown, find
a. the lateral area and
b. the surface area.

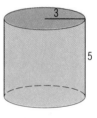

Solution

a. Begin by writing a formula for the lateral area of a right cylinder.
$$\text{L.A.} = ph$$
For a cylinder, if r is the radius of the base, $p = 2\pi r$. Here $r = 3$, so $p = 6\pi$.
Substituting,   L.A. = $6\pi h$.
Since $h = 5$,   L.A. = 30π square units.

b. In any cylinder, S.A. = L.A. + 2B.
Since the base is a circle, $B = \pi r^2$, and here $r = 3$.
From part **a**, L.A. = 30π.
Substituting,   S.A. = $30\pi + 2 \cdot (\pi \cdot 3^2)$
                      = $30\pi + 18\pi$
                      = 48π square units.

Notice that, since lateral area and surface area are areas, they are measured in square units.

Covering the Reading

8 cm
15 cm
20 cm

1. Which measures the boundary of a three-dimensional figure, surface area or volume? **surface area**

2. **a.** Define: lateral area. **the area of the lateral surface of a solid**
   b. What is a formula for the lateral area of a right prism? **L.A. = ph**

3. A small bag has dimensions as pictured at the left. What is its surface area? **1040 cm²**

4. In a prism or cylinder, S.A. = _?_ + _?_. **L.A., 2B**

In 5–7, a net for a surface is given.
   a. What is the surface?
   b. Calculate its lateral area.
   c. Calculate its surface area.

5.
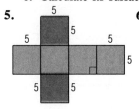

a) cube; b) 100 units²;
c) 150 units²

6.
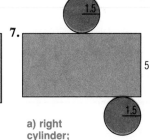

a) rt. triangular prism
b) 108 cm²; c) 120 cm²

7.
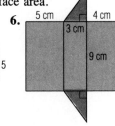

a) right cylinder;
b) 15π ≈ 47.12 units²;
c) 19.5π ≈ 61 units²

8. The lateral area of a right cylinder is the _?_ multiplied by the _?_ of the base. **height, circumference**

9. A right cylinder has height h and base with radius r. Write each formula in terms of r and h.
   a. area of either base **B = πr²**
   b. lateral area **L.A. = 2πrh**
   c. surface area **S.A. = 2πrh + 2πr², or 2πr(h + r)**

In 10 and 11, find the lateral area and surface area of each surface.

10.
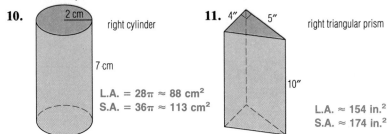

right cylinder

2 cm
7 cm

L.A. = 28π ≈ 88 cm²
S.A. = 36π ≈ 113 cm²

11.

right triangular prism

4″ 5″
10″

L.A. ≈ 154 in.²
S.A. ≈ 174 in.²

In 12–15, is the quantity related more to surface area or to volume?

12. how much a railroad box car will hold **volume**

13. how much metal is needed to build a box car **surface area**

14. how much you weigh **volume**

15. how much you sweat due to exercise **surface area**

LESSON 10-1 Surface Areas of Prisms and Cylinders **471**

MORE PRACTICE
For more questions on SPUR Objectives, use *Lesson Master 10-1*, shown below.

EXTENSION
Some students may be interested in obtaining a cardboard box from home or a store, and determining how much extra surface area is in the tabs and overlaps which are needed to make the box secure.

EVALUATION
Alternative Assessment
You may want several students to summarize the process of developing the formulas for the lateral area and surface area of a prism or cylinder from the general formulas given. Ask them to identify what is important to remember and what is not so important, and what each letter in the formulas represents.

NAME _____

LESSON **MASTER 10–1**
QUESTIONS ON **SPUR** OBJECTIVES

■SKILLS *Objectives A and B (See pages 516–519 for objectives.)*

1. **a.** What is the solid whose net is shown?
   rt. triangular prism
   b. What is its lateral area?
   2800 in.²
   c. What is its surface area?
   3220 in.²

   20 in. 21 in. 29 in.
   40 in.

2. The measure of the space enclosed by a three-dimensional figure is its ____ **volume**

3. If a cylinder has a radius of 5 and its lateral area is 30π, how high is the cylinder? **3**

4. Draw a right cylinder with a base of radius 1.5 cm and a height of 4 cm and give its lateral area and surface area.
   lateral area = **12π ≈ 37.7 cm²**
   surface area = **16.5π ≈ 51.8 cm²**
   4 cm
   1.5 cm

■USES *Objective I*
For 5–7, is the quantity related more to surface area or volume?
5. amount of paper needed to wrap a gift **surface area**
6. the number of pages in a book **volume**
7. how long a cartridge of ink will last **volume**

8. A new pencil is 17 cm long (not counting the eraser) and is shaped like a right hexagonal prism, with sides that are 4 mm long. How much surface area of the pencil has to be painted in square centimeters? **≈40.8 cm²**

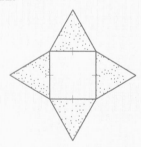
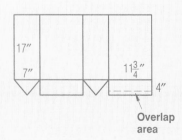
Applying the Mathematics

16. How many square centimeters of sheet metal are needed to make a closed cylindric can with height 20 cm and base radius 9 cm?
    $522\pi \approx 1640$ cm²

In 17–19, find the surface area of the given solid.

17. a box with dimensions 9 cm, 10 cm, and 11 cm 598 cm²

18. a box with dimensions ℓ, *w*, and *h* $2(\ell w + \ell h + wh)$

19. a cube with an edge of length *s* $6s^2$

20. The edges of a box are doubled in length. What happens to its surface area? (Hint: Try a few special cases.)
    S.A. is multiplied by 4 (quadrupled).

21. A fuel storage tank has a diameter of 50 meters and a height of 75 meters. If a gallon of paint can cover about 45 square meters and 2 coats of paint are required, about how many gallons are needed to paint the exterior sides and top of the tank? about 610 gallons

Review

22. Draw a net for a square pyramid and shade in the lateral surface. *(Lessons 9-7, 9-3)* See margin.

23. What is the center of a regular polygon? *(Lesson 7-6)*
    interior of the polygon that is equidistant from the vertices

24. Name the postulate applied here: $(2\ell + 2w)h = 2\ell h + 2wh$.
    (Lesson 1-7)
    Distributive Property of Multiplication

25. What is the cube of $\frac{2}{3}$? *(Previous course)* $\frac{8}{27}$

Exploration

26. Find a paper bag in your house.
    a. What are its dimensions? sample: 7″ by 11$\frac{3}{4}$″ by 17″
    b. What is its surface area? sample: 719.75 square inches
    c. To make the bag, some of the paper has to overlap for gluing. Carefully undo the bag to make it lie flat. Draw its net. See margin.
    d. How much paper is used to make the bag? sample: ≈ 789 square inches

27. Suppose you wish to make a box with no top and you have 100 square inches of cardboard, as well as scissors and tape. What might be its dimensions?
    sample: base 5 in. by 5 in. with a height of 3.75 in.

LESSON

10-2

Foam pyramids embedded with carbon line the steel walls of an anechoic chamber.

Surface Areas of Pyramids and Cones

Recall that the *height* of a pyramid or cone is the length of the perpendicular segment from its vertex to the plane of its base. The height also refers to that segment. Below are two square pyramids *A-BCDE* and *F-GHIJ* with the same height *h*. (Notice how the pyramids are named, with the vertex followed by a dash, followed by a name for the base.) The pyramid *F-GHIJ* is a regular pyramid, since the foot of the perpendicular from *F* to the plane of *GHIJ* is at the center of *GHIJ*.

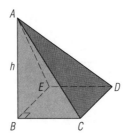
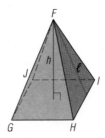

The lateral area of each of these pyramids is the sum of the areas of the four triangles that are its lateral faces.

L.A. of $A\text{-}BCDE$ = Area($\triangle ABC$) + Area($\triangle ACD$) + Area($\triangle ADE$) + Area($\triangle AEB$)
L.A. of $F\text{-}GHIJ$ = Area($\triangle FGH$) + Area($\triangle FHI$) + Area($\triangle FIJ$) + Area($\triangle FJG$)

Engineers place aircraft in a chamber built of steel walls with an echo-free interior to eliminate outside electronic signals and assure more accurate test results.

There is no simpler formula for the lateral area of *A-BCDE*. If you have enough information, you just calculate each of the four areas and add.

However, the lateral area of the regular pyramid *F-GHIJ* is easier to calculate, because the triangles are congruent isosceles triangles. Remember that the altitude of each of these triangles from the vertex *F* is the *slant height* of the pyramid. (Think of the slant height as the distance you would have to climb if you were trying to climb the pyramid starting at the midpoint of a base and proceeding straight toward its top.) The usual letter for slant height is ℓ, so

$$\begin{aligned}\text{L.A. of } F\text{-}GHIJ &= \tfrac{1}{2}\ell(GH) + \tfrac{1}{2}\ell(HI) + \tfrac{1}{2}\ell(IJ) + \tfrac{1}{2}\ell(JG) \\ &= \tfrac{1}{2}\ell(GH + HI + IJ + JG) \\ &= \tfrac{1}{2}\ell p,\end{aligned}$$

where *p* is the perimeter of the base.

LESSON 10-2 Surface Areas of Pyramids and Cones **473**

LESSON 10-2

RESOURCES
■ Lesson Master 10-2

OBJECTIVES

A Draw pyramids and cones, given their dimensions.
C Calculate surface areas of pyramids and cones from appropriate lengths, and vice versa.
F Develop formulas for specific figures from more general formulas.
I Apply formulas for surface area to real situations.

TEACHING NOTES

To find the surface area of a pyramid or cone, students should be taught to think of finding the lateral area and the area of the base separately and then to add these areas to find the surface area. (This is true of prisms and cylinders as well.) Formulas for lateral area are more important than formulas for surface area, because the latter can be found so easily from the former. For example, the Pyramid-Cone Surface Area Formula, S.A. = L.A. + B, is one which is understood simply by knowing the definitions of surface area, pyramids, and cones.

The area of the base of a cone is $\tfrac{1}{2}rp$, and the lateral area of a right cone is $\tfrac{1}{2}\ell p$. Since $r < \ell$, the lateral area of a cone is always greater than the area of its base. Suggest that students think of a rubber sheet fixed in a hoop. As the center is pushed in, the sheet must stretch, increasing the area.

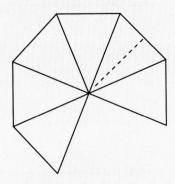
The formula L.A. $= \frac{1}{2}\ell p$ holds for any regular pyramid. Here is a proof.

Let s be a side of the base of a regular pyramid and ℓ be its slant height. Since the lateral faces are congruent, the area of each lateral face is $\frac{1}{2}\ell s$. Since there are n lateral faces,

$$\text{L.A.} = n \cdot \tfrac{1}{2}\ell s$$
$$= \tfrac{1}{2}\ell \cdot ns.$$

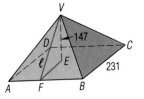

But ns is the perimeter of the base. Substituting p for ns,

$$\text{L.A.} = \tfrac{1}{2}\ell p.$$

Example 1 The pyramid of Khufu, a regular square pyramid 147 m tall and 231 m on a side, is the largest of the Egyptian pyramids.

a. What is the approximate slant height of this pyramid?
b. What is its lateral area?

Solution

a. Draw a picture.

To compute the slant height ℓ, focus on right triangle VEF. E is the center of the square, so $EF = \frac{1}{2} \cdot 231 = 115.5$ meters. VE is the height, 147 meters. By the Pythagorean Theorem,

$$\ell^2 = EF^2 + VE^2$$
$$= 115.5^2 + 147^2$$
$$\approx 34{,}950.$$

So $\qquad \ell \approx 187$ meters

b. To find the lateral area, use the formula L.A. $= \frac{1}{2}\ell p$. p is the perimeter of the base, so $p = 4 \cdot 231$ or 924.

$$\text{L.A.} = \tfrac{1}{2}\ell p$$
$$\approx \tfrac{1}{2} \cdot 187 \cdot 924$$
$$\approx 86{,}400 \text{ square meters}$$

Question 10 asks you to compare the answer in Example 1 with the area of a football field which, including the end zones, is less than 5400 square meters.

The formula L.A. $= \frac{1}{2}\ell p$ also applies to right cones. Imagine increasing n, the number of sides of the base of the regular pyramid. A cone is the limit of regular pyramids as n increases without bound. The slant height of the pyramids becomes the length of any lateral edge of the cone. The perimeter of the n-gon becomes the circumference of the circular base of the cone.

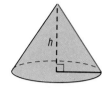

Regular Pyramid-Right Cone Lateral Area Formula:

The lateral area L.A. of a regular pyramid (or right cone) is half the product of the slant height ℓ and the perimeter (circumference) p of its base.
$$L.A. = \tfrac{1}{2}\ell p$$

All pyramids and cones have one base. So to calculate surface area, add the area of the base to the lateral area.

Pyramid-Cone Surface Area Formula:

The total surface area S.A. of any pyramid or cone is the sum of its lateral area L.A. and the area B of its base.
$$S.A. = L.A. + B$$

Example 2 Find the total surface area of a right cone with slant height 13 and radius of base 10.

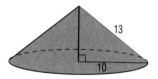

Solution Draw a picture, as at the left. Use the formula S.A. = L.A. + B. The lateral area can be found using the formula
$$L.A. = \tfrac{1}{2}\ell p.$$
Here, ℓ is 13. Now p is the perimeter of the base, that is, the circumference $2\pi r$. Thus, $p = 2\pi \cdot 10 = 20\pi$.
So
$$\begin{aligned} L.A. &= \tfrac{1}{2}\ell p \\ &= \tfrac{1}{2} \cdot 13 \cdot 20\pi \\ &= 130\pi. \end{aligned}$$
The base is a circle. So $B = \pi r^2$
$$= 100\pi.$$
The total surface area is L.A. + B, or 230π.

Check L.A. should be greater than B. (Do you see why?)
$130\pi > 100\pi$, a rough check.

ADDITIONAL EXAMPLES
1. A small pyramid discovered recently at an Inca ceremonial site on the top of a mountain in the Andes has a square base with vertices pointed in the four directions—north, south, east, and west. The ratio of the height of the pyramid to the edges of the base are near the golden ratio—about 1.6 to 1. If the height of the pyramid is 2 meters, what is the length of an edge of its base, what is its slant height, and what is its lateral area?
edge = 1.25 m; slant height ≈ 2.10 m; lateral area ≈ 5.24 m².

2. A pile of sand has been stored in the shape of a cone. The yardkeeper knows that the pile is about 20 feet tall and 102 feet in circumference around the base. What is the area of the tarpaulin needed to cover the pile?
about 1314 square feet

3. A rubber sheet is fastened in a circular hoop 1 meter in diameter. A stick is positioned in the center and pushed up as shown, stretching the rubber sheet in the shape of a cone. How far up does the rubber sheet need to be pushed before its lateral area has doubled?

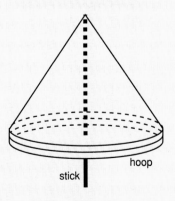

hoop

stick

$\frac{\sqrt{3}}{2}$ **or about .87 meters**

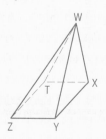

Covering the Reading

In 1–3, draw a picture. See margin.
1. a non-regular pyramid *W-XYZT*

2. a regular pentagonal pyramid *A-BCDEF* with slant height 5, height 4

3. a right cone with slant height ℓ, height *h,* and radius of base *r*

4. Each lateral face of a regular pyramid is a(n) _?_. isosceles triangle

In 5 and 6, what does each variable represent? Be as specific as you can.
5. In a pyramid, L.A. $= \frac{1}{2}\ell p$.
   L.A. = lateral area; ℓ = slant height; *p* = perimeter of base
6. In a cone, L.A. $= \frac{1}{2}\ell p$.
   L.A. = lateral area; ℓ = slant height; *p* = circumference of base

7. A right cone is the limit of regular pyramids as the number of _?_ increases without bound. sides of the base

8. At the left, a regular triangular pyramid is pictured. Its slant height is 10 cm and a side of the base is 12 cm. Find its lateral area. 180 cm²

9. The perpendicular from the vertex of a regular pyramid intersects the base at _?_. the center of the base

10. About how many times larger is the lateral area of the pyramid of Khufu than the area of a football field? 16

11. A second Egyptian pyramid is a regular square pyramid 450 ft tall, 755 ft on a side.
    a. What is its approximate slant height? ≈ 587.4 ft
    b. What is its approximate lateral area? ≈ 887,000 ft²

12. Use the right cone pictured below.
    a. Find its slant height. $\sqrt{130}$ ≈ 11.4 units
    b. Find its lateral area. $3\pi\sqrt{130}$ ≈ 107.5 units²
    c. Find its surface area. $3\pi\sqrt{130} + 9\pi$ ≈ 135.7 units²

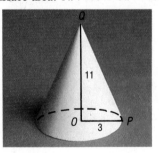

13. *Multiple choice.* For a given cone, which is larger, its lateral area or the area of its base?
    (a) lateral area   (b) area of the base
    (c) Neither; they are equal.   (d) The answer depends on the cone. (a)

476

14. a. In a pyramid, which is greater, its height or its slant height?
b. Explain your answer. a) slant height; b) The slant height is the hypotenuse of a right △. The height (a leg) is less than the hypotenuse.

In 15–17, **a.** draw the figure; **b.** find its lateral area; **c.** find its surface area.

15. a regular square pyramid with a base perimeter of 40 and a slant height of 50 a) See margin. b) 1000 units²; c) 1100 units²

16. a regular triangular pyramid with slant height 7 and with base of side 6 and area 9√3
a) See margin. b) 63 units²; c) 63 + 9√3 ≈ 79 units²

17. a right cone with slant height 17 and base diameter 14
a) See margin. b) 119π ≈ 374 units²; c) 168π ≈ 528 units²

18. Find the surface area of a box with dimensions 1′, 15″, and 18″.
(Lesson 10-1) 1332 sq in. = 9.25 sq ft

19. Small cans of frozen juice are about 9.5 cm tall and 5.5 cm in diameter. The tops and bottoms are metal; the rest is cardboard.
a. About how much metal is needed? ≈ 47.5 cm²
b. About how much cardboard is needed? *(Lesson 10-1)* ≈ 164 cm²

20. Draw a net for a regular square pyramid with dimensions of your choosing. *(Lesson 9-7)* See margin.

21. Find the length of each lateral edge in the pyramid of Question 8.
(Lessons 9-3, 8-7) √136 ≈ 11.66 cm

22. What are the four assumed properties of area? *(Lesson 8-3)*
See below.

23. Line *t* goes through the points (6, -4) and (8, 0).
a. Graph *t*. See margin.
b. Find the slope of *t*. 2
c. Find the slope of a line perpendicular to *t*. *(Lessons 3-5, 3-4)* $-\frac{1}{2}$

24. Solve in your head. *(Previous course)*
a. $x + 3 = 64$ 61
b. $y \cdot 3 = 64$ $\frac{64}{3}$
c. $z^3 = 64$ 4

25. Cut out a disc with radius 4″ or 10 cm from a sheet of paper. Then cut out a 90° sector from the disc. This leaves a figure with the shape of the shaded region at the left. Now fold $\overline{AB}$ onto $\overline{BC}$ to form a cone. What is the lateral area of this cone? If radius = 4 inches, L.A. ≈ 12π ≈ 37.7 square inches. If radius = 10 cm, L.A. ≈ 75π ≈ 235.6 cm².

22. Uniqueness property, rectangle formula, congruence property, additive property

---

FOLLOW-UP

MORE PRACTICE
For more questions on SPUR Objectives, use *Lesson Master 10-2,* shown below.

EVALUATION
Alternative Assessment
Use the questions dealing with applying the pyramid and cone formulas correctly (**Questions 11**, **12**, **15**, **16**, **17**). Have students discuss their answers in pairs and hand in one paper showing the answers. Ascertain both that the formulas and units are used properly and that the correct answers are given.

2., 3., 15.a., 16.a., 17.a., 20., 23.a. See Additional Answers in the back of this book.

NAME _____

RESOURCES
- Lesson Master 10-3
- Quiz for Lessons 10-1 Through 10-3

OBJECTIVES

B Calculate surface areas and volumes of cylinders and prisms from appropriate lengths, and vice versa.

E Calculate cube roots.

F Develop formulas for specific figures from more general formulas.

J Apply formulas for volume to real situations.

TEACHING NOTES

Reading Students can read this lesson independently, but be sure they pay attention to the similarities between the Volume Postulate and the Area Postulate (Chapter 8). You may wish to have them write summary statements about each of the four properties listed in the two postulates.

The unit cube in volume serves the same role as the unit square in area; that is, it is a convenient unit for measuring. Just as with area, the capacity of solids in which cubes do not fit snugly, such as spheres, will be determined later.

Finding the volume of a solid as simple as that in **Example 2** still requires the use of all four properties of the Volume Postulate. First, there is the unit cube whose volume must be found (Box Volume

---

10-3

Fundamental Properties of Volume

Each face of the cube below, with sides of length 1, has area 1 square unit. Since there are six faces, the surface area of the cube is 6 square units. But **volume** is quite different from surface area. The volume of this cube is 1 cubic unit or 1 unit^3. For this reason it is called the **unit cube.** Usually volume is measured in cubic units.

1 cubic unit

Volume measures how much a figure will hold, its *capacity*.

Example 1 What is the volume of a paper bag with base 12″ by 7″ and height 17″?

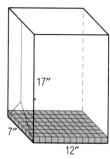

17″

7″

12″

Solution There are 12 · 7 unit cubes in the layer along a base. There are 17 layers. The volume is 12″ · 7″ · 17″, or 1428 cubic inches.

Notice that the volume of this bag is the product of its three dimensions. This is one of the four fundamental properties of volume assumed in the Volume Postulate. Compare these assumptions with the fundamental properties of area assumed in the Area Postulate in Lesson 8-3.

478

Volume Postulate:

   a. Uniqueness Property Given a unit cube, every polyhedral solid has a unique volume.

   b. Box Volume Formula The volume of a box with dimensions ℓ, w, and h is ℓwh.

   c. Congruence Property Congruent figures have the same volume.

   d. Additive Property The volume of the union of two nonoverlapping solids is the sum of the volumes of the solids.

In symbols, if Volume(S) is the volume of a solid S, then the Additive Property of Volume states that if A and B are two nonoverlapping solids, then:

$$\text{Volume}(A \cup B) = \text{Volume}(A) + \text{Volume}(B).$$

Using this property, volumes of more complicated figures can be calculated.

▪ ▪ ▪ ▪ ▪ ▪ ▪ ▪ ▪

Example 2   Figures I and II are the unions of 5 unit cubes. Give the surface area and volume of each.

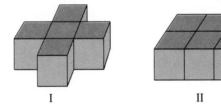

I   II

Solution   The volume for each solid is the same, since it is the sum of the volumes of the five cubes.

$$\text{Volume(I)} = \text{Volume(II)} = 5 \text{ cubic units}$$

In solid I, there are 12 lateral faces (3 on each of the four outside cubes), each with area 1 square unit, and each base has area 5 square units.

$$\begin{aligned}\text{S.A.} &= \text{L.A.} + 2 \cdot B \\ &= 12 + 2 \cdot 5 \\ &= 22 \text{ square units}\end{aligned}$$

In solid II, there are 10 lateral faces. Each base again has area 5 square units.

$$\begin{aligned}\text{S.A.} &= \text{L.A.} + 2 \cdot B \\ &= 10 + 2 \cdot 5 \\ &= 20 \text{ square units}\end{aligned}$$

LESSON 10-3 Fundamental Properties of Volume   **479**

Formula). There are five of these cubes and they all have the same volume (Congruence Property). The five volumes can be added to find the volume of the union (Additive Property). And the answer found is the only answer (Uniqueness Property).

The paragraph discussing the containers at the top of page 480 continues an important theme. Volume and surface area are quite different concepts, even though both measure the "size" of a figure. This is the subject of the Exploration **Questions 22** and **23**. Be sure to discuss them.

Calculators that are not scientific usually will not have a cube root key. Check that students know how to calculate cube roots; some options are given on page 480. You may wish to make a table of cubes of the integers from 1 to 10:

Edge n	Volume n^3
1	1
2	8
3	27
4	64
5	125
6	216
7	343
8	512
9	729
10	1000

Alternate Approach
One way to help students see the difference between the surface area of a box and its volume is to have them explore various models. A good model is a boxed deck of playing cards. The box itself represents the surface area, and the cards represent the amount (volume) that fits in the box. A single card can be used as the unit of measure for the volume of the box.

Example 2 illustrates that solids may have equal volumes, but unequal surface areas. However, many people judge the volume of a container by its surface area. They think, "if it looks big, then it holds a lot!"

Pictured at the left are a salad-dressing bottle and a yogurt container. The two containers hold the same amount; they have the same volume. The dressing bottle has greater surface area, giving the false impression that it has greater volume and holds more.

The formula for the volume of a cube is a special case of the formula for the volume of a box where each dimension is the same.

Cube Volume Formula:

The volume of a cube with edge s is s^3.

Proof

For a box,   Volume = ℓwh.
A cube is a box with $\ell = w = h = s$.
Substituting,   Volume = $s \cdot s \cdot s$
                                      = s^3.

Because of the Cube Volume Formula, we call s^3 the "cube of s." If a cube has volume 8, its edge will satisfy $s^3 = 8$, and so $s = 2$.

We say that 2 is the *cube root* of 8, and write $2 = \sqrt[3]{8}$. In general, $\sqrt[3]{y}$ is the edge of a cube whose volume is y.

Definition:

x is a **cube root** of y, written $x = \sqrt[3]{y}$, if and only if $x^3 = y$.

Scientific calculators differ in the keys they employ to calculate a cube root. Some have a $\boxed{\sqrt[3]{x}}$ key. On some there is a $\boxed{\sqrt[x]{x}}$ key; on these, to find $\sqrt[3]{n}$, press n $\boxed{\sqrt[x]{x}}$ 3 $\boxed{=}$. On others you can press n $\boxed{INV}$ $\boxed{x^y}$ 3 $\boxed{=}$.

Example 3 A cube has a volume of 50 cubic centimeters. What is the length of an edge?

Solution Let s be the length of an edge. Since $s^3 = 50$, s is exactly $\sqrt[3]{50}$ cm. To estimate $\sqrt[3]{50}$, use a calculator. 50 $\boxed{\sqrt[x]{x}}$ 3 $\boxed{=}$ displays 3.684... . An edge is approximately 3.7 cm long.

Check Is $3.7^3 \approx 50$? Yes, $3.7^3 = 50.653$, which is close enough.

480

Covering the Reading

1. What is the volume of a box with dimensions 30 cm, 70 cm, and 84 cm? **176,400 cm³**

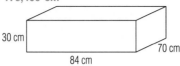

2. In a sugar cube, each edge has length 1 cm. What is the volume of the cube? **1 cm³**

3. Two solids have the same surface area. Must they have the same volume? **No**

4. Two cubes have the same surface area. Must they have the same volume? **Yes**

5. x is a cube root of y if and only if __?__ . $x^3 = y$

6. **a.** Give the cube of 8. **512**
   b. Give the cube root of 8. **2**

7. Write the exact cube root of 50. **$\sqrt[3]{50}$**

8. With a calculator, estimate the cube root of 100 to the nearest hundredth. **4.64**

Applying the Mathematics

9. A top is put on the paper bag of Example 1.
   a. By how much does the top change the bag's surface area?
   b. By how much does it change the bag's volume?
   a) adds 84 in.²; b) no change

10. Some people use the formula $V = Bh$ for the volume of a box.
    a. What is B in this formula? **area of a base**
    b. Why does this formula work? **The area of the base is ℓw, so the formula $V = Bh$ is equivalent to $V = \ell wh$.**

11. The volume of a bag is 576 in.³. If the base has an area of 48 in.², what is the height? **12 inches**

12. A cube has volume 29,791 cm³. What is its surface area? **5766 cm²**

13. Calculate $\sqrt[3]{25} + \sqrt[3]{100}$ to the nearest hundredth. **7.57**

14. One cube has edges x centimeters long. Another has edges $3x$ centimeters long. Find the ratio of:
    a. the total surface area of the smaller cube to that of the larger $\frac{1}{9}$
    b. the volume of the smaller cube to that of the larger. $\frac{1}{27}$

x $3x$

Sidebar (right column):

$\sqrt[3]{50}$. For a sense of the size of the cube, the first answer is useful. To express the idea that the cube holds 50 cubic units, use the second answer.

Question 10: In discussing this question, you may wish to make the analogy with the area of a rectangle.

Question 12: Students have to determine the measure in one dimension from the measure in another dimension. An analysis of the problem should begin with asking what must be known to find the desired measure. Write down the formula; then determine how the measures needed can be found from the given data.

Making Connections for Questions 14: In Chapter 12, the ratio of volumes as the cube of the ratio of similitude will be stressed. At this time, build the idea by having students see that 3 cubes are along each edge, and that 3^2 cubes are in each layer. Since there are 3 layers, there are 3^3 cubes in the whole.

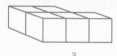

15. **a.** 1 yard = __?__ feet **3**
    b. 1 square yard = __?__ square feet **9**
    c. 1 cubic yard = __?__ cubic feet **27**

16. **a.** Complete this program so that it will print out the correct volume and surface area.

    ```
    10   PRINT "GIVE DIMENSIONS OF BOX"
    20   INPUT L, W, H
    30   PRINT "THE VOLUME IS " i. __?__ " CUBIC UNITS." i. L*W*H
    40   PRINT "THE SURFACE AREA IS " ii. __?__ " SQUARE UNITS."
    50   END                                ii. 2*(L*W + L*H + H*W)
    ```

    b. Check your program by letting L = 7, W = 12, and H = 17, and comparing the printout with Example 1 of this lesson and Example 1 of Lesson 10-1. **See margin.**

Review

17. **a.** Draw a right cone with radius 4 and slant height 12.
    b. Determine its lateral area. *(Lesson 10-2)*
    $48\pi \approx 150.8$ units²

18. Find the surface area of the regular square pyramid pictured at the left. *(Lesson 10-2)* S.A. = $2s\ell + s^2$

19. **a.** In square inches, how much wrapping paper is needed to cover a cylinder 12″ in diameter and 7″ high? $156\pi \approx 490$ in.²
    b. Suppose you can only buy the wrapping paper by the square foot. How many square feet will you need to buy to wrap the cylinder of part **a**? *(Lesson 10-1)* **4 square feet**

20. The tent at the right is in the shape of a right prism with isosceles triangle *GHI* as its base.
    a. Find the area of the base of this prism. $5\sqrt{11} \approx 16.6$ square feet
    b. If the length of the tent is 7 feet, find the surface area of the tent. (Assume no part of the tent is folded onto the ground.) *(Lessons 10-1, 8-7, 8-5)*
    $84 + 10\sqrt{11} \approx 117$ square feet

21. Give the singular of each term. *(Lessons 9-7, 2-5, 1-4)*
    a. polyhedra   **b.** radii   **c.** vertices
    polyhedron   radius   vertex

Exploration

22. Containers holding small amounts can be made to appear to hold more than they do by making them long and thin. Give some examples of these kinds of containers.
    samples: toothpaste tubes, cologne or perfume bottles

23. Two polyhedra made up of 5 unit cubes are shown in Example 2 of this lesson. **See margin.**
    a. Draw some of the other possible polyhedra that are the union of 5 unit cubes.
    b. Which has the most surface area?
    c. Which has the least surface area?

Box cars and other containers are being loaded onto a ship in Hampton, Virginia. Their total volume can be found in a variety of ways.

Multiplication, Area, and Volume

LESSON 10-4

RESOURCES
■ Lesson Master 10-4
▣ Computer Master 21

To obtain the area of a rectangle, you merely have to multiply its length by its width. Any positive numbers can be the length and the width. Thus the area of a rectangle is a *model* for the multiplication of two positive numbers. This enables multiplication to be pictured. For instance, the following picture shows that the product of 3.5 and 2.3 is larger than the product of 3 and 2.

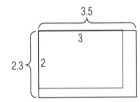

Turning a rectangle on its side does not change its area. But it switches its base and height.

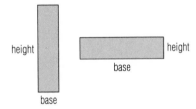

In terms of multiplication this means $hb = bh$, picturing the well-known Commutative Property of Multiplication.

The Box Volume Formula, $V = \ell wh$, models the multiplication of *three* numbers. Any face of a box can be its base, and any sides of the base its length and width, yet the volume will be the same. So not only is commutativity pictured because $V = (\ell w)h = h(\ell w)$, but also associativity because $V = (\ell w)h = \ell(wh)$.

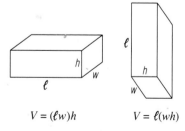

$$V = (\ell w)h \qquad V = \ell(wh)$$

LESSON 10-4 Multiplication, Area, and Volume **483**

OBJECTIVES

G Determine what happens to the surface area and volume of a figure when its dimensions are multiplied by some number.

K Represent products of two (or three) expressions as areas of rectangles (or volumes of boxes), and vice versa.

TEACHING NOTES

This lesson should help students see an application of the "mechanical" process of multiplying polynomials which they learned in algebra classes. Point out the different algebra properties used as well.

Reading To focus attention on how best to read the equations in this lesson, you might show the illustrations and Examples on the chalkboard as you read aloud the lesson together.

Alternate Approach
The results of **Example 2** are very important and a surprise for many students. The question of what happens to the volume of a figure as the dimensions change can be illustrated by using open, actual models and filling them up with unit cubes, sand, and so on.

Even the multiplication of polynomials can be pictured by area and volume. For instance, in algebra you probably saw the multiplication of two binomials pictured using areas of rectangles.

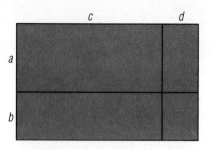

You may have seen the multiplication of two trinomials or other polynomials pictured in this way.

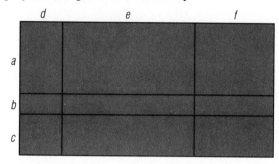

With volume, the multiplication of *three* binomials can be pictured. The big box below has dimensions $a+b$, $c+d$, and $e+f$. So its volume is the product of those three binomials. But the big box is made up of eight little boxes (parts of seven can be seen), so the volume of the big box is also the sum of the volumes of the eight little boxes.

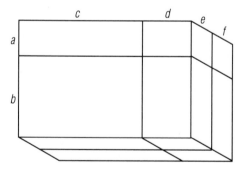

Notice that the product of the three binomials consists of all possible products in which one factor is taken from the first binomial, one from the second, and one from the third.

484

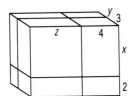

Example 1   Expand $(x + 2)(y + 3)(z + 4)$.

Solution 1   Think of the three factors as the dimensions of a box. The product is the volume of the box. The volume is the sum of the volumes of eight small boxes.

$V = 3zx + 3 \cdot 4 \cdot x + 3 \cdot z \cdot 2 + 3 \cdot 4 \cdot 2 + yzx + y \cdot 4 \cdot x + yz \cdot 2 + y \cdot 4 \cdot 2$
$\quad = 3xz + 12x + 6z + 24 + xyz + 4xy + 2yz + 8y$

Solution 2   Recall the Distributive Property from your study of algebra.

$(x + 2)(y + 3)(z + 4)$
$\quad = x(y + 3)(z + 4) + 2(y + 3)(z + 4)$
$\quad = x(yz + 4y + 3z + 12) + 2(yz + 4y + 3z + 12)$
$\quad = xyz + 4xy + 3xz + 12x + 2yz + 8y + 6z + 24$

Check 1   The two solutions give the same answer, which is a check.

Check 2   Substitute for x, y, and z. Suppose $x = 5$, $y = 10$, and $z = 8$. Then $(x + 2)(y + 3)(z + 4) = 7 \cdot 13 \cdot 12 = 1092$. Substituting in the answer yields

$5 \cdot 10 \cdot 8 + 4 \cdot 5 \cdot 10 + 3 \cdot 5 \cdot 8 + 12 \cdot 5 + 2 \cdot 10 \cdot 8 + 8 \cdot 10 + 6 \cdot 8 + 24$
$\quad = 400 + 200 + 120 + 60 + 160 + 80 + 48 + 24$
$\quad = 1092.$

Example 1 points out how complicated the change in volume is if you *add* 2 to one edge of a box, 3 to another edge, and 4 to the third edge. The increase in volume is the solution minus xyz, which is the polynomial $4xy + 3xz + 12x + 2yz + 8y + 6z + 24$. But if you *multiply* the edges by 2, 3, and 4, the change in volume is easy to find.

Example 2   A box has dimensions ℓ, w, and h. If the dimensions are multiplied by 2, 3, and 4, respectively, what happens to the volume of the box?

Solution   Draw a picture of the situation.

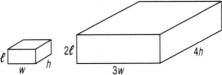

The new volume is $(2\ell)(3w)(4h)$, which is $24\ell wh$, 24 times the old volume.

In general, multiplying any one dimension of a box by a certain number multiplies the volume of the box by that number. In Example 2, if the length were doubled but nothing was done to the other dimensions, the volume would have been doubled. Adding to a dimension of a box does not affect the volume in such a simple way.

Questions

Covering the Reading

1. Use the area model for multiplication to show that $5.6 \cdot 7.8$ is larger than $5 \cdot 7$. **See margin.**

In 2–6, give the algebraic property illustrated.

2. has the same area as

    $ab = ba;$
    commutative property of multiplication

3. has the same volume as

    $(yz)x = (yx)z;$
    assoc. and comm. properties of mult.

4. At the left, the sum of the areas of the four little rectangles equals the area of the largest rectangle.
    $x^2 + 3x + x + 3 = (x + 1)(x + 3);$ **distributive property**

5. The sum of the areas of the six little rectangles equals the area of the largest rectangle. $da + db + dc + ea + eb + ec = (d + e)(a + b + c);$ **distributive property**

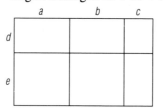

6. The sum of the volumes of the eight little boxes equals the volume of the large box.
    $(u + v)(w + x)(y + z)$
    $= uwy + uwz + uxy + uxz$
    $+ vwy + vwz + vxy + vxz;$
    distributive property

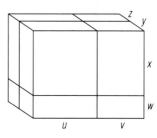

In 7–10, expand.

7. $(x + 9)(2x + 3)$ $2x^2 + 21x + 27$

8. $(3a + 5)(7a + 6)$ $21a^2 + 53a + 30$

9. $(a + 1)(a + 2)(a + 3)$ $a^3 + 6a^2 + 11a + 6$

10. $(a + b + 2)(3a + 8b)$ $3a^2 + 6a + 11ab + 16b + 8b^2$

486

486

In 11–13, how is the volume of a box changed if its dimensions are changed in the indicated way?

11. Its length is multiplied by 3 and all other dimensions are kept the same. **multiplied by 3**

12. Its length, width, and height are all multiplied by 3. **multiplied by 27**

13. Six is added to the length and all other dimensions are kept the same. **The volume is increased by six times the product of the height and the width.**

Applying the Mathematics

Rice harvesting in Indonesia

14. A coating of lead 1 mm thick is put on a steel box safe that has dimensions 28 cm, 20 cm, and 14 cm. What is the amount of lead needed? **about 249 cubic centimeters**

15. In a market you see two full bags of rice. Bag X is 1.4 times as high as bag Y, 1.2 times as wide, and 1.2 times as deep.
   a. How do the capacities of these bags compare?
   b. How should their prices compare? **a) Bag X holds about twice as much as bag Y. b) Bag X should cost about twice as much as bag Y.**

In 16–19, expand.

16. $(x - 1)(2x - 5)$ $2x^2 - 7x + 5$

17. $(y - x)(y + x)$ $y^2 - x^2$

18. $(3a + 2)(b - 6)(a - b)$ $-18a^2 - 12a + 3a^2b + 20ab - 3ab^2 + 12b - 2b^2$

19. $(a + b + c)^2$ $a^2 + b^2 + c^2 + 2ab + 2ac + 2bc$

Review

20. **a.** 1 meter = ___?___ centimeters **100**
   b. 1 square meter = ___?___ square centimeters **10,000**
   c. 1 cubic meter = ___?___ cubic centimeters *(Lesson 10-3, Previous course)* **1,000,000**

21. Estimate the cube root of π to the nearest hundredth. *(Lesson 10-3)* **1.46**

22. A cube has volume 27 in.^{3}. What is its surface area? *(Lessons 10-3, 10-2)* **54 in.^{2}**

23. A card in the game "Uno" is about 5.6 cm by 8.7 cm. If a stack of 72 cards is about 2.7 cm high, what is the volume of a single card? *(Lesson 10-3)* **about 1.8 cm^3**

24. **a.** Draw a regular pentagonal pyramid. *(Lesson 9-3)* **See margin.**
   b. If each side of the base is 18, and each lateral edge is 41, find its lateral area. *(Lesson 10-2)* **1800 square units**

25. Solve: $\pi r^2 = 10$. *(Previous course)* $\pm\sqrt{\frac{10}{\pi}} \approx \pm 1.8$

Exploration

26. Expand $(a + b)^3$ by finding the volume of an appropriate cube in two different ways. **The volume is $(a + b)^3$ and also $a^3 + 3a^2b + 3ab^2 + b^3$. So $(a + b)^3 = a^3 + 3a^2b + 3ab^2 + b^3$.**

FOLLOW-UP

MORE PRACTICE
For more questions on SPUR Objectives, use *Lesson Master 10-4,* shown below.

EXTENSION
Extend **Questions 16-19**. Give area models for the special products $(a + b)^2$, $(a + b)(a - b)$, and $(a - b)^2$, where $a > b$. Give volume models for $(a + b)^3$ and $(a - b)^3$.

ADDITIONAL ANSWERS
1. sample:

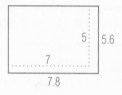

24. a. sample:

NAME _____

LESSON **MASTER 10–4**
QUESTIONS ON **SPUR** OBJECTIVES

■ **PROPERTIES** *Objective G (See pages 516–519 for objectives.)*

1. The dimensions of a box are all multiplied by four.
   a. What happens to its volume? **multiplied by 64**
   b. What happens to its surface area? **multiplied by 16**

2. The length and width of a box are each multiplied by six and the height remains the same. How will its volume change? **multiplied by 36**

■ **REPRESENTATIONS** *Objective K*

3. Compute the volume of the box.

$(a + 6)(b + 3)(c + 4) =$
$abc + 4ab + 6bc + 3ac$
$+ 12b + 24b + 18c + 72$

4. Compute the area of the rectangle.

$(x + 4)(x + 9) = x^2 +$
$13x + 36$

In 5–8, expand.

5. $(2x + 3)(x + 7)$
   $2x^2 + 17x + 21$

6. $(2t + 9)(3t + 2)$
   $6t^2 + 31t + 18$

7. $(y + 5)(2y + 2)(6y + 8)$
   $12y^3 + 88y^2 + 156y + 80$

8. $(x + 1)^3$
   $x^3 + 3x^2 + 3x + 1$

9. Five inches are added to one dimension of a square and 3 inches are added to the other.
   a. Represent this using a rectangle.
   b. Compute the area of the new figure. $(x^2 + 8x + 15)$ in.^{2}

RESOURCES
■ Lesson Master 10-5
◘ Visual for Teaching Aid 68 displays Cavalieri's Principle.

OBJECTIVES

B Calculate volumes of cylinders and prisms from appropriate lengths, and vice versa.
H Know the conditions under which Cavalieri's Principle can be applied.
J Apply formulas for volume to real situations.

TEACHING NOTES

Remind students that a cube and a box are prisms, so they have already calculated the volumes of some prisms. Specifically, the formula $V = \ell wh$ for the volume of a box could be interpreted as $V = Bh$, where the dimensions of the base are ℓ and w.

The use of physical models in this lesson will greatly enhance students' understanding. A stack of congruent sheets of paper is appropriate to illustrate Cavalieri's Principle, as shown on page 489. Note that the act of transforming the stack of paper (a transformation called "shearing") is not the same as "bending" a wire oblique prism. In shearing, the height of the stack of paper remains constant and the slant edge becomes longer. If the wire prism is bent, the height is shortened and thus volume is reduced.

LESSON

10-5

Volumes of Prisms and Cylinders

Oil, gas, and related products are often stored in huge cylindrical tanks like those pictured above. It is natural to wonder how much gas or oil is stored in each tank. The amount can be calculated if you know the dimensions of the tank and the formula for the volume of a cylinder. This formula and formulas for the volumes of other common three-dimensional figures can be derived from the Area and Volume Postulates you have already studied and from one other postulate to be stated in this lesson.

Consider a region with area B which is the base of a prism or cylinder. Then think of B unit squares covering the region, even if B is not an integer.

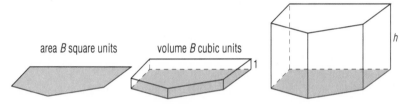

area B square units   volume B cubic units

If a prism with this base has height 1 unit, the prism contains B unit cubes, and so the volume of the prism is B cubic units. This is pictured in the middle figure above. The right figure shows a prism with this base and height h. That prism has h times the volume of the middle prism, and so its volume is Bh. This argument shows that, if a right prism or cylinder has height h and a base with area B, then its volume is Bh.

A cubic foot of liquid contains about 7.48 gallons. This information, which can be found in most almanacs, combined with the volume formula derived above, enables the capacity of an oil storage tank to be found.

488

Example 1 If a cylindrical storage tank has a diameter of 100 feet and is 70 feet high, how many gallons of oil can it hold? Make a guess before you go on.

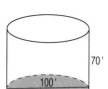

Solution It usually helps to draw a picture, as shown at the left.

Use the formula $V = Bh$. The radius of the base is 50′, so $B = \pi(50)^2$, or 2500π. (As usual, it is wise not to estimate π until absolutely necessary.) Thus

$$V = Bh$$
$$= 2500\pi \cdot 70$$
$$= 175{,}000\pi \text{ cubic feet}$$
$$\approx 550{,}000 \text{ cubic feet.}$$

Now each cubic foot contains about 7.48 gallons of fuel. So the capacity of the tank is

$$550{,}000 \text{ ft}^3 \cdot 7.48 \frac{\text{gal}}{\text{ft}^3} \approx 4{,}110{,}000 \text{ gallons.}$$

This is more than many people would estimate.

Now suppose you have an oblique prism or cylinder. Recall that in such figures, the lateral edges are not perpendicular to the planes of the bases. Pictured here are a right prism and an oblique prism with congruent bases and equal heights.

Imagine Prism I to be made up of a stack of thin slices like congruent sheets of paper. Shift the sheets of the first stack until it approximates the form of Prism II.

Note that the height, area of the base, and number of slices are the same in Prism I and Prism II. Consequently,

Volume(Prism II) = Volume(Prism I).

Or, since they have equal heights and bases,

Volume(Prism II) = Bh.

LESSON 10-5 Volumes of Prisms and Cylinders **489**

Making Connections
Oblique prisms and cylinders are to right prisms and cylinders as parallelograms are to rectangles. The space inside does not change, although the boundaries (perimeters or surface area) do. The key things to measure are the height and the base. Thus, just as parallelograms and rectangles both have the area formula $A = hb$, prisms and right prisms both have the volume formula $V = Bh$.

Reading There is a substantial amount of mathematics for students to understand in this lesson, so it may be an appropriate lesson for a cooperative effort. The Examples can be read aloud and explained thoroughly as can the key ideas behind Cavalieri's Principle. Students should discuss the derivations of the formulas and how they are applied to find the volume of a solid.

The key ideas of this argument are: (1) the prisms have their bases in the same planes; and (2) the slices in each prism have the same area. Such solids have the same volume. Francesco Bonaventura Cavalieri (1598–1647), an Italian mathematician, first realized the importance of this principle. It is named after him.

Volume Postulate:

e. (Cavalieri's Principle) Let I and II be two solids included between parallel planes. If every plane P parallel to the given planes intersects I and II in sections with the same area, then
Volume(I) = Volume(II).

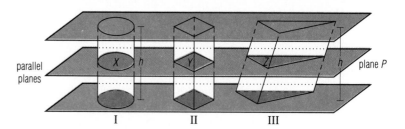

Above, plane P is parallel to the planes containing the bases, and all three solids have bases with area B. Since sections X, Y, and Z are translation images of the bases (this is how prisms and cylinders are defined), they also have area B. Thus the conditions for Cavalieri's Principle are satisfied. These solids have the same volume. But the volume of the box is known.

$$\text{Volume(II)} = \ell \cdot w \cdot h$$
$$= B \cdot h$$

Thus, using Cavalieri's Principle,

$$\text{Volume(I)} = B \cdot h \quad \text{and}$$
$$\text{Volume(II)} = B \cdot h.$$

This proves the following theorem for *all* cylinders and prisms.

Prism-Cylinder Volume Formula:

The volume V of *any* prism or cylinder is the product of its height h and the area B of its base.
$$V = Bh$$

490

For a cylinder, the base is a circle. If the radius is r, then the base has area πr^2. So a special formula for the volume of a cylinder is

$$V = \pi r^2 h,$$

but you should not have to remember it. You can derive it quickly from $V = Bh$.

In an oblique prism or cylinder, the height sometimes must be determined using the Pythagorean Theorem.

■ ■ ■ ■ ■ ■ ■ ■ ■

Example 2 Find the volume of the parallelepiped pictured below.

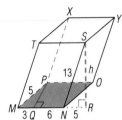

Solution The volume is $B \cdot h$. To find B, the area of the base $MNOP$, its height PQ must be found. Using the Pythagorean Theorem,
$$MQ^2 + PQ^2 = MP^2$$
$$3^2 + PQ^2 = 5^2.$$
So $\qquad\qquad\qquad\qquad PQ = 4.$
Thus $B = MN \cdot PQ = 9 \cdot 4 = 36$ square units. The height h of the prism is also found by applying the Pythagorean Theorem.
$$RS^2 + RN^2 = NS^2$$
$$h^2 + 5^2 = 13^2$$
So $\qquad\qquad\qquad\qquad h = 12.$
Thus $V = Bh = 432$ square units.

Questions

Covering the Reading

1. A cubic foot of liquid is how many gallons? about 7.48

2. How many gallons of oil can fill a cylindrical tank with diameter 120 feet and height 60 feet? ≈5,076,000

3. *Multiple choice.* In this lesson, a stack of paper is used to illustrate all but which of the following?
   (a) Cavalieri's Principle
   (b) that an oblique prism and a right prism can have the same volume
   (c) that the volume of an oblique prism is Bh
   (d) that a cylinder and a prism have the same volume formula (d)

4. Who was Cavalieri and in what century did he live most of his life?
   an Italian mathematician; 17th century

LESSON 10-5 Volumes of Prisms and Cylinders **491**

NOTES ON QUESTIONS
Question 12: You might compare the volume of the sewer to the amount of rain water which may fall on a given region in a period of time. For example, a parking lot might be 200′ by 150′. If one inch of rain falls in an hour, would the sewer pipe hold all the drainage from the lot?
(The volume of water over the lot is $200 \cdot 150 \cdot \frac{1}{12}$ cubic feet, or 2500 cubic feet. This sewer pipe would just hold that amount.)

5. State Cavalieri's Principle. See margin.

6. Give a formula for the volume of an oblique cylinder.
$V = Bh$ or $V = \pi r^2 h$

In 7–12, find the volume of each solid.

7.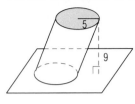

8.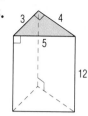

$225\pi \approx 707$ cubic units 72 units^3

9. a square prism whose base has edge 5 meters, and whose height is 20 meters 500 m³

10. the parallelepiped drawn below $96\sqrt{259} \approx 1545$ cubic units

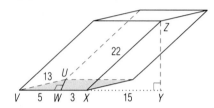

11. a right rectangular prism whose base is 3 feet by 7 feet, and whose height is 10 feet 210 ft³

12. a sewer pipe 200′ long with a radius of 2′ $800\pi \approx 2513$ ft³

13. Draw a rectangular prism and a cylinder which, according to Cavalieri, have identical volumes. Include the dimensions of each solid. See margin.

14. The volume of an oblique prism is 38 cubic meters. Its height is 4 meters. Find the area of the base. 9.5 m²

15. An artist constructed a prism as shown in the sketch below. What is its volume? 189 m³

9 m
base area 21 m²

16. Two cylindric glasses have the same height, but the diameters of the glasses are 2.3″ and 3.3″.
   a. Can the second glass hold twice as much as the first? Yes
   b. Why or why not? The larger glass has volume $\approx 2.7\pi h$. The smaller glass has volume $\approx 1.3\pi h$, less than half as much.

17. A cylinder and cone have bases of the same area and equal heights. Why can't Cavalieri's Principle be applied in this situation?
See margin.

492

18. If a cylinder of height h is compared with a cylinder which has the same height, but a radius half that of the first, how do the volumes compare?
The first cylinder has four times the volume of the second cylinder.

19. What does doubling the height of a prism without changing the size of its base do to its volume? doubles the volume

20. A milliliter of water has a mass of 1 gram and occupies 1 cm³ of space. If a cylindric can is 15 cm high, has radius 3 cm, and is filled with water, what is its mass (to the nearest gram)?
424 grams

Review

21. Expand $(4x - 5y)(x + 2y + 7)$. *(Lesson 10-4)*
$4x^2 + 3xy + 28x - 10y^2 - 35y$

22. The height of a box is multiplied by 4 and the length and width are each multiplied by 5. By how much does this multiply the volume of the box? *(Lesson 10-4)* 100

23. A closed lead box for vials of plutonium measures 4 cm by 3.5 cm by 2.5 cm on the outside. The inside dimensions are 3 cm by 2.5 cm by 2 cm. How much lead is used to make the box? *(Lesson 10-3)* 20 cm³

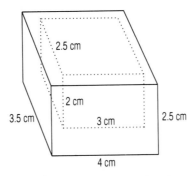

24. Find the surface area of the prism in Question 8. *(Lesson 10-1)*
156 square units

25. Refer to Example 2 on Page 491. Find the area of *MTSN*. *(Lesson 9-2)*
108 square units

26. Arrange these quadrilateral area formulas from most general to most specific: $A = s^2$, $A = \frac{1}{2}h(b_1 + b_2)$, $A = \ell w$, $A = hb$.
(Lessons 8-6, 8-4) $A = \frac{1}{2}h(b_1 + b_2)$; $A = bh$; $A = \ell w$; $A = s^2$

27. Refer to the figure at the right.
Given: $\overline{CD} \cong \overline{EF}$
$\overline{CD} \parallel \overline{EF}$.
Prove: $\angle FCE \cong \angle DEC$.
(Lessons 7-7, 7-3) See margin.

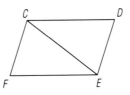

Exploration

28. Find a cylindric juice can in your house. Its volume is probably given in fluid ounces.
a. Calculate its volume in cubic inches. sample: ≈ 24.5 in.³
b. Use this information to determine about how many cubic inches there are to the fluid ounce. ≈ 2.0 in.³ per fluid oz

LESSON 10-5 Volumes of Prisms and Cylinders **493**

LESSON

10-6

Remembering Formulas

At this point, you have encountered formulas for perimeters and
areas of many two-dimensional regions and for lateral areas, surface
areas, and volumes of some three-dimensional figures. You will see
more formulas in other lessons of this chapter. At this point, you
may wonder: Which formulas should I remember? The answer to
that question is simple: *Remember formulas which apply to the most
figures*.

A hierarchy can help to organize the three-dimensional figures you
have seen. First organize by the number of bases, as shown in lines
(1) and (2) of the hierarchy below. Prisms and cylinders have two
parallel bases. Pyramids and cones have one base. Spheres, which
you will encounter later in this chapter, have no base. Some of these
figures include special types, shown in line (3). A very special type,
from which the volume of all figures is determined, is the one figure
in line (4).

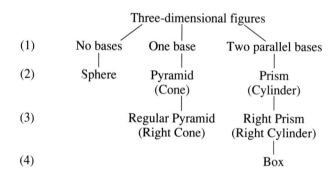

Three-dimensional figures

(1)	No bases	One base	Two parallel bases
(2)	Sphere	Pyramid (Cone)	Prism (Cylinder)
(3)		Regular Pyramid (Right Cone)	Right Prism (Right Cylinder)
(4)			Box

In this chapter, there are seven—only seven—basic formulas.
(Thus far you have seen four of the seven.) Here all seven formulas
are superimposed on the hierarchy. No formulas for total surface
area are given because all you have to do is add the area of all bases
to the lateral area to get a formula. Try to locate the four formulas
that have already been discussed.

494

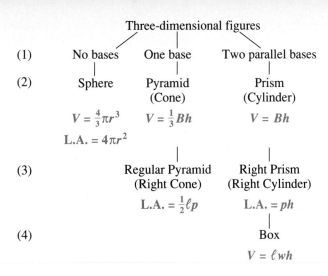

Three-dimensional figures

(1) No bases — One base — Two parallel bases

(2) Sphere — Pyramid (Cone) — Prism (Cylinder)

$V = \frac{4}{3}\pi r^3$ — $V = \frac{1}{3}Bh$ — $V = Bh$

L.A. $= 4\pi r^2$

(3) Regular Pyramid (Right Cone) — Right Prism (Right Cylinder)

L.A. $= \frac{1}{2}\ell p$ — L.A. $= ph$

(4) Box

$V = \ell w h$

One thing is obvious from the list: *To use a formula, you must know what each variable in the formula represents.*

You have seen formulas that are not on the hierarchy. For instance, the formula L.A. $= 2\pi rh$ for the lateral area of a right cylinder is not listed. This is because a few general ideas help reduce the load of formulas to remember. *For special formulas for cones and cylinders, substitute the circle formulas $B = \pi r^2$ and $p = 2\pi r$ in the corresponding formulas for pyramids and prisms.* The idea is simple: cones and cylinders are like pyramids and prisms, but with circular bases.

For example, to obtain a formula for the lateral area of a right cylinder, use the formula **L.A. $= ph$** from the hierarchy. Substitute $2\pi r$ for p to get L.A. $= (2\pi r)h = 2\pi rh$. Practice so that you can do the substitution quickly and thus avoid learning a special formula for the lateral area of a right cone.

In Lesson 10-3, you saw a formula for the volume of a box. You probably had seen this formula before. From this formula alone, all the other volume formulas can be deduced. The process we used—the process of proof—is the most powerful idea of all for remembering formulas. *If you cannot remember a formula, try to derive it from some simpler formulas you know to be true.* That is the way mathematicians recall many of the formulas they have to use. The difficulty with this advice is that it usually takes some time to derive a formula. Often there is not the time. So, if you do not want to spend your time proving or cannot do proofs, you must either learn some formulas by heart or have access to a book containing the formulas.

Another way to avoid learning lots of formulas is to *use general formulas to get formulas for special types of figures.* These ideas are applied in the Example.

Example Find a formula for the surface area of a box in terms of its height h, length ℓ, and width w.

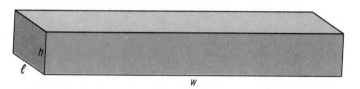

Solution A box is a prism. Begin with the formula for the lateral area of a prism.
$$\text{L.A.} = ph$$
h is given so it need not be touched. But p is the perimeter of the base. Since the base is a rectangle with length ℓ and width w, its perimeter is $2\ell + 2w$. Substituting,
$$\text{L.A.} = (2\ell + 2w)h.$$
For the surface area, the areas of the two bases must be added.
$$\text{S.A.} = \text{L.A.} + 2B$$
Each base has area ℓw. Thus a formula is
$$\text{S.A.} = (2\ell + 2w)\,h + 2\ell w.$$
Using the Distributive Property, the formula can be rewritten as
$$\text{S.A.} = 2\ell h + 2wh + 2\ell w.$$

Questions

Covering the Reading

1. What are the best formulas to remember?
   ones which apply to the most figures

In 2 and 3, choose from the following:
boxes, cones, cylinders, prisms, pyramids, spheres.

2. In which figures does S.A. = L.A. + $2B$? boxes, cylinders, prisms

3. In which figures does S.A. = L.A. + B? cones, pyramids

4. a. How many basic formulas are there to learn in this chapter? 7
   b. Which basic formulas have you seen already? See margin.

5. What do the variables represent in the formula L.A. = ph?
   See margin.

6. What is the process for obtaining special formulas for cones and cylinders? Substitute the circle formulas $B = \pi r^2$ and $p = 2\pi r$ into the corresponding formulas for pyramids and prisms.

496

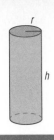

In 7 and 8, consider a right cylinder with height h and base with radius r.

7. Deduce a formula for its lateral area. **L.A. = $2\pi rh$**

8. Deduce a formula for its volume. **$V = \pi r^2 h$**

9. How do mathematicians recall formulas?
They try to prove them from simpler formulas known to be true.

10. Find a formula for the surface area of the right cylinder of Questions 7 and 8 in terms of its height h and the radius r of a base.
S.A. = $2\pi rh + 2\pi r^2$

11. A right cone has slant height ℓ and its base has radius r.
   a. Find a formula for its L.A. in terms of ℓ and r.
   b. Find a formula for its S.A. in terms of ℓ and r.
   a) L.A. = $\frac{1}{2}\ell(2\pi r) = \pi r\ell$; b) S.A. = $\pi r\ell + \pi r^2 = \pi r(\ell + r)$

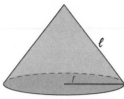

12. a. Find the area of an equilateral triangle with one side 400.
   b. Generalize part a to find the area of an equilateral triangle with one side s. a) $40{,}000\sqrt{3} \approx 69{,}282$ units^2;
   b) $A = \dfrac{s^2\sqrt{3}}{4}$

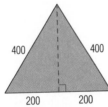

400   400

200   200

In 13–15, use the formula below for the area of any triangle given the lengths of its sides a, b, and c. It was discovered by Archimedes, but it is known as **Hero's** or **Heron's Formula,** after the Greek mathematician Hero (or Heron) of Alexandria, who lived about 50 A.D. Let s be half the perimeter of the triangle. Then Area($\triangle ABC$) = $\sqrt{s(s-a)(s-b)(s-c)}$.

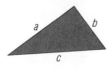

a b

c

Archimedes (287-212 B.C.)

13. a. Use Heron's Formula to find the area of a triangle with sides of lengths 9, 12, and 15. $\sqrt{(18)(9)(6)(3)} = 54$ units^2
   b. Use an alternate method to check your work. See margin.

14. Find the area of a triangle with sides 10, 17, and 21. 84 units^2

15. Use Heron's Formula to answer Question 12a.
$\sqrt{600 \cdot 200 \cdot 200 \cdot 200} \approx 69{,}282$ units^2

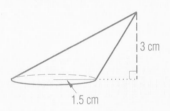
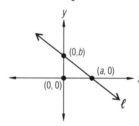

16. Suppose each base of a right prism is an isosceles trapezoid with dimensions as shown. *(Lessons 10-5, 10-1)*
    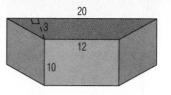
    a. Find its volume. **480 units³**
    b. Find its lateral area. **420 units²**
    c. Find its surface area. **516 units²**

17. The height of a cylinder equals the diameter of its base. If the radius of the base is 27, what is the volume of the cylinder? *(Lesson 10-5)* **39,366π ≈ 123,672 cubic units**

18. Expand $(x + y)^2$. *(Lesson 10-4)* **$x^2 + 2xy + y^2$**

19. By how much is the volume of a cube of side 8 changed if a is added to the length, a is subtracted from the width, and the height remains 8? *(Lesson 10-4)* **The volume is decreased by $8a^2$.**

20. Pyramids were built throughout the ancient world. Northeast of Mexico City is the regular square pyramid Teotihuacán. This pyramid is 66 m high and 442 m wide at its base. *(Lesson 10-2)*
    a. What is its lateral area? **≈203,900 m²**
    b. How does its lateral area compare with that of the pyramid of Khufu (see Lesson 10-2)? **It is more than twice as large.**

21. a. Draw an oblique cone with base radius 1.5 cm and height 3 cm.
    b. If the lateral area of the cone is 16 cm², what is the surface area of the cone? *(Lesson 10-2)* a) See margin. **b) $16 + 2.25π ≈ 23$ cm²**

22. A ring between two concentric circles is shaded, as at the left. If the radius of the small circle is h and the radius of the large circle is r, what is the area of the ring? *(Lesson 8-9)* **$π(r^2 - h^2)$**

23. Find the slope of line ℓ below. *(Lesson 3-4)* $-\frac{b}{a}$

24. Graph: $y = -\frac{1}{2}x + 3$. *(Lesson 1-3)*

25. a. Give dimensions for a cylinder whose surface area is 200π.
    b. Give dimensions for a second cylinder, not congruent to the first, whose surface area is 200π.
    a-b) sample:

Volumes of Pyramids and Cones

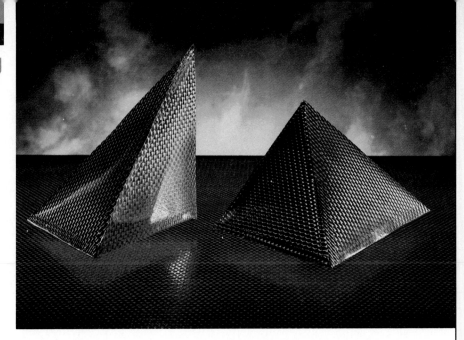

OBJECTIVES

C Calculate volumes of pyramids and cones from appropriate lengths, and vice versa.
F Develop formulas for specific figures from more general formulas.
H Know the conditions under which Cavalieri's Principle can be applied.
J Apply formulas for volume to real situations.

TEACHING NOTES

Reading This is a difficult lesson for many students to read. Students should pay particular attention to the notation for pyramids. The vertex is given first, a hyphen follows, and then the vertices of the base of the pyramid are given. This notation should help students classify the pyramids (how many vertices are in the base?) and also see the corresponding prism with bases congruent to the named base in the prism.

For many students, proofs are not as convincing as demonstrations. If you can, bring in a pyramid and a prism (or a cone and a cylinder) with the same height and identical bases. Fill the smaller one with sand or water. Empty it into the other. Show that one has three times the volume of the

In this lesson you will learn a simple formula for the volume of any pyramid or cone. The proof of that formula, however, is not so simple. It will help you to do part **a** of Question 23 before reading on. Use those models and examine the figures drawn as you read.

The cone and triangular pyramid pictured below have their bases in plane P and the bases have the same area B. Planes P, Q, and R are parallel, and the sections formed by plane Q are shaded. Their heights are the same, as both vertices lie in plane R. Under these conditions, the sections have the same area also. Cavalieri's Principle says that the two solids then have the same volume. Thus any cones or pyramids with bases of equal area and with equal heights have identical volumes.

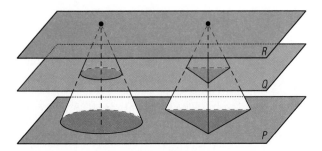

Thus, if the volume of a single pyramid is found, all others with the same height and base area will have the same volume. So pick a simple pyramid.

Consider the triangular pyramid *D-AGC* below in which $\overline{DC}$ is perpendicular to the plane of the base $\triangle AGC$. Let Area($\triangle AGC$) = *B* and *DC = h*. The volume of *D-AGC* is wanted.

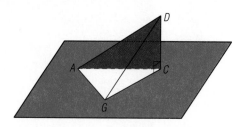

Form a triangular *prism* with congruent bases *AGC* and *FED,* and with edges parallel and equal to $\overline{DC}$. This prism has volume *Bh*. It will now be shown that this prism has 3 times the volume of the pyramid.

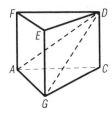

Draw $\overline{FG}$ in the prism above; it is a diagonal of rectangle *AGEF*. Notice that $\triangle AFG \cong \triangle EGF$. Now there are three nonoverlapping pyramids whose union is the prism. Each is outlined below in colored edges, while the rest of the prism is dashed.

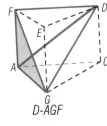
D-AGF

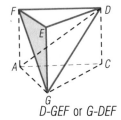
D-GEF or *G-DEF*

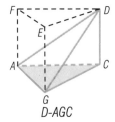
D-AGC

If you have your cutout models from Question 23, try to put the three of them together to form a prism, just as is done here.

The pyramids *D-AGF* and *D-GEF* have the same volume since the height of each is from *D* to the plane of parallelogram *AGEF,* and the bases are congruent. Similarly *G-DEF* and *D-AGC* are equal in volume because they have equal heights (*DC = EG*) and congruent bases. By the Transitive Property of Equality, the three pyramids have the same volume. So each pyramid has a volume that is one-third the volume of the prism. Consequently, the volume of pyramid *D-AGC* is $\frac{1}{3}Bh$.

The next step is to show that this formula works for any pyramid or cone. In general, the triangular base can be made to have *any* given area. By Cavalieri's Principle, the volume of any pyramid or cone can be equated with the volume of a pyramid of the same height and a given triangular base. For instance, if the base of a cone has area 6π units^2, a triangular pyramid of the same height can be constructed with a base of area 6π units^2. This argument proves the following theorem.

Pyramid-Cone Volume Formula:

The volume V of any pyramid or cone equals $\frac{1}{3}$ the product of its height h and its base area B.
$$V = \tfrac{1}{3}Bh$$

Notice that the volume of a pyramid may be easier to calculate than its surface area.

Example 1   Find the volume of the pyramid of Khufu. (Recall that this pyramid is a regular square pyramid 147 m high with each side of the base 231 m.)

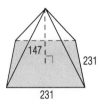

Solution   Use the formula
$$V = \tfrac{1}{3}Bh.$$

The base is a square, so $B = (231)^2 = 53,361$ square meters. From the given, $h = 147$ meters.
Thus $V = \tfrac{1}{3} \cdot 53,361 \cdot 147$
               $\approx 2,610,000$ cubic meters.

The volume is about 2,610,000 m^3. This is over 2500 times the capacity of a middle-size house with a volume of 1000 m^3!

The formula $V = \tfrac{1}{3}Bh$ holds for a cone. If the radius of the base of the cone is r, then $B = \pi r^2$. So a formula for the volume of a cone is
$$V = \tfrac{1}{3}\pi r^2 h.$$

This is a formula you should not have to memorize, but be able to derive.

ADDITIONAL EXAMPLES
1. A bin at a granary is in the shape of a cube with a pyramid underneath. If the cube is 5 feet tall and the entire bin is 9 feet tall, how many cubic feet of grain will it hold?
$\frac{475}{3} \approx$ **158 cu ft**

2. An ice cream cone is to hold 1/8 pint (about 5 cubic inches) of ice cream. (The rest will be above the cone.) If the cone has a diameter of 2 inches, how high does it need to be?
$\frac{\pi}{3}h = 5$, so $h \approx$ **4.8 inches.**

If you know all but one quantity in a formula, you can solve an equation to determine the unknown.

Example 2 If a cone has a height of 6 in. and a volume of 40 in.^{3}, what is the radius of its base?

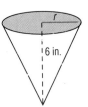

Solution The relevant formula is $V = \frac{1}{3} Bh$.
Here $h = 6$ and $V = 40$.
Substituting, $\qquad 40 = \frac{1}{3} B \cdot 6$
$\qquad\qquad\qquad 40 = 2B.$
So $\qquad\qquad\qquad B = 20.$
But $B = \pi r^2$. So $\qquad 20 = \pi r^2$
$\qquad\qquad\qquad r^2 = \frac{20}{\pi}.$
So $\qquad\qquad\qquad r = \sqrt{\frac{20}{\pi}} \approx 2.52$ in.

Questions

Covering the Reading

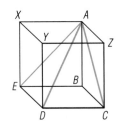

1. Two pyramids with congruent bases and heights have equal __?__.
   volumes
2. At the left, how does the volume of pyramid *A-BCDE* compare with the volume of the box?
   The volume of the pyramid is $\frac{1}{3}$ the volume of the box.
3. Find the volume V of a pyramid with height 6 and base area 57.
   114 units^3
4. A formula of the volume of a cone is $V = $ __?__ or $V = $ __?__.
   $\frac{1}{3} Bh$ or $\frac{1}{3} \pi r^2 h$
5. Find the volume of a cone with height 8′ and base of radius 2′.
   $\frac{32\pi}{3} \approx 33.5$ ft^3

In 6–8, find the volume of the solid.

6.
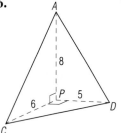
right triangular pyramid with base *PCD* and height *AP*
40 units^3

7.
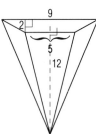
trapezoidal pyramid with height 12
56 units^3

8.
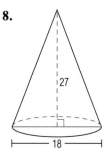
right cone with height 27 and diameter 18
$729\pi \approx 2290$ units^3

9. A cone has a volume of 40 cm^3. Its height is 5 cm. What must be the radius of the base? $\sqrt{\frac{24}{\pi}} \approx 2.8$ cm

502

10. A cone and a cylinder have identical bases and equal heights. If the volume of the cylinder is V, then the volume of the cone is __?__.
$\frac{1}{3}V$

11. The largest monument ever built is the Quetzalcóatl at Cholula de Rivadabia, a pyramid about 60 miles southeast of Mexico City. The Quetzalcóatl is 177 feet tall and its base covers 45 acres. (Recall 1 acre = 43,560 ft².) Determine the volume of the Quetzalcóatl to the nearest million cubic feet. 116,000,000 ft³

12. Consider the soft drink cup pictured below.
  a. How many cm³ of liquid will it hold? $\frac{160\pi}{3} \approx 168$ cm³
  b. How many times will it need to be used in order to fill a liter jug? (Note: 1 liter = 1000 cm³.) 6
  c. How much paper is needed to make the cup? $4\pi\sqrt{116} \approx 135$ cm²

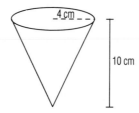

13. What happens to the volume of a cone if the height is kept the same but the radius of the base is multiplied by 7?
The volume is multiplied by 49.

14. What happens to the volume of a pyramid if its base is kept the same but its height is multiplied by 31.8? The volume is multiplied by 31.8.

15. If $\triangle ABC$ is spun about $\overleftrightarrow{AB}$, a right cone is formed.
  a. What is the height of the cone? 6 units
  b. Find the volume of the cone. $128\pi \approx 402$ units³

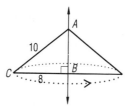

16. How much paper is needed to cover a box that is ℓ inches long, w inches wide, and h inches high? *(Lessons 10-6, 10-1)*
$2(\ell w + \ell h + wh)$ square inches

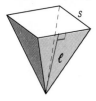

17. Give a formula for the lateral area of the regular square pyramid pictured at the left. *(Lesson 10-6)* L.A. = $4(\frac{1}{2}\ell s) = 2\ell s$

18. Find the volume and surface area of the right triangular prism pictured. *(Lessons 10-5, 10-1)* volume = 216 units³;
S.A. = $174 + 8\sqrt{117} \approx 261$ units²

LESSON 10-7 Volumes of Pyramids and Cones   **503**

Making Connections for Questions 13 and 14:
These questions can be used to review some algebra. Since $(kx)^2 = k^2x^2$, if x is multiplied by k, then its square is multiplied by k^2. Thus, if dimensions of a square are multiplied by k, the area is multiplied by k^2. Similarly, since $(kx)^3 = k^3x^3$, if dimensions of a cube are multiplied by k, the volume is multiplied by k^3.

EXTENSION
A good visual exercise for
students is to have them
draw a cube and then draw
four diagonals in the cube, all
from the top face. Ask what
figures are formed.
six congruent square
pyramids
If the edge of the cube is 2
inches, what would be the
volume of each pyramid?
$\frac{4}{3}$ in.^{3}

19. Find the area of the large rectangle pictured below. *(Lesson 10-4)*

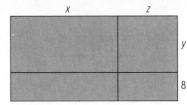

$(x + z)(y + 8) = xy + 8x + zy + 8z$

20. A two-by-four is a piece of wood that starts out measuring 2″ by 4″ by k' (it can have any length) but is planed to $1\frac{5}{8}″$ by $3\frac{5}{8}″$ by k'. What percent of the wood is lost in the planing? *(Lesson 10-3)* ≈ 26%

21. Bernard bought a 10-gallon fish tank. He was told a tank could support one guppy for every 168 in.^{3} of water. Bernard measured the tank and found it to be 20″ by 1′ by 10.5″. How many guppies can the tank support? *(Lesson 10-3)* 15

Exploration

22. **a.** Make a cone using a net like that at the left, but bigger.
    b. After the cone is made, make an open-top cylinder with height and base the same as the cone. a, b) Answers may vary.
    c. Fill the cone with dirt or sand. How many times must you empty the cone into the cylinder in order to fill up the cylinder? three

23. **a.** Trace two copies of net I and one of net II. Make a pyramid from each tracing. (Fold so the markings are "inside" the pyramids.)
    b. Fit the three pyramids together to form a right triangular prism.
    c. What have you shown? A pyramid has one-third the volume of a prism with the same base area and height.

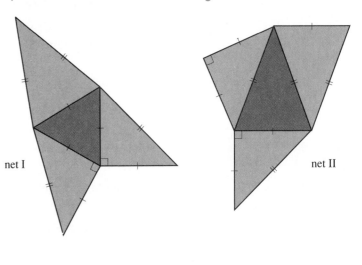

net I

net II

10-8

The Volume of a Sphere

RESOURCES
■ Lesson Master 10-8
⤵ Visual for Teaching Aid 70
displays the drawing on
page 505.

Here is how the volume formulas of this chapter have developed. It
began with a postulate in Lesson 10-3.

$$V = \ell wh \qquad \text{(volume of a box)}$$

Cavalieri's Principle was then applied and the following formula was
deduced in Lesson 10-5.

$$V = Bh \qquad \text{(volume of a prism or cylinder)}$$

A prism can be split into 3 pyramids with congruent heights and
bases. Using Cavalieri's Principle again, a formula was derived in
Lesson 10-7.

$$V = \tfrac{1}{3}Bh \qquad \text{(volume of a pyramid or cone)}$$

In this lesson, still another application of Cavalieri's Principle results
in a formula for the volume of a sphere.

Both the sphere and cylinder below have a height of $2r$ and each
cone in the cylinder has a height of r. An amazing result is that the
volume of the sphere equals the volume *between the cylinder and
the two cones*.

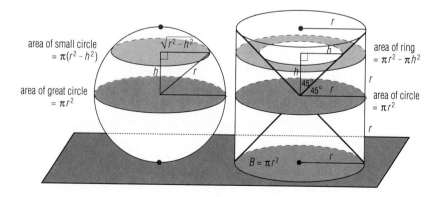

area of small circle
$= \pi(r^2 - h^2)$

area of great circle
$= \pi r^2$

area of ring
$= \pi r^2 - \pi h^2$

area of circle
$= \pi r^2$

$B = \pi r^2$

TEACHING NOTES

Reading You may wish to
read this lesson aloud with
as much use of visual aids
as possible. Even if students
do not understand the derivation, they should be able to
appreciate the interrelation-
ship of the cylinder, cone,
and sphere.

For all other figures, we derived the surface area formulas first, then the volume
formulas. Students may wonder why the order is reversed
here. The order could have
been reversed before; no
surface area formula was
used in deriving volume.
However, the formula for the
volume of the sphere is derived by using Cavalieri's
Principle. The surface area
will be found from the formula for the volume.

The figure used in the derivation of the Sphere Volume Formula is very complicated. A couple of images may help students visualize this drawing. Have them imagine a solid cylinder of wood from which two cones are carved out at either end. The remaining wood has the same volume as a sphere of the same radius as the cylinder. Imagine a beaker filled with water and two cones pushed in from each end, displacing the water. The water that remains would fill the sphere.

Some students may still think of π as a variable. Point out that variables in volume and surface area formulas are often those that determine the figure. For instance, a right cylinder is determined by its height h and the radius r of its base, so the surface area and volume formulas involve h and r. Thus, since a sphere is determined by its radius (all spheres with the same radius are congruent), a volume formula might involve only the radius. And the radius is cubed because cubic units are needed for volume. Thus, a formula for the volume of the sphere has the form $V = kr^3$. The value of k, which is $\frac{4}{3}\pi$, is determined in the proof.

ADDITIONAL EXAMPLES

1. Racquetballs come two to a can. The can is a cylinder and the balls are spheres. If the diameter of the can is d, what is the volume of a racquetball?

$\frac{1}{6}\pi d^3$

2. Jacques made a spherical cheese ball for a party. He formed it from cheese that came in a box 8 cm by 8 cm by 20 cm. What is the diameter of the cheese ball?

$\frac{4}{3}\pi r^3 = 1280$, so $r \approx 6.7$ cm, so $d \approx 13.4$ cm.

NOTES ON QUESTIONS

Questions 1-3: These questions lead students through the arguments in the lesson and should be discussed.

Here is how that can be shown. On the previous page, the blue sections are the plane sections resulting from a plane slicing these figures in their middles. These blue sections are congruent circles with area πr^2. At h units above each blue section is a section shaded in lavendar. In the sphere, by the Pythagorean Theorem, the lavendar section is a small circle with radius $\sqrt{r^2 - h^2}$. The area of this section is found using the familiar formula for the area of a circle.

$$\text{Area(small circle)} = \pi(\sqrt{r^2 - h^2})^2 = \pi(r^2 - h^2)$$

For the region between the cylinder and the cones, the section is the orange ring between circles of radius r and h. (The radius of that section of the cone is h because the acute angle measures 45°, so an isosceles triangle is formed.)

$$\text{Area(ring)} = \pi r^2 - \pi h^2 = \pi(r^2 - h^2)$$

Thus the orange sections have equal area. Since this works for any height h, Cavalieri's Principle can be applied. This means that the volume of the sphere is the difference in the volume of the cylinder $(B \cdot 2r)$ and the volume of the two cones (each with volume $\frac{1}{3}B \cdot r$).

$$\begin{aligned}\text{Volume of sphere} &= (B \cdot 2r) - 2 \cdot (\tfrac{1}{3}B \cdot r)\\ &= 2Br - \tfrac{2}{3}Br\\ &= \tfrac{4}{3}Br\end{aligned}$$

But here the bases of the cones and cylinder are circles with radius r. So $B = \pi r^2$. Substituting,

$$\begin{aligned}\text{Volume of sphere} &= \tfrac{4}{3} \cdot \pi r^2 \cdot r\\ &= \tfrac{4}{3}\pi r^3.\end{aligned}$$

Sphere Volume Formula:

The volume V of any sphere is $\frac{4}{3}\pi$ times the cube of its radius r.

$$V = \tfrac{4}{3}\pi r^3$$

To approximate the volume of a sphere, calculators are helpful.

Example 1 Find the volume of a sphere with radius 12.

Solution Substitute into the volume formula.

$$\begin{aligned}V &= \tfrac{4}{3}\pi r^3\\ &= \tfrac{4}{3}\pi(12)^3\\ &= 2304\pi \approx 7238 \text{ units}^3\end{aligned}$$

Example 2   A standard bowling ball cannot be more than 27 inches in circumference. What is the maximum volume of such a ball (to the nearest cubic inch) before the holes are drilled?

Solution   First find the radius of the ball. Use the circumference formula.

$$C = 2\pi r$$
$$27 = 2\pi r$$

So
$$r = \frac{27}{2\pi} \approx 4.3''.$$

Now substitute into the volume formula $V = \frac{4}{3}\pi r^3$.
$$V \approx \frac{4}{3} \cdot \pi \, (4.3)^3$$
$$\approx \frac{4}{3} \cdot \pi \cdot 79.507$$
$$\approx 333 \text{ cubic inches}$$

Even after drilling the holes, there are more than 300 cubic inches of rubber or plastic in a standard bowling ball.

Questions

Covering the Reading

In 1–3, use this drawing of a sphere, cylinder, and two cones. Sections formed by their intersections with a plane four units above and parallel to the horizontal plane through the figures' middles are colored.

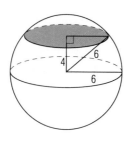
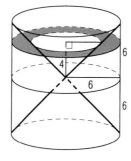

1. Give the area of:
   a. the section of the sphere; $20\pi \approx 62.8$ units^2
   b. the ring between the cylinder and the cone. $20\pi \approx 62.8$ units^2

2. Give the volume of:
   a. the cylinder; $432\pi \approx 1357$ units^3
   b. the two cones; $144\pi \approx 452.4$ units^3
   c. the solid region between the cylinder and the two cones;
   d. the sphere. c) $288\pi \approx 904.8$ units^3; d) $288\,\pi \approx 904.8$ units^3

3. By applying __?__ , the equal answers to parts **a** and **b** of Question 1 lead to equal answers to parts **c** and **d** of Question 2.
   Cavalieri's Principle

4. **a.** Draw a sphere with radius 8 cm. See margin.
   b. Find its volume. $\frac{2048\pi}{3} \approx 2145$ cm^3

Question 6:   The answer will surprise many students. Almost half of the cube is outside the basketball. Mention to students that it is easier to do this problem with diameter d than diameter 9.5″. Often algebra is easier than arithmetic.

Computer for Question 9:   Students may not realize that the situation described would be an emergency, because to have so little water in storage would be unhealthy. They also may not realize that water in storage tanks ultimately has to come from rainfall or snowfall. You might use a spreadsheet in which one column lists the different amounts of water removed per day. A second column should list how many days the water will last if x amount of water is replaced each day, where x is the value stored in a cell (hence, the students can see the effect as x is changed).

Question 10:   The answer suggests that a formula for the volume would be easier to remember in terms of the diameter than the radius. But it is traditional to learn the formula in terms of the radius.

Error Analysis for Question 20:   The answer 4.3 would indicate that students wrongly simplified $\sqrt[3]{85} - \sqrt[3]{5}$ to $\sqrt[3]{80}$.

ADDITIONAL ANSWERS
4. a. (Art is reduced in size.)

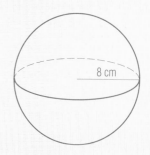

Applying the Mathematics

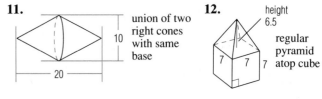

5. *Multiple choice.*
How much material is needed to make a standard bowling ball?
(a) less than 100 cubic inches
(b) between 100 and 200 cubic inches
(c) between 200 and 300 cubic inches
(d) between 300 and 400 cubic inches (d)

6. A basketball has a diameter of about 9.5 inches. If it is put into a cube-shaped box for shipping, what percent of the box is filled by the basketball? ≈52%

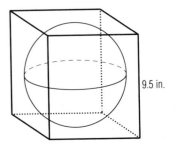

9.5 in.

7. The volume of a sphere is 268 cubic meters. Find its radius to the nearest meter. **4 m**

8. A filled ice cream cone has the shape of a hemisphere atop a cone. If the cone has height 10 cm, and the hemisphere radius is 3 cm, how much ice cream is there? **48π ≈ 151 cm³**

9. A spherical water tank with diameter 16 meters supplies water to a small town. The town uses about 500 cubic meters of water per day. How long would a full tank last if:
a. 300 cubic meters were replaced each day?
b. no water were replaced due to drought conditions?
   a) 10.7, or about 11 days; b) 4.3, or about 4 days

10. A sphere has diameter d. Give its volume. $\frac{\pi}{6} d^3$ **units³**

Review

In 11 and 12, find the volume of the solid. *(Lessons 10-7, 10-3)*

11.

10

20

union of two right cones with same base

$\frac{500\pi}{3} \approx 524$ **units³**

12.

height
6.5

7   7   7

regular pyramid atop cube

≈ 449 **units³**

13. Which of the fundamental properties of volume is needed in both Questions 11 and 12? *(Lesson 10-3)* **Additive Property**

14. a. A cube has surface area 96 m². Find its volume. **64 m³**
b. A cube has surface area x. Find its volume in terms of x.
(Lessons 10-6, 10-3) $V = \left(\sqrt{\frac{x}{6}}\right)^3$

508

In 15 and 16, choose from the following:
boxes, cones, cylinders, prisms, pyramids, spheres. *(Lesson 10-6)*

15. In which figures does $V = Bh$? **boxes, cylinders, prisms**

16. In which figures does L.A. $= \frac{1}{2}\ell p$? **cones, pyramids**

17. Two prisms have congruent bases and equal heights. One of the solids is oblique and one is right. *True* or *false*?
  a. The solids have the same volume. **True**
  b. The solids have the same surface area. *(Lesson 10-5)* **False**

18. Expand $(x + 3)(2y)(z + 4)$. *(Lesson 10-4)* **2xyz + 8xy + 6yz + 24y**

19. The dimensions of a box are tripled.
  a. What happens to its surface area? **It is multiplied by 9.**
  b. What happens to its volume? *(Lesson 10-4)* **It is multiplied by 27.**

20. To the nearest tenth, calculate $\sqrt[3]{85} - \sqrt[3]{5}$. *(Lesson 10-3)* **2.7**

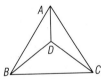

21. A hole is cut through the $3 \times 3 \times 3$ cube at the left, from top to bottom, as indicated. Then the big cube with the hole is dipped in white paint. *(Lesson 10-1)*
  a. What is the surface area of the big cube with the hole? **64 units²**
  b. How many of the 24 smaller cubes that are left are painted on exactly three faces? **16**
  c. How many of the 24 cubes that are left are painted on exactly two faces? **8**
  d. How many of the 24 cubes that are left are painted on exactly one face? **none**
  e. How many of the 24 cubes that are left are painted on no faces? **none**

22. Given: $\triangle ABC$ is isosceles with vertex $\angle A$.
              $\overline{AD}$ bisects $\angle BAC$.
      Prove: $\triangle BCD$ is isosceles. *(Lessons 5-1, 4-4)* **See margin.**

In 23 and 24, multiply. *(Previous course)*

23. $\frac{3}{r} \cdot \frac{1}{3} \cdot r \cdot x$ **x**

24. $\frac{3}{r} \cdot \frac{4}{3}\pi r^3$ **4πr²**

25. Unlike a cone or cylinder, it is impossible to make an accurate 2-dimensional net for a sphere. For this reason, maps of the earth on a sheet of paper must be distorted. The Mercator projection is one way to show the earth. How is this projection made? **The projection is from a point at the center of the earth through the surface of the globe onto a cylinder that touches the earth around the equator. That cylinder is then cut vertically and flattened.**

Exploration

NAME _____

■**SKILLS**   *Objectives A and D   (See pages 516–519 for objectives.)*

1. a. Draw a sphere with a radius of 3 cm.
   b. Find its volume. $36\pi \approx 113$ cm³

2. a. Draw a sphere with a diameter of 5 cm.
   b. Find its volume.   ≈65.45 cm³

3. What is the radius of a sphere with a volume of 288π cubic units?   **6 units**

4. What is the radius, to the nearest hundredth, of a sphere whose volume is 2000 cubic units?   **7.82 units**

5. The diameter of Neptune is about 3.5 times that of Earth. How do their volumes compare?
Neptune has 42.875 times the volume of Earth.

Geometry © Scott, Foresman and Company   *Continued* **93**

NAME _____
Lesson MASTER 10–8 (page 2)

■**PROPERTIES**   *Objective F*

6. Which of the following formulas is used to derive the formula for the volume of a sphere?   **(d)**
   (a) $V = Bh$ (b) $V = s^3$
   (c) L.A. $= \frac{1}{2}\ell p$ (d) $A = \pi r^2$

■**PROPERTIES**   *Objective H*
For 7–9, use the drawing below. Shaded sections are formed by intersections of the cone and cylinder with a plane eight units above the horizontal plane through the figures' middles.

7. Give the area of
   a. the section of the sphere;   **b.** the ring between the cylinder and the cone.
      36π units² 36π units²

8. Give the volume of
   a. the cylinder;   **b.** the two cones;
      2000π units³ $\frac{2000\pi}{3}$ units³
   c. the solid region between the cylinder and the two cones;   **d.** the sphere.
      $\frac{4000\pi}{3}$ units³ $\frac{4000\pi}{3}$ units³

9. Why are the answers to 8c and 8d equal?
      Cavalieri's Principle

■**USES**   *Objective J*

10. A spherical bowl whose diameter is 6 in. is one-half full with water. How much water is in the bowl? 18π in.³ ≈ 57 in.³

94   *Geometry © Scott, Foresman and Company*

OBJECTIVES

D Calculate the surface area of a sphere from appropriate lengths, and vice versa.
I Apply formulas for surface area to real situations.

TEACHING NOTES

The proof in this lesson is easier than those of the previous two lessons, but it still may be difficult for students to follow. Point out that there is no two-dimensional surface for a sphere, which is one reason why its surface area formula is derived from its volume formula.

Alternate Approach
The beach ball of the **Example** can make a good physical aid to demonstrate the surface area of a sphere formula. Deflate the ball as much as possible until it is apparently two circles (stuck together). If the ball is cut apart and laid out flat onto a circle of the same diameter as the original sphere, the pieces should fit into the circle four times. This method can only show an approximation, but it is easy to believe that the sphere has a surface area which is equal to four times the area of a great circle of the sphere. An alternate method is to cut out four circles with the same diameter as the beach ball, cut them apart, cover the beach ball with the pieces (like a puzzle), and show that it takes four circles to cover the sphere.

LESSON

10-9

The Surface Area of a Sphere

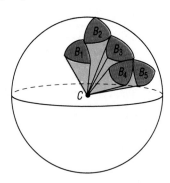

The only formula left from the hierarchy of Lesson 10-6 is for the surface area of a sphere. Surprisingly, this formula is derived from the volume formula. The idea is to consider a solid sphere as being made up of "almost pyramids" with vertices at the center of the sphere. One such "pyramid" is drawn above. The solid is not exactly a pyramid because its base is not exactly a polygon. Even so, when the base of the "almost pyramid" is small, its volume is close to that of a pyramid, namely $\frac{1}{3}Bh$. Since $h = r$, the radius of the sphere, each "almost pyramid" has volume $\frac{1}{3}Br$.

Now break up the entire sphere into "almost pyramids" with bases having areas B_1, B_2, B_3, and so on.

The volume V of the sphere is the sum of the volumes of all the "almost pyramids" with bases B_1, B_2, B_3, ...

$$V = \tfrac{1}{3}B_1 r + \tfrac{1}{3}B_2 r + \tfrac{1}{3}B_3 r + \tfrac{1}{3}B_4 r + \ldots$$
$$= \tfrac{1}{3}r(B_1 + B_2 + B_3 + B_4 + \ldots)$$

The sum of the bases is the surface area (S.A.) of the sphere. The volume V is $\frac{4}{3}\pi r^3$. Substituting,

$$\tfrac{4}{3}\pi r^3 = \tfrac{1}{3}r \cdot \text{S.A.}$$

To solve for the surface area, multiply both sides by $\frac{3}{r}$.

$$\frac{3}{r} \cdot \frac{4}{3}\pi r^3 = \frac{3}{r} \cdot \frac{1}{3} r \cdot \text{S.A.}$$

Thus $\qquad 4\pi r^2 = \text{S.A.}$

Sphere Surface Area Formula:

The surface area S.A. of a sphere with radius r is $4\pi r^2$.
$$\text{S.A.} = 4\pi r^2$$

Surprisingly, this formula indicates that the surface area of a sphere is equal to 4 times the area of a great circle of the sphere.

Example Find the surface area of a beach ball with radius 50 cm.

Solution S.A. $= 4\pi r^2 = 4 \cdot \pi \cdot 50^2 = 10{,}000\pi$ exactly, or approximately 31,416 square centimeters.

In the Example, the surface area measures how much plastic is needed for the surface of the beach ball. To determine how much air is inside the inflated beach ball, volume is needed. The volume of the beach ball above is $\frac{4}{3}\pi r^3 = \frac{4}{3}\pi(50^3) \approx 523{,}600 \text{ cm}^3$.

You now have encountered all of the surface area and volume formulas discussed in this book. The hierarchy given in Lesson 10-6 is shown below. These are the key formulas to remember. In all cases r represents radius, h represents height, p represents perimeter, and B represents area of a base. For regular pyramids, ℓ represents slant height, while for a box, ℓ represents length.

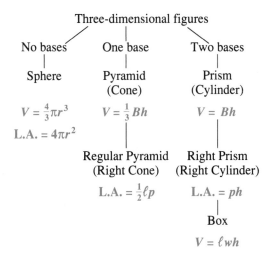

Three-dimensional figures

No bases — One base — Two bases

Sphere — Pyramid (Cone) — Prism (Cylinder)

$V = \frac{4}{3}\pi r^3$ $V = \frac{1}{3}Bh$ $V = Bh$

L.A. $= 4\pi r^2$

Regular Pyramid (Right Cone) — Right Prism (Right Cylinder)

L.A. $= \frac{1}{2}\ell p$ L.A. $= ph$

Box

$V = \ell wh$

ADDITIONAL EXAMPLES
1. Beads are to be gilded with a thin layer of gold. If the beads are spheres 1 cm in diameter, and if one container of gold will cover 100 square cm of surface with the desired thickness, how many beads can be covered with one container of gold?
About 32; however, of all metals, gold is the most malleable, and it can be made into very thin sheets. A small amount of gold can cover a very large surface.

2. Once, when a new solar system was discovered, a news reporter on TV said that its sun was "80 times as big as ours." Could the listeners be sure they knew how big it was?
No, since a reference to circumference, surface area, or volume was not given.

ADDITIONAL ANSWERS
21. $A' = (6, 3)$; $B' = (-3, -3)$; $C' = (0, -9)$

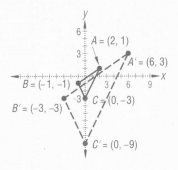

Questions

Covering the Reading

1. A sphere can be imagined as the union of __?__, whose base areas add up to the __?__ of the sphere. **"almost pyramids," surface area**

2. State the Sphere Surface Area Formula.
   The surface area S.A. of a sphere with radius r is $4\pi r^2$.

3. The surface area of a sphere is __?__ times the area of a great circle. **4**

In 4 and 5, find the surface area of the sphere: **a.** exactly; **b.** to the nearest square unit.

4. a sphere with radius 6 **a) 144π units²; b) 452 units²**

5. a sphere with diameter 100″
   a) $10,000\pi$ sq. inches; b) 31,416 sq. inches

6. Name the no-base, one-base, and two-base figures in the hierarchy of 3-dimensional figures you have studied in this chapter. **no base: sphere; one base: pyramid, cone, right cone, regular pyramid; two bases: prism, cylinder, right prism, right cylinder, box**

Applying the Mathematics

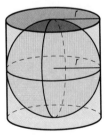

7. The area of the United States is about 3,600,000 square miles. What percent is this of the area of the earth, which is approximately a sphere with radius 3950 miles? **≈1.84%**

8. A sphere has diameter d. Give its surface area. **πd^2 units²**

9. A pavilion at the 1986 World's Fair in Vancouver, pictured at the left, had a dome with diameter 35 meters. Estimate the cost of covering the dome with gold foil that costs $3.20 per square meter. **≈ 75% the S.A. of a sphere yields a cost of about $9200.**

10. A baseball is nearly a sphere with a circumference (great circle) of about 9.1 inches.
    a. Estimate the volume of a baseball, to the nearest 0.1 cubic inch.
    b. Estimate the surface area of a baseball, to the nearest 0.1 square inch. **a) 12.7 in.³; b) 26.4 in.²**

11. The moon has diameter about $\frac{1}{4}$ that of the earth.
    a. How do their surface areas compare? **See margin.**
    b. How do their volumes compare? **See margin.**

12. A sphere has volume 36π cubic meters. What is the surface area? **36π m²**

13. A sphere of radius r fits exactly into a cylinder, touching the cylinder at the top, bottom, and sides. How does the surface area of the sphere compare to the lateral area of the cylinder? **They are the same; both are $4\pi r^2$.**

14. Refer to Question 7. Find the volume of the earth. *(Lesson 10-8)*
≈ **2.58 · 10¹¹ miles³**

15. a. Draw a sphere with radius 2.5 cm.

r = 2.5 cm
  b. Find its volume. *(Lesson 10-8)*
  ≈ **65.45 cubic cm**

16. A cone has base radius of 15 and a slant height of 17.
Picture this cone and find its volume. *(Lesson 10-7)* **See margin.**

17. One jar of jam is twice as tall as another, but only half as wide.
Which jar has more jam? *(Lessons 10-5, 10-4)*
The wider, shorter jar holds twice as much jam.

18. You can make two different cylinders by rolling an 8.5″ by 11″ piece
of notebook paper along its sides.
  a. What is the lateral area of each cylinder? **93.5 square inches**
  b. Which has the most volume? *(Lessons 10-5, 10-1)*
    the one with height of 8.5″

19. A cube has sides of length 13. A second cube has 5 times the volume
of the first cube. To the nearest tenth, what is the length of a side of
the second cube? *(Lesson 10-4)* **22.2 units**

20. Cheese is aged in large blocks. The block below is to be removed
from the aging cellar, wrapped in foil, and shipped. *(Lesson 10-1)*
  a. At a minimum, how many square cm of foil are needed?
  b. A distributor cuts the block into 15 cm × 7.5 cm × 3 cm slabs to
    sell to grocery stores. At a minimum, how much foil is needed to
    wrap all the slabs from the block?
    a) 2250 cm²; b) 7200 cm²

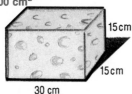
15 cm
15 cm
30 cm

21. A transformation T maps (*x*, *y*) onto (3*x*, 3*y*). Graph the image of
△*ABC* where *A* = (2, 1), *B* = (-1, -1), and *C* = (0, -3). *(Lesson 6-1)*
See margin.

In 22 and 23, an almanac, atlas, dictionary, or encyclopedia is necessary.

22. What three countries cover more of the surface of the earth than the
United States? What percent (to the nearest tenth) of the surface does
each cover?
Canada (≈1.96%), China (≈1.88%), Soviet Union (≈4.39%)

23. What percent (to the nearest tenth) of the surface of the earth is
covered by **a.** the Pacific Ocean; **b.** the Atlantic Ocean; **c.** all the
oceans together? **a) 32.5%; b) 16.2%; c) 64.3%**

LESSON 10-9   The Surface Area of a Sphere   **513**

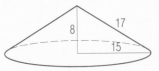

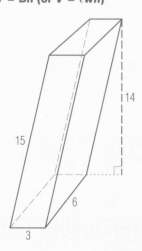

Summary

The lateral or surface area of a three-dimensional figure measures its boundary, which is two-dimensional. So these areas, like the areas you studied in Chapter 8, are measured in square units. Volume measures the space enclosed by a three-dimensional figure. Beginning with the formula $V = \ell wh$ for the volume of a box, this chapter developed formulas for the volumes of other figures. Four basic properties of volume and Cavalieri's Principle were employed. The following chart contains a summary of these formulas.

	Volume	Lateral Area Right or regular	Surface Area
Prism (Cylinder)	Bh	ph	L.A. $+ 2B$
Pyramid (Cone)	$\frac{1}{3}Bh$	$\frac{1}{2}p\ell$	L.A. $+ B$
Sphere	$\frac{4}{3}\pi r^3$		$4\pi r^2$
Cube	s^3		$6s^2$

In these formulas, B is the area of a base, p the perimeter of a base, h the height, ℓ the slant height, L.A. the lateral area, and r the radius. You can obtain special formulas for cones and cylinders by substituting πr^2 for B and $2\pi r$ for p.

Vocabulary

Below are the most important terms and phrases for this chapter.
For the starred (*) terms you should be able to give a definition of the term.
For the other terms you should be able to give a general description and specific example of each.

Lesson 10-1
surface area, S.A.
lateral area, L.A.
Right Prism-Cylinder Lateral Area Formula
Prism-Cylinder Surface Area Formula

Lesson 10-2
regular pyramid
Regular Pyramid-Right Cone Lateral Area Formula
Pyramid-Cone Surface Area Formula

Lesson 10-3
volume
unit cube
*cube root, $\sqrt[3]{}$
Volume Postulate (parts **a–d**)
Cube Volume Formula

Lesson 10-5
Cavalieri's Principle (Volume Postulate **e**)
Prism-Cylinder Volume Formula

Lesson 10-6
Heron's Formula

Lesson 10-7
Pyramid-Cone Volume Formula

Lesson 10-8
Sphere Volume Formula

Lesson 10-9
Sphere Surface Area Formula

514

Progress Self-Test

See margin for answers not shown below.

Directions: Take this test as you would take a test in class. Use a ruler and calculator. Then check your work with the solutions in the Selected Answers section in the back of the book.

1. An oblique rectangular prism has dimensions 3 cm by 6 cm by 15 cm and height 14 cm.
   a. Draw an appropriate figure and indicate the formula you would use to find its volume.
   b. Find its volume. **252 cm³**

2. A regular square pyramid has base edges of length 20 and slant height of length 26.
   a. Draw an appropriate figure and indicate the formula you would use to find its lateral area.
   b. Find its lateral area. **1040 units²**

3. The largest asteroid, Ceres, has a diameter of 620 miles. Assuming Ceres is spherical in shape, what is its volume? **≈ 1.25 · 10⁸ miles³**

4. How much paper is needed for a cone-shaped megaphone with radius 4″ and slant height 18″? (Ignore the small open end.) **72π ≈ 226 in.²**

5. Find the volume of the inside of a pipe 20″ long and with an inside radius of 3″, as drawn below. **180π ≈ 565.5 in.³**

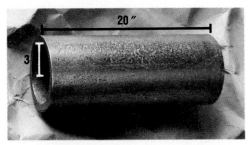

20″

3

6. Find the volume of this right cone.
   320π ≈ 1005.3 units³

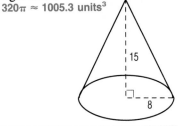

15

8

In 7 and 8, the base of a right prism has area 40 and perimeter 32. Its height is 30.

7. What is its lateral area? **960 units²**
8. What is its volume? **1200 units³**

In 9 and 10, a box has a volume of 400 cubic cm, a height of 10 cm, and a width of 5 cm.

9. What is its length? **8 cm**
10. What is its surface area? **340 cm²**

11. A sphere has a surface area of 100π. What is its radius? **5**

12. Give the cube root of 400 to the nearest whole number. **7**

13. State Cavalieri's Principle.

14. A prism and a pyramid have congruent bases and their heights are equal. How do their volumes compare?

15. Jupiter has 11 times the diameter of the earth. How do their surface areas compare?
    Jupiter's is 121 times as large.

In 16 and 17, choose from the following figures: box, cube, regular pyramid, prism, right cylinder, sphere, cone.

16. For which figure does
    S.A. = L.A. + B? **regular pyramid, cone**

17. For which figure does L.A. = ph?
    box, cube, prism, right cylinder

18. Find the volume of the box pictured below.

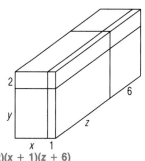

2

6

y

z

x 1

$(y + 2)(x + 1)(z + 6)$
$= xyz + yz + 2xz + 2z + 6xy + 6y + 12x + 12$

Whereas end-of-chapter materials may be considered optional in some texts, they should not be considered optional in UCSMP *Geometry*. The Progress Self-Test provides the opportunity for feedback and correction; the Chapter Review provides additional opportunities for practice. It is at this point that the material "gels" for many students, allowing them to solidify skills and concepts before a test. In general, student performance is markedly improved after these pages.

USING THE PROGRESS SELF-TEST
Assign the Progress Self-Test as a one-night assignment. Worked-out *solutions* for all questions are in the Selected Answers section of the student text. Encourage students to take the Progress Self-Test honestly, grade themselves, and then be prepared to discuss the test in class.

Advise students to pay special attention to those Chapter Review questions (pages 516-519) which correspond to questions missed on the Progress Self-Test. A chart provided with the Selected Answers keys the Progress Self-Test questions to the lettered SPUR Objectives in the Chapter Review or to the Vocabulary. It also keys the questions to the corresponding lessons where the material is covered.

2. a. L.A. = $\frac{1}{2}\ell p$

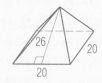

26   20

20

13., 14. See Additional Answers in the back of this book.

515

CHAPTER REVIEW

The main objectives for the chapter are organized here into sections corresponding to the four main types of understanding this book promotes: Skills, Properties, Uses, and Representations. We call these the SPUR objectives.

The four types of understanding are not in increasing order of difficulty. There may be hard skills and easy representations; some uses may be easier than anything else; and so on.

USING THE CHAPTER REVIEW
Students should be able to answer questions like these with about 85% accuracy. But they will not always be able to do so by the end of the chapter; the continual review in later chapters will help.

You may assign these questions over a single night to help students prepare for a test the next day, or you may assign the questions over a two-day period.

If you assign the questions over two days, then we recommend assigning the *evens* for homework the first night so that students get feedback in class the next day. Then assign the *odds* for the second night (the night before the test) so that students can use the answers provided in the book as a study aid.

Chapter Review

See margin for answers not shown below.

Questions on **SPUR** Objectives

SPUR stands for **S**kills, **P**roperties, **U**ses, and **R**epresentations.
The Chapter Review questions are grouped according to the
SPUR Objectives for this chapter.

SKILLS deal with the procedures used to get answers.

■ **Objective A:** *Draw 3-dimensional figures, given their dimensions. (Lessons 10-1, 10-2, 10-8)*

In 1–4, show the given information on the figure.

1. Draw a cylinder whose height is twice its diameter.

2. Draw a cone with radius 3 and slant height 5.

3. Draw a sphere with diameter $1\frac{3}{4}''$.

4. Draw a square pyramid with slant height 15 and height 9.

■ **Objective B:** *Calculate surface areas and volumes of cylinders and prisms from appropriate lengths, and vice-versa. (Lessons 10-1, 10-3, 10-5)*

5. Refer to the right cylinder drawn below. Find its **a.** lateral area; **b.** surface area; **c.** volume.

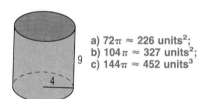

a) $72\pi \approx 226$ units²;
b) $104\pi \approx 327$ units²;
c) $144\pi \approx 452$ units³

6. Refer to the right square prism drawn below. Find its **a.** volume; **b.** surface area.
a) 90 units³; b) 138 units²

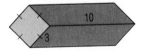

7. The base of the prism drawn below is a right triangle with legs of lengths 5 and 12. The distance between the bases of the prism is 24. Find the volume of the prism. **720 units³**

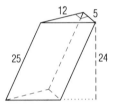

8. If a cylinder is to have a volume of 30π cubic units and a base with radius 3, what must its height be? $\frac{30}{9} \approx$ **3.33 units**

9. Find the surface of a cube whose volume is 125 cubic units. **150 units²**

10. Find the volume of a right cylinder whose lateral area is 60π square centimeters and whose base has diameter 12 centimeters. **180π ≈ 565.5 cm³**

■ **Objective C:** *Calculate surface areas and volumes of pyramids and cones from appropriate lengths, and vice-versa. (Lessons 10-2, 10-7)*

11. Find the surface area and volume of the right cone drawn below.

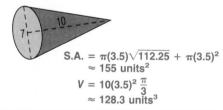

S.A. $= \pi(3.5)\sqrt{112.25} + \pi(3.5)^2$
≈ 155 units²

$V = 10(3.5)^2 \frac{\pi}{3}$
≈ 128.3 units³

In 12 and 13, refer to the square pyramid drawn below.

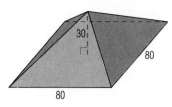

12. Find its volume. **64,000 units³**

13. Find **a.** the slant height;
b. its lateral area; **c.** its total surface area.
a) 50 units; b) 8000 units²; c) 14,400 units²

14. Find the volume of the cone drawn below.
18π ≈ 56.5 units³

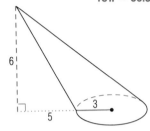

15. The slant height of a regular pentagonal pyramid is 20. The perimeter of the base is also 20. What is the lateral area of the pyramid? **200 units²**

16. If a pyramid has volume 75 cubic centimeters and its base has area 5 square centimeters, what is its height? **45 cm**

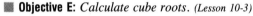

■ **Objective D:** *Calculate the surface area and volume of a sphere from appropriate lengths, and vice-versa.* *(Lessons 10-8, 10-9)*

17. Give the surface area and volume of a sphere with radius 72.

18. Give the surface area and volume of a sphere with diameter 3 mm.

19. A sphere has volume 288π. What is its radius? **6 units**

20. A sphere has volume 40π cubic units. What is its surface area?
$4\pi(\sqrt[3]{30})^2 \approx 121.3$ **units²**

■ **Objective E:** *Calculate cube roots.* *(Lesson 10-3)*

21. Give the cube root of 27,000. **30**

22. Approximate the cube root of 50 to the nearest tenth. **3.7**

23. One cube has side length 4. A second cube has twice the volume of the first cube. To the nearest hundredth, what is the length of a side of the second cube? **5.04**

24. To the nearest hundredth, calculate $\sqrt[3]{15} + \sqrt[3]{21}$. **5.23**

PROPERTIES deal with the principles behind the mathematics.

■ **Objective F:** *Develop formulas for specific figures from more general formulas.*
(Lessons 10-2, 10-3, 10-6, 10-7, 10-8)

25. Find a formula for the surface area of a regular square pyramid with edge s and slant height ℓ. **s² + 2sℓ**

26. A right cone has slant height ℓ and its base has radius r. Find a formula for its volume.
$\frac{1}{3}\pi r^2 \sqrt{\ell^2 - r^2}$

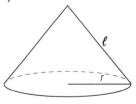

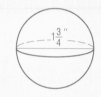
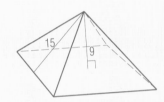

■ **Objective G:** *Determine what happens to the surface area and volume of a figure when its dimensions are multiplied by some number.*
(Lesson 10-4)

27. All of the dimensions of a box are tripled.
  a. What happens to the surface area?
  b. What happens to the volume?

28. The sides of a cube are multiplied by 9. What happens to its volume? **It is multiplied by 729.**

29. The diameter of a pizza is doubled. If it remains the same thickness, how do the volumes of the new and old pizzas compare? **The new volume is 4 times as large.**

30. The diameter of the earth is multiplied by 109 to give the diameter of the sun. How do their volumes compare?
The volume of the sun is approximately 1,300,000 times the volume of the earth.

■ **Objective H:** *Know the conditions under which Cavalieri's Principle can be applied.*
(Lessons 10-5, 10-7, 10-8)

31. A prism and pyramid have bases of the same area and equal heights. Why can't Cavalieri's Principle be applied in this situation?

32. In deriving the formula for the volume of a sphere, a plane section of a sphere was shown to be equal in area to what other figure?

33. Two cylindric solids have congruent bases and equal heights. One of the solids is oblique and one is right. *True or false?*
  a. The solids have the same volume. **True**
  b. The solids have the same surface area. **False**

USES deal with applications of mathematics in real situations.

■ **Objective I:** *Apply formulas for surface area to real situations. (Lessons 10-1, 10-2, 10-9)*

34. Venus is almost spherical with a radius of about 6000 km. To survey Venus completely, about how many square kilometers must be covered? **≈ 4.52 · 10⁸ km²**

35. To the nearest square foot, how much canvas is needed to cover a beach ball that is about 5 feet around? **8 ft²**

36. How much paper is needed to make a cylindrical paper cup with a base diameter of 10 cm and a height of 12 cm? **145π ≈ 455.5 cm²**

37. An ancient square pyramid is 100 cubits (an ancient unit) on a side. It is 50 cubits high. Find its lateral area. **200√5000 ≈ 14,142 cubits²**

■ Objective J: *Apply formulas for volume to real situations.* *(Lessons 10-3, 10-5, 10-7, 10-8)*

38. A silo is a cylinder whose base is a circle with diameter 6 meters and whose height is 10 meters. What is the volume of this silo? $90\pi \approx 282.7\ m^3$

39. How much can the paper cup of Question 36 hold? $300\pi \approx 942.5\ cm^3$

40. How much wood goes into making a solid cube 2.5″ on a side? $15.625\ in.^3$

41. Find the volume of the pyramid in Question 37. $\frac{500,000}{3} \approx 167,000\ cubits^3$

42. Can a suitcase 3 feet long, 1 foot wide, and 2 feet high hold one million dollar bills, if a dollar bill is 6.125″ long, 2.562″ wide, and 0.004″ thick? No; the suitcase has volume 10,368 in.³; the bills have volume 62,769 in.³

REPRESENTATIONS deal with pictures, graphs, or objects that illustrate concepts.

■ Objective K: *Represent products of two (or three) expressions as areas of rectangles (or volumes of boxes), and vice-versa.* *(Lesson 10-4)*

In 43 and 44, expand.

43. $(5x + 2)(4y + 3)$ 20xy + 15x + 8y + 6

44. $(a + 6)(2a + 1)(a + 8)$
$2a^3 + 29a^2 + 110a + 48$

45. Give two ways to compute the area of the rectangle below.

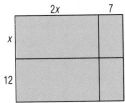

$(2x + 7)(x + 12) = 2x^2 + 7x + 24x + 84 =$
$2x^2 + 31x + 84$

46. Give two ways to compute the volume of the box below.

$(a + 15)(b + 9)(c + 8) =$
$abc + 8ab + 9ac + 72a + 15bc + 120b + 135\ c + 1080$

EVALUATION
Three tests are provided for this chapter in the Teacher's Resource File. Chapter 10 Test, Forms A and B cover just Chapter 10. The third test is Chapter 10 Test, Cumulative Form. About 50% of this test covers Chapter 10, 25% covers Chapter 9, and 25% covers previous chapters. For information on grading, see *General Teaching Suggestions: Grading* on page T44 in the Teacher's Edition.

ASSIGNMENT RECOMMENDATION
We strongly recommend that you assign the reading and questions from Lesson 11-1 for homework the evening of the test. It gives students work to do if they complete the test before the end of the period and keeps the class moving.

CHAPTER 11 ■ COORDINATE GEOMETRY

DAILY PACING CHART ■ CHAPTER 11

Every chapter of UCSMP *Geometry* includes lessons, a Progress Self-Test, and a Chapter Review. For optimal student performance, the self-test and review should be covered. (See *General Teaching Suggestions: Mastery* on page T36 of the Teacher's Edition.) By following the pace of the Full Course given here, students can complete the entire text by the end of the year. Students following the pace of the Minimal Course spend more time when there are quizzes and on the Chapter Review and will generally not complete all of the chapters in this text.

When all lessons are covered from the beginning (the recommendation of the authors), then students in the Minimal Course can cover through Lesson 13-4 and will cover all they need for future courses. For more information on pacing, see *General Teaching Suggestions: Pace* on page T35 of the Teacher's Edition.

DAY	MINIMAL COURSE	FULL COURSE
1	11-1	11-1
2	11-2	11-2
3	11-3	11-3
4	Quiz (TRF); Start 11-4.	Quiz (TRF); 11-4
5	Finish 11-4.	11-5
6	11-5	11-6
7	11-6	Progress Self-Test
8	Progress Self-Test	Chapter Review
9	Chapter Review	Chapter Test (TRF)
10	Chapter Review	
11	Chapter Test (TRF)	

TESTING OPTIONS

■ Quiz for Lessons 11-1 Through 11-3　■ Chapter 11 Test, Form A　■ Chapter 11 Test, Cumulative Form
■ Chapter 11 Test, Form B

PROVIDING FOR INDIVIDUAL DIFFERENCES

The student text has been written for, and tested with, average students. It also has been used successfully with better and more poorly prepared students.

The Lesson Notes often include Error Analysis and Alternate Approach features to help you with those students who need more help. A blackline Lesson Master (in the Teacher's Resource File), keyed to the chapter objectives is provided for each lesson to allow more practice. (However, since it is very important to keep up with the daily pace, you are not expected to use all of these masters. Again, refer to the suggestions for pacing on page T35.) Extension activities are provided in the Lesson Notes for those students who have completed the particular lesson in a shorter amount of time than is expected, even in the Full Course.

OBJECTIVES ■ CHAPTER 11

The objectives listed here are the same as in the Chapter 11 Review on pages 559-561 of the student text. The Progress Self-Test on page 558 and the tests in the Teacher's Resource File cover these objectives. For recommendations regarding the handling of this end-of-chapter material, see the notes in the margin on the corresponding pages of the Teacher's Edition.

OBJECTIVES FOR CHAPTER 11 (Organized into the SPUR Categories—Skills, Properties, Uses, and Representations)	Progress Self-Test Questions	Chapter Review Questions	Lesson Master from Teacher's Resource File*
SKILLS (There are no objectives for skills in this chapter.)			
PROPERTIES			
A Using coordinates in individual figures, prove that segments in them are congruent, perpendicular, or parallel.	6, 9	1 through 4	11-1, 11-2
B Using coordinates, prove theorems involving parallel or perpendicular sides, congruent segments, midpoints, or combinations of these in triangles and quadrilaterals.	14	5 through 8	11-1, 11-2, 11-4, 11-5
C Apply the Midpoint Connector Theorem.	1, 2	9 through 12	11-5
USES			
D Determine the center of gravity of a segment or a set of points.	4	13 through 16	11-4
E Apply the Distance Formula and Diagonal of a Box Formula in real situations.	7	17 through 20	11-2, 11-6
REPRESENTATIONS			
F Determine the distance between two points in the coordinate plane.	3	21 through 24	11-2
G Write an equation for a circle given its center and radius, and vice versa.	5	25 through 30	11-3
H Determine the coordinates of the midpoint of a segment in the coordinate plane.	8	31 through 34	11-4
I Give convenient locations for triangles and quadrilaterals in the coordinate plane.	10	35 through 38	11-5
J Apply coordinate geometry in three dimensions.	11, 12	39 through 42	11-6
K Find the point of intersection of two lines in the coordinate plane.	13	43 through 45	11-1, previous course

*The masters are numbered to match the lessons.

OVERVIEW ■ CHAPTER 11

Coordinate geometry is a very powerful branch of mathematics that can be used to describe or deduce information about geometric figures. Students were introduced to the description aspect of coordinate geometry in Lesson 1-3, in which points and lines were graphed. The coordinate descriptions of parallel and perpendicular lines were presented in Chapter 3, of reflections in Chapter 4, and of other transformations in Chapter 6.

The use of coordinates to deduce information about figures was presented first in Chapter 3, where lines were concluded to be parallel

or perpendicular based on their slopes. In Chapter 8, coordinate descriptions of polygons were used to calculate the areas of polygons.

This chapter broadens the scope of the deductions made with figures on the coordinate plane by deducing general theorems. Some of the theorems are proved more easily using coordinate methods than synthetic methods.

Chapter 11 is located at this position in the book for two reasons. First, coordinates are needed for the study of similarity (in particular, the Distance Formula). Second, the

proofs serve as a nice counterpart to the synthetic proofs presented earlier in the book.

Lesson 11-1 reviews slope and introduces the idea of coordinate proof. The Distance Formula is derived in Lesson 11-2 and used in Lesson 11-3 to find the equation for a circle. In Lesson 11-4, the Midpoint Formula is proved and then used in Lesson 11-5 to prove the Midpoint Connector Theorem. Lesson 11-6 introduces the three-dimensional analogues to the two-dimensional ideas presented earlier.

PERSPECTIVES ■ CHAPTER 11

The Perspectives provide the rationale for the inclusion of topics or approaches, provide mathematical background, and make connections with other lessons and within UCSMP.

11-1

PROOFS WITH COORDINATES

The proofs in this lesson are of three types: (1) prove lines are parallel; (2) prove lines are perpendicular; and (3) use the previous facts to prove that a polygon is a special type of polygon.

To prove that lines are parallel or perpendicular, students first calculate their slopes (the justification is the definition of slope). They then apply either the Parallel Lines and Slopes Theorem (if slopes are equal, the lines are parallel) or the Perpendicular Lines and Slopes Theorem (if the product of the slopes is -1, then the lines are perpendicular). These steps can be repeated for as many pairs of lines as are needed.

To prove that a figure is a right triangle, parallelogram, or rectangle (that is, figures whose definitions depend on perpendicularity or parallelism), students simply add a third step whose justification is the definition of the figure.

11-2

THE DISTANCE FORMULA

The application of the Pythagorean Theorem to prove the Distance Formula is simple and powerful. Students should be expected not only to know the formula but also to know the idea (not necessarily the details) behind its derivation. Students who have studied UCSMP *Algebra* should have seen this formula before.

The Distance Formula enables segments to be proved congruent. Therefore, by using the Distance Formula, triangles can be proved to be equilateral or isosceles, quadrilaterals can be proved to be kites, and so on.

11-3

EQUATIONS FOR CIRCLES

This lesson is a nice application of the Pythagorean Theorem to circles. The content is important and will be seen again in later courses.

At this time, students are expected to be able to write an equation for a circle given its center and radius. Conversely, given an equation of a circle in standard form, $(x - h)^2 + (y - k)^2 = r^2$, students are expected to find the center and radius.

11-4

THE MIDPOINT FORMULA

This lesson covers the derivation of the formula for finding the midpoint of a segment and its application to the center of gravity.

The proof of the Midpoint Formula is difficult for students at this level, and they should not be expected to reproduce it.

The center of gravity of a polygonal region is important in physical applications. If an object is thrown into the air, it may wobble or turn, but its center of gravity will trace the path of a parabola. If you wish to move a piece of furniture, the piece acts as if all of its mass is concentrated at its center of gravity. In this way, the center of gravity provides another description of a point that can be added to the four descriptions found in Chapter 1. The center of gravity description of a point is fundamental in physics and is one reason that forces can be treated mathematically.

11-5

THE MIDPOINT CONNECTOR THEOREM

This lesson covers three major ideas. The first is the proof of a theorem using coordinates, the Midpoint Connector Theorem. The second idea is the notion of convenient locations for figures. The third major idea is the use of convenient coordinates that arise from a convenient location, as in the proof of the Midpoint Connector Theorem.

11-6

THREE-DIMENSIONAL COORDINATES

Now that students are familiar with coordinates, it is appropriate to expose them to three-dimensional coordinates. Throughout the book, two-dimensional ideas are extended to three dimensions.

The formulas presented earlier in the chapter on distance, circles, and midpoints are all extended to three dimensions in this lesson. The Diagonal of a Box Formula also is included in this lesson because it is an immediate application of the distance formula in three dimensions.

We recommend 9 to 11 days for this chapter: 6 to 7 for the lessons and quiz; 1 for the Progress Self-Test; 1 or 2 for the Chapter Review; and 1 for a Chapter test. (See the Daily Pacing Chart on page 520A.) If you spend more than 11 days on this chapter, you are moving too slowly. Keep in mind that each lesson includes Review questions to help students firm up content studied previously.

CHAPTER 11

Coordinate Geometry

11-1: Proofs with Coordinates

11-2: The Distance Formula

11-3: Equations for Circles

11-4: The Midpoint Formula

11-5: The Midpoint Connector Theorem

11-6: Three-Dimensional Coordinates

The reading on these pages gives background information for the chapter, focusing on historical and practical perspectives. The main points are that (1) algebra and coordinate geometry are relatively new, more recent than many students realize; (2) Descartes thought he had a method by which all problems could be solved; and (3) coordinate geometry is now applied whenever computer graphics are used.

Sometimes a distinction is made between *analytic geometry* and *coordinate geometry.* You might want to make this distinction. Analytic geometry refers to the use of graphs to describe equations and inequalities as well as to the study of geometric figures. Coordinate geometry refers to the use of the coordinate plane to study geometric figures. That is, in coordinate geometry the figure comes first and it is placed on a coordinate plane for study. In analytic geometry, an equation often comes first, and the geometry is used to study the equation.

The computer animated figures above were designed using a three-dimensional coordinate system.

The use of variables to solve equations as people do today dates only from the work of François Vieté (1540–1603) in the late 1500s. Before that time mathematics was almost entirely arithmetic and geometry. The invention of algebra by Vieté provided people a tool as powerful then as the invention of computers in our century. People wondered what could and could not be done with this new tool. Among the wonderers was René Descartes, who was born in 1596.

You may recall that Descartes, along with Pierre Fermat, invented the idea of geometrically representing ordered pairs of numbers. He was thrilled with his invention, which he called a *method,* for it used algebra to combine arithmetic and geometry, and so unified all the mathematics known up to that time. He used his method, which is now called **coordinate geometry** or **analytic geometry,** to solve many problems which were then very difficult or not able to be solved.

Descartes believed that he had found a method whereby any mathematics problem could be solved or any conjecture proved or disproved. In fact, he thought that mathematics and logic could provide the means whereby any problem in *any* field of endeavor could be solved. Today we know that his belief is not even theoretically possible, but Descartes' dream reflects the power of the coordinate geometry methods he discovered.

In the 20th century, coordinate geometry has found an entirely new area of applications—to computer graphics. By specifying the pixels on a computer screen, computer programmers can generate all sorts of figures and designs. They can show and rotate three-dimensional images, as you have probably seen many times on television. For fun, they can produce animated cartoons and video games. For serious pursuits, they can model the design of anything from atoms to stars, from small animals to large buildings. All of the graphics on the facing page were computer generated using coordinates.

You already know how to graph points and lines and how to determine whether lines are perpendicular or parallel. In this chapter, you will learn how to calculate the distance between points and use that idea to describe circles. You will also learn how to calculate coordinates of midpoints. Many of these ideas can be used the way Descartes used them, to *deduce* properties of figures.

CHAPTER 11 Coordinate Geometry **521**

OBJECTIVES

A Using coordinates in individual figures, prove that segments in them are perpendicular or parallel.

B Using coordinates, prove theorems involving parallel or perpendicular sides in triangles and quadrilaterals.

K Find the point of intersection of two lines in the coordinate plane.

TEACHING NOTES

You might begin by going over **Example 1** carefully with the class. Emphasize what needs to be written; you may wish to state a preference for either the paragraph or two-column format.

The work of David Hilbert, discussed at the top of page 523, was not done earlier because up until the late 1800s it was felt that the logical foundations of arithmetic and algebra were firmer than those of geometry. Hilbert's work established that the postulates normally taken for Euclidean geometry (postulates equivalent to the ones stated in this book) are as consistent as the postulates of normal arithmetic. *Consistency* in a set of postulates means that there is no known internal contradiction. Consistency is a critical property because, if an internal contradiction were known, anything could be deduced.

Proofs with Coordinates

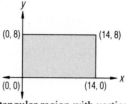

rectangular region with
length 14, width 8

Figures can be described with or without coordinates. Above and below are three descriptions of congruent rectangular regions. Two of these descriptions use coordinates.

rectangular region with vertices
(0, 0), (14, 0), (14, 8), and (0, 8)

set of points (x, y) with
$0 \le x \le 14$ and $0 \le y \le 8$

Any polygon or polygonal region can be described using a description like the one just above on the left. Just list its vertices in order. Some polygons can be proved to be special.

Example 1 Consider quadrilateral *ABCD* with vertices $A = (0, 0)$, $B = (8, 0)$, $C = (11, 12)$, and $D = (3, 12)$. Prove that *ABCD* is a parallelogram.

Solution 1 First draw a picture, as done at the left. In the drawing, it appears that *ABCD* is a parallelogram. The idea is to use slopes to prove opposite sides parallel. Here is what you might write.

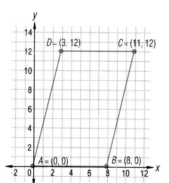

Using the slope formula, $\overline{AD}$ and $\overline{BC}$ have slope 4 and $\overline{DC}$ and $\overline{AB}$ have slope 0. So because of the Parallel Lines and Slopes Theorem, $\overline{AD} \parallel \overline{BC}$ and $\overline{DC} \parallel \overline{AB}$. Thus, by the definition of parallelogram (sufficient condition), *ABCD* is a parallelogram.

Solution 2 Here is a proof of the same statement, written in two-column form.

Conclusions	Justifications
1. slope of $\overline{AD} = \dfrac{12 - 0}{3 - 0} = 4$	definition of slope (meaning)
slope of $\overline{BC} = \dfrac{12 - 0}{11 - 8} = 4$	
slope of $\overline{DC} = \dfrac{12 - 12}{11 - 3} = \dfrac{0}{8} = 0$	
slope of $\overline{AB} = \dfrac{0 - 0}{8 - 0} = \dfrac{0}{8} = 0$	
2. $\overline{AD} \parallel \overline{BC}, \overline{DC} \parallel \overline{AB}$	Parallel Lines and Slopes Theorem
3. *ABCD* is a parallelogram.	definition of parallelogram (sufficient condition)

522

David Hilbert

Until the 1800s, it was taken for granted that coordinate methods would lead to the same geometry as the older methods, for there was only one geometry known. The discovery of non-Euclidean geometry brought doubt to this assumption. Only in 1901 did the great German mathematician David Hilbert (1862–1943) prove that analytic and traditional methods could lead to the same conclusions. In the language of this book, the location description and ordered pair description of points are equivalent. They lead to the same properties of figures. That is why you can use them interchangeably.

For example, since *ABCD* (page 522) has been shown to be a parallelogram, you can apply any of the properties of parallelograms to determine more about *ABCD*. For instance, $m\angle A = m\angle C$ because they are opposite angles. The area of $ABCD = \frac{1}{2} hb$. Here $b = AB = 8$, and h, the perpendicular from D to $\overleftrightarrow{AB}$, is 12. So the area of *ABCD* is $12 \cdot 8 = 96$ units^2.

Recall that horizontal and vertical lines are perpendicular; this is how the coordinate plane is defined. Other pairs of lines are perpendicular if the product of their slopes is -1. This enables lines to be proved perpendicular if their slopes are known.

Example 2   If $T = (3, 5)$, $O = (-1, -2)$, and $W = (-3, 1)$, prove that $\triangle TOW$ is a right triangle.

Solution   A drawing shows $\angle W$ to be the possible right angle. So try to show $\overline{WO} \perp \overline{WT}$. This can be done by using slope.

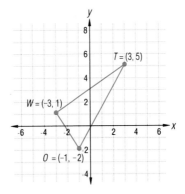

Write

Conclusions	Justifications
1. slope of $\overline{WO} = \dfrac{-2 - 1}{-1 - (-3)} = \dfrac{-3}{2}$	definition of slope (meaning)
slope of $\overline{WT} = \dfrac{5 - 1}{3 - (-3)} = \dfrac{4}{6}$	
2. $-\dfrac{3}{2} \cdot \dfrac{4}{6} = -1$	arithmetic
3. $\overline{WO} \perp \overline{WT}$	Perpendicular Lines and Slopes Theorem
4. $\triangle TOW$ is a right triangle.	definition of right triangle (sufficient condition)

Notice how automatic these proofs of parallelism and perpendicularity are. Just calculate and compare slopes! This is why Descartes was so optimistic about his method.

LESSON 11-1   Proofs with Coordinates   **523**

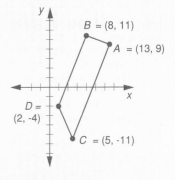

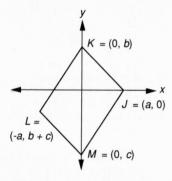
Covering the Reading

1. Name the mathematician(s) who discovered or invented each field.
  a. algebra
    Francois Viete
  b. analytic geometry
    Rene Descartes
2. What was Descartes' dream? Any mathematics problem could be solved, or any conjecture proved or disproved.
3. What is another name for analytic geometry? coordinate geometry
4. State the Parallel Lines and Slopes Theorem. Two nonvertical lines are parallel if and only if they have the same slope.
5. State the Perpendicular Lines and Slopes Theorem. Two nonvertical lines are ⊥ if and only if the product of their slopes is -1.
6. Given *A* = (0, 0), *B* = (6, 0), *C* = (9, 1), and *D* = (3, 1). Complete the proof that *ABCD* is a parallelogram.

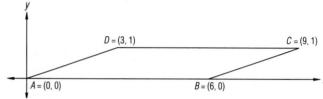

Conclusions	Justifications
1. slope of $\overline{AD} = \frac{1}{3}$	**a.** _?_ definition of slope (meaning)
slope of $\overline{BC} =$ **b.** _?_ $\frac{1}{3}$
slope of $\overline{AB} =$ **c.** _?_ 0
slope of $\overline{DC} =$ **d.** _?_ 0
2. $\overline{AB} \parallel \overline{DC}$ and $\overline{AD} \parallel \overline{BC}$	**e.** _?_ Parallel Lines and Slope Theorem
3. **f.** _?_ *ABCD* is a parallelogram.	Definition of parallelogram (meaning)

7. If *X* = (3, 7), *Y* = (11, 3), and *Z* = (4, 9), prove that △*XYZ* is a right triangle. See margin.

8. Name four areas where figures graphed on coordinate systems are used. samples: graphic design, computer animation, video games, and laser shows

Applying the Mathematics

In 9 and 10, use quadrilateral *EFGH* shown below.

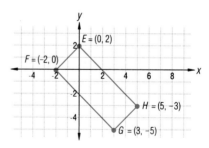

9. Prove: *EFGH* is a rectangle. See margin.

10. Show that $\overline{EG}$ and $\overline{FH}$ are not perpendicular. See margin.

11. Given: $W = (0, 0)$, $X = (a, 0)$, $Y = (a + b, c)$, and $Z = (b, c)$.
$a \neq 0$, $c \neq 0$.
Prove: $WXYZ$ is a parallelogram. **See margin.**

12. Given $S = (1, 3)$, $P = (4, 4)$, $A = (3, 1)$, and $T = (0, 0)$.
a. Draw $SPAT$. **See margin.**
b. Prove $\overline{SA} \perp \overline{PT}$. **The slope of $\overline{SA}$ is -1, and the slope of $\overline{PT}$ is 1.**
-1 · 1 = -1, so $\overline{SA} \perp \overline{PT}$.

13. Full-grown zebras can range from 46 to 55 inches high at the shoulder and their weights can range from 550 to 650 pounds. Let h be these possible heights and w be these possible weights.
a. Graph all possible ordered pairs (h, w). **See margin.**
b. Describe the graph. **The graph is the rectangular region with vertices (46, 550), (55, 550), (55, 650), and (46, 650).**

Review

In 14–16, find the intersection of the given lines by solving a system. Here is an example. Suppose the lines have equations

$$\begin{cases} 2x + y = 3 \\ x - 3y = 5. \end{cases}$$

Multiply both sides of the top equation by 3 to make the coefficients of y in the equations opposites. (You could also multiply both sides of the bottom equation by -2; this would make the coefficients of x opposites.)

$$\begin{cases} 6x + 3y = 9 \\ x - 3y = 5 \end{cases}$$

Now add, $\qquad\qquad 7x = 14$

so $\qquad\qquad\qquad x = 2.$

This is the x-coordinate of the point of intersection. Substitute into either original equation to find the y-coordinate. We use the first.

$$2(2) + y = 3$$
$$4 + y = 3$$
$$y = -1$$

Thus the point of intersection is $(2, -1)$. *(Previous course)*

14. $\begin{cases} 3x + y = 7 \\ x - y = 1 \end{cases}$ **(2, 1)**

15. $\begin{cases} 2x - 5y = 20 \\ 4x + y = 18 \end{cases}$ **(5, -2)**

16. $\begin{cases} y = \frac{1}{2}x \\ y = 2x - 5 \end{cases}$ $\left(\frac{10}{3}, \frac{5}{3}\right)$

NAME _____

NAME _____
Lesson MASTER 11–1 (page 2)

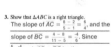

525

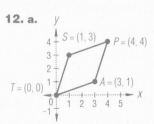
17. The side of a circular silo 10′ in diameter and 20′ high is to be painted. *(Lessons 10-4, 10-1)*
   a. How large is the area to be painted? 200π ≈ 628.3 sq ft
   b. If a bushel is about $1\frac{1}{4}$ cubic feet, about how many bushels of corn could be stored in this silo? ≈1257 bushels

18. The diamond crystal below is in the shape of a regular octahedron. Give the number of vertices, faces, and edges of this crystal. *(Lesson 9-7)* six vertices, eight faces, and twelve edges

In 19 and 20, a conclusion is made from the given statement. Name the justification. *(Lessons 8-7, 3-3, 2-5)*

19. Given: ABC is a right triangle with hypotenuse $\overline{AB}$.
    Conclusion: $AB^2 = AC^2 + CB^2$. Pythagorean Theorem

20. Given: $\odot P$ contains Q and R.
    Conclusion: $PQ = PR$. definition of circle (meaning)

21. a. What is the distance between two points on a number line with coordinates 50 and 500? 450
    b. What is the distance between (50, 100) and (500, 100)? *(Lesson 1-2)* 450

Exploration

22. Three vertices of a parallelogram are (2, 6), (-1, 5), and (0, -4).
    a. Find at least two possible locations of the fourth vertex.
    b. Are there other possible locations?
       a, b) There are only 3 possibilities: (-3, -5), (1, 15), (3, -3).

LESSON

11-2

The gates on a slalom course are placed at specific distances apart.

The Distance Formula

In the previous lesson, polygons were described by the coordinates of their vertices. It is possible to calculate the lengths of sides, diagonals, or other segments for such polynomials using a formula to be derived in this lesson.

If two points are on the same horizontal or vertical line, the distance between them can be found by the definition of distance on a number line. Below,

$$PQ = |6 - 2| = 4.$$

(Ignore the second coordinates of P and Q because they are equal.)
Similarly, $\qquad QR = |{-3} - 5| = 8.$

(Ignore the first coordinates of Q and R because they are equal.)

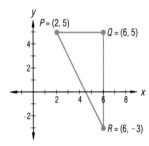

P and R are on an oblique line, but PR can now be found using the Pythagorean Theorem. Because $\overline{PQ} \perp \overline{QR}$, $\triangle PQR$ is a right triangle with hypotenuse $\overline{PR}$. By the Pythagorean Theorem,

$$\begin{aligned} PR^2 &= PQ^2 + QR^2 \\ &= 4^2 + 8^2 \\ &= 16 + 64 \\ &= 80. \end{aligned}$$

So $\qquad PR = \sqrt{80}$, or about 8.94.

You could draw a right triangle every time you had to calculate distances on an oblique line, but it is easier to have a general formula. The desired formula for PR should use only the coordinates of P and R. The idea is to repeat the above process, but use variables.

RESOURCES
■ Lesson Master 11-2

OBJECTIVES

A Using coordinates in individual figures, prove that segments in them are congruent, perpendicular, or parallel.
B Using coordinates, prove theorems involving congruent segments in triangles and quadrilaterals.
E Apply the Distance Formula in real situations.
F Determine the distance between two points in the coordinate plane.

TEACHING NOTES

Every line in the coordinate plane is a number line, but only horizontal and vertical lines have points whose coordinates are obvious. To find distances along these lines, the familiar distance formula $|a - b|$ can be used; all one does is ignore the coordinates that are alike. However, along an oblique line segment, the coordinates are not obvious (and, in fact, they are seldom indicated), and the Pythagorean Theorem is needed.

It is important to go through the proof of the Distance Formula in detail. Students need to understand that one reason for a proof is to save work. Once the Distance Formula is proved, it can be used to find distances because it always works. Thus, it is not necessary to draw a right triangle every time a distance must be found.

A possibly confusing step in the derivation of the Distance Formula is the move from absolute value to parentheses. The logic is as follows: Either $|a| = a$ or $|a| = -a$, and since $a^2 = (-a)^2$, the number a and its absolute value (either a or $-a$, depending on whether a is positive or negative) have the same square.

Example 1 is straightforward. **Example 2** points out the usefulness of the Distance Formula. It is more difficult to answer this type of question without using coordinates.

There are five proofs in this lesson, three involving the Distance Formula (**Questions 8, 9** and **13**) and two review proofs (**Questions 14** and **15**). The idea in all of these proofs is to show that the definition (sufficient condition) for the figure can be applied.

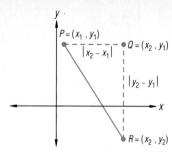

Let $P = (x_1, y_1)$ and $R = (x_2, y_2)$. First find Q so that $\overline{PR}$ is the hypotenuse of a right triangle. Such a point is $Q = (x_2, y_1)$.

$$PR^2 = PQ^2 + QR^2$$
$$= |x_2 - x_1|^2 + |y_2 - y_1|^2$$

Since a number and its absolute value have the same square,

$$|x_2 - x_1|^2 = (x_2 - x_1)^2 \text{ and}$$
$$|y_2 - y_1|^2 = (y_2 - y_1)^2.$$

Thus $\quad\quad PR^2 = (x_2 - x_1)^2 + (y_2 - y_1)^2.$

Taking square roots, $\quad PR = \sqrt{(x_2 - x_1)^2 + (y_2 - y_1)^2}$.

This gives a formula you should memorize.

Distance Formula:

The distance between two points (x_1, y_1) and (x_2, y_2) in the coordinate plane is

$$\sqrt{(x_2 - x_1)^2 + (y_2 - y_1)^2}.$$

Example 1 Find the distance between (-8, 50) and (30, -11).

Solution Let $(x_1, y_1) = (-8, 50)$ and let $(x_2, y_2) = (30, -11)$. If d is the distance between these points,

$$d = \sqrt{(x_2 - x_1)^2 + (y_2 - y_1)^2}$$
$$= \sqrt{(30 - -8)^2 + (-11 - 50)^2}$$
$$= \sqrt{(38)^2 + (-61)^2}$$
$$= \sqrt{1444 + 3721}$$
$$= \sqrt{5165}$$
$$\approx 71.87.$$

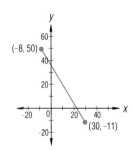

Check Draw a rough picture and mark off units on the line segment, as done at the left. The segment seems to have a length of about 70.

528

A grid can be put behind any drawing (blueprint, map, picture, etc.) to assign coordinates to points. With the Distance Formula, you can calculate distances between any two points on the drawing without having to measure.

Example 2 Tom bikes from his apartment to Doris' house following the path shown below in black: 3 miles north, then 2 miles east, then $\frac{1}{2}$ mile north, then $\frac{1}{4}$ mile west. By air, how far apart are these places?

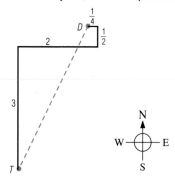

Solution Think of the path as being on a coordinate grid with Tom's place at (0, 0). Doris' house is at the point (1.75, 3.5). The air distance between them is the length of $\overline{TD}$.

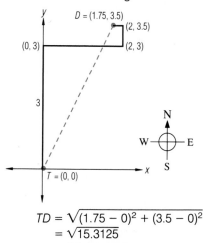

$$TD = \sqrt{(1.75 - 0)^2 + (3.5 - 0)^2}$$
$$= \sqrt{15.3125}$$
$$\approx 3.9$$

They are about 3.9 miles apart.

LESSON 11-2   The Distance Formula   **529**

NOTES ON QUESTIONS
Question 9: *Drawing a picture* can shorten work by indicating which sides are probably the same length.

Question 10:   Without co-ordinates, this would be a more difficult question, but it could be done by using the Pythagorean Theorem.

Making Connections for Question 15:   You might have **small groups** of students graph the triangle, assigning each group a different value for z. Elicit the observation that the triangles are the same shape but different sizes. This will help prepare students for the next chapter for similarity.

Making Connections for Question 18:   The generalization of part **b** is used in a theorem in Lesson 14-1.

Making Connections for Question 21:   This question reviews how to find the mean of a set of numbers in preparation for Lesson 11-4. A nice algebra problem students always want to know the answer to is: What score does Lynne need to get on the next test to have an A average for the four tests?

EXTENSION
Computer Students who
can program a computer may
be interested in writing a
short program to find the distance between two points
which have been inputted.
The program also could be
extended to print out whether
the segment is horizontal,
vertical, or oblique.

ADDITIONAL ANSWERS
8. a. $KL = \sqrt{82}$ and
$LJ = \sqrt{82}$ by the Distance
Formula. $KL = LJ$ by the
Transitive Property of
Equality. Thus, $\triangle JKL$ is
isosceles by the definition
of isosceles $\triangle$ (sufficient
condition).

9. $AB = \sqrt{20}$, $BC = \sqrt{20}$,
$CD = \sqrt{212}$, and $AD = \sqrt{212}$
by the Distance Formula.
$AB = BC$ and $CD = AD$ by
the Transitive Property of
Equality. Thus, $ABCD$ is a
kite by the definition of
kite (sufficient condition).

11. a. False; sample
counterexample:
Let $x_1 = 4$; $x_2 = 1$.
$|x_2 - x_1| = 3$, but $x_2 - x_1 = -3$.

14. The slope of $\overline{BC} =$
$\frac{5-4}{1-0} = 1$ and the slope of
$\overline{AD} = \frac{3-0}{3-0} = 1$ by the
definition of slope
(meaning). $\overline{BC} \parallel \overline{AD}$ by the
Parallel Lines and Slopes
Theorem. Thus, $ABCD$ is a
trapezoid by the definition
of trapezoid (sufficient
condition).

15. The slope of $\overline{PQ} =$
$\frac{2z - 4z}{7z - 3z} = -\frac{1}{2}$ and the slope of
$\overline{QR} = \frac{-8z - 2z}{2z - 7z} = 2$ by the
definition of slope
(meaning). $\overline{PQ} \perp \overline{QR}$ by the
Perpendicular Lines and
Slopes Theorem. Thus,
$\triangle PQR$ is a right triangle by
the definition of right
triangle (sufficient
condition).

Questions

Covering the Reading

In 1–6, use the figure below when necessary. Give the distance between
the named points.

1. A and B **11**

2. B and C **5**

3. A and C $\sqrt{146} \approx$ **12.08**

4. A and the origin $\sqrt{29} \approx$ **5.39**

5. B and D $\sqrt{52} \approx$ **7.21**

6. (x_1, y_1) and (x_2, y_2) $\sqrt{(x_2 - x_1)^2 + (y_2 - y_1)^2}$

7. To get to a hospital from the middle of a nearby town, you can drive
8 miles east, turn and go 4 miles south, and then go 1 mile west. By
helicopter, how far is it from the middle of the town to the hospital?
$\sqrt{65} \approx$ **8.06 miles**

Applying the Mathematics

8. Let $J = (-5, 0)$, $K = (5, 8)$, and $L = (4, -1)$.
   a. Prove that $\triangle JKL$ is isosceles by using the Distance Formula.
   b. Is $\triangle JKL$ equilateral?
   a) See margin. b) No

9. Given: $A = (4, -7)$, $B = (6, -3)$, $C = (4, 1)$, and $D = (-10, -3)$.
   Prove: $ABCD$ is a kite. See margin.

10. On a map, it can be seen that Charles lives 1 mile east and 1.5 miles
south of school, while Cynthia lives 2 miles west and 0.8 miles
south of school. By air, how far do Charles and Cynthia live from
each other? $\sqrt{9.49} \approx$ **3.08 miles**

11. Tell whether the statement is *true* or *false*. If false, give a
counterexample.
    a. $|x_2 - x_1| = (x_2 - x_1)$ b. $|x_2 - x_1|^2 = (x_2 - x_1)^2$
    c. $|x_2 - x_1| = |x_1 - x_2|$ d. $(x_1 - x_2)^2 = (x_2 - x_1)^2$
    a) See margin. b) True; c) True; d) True

12. a. Find the distance between $(1, 2)$ and $(3, 4)$. $\sqrt{8} \approx$ **2.83**
    b. Is the answer to part **a** the same as the distance between
    $(3, 4)$ and $(1, 2)$? Yes
    c. Generalize the result. The distance between (x_1, y_1) and (x_2, y_2) is the
    same as the distance between (x_2, y_2) and (x_1, y_1).

13. Let $A = (-1, 3)$ and $B = (11, 2)$. Prove that the point $C = (3, -7)$ is
on the circle with center B and radius BA. $BC = \sqrt{145}$ and $BA = \sqrt{145}$.
Thus, by the definition of circle (sufficient condition), C and A are on the
same circle with center B.

530

530

14. Prove: $A = (0, 0)$, $B = (4, 0)$, $C = (5, 1)$, and $D = (3, 3)$ are vertices of a trapezoid. *(Lesson 11-1)* **See margin.**

15. Prove that the triangle with vertices $P = (3z, 4z)$, $Q = (7z, 2z)$, and $R = (2z, -8z)$ is a right triangle. *(Lesson 11-1)* **See margin.**

In 16 and 17, find the point of intersection of the lines by solving a system. *(Lesson 11-1, Previous course)*

16. $\begin{cases} -2x + y = 11 \\ x + 2y = 6 \end{cases}$
$(\frac{-16}{5}, \frac{23}{5})$ **or (-3.2, 4.6)**

17. $\begin{cases} y = 13 \\ 4x - 3y = 10 \end{cases}$
(12.25, 13)

18. a. A square has sides of length 100. What is the length of either diagonal? **$100\sqrt{2}$ units**
   b. Generalize part **a.** *(Lesson 8-7)*
   A square of side s has diagonals of length $s\sqrt{2}$.

19. A parallelogram and triangle have the same base and same altitude. How are their areas related? *(Lessons 8-6, 8-5)*
   The area of the triangle is one-half the area of the parallelogram.

20. The measure of one acute angle of a right triangle is 45° more than the measure of the other.
   a. Is this possible? **Yes**
   b. If so, find the measures. If not, tell why not. *(Lessons 5-7, 3-2)*
   22.5, 67.5

21. Lynne has scored 92, 83, and 95 on her three tests so far this grading period. What is her average (or mean) score? *(Previous course)* **90**

22. The distance from point X to (2, 8) is 17.
   a. Show that X could be (10, 23).
   b. Name five other possible locations of point X. (Hint: Draw a picture.)
   a) $\sqrt{(10-2)^2 + (23-8)^2} = \sqrt{64 + 225} = \sqrt{289} = 17$
   b) samples: (2, 25), (2, -9), (19, 8), (-15, 8) (10, -7)

LESSON 11-2   The Distance Formula   **531**

RESOURCES
■ Lesson Master 11-3
■ Quiz for Lessons 11-1
  Through 11-3
▶ Visual for Teaching Aid 71
  displays the graph of the
  circle on page 532.

OBJECTIVE

G Write an equation for a
circle given its center and
radius, and vice versa.

TEACHING NOTES

Reading Using the standard form of the equation of
a circle can be difficult for
some students because there
is a subtraction in the equation (representing a difference in coordinates). Caution
students to read the equation
in **Example 2,** for example,
as a circle with center (-1, -3),
not (1, 3).

You might wish to begin by
discussing **Question 11.**
Then consider the equation
$(x - 4)^2 + (y - 11)^2 = 25$.
This equation has many lattice point solutions, among
them the obvious four points
(9, 11), (-1, 11), (4, 16), and
(4, 6). But there are also the
solutions from the relationship $3^2 + 4^2 = 25$. Some of
the other points are (7, 15),
(1, 15), (8, 14), (8, 8), (0, 14),
(0, 8), (7, 7), (1, 7). Have students graph these points.
The graph demonstrates that
they all lie on a circle.

The equation $(x - 4)^2 +$
$(y - 11)^2 = 25$ is *an* equation for a circle. There are
many equations equivalent to
this one. Point out, however,
that this one is *the* equation
written in standard form.

Equations for Circles

You are familiar with equations for lines. There are also equations
for circles. Below, a circle is drawn with center (3, 2) and radius
10. By adding or subtracting 10 from either coordinate of (3, 2),
four points on the circle can be found. They are (13, 2), (3, 12),
(-7, 2), and (3, -8). It would be nice to find an equation satisfied by
these four points and all other points on the circle.

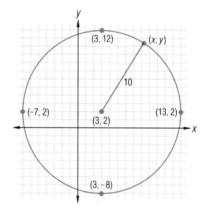

If a point (x, y) is on the circle, then by the Distance Formula,
$$\sqrt{(x - 3)^2 + (y - 2)^2} = 10.$$

This equation is an equation for the circle. However, most people
prefer equations without square roots. Squaring both sides gives an
equivalent equation.

$$(x - 3)^2 + (y - 2)^2 = 100$$

To check if this is correct, try the point (-7, 2). It should satisfy the
equation. Substitute -7 for x and 2 for y.

Does $\quad (-7 - 3)^2 + (2 - 2)^2 = 100$?
Does $\qquad\qquad (-10)^2 + 0^2 = 100$? Yes.

It is easy to generalize this example.

532

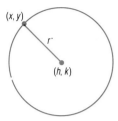

Theorem (Equation for a Circle):

The circle with center (h, k) and radius r is the set of points (x, y) satisfying

$$(x - h)^2 + (y - k)^2 = r^2.$$

Proof

Since r is the radius, by the definition of circle, the distance from (h, k) to any point (x, y) on the circle is r.

That distance is given by the Distance Formula.

$$\sqrt{(x - h)^2 + (y - k)^2} = r$$

Squaring both sides:

$$(x - h)^2 + (y - k)^2 = r^2.$$

Example 1   Write an equation for the circle with center (0, -4) and radius 7.

Solution   Here $r = 7$ and $(h, k) = (0, -4)$. So $h = 0$ and $k = -4$. Substitute the values of h, k, and r into the equation for a circle.

$$(x - 0)^2 + (y - -4)^2 = 7^2$$

Simplify: $x^2 + (y + 4)^2 = 49$ is the desired equation.

Check   Draw a picture and find a point on the circle.

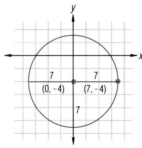

One point on the circle is (7, -4). Does (7, -4) satisfy the equation? Substitute 7 for x and -4 for y.

Does $7^2 + (-4 + 4)^2 = 49$?
Does $7^2 + 0^2 = 49$?   Yes.

You could try other points, such as (0, 3), (-7, -4), or (0, -11). Remember that the center is not on the circle, so its coordinates will not satisfy the equation.

Some students might think that the coordinates of a circle must be integers. To help students see that this is not true, pick one of the circles in the lesson and have each student find the coordinates of a point that is not a lattice point. This is not as hard to do as it might seem. For instance, for the circle on page 532, if $x = 0$, then $9 + (y - 2)^2 = 100$. Thus, $(y - 2)^2 = 91$, $y - 2 = \pm\sqrt{91}$, and $y = 2 \pm \sqrt{91}$. Thus, two points are $(0, 2 - \sqrt{91})$ and $(0, 2 + \sqrt{91})$. Students can check that these points are on the circle by using a decimal approximation to $\sqrt{91}$.

Error Analysis   A major difficulty some students have in understanding the equation for a circle is that the use of the variables x and y in the formula is different from the uses of h, k, and r. The variables x and y may stand for any point on the circle, but h, k, and r are constants. You might point out that the expression

$$\sqrt{(x - 3)^2 + (y - 2)^2}$$ gives

the distance from any point (x, y) to (3, 2). By setting the expression equal to 10, only those points 10 units away from (3, 2) will satisfy the equation. The constants are 3, 2, and 10.

Making Connections
Point out the simplicity of the equation for a circle whose center is at the origin, as shown on page 534. Tell students that there are reasonably simple equations for certain placements of conic sections. They may have seen equations for some parabolas ($y = ax^2 + bx + c$) and some hyperbolas ($xy = k$) in algebra.

Alternate Approach
You might want to prepare several transparencies of circles with integral radii and use them to demonstrate the equation for a circle. Superimpose each circle on a coordinate plane and line up its

533

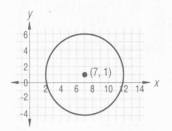
From the equation for a circle you can figure out its center and radius.

Example 2 Find the center and radius of the circle with equation $(x + 1)^2 + (y + 3)^2 = 25$.

Solution Compare the general equation to the given equation.
$$(x - h)^2 + (y - k)^2 = r^2$$
$$(x + 1)^2 + (y + 3)^2 = 25$$

h must be -1 to get $(x + 1)$. k must be -3 to get $(y + 3)$. The center is (h, k), so it is (-1, -3). $r^2 = 25$, so the radius is 5. (r is a length, so r cannot be negative.)

Check Draw a picture of the circle with center (-1, -3) and radius 5.

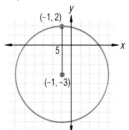

One point on the circle is (-1, 2). Does it satisfy the equation?

Does $(-1 + 1)^2 + (2 + 3)^2 = 25$?
Does $0^2 + 5^2 = 25$? Yes.

The circles with the simplest equations are those with center (0, 0), the origin. Then $h = 0$ and $k = 0$, so an equation is
$$(x - 0)^2 + (y - 0)^2 = r^2,$$
or just
$$x^2 + y^2 = r^2.$$

Pictured below is the circle with center (0, 0) and radius 9. Its equation is $x^2 + y^2 = 81$.

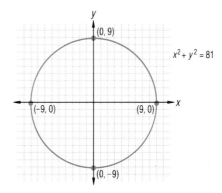

534

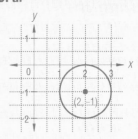

Covering the Reading

1. Is the point on the circle with center (3, 2) and radius 10?
   a. (13, 2) Yes
   b. (3, -8) Yes
   c. (8, 7) No
   d. (9, -6) Yes

2. a. What is an equation for the circle with center (-3, 5) and radius 1? $(x + 3)^2 + (y - 5)^2 = 1$
   b. Give the coordinates of four points on the circle.
      samples: (-4, 5), (-3, 6), (-2, 5), (-3, 4)

3. a. What is the distance between (x, y) and (7, 1)? $\sqrt{(x - 7)^2 + (y - 1)^2}$
   b. Give an equation for the circle with center (7, 1) and radius 5.
   c. Graph this circle. See margin.
   d. Give the coordinates of four points on this circle.
      b) $(x - 7)^2 + (y - 1)^2 = 25$; d) samples: (2, 1), (12, 1), (7, 6), (7, -4)

4. The circle below has center at the origin and contains (3, 0). What is an equation for it? $x^2 + y^2 = 9$

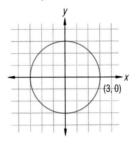

11. (0, 5), (3, 4), (4, 3), (5, 0), (4, -3), (3, -4), (0, -5), (-3, -4), (-4, -3), (-5, 0), (-4, 3), (-3, 4)

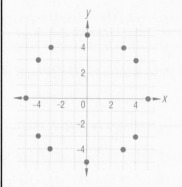

5. The proof of the equation for a circle relies on what formula?
   The Distance Formula

In 6–9, determine a. the center, b. the radius, and c. one point on the circle with the given equation.

6. $(x - 5)^2 + (y - 11)^2 = 81$ a) (5, 11); b) 9; c) sample: (5, 20)

7. $(x + 1)^2 + y^2 = 2$ a) (-1, 0); b) $\sqrt{2}$; c) sample: (0, 1)

8. $x^2 + y^2 = 25$ a) (0, 0); b) 5; c) sample: (0, 5)

9. $(x + 6)^2 + (y + 2)^2 = 1$ a) (-6, -2); b) 1; c) sample: (-6, -3)

12. See the margin on p. 536.

13. See Additional Answers in the back of this book.

Applying the Mathematics

10. A circle has center (2, -1) and touches the x-axis at exactly one point. The circle is called **tangent** to the axis.
    a. Draw a picture. See margin.
    b. What are the coordinates of the *point of tangency*? (2, 0)
    c. Find an equation for the circle. $(x - 2)^2 + (y + 1)^2 = 1$
    d. Find the area of this circle. π square units

11. Give the coordinates of the 12 lattice points on the circle $x^2 + y^2 = 25$. (Recall that a lattice point is a point with integer coordinates.) Graph the points. See margin.

In 12 and 13, graph.

12. $x^2 + y^2 = 16$
    See margin.

13. $(x + 5)^2 + (y - 8)^2 = 121$
    See margin.

LESSON 11-3   Equations for Circles   **535**

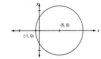

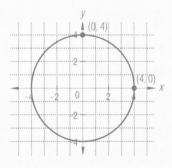

Review

In 14 and 15, calculate the distance between the points. Assume $x > 0$. *(Lesson 11-2)*

14. (4, -7) and (-1, 5) **13**

15. $(9x, -40x)$ and the origin **41x**

16. Nancy lives 6 blocks west and 3 blocks north of the park. Domaso lives 5 blocks south of the park. How many blocks by air is it from where Nancy lives to where Domaso lives? *(Lesson 11-2)* **10 blocks**

17. Prove that the quadrilateral $QRST$ with vertices $Q = (9a, 4b)$, $R = (6a, 2b)$, $S = (a, -7b)$, and $T = (-a, -14b)$ is a trapezoid. *(Lesson 11-1)* **See margin.**

18. Find the intersection of the following lines: *(Lesson 11-1, Previous course)*
$$\begin{cases} x - 7y = 15 \\ 4x + 5y = -6. \end{cases}$$ **(1, -2)**

19. Suppose $\overleftrightarrow{AB}$ and $\overleftrightarrow{BC}$ have the same slope. What can you conclude about points A, B, and C? *(Lessons 3-4, 1-7)* **They are collinear.**

In 20 and 21, draw the diagram. *(Lessons 9-2, 9-1)*

20. two perpendicular planes **See margin.**

21. a parallelepiped **See margin.**

22. Given: $\triangle XYZ$ below is isosceles with vertex angle X.
V is the midpoint of $\overline{XY}$.
W is the midpoint of $\overline{XZ}$.
Prove: $\triangle XVW$ is isosceles. *(Lessons 5-1, 4-4)* **See margin.**

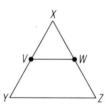

Exploration

23. Give an equation for a circle on which there are no lattice points and whose interior contains no lattice points. (See Question 11 if you have forgotten the meaning of "lattice point.")
sample: $(x - \frac{1}{2})^2 + (y - \frac{1}{2})^2 = \frac{1}{16}$

LESSON 11·4

The Midpoint Formula

RESOURCES
■ Lesson Master 11-4

Suppose you score 90, 85, and 83 on three tests. Your average or **mean** score is the sum of these numbers divided by 3. It is

$$\frac{90 + 85 + 83}{3} = 86.$$

The mean has a physical interpretation. Think of a weightless ruler with hooks for attaching weights. If equal weights are hung from 90, 85, and 83, the ruler will balance on 86, their mean. The mean is the **center of gravity** of the weighted ruler.

A similar idea is true in two dimensions. Suppose you wish to find the center of gravity of a set of points. The coordinates of the center of gravity are found by computing the mean of the x-coordinates and the mean of the y-coordinates of the points. (The proof of the result depends on laws of physics, and is not presented.)

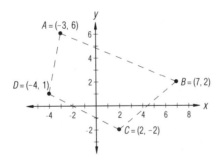

Find the mean of the x-coordinates:

$$\frac{-3 + 7 + 2 + {}^-4}{4} = \frac{2}{4} = 0.5.$$

Find the mean of the y-coordinates:

$$\frac{6 + 2 + {}^-2 + 1}{4} = \frac{7}{4} = 1.75.$$

LESSON 11-4 The Midpoint Formula **537**

So the center of gravity is (0.5, 1.75), as shown below.

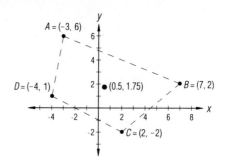

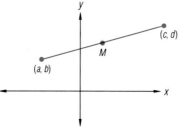

In the simplest case, as shown at the left, there are only two points (or weights) to begin with, and the center of gravity is the midpoint of the segment connecting them.

Coordinates of midpoints are easy to find, though the proof is complicated.

Midpoint Formula:

If a segment has endpoints (a, b) and (c, d), its midpoint is

$$\left(\frac{a + c}{2}, \frac{b + d}{2}\right).$$

Proof

Draw a picture with $P = (a, b)$, $Q = (c, d)$, and $M = \left(\frac{a+c}{2}, \frac{b+d}{2}\right)$.

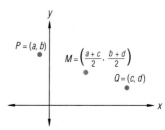

Recall the definition of midpoint. To show that M is the midpoint of $\overline{PQ}$, we need to show that $PM = MQ$ and M is on $\overleftrightarrow{PQ}$.

The algebra that follows is cumbersome, but it works out. To show that $PM = MQ$, we calculate distances using the Distance Formula.

538

$$PM = \sqrt{\left(\frac{a+c}{2} - a\right)^2 + \left(\frac{b+d}{2} - b\right)^2}$$

$$= \sqrt{\left(\frac{a+c-2a}{2}\right)^2 + \left(\frac{b+d-2b}{2}\right)^2}$$

$$= \sqrt{\left(\frac{c-a}{2}\right)^2 + \left(\frac{d-b}{2}\right)^2}$$

$$MQ = \sqrt{\left(c - \frac{a+c}{2}\right)^2 + \left(d - \frac{b+d}{2}\right)^2}$$

$$= \sqrt{\left(\frac{2c-(a+c)}{2}\right)^2 + \left(\frac{2d-(b+d)}{2}\right)^2}$$

$$= \sqrt{\left(\frac{c-a}{2}\right)^2 + \left(\frac{d-b}{2}\right)^2}$$

Thus $PM = MQ$. To show that M is on $\overline{PQ}$, we calculate the slopes of $\overleftrightarrow{PM}$ and $\overleftrightarrow{MQ}$.

$$\text{slope of } \overleftrightarrow{PM} = \frac{\frac{b+d}{2} - b}{\frac{a+c}{2} - a} = \frac{b+d-2b}{a+c-2a} = \frac{d-b}{c-a}$$

$$\text{slope of } \overleftrightarrow{MQ} = \frac{d - \frac{b+d}{2}}{c - \frac{a+c}{2}} = \frac{2d-(b+d)}{2c-(a+c)} = \frac{d-b}{c-a}$$

The slopes are equal so $\overleftrightarrow{PM} \parallel \overleftrightarrow{MQ}$. Both lines contain point M, so $\overleftrightarrow{PM} = \overleftrightarrow{MQ}$ and M is on $\overleftrightarrow{PQ}$. So M is the midpoint of $\overline{PQ}$.

Fortunately, applying the Midpoint Formula is easier than proving it.

Example 1   If $P = (-10, 6)$ and $Q = (1, 8)$, find the midpoint of $\overline{PQ}$.

Solution   Call the midpoint M. Use the Midpoint Formula.

$$M = \left(\frac{-10+1}{2}, \frac{6+8}{2}\right)$$
$$= \left(\frac{-9}{2}, \frac{14}{2}\right)$$
$$= (-4.5, 7)$$

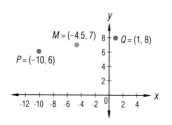

Check   Graph the points on a coordinate plane. (-4.5, 7) looks like it is halfway between (-10, 6) and (1, 8). This gives a rough check. You could calculate slopes and lengths of $\overline{PM}$ and $\overline{MQ}$ for an exact check.

The Midpoint Formula is often applied to prove theorems or solve problems. Example 2 is an instance of a theorem proved in the next lesson.

■ ■ ■ ■ ■ ■ ■ ■

Example 2 Let $A = (0, 12)$, $B = (2, -4)$, and $C = (8, 10)$, as shown below. Let M and N be the midpoints of $\overline{AB}$ and $\overline{AC}$.
Prove: $\overline{MN} \parallel \overline{BC}$.

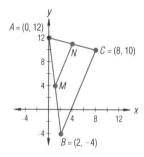

Analyze $\overline{MN}$ and $\overline{BC}$ are parallel if and only if their slopes are equal. So first find the coordinates of M and N.

Write

Conclusions	Justifications
1. $M = \left(\frac{0+2}{2}, \frac{12+-4}{2}\right) = (1, 4)$	**Midpoint Formula**
$N = \left(\frac{0+8}{2}, \frac{12+10}{2}\right) = (4, 11)$	
2. The slope of $\overline{MN}$ is $\frac{11-4}{4-1} = \frac{7}{3}$.	**definition of slope (meaning)**
The slope of $\overline{BC}$ is $\frac{10-(-4)}{8-2} = \frac{14}{6} = \frac{7}{3}$.	
3. $\overline{MN} \parallel \overline{BC}$	**Parallel Lines and Slopes Theorem**

You may be surprised to learn another relationship in Example 2 above: $\overline{MN}$ has half the length of $\overline{BC}$. You can verify this result using the Distance Formula. (See Question 10.)

Questions

Covering the Reading

In 1–3, find the mean of the given numbers.
1. 100, 50, 200 $\frac{350}{3} = 116\frac{2}{3}$

2. -1, -3, -5, -7 **-4**

3. 1492, 1776 **1634**

4. Equal weights are hung from a (weightless) number line at the points -81 and 47. At what point will the number line balance? **-17**

540

5. Find the center of gravity of the vertices of the figure shown below. **(5.5, 5)**

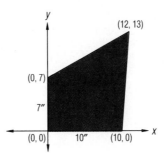

6. Give the coordinates of the midpoint of the segment connecting (x_1, y_1) to (x_2, y_2). $\left(\frac{x_1 + x_2}{2}, \frac{y_1 + y_2}{2}\right)$

7. a. Give the coordinates of the midpoint of the segment joining (12, -4) and (-2, -8). **(5, -6)**
   b. Check your answer by using distance and slope. **See margin.**

8. Give the coordinates of the midpoint of the segment with endpoints (a, b) and the origin. $\left(\frac{a}{2}, \frac{b}{2}\right)$

9. Use $\triangle DEF$ below. L, M, and N are midpoints of the sides.
   a. Find the coordinates of L, M, and N.
   b. Prove $\overline{LM} \parallel \overline{DE}$.
   c. Prove $\overline{MN} \parallel \overline{EF}$.
   d. Prove $MN = \frac{1}{2}EF$.

   a) $L = (6.5, 0)$, $M = (8, 6)$, $N = (1.5, 6)$; b-d) See margin.

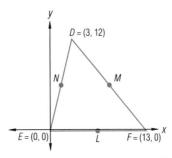

10. In the triangle of Example 2, show that $MN = \frac{1}{2}BC$. **See margin.**

In 11–13, write each expression as a single fraction with no fractions in the numerator or denominator.

11. $\dfrac{a + c}{2} - a$

$\dfrac{a + c - 2a}{2}$ or $\dfrac{c - a}{2}$

12. $c - \dfrac{a + c}{2}$

$\dfrac{2c - (a + c)}{2}$ or $\dfrac{c - a}{2}$

13. $\dfrac{d - \dfrac{b + d}{2}}{c - \dfrac{a + c}{2}}$ $\dfrac{2d - (b + d)}{2c - (a + c)}$ or $\dfrac{d - b}{c - a}$

MORE PRACTICE
For more questions on SPUR
Objectives, use *Lesson
Master 11-4,* shown on page
543.

EXTENSION
You may want to point out
that the coordinates of the
midpoint of a segment (m, n)
satisfy the following relationships:
$m = a + \frac{1}{2}(c - a) = \frac{1}{2}a + \frac{1}{2}c$
and $n = b + \frac{1}{2}(d - b) =$
$\frac{1}{2}b + \frac{1}{2}d$.
The coordinates of the point
(m, n) one-third of the way
from (a, b) to (c, d) satisfy
the following relationships:
$m = a + \frac{1}{3}(c - a) = \frac{2}{3}a + \frac{1}{3}c$
$n = b + \frac{1}{3}(d - b) = \frac{2}{3}b + \frac{1}{3}d$.
In general, the point $\frac{p}{q}$ of the
way from (a, b) to (c, d) is
$((1 - \frac{p}{q})a + \frac{p}{q}c, (1 - \frac{p}{q})b + \frac{p}{q}d)$.

ADDITIONAL ANSWERS
18. a.

Conclusions	Justifications
1. $M =$	Midpoint
(11.5, 9.5)	Formula
$N =$	
(20, 12)	
$P =$	
(14.5, 22.5)	
$Q =$	
(6, 20)	
2. $MN =$	Distance
$\sqrt{78.5}$	Formula
$PQ =$	
$\sqrt{78.5}$	
3. $MN = PQ$	Transitive
	Prop. of Eq.

b. The slope of $\overline{MN} = \frac{2.5}{8.5}$
and the slope of $\overline{PQ} = \frac{2.5}{8.5}$
by the definition of slope
(meaning). $\overline{MN} \parallel \overline{PQ}$ by the
Parallel Lines and Slopes
Theorem.

20.

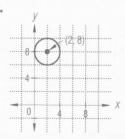

14. Below is a graph of the population of non-white families in the United
States for two years.

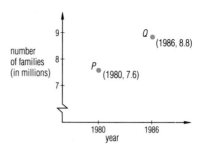

a. Find the midpoint of $\overline{PQ}$. **(1983, 8.2)**
b. What does each coordinate of the midpoint mean? **In 1983 one
might estimate that there were 8.2 million non-white families in the U.S.**

15. Give the slope of the segment connecting the origin to the midpoint of
the segment with endpoints (14, -11) and (-4, -35). $-\frac{23}{5} = -4.6$

16. In $\triangle ABC$, $A = (5,7)$, $B = (-2, 0)$, and $C = (-13, 11)$. Find the
length of the median from B to $\overline{AC}$. $\sqrt{85} \approx 9.22$

17. A meter stick is shortened by cutting off 12 centimeters from one end
and 20 centimeters from the other. What is the reading at the point on
which the new stick balances?
46 or 54, depending on which piece was cut from each end

18. $M, N, P,$ and Q are the midpoints of the sides of quadrilateral
ABCD below.
a. Prove $MN = PQ$. **See margin.**
b. Prove $\overline{MN} \parallel \overline{PQ}$. **See margin.**
c. What kind of quadrilateral is *MNPQ*? **parallelogram**

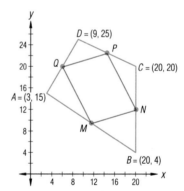

19. The equation of a given circle is $x^2 + y^2 = 75$.
a. Find its center. **(0, 0)**
b. Find its radius. $\sqrt{75} \approx 8.66$ **units**
c. Find one point on the circle. **sample:** $(\sqrt{75}, 0)$
d. Find its area. *(Lesson 11-3)* 75π **units²**

20. Graph: $(x - 2)^2 + (y - 8)^2 = 4$. *(Lesson 11-3)* **See margin.**

542

In 21 and 22, solve the system. *(Lesson 11-1)*

21. $\begin{cases} 5x - 2y = 25 \\ 3x + y = 4 \end{cases}$ (3, -5)

22. $\begin{cases} x = 14y - 13 \\ 2x + 3y = 36 \end{cases}$ (15, 2)

23. The regular square pyramid below has a height of 30 cm. The perimeter of the base is 64 cm.

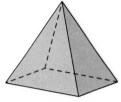

    a. Find its volume. **2560 cm³**
    b. Find its surface area. *(Lessons 10-6, 10-2)* **≈1249.6 cm²**

24. What is the slope of the line connecting $(a, 0)$ and $(0, -a)$? (Assume $a \neq 0$.) *(Lesson 3-1)* **1**

25. If $x > 0$, simplify: **a.** $\sqrt{x^2}$; **b.** $\sqrt{4x^2}$; **c.** $\sqrt{5x^2}$. *(Previous course)*
a) x; b) $2x$; c) $x\sqrt{5}$

Exploration

26. The center of gravity of a polygonal region with more than three sides is not generally the same point as the center of gravity of its vertices. Cut a nonsymmetric convex polygonal region out of cardboard.
    a. By trial and error, find the point where the region will balance on the tip of a pin.
    b. By putting the region on graph paper, find the center of gravity of its vertices and determine how close your point in part **a** is to this point.

Answers will vary; the center of gravity found in part a should be very close to that found in part b.

LESSON 11-4 The Midpoint Formula   **543**

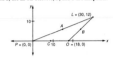
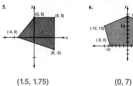

11-5

The Midpoint Connector Theorem

OBJECTIVES

B Using coordinates, prove theorems involving parallel or perpendicular sides, congruent segments, midpoints, or combinations of these in triangles and quadrilaterals.

C Apply the Midpoint Connector Theorem.

I Give convenient locations for triangles and quadrilaterals in the coordinate plane.

TEACHING NOTES

Historically, the Midpoint Connector Theorem was proved by the Greeks without coordinates and was a mathematical link from congruence to similarity. The Greeks were troubled by the fact that ratios of sides in similar figures could be irrational. They called these ratios *incommensurable*, which means unmeasurable. Today's conception of real numbers covers both rationals and irrationals, and the use of coordinates enables the general theorem to be proved without introducing an additional postulate to deal with similarity. This will be done in Lesson 12-10.

The use of convenient coordinates, such as 2a, when a midpoint is to be obtained, is a difficult idea for some students. Point out that mathematicians try to do things easily, and one way to do this is to avoid fractions.

The midpoints of the sides of polygons often determine figures with interesting characteristics. You saw an example in Example 2 of Lesson 11-4. In this lesson, you will see these properties further developed.

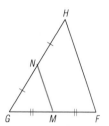

A basic property of midpoints is pictured at the left. Segment $\overline{MN}$ joins the midpoints of $\overline{FG}$ and $\overline{GH}$. It is parallel to $\overline{FH}$. It is also half the length of $\overline{FH}$. (Measure to check this.)

These two results can be proved for any triangle. Given any triangle *PQR*, a coordinate plane can be put on the plane of $\triangle PQR$ so that *Q* is the origin and $\overline{QR}$ is on the *x*-axis.

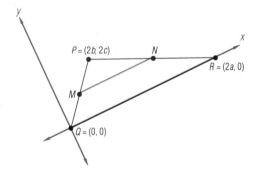

Since *R* is on the *x*-axis, its second coordinate is 0. Its first coordinate is not known. You could call it *x* or any other unknown. Pick 2*a* to more easily calculate midpoints. $R = (2a, 0)$.

544

Neither coordinate of P is known or determined by R or Q. So call the coordinates $2b$ and $2c$, again to more easily calculate midpoints. $P = (2b, 2c)$. You can use these coordinates to prove the following theorem.

Midpoint Connector Theorem:

The segment connecting the midpoints of two sides of a triangle is parallel to and half the length of the third side.

Proof

Draw: Use $\triangle PQR$ drawn on page 544 with midpoints M and N.

Given: $\triangle PQR$, M the midpoint of $\overline{PQ}$, N the midpoint of $\overline{PR}$.

Prove: a. $\overline{MN} \parallel \overline{QR}$
       b. $MN = \frac{1}{2} QR$.

Analyze The coordinates of M and N are needed. For part a, slopes can be used to prove the segments parallel. The Distance Formula can show part b.

Write Place $\triangle PQR$ on a coordinate system with $Q = (0, 0)$, $R = (2a, 0)$, and $P = (2b, 2c)$.

Conclusions	Justifications
1. $M = \left(\dfrac{2b + 0}{2}, \dfrac{2c + 0}{2}\right) = (b, c)$	Midpoint Formula
$ N = \left(\dfrac{2b + 2a}{2}, \dfrac{2c + 0}{2}\right) = (b + a, c)$	
2. slope of $\overline{MN} = \dfrac{c - c}{b + a - b} = \dfrac{0}{a} = 0$	definition of slope (meaning)
 slope of $\overline{QR} = \dfrac{0 - 0}{2a - 0} = \dfrac{0}{2a} = 0$	
3. $\overline{MN} \parallel \overline{QR}$	Parallel Lines and Slopes Theorem
4. $QR = \sqrt{(2a - 0)^2 + (0 - 0)^2}$ $ = \sqrt{4a^2}$ $ = 2\sqrt{a^2}$	Distance Formula
5. $MN = \sqrt{((b + a) - b)^2 + (c - c)^2}$ $ = \sqrt{a^2 + 0}$ $ = \sqrt{a^2}$	Distance Formula
6. $2MN = QR$	Substitution [MN for $\sqrt{a^2}$] (step 5 into step 4)
7. $MN = \frac{1}{2} QR$	Multiplication Property of Equality

Except for the parallelogram, the convenient coordinates for the various special triangles and quadrilaterals, shown on page 546, all result from the definition or symmetry of the figure. For the parallelogram, the only nonobvious vertex is $(a + b, c)$. The second coordinate is c because the side is parallel to the x-axis. Let the first coordinate be x. Now the oblique sides must be parallel, and since the slope of the left side is $\frac{c}{b}$, the slope of the right side must be $\frac{c}{b}$. From the slope formula $\frac{c - 0}{x - a} = \frac{c}{b}$, from which $x - a = b$, and therefore $x = a + b$.

Students may find coordinate proofs quite difficult if the algebra gets too complicated. The easiest proof is usually done with the least number of variables for vertices, and that is accomplished by using the x- or y-axis as lines containing the sides of the figure, if possible.

Alternate Approach
Although the algebra used in the proofs in this lesson is fairly straightforward, students may better understand the usage of the Midpoint Connector Theorem and the statement proved in the **Example** if a worksheet is prepared showing several triangles. Have students measure the segments involved to verify the relationships. For the Midpoint Connector Theorem, have students measure all three segments connecting the three midpoints of a triangle. They can use their protractors to verify that the segment connecting the midpoints of two sides of a triangle is parallel to the third side.

The Midpoint Connector Theorem could be proved starting with the most general vertices possible, namely (a, b), (c, d), and (e, f). The proof would be the same, but the algebra would be more complicated. By *conveniently locating* the coordinate plane, the proof is simplified. Convenient locations use the *x*-axis or *y*-axis as symmetry lines, or place one vertex at the origin, or both. Here are convenient locations for some other figures you have studied.

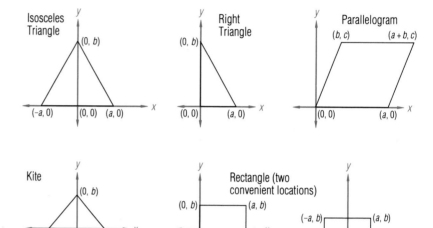

If midpoints will be used, it is better to double the coordinates. In the Example below, this is done to deduce a property of all right triangles.

■ ■ ■ ■ ■ ■ ■ ■

Example   **Prove:**   In a right triangle, the segment connecting the vertex of the right angle to the midpoint of the hypotenuse has half the length of the hypotenuse.

Draw

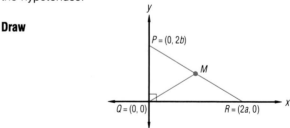

Given: Right $\triangle PQR$ with right angle Q. M is the midpoint of $\overline{PR}$.
Prove: $QM = \frac{1}{2} PR$.

Analyze Place the figure on a coordinate system. Find the coordinates of *M*, then use the Distance Formula to calculate *QM* and *PR*.

Write Place $\triangle PQR$ on a coordinate system with $Q = (0, 0)$, $R = (2a, 0)$, $P = (0, 2b)$.

Conclusions	Justifications
1. $M = \left(\frac{0 + 2a}{2}, \frac{2b + 0}{2}\right) = (a, b)$	Midpoint Formula
2. $PR = \sqrt{(2a - 0)^2 + (0 - 2b)^2}$ $\quad = \sqrt{4a^2 + 4b^2}$ $\quad = 2\sqrt{a^2 + b^2}$	Distance Formula
3. $QM = \sqrt{(a - 0)^2 + (b - 0)^2}$ $\quad = \sqrt{a^2 + b^2}$	Distance Formula
4. $2QM = PR$	Substitution (step 3 into step 2) [QM for $\sqrt{a^2 + b^2}$]
5. $QM = \frac{1}{2}PR$	Multiplication Property of Equality

Questions

Covering the Reading

In 1 and 2, *A*, *B*, and *C* are midpoints of the sides of $\triangle LMN$ at the left.

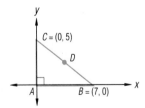

1. If $LN = 12$, what other lengths can be found? *AL = AN = BC = 6*

2. If $AB = 5.2$, what other lengths can be found?
NC = CM = 5.2, NM = 10.4

3. State the Midpoint Connector Theorem. See margin.

In 4–7, draw a figure of the indicated type conveniently placed on a coordinate system.

4. triangle See margin.   **5.** kite See margin.

6. right triangle See margin.   **7.** parallelogram See margin.

8. In right triangle *CAB* with m$\angle A = 90$, *D* is the midpoint of $\overline{BC}$. $B = (7, 0)$ and $C = (0, 5)$. What is the length of $\overline{AD}$?
$\frac{\sqrt{74}}{2} \approx 4.30$ units

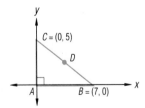

9. Fill in the blanks. $(a^2 + b^2)$, 4, $a^2 + b^2$
$\sqrt{4a^2 + 4b^2} = \sqrt{4(\underline{\ ?\ })} = \sqrt{\underline{\ ?\ }} \cdot \sqrt{\underline{\ ?\ }} = 2\sqrt{a^2 + b^2}$

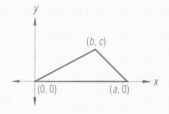
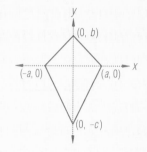
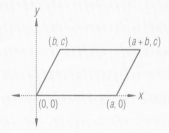

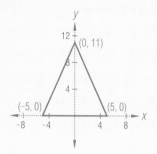
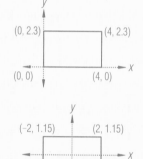
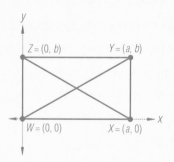

10. An isosceles triangle has base 10 and altitude 11. Place this triangle conveniently on a coordinate system. **See margin.**

11. A rectangular metal sheet has length 4 meters and width 2.3 meters. If you wished to analyze this sheet with a computer, you might need to put it on a coordinate system. Show two convenient sets of locations for the vertices of the rectangle. **See margin.**

12. For the figure of Question 1, give justifications in this proof that ABCN is a parallelogram.

Conclusions	Justifications
1. $\overline{BC} \parallel \overline{LN}$; $\overline{AB} \parallel \overline{MN}$	**a.** ? Midpoint Connector Theorem
2. ABCN is a parallelogram.	**b.** ? definition of parallelogram (sufficient condition)

13. L, M, and N are the midpoints of the sides of △DEF below. If DE = 20, EF = 16, and DF = 24, what is the perimeter of △LMN? **30 units**

In 14 and 15, RECT below is a rectangle. Y and D are the midpoints of sides $\overline{RE}$ and $\overline{EC}$.

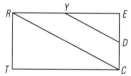

14. Explain why YDCR is a trapezoid. **See margin.**

15. If RC = 58 and ED = 20, find the lengths of all of the other segments drawn in the figure.
DC = 20, EC = RT = 40, YD = 29, EY = RY = 21, ER = TC = 42

16. By placing a general rectangle in a convenient location, prove that the diagonals of a rectangle have the same midpoint. **See margin.**

548

17. Find the center of gravity of the vertices of the figure shown below.
(Lesson 11-4)

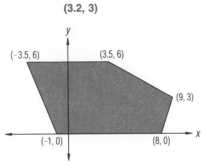

(3.2, 3)

(-3.5, 6)   (3.5, 6)

(9, 3)

(-1, 0)   (8, 0)

18. Find the center of gravity of the region bounded by the kite with vertices $(a, 0)$, $(0, b)$, $(-a, 0)$ and $(0, -c)$ graphed on page 546.
(Lesson 11-4) $\left(0, \frac{b-c}{4}\right)$

19. Let $V = (11, 21)$ and $L = (6, 33)$. Calculate each value.
  a. VL **13**
  b. the slope of $\overline{VL}$ $-\frac{12}{5}$ **= -2.4**
  c. the coordinates of the midpoint of $\overline{VL}$ **(8.5, 27)**
  (Lessons 11-4, 11-2, 3-4)

20. Answer Question 19 if $V = (a, b)$ and $L = (c, d)$.
  (Lessons 11-4, 11-2, 3-4)
  a) $\sqrt{(c - a)^2 + (d - b)^2}$; **b)** $\frac{d-b}{c-a}$; **c)** $\left(\frac{a+c}{2}, \frac{b+d}{2}\right)$

21. The circle at the right has center (-2, 0). What is an equation for it?
  (Lesson 11-3)
  $(x + 2)^2 + y^2 = 25$

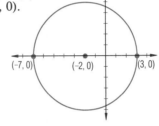

(-7, 0)   (-2, 0)   (3, 0)

22. Twice one number plus three times a second number is 462. The sum of the numbers is 254. What are the numbers?
  (Lesson 11-1, Previous course) **300, -46**

23. Draw at least five quadrilaterals with different shapes. In each quadrilateral, connect the midpoints of the sides in order so as to form a smaller quadrilateral. What is true about all these smaller quadrilaterals?
  All the smaller quadrilaterals are parallelograms.

Samples: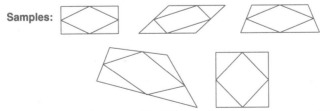

LESSON 11-5   The Midpoint Connector Theorem   **549**

FOLLOW-UP

MORE PRACTICE
For more questions on SPUR Objectives, use *Lesson Master 11-5*, shown below.

NAME _____

LESSON **MASTER   11–5**
QUESTIONS ON **SPUR** OBJECTIVES

■ **PROPERTIES**   *Objectives B and C* (See pages 559–561 for objectives.)
In 1 and 2, Q and R are midpoints of $\overline{AB}$ and $\overline{BC}$ in the figure below.

1. If $QA = 18$ and $AC = 34$, determine as many other lengths as possible.
  $QB = 18, AB = 36, QR = 17$

2. Prove: m∠BQR = m∠QAC.

Conclusions	Justifications
1. $QR \parallel AC$	Midpt. Connector Thm.
2. m∠BQR = m∠QAC	∥ lines ⇒ corr. ∠s ≅

In 3 and 4, ABCD is a kite with ends B and D. W and V are the midpoints of $\overline{AB}$ and $\overline{BC}$.

3. Explain why WVCA is an isosceles trapezoid.
  By the Midpt. Connector Thm., $\overline{WV} \parallel$
  $\overline{AC}$, making WVCA a trapezoid. Since
  ABCD is a kite, $AB = BC$, so ∠BAC ≅
  ∠BCA by the Isosceles Triangle Thm.
  Thus, by def., WVCA is an isosceles
  trapezoid.

4. If $WB = 10$ and $WV = 8$, find as many other lengths as possible.
  $WA = BV = VC = 10; AB = BC = 20; AC = 16$

NAME _____
Lesson MASTER 11-5 (page 2)

■ **REPRESENTATIONS**   *Objective I*

5. An isosceles triangle has a base of 14 and an altitude of 8. Place it in a convenient position on the coordinate plane below and give the coordinates of its vertices.

6. An isosceles trapezoid has bases 2a and 2b, and an altitude of c. Place the trapezoid on the coordinate plane below so that it is symmetric about the y-axis.

sample

7. Three consecutive vertices of a parallelogram are (3, 2), (4, 8), and (11, 16). What is the fourth vertex?   **(10, 10)**

8. Give convenient coordinates for the vertices of the kite with diagonals of length 40 and 64 if the symmetry diagonal is divided by the other diagonal into segments of length 40 and 24.
  (20, 0), (0, 40), (-20, 0), (0, -24)

OBJECTIVES

E Apply the Diagonal of a Box Formula in real situations.
J Apply coordinate geometry in three dimensions.

TEACHING NOTES

Plotting points in three dimensions with paper and pencil is not easy. A grid is needed, as the picture on the bottom of this page indicates. In that picture, (*x, y, z*) could be in the *x-y* plane and behind the *y*-axis, or directly below the *x*-axis, or near the viewer and quite high above the *x-y* plane. The lines, as shown for the point (4, 7, 8) on that page, or a box, as shown for (-5, 2, 1) on page 551, are needed. Do not expect your students to become expert graphers, but do expect them to know how to graph a point.

Students may wonder why *x* is not the horizontal axis in three-dimensional graphing. Point out that when the *x-y* plane is viewed from the top, the *x*-axis and *y*-axis should be in their usual positions.

Point out that all of the theorems in this lesson are analogous to theorems in two dimensions. This is not always the case because a theorem in two dimensions cannot always be extended to three dimensions.

Three-Dimensional Coordinates

Points in space can be located by using a **three-dimensional coordinate system.** For instance, to locate points in a room, let the origin be at a corner of the room where two walls and the floor intersect. With two coordinates, *x* and *y,* you can describe the location of an object on the floor. To describe an object in the room which is not on the floor (such as a light hanging from the ceiling), use a third number to indicate the height from the floor. This is the **z-coordinate.** Thus, if the light is 4 ft from the origin in the *x*-direction, 7 ft in the *y*-direction, and 8 ft in the *z*-direction (up), you could uniquely specify the position of the light by the **ordered triple** (4, 7, 8). The *x*-coordinate is 4, the *y*-coordinate is 7, and the *z*-coordinate is 8. The lines where the walls and floor meet are the **axes** of this 3-dimensional coordinate system.

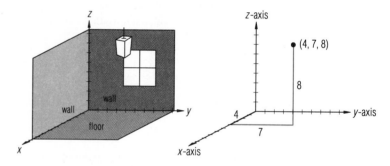

Now imagine extending each axis in its negative direction, as shown in the figure below. The positive direction is shown on each axis by a single arrowhead. The three axes are called the **x-axis,** the **y-axis,** and the **z-axis.** The ordered triple (*x, y, z*) represents a point in 3-space. The position of a point is given by its three distances from the origin (0, 0, 0). The following example shows how to locate points in three dimensions.

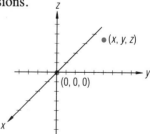

550

Example 1 Plot the point $R = (-5, 2, 1)$ on a three-dimensional coordinate system.

Solution To plot point R:

1. Move 5 units backward (in a negative direction) on the x-axis.
2. Move 2 units to the right parallel to the y-axis.
3. Move 1 unit up parallel to the z-axis.

It helps to think of the point as the back, upper, right vertex of a box with base dimensions 5 and 2, and height 1.

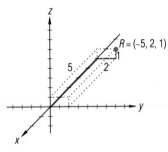

Many of the formulas for 2-dimensional coordinates have counterparts in three dimensions. For instance, the Distance Formula states that the distance between (x_1, y_1) and (x_2, y_2) in the coordinate plane is $\sqrt{(x_2 - x_1)^2 + (y_2 - y_1)^2}$. Its counterpart is the 3-dimensional Distance Formula below.

Distance Formula in Three Dimensions:

The distance between two points (x_1, y_1, z_1) and (x_2, y_2, z_2) is

$$\sqrt{(x_2 - x_1)^2 + (y_2 - y_1)^2 + (z_2 - z_1)^2}.$$

The proof of the formula is based on two applications of the Pythagorean Theorem.

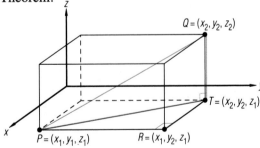

In right $\triangle PRT$, $PT^2 = RT^2 + PR^2$
In right $\triangle PTQ$, $PQ^2 = PT^2 + QT^2 = RT^2 + PR^2 + QT^2.$
So $PQ^2 = (x_2 - x_1)^2 + (y_2 - y_1)^2 + (z_2 - z_1)^2.$

The formula is found by taking the square root of each side.

An example of the use of three coordinates is to determine the position of an airplane relative to an airport. This position may be given as the airplane's distance east and south of the airport and its altitude above sea level.

Reading This lesson can be read independently even though many students have never worked with three-dimensional graphing before. Encourage students to summarize the theorems and their analogues in two dimensions and to make sure they can justify the calculations given in the Examples.

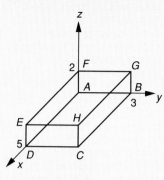
Example 2 Find the distance between points P and Q, where $P = (-5, 2, 1)$ and $Q = (4, 0, -3)$.

Solution   Let $P = (-5, 2, 1) = (x_1, y_1, z_1)$
and let $Q = (4, 0, -3) = (x_2, y_2, z_2)$.
Then
$$PQ = \sqrt{(x_2 - x_1)^2 + (y_2 - y_1)^2 + (z_2 - z_1)^2}$$
$$= \sqrt{(4 - -5)^2 + (0 - 2)^2 + (-3 - 1)^2}$$
$$= \sqrt{81 + 4 + 16}$$
$$= \sqrt{101}$$
$$\approx 10.05 \text{ units.}$$

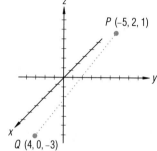

The Distance Formula for Three Dimensions helps to answer the question: What is the length of the diagonal of a box? A box with dimensions a, b, and c is conveniently located below with its edges on the axes, one endpoint of the diagonal at the origin, the other at (a, b, c).

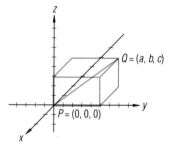

Simply find PQ.

$$PQ = \sqrt{(a - 0)^2 + (b - 0)^2 + (c - 0)^2}$$
$$= \sqrt{a^2 + b^2 + c^2}$$

This proves the following formula.

Diagonal of a Box Formula:

In a box with dimensions a, b, and c, the length of the diagonal is
$$\sqrt{a^2 + b^2 + c^2}.$$

552

In Lesson 11-3, the equation for the circle with center (h, k) and radius r was given as $(x - h)^2 + (y - k)^2 = r^2$. The three-dimensional counterpart to the circle is the sphere. An equation for the sphere is analogous to the equation for a circle.

Theorem (Equation for a Sphere):

The sphere with center (h, k, j) and radius r is the set of points (x, y, z) satisfying

$$(x - h)^2 + (y - k)^2 + (z - j)^2 = r^2.$$

Proof

Since r is the radius, by the definition of sphere, the distance from (h, k, j) to (x, y, z) is r. That distance is given by the Distance Formula for Three Dimensions:

$$\sqrt{(x - h)^2 + (y - k)^2 + (z - j)^2} = r.$$

Squaring both sides results in the theorem.

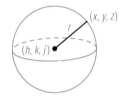

Example 3 Find an equation for the sphere with center $(3, 0, -1)$ and radius 8.

Solution Here $(h, k, j) = (3, 0, -1)$. So $h = 3$, $k = 0$, and $j = -1$.
Also, $r = 8$. Substitute into the equation for a sphere.
$$(x - 3)^2 + (y - 0)^2 + (z - -1)^2 = 8^2$$
Simplify: $(x - 3)^2 + y^2 + (z + 1)^2 = 64$ is the desired equation.

Finally, the Midpoint Formula adapts easily to three dimensions.

Midpoint Formula in Three Dimensions:

If a segment has endpoints (a, b, c) and (d, e, f), then its midpoint is

$$\left(\frac{a + d}{2}, \frac{b + e}{2}, \frac{c + f}{2}\right).$$

You can verify the Midpoint Formula in Three Dimensions by calculating the distances between the endpoints and the midpoint, just as in two dimensions.

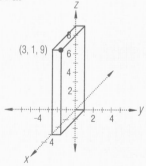

Covering the Reading

1. Any point in three dimensions can be located with an ordered __?__.
   triple
2. *True* or *false*? The intersection of two walls and the floor of a room can represent the origin of a coordinate system in three dimensions.
   True
3. Draw a coordinate system and plot the points $B = (7, -1, -3)$ and $C = (0, -6, 1)$. See margin.

4. Find PQ where $P = (3, 7, -2)$ and $Q = (5, -11, 0)$.
   $\sqrt{332} \approx 18.22$ units
5. In the box pictured below, calculate CF. $\sqrt{227} \approx 15.07$ units

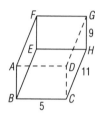

6. Find an equation for the sphere with center $(-5, 3, -10)$ and radius 13.
   $(x + 5)^2 + (y - 3)^2 + (z + 10)^2 = 169$
7. Refer to Question 4. Find the midpoint of $\overline{PQ}$. (4, -2, -1)

8. Given the equation
   $$(x - 18)^2 + (y - 5)^2 + (z + 11)^2 = 36.$$
   a. Where is the center of the sphere? (18, 5, -11)
   b. What is the radius of the sphere? 6
   c. Give the coordinates of two points on the sphere.
      samples: (12, 5, -11) and (18, 11, -11)

Applying the Mathematics

9. A box has the following vertices: the origin, $(0, 1, 0)$, $(3, 0, 0)$, $(3, 1, 0)$, $(3, 1, 9)$, $(3, 0, 9)$, $(0, 0, 9)$, and $(0, 1, 9)$.
   a. Draw the box on a 3-dimensional coordinate system. See margin.
   b. Determine its volume. 27 units^3

10. In the rectangular box below, $D = (10, 1, 2)$ and F is the origin.
    a. Find the coordinates of points A, B, C, E, G, and H. See below.
    b. Determine the volume of the box. 20 units^3
    c. Determine its surface area. 64 units^2

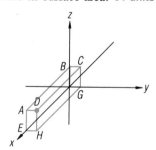

a) $A = (10,0,2)$, $B = (0,0,2)$, $C = (0,1,2)$, $E = (10,0,0)$, $G = (0,1,0)$, $H = (10,1,0)$

In 11 and 12, triangle *ABC* has vertices *A* = (2, -1, 7), *B* = (4, 0, -5), and *C* = (-11, 8, 2).

11. Find the perimeter of △*ABC*. $\sqrt{149} + \sqrt{338} + \sqrt{275} \approx 47.17$

12. Find the midpoints of all the sides. $\overline{AB}$: (3, -.5, 1); $\overline{BC}$: (-3.5, 4, -1.5); $\overline{AC}$: (-4.5, 3.5, 4.5)

13. What is the length of the longest thin cylindrical tube that can be carried in a 20″ × 40″ × 5″ carrying case? 45 inches

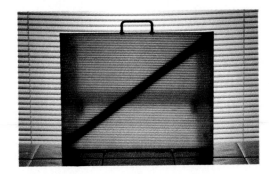

14. Find an equation for the sphere below with center (0, 0, 0).
$x^2 + y^2 + z^2 = 25$

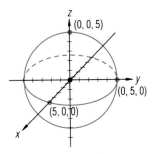

(0, 0, 5)
(0, 5, 0)
(5, 0, 0)

Review

15. A right triangle has sides of lengths 12, 16, and 20. To study this triangle on a coordinate plane, where would be a convenient place to locate its vertices? *(Lesson 11-5)*
(0, 0), (12, 0) and (0, 16) or (0, 0), (0, 12) and (16, 0)

16. a. The figure below is a(n) __?__. trapezoid
b. Use this figure to complete the sentence and prove: The segment joining the midpoints of the non-base sides of a(n) __?__ is parallel to the bases. *(Lessons 11-5, 5-2)*
trapezoid; See margin.

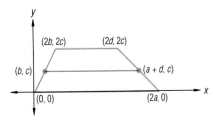

(2b, 2c)   (2d, 2c)
(b, c)   (a + d, c)
(0, 0)   (2a, 0)

Question 14: Ask students to find any lattice points on this sphere other than the three given. (There are many: the other points of intersection with the axes, (-5, 0, 0), (0, -5, 0), and (0, 0, -5), and also many points like (3, 4, 0) and (0, -3, 4).)

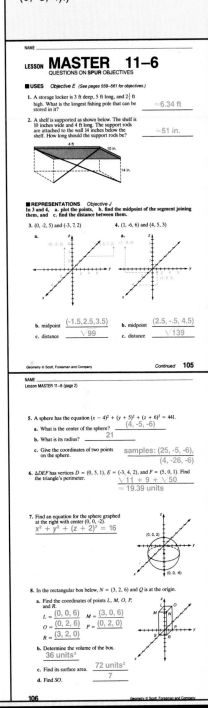

Question 17: This proof is meant to be done as a synthetic proof, but it uses a theorem proved with the aid of coordinates.

Error Analysis for Question 19: It may have been a while since students have seen the word *median*. Remind them that there is a glossary and an index at the back of the book which can be helpful in remembering the meanings of forgotten terms. The general theorem for triangular regions is that the center of gravity is at the point of concurrency of the three medians of the triangle.

FOLLOW-UP

MORE PRACTICE
For more questions on SPUR Objectives, use *Lesson Master 11-6*, shown on page 555.

EXTENSION
Students can explore plotting polyhedra in three dimensions. Ask them to first draw and then plot a tetrahedron, a cube (a hexahedron), and an octahedron.

EVALUATION
Alternative Assessment
You might bring closure to the chapter by having students make a summary list of all the theorems and formulas in the chapter. They should pay careful attention to the analogous two and three-dimensional formulas and be able to give an example of each.

ADDITIONAL ANSWERS
17.

Conclusions	Justifications
1. $\overline{PL} \parallel \overline{MN}$	Midpoint Connector Thm.
2. $\angle QLP \cong$ $\angle QNM$	$\parallel$ lines $\Rightarrow$ corr. $\angle$s =

In 17 and 18, use the figure below. P and L are the midpoints of $\overline{QM}$ and $\overline{QN}$. *(Lesson 11-5)*

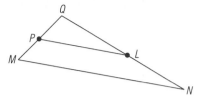

17. Prove: $\angle QLP \cong \angle QNM$. **See margin.**

18. If $QL = 3x$, $PL = 2x + 1$, and $QM = 4x$, find the perimeter of $\triangle QMN$. **14x + 2**

19. Below, $\overline{AD}$ is a median of $\triangle ABC$.
   a. Find the coordinates of D. **(14, 5)**
   b. Calculate the length of $\overline{AD}$. **$\sqrt{109} \approx$ 10.44 units**
   c. *True* or *false*? The center of gravity of triangular region ABC is on $\overline{AD}$. *(Lesson 11-4)* **True**

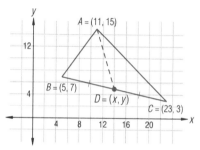

20. A triangle has vertices $(4, -7)$, $(-12, 5)$, and $(9, -7)$. Find its perimeter. *(Lesson 11-2)* **25 + $\sqrt{585} \approx$ 49.19 units**

21. Find the intersection of the lines with equations $5x - 2y = 15$ and $y = 6$. *(Lesson 11-1, Previous course)* **(5.4, 6)**

Exploration

22. Set up a coordinate system in your bedroom or classroom and determine the coordinates of the lights and windows.
   Answers will vary.

23. What is a hypersphere? What is a hypercube? **See below.**

---

23. A hypersphere is all points that are a given distance from a given point in four dimensions. A hypercube is a four-dimensional cube.

556

Summary

In coordinate geometry, figures are described by equations or by giving coordinates of key points. To deduce a general property of a polygon using coordinates, it is efficient to place the polygon in a convenient location on the coordinate plane. Either the figure is placed with one vertex at the origin and one or more sides on axes, or the figure is placed so that it is symmetric to the x-axis or y-axis.

Three formulas are involved in the coordinate proofs of this chapter. Let (a, b) and (c, d) be two points. The slope of the line through them, $\frac{d-b}{c-a}$, gives a way of telling whether this line is perpendicular or parallel to another. The distance between these points, deduced using the Pythagorean Theorem, is $\sqrt{(c-a)^2 + (d-b)^2}$. This gives a way to tell whether segments are congruent. The midpoint of the segment joining the points is $\left(\frac{a+c}{2}, \frac{b+d}{2}\right)$. Many theorems about triangles and quadrilaterals which involve midpoints can be deduced using the Midpoint Formula.

Just as there are equations for lines, there are equations for circles. An equation for the circle with center (h, k) and radius r is
$$(x - h)^2 + (y - k)^2 = r^2.$$
A coordinate geometry of three dimensions can be built by extending the two-dimensional coordinate system. An ordered pair becomes an ordered triple. The equation for a circle has an analogous equation for a sphere. The Distance Formula and the Midpoint Formula have their three-dimensional counterparts. Many properties of three-dimensional figures can be deduced using three-dimensional coordinates. One example given in this chapter was the formula for the length of a diagonal of a box.

Vocabulary

Below are the most important terms and phrases for this chapter.
For these terms you should be able to give a general description and a specific example of each.

Lesson 11-1
coordinate geometry
analytic geometry

Lesson 11-2
Distance Formula

Lesson 11-3
equation for a circle

Lesson 11-4
mean
center of gravity
Midpoint Formula

Lesson 11-5
Midpoint Connector Theorem

Lesson 11-6
three-dimensional coordinate
   system
ordered triple, z-coordinate
x-axis, y-axis, z-axis
Distance Formula in Three
   Dimensions
Diagonal of a Box Formula
equation for a sphere
Midpoint Formula in Three
   Dimensions

ADDITIONAL ANSWERS FOR PROGRESS SELF-TEST

3. $10 + \sqrt{80} \approx 18.94$ units

5. a. $(-1, 9)$
   b. $r = 5$
   c. sample: $(4, 9)$

7. $\sqrt{11817} \approx 108.7$ miles

8. $E = (11, 8)$; $I = (13, 4)$; $O = (5, 0)$; $U = (3, 4)$

9. Slope of $\overline{EU} = \frac{1}{2}$, slope of $\overline{EI} = -2$, slope of $\overline{IO} = \frac{1}{2}$, slope of $\overline{OU} = -2$.
From the Perpendicular Lines and Slopes Theorem, $\overline{EU} \perp \overline{EI}$, $\overline{EI} \perp \overline{IO}$, $\overline{IO} \perp \overline{OU}$, and $\overline{OU} \perp \overline{EU}$, so by the definition of rectangle (sufficient condition) $EIOU$ is a rectangle.

12. $x^2 + (y + 19)^2 + (z - 4)^2 = 36$

14. midpoint of $\overline{XZ} = (\frac{2a + 2b}{2}, \frac{0 + 2c}{2}) = (a + b, c)$
midpoint of $\overline{YW} = (\frac{2a + 2b + 0}{2}, \frac{2c + 0}{2}) = (a + b, c)$

557

Whereas end-of-chapter materials may be considered optional in some texts, they should not be considered optional in UCSMP *Geometry*. The Progress Self-Test provides the opportunity for feedback and correction; the Chapter Review provides additional opportunities for practice. It is at this point that the material "gels" for many students, allowing them to solidify skills and concepts before a test. In general, student performance is markedly improved after these pages.

USING THE PROGRESS SELF-TEST
Assign the Progress Self-Test as a one-night assignment. Worked-out *solutions* for all questions are in the Selected Answers section of the student text. Encourage students to take the Progress Self-Test honestly, grade themselves, and then be prepared to discuss the test in class.

Advise students to pay special attention to those Chapter Review questions (pages 559-561) which correspond to questions missed on the Progress Self-Test. A chart provided with the Selected Answers keys the Progress Self-Test questions to the lettered SPUR Objectives in the Chapter Review or to the Vocabulary. It also keys the questions to the corresponding lessons where the material is covered.

ADDITIONAL ANSWERS
1. $\overline{DF} \parallel \overline{BE}$ by the Midpoint Connector Theorem; $\overline{EF} \parallel \overline{BD}$ by the Midpoint Connector Theorem. By the definition of a parallelogram (meaning), *BDFE* is a parallelogram.

2. $AE = EB = DF = 5.5$; $EF = BD = DC = 11.15$

3., 5., 7., 8., 9., 12., 14. See the margin on p. 557.

Progress Self-Test

See margin for answers not shown below.

Directions: Take this test as you would take a test in class. Use a ruler and calculator. Then check your work with the solutions in the Selected Answers section in the back of the book.

In 1 and 2, *D, E,* and *F* are midpoints of the sides of $\triangle ABC$ below.

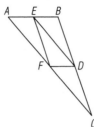

1. Explain why *BDFE* is a parallelogram.
2. If $AB = 11$ and $BC = 22.3$, find as many other lengths as you can.

3. Let $R = (3, 4)$, $S = (8, 4)$, and $T = (11, 8)$. Find the perimeter of $\triangle RST$.

4. What are the coordinates of the center of gravity of the vertices of the figure graphed below? **(1.6, 0)**

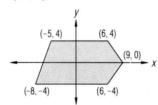

5. For the circle with equation $(x + 1)^2 + (y - 9)^2 = 25$, determine
   a. the center, **b.** the radius, and
   c. one point on the circle.

6. *Multiple choice.* Quadrilateral *ABCD* has coordinates $A = (3, 6)$, $B = (7, 9)$, $C = (13, 1)$, and $D = (9, -2)$. Most specifically, *ABCD* is a
   (a) rectangle   (b) rhombus
   (c) kite   (d) square. **(a)**

7. Selkirk, Kansas, does not have a local airport. The nearest airports are in Goodland, about 60 miles north and 12 miles west of Selkirk, and in Garden City, about 36 miles south and 39 miles east of Selkirk. What is the flying distance from Goodland to Garden City?

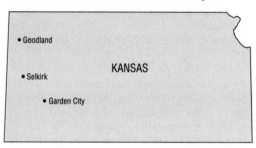

In 8 and 9, a rhombus *RHMB* is located on the coordinate system below. *E, I, O,* and *U* are midpoints of the sides.

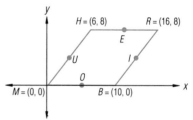

8. Give the coordinates of *E, I, O,* and *U*.
9. Prove: *EIOU* is a rectangle.

10. Give convenient coordinates for the vertices of a trapezoid. **(0, 0), (a, 0), (b, c), and (d, c)**

11. Find *PQ* where $P = (3, -1, 8)$ and $Q = (-4, 9, 0)$. $\sqrt{213} \approx$ **14.59 units**

12. What is an equation for a sphere with center $(0, -19, 4)$ and radius 6?

13. Find the point of intersection of the lines $2x - 3y = 8$ and $4x - 5y = 20$. **(10, 4)**

14. Prove that the diagonals of the quadrilateral below have the same midpoint.

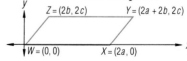

558

Chapter Review

Questions on **SPUR** Objectives

SPUR stands for **S**kills, **P**roperties, **U**ses, and **R**epresentations. The Chapter Review questions are grouped according to the SPUR Objectives for this chapter.

SKILLS deal with the procedures used to get answers.

There are no objectives for skills in this chapter.

PROPERTIES deal with the principles behind the mathematics.

■ **Objective A:** *Using coordinates in individual figures, prove that segments in them are congruent, perpendicular, or parallel.*
(Lessons 11-1, 11-2)

1. Prove that the triangle with vertices $A = (11, 2)$, $B = (23, 1)$, and $C = (2, 10)$ is isosceles.

2. Prove that the triangle with vertices $X = (q, 0)$, $Y = (0, q)$, and $Z = (2q, 3q)$ is a right triangle.

3. Determine whether the quadrilateral with vertices $A = (0, 5)$, $B = (0, 1)$, $C = (7, 4)$, and $D = (7, 9)$ is a trapezoid or kite. **trapezoid**

4. Prove that $X = (-1, 10)$, $Y = (6, 8)$, $Z = (3, -2)$, and $W = (-4, 0)$ are vertices of a parallelogram.

■ **Objective B:** *Using coordinates, prove theorems involving parallel or perpendicular sides, congruent segments, midpoints, or combinations of these in triangles and quadrilaterals.*
(Lessons 11-1, 11-2, 11-4, 11-5)

5. Prove that the four segments joining consecutive midpoints of the rectangle below all have the same length.

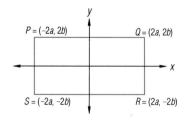

6. Prove that both pairs of opposite sides of the parallelogram below have the same length.

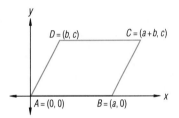

7. Prove that the diagonals of the square below are perpendicular to each other.

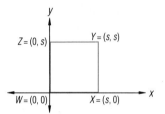

8. Use the figure below to prove that any isosceles triangle has two medians of the same length.

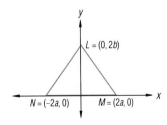

CHAPTER REVIEW

The main objectives for the chapter are organized here into sections corresponding to the four main types of understanding this book promotes: Skills, Properties, Uses, and Representations. We call these the SPUR objectives.

The four types of understanding are not in increasing order of difficulty. There may be hard skills and easy representations; some uses may be easier than anything else; and so on.

You may be surprised to see no objectives for skills in this chapter. This is because we view the algebra of coordinate geometry *in a geometry class* as a representation of the geometry. Objective K is appropriately classified as a skill in algebra but as a representation in geometry.

USING THE CHAPTER REVIEW
Students should be able to answer questions like these with about 85% accuracy by the end of the chapter.

You may assign these questions over a single night to help students prepare for a test the next day, or you may assign the questions over a two-day period.

If you assign the questions over two days, then we recommend assigning the *evens* for homework the first night so that students get feedback in class the next day. Then

Objective C: *Apply the Midpoint Connector Theorem. (Lesson 11-5)*

In 9 and 10, *W* and *Y* are midpoints of $\overline{XV}$ and $\overline{XZ}$ in the figure below.

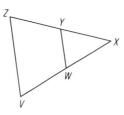

9. If *YW* = 40 and *WV* = 41, what other lengths can be determined? **WX = 41, VX = 82, VZ = 80**

10. Prove: $m\angle XWY = m\angle XVZ$.

In 11 and 12, *ABCD* below is a rhombus. *F* and *E* are midpoints of sides $\overline{BC}$ and $\overline{CD}$.

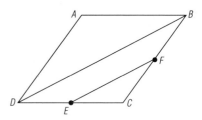

11. Explain why *BDEF* is a trapezoid.

12. If *BD* = 10 and *BC* = 6, find the lengths of as many other segments as possible. **EF = 5, DC = AB = AD = 6, DE = EC = CF = BF = 3**

USES deal with applications of mathematics in real situations.

Objective D: *Determine the center of gravity of a segment or a set of points. (Lesson 11-4)*

13. Think of the region below as a very thin sheet of metal with no weight except at its vertices. Find the center of gravity of its vertices. **(0, -1.2)**

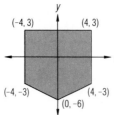

14. Locate the center of gravity of the vertices of this 3–4–5 right triangular region. **($\frac{4}{3}$, 1)**

15. Where is the center of gravity of a segment located? **at its midpoint**

16. A meter stick is shortened by cutting it at a point 8 centimeters from one end and 3 centimeters from the other. What is the reading at the point on which the new stick balances? **47.5 or 52.5 (depending on which piece was cut from each end)**

Objective E: *Apply the distance and diagonal of a box formulas in real situations. (Lessons 11-2, 11-6)*

17. A car drives 5 miles north, 2 miles east, then another 6 miles north, and another 3 miles east. By plane, how far is the car from its starting point? $\sqrt{146} \approx$ **12.1 miles**

18. A ship is located 2.3 km south and 1.4 km west of a lighthouse. Another ship is 1.6 km south and 0.8 km east of the lighthouse.
   a. Draw a picture of this situation.
   b. Calculate the distance between the ships.

19. A storage niche is 8 inches by 12 inches by 24 inches. What is the longest dowel rod that can fit in it? **28 inches**

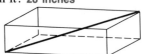

20. A wooden crate is 45 mm by 30 mm by 80 mm. What is the length of the longest straw that will fit in it? $\sqrt{9325} \approx$ **96.6 mm**

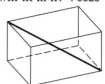

REPRESENTATIONS deal with pictures, graphs, or objects that illustrate concepts.

■ **Objective F:** *Determine the distance between two points in the coordinate plane.* *(Lesson 11-2)*

21. Calculate the distance between $(3, -5)$ and $(-7, -1)$. **$\sqrt{136} \approx 11.66$ units**

22. What is the distance between (a, b) and the origin? **$\sqrt{a^2 + b^2}$**

23. A triangle has vertices $(3, 2)$, $(3, 7)$, and $(6, 11)$. What is its perimeter?

24. What is the length of the longest side of trapezoid $ABCD$ if $A = (0, 0)$, $B = (3, 0)$, $C = (10, 1)$, and $D = (6, 1)$? **$\sqrt{50} \approx 7.07$ units**

■ **Objective G:** *Write an equation for a circle given its center and radius, and vice versa.* *(Lesson 11-3)*

25. What is an equation for the circle with center $(8, -1)$ and radius 15? **$(x - 8)^2 + (y + 1)^2 = 225$**

26. The circle has center at $(0, 6)$. What is an equation for it?
$x^2 + (y - 6)^2 = 16$

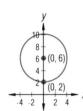

In 27 and 28, determine **a.** the center, **b.** the radius, and **c.** one point on the circle with the given equation. **a) (6, -3); b) 13; c) sample: (19, -3)**

27. $(x - 6)^2 + (y + 3)^2 = 169$

28. $x^2 + y^2 = 50$
a) (0, 0); b) $\sqrt{50} \approx 7.07$; c) sample: (5, 5)

In 29 and 30 graph.

29. $(x + 1)^2 + (y - 4)^2 = 9$

30. $x^2 + (y + 2)^2 = 1$

■ **Objective H:** *Determine the coordinates of the midpoint of a segment in the coordinate plane.* *(Lesson 11-4)*

31. Give the coordinates of the midpoint of the segment joining $(3, 2)$ and $(6, -2)$. **(4.5, 0)**

32. Give the coordinates of the midpoint of the segment joining $(2a, 2b)$ and $(0, 2c)$. **(a, b + c)**

33. Give the slope of the segment connecting the origin to the midpoint of the segment with endpoints $(50, -10)$ and $(60, 70)$. **$\frac{30}{55} = \frac{6}{11}$**

34. Let $A = (3, 0)$, $B = (4, 5)$, and $C = (9, 8)$. Find the length of the segment connecting B to the midpoint of $\overline{AC}$. **$\sqrt{5} \approx 2.24$ units**

■ **Objective I:** *Give convenient locations for triangles and quadrilaterals in the coordinate plane.* *(Lesson 11-5)*

35. Give convenient coordinates of a rectangle placed on the coordinate plane so that it is symmetric to both the x-axis and the y-axis.

36. Give convenient coordinates for the vertices of an isosceles triangle. **(0, 0), (2a, 0), (a, b)**

37. Three consecutive vertices of a parallelogram are $(17, 5)$, $(0, 0)$, and $(8, 0)$. What is the fourth vertex? **(25, 5)**

38. Give convenient coordinates for the vertices of a kite with diagonals of lengths 30 and 48 if the other diagonal divides the symmetry diagonal in pieces of length 20 and 28.
(15, 0), (0, 20), (-15, 0), (0, -28) or (15, 0), (0, 28), (-15, 0), (0, -20)

■ **Objective J:** *Apply coordinate geometry in three dimensions.* *(Lesson 11-6)*

In 39 and 40, **a.** draw a coordinate system and plot the points. **b.** Find the midpoint of the segment joining them. **c.** Find the distance between them.

39. $P = (-2, 3, 6)$ and $Q = (0, -5, 1)$

40. $R = (13, -5, 8)$ and $S = (0, 16, -3)$

41. Find an equation for the sphere with center $(4, -3, 0)$ and radius 10.

42. Find the center and radius of the sphere $(x - 1)^2 + (y + 2)^2 + (z - 5)^2 = 4$.
center: (1, -2, 5), radius: 2

■ **Objective K:** *Find the point of intersection of two lines in the coordinate plane.*
(Lesson 11-1, Previous course)

In 43–45, find the point of intersection of the lines by solving a system.

43. $\begin{cases} 2x + y = 5 \\ -x - 5y = 11 \end{cases}$ **(4, -3)**

44. $\begin{cases} x + y = 180 \\ x - y = 25 \end{cases}$ **(102.5, 77.5)**

45. $\begin{cases} y - 3x = 8 \\ x = 7 \end{cases}$ **(7, 29)**

EVALUATION
Three tests are provided for this chapter in the Teacher's Resource File. Chapter 11 Test, Forms A and B cover just Chapter 11. The third test is Chapter 11 Test, Cumulative Form. About 50% of this test covers Chapter 11, 25% covers Chapter 10, and 25% covers previous chapters. For information on grading, see *General Teaching Suggestions: Grading* on page T44 in the Teacher's Edition.

ASSIGNMENT RECOMMENDATION
We strongly recommend that you assign the reading and questions from Lesson 12-1 for homework the evening of the test. It gives students work to do if they complete the test before the end of the period and keeps the class moving.

8. Let G and H be the midpoints of $\overline{LM}$ and $\overline{LN}$. $G = (a, b)$, $H = (-a, b)$. $GN = \sqrt{(-2a - a)^2 + (0 - b)^2} = \sqrt{(-3a)^2 + (-b)^2} = \sqrt{9a^2 + b^2}$; $HM = \sqrt{(2a - -a)^2 + (0 - b)^2} = \sqrt{(3a)^2 + (-b)^2} = \sqrt{9a^2 + b^2}$; so $GN = HM$.

10. From the Midpoint Connector Theorem, $\overline{WY} \parallel \overline{VZ}$. Thus, m$\angle XWY =$ m$\angle XVZ$ by $\parallel$ lines $\Rightarrow$ corr. $\angle$s =.

11. Applying the Midpoint Connector Theorem to $\triangle BCD$, $\overline{EF} \parallel \overline{DB}$. Thus, $BDEF$ is a trapezoid by the definition of trapezoid (sufficient condition).

18., 29., 30., 39., 40. See Additional Answers in the back of this book.

23. $10 + \sqrt{90} \approx 19.49$ units

35. (a, b), $(a, -b)$, $(-a, -b)$, $(-a, b)$

41. $(x - 4)^2 + (y + 3)^2 + z^2 = 100$

CHAPTER 12 ■ SIMILARITY

DAILY PACING CHART ■ CHAPTER 12

Every chapter of UCSMP *Geometry* includes lessons, a Progress Self-Test, and a Chapter Review. For optimal student performance, the Self-Test and Review should be covered. (See *General Teaching Suggestions: Mastery* on page T36 of the Teacher's Edition.) By following the pace of the Full Course given here, students can complete the entire text by the end of the year. Students following the pace of the Minimal Course spend more time when there are quizzes and on the Chapter Review and will generally not complete all of the chapters in this text.

When all lessons are covered from the beginning (the recommendation of the authors), then students in the Minimal Course can cover through Lesson 13-4 and will cover all they need for future courses. For more information on pacing, see *General Teaching Suggestions: Pace* on page T35 of the Teacher's Edition.

DAY	MINIMAL COURSE	FULL COURSE
1	12-1	12-1
2	12-2	12-2
3	12-3	12-3
4	Quiz (TRF); Start 12-4.	Quiz (TRF); 12-4
5	Finish 12-4.	12-5
6	12-5	12-6
7	12-6	12-7
8	12-7	Quiz (TRF); 12-8
9	Quiz (TRF); Start 12-8.	12-9
10	Finish 12-8.	12-10
11	12-9	Progress Self-Test
12	12-10	Chapter Review
13	Progress Self-Test	Chapter Test (TRF)
14	Chapter Review	Comprehensive Test (TRF)
15	Chapter Review	
16	Chapter Test (TRF)	
17	Comprehensive Test (TRF)	

TESTING OPTIONS
■ Quiz for Lessons 12-1 Through 12-3 ■ Chapter 12 Test, Form A ■ Chapter 12 Test, Cumulative Form
■ Quiz for Lessons 12-4 Through 12-7 ■ Chapter 12 Test, Form B ■ Comprehensive Test, Chapters 1-12

PROVIDING FOR INDIVIDUAL DIFFERENCES
The student text has been written for, and tested with, average students. It also has been used successfully with better and more poorly prepared students.

The Lesson Notes often include Error Analysis and Alternate Approach features to help you with those students who need more help. A blackline Lesson Master (in the Teacher's Resource File), keyed to the chapter objectives, is provided for each lesson to allow more practice. (However, since it is very important to keep up with the daily pace, you are not expected to use all of these masters. Again, refer to the suggestions for pacing on page T35.) Extension activities are provided in the Lesson Notes for those students who have completed the particular lesson in a shorter amount of time than is expected, even in the Full Course.

OBJECTIVES ■ CHAPTER 12

The objectives listed here are the same as in the Chapter 12 Review on pages 624-627 of the student text. The Progress Self-Test on pages 622-623 and the tests in the Teacher's Resource File cover these objectives. For recommendations regarding the handling of this end-of-chapter material, see the notes in the margin on the corresponding pages of the Teacher's Edition.

OBJECTIVES FOR CHAPTER 12 (Organized into the SPUR Categories—Skills, Properties, Uses, and Representations)	Progress Self-Test Questions	Chapter Review Questions	Lesson Master from Teacher's Resource File*
SKILLS			
A Draw size transformation images of figures.	1, 2	1 through 5	12-2, 12-3
B Find the lengths in figures by applying the Side-Splitting Theorem and the Side-Splitting Converse.	6-8	6 through 10	12-10
C Find angle measures, lengths, perimeters, areas, and volumes in similar figures.	10, 11	11 through 18	12-5, 12-6
PROPERTIES			
D Recognize and apply properties of size transformations and similar figures.	3, 4, 12	19 through 24	12-2, 12-3, 12-5, 12-6, 12-7
E Given a true proportion, find other true proportions with the same terms.	9	25 through 28	12-4
F Determine whether or not triangles are similar using the AA, SAS, or SSS Similarity Theorems.	14, 15	29 through 33	12-8, 12-9
USES			
G Identify and determine proportional lengths and distances in real situations.	16-18	34 through 39	12-4, 12-5, 12-10
H Apply the Fundamental Theorem of Similarity in real situations.	13, 19	40 through 45	12-6, 12-7
REPRESENTATIONS			
I Use the definition of size transformations for figures on the coordinate plane.	20	46 through 50	12-1

*The masters are numbered to match the lessons.

562B

OVERVIEW ■ CHAPTER 12

If a few students are asked to draw a 3-4-5 right triangle, they will not necessarily draw congruent triangles, but they will draw similar triangles, and all the formulas and relationships they have learned will apply in these similar figures. Thus, Euclidean geometry can be thought of as the study of similar figures.

With the use of transformations, similarity becomes analogous to congruence. In place of reflections, a new type of transformation, the *size change* or *size transformation,* is utilized. Lesson 12-1 introduces this transformation on the coordinate plane and deduces two of its properties. Lesson 12-2 shows students how to do size changes without coordinates. The properties of these transformations are summarized in Lesson 12-3. The preser-

vation properties of size changes are like those of reflections, except that they multiply distances by a constant amount. The result is that the ratios of lengths of images and their preimages are equal, forming proportions. Solving proportions is reviewed in Lesson 12-4.

Students are ready for a formal definition of similarity by Lesson 12-5. Given the definition, there can be similar figures of any type. Lesson 12-6 covers what may be the most important theorem in geometry, the Fundamental Theorem of Similarity. This theorem gives the relations between ratios of volumes, areas, perimeters, and lengths in similar figures. A very nice application of this theorem is presented in Lesson 12-7. The application explains why there cannot

be humans twice the height of normal humans. Many students do not understand Lesson 12-6 until they encounter this concrete application.

From the definition of similar figures, criteria also can be developed for the existence of similar triangles. The SSS Similarity Theorem is deduced and used in Lesson 12-8, and the AA and SAS Similarity Theorems are discussed in Lesson 12-9. In Lesson 12-10, the AA Similarity Theorem is applied to prove the Side-Splitting Theorem, namely that a line parallel to a side of a triangle splits the other two sides proportionally.

Students who have studied UCSMP *Transition Mathematics* or UCSMP *Algebra* will have had size changes and will have studied proportions in similar figures.

PERSPECTIVES ■ CHAPTER 12

The Perspectives provide the rationale for the inclusion of topics or approaches, provide mathematical background, and make connections with other lessons and within UCSMP.

12-1

SIZE CHANGES ON A COORDINATE PLANE

Outside of mathematics, there are two common paper-and-pencil methods for changing the size of a figure (perhaps for artwork or for the design of a product). One method is to draw a grid of squares over the figure, then draw another grid of different-size squares, and finally to work in the second grid, making the figure in each new square the appropriate size. The second method is to project the first figure onto a wall or other flat surface and trace the image.

The work of this lesson and the next one is related to these two methods. In this lesson, the transformation which maps (x, y) onto

(kx, ky) is considered. This transformation is the size change of magnitude k with center $(0, 0)$. However, it is not called a size change; it is called S_k and students are asked to explore its properties.

The advantage of using coordinates is the ease with which sizes of figures can be changed and the speed with which certain properties can be deduced. Proved in this lesson is the fact that under S_k, distances between images are k times distances between corresponding preimages. This is the fundamental property of size changes, and S_k could be thought of as multiplying the lengths of sides of the squares in the grid by a factor of k. Also deduced is that a line is parallel to its image.

12-2

SIZE CHANGES WITHOUT COORDINATES

The disadvantage of using coordinates is that often figures are not given on a coordinate plane. Thus, in this lesson, a synthetic formal definition of the size change with center P and magnitude k is given. Students are expected to draw images of figures without the use of coordinates.

Then it is proved that the transformation S_k, studied in the preceding lesson, is such a size change. Since any point can be the origin of a coordinate system, the properties of S_k deduced in Lesson 12-1 apply to all size changes. This is verified in the drawings students have made.

12-3
PROPERTIES OF SIZE CHANGES

The Size Change Distance Theorem implies that size changes do not preserve distance. It is surprising to many students that size changes preserve all of the other properties that were preserved by reflections, namely collinearity, betweenness, and angle measure. This lesson deduces the properties of size changes and gives students the opportunity to apply them to drawing images of figures.

12-4
PROPORTIONS

This lesson is a review of the algebra needed to solve proportions which arise when size changes and similar figures are present. The Means-Extremes Property is deduced and various ways of rewriting proportions are given.

12-5
SIMILAR FIGURES

Two figures are defined to be *similar* if one can be mapped onto the other by a composite of size transformations and reflections. This is a perfect analogue to the definition of congruent figures and is a definition that applies to all figures.

The properties of similar figures come immediately from the properties of size changes and reflections. In similar figures, corresponding distances are proportional and corresponding angles have the same measure.

12-6
THE FUNDAMENTAL THEOREM OF SIMILARITY

The theorem states that in similar figures with ratio of similitude k, (1) corresponding distances are in the ratio k, (2) corresponding areas are in the ratio k^2, and (3) corresponding volumes are in the ratio k^3. The theorem is not covered in some geometry courses, because it requires a knowledge of similarity, perimeter, area, and volume, all topics which may be encountered late in the school year. It is placed earlier in this book so that it can be covered during the school year.

12-7
CAN THERE BE GIANTS?

When Lesson 12-7 was first tested, it was discovered that students neither understood nor *believed* the effects of the Fundamental Theorem of Similarity until they read this lesson. The reason is that the physical and biological instances of the Fundamental Theorem of Similarity are not given accurate accounts in the media. The example of small birds eating many times their weight is often cited, as if it indicates something special. It does not because small birds have more surface area for their volume than larger birds, such as eagles and hawks, which do not consume as many times their weight in food each day as smaller birds.

As indicated in the lesson, Galileo was the first to realize that there could not be giants with the shapes of normal humans because the strength of human bones would not allow it. His discovery was the first to indicate that the shapes of animals can often be explained with mathematical arguments.

12-8
THE SSS SIMILARITY THEOREM

This lesson begins a two-lesson sequence in which three triangle similarity theorems are presented. The proofs of the similarity theorems all employ the same strategy of applying a size change to one triangle and showing that its image is congruent to the other. Students should note that the SSS Congruence Theorem is needed to prove the SSS Similarity Theorem.

12-9
THE AA AND SAS SIMILARITY THEOREMS

There is a triangle similarity theorem corresponding to every triangle congruence theorem.

Congruence	Similarity
SSS	SSS
SAS	SAS
ASA or AAS	AA
HL	HL
SsA	SsA

It is quite common for geometry books to discuss SSS, SAS, and AA, and to ignore HL and SsA, as is done in this text, because HL Similarity can be deduced by using the Pythagorean Theorem and the SSS Similarity Theorem.

12-10
THE SIDE-SPLITTING THEOREM

The theorem presented in this lesson states that if a line is parallel to a side of a triangle and intersects the other two sides in distinct points, it "splits" these sides into proportional segments. The proof of the theorem depends on similar triangles. The Side-Splitting Converse Theorem also is stated and proved in the lesson. The proofs of both theorems are generally difficult for most students to understand but should be presented in class and discussed thoroughly.

CHAPTER 12

Similarity

We recommend 14 to 17 days for this chapter: 10 to 12 on the lessons and quizzes; 1 for the Progress Self-Test; 1 or 2 for the Chapter Review; 1 for a Chapter test; and 1 for the Comprehensive Test. (See the Daily Pacing Chart on page 562A.) If you spend more than 17 days on this chapter, you are moving too slowly. Keep in mind that each lesson includes Review questions to help students firm up content studied previously.

12-1: Size Changes on a Coordinate Plane
12-2: Size Changes Without Coordinates
12-3: Properties of Size Changes
12-4: Proportions
12-5: Similar Figures

12-6: The Fundamental Theorem of Similarity
12-7: Can There Be Giants?
12-8: The SSS Similarity Theorem
12-9: The AA and SAS Similarity Theorems
12-10: The Side-Splitting Theorem

USING PAGES 562-563
The given situation illustrates how geometry can be used to analyze statistical drawings and is an important idea for consumers.

The figure for the 1980 population is about 1.35 times the height of the figure for 1970, but appears to be about twice the size because it covers 1.8 times the area and 2.5 times the volume. You might begin the discussion of this chapter with the question in the text on this page: Do you think the graph is misleading?

In 1970, the population of Saline, Michigan, was 4811. By 1980, the population had grown to 6483.

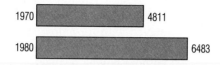

This *bar graph* depicts the change, but it has no "oomph." One way to make it more appealing is to use repetitions of congruent figures. Here each picture of a person represents 1000 people. Part of a picture is part of a thousand. The result is called a *picture graph*.

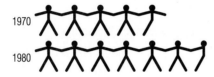

Still another way to compare data in a display is to show two figures of the same shape but of different size. The shorter figure represents the 1970 population, and the taller one represents the 1980 population. Since $\frac{6483}{4811}$ is about 1.35, the height of the 1980 figure is about 1.35 times the height of the 1970 figure.

However, the area of the 1980 figure is about $(1.35)^2 \approx 1.8$ or almost twice the area of the 1970 figure. And if these figures were three-dimensional, the volume of the 1980 figure would be about $(1.35)^3 \approx 2.5$ times the volume of the figure for 1970. Do you think the graph is misleading?

Figures with the same shape (but not necessarily the same size) are *similar figures*. The concept of *similarity* is as important in analyzing figures as the concept of congruence. In this chapter, you will learn how to draw similar figures, study their basic properties and the transformations relating them, and see a few of their many applications.

CHAPTER 12 Similarity **563**

OBJECTIVE

I Apply size transformations to figures on the coordinate plane.

TEACHING NOTES

This lesson uses coordinate methods developed in Chapter 11. The proof on pages 565-566 is difficult for some students. They may be rusty with the simplifications in part (2), and you should go over these in detail.

You may wish to review the definition of transformation and the notation used before starting this lesson. Ask students to summarize the properties of reflections and describe the result of reflecting points in the coordinate plane.

Making Connections
Students who have studied earlier UCSMP courses have encountered the transformation S_k as a picture of multiplication by k. They have seen figures on a coordinate plane; they have multiplied the coordinates by a nonzero number; and they have graphed the image. They have seen cases where k is negative (that is, rotated 180°). This shows graphically that multiplication by a negative number reverses sign. They have been introduced to the phrase *size change* as a name for this transformation. S_k is not proved to be a

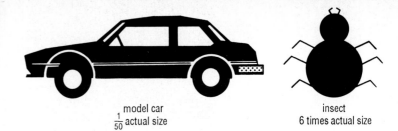

model car
$\frac{1}{50}$ actual size

insect
6 times actual size

Size Changes on a Coordinate

Figures with different sizes but the same shape are found both in fun and serious pursuits. Model planes, model cars, model trains, dolls, and doll houses can all be considered as scale models of real figures played with for enjoyment. Clothes designers, inventors, architects, and city planners use scale models to see how an object will look without having to make it actual size. Scientists magnify small things like insects or the atom, or make models of large objects like the earth or our solar system, in order to study them.

Changing the size is remarkably easy if the figure is given on a coordinate plane. You need only multiply the coordinates of every point on the figure by a fixed number.

Example 1 In pentagon *ABCDE*, *A* = (-9, 15), *B* = (-15, -6), *C* = (0, 3), *D* = (12, 0), and *E* = (3, 12). Describe the result when all coordinates of points on this figure are multiplied by $\frac{2}{3}$.

Solution First draw *ABCDE*. Then multiply the coordinates of the vertices of *ABCDE* by $\frac{2}{3}$. The resulting five image points are called *A'*, *B'*, *C'*, *D'*, and *E'* and are connected below.

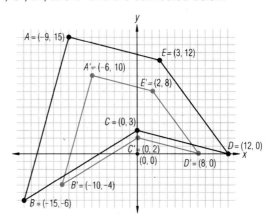

564

To describe the result, examine the preimage and the image sides closely. You could write:

(1) Image and preimage sides seem to be parallel.

(2) Image sides appear to be $\frac{2}{3}$ as long as preimage sides.

Closer examination gives something else:

(3) The image of a point is between the preimage and the origin.

Do you see anything else?

Example 1 describes a transformation in which the image of (x, y) is $(\frac{2}{3}x, \frac{2}{3}y)$. This transformation is denoted $S_{\frac{2}{3}}$. To verify the first property of $S_{\frac{2}{3}}$ found in Example 1, you could focus on a segment and its image, say $\overline{AE}$ and $\overline{A'E'}$. Using slopes, it is easy to show that $\overline{AE} \parallel \overline{A'E'}$.

$$\text{slope of } \overline{AE} = \frac{12 - 15}{3 - -9} = \frac{-3}{12} = -\frac{1}{4}$$

$$\text{slope of } \overline{A'E'} = \frac{8 - 10}{2 - -6} = \frac{-2}{8} = -\frac{1}{4}$$

Since the slopes are equal, $\overline{AE}$ and $\overline{A'E'}$ are parallel.

Now we generalize this example. The transformation which maps (x, y) onto (kx, ky) is denoted by the symbol $\mathbf{S}_k$. The number k is called the **magnitude** of $\mathbf{S}_k$. Any number but zero can be the magnitude, but in this book $k > 0$ unless otherwise stated. This transformation has many important properties, all of which can be proved using coordinate geometry. Here are two important ones.

Theorem

Let S_k be the transformation mapping (x, y) onto (kx, ky). Let $P' = S_k(P)$ and $Q' = S_k(Q)$. Then

(1) $\overleftrightarrow{P'Q'} \parallel \overleftrightarrow{PQ}$,

(2) $P'Q' = k \cdot PQ$.

Proof

Let $P = (a, b)$ and $Q = (c, d)$ be the preimages.
Then $P' = (ka, kb)$ and $Q' = (kc, kd)$.

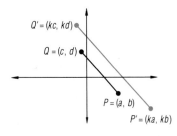

size change until the next lesson, because a definition of size change is needed first.

Alternate Approach

You might want students to do example size transformations like **Example 1** in **small groups**. Prepare several examples on a worksheet or have students make up their own examples on graph paper. Have students label the preimage points with the correct coordinates and then find the image points under S_k for $k = 1, 1.5,$ and $.5$. Have them write down their results and try to make conjectures. Other members of the groups can analyze the conjectures and summarize them for the class.

ADDITIONAL EXAMPLES

1. Let $W = (3, 0)$, $X = (5, 0)$, and $Y = (-1, 2)$.

a. Find the image $\triangle W'X'Y'$ of $\triangle WXY$ under S_3.
W' = (9, 0), X' = (15, 0), Y' = (-3, 6)

b. How many times longer than XY is $X'Y'$?
3

c. $\triangle W'X'Y'$ has how many times the area of $\triangle WXY$?
9

2. In Additional Example 1 above, deduce that $\overline{XY} \parallel \overline{X'Y'}$.

Each line has slope $-\frac{1}{3}$, so they are parallel.

NOTES ON QUESTIONS

Question 8: This question will take some time for students to do, but notice how much more vivid the idea of similarity is with a complicated figure than with triangles. Ask students to compare the lengths of the sides of the image with those of the preimage (the image is 2 times the preimage); the area of the circles on the image and preimage (the image is 4 times the preimage); and the angle measures of corresponding angles (they are equal). Thus, this one problem exemplifies many of the ideas of the chapter.

Question 10: This is an important problem in calculating scaled values and should be discussed.

Question 12: This is the first of many questions in the chapter that continues the work on triangle congruence proofs. The purpose is to help students make the connection between congruence and similarity. The two parts of the question should be part of an extended proof; that is, do not expect students to start part **b** from the beginning once they have done part **a**.

Making Connections for Question 13: The analogous theorem for size transformations is found in Lesson 12-3.

Questions 15 and 16: These questions begin a three-day review of solving algebraic proportions, in preparation for Lesson 12-4.

Question 18: In general, S_{-k} is the composite of S_k and a rotation of 180°. Notice that both S_k and S_{-k} preserve orientation.

ADDITIONAL ANSWERS

2. slope of $\overline{BC}$ =
$$\frac{-6-3}{-15-0} = \frac{-9}{-15} = \frac{3}{5};$$
slope of $\overline{B'C'}$ =
$$\frac{-4-2}{-10-0} = \frac{-6}{-10} = \frac{3}{5}$$

3.
$$BC=\sqrt{(-15-0)^2+(-6-3)^2} = \sqrt{306} = 3\sqrt{34};$$
$$B'C' = \sqrt{(-10-0)^2+(-4-2)^2} = \sqrt{136} = 2\sqrt{34} = \frac{2}{3} \cdot BC$$

5. a.

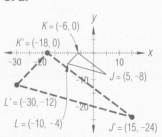

---

(1) $\overleftrightarrow{P'Q'}$ is parallel to $\overleftrightarrow{PQ}$ if the slopes are the same.

$$\text{slope of } \overleftrightarrow{P'Q'} = \frac{kd - kb}{kc - ka} = \frac{k(d - b)}{k(c - a)} = \frac{d - b}{c - a}$$

$$\text{slope of } \overleftrightarrow{PQ} = \frac{d - b}{c - a}$$

Thus $\overleftrightarrow{PQ} \parallel \overleftrightarrow{P'Q'}$.

(2) The goal is to show that $P'Q' = k \cdot PQ$.
From the Distance Formula,
$$PQ = \sqrt{(c - a)^2 + (d - b)^2}.$$
Also from the Distance Formula,

$$
\begin{aligned}
P'Q' &= \sqrt{(kc - ka)^2 + (kd - kb)^2} \\
&= \sqrt{(k(c - a))^2 + (k(d - b))^2} && \text{Distributive Property} \\
&= \sqrt{k^2(c - a)^2 + k^2(d - b)^2} && \text{Power of a Product} \\
&= \sqrt{k^2((c - a)^2 + (d - b)^2)} && \text{Distributive Property} \\
&= \sqrt{k^2} \sqrt{(c - a)^2 + (d - b)^2} && \text{Square Root of a Product} \\
&= k\sqrt{(c - a)^2 + (d - b)^2} && \text{Since } k > 0, \sqrt{k^2} = k \\
&= k \cdot PQ. && \text{Substitution}
\end{aligned}
$$

Property (2) in the theorem is verified in Example 2.

Example 2   **a.** Find the images of $M = (2, 2)$ and $N = (-1, 3)$ under S_4.
b. Verify that $M'N' = 4MN$.

Solution   It helps to draw a figure.

a. $M' = (4 \cdot 2, 4 \cdot 2) = (8, 8)$
$N' = (4 \cdot -1, 4 \cdot 3) = (-4, 12)$

Graph the preimages and images. The graph shows that the segment and its image are parallel. That is a good check that the points are correctly graphed.

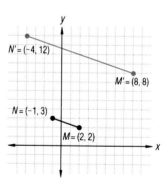

b. $M'N' = \sqrt{(8 - -4)^2 + (8 - 12)^2} = \sqrt{12^2 + (-4)^2}$
$= \sqrt{160} = \sqrt{16}\sqrt{10} = 4\sqrt{10}$
$MN = \sqrt{(2 - -1)^2 + (2 - 3)^2} = \sqrt{3^2 + (-1)^2} = \sqrt{10}$
So $M'N' = 4MN$.

Other properties of these transformations are proved in Lesson 12-3.

1. Name four occupations which use scale models.
samples: clothes designers, inventors, architects, and city planners

In 2 and 3, refer to Example 1.

2. Verify that $\overline{B'C'} \parallel \overline{BC}$ by calculating slopes. **See margin.**

3. Verify that $B'C' = \frac{2}{3}BC$ by using the Distance Formula.
See margin.

4. a. S_k is the transformation which maps (x, y) onto __?__. **(kx, ky)**
   b. k is the __?__ of S_k. **magnitude**

5. Let $J = (5, -8)$, $K = (-6, 0)$, and $L = (-10, -4)$.
   a. Graph $\triangle JKL$ and its image under S_3.
   b. Describe the result.
   See margin.

6. Let $P = (-2, 11)$ and $Q = (3, -5)$. Let $P' = S_7(P)$ and $Q' = S_7(Q)$.
   a. What are the coordinates of P' and Q'?
   b. Show that the slopes of $\overline{QP}$ and $\overline{Q'P'}$ are equal.
   c. Show that $Q'P' = 7 \cdot QP$ using the Distance Formula.
   See margin.

7. Refer to the solution of Example 1. Verify property (3) for the points O, A', and A. (Hint: calculate distances.) **See margin.**

8. An artist wished to double the dimensions of the insect shown in this lesson. So the artist traced the insect onto graph paper. (This is shown at the right.) Then the coordinates of key points on the insect were multiplied by 2 and the image drawn. Repeat what the artist did using your own paper. **See margin.**

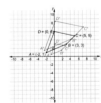

9. a. What is the image of (x, y) under S_1? **(x, y)**
   b. Describe S_1. **S₁ maps any preimage onto itself.**

10. Below is a scale drawing of the side of a cabin. If each unit on the paper is $\frac{1}{4}$ inch, and the figure is $\frac{1}{48}$ actual size, what is the height of the real cabin? **144 inches = 12 feet**

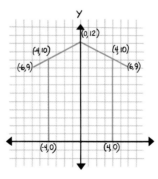

LESSON 12-1 Size Changes on a Coordinate Plane **567**

---

b. The sides of $\triangle J'K'L'$ are parallel to and 3 times the length of the corresponding sides of $\triangle JKL$. Each preimage-image pair of points is collinear with the origin.

6. a. $P' = (-14, 77)$;
$Q' = (21, -35)$

b. slope of $\overline{QP} = \frac{-5 - 11}{3 - -2} = \frac{-16}{5}$
slope of $\overline{Q'P'} = \frac{-35 - 77}{21 - -14} =$
$\frac{-112}{35} = \frac{-16}{5}$

c. $QP = \sqrt{(3--2)^2 + (-5-11)^2}$
$= \sqrt{281}$
$Q'P' =$
$\sqrt{(21--14)^2 + (-35-77)^2} =$
$\sqrt{13,769} = 7\sqrt{281} = 7 \cdot QP$

7. $OA = \sqrt{(-9-0)^2 + (15-0)^2}$
$= \sqrt{306} = 3\sqrt{34}$
$OA' = \sqrt{(-6-0)^2 + (10+0)^2}$
$= \sqrt{136} = 2\sqrt{34}$
$AA' = \sqrt{(-9--6)^2 + (15-10)^2}$
$= \sqrt{34}$
Since $OA' + AA' = OA$, A' is between O and A.

8. See Additional Answers in the back of this book.

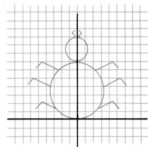

MORE PRACTICE
For more questions on SPUR
Objectives, use *Lesson Master 12-1*, shown on page 567.

EXTENSION
Have students design their own preimage like the one in **Question 8** (on graph paper). Then, using graph paper with a larger or smaller unit, draw an image of their preimage. How can the magnitude of S_k be determined?

EVALUATION
Alternative Assessment
You might ask several students to summarize the results of doing size changes with coordinates and how size changes are related to other transformations.

ADDITIONAL ANSWERS
11. See Additional
Answers in the back of this book.

12. a.
Conclusions	Justifications
1. ∠KLM ≅ ∠GFM, ∠LKM ≅ ∠FGM	‖ Lines ⇒ AIA = Thm.
2. $\overline{LM} \cong \overline{MF}$	def. of midpoint (meaning)
3. △KLM ≅ △GFM	AAS Congruence Thm. (steps 1 and 2)

b. Since △KLM ≅ △GFM by the CPCF Theorem, MG = MK.

14. See Additional
Answers in the back of this book.

11. In three dimensions, S_k is the transformation mapping (x, y, z) onto (kx, ky, kz).
    a. Find the image of $P = (-3, 12, 4)$ under S_5. Call this point P'.
    b. Find the image of $Q = (2, -8, 0)$ under S_5. Call this point Q'.
    c. Using the Distance Formula in Three Dimensions, verify that $Q'P' = 5 \cdot QP$.
    a) $P' = (-15, 60, 20)$; b) $(10, -40, 0)$; c) See margin.

Review

12. In the figure below, $\overleftrightarrow{KL} \parallel \overleftrightarrow{FG}$ and M is the midpoint of $\overline{LF}$.
    a. Prove $\triangle KLM \cong \triangle GFM$.
    b. Prove $MG = MK$. *(Lessons 7-3, 6-7)* See margin.

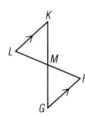

13. If a figure is determined by certain points, then its reflection image is determined by the reflection images of those points.

13. State the Figure Reflection Theorem. *(Lesson 4-2)*

14. Copy segment $\overline{AB}$ below. Construct its perpendicular bisector. *(Lesson 3-6)* See margin.

In 15–17, solve. *(Previous course)*

15. $\dfrac{2}{9} = \dfrac{3}{x}$ 13.5

16. $\dfrac{2y - 5}{5} = \dfrac{3y + 14}{8}$ 110

17. $AB - 9 = \frac{3}{4} \cdot AB$. (Here, A and B are points.) 36

Exploration

18. Use $\triangle JKL$ of Question 5.
    a. Multiply all the coordinates of the vertices by -3.
    b. Describe the figure that results.
    c. Generalize parts **a** and **b**.
    See below.

a) $J' = (-15, 24)$, $K' = (18, 0)$, $L' = (30, 12)$
b) Its dimensions are 3 times those of $\triangle JKL$, and it is rotated 180° about the origin.
c) If $k > 0$, then S_{-k} makes a figure whose sides are k times as long and rotates it 180° about the origin.

568

12-2

Size Changes Without Coordinates

Not all figures, of course, are given on the coordinate plane. It sometimes is necessary to be able to change sizes of figures without coordinates. Below is a face made up of segments and circular arcs. Suppose you wanted to draw a face like this one, but 2.5 times as large. The number 2.5 is the **magnitude** or **scale factor** or **size change factor**.

To begin, choose a point in the plane. The point can be anywhere in the plane, but, for clarity, we select a point O outside the face. O is the **center** of a *size transformation*. Then choose and label key points on the face. Some key points are endpoints of the segments and the centers of the arcs. We have chosen A, B, C, D, E, F, G, and H. Draw rays from O through the named points.

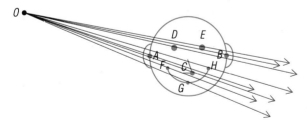

Now find the image of each point. Here is how to do it for point A.

Step 1. Measure OA.
Step 2. On $\overrightarrow{OA}$, locate A' so that $OA' = 2.5 \cdot OA$. That is, A' is 2.5 times as far from the center as A is. Point A' is the *size change image* of A.

LESSON 12-2

RESOURCES
- Lesson Master 12-2
- Visual for Teaching Aid 74 shows size changes on page 570.
- Visual for Teaching Aid 75 can be used with **Questions 6 and 14-16**.
- Computer Master 24

OBJECTIVES

A Draw size transformation images of figures.
D Recognize and apply properties and size transformations.

TEACHING NOTES

Students who have taken earlier UCSMP courses will not have seen how to do a size transformation *without* using coordinates, so the material of Lesson 12-2 is new but the ideas are not. For all students, it may be helpful to begin the lesson with two or three simple polygons and directions to find a size change image with some point as center and some magnitude. (You could use any of **Questions 3, 4, 6, 17,** or **18** for this purpose or use the Lesson Master.)

Reading You might need to point out that certain synonyms are used interchangeably: size change, size transformation, and dilation; and magnitude, scale factor, and size change factor. A dilation can also be called a dilatation. A description of a size change without coordinates needs to include the name of the center and the magnitude.

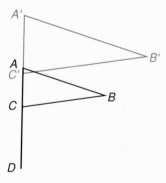
Repeat steps 1 and 2 for all the labeled points of the figure. Connect the image points in the manner of the preimages. The result is shown below. Because the scale factor is greater than one, the image is larger than the preimage.

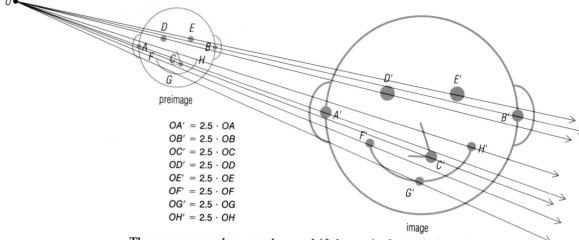

$OA' = 2.5 \cdot OA$
$OB' = 2.5 \cdot OB$
$OC' = 2.5 \cdot OC$
$OD' = 2.5 \cdot OD$
$OE' = 2.5 \cdot OE$
$OF' = 2.5 \cdot OF$
$OG' = 2.5 \cdot OG$
$OH' = 2.5 \cdot OH$

The same procedure can be used if the scale factor is less than or equal to one. Below is shown the face and its image when the scale factor is $\frac{1}{3}$ and the center is O. Notice OC'' is $\frac{1}{3}$ of OC. The image is now smaller than the preimage.

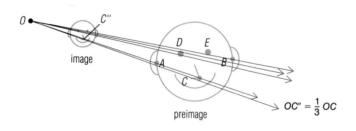

$OC'' = \frac{1}{3} OC$

The transformation described in this section has various names. It is called a **size change** or a **size transformation.** Some others call it a **dilation** or **dilatation.**

Definition:

Let O be a point and k be a positive real number. For any point P, let $S(P) = P'$ be the point on $\overrightarrow{OP}$ with $OP' = k \cdot OP$. Then S is the **size change with center O and magnitude k.**

When $k > 1$, S is called an **expansion.** When $0 < k < 1$, S is a **contraction.** When $k = 1$, S is called the **identity transformation** because each point coincides with its image, so the image is identical to the preimage. In this lesson you have seen an expansion with magnitude 2.5 and a contraction with magnitude $\frac{1}{3}$.

The next theorem relates a size change to the transformation S_k of the last lesson.

Theorem

The transformation S_k, where $S_k(x, y) = (kx, ky)$, is the size change with center $(0, 0)$ and magnitude k.

Proof

It must be shown that a point and its image under S_k satisfy the sufficient conditions of the definition of size change. So let $P = (a, b)$. Then $P' = (ka, kb)$ by the definition (meaning) of S_k.

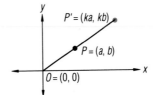

Two things need to be shown:
(1) P' lies on $\overrightarrow{OP}$, and
(2) $OP' = k \cdot OP$.

(1) P' lies on $\overrightarrow{OP}$ if the points O, P, and P' are collinear and in the same quadrant. O, P, and P' are collinear if the slope of $\overline{OP}$ equals the slope of $\overline{OP'}$.

$$\text{slope of } \overline{OP} = \frac{b - 0}{a - 0} = \frac{b}{a}$$

$$\text{slope of } \overline{OP'} = \frac{kb - 0}{ka - 0} = \frac{kb}{ka} = \frac{b}{a}$$

Thus O, P, and P' are collinear.

If a and b are not zero, the quadrant of (a, b) depends on the signs (positive or negative) of a and b. Since k is positive, the numbers a and ka have the same sign. Similarly, b and kb have the same sign. So (a, b) and (ka, kb) are in the same quadrant. If $a = 0$ or $b = 0$, then the points are on the axes and a similar argument can be given.

(2) Use the Distance Formula and algebraic simplification. This is similar to the proof in the last lesson.

$$OP = \sqrt{(a - 0)^2 + (b - 0)^2} = \sqrt{a^2 + b^2}$$
$$OP' = \sqrt{(ka - 0)^2 + (kb - 0)^2} = \sqrt{(ka)^2 + (kb)^2}$$
$$= \sqrt{k^2 a^2 + k^2 b^2}$$
$$= \sqrt{k^2(a^2 + b^2)}$$
$$= \sqrt{k^2} \cdot \sqrt{a^2 + b^2}$$
$$= k\sqrt{a^2 + b^2} \text{ (because } k > 0)$$
$$= k \cdot OP$$

Although the proof of the above theorem is long, the theorem is worth it, because it enables you to work either with or without coordinates when doing size changes.

LESSON 12-2 *Size Changes Without Coordinates* **571**

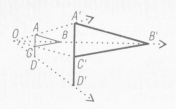
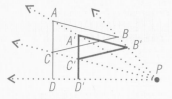
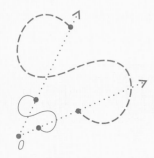
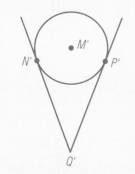
Covering the Reading

1. In the expansion of the face in this lesson, what are the center and magnitude? O, 2.5

2. In the contraction of the face in this lesson, what are the center and magnitude? O, $\frac{1}{3}$

In 3 and 4, trace the drawing below. Find the image of the flag under:

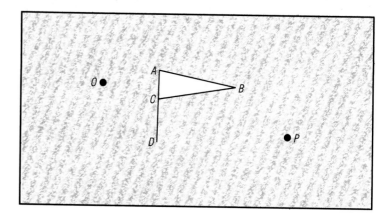

3. the size change with center O and magnitude 3; See margin.

4. the size change with center P, magnitude $\frac{3}{4}$. See margin.

5. Let S be a size transformation with scale factor 6 and center O. Let A be any point. Then S(A) is __?__ times as far from O as A is. 6

6. In the figure below, $A'B'C'D'$ is a size change image of $ABCD$ with center O.
   a. Is this size change an expansion or a contraction? expansion
   b. If $OA = 10$ and $AA' = 4$, what is the magnitude of the size change? 1.4

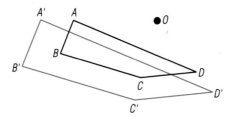

7. If k is the scale factor of an expansion, then __?__. $k > 1$

8. If k is the scale factor of a contraction, then __?__. $0 < k < 1$

9. In order to show that the transformation S_k is a size change of magnitude k with center O, what two statements needed to be proved? P' lies on $\overrightarrow{OP}$, and $OP' = k \cdot OP$.

572

In 10–13, use the figure below. S is a size change with center O and $S(\triangle ABC) = \triangle A'B'C'$. The figure is a guide and not necessarily accurate.

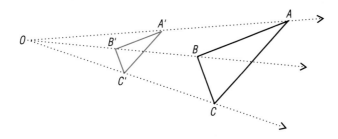

10. If $k = \frac{2}{3}$ and $OA = 9$, then $OA' = \underline{\ ?\ }$ and $AA' = \underline{\ ?\ }$. **6, 3**

11. If $OB = 5$ and $OB' = 3$, then $k = \underline{\ ?\ }$. $\frac{3}{5}$

12. If $OC' = 2 \cdot OC$, then $k = \underline{\ ?\ }$. **2**

13. If $\dfrac{OB}{OB'} = \dfrac{4}{3}$, then $k = \underline{\ ?\ }$. $\frac{3}{4}$

In 14–16, trace each figure. Use a ruler to determine the center and the scale factor k for the size transformation represented. (The image is blue.)
See margin.

14.

15.

16.

17. Draw a figure 1.5 times as large as the figure below.
See margin.

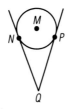

LESSON 12-2 Size Changes Without Coordinates **573**

18. Trace $\triangle ABC$ below and draw its image under a size change with center A and magnitude $\frac{1}{3}$.

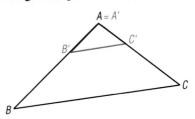

Review

19. Let $A = (0, -4)$, $B = (-13, \frac{1}{3})$, and $C = (7, 11)$. Find the image of $\triangle ABC$ under S_3. *(Lesson 12-1)* $A' = (0,-12)$, $B' = (-39, 1)$, $C' = (21, 33)$

20. Given $P = (9, 2)$, $Q = (-4, 8)$, and $R = (35, -10)$. See margin.
    a. Show that P, Q, and R are collinear.
    b. Show that P is between Q and R.
    c. Find the images P', Q', and R' of P, Q, and R under S_4.
    d. Show that P', Q', and R' are collinear.
    e. Show that P' is between Q' and R'. *(Lessons 12-1, 1-8)*

21. The rectangular field $ABCD$ pictured below is 300' by 400'. What is the perimeter of $\triangle ABC$? *(Lessons 8-7, 8-1)* 1200'

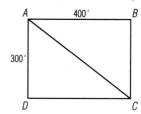

22. Is the figure of Question 21 traversable? *(Lesson 1-4)* Yes

23. a. How many inches are there in a mile? 63,360
    b. How many millimeters are there in a kilometer?
       (Previous course) 1,000,000

24. Solve each equation. *(Previous course)*
    a. $\frac{z+1}{2} = \frac{30}{40}$ .5   b. $\frac{M}{5} = \frac{6}{M}$ $\pm\sqrt{30} \approx \pm 5.48$

Exploration

25. Draw a pentagon (but not a regular pentagon). Draw the images of this pentagon under two size changes with the same magnitude but different centers, one inside the pentagon, one outside. (You pick the magnitude and the two centers.) How do the images compare? Sample: let $k = 1.5$ and centers be P and Q. The images are congruent.

12-3

Properties of Size Changes

LESSON 12-3

RESOURCES
■ Lesson Master 12-3
■ Quiz for Lessons 12-1
　Through 12-3
◨ Visual for Teaching Aid 76
　can be used with
　Questions 11, 12, and **18**.

You have now seen ways to find size changes with and without coordinates. Working without coordinates is more flexible because figures are not always given on a coordinate plane. However, coordinates enable some properties of size changes to be deduced rather easily. And, since any point can be the origin for a coordinate system, if a property of S_k can be deduced, then it holds for size changes with other centers.

In the questions of the last two lessons, you have been asked to verify some of the properties of size changes. The first of these is the most important property of size changes and was proved in Lesson 12-1.

Size Change Distance Theorem:

Under a size change with magnitude $k > 0$, the distance between any two image points is k times the distance between their preimages.

Remember the A-B-C-D properties of reflections and other isometries. Size changes may not preserve distances, but they preserve the other three. First, look at betweenness and collinearity.

OBJECTIVES

A Draw size transformation
images of figures.
D Recognize and apply properties of size transformations.

TEACHING NOTES

Making Connections　In Chapter 4, students learned that reflections have the A-B-C-D preservation properties. In Chapter 6, it was shown that translations, rotations, and all other isometries possess these properties. This lesson explains that size transformations have the A-B-C properties but not the D (for distance). Many students will first understand what it means to "preserve" a property only after seeing some of the examples.

You might wish to begin the lesson by asking students for the preservation properties of reflections. Point out to students that whereas the reflections were assumed, all the properties of size transformations can be proved.

You might need to go over the proofs of the theorems in this lesson in some detail. Emphasize that the proofs are algebraic, so students can use the problem-solving skill *try a simpler case* to verify the theorems. Ask students to explain why

Theorem:

Size transformations preserve betweenness and collinearity.

Proof

Let the images of P, Q, and R under size change S_k be P', Q', and R'. For betweenness, we need to show: If Q is between P and R, then Q' is between P' and R'.

Given: Q is between P and R.

Conclusions	Justifications
1. $PQ + QR = PR$	Def. of betweenness (meaning)
2. $k(PQ + QR) = k \cdot PR$	Multiplication Property of Equality
3. $k \cdot PQ + k \cdot QR = k \cdot PR$	Distributive Property
4. $k \cdot PQ = P'Q'$	Size Change Distance Theorem
$\quad\ k \cdot QR = Q'R'$	
$\quad\ k \cdot PR = P'R'$	
5. $P'Q' + Q'R' = P'R'$	Substitution (step 4 into step 3)
6. Q' is between P' and R'.	Def. of betweenness (suff. cond.)

Collinearity is preserved means that when three points are collinear, so are their images. But if three different points are collinear, one must be between the other two. So the image of that one is between the images of the other two, which means the images are collinear.

Because size changes preserve collinearity, the image of a line is a line. Because size changes preserve betweenness, the image of a segment is a segment, the image of a ray is a ray, and the image of an angle is an angle.

In Lesson 12-1, the following property was proved.

Theorem:

A line and its image under a size transformation are parallel.

You can use this theorem to quickly draw images of polygons.

■ ■ ■ ■ ■ ■ ■ ■

Example S is a size transformation with magnitude 0.6 and center O. Draw S($ABCD$).

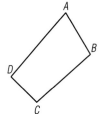

576

Solution S(ABCD) is determined by the images of A, B, C, and D. Draw guide rays $\overrightarrow{OA}$, $\overrightarrow{OB}$, $\overrightarrow{OC}$, and $\overrightarrow{OD}$. Measure OA: OA ≈ 56 mm. So OA' = 0.6 · OA = 0.6 · 56 mm ≈ 34 mm. This locates A'. Since $\overline{A'B'} \parallel \overline{AB}$, find B' by drawing a line through A' parallel to $\overleftrightarrow{AB}$ which intersects $\overrightarrow{OB}$ in B'. Likewise, since $\overline{A'D'} \parallel \overline{AD}$, find D by drawing a line through A' parallel to $\overrightarrow{OB}$ which intersects $\overrightarrow{OD}$ in D'. Continue this process until all the vertices of the image polygon are located.

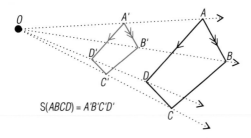

S(ABCD) = A'B'C'D'

In the Example, it certainly looks as if corresponding angles in ABCD and A'B'C'D' have the same measure. This can be proved easily. For instance, here is a proof that m∠ABC = m∠A'B'C'.

Conclusions	Justifications
1. $\overleftrightarrow{BC} \parallel \overleftrightarrow{B'C'}$ $\overleftrightarrow{AB} \parallel \overleftrightarrow{A'B'}$	A line and its image under a size transformation are parallel.
2. m∠ABO = m∠A'B'O m∠OBC = m∠OB'C'	∥ lines ⇒ corr ∠s =
3. m∠ABO + m∠OBC = m∠A'B'O + m∠OB'C'	Addition Property of Equality
4. m∠ABO + m∠OBC = m∠ABC m∠A'B'O + m∠OB'C' = m∠A'B'C'	Angle Addition Property
5. m∠ABC = m∠A'B'C'	Substitution (step 4 into step 3)

This proves that size transformations preserve angle measure. Combining this all into one theorem:

Size Change Theorem:

Under a size transformation:

(a) angle measure preserved;
(b) betweenness is preserved;
(c) collinearity is preserved; and
(d) lines and their images are parallel.

NOTES ON QUESTIONS

Question 2: The Exploration question of the previous lesson is related.

Question 5: Although the expected answers are given here, there are other correct answers: perpendicularity (if two lines are perpendicular, so are their size transformation images), triangles (the image of a triangle is a triangle), and so on.

Question 10: Ask: Does the use of the words *TINY* and *HUGE* lead students to believe that S is an expansion? (Despite the words, no information is given about the magnitude of S.)

Question 11: You might ask students to prove that ∠*ABO* ≅ ∠*DEO*. It is a nice two-step proof. $\overline{AB} \parallel \overline{DE}$ because of the Size Change Theorem. Then the angles are corresponding angles and are congruent because of the Parallel Lines Postulate.

Question 12: Ask students to give the relationship between the answers to this question and the answers to the related question, "If T(*MICRO*) = *MEGAS*, what is the magnitude of T?" (the reciprocal of .625, or $\frac{8}{5}$)

Questions 13 and 14: These questions verify that the center of a size transformation determines where the image is located but not the size of the image. In the next lesson, students learn exactly how the magnitude affects the size.

Questions 16, 18, and 19: These are three basic applications of size changes: to photographs (Question 16), scale drawings (Question 18), and map scales (Question 19). Although many of the questions in this lesson involve polygons, be sure to emphasize the general nature of the effect of size changes on distance.

The preservation properties imply that images of figures are determined by images of key points.

Figure Size Change Theorem:

If a figure is determined by certain points, then its size change image is the corresponding figure determined by the size change images of those points.

The Figure Size Change Theorem was applied as early as Lesson 12-1 to find the image of a pentagon.

Questions

Covering the Reading

1. Suppose you know the lengths of a segment and its image under a size change. How can the magnitude of the size change be calculated? **Divide the length of the image segment by the length of the preimage segment.**

2. *True* or *false*? The length of the image of a segment under a size transformation depends upon the location of the center of the size transformation. **False**

3. *True* or *false*? Size transformations preserve distance. **False**

4. A picture of an insect is *k* times actual size. If a leg on the picture is 3 cm long, how long is the leg on the actual insect? $\frac{3}{k}$ **cm**

5. Size transformations preserve __?__ , __?__ , and __?__ .
   angle measure, betweenness, collinearity

6. S is a size transformation of magnitude 2. If S(∠*TJK*) = ∠*T'J'K'* and m∠*T'J'K'* = 43, find m∠*TJK*. **43**

7. Suppose S($\overleftrightarrow{AB}$) = $\overleftrightarrow{CD}$. How are $\overleftrightarrow{AB}$ and $\overleftrightarrow{CD}$ related?
   They are parallel.

   In 8 and 9, S(*A*) = *X*, S(*B*) = *T*, S(*C*) = *E*, and S(*D*) = *J*.

8. S(∠*BCD*) = __?__ ∠*TEJ*

9. If m∠*BAD* = 73, then m∠ __?__ .
   TXJ = 73

10. If S(*TINY*) = *HUGE*, then S(*N*) = __?__ . **G**

Applying the Mathematics

11. Below, △*DEF* is a size transformation image of △*ABC* with center *O*. *AB* = 6, *BC* = 8, *EF* = 20, and *DF* = 30. Find each value.
    a. *k*, the magnitude of the size change **2.5**
    b. *DE* **15**
    c. *AC* **12**

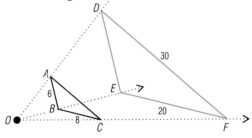

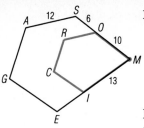

12. T is a size change with T(*MEGAS*) = *MICRO* and lengths as indicated at the left.
  a. What is the magnitude of T? .625
  b. What is the center of T? **M**
  c. Give the value of *OR*. 7.5
  d. Give the value of *ME*. 20.8

In 13–15, trace each figure. Draw the image of the figure under the size change with center *P* and the given magnitude *k*.

13. $k = \frac{5}{6}$ See margin. **14.** $k = \frac{5}{6}$ See margin. **15.** $k = 4$ See margin.

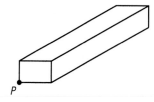

16. A photograph that measures 5 cm by 12 cm is enlarged to a width of 7 cm.
  a. Find the scale factor of the enlargement. 1.4
  b. Find the length of the enlargement. 16.8 cm
  c. Find the areas of the photograph and its enlargement.
  d. How many times larger in area is the enlargement than the original? 1.96
  e. How many times larger in perimeter is the enlargement than the original? 1.4
  c) 60 cm² and 117.6 cm²

17. Use the figure at the right.
  Given: S(△*OAC*) = △*OBD*,
  OA = 6, *AB* = 1,
  BD = 4, *OC* = 6.1.
  Find the lengths of as many other segments as you can.
  $AC = \frac{24}{7} \approx 3.429$; $OD \approx 7.117$; $CD \approx 1.017$; $OB = 7$

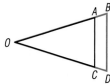

Review

18. Figure A below is a size change image of Figure B. Find the center and scale factor *k*. *(Lesson 12-2)* $k = \frac{1}{2}$

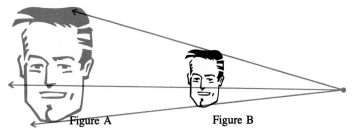

  Figure A   Figure B

19. Many road maps can be thought of as contractions of a part of the earth. Suppose 1 cm on a map equals 1 km on the earth. What is the scale factor of the contraction for this map? (That magnitude is the *scale* of the map.) *(Lesson 12-2)* .00001 = 10⁻⁵

14.

15. See Additional Answers in the back of this book.

NAME _____

LESSON **MASTER 12–3**
QUESTIONS ON **SPUR** OBJECTIVES

■ **SKILLS** *Objective A (See pages 624–627 for objectives.)*
In 1 and 2 below, draw the image of the figure under the size change with center *P* and the given magnitude *k*.

1. *k* = 3   2. $k = \frac{1}{4}$

■ **PROPERTIES** *Objective D*

3. A photograph that measures 4 cm by 9 cm (length by width) is enlarged to a width of 15 cm.
  a. What is the scale factor of the expansion? $\frac{5}{3}$
  b. What is the length of the larger picture? $\frac{20}{3}$ cm
  c. How many times larger in area is the enlargement than the original? $\frac{25}{9}$

For 4–7, use the figure at the right. △*DEF* is a size transformation image of △*ABC* with center *O*. *AB* = 2, *AC* = 3, *ED* = 5, and *FD* = 7.

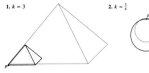

4. What is the scale factor of the size change? 2.5
5. *EF* = 7.5   6. *CB* = 2.8
7. Explain why $\overline{FD} \parallel \overline{CB}$. Lines and their images are parallel under a size change (or transformation).

110   *Geometry © Scott, Foresman and Company*

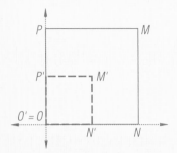
20. Suppose $P'Q'R'T'$ is the image of $PQRT$ under S_k with $P = (4, -6)$, $Q = (-9, 12)$, $R' = (5, 13)$, $T = (0, -8)$, and $P' = (2, -3)$. Find k and the coordinates of Q', R, and T'. *(Lesson 12-1)*
$k = \frac{1}{2} = .5$, $Q' = (-4.5, 6)$, $R = (10, 26)$, $T' = (0, -4)$

21. Nina and Kathryn are about to replace the anchor line for their boat. When they go fishing at their favorite spot on Lake Congora, which is about 15 feet deep, they like to be able to drift 9 feet from the location where they drop the anchor. How long should the anchor line be? *(Lesson 8-7)* $\sqrt{306} \approx 17.5$ ft

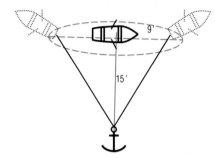

22. Complete this hierarchy for isometries. *(Lesson 6-6)*

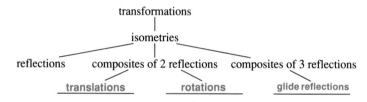

In 23 and 24, suppose $\frac{2x}{k} = \frac{b}{y}$. *(Previous course)*

23. Find k if $x = 9$, $b = 7$, and $y = 50$. $\frac{900}{7} \approx 128.57$

24. If $x = 1$ and $y = 1$, what can you say about the value of k? $k = \frac{2}{b}$

25. Solve for t: $\frac{t+3}{100} = \frac{t-5}{200}$. *(Previous course)* -11

26. a. Does the definition of size change given in Lesson 12-2 hold in three dimensions or must it be modified? If so, how would you modify it? It holds in three dimensions.
  b. What properties mentioned in this lesson are preserved with size changes of three dimensions? angle measure, betweenness, collinearity, and lines and their images are parallel

27. Consider this conjecture:
If $MNOP$ is a square, then $S_k(MNOP)$ is a square.
  a. Draw an instance of this conjecture.
  b. Is this conjecture true? If so, prove it. If not, draw a counterexample.
  See margin.

580

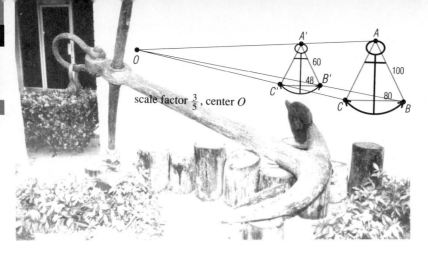

scale factor $\frac{3}{5}$, center O

LESSON 12-4

RESOURCES
■ Lesson Master 12-4

A **ratio** is a quotient of two numbers, $\frac{m}{n}$ or m/n. Sometimes the ratio m/n is written $m{:}n$. In a ratio $\frac{m}{n}$, m and n must be quantities of the same kind, such as lengths, populations, or areas. (If the quantities are of different kinds, $\frac{m}{n}$ is called a *rate*.)

Ratios appear whenever there is a size change. For example, above is pictured the size change with center O and magnitude $\frac{3}{5}$. Then, by the Size Change Distance Theorem,

$$A'B' = \tfrac{3}{5} \cdot AB \quad \text{and} \quad B'C' = \tfrac{3}{5} \cdot BC.$$

Consequently, $\quad \dfrac{A'B'}{AB} = \dfrac{3}{5} \quad$ and $\quad \dfrac{B'C'}{BC} = \dfrac{3}{5}.$

Thus in a size transformation, the ratios of image lengths to pre-image lengths are equal; that is, $\frac{A'B'}{AB} = \frac{B'C'}{BC}$. That ratio is equal to the magnitude of the size change.

A statement that two ratios are equal is called a **proportion.** Each equation below is a proportion.

$$\frac{CB}{C'B'} = \frac{5}{3} \qquad \frac{2}{7} = \frac{x}{9} \qquad \frac{y+3}{5} = \frac{7}{y} \qquad \frac{A'B'}{AB} = \frac{B'C'}{BC}$$

You learned how to solve proportions in previous years and have reviewed them in questions in previous lessons. In this lesson, there are two more goals for proportions:

1. to learn some terms used to talk about proportions;
2. to derive other true proportions when given a true one.

Four numbers that form a true proportion are called **proportional.** The numbers 5, 3, 10, and 6, in that order, are proportional because $\frac{5}{3} = \frac{10}{6}$. The numbers 1, 2, 3, and 4 are not proportional, for $\frac{1}{2} \neq \frac{3}{4}$.

LESSON 12-4 *Proportions* **581**

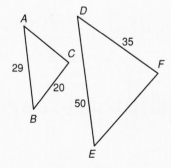
Proportional numbers are always around when there is a size change. For instance, when $\triangle ABC$ is a size transformation image of $\triangle XYZ$, you can say "The sides of the triangles are proportional." This means the three ratios of corresponding sides are equal.

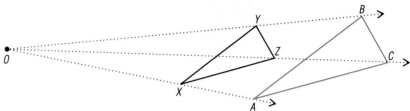

That is, $\frac{XY}{AB} = \frac{XZ}{AC} = \frac{YZ}{BC}$. You can equate any two of these ratios to form a true proportion.

$$\frac{XY}{AB} = \frac{XZ}{AC} \qquad \frac{XY}{AB} = \frac{YZ}{BC} \qquad \frac{XZ}{AC} = \frac{YZ}{BC}$$

Notice that in each proportion, *the numerators come from one figure and the denominators from the other*.

The four parts of a proportion have names and are numbered in order. The 1st and 4th terms are the **extremes** and the 2nd and 3rd terms are the **means.**

1st term → a c ← 3rd term
2nd term → $\frac{a}{b} = \frac{c}{d}$ ← 4th term

extremes
$$\frac{a}{b} = \frac{c}{d}$$
means

In algebra, you learned the Means-Extremes Property: In any proportion, the product of the means equals the product of the extremes.

Theorem (Means-Extremes Property):

If $\frac{a}{b} = \frac{c}{d}$, then $ad = bc$.

Proof

Multiply both sides of $\frac{a}{b} = \frac{c}{d}$ by bd.
$$bd \cdot \frac{a}{b} = bd \cdot \frac{c}{d}$$
$$b \cdot d \cdot a \cdot \frac{1}{b} = b \cdot d \cdot c \cdot \frac{1}{d}$$
Since the product of a number and its reciprocal is 1, these products can be simplified.
$$ad = bc$$

582

Example $\triangle QRS$ is the image of $\triangle TUV$ under a size change with center O. If $QR = 10$, $RS = 15$, and $TU = 25$, find UV.

Solution The sides of the triangles are proportional.

Thus $\frac{TU}{QR} = \frac{UV}{RS}$. Substituting, $\frac{25}{10} = \frac{UV}{15}$.

Solve for UV, using the Means-Extremes Property.
$$25 \cdot 15 = 10 \cdot UV$$
$$UV = \frac{375}{10}$$
$$= 37.5$$

Check The magnitude of the size change is $\frac{10}{25} = .4$, which is the same as $\frac{15}{37.5}$.

When four numbers are proportional, many true proportions can be stated. For instance, if the proportional numbers are 30, 7.5, 20, and 5, the following is a true proportion.
$$\frac{30}{7.5} = \frac{20}{5}$$
You can *exchange the means* (or the *extremes*) to form two other true proportions.
$$\frac{30}{20} = \frac{7.5}{5} \qquad \frac{5}{7.5} = \frac{20}{30}$$
You can take *reciprocals* to form still other true proportions.
$$\frac{20}{30} = \frac{5}{7.5} \qquad \frac{7.5}{5} = \frac{30}{20}$$
These examples are generalized in the following theorem.

Theorem:

If $\frac{a}{b} = \frac{c}{d}$, then $\frac{a}{c} = \frac{b}{d}$ **(Means Exchange Property)**

and $\frac{b}{a} = \frac{d}{c}$ **(Reciprocals Property).**

Proof

If $\frac{a}{b} = \frac{c}{d}$, then by the Means-Extremes Property, $ad = bc$.
Dividing both sides of $ad = bc$ by cd yields the Means Exchange Property.
Since $ad = bc$, by the Symmetric Property of Equality, $bc = ad$.
Dividing both sides of $bc = ad$ by ac yields the Reciprocals Property.

LESSON 12-4 Proportions **583**

NOTES ON QUESTIONS
It is useful to discuss all the questions in Covering the Reading quickly and in sequential order to ascertain that students have the terminology of the lesson.

Question 1: You might want to include the extended ratio in the discussion: "What is a way of writing the ratio of 2 to 3 to 5?" (2:3:5. Use colons for extended ratios.)

Question 12: Ask students how they could check their answers to this question. (They could substitute numbers for a, b, and c, solve the equation for x, and see if the solution is the same as that given by substituting into $\frac{ac}{b}$.)

Questions 13 and 14: These questions indicate that the Side-Splitting Theorem (Lesson 12-10) could be deduced even now.

Questions 15 and 16: These questions should be review of material students have had in algebra or in previous courses.

Question 16: Students could use the pattern of part **a** to do part **b**. Another method is that the two equal rates are
$$\frac{m \text{ miles}}{h \text{ hours}} = \frac{x \text{ miles}}{r \text{ hours}},$$
where x is the unknown distance. (Students who have studied previous UCSMP courses may think this way.) Then solve the proportion to find $x = \frac{rm}{h}$.

Question 21: Applications like this one are the relationship between the size of the negative in a motion picture film and the size of the picture on a screen, or the size of a figure on a transparency and the size of its image on a screen.

Making Connections for Question 22: This question is an appropriate lead into Lesson 12-5.

583

Covering the Reading

1. *Multiple choice.* Which is *not* a way of writing the ratio of 7 to 9?
   (a) 7 : 9   (b) 7/9
   (c) $\frac{7}{9}$ (d) 7.9 (d)

2. A ratio is a(n) __?__ of two numbers. quotient

3. A proportion is a statement that two __?__ are __?__. ratios, equal

4. Given $\frac{7}{x} = \frac{11}{y}$, name the
   a. extremes 7, y   b. means x, 11
   c. first term 7   d. 4th term y
   e. 3rd term 11   f. 2nd term. x

5. Suppose $\frac{r}{s} = \frac{t}{u}$. Make a conclusion using each justification.
   a. Means-Extremes Property ru = st
   b. Means Exchange Property $\frac{r}{t} = \frac{s}{u}$
   c. Reciprocals Property $\frac{s}{r} = \frac{u}{t}$

6. Form three true proportions using the numbers 2, 93, 62, and 3.
   See margin.

7. Why are the numbers 2, 4, 6, and 8 *not* proportional?
   $\frac{2}{4} \neq \frac{6}{8}, \frac{2}{6} \neq \frac{4}{8}, \frac{2}{8} \neq \frac{4}{6}$

In 8 and 9, *ABCD* at the left is the image of *FGHE* under a size change with center *V*.

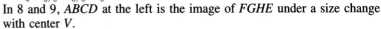

8. Fill in the space: $\frac{AB}{FG} = \frac{AD}{\square}$. FE

9. If *FG* = 10, *AB* = 12, and *BC* = 15, what is *GH*? 12.5

10. a. What equation results if both sides of the equation *ad = bc* are divided by *bd*? $\frac{a}{b} = \frac{c}{d}$
    b. What equation results if both sides of the equation *ad = bc* are divided by *ac*? $\frac{d}{c} = \frac{b}{a}$

11. Suppose $\frac{u}{v} = \frac{w}{x} = \frac{y}{z}$. From this information, form three true proportions. samples: $\frac{u}{w} = \frac{v}{x}; \frac{u}{y} = \frac{v}{z}; \frac{v}{u} = \frac{z}{y}$

Applying the Mathematics

12. Solve for *x*: $\frac{a}{x} = \frac{b}{c}$. x = $\frac{ac}{b}$

In 13 and 14, △*GJK* at the left is a size change image of △*GHI*.

13. *True* or *false*?
    a. $\frac{GJ}{GH} = \frac{GK}{GI}$ True   b. $\frac{GH}{GJ} = \frac{GI}{GK}$ True   c. $\frac{JK}{HI} = \frac{GI}{GK}$ False

14. If *GH* = 100, *GJ* = 130, and *HI* = 120, then *JK* = __?__. 156

15. Weights and prices of fruit are often proportional. If 2.3 pounds of apples cost $1.05, what should 4 pounds of apples cost? ≈$1.83

584

16. a. If you bike 13 miles in $1\frac{1}{2}$ hours, at that rate how many miles would you bike in $2\frac{1}{2}$ hours? $21\frac{2}{3}$ **miles**

b. If you drive m miles in h hours, at that rate how many miles can you drive in r hours? $\frac{mr}{h}$ **miles**

17. If $wx = yz$, write three true proportions using w, x, y, and z.
samples: $\frac{w}{y} = \frac{z}{x}$, $\frac{w}{z} = \frac{y}{x}$, $\frac{y}{w} = \frac{x}{z}$

Review

18. Suppose S is a size change of magnitude 1.5, and suppose $S(ABCDE) = UVWXY$. If m$\angle BDE = 47$ and $AE = 30$, find two other measures. *(Lessons 12-3, 12-2)* m$\angle VXY = 47$ and $UY = 45$

19. Let S be a size transformation of magnitude $\frac{1}{2}$ centered at the origin. If $A = (16, -6)$ and $B = (10, 8)$, verify that the distance between $S(A)$ and $S(B)$ is half the distance between A and B. *(Lessons 12-3, 12-1)* **See margin.**

20. Trace the figure below. Draw the image of the figure under the size change with center H and magnitude $\frac{3}{5}$. *(Lesson 12-2)*

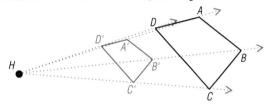

21. The distance between the lens and the negative is 2 inches. How far away from the lens must Ann place the photo paper if the developed picture is to be 5 times as large as the negative? *(Lesson 12-2)* **10 in.**

22. Finish this definition. Two figures α and β are congruent, written $\alpha \cong \beta$, if and only if __?__. *(Lesson 6-5)*
β **is the image of** α **under a reflection or composite of reflections**

23. Given: $GHJKL$, FGL, and HIJ are regular polygons.
a. Prove: $\triangle FGL \cong \triangle HIJ$. **See margin.**
b. What is m$\angle GHI$? *(Lesson 7-6, 7-3)* **168**

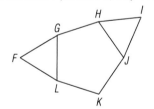

Exploration

24. Here are sets of numbers that could be lengths of sides of triangles.

$\{3, 4, 5\}$ $\quad$ $\{8, 6, 12\}$ $\quad$ $\{5, 4, 3\}$ $\quad$ $\{9, 12, 18\}$

$\{2, 4.5, 4\}$ $\quad$ $\{1.8, 2.4, 3\}$ $\quad$ $\{8, 16, 18\}$

a. Which sets could be paired so that one triangle is a size transformation image of the other?
b. What possible scale factors are there for each pair?
c. Could there be more than one scale factor for a pair? Why or why not?
See margin.

FOLLOW-UP

MORE PRACTICE
For more questions on SPUR Objectives, use *Lesson Master 12-4,* shown below.

EXTENSION
A cake recipe calls for a 9" × 13" pan. If the only pan available is 8" × 8", what ratio should be used to reduce the recipe?
64/117, but using 1/2 might be close enough.

EVALUATION
Alternative Assessment
Questions 18-23 can be used for **oral** assessment. Have students read the questions, answer them, and explain their solutions out loud; discuss alternate ways to answer the questions.

NAME _____

LESSON **MASTER 12-4**
QUESTIONS ON **SPUR** OBJECTIVES

■ **PROPERTIES** *Objective E (See pages 624–627 for objectives.)*

1. Write three true proportions involving the numbers 5, 9, 15, 27.
any 3 of: $\frac{5}{15} = \frac{9}{27}$, $\frac{15}{5} = \frac{27}{9}$, $\frac{5}{9} = \frac{15}{27}$, $\frac{9}{27} = \frac{5}{15}$, $\frac{15}{27} = \frac{9}{15}$

2. Write three true proportions involving the numbers 12, 16, 21, 28.
any 3 of: $\frac{12}{16} = \frac{21}{28}$, $\frac{16}{12} = \frac{28}{21}$, $\frac{12}{21} = \frac{16}{28}$, $\frac{16}{21} = \frac{12}{28}$, $\frac{28}{12} = \frac{16}{21}$

3. If $\frac{a}{n} = \frac{a}{p}$, write three other true proportions.
$\frac{\ell}{n} = \frac{p}{a}$, $\frac{\ell}{p} = \frac{n}{a}$, $\frac{n}{\ell} = \frac{p}{a}$, $\frac{a}{n}$

4. If the Means-Exchange Property is applied to $\frac{4}{y} = \frac{9}{15}$, what proportion results? $\frac{4}{9} = \frac{y}{15}$

5. If the Reciprocals Property is applied to the proportion $\frac{1}{a} = \frac{x}{b}$, what proportion results? $\frac{a}{1} = \frac{x}{b}$

6. If $5x = 7y$, write three true proportions using 5, x, 7, and y.
any 3 of: $\frac{5}{7} = \frac{y}{x}$, $\frac{7}{5} = \frac{x}{y}$, $\frac{5}{y} = \frac{7}{x}$, $\frac{y}{5} = \frac{x}{7}$

■ **USES** *Objective G*

7. If 15 pencils cost 65 cents, about how much will 50 pencils cost? | **217 cents**

8. If 3 pounds of apples cost $2.15, how much would 4.8 pounds cost? | **$3.44**

9. The amount of pull that a spring exerts is proportional to the distance it is stretched from its rest position. If a spring exerts a pull of 2 pounds when it is stretched 9 inches, how much of a pull would it exert when stretched 12 inches? | $2\frac{2}{3}$ **lb**

10. If you can drive b miles in h hours, how many miles can you drive in s hours? | $\frac{sb}{h}$

Geometry © Scott, Foresman and Company | **111**

OBJECTIVES

C Find angle measures, lengths, perimeters, areas, and volumes in similar figures.

D Recognize and apply properties of size transformations and similar figures.

G Identify and determine proportional lengths and distances in real situations.

TEACHING NOTES

Just as you may have begun the discussion of properties of size transformations by writing down the properties of reflections, you might begin the discussion of similar figures by writing down the definition of congruence. Then put parentheses around certain words and show replacements as indicated below. Two figures *F* and *G* are (congruent) **similar,** written *F* (≅) ~ *G*, if and only if there is a composite of (reflections) **reflections and size changes** mapping *F* onto *G*.

The Similar Figures Theorem is also analogous to a theorem of congruence. There are only two words changed.

If two figures are (congruent) **similar,** then:
(a) corresponding angles are congruent;
(b) corresponding lengths are (congruent) **proportional.**

You may wish to spend some time discussing scale models, such as model airplanes, dolls, and so on. Because

LESSON

12-5

Similar Figures

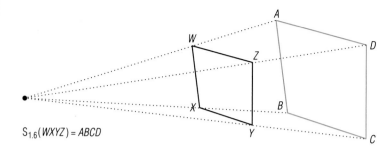

$S_{1.6}(WXYZ) = ABCD$

In geometry, the word "similar" has a very precise meaning. Quadrilaterals *ABCD* and *WXYZ* above are similar to each other. Triangles *ABC*, *PQR*, *SQT*, and *XYZ* below are also similar.

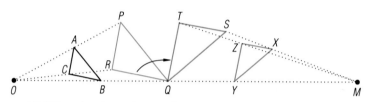

$\triangle PQR$ is a size change image of $\triangle ABC$.   (center *O*, magnitude 1.8)
$\triangle SQT$ is a rotation image of $\triangle PQR$.   (center *Q*, magnitude 90°)
$\triangle XYZ$ is a size change image of $\triangle SQT$.   (center *M*, magnitude 0.8)

The definition of *similarity transformation* encompasses all these possibilities.

Definition:

A transformation is a **similarity transformation** if and only if it is the composite of size changes and reflections.

A figure and its image under these transformations are called *similar*.

Definition:

Two figures F and G are **similar,** written F ~ G, if and only if there is a similarity transformation mapping one onto the other.

586

When the size changes have magnitude 1, then the similarity transformation is a composite solely of reflections. Figures and their images are then congruent. Thus two congruent figures are also similar.

Here is a hierarchy of transformations you have studied, with similarity transformations and size changes included.

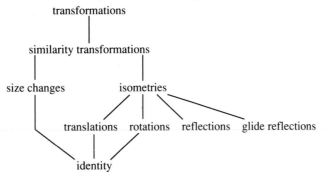

The basic properties of similar figures come from preservation properties of similarity transformations. Compare these lists.

Preserved under reflections	Preserved under size transformations
Angle measure	Angle measure
Betweenness	Betweenness
Collinearity	Collinearity
Distance	

Those properties common to both columns are preserved by similarity transformations. Thus similarity transformations have the A-B-C preservation properties. However, distance is not preserved. Because size transformations are involved, similarity transformations multiply distance by a constant amount. Thus the ratios of image lengths to preimage lengths are equal.

Similar Figures Theorem:

If two figures are similar, then:
(a) corresponding angles are congruent;
(b) corresponding lengths are proportional.

The ratio of the length of an image to the length of a preimage is called the **ratio of similitude.** It is the product of the scale factors of all size transformations used in the composite similarity transformation. Unless otherwise specified, F ~ G with *ratio of similitude k* means that lengths in G divided by corresponding lengths in F equal k. As with congruence, corresponding vertices are put in order.

corresponding angles are congruent, the scale models look like the real thing. Given lengths of *any* pair of corresponding segments on the model and the real object, one can determine the scale.

The transformation approach is more powerful than Euclid's; without it one needs to spend time proving individual theorems such as: If two triangles are similar, then corresponding altitudes are in the same ratio as the ratio of similitude. Using the transformation approach, all corresponding lengths are dealt with intuitively at the same time.

Reading You may wish to read this lesson aloud together with an emphasis on the main ideas. Ask what clues are given to help students remember the properties of similarity transformations and how these clues can be used to find the solutions to the Examples.

Error Analysis Setting up the proportions used in the Examples may be difficult for some students if they are not careful to match up the corresponding sides correctly. A good rule to remember is to put the corresponding sides of the same figure "all on the top" or "all on the bottom" of the proportion. That is, the corresponding sides of the same figure should both be numerators or both be denominators in the proportion.

LESSON 12-5 *Similar Figures* **587**

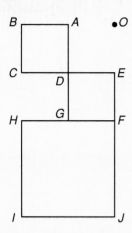
Example 1 In the figure, $r_\ell \circ S_{2.5}(ABCD) = WXYZ$, where the center of $S_{2.5}$ is point *O*.

a. If m∠*B* = 85, what other angle has measure 85?
b. If *CD* = 12, what other length can be determined and what is this length?

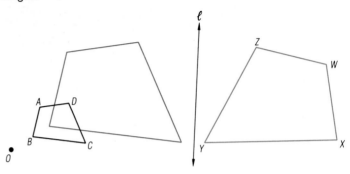

Solution The figures are similar, since $r_\ell \circ S_{2.5}$ is a composite of a reflection and a size change.

a. By the Similar Figures Theorem, corresponding angles are congruent:

∠*A* ≅ ∠*W*, ∠*B* ≅ ∠*X*, ∠*C* ≅ ∠*Y*, and ∠*D* ≅ ∠*Z*.

Since m∠*B* = 85, so also m∠*X* = 85.

b. By the Similar Figures Theorem, corresponding sides are proportional. These ratios equal 2.5, the ratio of similitude.

$$\frac{WX}{AB} = \frac{XY}{BC} = \frac{YZ}{CD} = \frac{ZW}{DA} = 2.5$$

Since *CD* = 12, the length of the corresponding side *YZ* can be determined.

$$\frac{YZ}{12} = 2.5$$
$$YZ = 12 \cdot 2.5 = 30$$

When examining similar figures, always look first for corresponding vertices. These give the pairs of congruent angles. Look next at corresponding sides.

Example 2 △*ABC* ~ △*TOP* with lengths and angle measures as indicated.

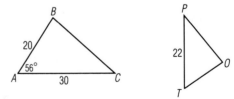

Find as many lengths and angle measures in △*TOP* as you can.

Solution Angle measures: $\angle T$ corresponds to $\angle A$. In similar figures, corresponding angles are congruent. So $m\angle T = m\angle A = 56$.

Lengths: Since corresponding sides are proportional, $\dfrac{PT}{CA} = \dfrac{TO}{AB} = \dfrac{OP}{BC}$.

Now substitute the three known lengths.

$$\frac{22}{30} = \frac{TO}{20} = \frac{OP}{BC}$$

Use the equality of the left and middle ratios.

$$\frac{22}{30} = \frac{TO}{20}$$

By the Means-Extremes Property, $30 \cdot TO = 440$, so

$$TO = \frac{440}{30} = 14\frac{2}{3} \approx 14.67.$$

Neither BC nor OP can be found using the Similar Figures Theorem.

In Example 2, enough information is given to determine all sides and angle measures in each triangle, but a theorem from trigonometry (the Law of Cosines) is needed. That theorem is not covered in this book.

Here is a problem you have learned to solve in previous years. Now you can analyze it using the language of similarity.

■ ■ ■ ■ ■ ■ ■ ■

Example 3   A dollhouse is $\frac{1}{12}$ actual size. If a table in the house is an oval $6\frac{1}{2}''$ long and $4\frac{3}{8}''$ wide, how long and wide is the actual table it models?

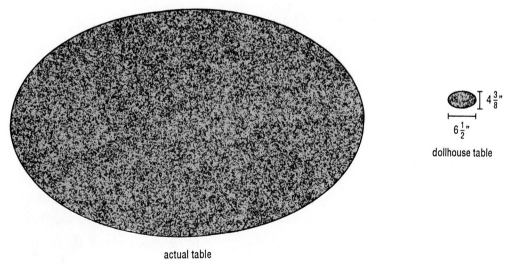

actual table

dollhouse table

Questions 1-3: Often the more complicated a figure is, the easier it is to see the similarity. Thus, the figures used in these questions are seen to be similar easily, whereas with the pentagons of **Questions 15-17,** it is more difficult to see the similarity, and, in fact, the triangles on page 586 may be the most difficult figures to see the similarity.

Questions 11-14:
Students may wonder whether there is any transformation that is *not* a similarity transformation. Refer them back to Lesson 6-1 in which there are numerous examples of transformations that are not similarities.

Questions 15-17: You may wish to add some angle measurements and side lengths to these figures and have students calculate the corresponding angles and sides.

Question 20: In general, scale factors are multiplicative. That is, the composite of a size change of magnitude *x* with a size change of magnitude *y* is a size change of magnitude *xy*. However, many students think the magnitudes should be added. This is probably because students have far less experience with multiplication than addition. You might ask: Suppose a copy machine can reduce a picture to 70% of its original length. What is the result of two consecutive reductions? (The result is a picture whose length is 49% of the original length.)

Solution The two tables D (for doll) and A (for actual) are similar. So A ~ D and the ratio of similitude is $\frac{1}{12}$.

Corresponding lengths are proportional. So

$$\frac{\text{dollhouse width}}{\text{actual width}} = \frac{\text{dollhouse length}}{\text{actual length}} = \frac{1}{12}.$$

Substitute for the doll house table dimensions and let *L* and *W* be the actual length and width.

$$\frac{4\frac{3}{8}}{W} = \frac{6\frac{1}{2}}{L} = \frac{1}{12}$$

Now solve. Since $\frac{4\frac{3}{8}}{W} = \frac{1}{12}$, $W = 12 \cdot 4\frac{3}{8}'' = 52\frac{1}{2}''$.

Since $\frac{6\frac{1}{2}}{L} = \frac{1}{12}$, $L = 12 \cdot 6\frac{1}{2}'' = 78''$.

Check $\frac{78}{6.5} = 12$ and $\frac{52.5}{4.375} = 12$, so the actual measurements are 12 times the measurements of the model.

Questions

Covering the Reading

In 1–3, use the sketch at the right. Figure III is the image of Figure I under S ∘ r$_\ell$, where S is the size transformation with center *C*, magnitude 2.3.

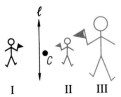

I   II   III

1. S · r$_\ell$ is what kind of transformation? **a similarity transformation**

2. Figures I and III are __?__ · **similar**

3. Figures I and II are both __?__ and __?__ · **congruent, similar**

4. The symbol "~" is read __?__ · **is similar to**

5. Define: similar figures. **Two figures are similar if and only if there is a similarity transformation mapping one onto the other.**

In 6–10, does every similarity transformation preserve the given property?

6. betweenness **Yes**   **7.** angle measure **Yes**   **8.** orientation **No**

9. distance **No**   **10.** "tilt" **No**

In 11–14, is the transformation a similarity transformation?

11. a reflection **Yes**   **12.** a size change with magnitude $\frac{1}{3}$ **Yes**

13. a translation **Yes**   **14.** the composite of a rotation and a size change
Yes

In 15–17, $ABCDE \sim FGHIJ$. The ratio of similitude is $\frac{4}{7}$.

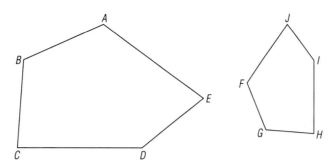

15. *True* or *false*? $m\angle I = \frac{4}{7} \cdot m\angle D$ False

16. Suppose $FJ = 10$.
   a. What other segment length can be determined? *AE*
   b. What is that length? $\frac{70}{4} = 17.5$

17. If $DE = x$, then $IJ = \underline{\ ?\ }$. $\frac{4x}{7}$

Applying the Mathematics

18. A photograph measures 40 mm by 30 mm. The longer side of an enlargement measures 150 mm. What is the length of the shorter side of the enlargement? 112.5 mm

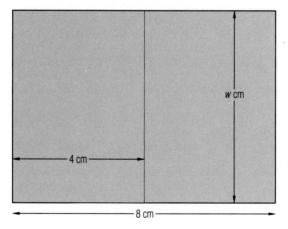

19. a. Draw the image of the logo at the left under a size change with magnitude 2. Then draw an enlargement of the image with a scale factor of 1.5. See margin.
   b. How does the final image compare to the original logo?
   It is the image under an expansion with scale factor 3.

20. If you were to enlarge the logo in Question 19 by a factor of 4, and then transform the image with a scale factor of $\frac{1}{5}$, using a different center than the first transformation, what would be the result?
a size change with scale factor $\frac{4}{5}$

21. Presto Printing makes cards which, when opened, have an outside boundary similar to that when they are folded. Find the width w of the card for the dimensions given. $w = \sqrt{32} \approx 5.66$ cm

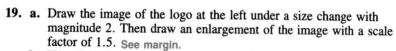

w cm

4 cm

8 cm

FOLLOW-UP

MORE PRACTICE
For more questions on SPUR Objectives, use *Lesson Master 12-5*, shown below.

EXTENSION
The concept of similarity is used often in architecture or design. Interested students could make posters out of pictures of similar figures they find in magazines or newspapers. Emphasize that they should not limit themselves to polygons or to two-dimensional images. Three-dimensional images will tie into the next lesson.

ADDITIONAL ANSWERS
19. a. See Additional Answers in the back of this book.

NAME _____

LESSON **MASTER   12–5**
QUESTIONS ON **SPUR** OBJECTIVES

■**SKILLS**   *Objective C (See pages 624–627 for objectives.)*

1. *BALE ~ CARD*, with sides and measures as indicated. Find as many missing lengths and angle measures as possible.
$m\angle R = 95$,
$\overline{CD} = 12, EL = 15$

In 2–4, *MNOPQ ~ DEFGH*. The ratio of similitude is $\frac{5}{8}$.

2. *True* or *false*? $m\angle N = \frac{5}{8}m\angle E$.   False

3. a. If $MN = 12$, what other segment length can be determined?   *DE*
   b. What is that length?   7.5

4. If $OP = y$, then $FG = \underline{\ \frac{5y}{8}\ }$.

5. $\triangle ABC \sim \triangle DEF$. If $BC = 15$, $EF = 40$, and $AB = 9$, find DE.   24

■**PROPERTIES**   *Objective D*

6. Which properties are preserved under a size transformation? Write *Yes* or *No*.
   a. betweenness   Yes   **b.** distance   No
   b. orientation   No   **d.** angle measure   Yes

■**USES**   *Objective G*

7. A painting measures 24 inches wide and 30 inches high. A reproduction which is similar to the original is 20 inches wide. How high is the reproduction?   25 in.

8. The two triangular ramp supports shown are similar. The smaller support has a side of 40 cm, and the other has a side of 75 cm. If the smaller support has a base of 8 cm, what is the length of the base of the larger support?   15 cm

112   *Geometry © Scott, Foresman and Company*

591

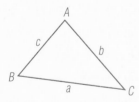
In the figure below, the two right cones are similar. $QS = 10$, $MZ = 5$. T and L are centers of the bases.

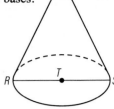

22. **a.** What is the ratio of similitude? $\frac{1}{2}$ (or 2)
    b. If $ST = 6$, find LM. 3

23. $\triangle ABC \sim \triangle DEF$. If $BC = 12$, $DE = 8$, and $EF = 16$, find AB. 6

24. Let S be a similarity transformation and ℓ and m be lines. Tell whether the statement is true or false and justify your answer.
    a. S(ℓ) $\parallel$ ℓ
    b. If $\ell \parallel m$, then S(ℓ) $\parallel$ S(m).
    See margin.

Review

25. If 3 cans of tuna cost $2.00, at this rate how much would 5 cans cost? *(Lesson 12-4)* $\approx$$3.34

26. Given $\frac{a}{b} = \frac{c}{d}$. *True* or *false*?
    a. $\frac{a}{c} = \frac{b}{d}$ True
    b. $\frac{a+b}{b} = \frac{c+d}{d}$ True
    c. $\frac{a}{d} = \frac{c}{b}$ *(Lesson 12-4)* False

27. In the figure at the left, $\triangle ABC$ is the image of $\triangle DBE$ under a size change.
    a. *True* or *false*? $\overleftrightarrow{DE} \parallel \overleftrightarrow{AC}$ **b.** *True* or *false*? $\frac{BD}{AB} = \frac{ED}{AC}$
    c. Solve for x. *(Lessons 12-4, 12-3, 12-2)*
    a) True; b) True; c) 15

28. A spherical rubber ball has an outside diameter of 10 cm. The ball is hollow and the rubber is 1 cm thick. How much rubber is used in making the ball? *(Lesson 10-7)* $\frac{244\pi}{3} \approx 256$ cm^3

29. In triangles XYZ and APD, $\angle X \cong \angle A$, $\angle Y \cong \angle P$, and $\angle Z \cong \angle D$.
    a. Is $\triangle XYZ$ necessarily congruent to $\triangle APD$? No
    b. Justify your answer to **a.** *(Lesson 7-2)*
    The triangles could be similar with a ratio of similitude not equal to 1.

Exploration

30. Scale models are objects that are similar to larger objects. Find a scale model. For the scale model you find:
    a. What is the ratio of similitude?
    b. A length of 1″ on the model corresponds to what length on the larger object it models?
    Answers will vary.

31. In Example 2, BC can be found using a theorem called the Law of Cosines. Look in some other book to find out what this "law" is.
    See margin.

12-6

The Fundamental Theorem of Similarity

In the last lesson, a similarity transformation was defined as a composite of size changes, reflections, rotations, or translations. Similar figures may be 2-dimensional or 3-dimensional because a similarity transformation can be done in three dimensions just as easily as in two. Any point can be the center of the size change and any real number the scale factor. The characteristics of corresponding parts that hold for similar plane figures hold for similar space figures—corresponding distances are multiplied by the scale factor and corresponding angles are congruent.

In similar figures, perimeters, areas, and volumes satisfy a very important relationship, which is the subject of this lesson.

Example 1 Two models of the same schooner (a boat with front and rear masts) are made. Each is similar to the original, so they are similar to each other. The bigger model is 120 cm long, the smaller 30 cm long.

a. How do their heights compare?
b. How do the areas of their sails compare?
c. How do the volumes of their hulls (the bodies of the boats) compare?

30 cm   120 cm

OBJECTIVES

C Find angle measures, lengths, perimeters, areas, and volumes in similar figures.
D Recognize and apply properties of size transformations and similar figures.
H Apply the Fundamental Theorem of Similarity in real situations.

TEACHING NOTES

You may wish to restate the Fundamental Theorem of Similarity in the following way: In similar figures with ratio of similitude k:

$$\frac{V'}{V} = k^3$$

$$\frac{A'}{A} = k^2$$

$$\frac{p'}{p} = k$$

Here is still another way. In similar figures with ratio of similitude k:

$$\frac{V'}{V} = \left(\frac{p'}{p}\right)^3 = \frac{p'^3}{p^3}$$

$$\frac{A'}{A} = \left(\frac{p'}{p}\right)^2 = \frac{p'^2}{p^2}$$

There is no better way to explain the ideas of this lesson than to use physical models. Possible examples other than those mentioned in the lesson are basketballs of different sizes and U.S. flags.

593

Alternate Approach
You might want to demonstrate the Fundamental Theorem of Similarity by setting up proportions using the ratio of similitude. For example, in **Question 11a,** the proportion would be $(\frac{8}{12})^3 = \frac{100}{x}$. Students would then solve the proportion by the Means-Extremes Property.

Solution

a. Corresponding lengths in similar figures are proportional. Thus

$$\frac{\text{height of large schooner}}{\text{height of small schooner}} = \frac{\text{length of large schooner}}{\text{length of small schooner}} = \frac{120 \text{ cm}}{30 \text{ cm}} = 4.$$

So the height of the large schooner is 4 times that of the small schooner.

b. Let the dimensions of a sail in the small schooner be ℓ and w. The sail's area is thus ℓw. The dimensions of the corresponding sail in the larger schooner must be 4ℓ and $4w$, because the ratio of lengths is 4. So the corresponding sail's area is $4\ell \cdot 4w = 16\ell w$. Thus the areas of sails in the large schooner are 16 times those of the small schooner.

c. Think of the smaller hull as being made up of small cubes with sides s. The larger hull is made up of the same number of cubes, each of side $4s$.

$$\frac{\text{volume of part of larger hull}}{\text{volume of part of smaller hull}} = \frac{(4s)^3}{s^3} = \frac{64s^3}{s^3} = 64$$

The volume of the larger hull is 64 times the volume of the smaller.

The ratio of similitude in Example 1 is 4. Lengths in the smaller model are multiplied by 4 to yield corresponding lengths in the larger model. Areas are multiplied by 16, which is 4^2, and volumes are multiplied by 64, which is 4^3. All this verifies the *Fundamental Theorem of Similarity*, which applies to all plane or solid figures.

Fundamental Theorem of Similarity:

If $G \sim G'$ and k is the ratio of similitude, then

(a) $\text{Perimeter}(G') = k \cdot \text{Perimeter}(G)$ or $\dfrac{\text{Perimeter}(G')}{\text{Perimeter}(G)} = k$;

(b) $\text{Area}(G') = k^2 \cdot \text{Area}(G)$ or $\dfrac{\text{Area}(G')}{\text{Area}(G)} = k^2$; and

(c) $\text{Volume}(G') = k^3 \cdot \text{Volume}(G)$ or $\dfrac{\text{Volume}(G')}{\text{Volume}(G)} = k^3$.

Proof

(a) Perimeter is just the sum of the lengths. Suppose lengths $a, b, c, d, e, \ldots$ make up the perimeter of G. Then lengths $ka, kb, kc, kd, ke, \ldots$ make up the perimeter of G'.

$$\text{Perimeter}(G') = ka + kb + kc + kd + ke + \ldots$$
$$= k(a + b + c + d + e + \ldots)$$
$$= k \cdot \text{Perimeter}(G)$$

594

(b) Let A = the area of G. Then you could think of the area of G as the sum of areas of A unit squares. Then the area of G′ is the sum of areas of A squares k units on a side. Since each square in G′ has area k^2,

$$\text{Area of G}' = A \cdot k^2 = k^2 \cdot \text{Area of G}.$$

(c) The argument is identical to that in part (c) of Example 1, except that you should use k for the ratio of similitude and make it apply to more than schooners.

Example 2 $\triangle ABC \sim \triangle DEF$. Give the ratios of the perimeters and areas of those triangles.

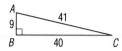 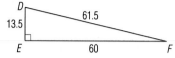

Solution   Use the Fundamental Theorem of Similarity. The ratio of similitude is $\frac{60}{40} = 1.5$. So the ratio of perimeters is 1.5 and the ratio of areas is 1.5^2, which is 2.25.

Check   The perimeters and areas can be calculated directly.

$\triangle ABC$
Perimeter = 9 + 40 + 41
= 90 units
Area $= \frac{1}{2} \cdot 40 \cdot 9$
= 180 square units

$\triangle DEF$
Perimeter = 13.5 + 60 + 61.5
= 135 units
Area $= \frac{1}{2} \cdot 13.5 \cdot 60$
= 405 square units

Thus ratio of perimeters = $\frac{135}{90}$ = 1.5

ratio of areas = $\frac{405}{180}$ = 2.25.

The Fundamental Theorem of Similarity can be verified by looking at area formulas. Here are some area formulas: $A = \pi r^2$ (circles), $A = \ell w$ (rectangles), $A = \frac{1}{2} h(b_1 + b_2)$ (trapezoids), L.A. $= ph$ (cylinders or prisms). Notice that each area formula involves the product of two lengths. (That's why the result is measured in *square* units.) So if every length is multiplied by k, the area will be multiplied by k^2.

Volume formulas also verify the Fundamental Theorem of Similarity. Consider some volume formulas: $V = \ell wh$ (boxes), $V = \frac{4}{3}\pi r^3$ (spheres), $V = \frac{1}{3}Bh$ (pyramids or cones). Each formula involves the product of three lengths. (For pyramids or cones, it looks as if there are only two lengths multiplied, but B is an area, so B itself is the product of two lengths.) When each length is multiplied by k, the volume will be multiplied by k^3.

LESSON 12-6   The Fundamental Theorem of Similarity   **595**

ADDITIONAL EXAMPLES
1. $\triangle ABC$ has sides of lengths 12, 15, and 17. The smallest side of a similar triangle has length 5.
a. What is the perimeter of the similar triangle?
Solve $\frac{44}{x} = \frac{12}{5}$ to get
$x = 18\frac{1}{3}$.
b. How do their areas compare?
The first triangle has 5.76 times the area of the second.

2. A wooden shed is to be built, and a model of the shed is made $\frac{1}{6}$ of the actual size and from the same material. If the model weighs 5 pounds, what will be the weight of the wood needed for the actual shed?
1080 pounds

NOTES ON QUESTIONS

Question 1: The answers to this question can be found in two ways: (1) by calculating the quantities for each box and then dividing, or (2) by using the ratio of similitude and the Fundamental Theorem of Similarity. Students will answer the questions either way; use one answer to check the other.

Question 9: The answer to part **a** is found by calculating $10 + 10 + \sqrt{40}$. There have not been many expressions of the form $a + \sqrt{b}$ in this book, and students may want to combine 20 and $\sqrt{40}$. Remind students that they could estimate $20 + \sqrt{40}$ by using their calculators.

Question 12: Notice that the individual side lengths do not need to be known.

Making Connections for Question 13: In general, larger objects made from the same material as smaller objects are far heavier than one would think. (See also Additional Example 2.) This question is directly related to the next lesson.

To summarize the basic properties of measures in similar figures: If two figures are similar with ratio of similitude k, then

corresponding angle measures are equal;
corresponding lengths and perimeters are in the ratio k;
corresponding areas and surface areas are in the ratio k^2;
corresponding volumes are in the ratio k^3.

Some people remember the Fundamental Theorem of Similarity by remembering the units in which objects are measured. Since volume is measured in cubic units, the ratio of volumes of similar figures is k^3. Since area and surface area are measured in square units, the ratio of areas or surface areas of similar figures is k^2. Since lengths and perimeter are measured in linear units, the ratio of linear measures in similar figures is k^1, which is k.

Questions

Covering the Reading

1. Here are two similar boxes.

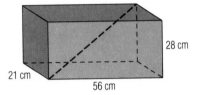

   a. What is the ratio of the lengths of their longest diagonals? $\frac{5}{7}$
   b. What is the ratio of the areas of their largest faces? $\frac{25}{49}$
   c. What is the ratio of their volumes? $\frac{125}{343}$ (or $\frac{343}{125}$)

2. Area is a product of __?__ lengths. two

3. Volume is a product of __?__ lengths. three

4. The ratio of similitude of two figures is $\frac{5}{3}$. Find the ratio of their
   a. perimeters $\frac{5}{3}$ **b.** areas $\frac{25}{9}$
   c. volumes $\frac{125}{27}$ **d.** corresponding sides. $\frac{5}{3}$

5. R ~ R', $k = 4$, and Volume(R) = 34 cubic units. Find Volume(R').
   2176 units³

6. G ~ G', $k = \frac{2}{3}$, and Area(G) = 72 square meters. Find Area(G').
   32 meters²

7. Two squares have sides 5 in. and 13 in. Find the ratio of their perimeters. $\frac{5}{13}$ (or $\frac{13}{5}$)

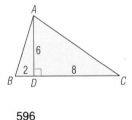

8. **a.** Find the area of $\triangle ABC$ at the left. **30 units²**
   b. If $\triangle ABC \sim \triangle EFG$ with ratio of similitude 5, what is the area of $\triangle EFG$? **750 units²**

Martin Luther King, Jr.

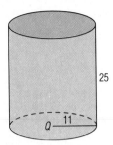

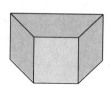

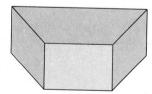

9. a. Find the perimeter of $\triangle ABC$ in Question 8.
   b. Find the perimeter of $\triangle EFG$ in Question 8.
   a) $20 + \sqrt{40} \approx 26.32$ units; b) $100 + 5\sqrt{40} \approx 131.62$ units

10. a. Find the volume and surface area of right cylinder Q below.
   b. Let cylinder R be the image of cylinder Q under a size change with magnitude 3. Cylinder R will have __?__ times the volume of cylinder Q and __?__ times the surface area.
   c. Find the volume and surface area of cylinder R.
   a) $V = 3025\pi$ units^3; S.A. $= 792\pi$ units^2 b) 27, 9
   c) $V = 81{,}675\pi$ units^3
   S.A. $= 7128\pi$ units^2

25

Q   11

11. Corresponding sides of two similar pyramids are 8 and 12 inches.
   a. Find the volume of the larger solid, if the smaller has volume 100 cubic inches. 337.5 in.^{3}
   b. Find the volume of the smaller solid, if the larger has volume 100 cubic inches. $\approx$29.63 in.^{3}

12. Two similar nonregular 15-gons have perimeters of 20 ft and 28 ft, respectively. What is the ratio of the length of a side of the smaller to the length of the corresponding side of the larger? $\frac{20}{28} = \frac{5}{7} \approx .71$.

13. On two similar solid brass statues of Martin Luther King, Jr., the length of the left ear on one is 3 cm and on the other is 5 cm.
   a. If the base area of the larger statue is 50 cm^2, find the base area of the smaller statue. 18 cm^2
   b. The volume of brass used to make the smaller was 216 cm^3. What volume of brass was used to make the larger? 1000 cm^3

14. The volumes of two spheres are 288π and 7776π cubic mm.
   a. What is a ratio of similitude for these spheres? 3 or $\frac{1}{3}$
   b. What is a ratio of their surface areas? 9 or $\frac{1}{9}$

15. *Multiple choice.* The bases of two quadrangular prisms are similar with ratio of similitude 1.5, but the prisms have the same height. What is the ratio of the volumes?

   (a) 1.5   (b) 2.25
   (c) 3   (d) 4.5
   (e) cannot be determined from the given information (b)

LESSON 12-6   The Fundamental Theorem of Similarity   **597**

16. Below, Figure Q ~ Figure R. Name the ratio of similitude. *(Lesson 12-5)* $\frac{3}{2}$

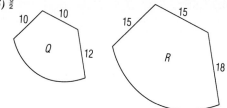

17. $\triangle ABC \sim \triangle DEF$ with ratio of similitude 2.5. If $AB = 3$, $BC = 5$, and m∠B = 135, find as many lengths and angle measures in $\triangle DEF$ as you can. *(Lesson 12-5)* See margin.

18. A comic strip measures 6″ by 2″. The smaller sides of a reduction measure $\frac{1}{2}$″. What are the lengths of the larger sides of the reduction? *(Lesson 12-5)* $1\frac{1}{2}$″

19. Given $\frac{x}{10} = \frac{11}{y}$. Find three other true proportions involving these numbers. *(Lesson 12-4)* $\frac{x}{11} = \frac{10}{y}$; $\frac{10}{x} = \frac{y}{11}$; $\frac{11}{x} = \frac{y}{10}$

20. A goal post and its shadow are shown. The sides of the goal post cast shadows 20 meters long. The crossbar is 3 m high; the post part beneath the crossbar casts a shadow 8 m long. What is the height of the goalpost? *(Lesson 12-4)* 7.5 m

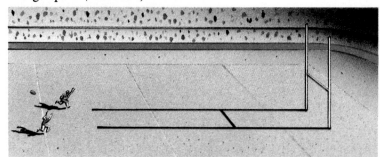

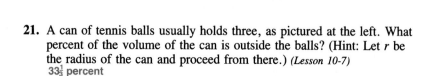

21. A can of tennis balls usually holds three, as pictured at the left. What percent of the volume of the can is outside the balls? (Hint: Let r be the radius of the can and proceed from there.) *(Lesson 10-7)* $33\frac{1}{3}$ percent

22. In the Exploration to Lesson 12-5, you were asked to find a scale model of an actual object. Weigh the scale model you found. If the actual object were made from the same materials, what would be its weight? Answers will vary.

LESSON 12-7

Can There Be Giants?

Giants are common characters in children's stories; an example is the giant from *Jack and the Beanstalk.* Saturday morning cartoons often have giant creatures with human shape. But according to the *Guinness Book of World Records,* the tallest man on record was Robert Wadlow from Alton, Illinois. On June 27, 1940, at age 22, he was measured at 8 feet, 11.1 inches. Wadlow was about 1.5 times the height of a typical male. Can humans be much taller? The Fundamental Theorem of Similarity provides the answer.

Let's look at what the theorem reveals, using an example from a famous novel. In *Gulliver's Travels,* Jonathan Swift writes about Gulliver visiting the land of Brobdingnag, where the Brobdingnagians are similar to us but 12 times as tall. Their volume, and thus their weight, would be 12^3 times ours. Since $12^3 = 1728$, they would weigh about 1728 times what we weigh. If you weigh 140 pounds, a similar Brobdingnagian would weigh 241,920 pounds! They would support this weight on feet covering a region whose area is only 12^2 or 144 times what we stand on. So each bone of a Brobdingnagian would have to carry 12 times as much weight as ours.

Even champion weightlifters seldom lift more than twice their body weight—and when they do, it is only for a few seconds. You can imagine what lifting 12 times your weight would do. It would quickly break your bones!

You might think that a giant's body would find some way of dealing with the extra weight. But it can't. Wadlow had to wear a brace to support his weight. He had an accident involving the brace and cellulitis set in. Eighteen days after his height was measured in June, 1940, he died in Manistee, Michigan.

Animals in nature have developed within the constraints imposed by the Fundamental Theorem of Similarity. Elephants have legs with large horizontal cross-sectional surface areas to support their great weight. Thoroughbred race horses have skinny legs which enable

LESSON 12-7 Can There Be Giants? **599**

RESOURCES
- Lesson Master 12-7
- Quiz for Lessons 12-4 through 12-7

OBJECTIVES

D Recognize and apply properties of size transformations and similar figures.
H Apply the Fundamental Theorem of Similarity in real situations.

TEACHING NOTES

Reading Although there is a substantial amount of reading in this lesson, students find the material interesting and can read it on their own. However, be certain to discuss all the Covering the Reading questions.

The cartoons seen by young children illustrate incorrectly many physical and biological laws. For instance, cartoon characters walk off cliffs and do not fall until they realize that there is nothing under them, and there are giant and small creatures with the same shape. Some people believe there can be giant humans. This lesson is designed to show why there cannot be giant humans.

In the first part of this century, many people tried to build ships that would fly. They would build a small model and find that it could fly (much like the paper airplanes and gliders that are toys for children). Then they would use the same materials for the actual plane. They forgot that a larger model would have the cube of the weight but only the square of them to run fast, but the legs are small for their bodies and break easily. When a thoroughbred falls, its legs often break. Draught horses do not have this problem, but they are slow. A mosquito can walk on the surface of water without sinking. It is so light that it will not break the surface tension of the water. It also has thin legs which are fine to support its light body. But that body has a relatively large surface area. Should a raindrop force the body into the water, the surface tension acts like glue on the body's surface and the thin legs cannot pull the mosquito from the water.

The amount of food needed by an animal is proportional to its volume. The Brobdingnagians would consume 1728 times the food needed by Gulliver. A person like Gulliver needs about 19 calories per day per pound of body weight (perhaps 3000 calories) to maintain body weight. The Brobdingnagians would require 1728 times 3000 calories daily to maintain their body weights. That's a lot of food.

Gulliver also visited the land of Lilliput, where people were $\frac{1}{12}$ his height. For Gulliver as for us, a new coat would require about two square yards of material. Clothing is proportional to surface area and is multiplied by k^2, the square of the ratio of similitude. So the Brobdingnagians would require 12^2 or 144 times as much material. The Lilliputians, being $\frac{1}{12}$ Gulliver's height, would require only $(\frac{1}{12})^2$ or $\frac{1}{144}$ times the two square yards needed by Gulliver. Thus similarity answers questions about clothing and food needs as well as the properties of giants.

Example 1 In 1987, Domino's® Pizza sold 12″-diameter pizzas with cheese and one topping for $6.05 (plus tax). Suppose they base their prices on the amount of ingredients and the pizzas have the same thickness. Then what should they charge for a 14″-diameter pizza?

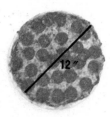 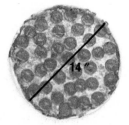

Solution The pizza tops are similar with $k = \frac{14}{12} = \frac{7}{6}$. An immediate response is to charge $\frac{7}{6} \cdot$ $6.05. This is not correct because the crust and toppings are proportional to the *area,* not the linear dimensions. Thus the price, based only on amount of ingredients, would be $6.05 $\cdot (\frac{7}{6})^2 =$ $6.05 $\cdot \frac{49}{36} \approx$ $8.23.

600

Example 2 A solid clay figurine weighs 5 kilograms. A similar one which is twice as tall stands next to it. Could a 4-year old child pick up the taller figurine?

Solution Weight is dependent upon volume. Thus the multiplying factor for weight is the cube of the ratio of similitude, in this case 2^3. The taller figurine weighs $2^3 \cdot 5 = 40$ kg (about 90 pounds). Most children of 4 would not be able to pick up the figurine, and many adults would be surprised at the weight of the figurine.

The Fundamental Theorem of Similarity was known to Euclid, but the structural applications to giants were not recognized until over 1800 years later by the Italian scientist Galileo. He considered this discovery as important as his most famous discovery that when heavier-than-air objects of different weights are dropped from the same height, they fall to the ground at the same time.

Questions

Covering the Reading

In 1–3, according to *Gulliver's Travels,*

1. Brobdingnagians are __?__ times the height of Gulliver, and weigh __?__ times as much. 12, 1728

2. Lilliputians are __?__ times the height of Gulliver and weigh __?__ times as much. $\frac{1}{12}$, $\frac{1}{1728}$

3. Brobdingnagians are __?__ times the height of Lilliputians and weigh __?__ times as much. 144; $144^3 = 2{,}985{,}984$

4. Who was Robert Wadlow? the tallest man on record

In 5–8, consider an imaginary giantess 27 feet tall, which is about 5 times the height of an average woman. If the giantess and woman had similar shapes, how would the quantities compare? See margin.

5. weight
6. nose lengths
7. area of bottom of foot
8. wrist circumference

9. *True* or *false*? Champion weightlifters often lift weights five times their own weight. False

10. *True* or *false*? Prices of pizza are proportional to their diameters. False

11. Why does an elephant need thicker legs for its height than a mosquito? See margin.

12. A scale model is $\frac{1}{15}$ actual size. If it is made from the same materials as the original object, then its weight will be __?__ the weight of the object. The amount of paint to cover the exterior will be __?__ times the paint used to cover the original. $\frac{1}{3375}$, $\frac{1}{225}$

LESSON 12-7 Can There Be Giants?   **601**

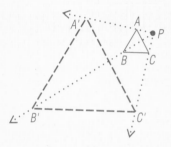
Applying the Mathematics

13. Two similar solid clay figurines are 40 cm and 50 cm tall. If the shorter one weighs 8 kg, how much will the taller one weigh? **15.625 kg**

14. A pizza store manager calculates that the ingredients in a 16″ pizza cost the store $1.50. At this rate, what do the ingredients cost in a 12″ pizza with the same thickness? **≈$0.84**

15. Suppose two boxes have congruent bases, but one box is twice the height of the other.
  a. Are the boxes similar? **No**
  b. How do their volumes compare? **See margin.**
  c. How do their surface areas compare? **See margin.**

16. If a 6-foot-tall basketball player weighs 200 lb, what would you expect a similarly shaped, 7-foot-tall player to weigh? **≈318 lb**

17. The surface area of the earth is about 13 times that of the moon.
  a. What is the ratio of their radii, considering them both to be spheres? $\sqrt{13} \approx 3.6$
  b. What is the ratio of their volumes? $\sqrt{13})^3 \approx 46.9$

Review

18. A hexagon has area 70 units². What is the area of its image under a size change of magnitude $\frac{2}{5}$? *(Lesson 12-6)* **11.2 units²**

19. Below, $\triangle PQR \sim \triangle MST$. Find as many missing lengths and angle measures as possible. *(Lessons 12-5, 12-4)*
$m\angle R = 42$; $m\angle T = 42$; $m\angle S = 43$; $MT = 12.24$; $RQ = 29.8$

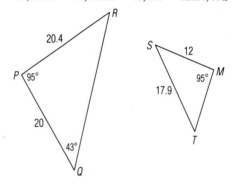

20. Define: similar figures. *(Lesson 12-5)* **See margin.**

21. Draw the image of $\triangle ABC$ below under a size change with center P, magnitude 4. *(Lesson 12-3)* **See margin.**

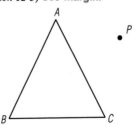

22. Use the figure below.
Given: K is the midpoint of $\overline{FJ}$.
The segments $\overline{KI}$ and $\overline{KG}$ are parallel to $\overline{FH}$ and $\overline{HJ}$, respectively.
Prove: $\triangle FGK \cong \triangle KIJ$. *(Lesson 7-3)* See margin.

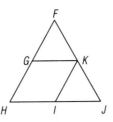

Exploration

23. Below are the men's world weightlifting records as of October 1, 1988, in the clean and jerk.
  a. Calculate the ratios of weight lifted to weightlifter's maximum weight.
  b. What trends do you see?
  c. Give an explanation for any trends you find. See margin.

Naim Suleymanoglu

Weight Class	Men	Country	C & J
52.0 kg	He Zhuoqiang	China	153.0 kg
56.0 kg	Neno Terziiski	Bulgaria	171.0 kg
60.0 kg	Naim Suleymanoglu	Turkey	190.0 kg
67.0 kg	Mikhail Petrov	Bulgaria	200.5 kg
75.0 kg	Alexander Varbanov	Bulgaria	215.5 kg
82.5 kg	Asen Zlatev	Bulgaria	225.0 kg
90.0 kg	Anatoli Khrapaty	USSR	235.0 kg
100.0 kg	Pavel Kuznietsov	USSR	241.5 kg
110.0 kg	Yuri Zacharevich	USSR	250.5 kg
Over 110.0 kg	Leonid Taranenko	USSR	265.5 kg

24. Find the costs of two different size pizzas (with the same ingredients) at a local pizza parlor.
  a. What is the ratio of the diameters of the pizzas?
  b. What is the ratio of the costs of the pizzas?
  c. Are costs based on area?
  d. What are the costs in making a pizza?
  Answers may vary.

FOLLOW-UP

MORE PRACTICE
For more questions on SPUR Objectives, use *Lesson Master 12-7,* shown below.

EXTENSION
You might wish to assign an extra credit report on one of the topics discussed in this lesson: Robert Wadlow, *Gulliver's Travels,* weightlifting trends, or the pizza topic of **Question 24.**

EVALUATION
A quiz covering Lessons 12-4 through 12-7 is provided in the Teacher's Resource File.

NAME _____

LESSON **MASTER   12–7**
QUESTIONS ON **SPUR** OBJECTIVES

■**PROPERTIES** *Objective D (See pages 624–627 for objectives.)*

1. If there were a person who was $\frac{1}{2}$ as tall as you and similar to you, that person would weigh ___1/8___ as much as you weigh.

2. Why does a dog need thicker legs for its height than an insect?
The strength of the bones in the insect and the
dog is relatively constant, but the weight of the
animal grows as the cube of their heights; thus, to
support this greater weight, the bones of the dog
must be thicker.

■**USES** *Objective H*

3. A scale model of a bridge is $\frac{1}{50}$ the size of the actual bridge. How many times more material would be required to build the larger bridge? ___250,000___

4. A small, similar model is made of a sculpture that is $\frac{1}{3}$ the height of the projected sculpture. If 15 pounds were the weight of the scale model, how much would the full-size sculpture weigh? ___≈555.6 lb___

5. If the price of a pizza is proportional to the amount of ingredients covering it, and a 12-inch pizza costs $8.00, how much should a 16-inch pizza of the same thickness cost? ___$14.22___

6. The gravitational pull of an object is proportional to its mass (volume). If a certain star had a diameter twice that of our sun, how many times greater would its gravitational pull be? ___8___

7. The amount of drag that a parachute provides is proportional to its surface area. A parachute has a diameter of 5 feet. An engineer wants to multiply the drag of a parachute by a factor of 20. What should the diameter of the desired parachute be? ___≈22.36 ft___

114   Geometry © Scott, Foresman and Company

OBJECTIVE

F Determine whether or not triangles are similar using the SSS Similarity Theorem.

TEACHING NOTES

Recall that we indicated (in Lesson 12-5) that determining similarity in triangles by sight in more difficult than determining similarity in more complicated figures. Thus, it is particularly useful to have theorems indicating when triangles are similar.

In this lesson, the correspondences with congruence theorems are more than analogies, because each congruence theorem is used to deduce its similarity counterpart. For instance, the SSS Congruence Theorem is critical in deducing the SSS Similarity Theorem. Go through the example on this page and the proof on page 605 in detail.

The difficult part of **Example 2** is determining which vertices correspond. The following are two ways of doing this. (1) Order the sides by length. Then the intersection of the two longest sides in each triangle corresponds, the intersection of the two shortest sides corresponds, and the third vertices correspond. (2) Order the sides by length. Then the vertices opposite the longest sides correspond; the vertices opposite the middle sides

LESSON

12-8

The SSS Similarity Theorem

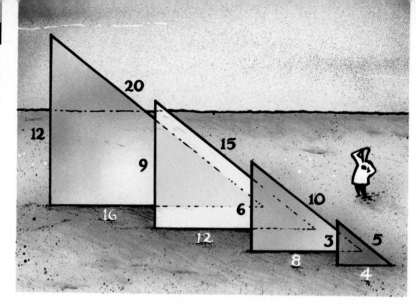

Recall the SSS Congruence Theorem: If three sides of one triangle are congruent to three sides of a second triangle, then the triangles are congruent.

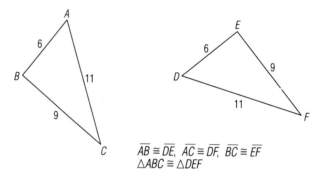

$$\overline{AB} \cong \overline{DE}, \ \overline{AC} \cong \overline{DF}, \ \overline{BC} \cong \overline{EF}$$
$$\triangle ABC \cong \triangle DEF$$

There is also an SSS Similarity Theorem. For it, the sides of the triangles need to be proportional. That is, their ratios must be equal. Below, each ratio of corresponding sides equals 2: $\frac{12}{6} = \frac{22}{11} = \frac{18}{9}$. The SSS Similarity Theorem asserts that $\triangle ABC \sim \triangle GHI$.

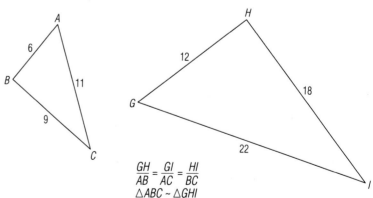

$$\frac{GH}{AB} = \frac{GI}{AC} = \frac{HI}{BC}$$
$$\triangle ABC \sim \triangle GHI$$

604

SSS Similarity Theorem:

If the three sides of one triangle are proportional to the three sides of a second triangle, then the triangles are similar.

Proof

Draw   As usual, the first task is to draw a figure and state the given and what is to be proved in terms of that figure.

Given: $\dfrac{XY}{AB} = \dfrac{YZ}{BC} = \dfrac{XZ}{AC}$.

Prove: $\triangle ABC \sim \triangle XYZ$.

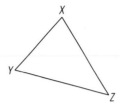

Analyze   The idea is to prove that there is a size transformation image of $\triangle ABC$ which is *congruent* to $\triangle XYZ$. Then the definition of similar figures (sufficient condition) shows the triangles are similar.

Write   Let $k = \dfrac{XY}{AB}$. Then by transitivity, $k = \dfrac{YZ}{BC}$ and $k = \dfrac{XZ}{AC}$. Apply *any* size transformation with magnitude k to $\triangle ABC$.

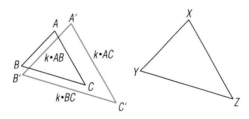

In the image $\triangle A'B'C'$, $A'B' = k \cdot AB$, $B'C' = k \cdot BC$, and $A'C' = k \cdot AC$.

But $k \cdot AB = \dfrac{XY}{AB} \cdot AB = XY$

$k \cdot BC = \dfrac{YZ}{BC} \cdot BC = YZ$

$k \cdot AC = \dfrac{XZ}{AC} \cdot AC = XZ$.

Thus the three sides of $\triangle A'B'C'$ have the same lengths as the sides of $\triangle XYZ$. So by the SSS Congruence Theorem, $\triangle A'B'C' \cong \triangle XYZ$. The definition of congruence tells us there is an isometry mapping $\triangle A'B'C'$ onto $\triangle XYZ$. So there is a composite of a size change (the one we started with) and an isometry mapping $\triangle ABC$ onto $\triangle XYZ$. By the definition of similarity, $\triangle ABC \sim \triangle XYZ$.

Alternate Approach
You might ask several students to state the SSS Congruence Theorem and use it to name the congruent sides and angles of two congruent triangles. Then you can change the wording to fit the SSS Similarity Theorem. Have them name the congruent angles and set up the proportions which fit the sides.

ADDITIONAL EXAMPLES
1. *True* or *false*? A triangle with sides 8, 12, and 16 is similar to a triangle with sides 12, 16, and 24.

False, since not all of $\frac{8}{12}$, $\frac{12}{16}$, and $\frac{16}{24}$ are equal.

2. The large triangle *DEF* has been drawn such that $\triangle ABC \sim \triangle DEF$ with ratio of similitude 2. But someone forgot to put in the vertices and the lengths of sides in the large triangle. Label the triangle correctly.

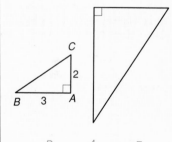

605

Example 1 *True* or *false*? A triangle with sides 3, 4, and 5 is similar to a triangle with sides 8, 6, and 10.

Solution Put the sides in order and take the ratios:

$$\frac{6}{3} \qquad \frac{8}{4} \qquad \frac{10}{5}$$

Since all the ratios are equal, the triangles are similar. The answer is *true*.

Check $3^2 + 4^2 = 5^2$ and $6^2 + 8^2 = 10^2$, so both triangles are right triangles. Since $\angle I$ and $\angle Y$ are both right angles, $\angle I \cong \angle Y$.

In Example 1, the ratio of similitude is either 2 or $\frac{1}{2}$, dependent on which triangle is first. The corresponding sides tell you which vertices correspond. Write the similarity with vertices in corresponding order. Here you could write $\triangle AEI \sim \triangle UOY$. This tells which corresponding angles are congruent. For instance, $\angle E \cong \angle O$. Similar right triangles form the basis for the trigonometry concepts introduced in Chapter 14.

Example 2 Given the two triangles below with sides and approximate angle measures as indicated.

a. Ratios of which sides are equal?
b. Are the triangles similar?
c. Find the measure of each angle of $\triangle XYZ$.
d. $\triangle BAC \sim$ ___?___

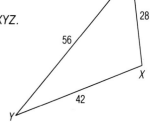

Solution

a. The shortest side in $\triangle ABC$ would have to correspond to the shortest in $\triangle XYZ$. In general, the sides correspond in order of their lengths. Write the extended proportion.

$$\frac{28}{20} = \frac{42}{30} = \frac{56}{40}. \text{ That is, } \frac{XZ}{AC} = \frac{XY}{AB} = \frac{YZ}{BC}.$$

b. Since all three ratios of sides are equal, the triangles are similar due to the SSS Similarity Theorem.

c. The congruent angles are opposite the corresponding sides.
$\overline{BC}$ corresponds to $\overline{YZ}$, so $\angle A \cong \angle X$, so $m\angle X \approx 104.5$.
$\overline{AC}$ corresponds to $\overline{XZ}$, so $\angle B \cong \angle Y$, so $m\angle Y \approx 29$.
$\overline{AB}$ corresponds to $\overline{XY}$, so $\angle C \cong \angle Z$, so $m\angle Z \approx 46.5$.
d. Using the correspondence of angles, $\triangle BAC \sim \triangle YXZ$.

606

Covering the Reading

In 1 and 2, the triangles are similar. See margin.

  a. Determine the corresponding vertices.
  b. Find a ratio of similitude.
  c. Determine as many missing angle measures or side lengths as possible.

1.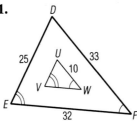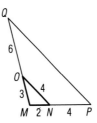

2.

3. If $\triangle RST \sim \triangle UVW$, name two ratios equal to $\frac{RS}{UV}$. $\frac{ST}{VW}, \frac{TR}{WU}$

4. One way to prove $\triangle ABC \sim \triangle DEF$ is to find a size change image of $\triangle ABC$ that is __?__ to $\triangle DEF$. congruent

5. State the SSS Similarity Theorem. See margin.

6. *True* or *false*?   The right triangle with sides 5, 12, and 13 is similar to the right triangle with sides 60, 65, and 25. True

7. *True* or *false*?   The right triangle with sides 20, 21, and 29 is similar to the right triangle with sides 41, 9, and 40. False

Applying the Mathematics

8. a. Are these two triangles similar? Yes
  b. Why or why not? See margin.

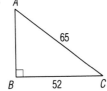

9. The two triangles below are similar by the SSS Similarity Theorem.
  a. Write the similarity with the vertices in proper order. $\triangle PQR \sim \triangle TVU$
  b. Describe a similarity transformation which maps the smaller triangle onto the larger. See margin.

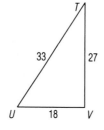

MORE PRACTICE
For more questions on SPUR Objectives, use *Lesson Master 12-8,* shown below.

2. a. $\triangle MNO \sim \triangle MPQ$
b. 3 or $\frac{1}{3}$
c. $QP = 12$

5. If the three sides of one triangle are proportional to the three sides of a second triangle, then the triangles are similar.

8. b. Using the Pythagorean Theorem, $AB = 39$ and $DF = 32$. Since $\frac{24}{39} = \frac{32}{52} = \frac{40}{65}$, $\triangle ABC \sim \triangle EDF$ by the SSS Similarity Theorem.

9. b. Sample: Apply the size change with magnitude 3, center Q to $\triangle PQR$. Take the image and reflect over the perpendicular bisector of $\overline{P'T}$. Then rotate with center T magnitude $m\angle Q''TV$.

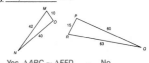

10. Given: X is the midpoint of $\overline{WY}$.
V is the midpoint of $\overline{WZ}$.
Prove: $\triangle WXV \sim \triangle WYZ$. See margin.

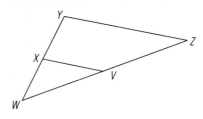

11. An altitude of $\triangle ABC$ is k times the altitude of $\triangle PQR$ and the base of $\triangle ABC$ is k times the base of $\triangle PQR$. Explain why the two triangles might not be similar. See margin.

Review

12. If there were a person $\frac{1}{6}$ as tall as you are and with your physique, the person would weigh __?__ times as much as you. This weight would be supported by __?__ times the area that supports you. (Lesson 12-7) $\frac{1}{216}$, $\frac{1}{36}$

13. A certain box 10″ high holds 20 lb of paper when filled. How many pounds of paper would be in a similar box 13″ high filled with the same kind of paper? (Lessons 12-7, 12-6) 43.94 lb

14. A right triangle has area 120 cm². A similar right triangle has area 30 cm². The length of the hypotenuse of the larger triangle is __?__ times the length of the hypotenuse of the smaller triangle. (Lesson 12-6) 2

15. The radius of a sphere is tripled to create a new sphere. If the original sphere had volume 36π units³, what is the volume of the new sphere? (Lesson 12-6) 972π units³

16. $\triangle DEF$ is the image of $\triangle ABC$ under a size change of magnitude 5. Then $\triangle ABC$ is the image of $\triangle DEF$ under a size change of magnitude __?__. (Lesson 12-2) $\frac{1}{5}$

17. The given formula finds what quantity in what figure? (Lessons 10-6, 10-5)
a. $V = \frac{1}{3}Bh$ **b.** S.A. $= 2\ell w + 2wh + 2\ell h$
c. $p = a + b + c$ **d.** $V = \pi r^2 h$
e. L.A. $= \pi r \ell$
See margin.

18. Multiple choice. $\frac{2x + 10}{2} =$
(a) $\frac{x + 5}{2}$ (b) $x + 5$
(c) $x + 10$ (d) $2x + 5$ (Previous course) (b)

Exploration

19. Is there an SSSS Similarity Theorem for quadrilaterals? If so, how do you know? If not, draw a counterexample. See margin.

LESSON 12-9

The AA and SAS Similarity Theorems

For each triangle congruence theorem there is a counterpart triangle similarity theorem. In the triangle similarity theorems, "A" still denotes a pair of congruent angles but "S" denotes a *ratio* of corresponding sides.

Three triangle similarity theorems are used more often than the others.

Triangle Congruence Theorem	Triangle Similarity Theorem
SSS ————————————→	SSS
SAS ————————————→	SAS
ASA ——————————→	AA
AAS ——————————→	

The strategy used in proving all these triangle similarity theorems is the same. A size change is applied to one triangle so that its image is congruent to the other triangle. The key decision is the choice of the magnitude k of the size change. Once that is done, the only other thing to do is to identify the triangle congruence theorem to use. That turns out always to be the corresponding triangle congruence theorem.

RESOURCES
■ Lesson Master 12-9
▯ Visual for Teaching Aid 77 can be used with **Questions 5-9**.
▯ Computer master 25

OBJECTIVE

F Determine whether or not triangles are similar using the AA, SAS, or SSS Similarity Theorems.

TEACHING NOTES

The goals of this lesson are to have students (1) realize that the proofs of the various triangle similarity theorems all follow the same idea; (2) determine whether two triangles are similar given various angle measures and side lengths; and (3) use the triangle similarity theorems in simple proofs.

Alternate Approach
There is an alternate proof in **Example 2.** Consider the size change C with center P and magnitude 2. $C(P) = P$, $C(T) = S$, and $C(Q) = R$, so $C(\triangle PTQ) = \triangle PSR$. Thus, by the definition of similarity, $\triangle PTQ \sim \triangle PSR$. There is always such an alternate proof going back to the definition of similarity.

Error Analysis Students often have difficulty knowing which triangle similarity theorem to use in a proof. Here is a way to remember:
If 2 angles, use AA.
If 1 angle, use SAS.
If 0 angles, use SSS.

609

1. Prove that at least two of the four triangles formed by the diagonals of a trapezoid are similar.

Let the trapezoid be *ABCD* with $\overline{AB} \parallel \overline{CD}$ and diagonals intersecting at *E* as shown below.

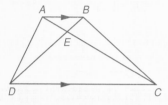

Then $\angle EAB \cong \angle ECD$ and $\angle EBA \cong \angle EDC$ because they are pairs of alternate interior angles formed by parallel lines. Thus, by the AA Similarity Theorem, $\triangle AEB \sim \triangle CED$.

2. Two similar triangles each have a 37° angle. The sides including the 37° angle in one of the triangles have lengths 6 cm and 5 cm. One side including the 37° angle in the other triangle has length 15. What must be the length of the other including side?

either 12.5 or 18, depending on whether it corresponds to the 5-cm or the 6-cm side

AA Similarity Theorem:

If two triangles have two angles of one congruent to two angles of the other, then the triangles are similar.

Proof

Given: Triangles *ABC* and *XYZ* with $\angle A \cong \angle X$ and $\angle B \cong \angle Y$.
Prove: $\triangle ABC \sim \triangle XYZ$.

The congruent angles signal the corresponding vertices. This indicates the corresponding sides and enables a picture to be drawn.

Since $\overline{XY}$ and $\overline{AB}$ are corresponding sides, let $k = \frac{XY}{AB}$ be the magnitude of a size transformation applied to $\triangle ABC$.

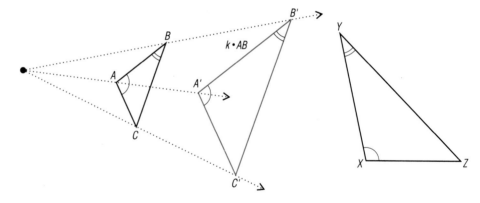

Then
$$A'B' = k \cdot AB$$
$$= \frac{XY}{AB} \cdot AB$$
$$= XY.$$

Also, since size transformations preserve angle measure, $\angle A \cong \angle A'$ and $\angle B \cong \angle B'$. With transitivity, $\angle A' \cong \angle X$ and $\angle B' \cong \angle Y$. So $\triangle A'B'C' \cong \triangle XYZ$ by the ASA Congruence Theorem. Thus $\triangle ABC$ can be mapped onto $\triangle XYZ$ by a composite of size changes and reflections. So $\triangle ABC \sim \triangle XYZ$.

610

Example 1 Given the triangles at the right with lengths and congruent angles as indicated.

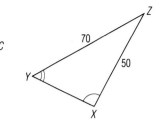

a. Prove that the triangles are similar.

b. Find the ratio of similitude.

c. Find AC.

Solution

a. $\angle A \cong \angle X$ and $\angle B \cong \angle Y$, so $\triangle ABC \sim \triangle XYZ$ by the AA Similarity Theorem.

b. The ratio of similitude is any of the equal ratios $\frac{XY}{AB} = \frac{YZ}{BC} = \frac{XZ}{AC}$. Use sides $\overline{BC}$ and $\overline{YZ}$ whose lengths are known: $\frac{YZ}{BC} = \frac{70}{20} = \frac{7}{2}$.

(The ratio would be $\frac{2}{7}$ if you considered the triangles in reverse order.)

c. Substituting into the proportion $\frac{YZ}{BC} = \frac{XZ}{AC}$, $\frac{70}{20} = \frac{50}{AC}$, from which $AC = \frac{100}{7} = 14\frac{2}{7}$.

Another triangle similarity theorem is the *SAS Similarity Theorem*. You are asked to prove it in the Questions.

SAS Similarity Theorem:

If, in two triangles, the ratios of two pairs of corresponding sides are equal and the included angles are congruent, then the triangles are similar.

Example 2 **Given:** T is the midpoint of $\overline{PS}$; Q is the midpoint of $\overline{PR}$.

Prove: $\triangle PTQ \sim \triangle PSR$.

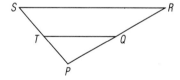

Analyze Since T and Q are midpoints, the ratio of two pairs of corresponding sides is 2:1. The angle included by these sides is in both triangles.

Write

Conclusions	Justifications
1. $PT = \frac{1}{2} PS$, $PQ = \frac{1}{2} PR$	definition of midpoint (meaning)
2. $\frac{PT}{PS} = \frac{1}{2}$, $\frac{PQ}{PR} = \frac{1}{2}$	Mult. Prop. of Equality
3. $\angle P \cong \angle P$	Reflexive Prop. of Congruence
4. $\triangle PTQ \sim \triangle PSR$	SAS Similarity Theorem (steps 2, 3)

Questions

Covering the Reading

In 1 and 2, the triangles are similar. See margin.
  a. Determine the correspondence for the vertices.
  b. Find a ratio of similitude.
  c. Determine as many missing angle measures or side lengths as possible.

1.

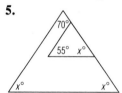

2.

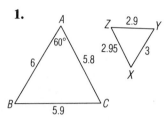

3. State the AA Similarity Theorem. See margin.

4. For each triangle similarity theorem, give the corresponding triangle congruence theorem.
  a. SSS Similarity Theorem SSS Congruence Theorem
  b. AA Similarity Theorem ASA or AAS Congruence Theorem
  c. SAS Similarity Theorem SAS Congruence Theorem

In 5–9, each figure contains two triangles. **a.** Are the triangles similar?
b. If so, what triangle similarity theorem guarantees their similarity?

5.

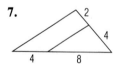

a) Yes;
b) AA Similarity Theorem

6. a) No

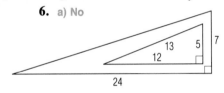

7.

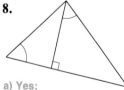

a) Yes;
b) SAS Similarity Theorem

8.

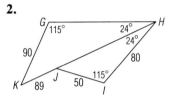

a) Yes;
b) AA Similarity Theorem

9.

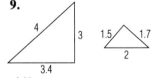

a) Yes;
b) SSS Similarity Theorem

612

612

10. The triangles below are similar.

   a. What is the magnitude of a size change applied to △PQR which would cause its image to be congruent to △XYZ? 2.4

   b. How do you know the image of the smaller triangle would be congruent to the larger? by the SAS Congruence Theorem

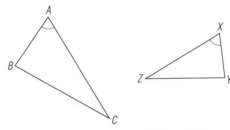

11. Prove the SAS Similarity Theorem using the figure below.

   Given: ∠A ≅ ∠X.

   $$\frac{AB}{XY} = \frac{AC}{XZ}.$$

   Prove: △ABC ~ △XYZ.

   (Hint: Use the general idea of the proofs of the other two triangle similarity theorems.) See margin.

12. In the beach chair pictured below, $\overline{AE}$ and $\overline{BD}$ intersect at C, and $\overleftrightarrow{AB} \parallel \overleftrightarrow{DE}$. Prove that the triangles are similar. See margin.

13. Use the figure at the right.

   Given: $WY = 3 \cdot VY$
   $XY = 3 \cdot YZ$.

   Prove: △WXY ~ △VZY.
   See margin.

LESSON 12-9   The AA and SAS Similarity Theorems   **613**

12. ∠ABC ≅ ∠EDC, and ∠BAC ≅ ∠DEC from the ∥ Lines ⇒ AIA = Theorem. Thus, △CED ~ △CAB by the AA Similarity Theorem.

13.

Conclusions	Justifications
1. m∠**WYX** = m∠**ZYV**	Vertical Angle Thm.
2. $\frac{WY}{VY} = 3$, $\frac{XY}{YZ} = 3$	Mult. Prop. of Eq.
3. $\frac{WY}{VY} = \frac{XY}{YZ}$	Transitive Prop. of Eq.
4. △**WXY** ~ △**VZY**	SAS Similarity Thm. (steps 1 and 3)

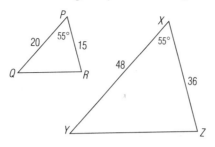

14. A garage casts a shadow 5 meters long. At the same time, a meter stick casts a shadow 1.2 meters long. Determine the height of the garage. $\approx$**4.17m**

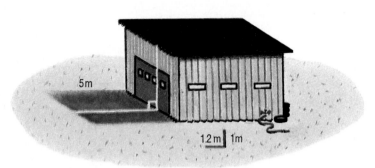

5m

1.2 m | 1m

Review

15. a. Are triangles *LMN* and *PQR*, pictured here, similar? **No**
b. If so, why? If not, why not? *(Lesson 12-8)* $\frac{12}{8} \neq \frac{16}{12} \neq \frac{20}{16}$

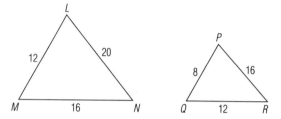

16. Consider the sun and Jupiter to be of similar shape. The equatorial diameter of the sun is 865,400 miles. The equatorial diameter of Jupiter is 88,000 miles.
a. What is the ratio of the surface area of the sun to that of Jupiter?
b. What is the ratio of the volume of the sun to that of Jupiter?
(Lessons 12-7, 12-6) **a)** $\approx$**96.7; b)** $\approx$**951**

17. Find the image of path *HIJHG* under a size change with center *G*, magnitude $\frac{3}{4}$. *(Lesson 12-3)*

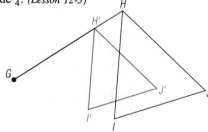

18. Solve for *x*: $\dfrac{x^2}{90} = \dfrac{3}{10}$. *(Lesson 12-4)* $\pm\sqrt{27} \approx \pm 5.2$

Exploration

19. Is there an HL Similarity Theorem and an SsA Similarity Theorem for triangles? If so, how do you know? If not, draw a counterexample.
Yes, because there exist HL and SsA Congruence Theorems.

LESSON 12-10

The Side-Splitting Theorem

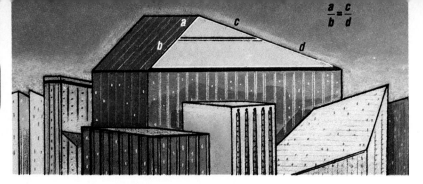

$$\frac{a}{b} = \frac{c}{d}$$

Above is pictured an asymmetric roof. Amazingly, the parallel beams split the sides of the roof into proportional lengths. This result is called the Side-Splitting Theorem, and its proof depends on similar triangles.

Side-Splitting Theorem:

If a line is parallel to a side of a triangle and intersects the other two sides in distinct points, it "splits" these sides into proportional segments.

Proof

A figure is drawn at the right.

Given: $\overleftrightarrow{PQ} \parallel \overleftrightarrow{BC}$.

Prove: $\dfrac{AP}{PB} = \dfrac{AQ}{QC}$.

$\angle 1 \cong \angle 2$ and $\angle 3 \cong \angle 4$ since $\parallel$ lines $\Rightarrow$ corr. $\angle$s $=$. Thus, by the AA Similarity Theorem, $\triangle APQ \sim \triangle ABC$. Thus in these triangles, corresponding sides are proportional.

$$\frac{AB}{AP} = \frac{AC}{AQ}$$

Now we split AB and AC into two parts.

$$\frac{AP + PB}{AP} = \frac{AQ + QC}{AQ}$$

Separate the fractions, as you might do in algebra.

$$\frac{AP}{AP} + \frac{PB}{AP} = \frac{AQ}{AQ} + \frac{QC}{AQ}$$

$$1 + \frac{PB}{AP} = 1 + \frac{QC}{AQ}$$

Subtract 1 from both sides. $\qquad \dfrac{PB}{AP} = \dfrac{QC}{AQ}$

Use the Reciprocals Property. $\qquad \dfrac{AP}{PB} = \dfrac{AQ}{QC}$

LESSON 12-10 The Side-Splitting Theorem **615**

RESOURCES
■ Lesson Master 12-10
⬆ Visual for Teaching Aid 78 can be used with **Questions 10, 12,** and **13**.
⬛ Computer Master 26.

OBJECTIVES

B Find the lengths in figures by applying the Side-Splitting Theorem and the Side-Splitting Converse.
G Identify and determine proportional lengths and distances in real situations.

TEACHING NOTES

The Side-Splitting Theorem is an easy theorem to learn, but its proof is not easy for most students to follow. Students have trouble with all the variations due to the reciprocals, the means exchange, the parts and the wholes, and the segments of the parallel lines. If students are confused, explain that there are only two things to remember: (1) the properties of size changes, under which ratios of lengths of images to pre-images is constant (this takes care of the segments on the parallel lines as well as the parts to the wholes), and (2) the theorem itself.

The proof of the Side-Splitting Converse goes through the same steps as the proof of the theorem but in reverse order. Different letters are used so that the proofs are not confusing, but you may wish to write the steps on this page in reverse order and ask students for the reasons to get from one step to the next. They will then have proved the converse.

You may wish to state the two theorems in if-and-only-if language: A line which intersects two sides of a triangle in two distinct points is parallel to the third side if and only if it splits the two sides proportionally.

Making Connections

Any discussion about converses and if-and-only-if statements will prepare students for the next chapter in which the logic of proof is examined in more detail.

Note that the Midpoint Connector Theorem (Lesson 11-5) described a special case of the Side-Splitting Converse, one in which the ratio of the proportional segments is one to one. The Midpoint Connector Theorem includes the bonus that the segment is also equal to half of the third side.

Error Analysis
After learning the Midpoint Connector Theorem, students may think that the Side-Splitting Theorem also should include the statement that the segment drawn should be in the same ratio with the third side as the other two proportional sides are. This, of course, is not true because the "pieces" of the sides do not have the same ratio as the ratio of similitude of the (similar) triangles.

ADDITIONAL EXAMPLES
1. In $\triangle RIG$ below, $\overline{AN} \parallel \overline{RI}$. If $IG = 9$, what are the lengths of $\overline{IN}$ and $\overline{NG}$?

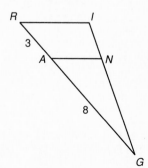

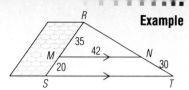

Example Suppose beams $\overline{MN}$ and $\overline{ST}$ are parallel and split the sides of the roof into the lengths as shown at the left. (All lengths are in decimeters. One decimeter $= \frac{1}{10}$ meter.)

a. Find the length of $\overline{RN}$.   **b.** Find ST.

Solution

a. From the Side-Splitting Theorem, $\frac{RM}{MS} = \frac{RN}{NT}$.

Substitute. $\frac{35}{20} = \frac{RN}{30}$

Solve for RN. $20 \cdot RN = 30 \cdot 35$

$RN = 52.5$ decimeters

b. $\triangle RMN \sim \triangle RST$ so $\frac{RM}{RS} = \frac{MN}{ST}$. Substituting, $\frac{35}{55} = \frac{42}{ST}$. Thus $35 \cdot ST = 42 \cdot 55$ and $ST = 66$ decimeters.

The converse of the Side-Splitting Theorem is also true: A line intersecting two sides of a triangle and forming proportional segments is parallel to the third side. You may use it to conclude that lines are parallel.

Side-Splitting Converse:

If a line intersects $\overrightarrow{OP}$ and $\overrightarrow{OQ}$ in distinct points X and Y so that $\frac{OX}{XP} = \frac{OY}{YQ}$, then $\overleftrightarrow{XY} \parallel \overleftrightarrow{PQ}$.

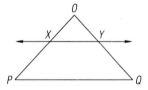

Proof

Analyze It looks like the triangles are similar. Prove this first. Then corresponding angles can be used to get the parallel lines.

Write   Given is $\frac{OX}{XP} = \frac{OY}{YQ}$.

Using the Reciprocals Property, $\frac{XP}{OX} = \frac{YQ}{OY}$.

Adding 1 to both sides ($\frac{OX}{OX}$ to the left side, and $\frac{OY}{OY}$ to the right), and adding the fractions,

$$\frac{OX + XP}{OX} = \frac{OY + YQ}{OY}.$$

Since $OX + XP = OP$ and $OY + YQ = OQ$, substituting,

$$\frac{OP}{OX} = \frac{OQ}{OY}.$$

Thus, in the triangles, two pairs of sides are proportional. Also, by the Reflexive Property, $\angle XOY \cong \angle POQ$. So $\triangle OPQ \sim \triangle OXY$ by the SAS Similarity Theorem. The corresponding angles in the similar triangles are congruent, so $\angle OPQ \cong \angle OXY$. These are corresponding angles for the lines $\overleftrightarrow{XY}$ and $\overleftrightarrow{PQ}$ with transversal $\overleftrightarrow{OP}$. Since corr. $\angle s = \Rightarrow \parallel$ lines, $\overleftrightarrow{XY} \parallel \overleftrightarrow{PQ}$.

616

1. Given $m \parallel \overleftrightarrow{XY}$, finish the proportions.

a. $\dfrac{AC}{AX} = \underline{\ ?\ } = \underline{\ ?\ }$ $\frac{AB}{AY} = \frac{CB}{XY}$

b. $\dfrac{AB}{BY} = \underline{\ ?\ }$ $\frac{AC}{CX}$

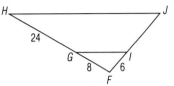

2. In the triangle below at the left, if $\overleftrightarrow{BC} \parallel \overleftrightarrow{DE}$, then $CE = \underline{\ ?\ }$. 7.5

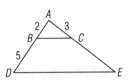

3. In the triangle above at the right, if $\overleftrightarrow{GI} \parallel \overleftrightarrow{HJ}$ then $FJ = \underline{\ ?\ }$. 24

4. Given $\overleftrightarrow{MN} \parallel \overleftrightarrow{PQ}$, $MP = 6$, $NQ = 5$, $ON = 30$, $MN = 14$. Find each number.

a. $\dfrac{NQ}{ON}$ $\frac{1}{6}$　　b. $\dfrac{MP}{MO}$ $\frac{1}{6}$　　c. MO 36　　d. OP 42

e. $\dfrac{ON}{OQ}$ $\frac{6}{7}$　　f. $\dfrac{OM}{OP}$ $\frac{6}{7}$　　g. $\dfrac{MN}{PQ}$ $\frac{6}{7}$　　h. PQ $\frac{98}{6} = 16\frac{1}{3}$

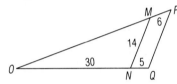

5. In Question 4, what is the magnitude of the size change S with center O and $S(\triangle MNO) = \triangle PQO$? $\frac{7}{6}$

6. *Multiple choice.* $\dfrac{x + y}{x} =$

(a) $1 + y$　　(b) $1 + \dfrac{y}{x}$　　(c) $\dfrac{y}{x}$　　(d) none of these (b)

7. *Multiple choice.* $\dfrac{z}{z} + \dfrac{y}{z} =$

(a) $\dfrac{z + y}{2z}$　　(b) $\dfrac{z + y}{z^2}$　　(c) $\dfrac{z + y}{z}$　　(d) none of these (c)

8. State the Side-Splitting Converse. See margin.

9. Below, the horizontal beam splits the sides of this asymmetric roof. If $AB = 20$, $BD = 30$, and $AE = 60$, find AC and CE.
$AC = 24$, $CE = 36$

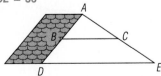

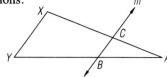

Let $x = IN$. Then $NG = 9 - x$ and so $\frac{3}{8} = \frac{x}{9-x}$. Solving this equation, $x = \frac{27}{11}$, so $IN = \frac{27}{11}$ and $NG = \frac{72}{11}$. Another method of solution is to use the similar triangles. $\frac{AG}{RG} = \frac{NG}{IG}$, so $\frac{8}{11} = \frac{NG}{9}$. From this again, $NG = \frac{72}{11}$.

2. $\overline{BE}$ is a segment which splits the sides of $\triangle ACD$ as shown below. Is $\overline{BE} \parallel \overline{CD}$?

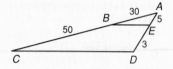

No; $\frac{30}{50} \neq \frac{5}{3}$.
(Some students may think that since there is a proportion $\frac{3}{30} = \frac{5}{50}$, which can be made using the four numbers, $\overline{BE} \parallel \overline{CD}$.)

NOTES ON QUESTIONS
Questions 6 and 7:
These questions involve some of the algebra used in the proof of the Side-Splitting Theorem. Either do these questions before going over the proof in detail or use them to reinforce the proof.

Question 9: Only because $\overline{BC}$ is parallel to $\overline{DE}$ does the Side-Splitting Theorem apply.

ADDITIONAL ANSWERS
8. If a line intersects $\overrightarrow{OP}$ and $\overrightarrow{OQ}$ in distinct points X and Y so that $\frac{OX}{XP} = \frac{OY}{YQ}$, then $\overleftrightarrow{XY} \parallel \overleftrightarrow{PQ}$.

10. Given $\overleftrightarrow{DE} \parallel \overleftrightarrow{AC}$, $\overleftrightarrow{EF} \parallel \overleftrightarrow{AB}$; lengths as indicated below.
   a. Find *DB*. 7.5
   b. Find *FA*. 9
   c. ∠*A* and ∠*AFE* are __?__ angles. supplementary
   d. Write a true proportion using *BD*, *DA*, *CF*, and *FA*. $\frac{BD}{DA} = \frac{FA}{CF}$

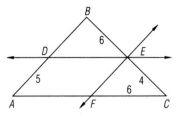

11. Given $m \parallel n$, then the Side-Splitting Theorem guarantees $\frac{x}{y} = \frac{z}{w}$.
Write five other true proportions involving *x*, *y*, *z*, and *w*.
See margin.

12. Fill in the justifications for the proof of the following generalization of the Side-Splitting Theorem:

If $m \parallel n \parallel p$, then $\frac{a}{b} = \frac{c}{d}$.

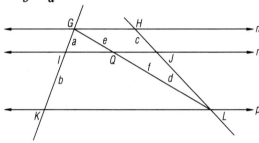

Conclusions

1. $\frac{a}{b} = \frac{e}{f}$

2. $\frac{e}{f} = \frac{c}{d}$

3. $\frac{a}{b} = \frac{c}{d}$

Justifications

a. __?__ Side-Splitting Theorem

b. __?__ Side-Splitting Theorem

c. __?__ Transitive Property of Equality (steps 1 and 2)

13. 8th, 9th, and 10th Streets are parallel. Given the distances on Rasci Road, find *x* and *y*, the distances on Elm Street between these streets.
x = 125 m; y = 100 m

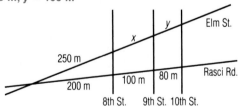

618

<table>
<tr><td style="background:gray">Review</td><td>

14. Refer to the figure below.
Given: $\overleftrightarrow{BE}$ bisects $\angle ABC$;
$\overline{AE} \perp \overline{AB}; \overline{DC} \perp \overline{CB}$.
Prove: $\triangle ABE \sim \triangle CBD$. *(Lesson 12-9)* See margin.

</td></tr>
</table>

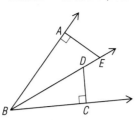

In 15–17, determine from the markings and other information if the pair of triangles is similar. If so, indicate the corresponding vertices and state the theorem or definition that justifies your conclusion. *(Lessons 12-9, 12-8)*

15. No

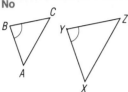

16.

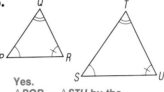

Yes.
$\triangle PQR \sim \triangle STU$ by the AA Similarity Theorem.

17.

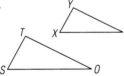

$\dfrac{ST}{XY} = \dfrac{TO}{YZ} = \dfrac{OS}{ZX}$

Yes, $\triangle STO \sim \triangle XYZ$ by the SSS Similarity Theorem

18. $ABCDE \sim JFGHI$ with sides and angle measures as indicated below. Find as many missing lengths and angle measures as possible.
(Lesson 12-5) $m\angle B = 75$; $m\angle H = 40$; $AB = 175$; $HI = 21$

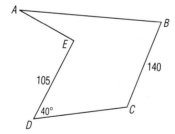

19. On a certain map, a distance of 150 miles is 4 inches. If two cities are $2\frac{1}{2}$ inches apart on the map, what is the actual distance between them?
(Lesson 12-4) 93.75 miles

20. Let S be a size change of magnitude 5 centered at the origin. Graph $S(\triangle PQR)$ if $P = (2, -.6)$, $Q = (-1.4, 0)$, and $R = (.8, 1.2)$.
(Lesson 12-1) See margin.

NAME _____

LESSON **MASTER   12–10**
QUESTIONS ON **SPUR** OBJECTIVES

■ **SKILLS** *Objective B* (See pages 624–627 for objectives.)

1. If $\overleftrightarrow{EF} \parallel k$, finish the proportions.
  a. $\dfrac{CG}{CE} = \dfrac{DG}{FG}$
  $\dfrac{GC}{}$
  b. $\dfrac{GD}{DF} = \dfrac{}{CE}$

In 2 and 3, use the figure at the right. $\overline{EC} \parallel \overline{AB}$. $DC = 20$, $BC = 30$.

2. If $AD = 75$, what is AE?   45

3. If $FB = 24$, what would AF have to be in order to have $\overline{FC} \parallel \overline{AD}$?   16

4. In the figure below, $\overline{WV} \parallel \overline{XZ}$. Find XW.   16

5. Use the figure below (not necessarily drawn accurately). Name all pairs of parallel lines and explain why they are parallel.

$\overleftrightarrow{CE} \parallel \overleftrightarrow{BF}$ by the Side-Splitting Converse, since $\dfrac{60}{12} = \dfrac{50}{10}$.

Geometry © Scott, Foresman and Company   Continued **117**

NAME _____
Lesson MASTER 12–10 (page 2)

■ **USES** *Objective G*

6. A support is to be placed 100 m from the top of the ramp. The ramp is 30 m long.

  a. How long should the support beam be?   8 m
  b. How far from the end of the ramp (where it meets the ground) is the base of the support? $\sqrt{336} \approx 18.33$ m

7. In the roof below, the beam is 20 ft long, and the base of the roof is 30 ft long. If the beams in the roof are 18 ft long, find AB, where the joint with the cross beam on the roof beam is located.   12 ft

8. In the street-map below, Main Street is parallel to Broadway. From the intersection of Broadway and Grant to Grant and Main is 300 ft, and then it is another 250 ft to Grant and Lincoln. From Grant and Broadway to Lincoln and Broadway is 700 ft. How far is it from Grant and Main to Lincoln and Main?   ≈318 ft

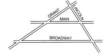

118   Geometry © Scott, Foresman and Company

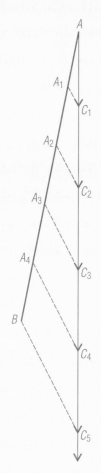

21. In the figure below, $AB = AC$, and D and E split $\overline{BC}$ into three equal segments. Carefully trace the figure (or use an automatic drawer) and draw $\overline{AD}$ and $\overline{AE}$. Do they trisect $\angle BAC$? That is, do they split $\angle BAC$ into three angles of equal measure? Justify your answer.
No, the three angle measures ≈ 30, 50, and 30.

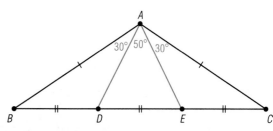

22. Here is how to divide a line segment $\overline{AB}$ into n congruent parts. (The figure shows the case $n = 5$.)

Step 1. Draw any ray $\overrightarrow{AC_1}$ that is not collinear with $\overrightarrow{AB}$. (Make C_1 close to A for convenience.)

Step 2. Mark off n segments AC_1, C_1C_2, C_2C_3, ... of equal lengths on $\overrightarrow{AC_1}$.

Step 3. Draw $\overline{BC_n}$. (Below, $n = 5$ so $\overline{BC_5}$ is drawn.)

Step 4. Draw parallels to $\overline{BC_n}$ through C_1, C_2, C_3, etc.

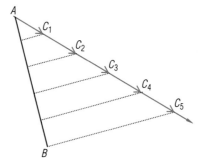

b. $\frac{AA_1}{AB} = \frac{AC_1}{AC_5} = \frac{1}{5}$ from the AA Similarity Theorem. The other segments are $\frac{1}{5}$ of AB from the Side-Splitting Theorem.

a. Follow the algorithm to divide $\overline{AB}$ below into 5 equal parts.

b. How do you know that each part of $\overline{AB}$ in the figure above is $\frac{1}{5}$ of $\overline{AB}$?
See margin.

620

Summary

In the coordinate plane, a size change centered at the origin can be achieved by multiplying coordinates of points by a given scale factor. Since a coordinate system can be created with any point as the origin, size transformations can be centered anywhere. Size transformations can occur in two or three dimensions.

Two figures are similar if and only if one can be mapped onto the other by a composite of reflections and size transformations. In similar figures, angles and their images are congruent. Lengths of image segments are k times the lengths of preimage segments, where k is a positive number called the ratio of similitude. Areas of images are k^2 times the areas of their preimages. Volumes of images are k^3 times the volumes of their preimages. These relationships between two similar figures help explain why large animals need relatively thicker legs than small animals, and why there cannot be giants.

When one quantity is k times another, then the ratio of the quantities equals k. An equality of two ratios is called a proportion. Whenever there are similar figures, lengths are proportional. Solving proportions can help you determine unknown measurements.

The ability to draw or construct similar figures is necessary in the making of scale drawings, toys or scale models, maps, blueprints, and other diagrams. It is just as important to know when figures are similar. For triangles, the conditions guaranteeing similarity correspond to those for congruence. The most commonly used are SSS, AA, and SAS; A indicates equal angle measures and S indicates equal ratios of sides.

Vocabulary

Below are the most important terms and phrases for this chapter.
For the starred (*) terms you should be able to give a definition of the term.
For the other terms you should be able to give a general description and a specific example of each.

Lesson 12-1
S_k, magnitude

Lesson 12-2
*size change
size transformation
dilation, dilatation
center of size transformation
magnitude
scale factor
size change factor
size change image
*expansion
*contraction
*identity transformation

Lesson 12-3
Size Change Distance Theorem
Size Change Theorem
Figure Size Change Theorem

Lesson 12-4
*ratio, rate,
*proportion, proportional
means, extremes
Means-Extremes Property
Means Exchange Property
Reciprocals Property

Lesson 12-5
*similarity transformation
*similar figures
ratio of similitude
Similar Figures Theorem

Lesson 12-6
Fundamental Theorem of
  Similarity

Lesson 12-8
SSS Similarity Theorem

Lesson 12-9
AA Similarity Theorem
SAS Similarity Theorem

Lesson 12-10
Side-Splitting Theorem
Side-Splitting Converse

SUMMARY

The Summary gives an overview of the entire chapter and provides an opportunity for students to consider the material as a whole. Thus, the Summary can be used to help students relate the various concepts presented in the chapter.

VOCABULARY

Terms, symbols, and properties are listed by lesson to provide a checklist of concepts a student must know. Emphasize to students that they should read the vocabulary list carefully before starting the Progress Self-Test. If students do not understand the meaning of a term or a statement of a theorem, they should refer back to the individual lesson.

Whereas end-of-chapter materials may be considered optional to some texts, they should not be considered optional in UCSMP *Geometry*. The Progress Self-Test provides the opportunity for feedback and correction; the Chapter Review provides additional opportunities for practice. It is at this point that the material "gels" for many students, allowing them to solidify skills and concepts before a test. In general, student performance is markedly improved after these pages.

USING THE PROGRESS SELF-TEST
Assign the Progress Self-Test as a one-night assignment. Worked-out *solutions* for all questions are in the Selected Answers section of the student text. Encourage students to take the Progress Self-Test honestly, grade themselves, and then be prepared to discuss the test in class.

Advise students to pay special attention to those Chapter Review questions (pages 624-627) which correspond to questions missed on the Progress Self-Test. A chart provided with the Selected Answers keys the Progress Self-Test questions to the lettered SPUR Objectives in the Chapter Review or to the Vocabulary. It also keys the questions to the corresponding lessons where the material is covered.

ADDITIONAL ANSWERS
2. (Art is reduced in size.)

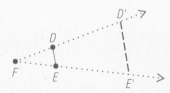

Progress Self-Test

See margin for answers not shown below.

Directions: Take this test as you would take a test in class. Use a ruler. Then check your work with the solutions in the Selected Answers section in the back of the book.

1. Trace the figure. Draw the image of △*ABC* under a size transformation with center *O*, magnitude $\frac{3}{4}$.

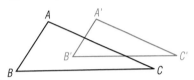

2. Draw the image of $\overline{DE}$ under a size change with center *F*, magnitude 2.8.

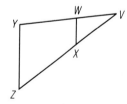

3. *Multiple choice.* Size changes preserve
   (a) angle measure
   (b) distance
   (c) area
   (d) volume. **(a)**

4. In Question 1, how does the area of △*ABC* compare with the area of its image?

5. Define: similar figures.

In 6–8, use the figure below, in which $\overleftrightarrow{WX} \parallel \overleftrightarrow{YZ}$.

6. $\frac{VW}{WY} = \underline{\quad ? \quad} \frac{VX}{XZ}$

7. If *VW* = 11, *WY* = 13, and *VZ* = 30, what is *VX*? **13.75**

8. If *WX* = 8, *YZ* = 20, and *WV* = 10, find *VY*.

9. If $\frac{a}{b} = \frac{c}{d}$, write three other true proportions using *a, b, c,* and *d*.

10. In the figure below, $\overleftrightarrow{AB} \parallel \overleftrightarrow{DE}$. If *AC* = 32, *CE* = 24, and *DC* = 20, find *BC*. $26\frac{2}{3} = 26.\overline{6}$

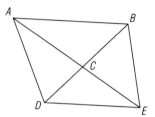

11. *QUAD* ~ *FOUR* with sides and angle measures as indicated below. Find as many missing lengths and angle measures as possible.
m∠*AUQ* = 37; *DA* = 20.25; *OU* = 32

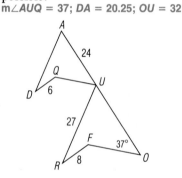

12. Two figures are similar and the ratio of corresponding sides is 5:1. What is the ratio of their volumes? **125:1**

13. A solid figurine is 4″ tall and weighs 5 pounds. What will a similar figurine of the same material weigh if it is 12″ tall? **135 lb**

In 14 and 15, are the triangles similar? If so, why?

14.

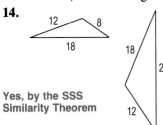

Yes, by the SSS
Similarity Theorem

15. Yes; by the AA Similarity Theorem

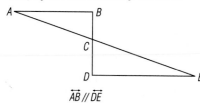

$\overrightarrow{AB} \parallel \overrightarrow{DE}$

16. Washington, Adams, and Jefferson streets are parallel. Given the distances on Martha Lane, find x, the length on Abigail Avenue between Washington and Adams. **220 m**

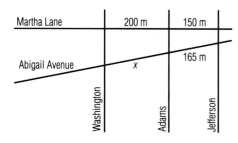

17. A photo slide is 5 cm by 3 cm. If a similar print from the slide is 25 cm in its shorter dimension, what is its longer dimension? $41\frac{2}{3} = 41.\overline{6}$ cm

18. A man 2 meters tall has a foot 30 cm long. If a man with a similar physique were 0.4 meters tall, how long would his foot be? **6 cm**

19. If there were a person 6 times as tall as you, the person would weigh about __?__ times as much. This weight would be supported by about __?__ times the area. **216; 36**

20. Let S be a size change of magnitude $\frac{1}{3}$ centered at the origin. Graph S($\triangle ABC$) if $A = (6, -2)$, $B = (9, 0)$, and $C = (-30, 10)$.

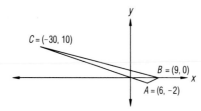

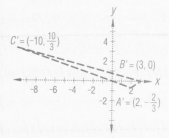

CHAPTER REVIEW

The main objectives for the chapter are organized here into sections corresponding to the four main types of understanding this book promotes: Skills, Properties, Uses, and Representations. We call these the SPUR objectives.

The four types of understanding are not in increasing order of difficulty. There may be hard skills and easy representations; some uses may be easier than anything else; and so on.

USING THE CHAPTER REVIEW
Students should be able to answer questions like these with about 85% accuracy by the end of the chapter.

You may assign these questions over a single night to help students prepare for a test the next day, or you may assign the questions over a two-day period.

If you assign the questions over two days, then we recommend assigning the *evens* for homework the first night so that students get feedback in class the next day. Then assign the *odds* for the second night (the night before the test) so that students can use the answers provided in the book as a study aid.

Chapter Review

See margin for answers not shown below.

Questions on **SPUR** Objectives

SPUR stands for **S**kills, **P**roperties, **U**ses, and **R**epresentations. The Chapter Review questions are grouped according to the SPUR Objectives for this chapter.

SKILLS deal with the procedures used to get answers.

■ **Objective A:** *Draw size transformation images of figures. (Lessons 12-2, 12-3)*

In 1–4, first trace the figure.

1. Draw the image of $\triangle ABC$ under a size change with center O, magnitude 1.5.

2. Draw the image of $\triangle ABC$ under a size transformation with center A, magnitude 0.8.

3. Draw the image of $DEFG$ under a size transformation with center I, scale factor $\frac{2}{3}$.

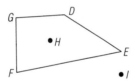

4. Draw the image of $DEFG$ under a size change with scale factor $\frac{5}{3}$, center H.

5. Describe the image of $DEFG$ in Question 4 under a size change with center F, magnitude 1.
It is *DEFG* itself.

■ **Objective B:** *Find the lengths in figures by applying the Side-Splitting Theorem and the Side-Splitting Converse. (Lesson 12-10)*

6. Given: S is a size transformation and $S(\triangle JKL) = \triangle JMN$. What is the value of LN?
2.5

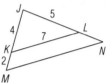

In 7 and 8, use the figure below. $\overleftrightarrow{NP} \parallel \overleftrightarrow{QS}$, $MP = 30$, and $PS = 120$.

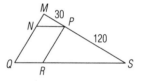

7. If $QR = 25$, what must RS be in order for $\overleftrightarrow{PR}$ to be parallel to $\overleftrightarrow{MQ}$? 100

8. If $MQ = 90$, then $MN = \underline{\ ?\ }$. 18

9. If $\overline{AB} \parallel \overline{CD}$, find DE. 8

10. Below, if $\overleftrightarrow{WV} \parallel \overleftrightarrow{UT}$, what is SW? 22

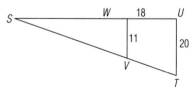

■ **Objective C:** *Find angle measures, lengths, perimeters, areas, and volumes in similar figures.*
(Lessons 12-5, 12-6)

In 11 and 12, $\overline{TU} \parallel \overline{WX}$.

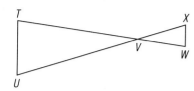

11. If $TV = 10$, $VW = 5$, and $VX = 6$, what is VU? **12**

12. If $TU = 70$, $XW = 42$, and $TV = 112.5$, what other length can be found? **VW = 67.5**

13. *PENTA ~ HOURS* with sides and angle measures as indicated below. Find as many missing lengths and angle measures as possible. (Be careful about which vertices correspond.)
m∠H = 100, PE = 4.16, OU = 7.92

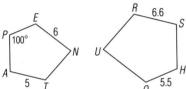

14. A hexagon has area 20 cm² and a smallest side with length 6 cm. A similar hexagon has a smallest side of length 8 cm. What is the area of this similar hexagon? **≈35.6 cm²**

15. A right triangle has hypotenuse 10 and two angles with measures 57 and 33. What are the angle measures in a similar triangle whose hypotenuse has length 5? **90, 57, 33**

16. A prism has volume 64 cubic meters. What is the volume of a similar prism $\frac{3}{4}$ as high?
27 cubic meters

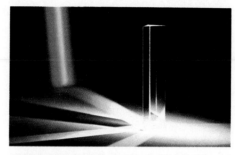

17. A polygon has area 100. What is the area of its image under a size change of magnitude 2.5? **625 units²**

18. In Question 1, if $\triangle A'B'C'$ is the image of $\triangle ABC$, how do the areas of $\triangle A'B'C'$ and $\triangle ABC$ compare?
area ($\triangle A'B'C'$) = 2.25 · area ($\triangle ABC$)

PROPERTIES deal with the principles behind the mathematics.

■ **Objective D:** *Recognize and apply properties of size transformations and similar figures.*
(Lessons 12-2, 12-3, 12-5, 12-6, 12-7)

19. Refer to the figure in Question 6.
   a. What is the center of S? **J**
   b. What is the magnitude of S? **1.5**
   c. *True* or *false*? $\overleftrightarrow{MN} \parallel \overleftrightarrow{KL}$. **True**

20. *Multiple choice.*
   Size changes do *not* preserve
   (a) angle measure
   (b) betweenness
   (c) collinearity
   (d) distance. **(d)**

21. How are the volumes of similar figures related to the ratio of similitude?

22. $\triangle RST$ is the image of $\triangle OQP$ under a size change.

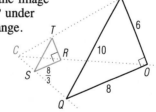

   a. Trace the figure and locate the center of the size change.
   b. What is the magnitude of the size change?
   c. Find the lengths of $\overline{RT}$ and $\overline{ST}$.

23. If two figures are similar and the ratio of their areas is 4:1, what is the ratio of the lengths of corresponding sides? **2:1**

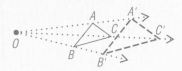
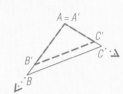
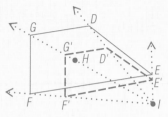
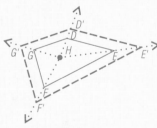

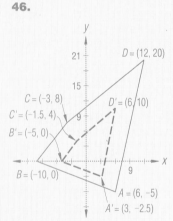
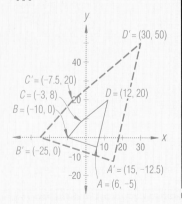
24. One kite has sides of lengths 12, 12, 14, and 14. Another has sides of lengths 6, 6, 7, and 7.
    a. Must they be similar? **No**
    b. If so, why? If not, why not?

■ **Objective E:** *Given a true proportion, find other true proportions with the same terms. (Lesson 12-4)*

25. If $\frac{m}{a} = \frac{t}{e}$, write three other true proportions using m, a, t, and e.

26. *Multiple choice.* If $\frac{u}{v} = \frac{w}{x}$, which is true?

    (a) $\frac{u + v}{v} = \frac{w + v}{x}$ (b) $\frac{u}{v} = \frac{x}{w}$

    (c) $\frac{u + v}{v} = \frac{w + x}{x}$ (d) $\frac{u}{x} = \frac{w}{v}$ **(c)**

27. Write three true proportions involving the numbers 8, 12, 24, and 16.

28. If the Means Exchange Property is applied to $\frac{3}{x} = \frac{4}{5}$, what proportion results? **$\frac{3}{4} = \frac{x}{5}$**

■ **Objective F:** *Determine whether or not triangles are similar using the AA, SAS, or SSS Similarity Theorems. (Lessons 12-8, 12-9)*

29. One triangle has sides 40, 45, and 50.
    a. Is this triangle similar to a second triangle with sides 10, 9, and 8?
    b. If so, why? If not, why not?
    a) Yes; b) by the SSS Similarity Theorem

In 30 and 31, are the triangles similar? If so, why? If not, why not?

30.

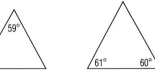

Yes, by the AA Similarity Theorem

31.

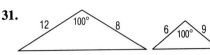

Yes, by the SAS Similarity Theorem

32. $ABDC$ is a trapezoid with $\overleftrightarrow{AB} \parallel \overleftrightarrow{CD}$ and diagonals intersecting at E.
    Prove: $\triangle ABE \sim \triangle DCE$.

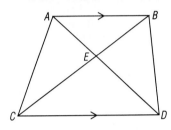

33. Refer to the figure below.
    Given: $\overline{AC} \perp \overline{BD}$, $BC = x$,
    $AC = 2x$, and $DC = 4x$.
    Prove: $\triangle ABC \sim \triangle DAC$.

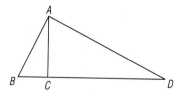

USES deal with applications of mathematics in real situations.

■ **Objective G:** *Identify and determine proportional lengths and distances in real situations.*
(Lessons 12-4, 12-5, 12-10)

34. First Street runs north-south. Elm, Maple, and Pine run east-west. Distances between them are as indicated. There is 2000 ft of frontage on Slant Street between Elm and Maple. How much frontage is there on Slant Street between Maple and Pine? **3000′**

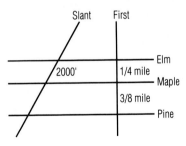

35. A photograph is 5″ by 8″. If a similar photograph is 10″ in its longer dimension, what is its shorter dimension? **6.25″**

36. 1.5 meters from its bottom, a slide is 1.3 m tall. If the slide runs for 4 m along the ground, what is its height at its highest point? (Round your answer to the nearest 0.1 m.) **3.5 m**

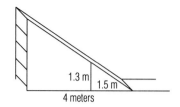

1.3 m   1.5 m
4 meters

37. At 4 PM, a tree casts a shadow 9 meters long. At the same time, a vertical meter stick casts a shadow 60 cm long. How tall is the tree? **15 m**

38. If 4 pounds of navel oranges cost $1.89, what should 5 pounds of navel oranges cost? **$2.37**

39. TV screens are nearly all similar. If a 9″ screen (measured along a diagonal) is 7″ wide, how wide is a 26″ screen? **≈20.2″**

Objective H: *Apply the Fundamental Theorem of Similarity in real situations.* (*Lessons 12-6, 12-7*)

40. A solid figurine is 20 cm tall and weighs 3 kg. How much will a similar figurine of the same material weigh if it is 32 cm tall? **≈12.3 kg**

41. If a 10-inch-diameter pizza costs $5.89, and cost is proportional to ingredients, what should a 16-inch-diameter pizza with the same kinds of ingredients cost? **≈$15.08**

42. Dolls are often $\frac{1}{12}$ actual size. The same material used for a real coat can be used to make how many doll coats? **144**

43. An elephant 16 feet high can weigh 7 tons. (A ton is 2000 pounds.) If a similarly shaped elephant were 1 foot high, how many pounds would it weigh? **≈3.4 lb**

44. If there were a person 8 times as tall as you are with your physique, the person would weight about __?__ times as much. This weight would be supported by about __?__ times the area. **512, 64**

45. *True* or *false*? Larger animals need thicker legs than smaller animals to hold their weight. **True**

REPRESENTATIONS deal with pictures, graphs, or objects that illustrate concepts.

Objective I: *Use the definition of size transformations for figures on the coordinate plane.* (*Lesson 12-1*)

In 46–48, $A = (6, -5)$, $B = (-10, 0)$, $C = (-3, 8)$, $D = (12, 20)$.

46. Graph *ABCD* and its image under $S_{\frac{1}{2}}$.

47. Graph *ABCD* and its image under $S_{2.5}$.

48. List the coordinates of the image of *ABCD* under S_k.

49. Let $O = (0, 0, 0)$ and $P = (-5, -8, 11)$.
  a. Find P', the image of P under S_4.
  b. Verify that $OP' = 4 \cdot OP$.

50. Let S be a size transformation of magnitude 5.
  a. Using the graph, find $S(P)$, $S(Q)$, and $S(R)$.
  b. Fill in the blank and answer the question. Prove that the distance between $S(P)$ and $S(Q)$ is __?__ times the distance between *P* and *Q*.
  c. Verify that the slope of $\overline{PQ}$ equals the slope of the line through $S(P)$ and $S(Q)$.
  d. Verify that $S(P)$, $S(Q)$, and $S(R)$ are collinear.
  e. Verify that $S(Q)$ is between $S(P)$ and $S(R)$.

Graph: $P = (1, 4)$, $Q = (2, -1)$, $R = (3, -6)$

CHAPTER 13 ■ LOGIC AND INDIRECT REASONING

DAILY PACING CHART ■ CHAPTER 13

Every chapter of UCSMP *Geometry* includes lessons, a Progress Self-Test, and a Chapter Review. For optimal student performance, the self-test and review should be covered. (See *General Teaching Suggestions: Mastery* on page T36 of the Teacher's Edition.) By following the pace of the Full Course given here, students can complete the entire text by the end of the year. Students following the pace of the Minimal Course spend more time when there are quizzes and on the Chapter Review and will generally not complete all of the chapters in this text.

When all lessons are covered from the beginning (the recommendation of the authors), then students in the Minimal Course can cover through Lesson 13-4 and will cover all they need for future courses. For more information on pacing, see *General Teaching Suggestions: Pace* on page T35 of the Teacher's Edition.

DAY	MINIMAL COURSE	FULL COURSE
1	13-1	13-1
2	13-2	13-2
3	13-3	13-3
4	Quiz (TRF); Start 13-4.	Quiz (TRF); 13-4
5	Finish 13-4.	13-5
6	13-5	13-6
7	13-6	Quiz (TRF); 13-7
8	Quiz (TRF); Start 13-7.	13-8
9	Finish 13-7.	Progress Self-Test
10	13-8	Chapter Review
11	Progress Self-Test	Chapter Test (TRF)
12	Chapter Review	
13	Chapter Review	
14	Chapter Test (TRF)	

TESTING OPTIONS
■ Quiz for Lessons 13-1 Through 13-3   ■ Chapter 13 Test, Form A   ■ Chapter 13 Test, Cumulative Form
■ Quiz for Lessons 13-4 Through 13-6   ■ Chapter 13 Test, Form B

PROVIDING FOR INDIVIDUAL DIFFERENCES
The student text has been written for, and tested with, average students. It also has been used successfully with better and more poorly prepared students.

The Lesson Notes often include Error Analysis and Alternate Approach features to help you with those students who need more help. A blackline Lesson Master (in the Teacher's Resource File), keyed to the chapter objectives, is provided for each lesson to allow more practice. (However, since it is very important to keep up with the daily pace, you are not expected to use all of these masters. Again, refer to the suggestions for pacing on page T35.) Extension activities are provided in the Lesson Notes for those students who have completed the particular lesson in a shorter amount of time than is expected, even in the Full Course.

628A

OBJECTIVES ■ CHAPTER 13

The objectives listed here are the same as in the Chapter 13 Review on pages 678-681 of the student text. The Progress Self-Test on pages 676-677 and the tests in the Teacher's Resource File cover these objectives. For recommendations regarding the handling of this end-of-chapter material, see the notes in the margin on the corresponding pages of the Teacher's Edition.

OBJECTIVES FOR CHAPTER 13 (Organized into the SPUR Categories—Skills, Properties, Uses, and Representations)	Progress Self-Test Questions	Chapter Review Questions	Lesson Master from Teacher's Resource File*
SKILLS			
A Draw regular polygons using LOGO programs.	7	1 through 2	13-8
B Determine measures of exterior angles in polygons.	6	3 through 4	13-8
PROPERTIES			
C Write the converse, inverse, or contrapositive of a conditional.	1, 2	5 through 8	13-2
D Follow the basic laws of reasoning to make conclusions.	3	9 through 18	13-1, 13-2, 13-3, 13-4
E Write indirect proofs.	4, 5	19 through 21	13-4
F Make deductions from properties of radii perpendicular to tangents.	14, 15	22 through 25	13-5
G Justify auxiliary lines.	12, 13	26 through 29	13-6
H From given information, deduce which sides or angles of triangles are smallest or largest.	9	30 through 33	13-7
I Use the Exterior Angle Inequality to determine angle measures.	10	34 through 35	13-7
USES			
J Apply laws of reasoning in real situations.	8, 16	36 through 39	13-1, 13-2, 13-3, 13-4
REPRESENTATIONS			
(There are no representation objectives in this chapter.)			
HISTORY			
K Know the history and impact of Playfair's Parallel Postulate on the development of geometry.	11	40 through 42	13-6

*The masters are numbered to match the lessons.

628B

OVERVIEW ■ CHAPTER 13

What makes mathematics interesting to many professional mathematicians is the variety of proofs that exist. The number of different types of proofs seems infinite. It is a challenge and a pleasure to discover or rediscover them.

Although for students, this aspect of mathematics can be extremely frustrating, this chapter's work with logic and proof has been very popular. Students see it as worthwhile and applicable.

The proofs mathematicians do are based on just a few laws of logic. Two of these laws, Detachment and Transitivity, are discussed in Lesson 13-1. The other

laws, Contrapositive, Ruling Out Possibilities, and Indirect Reasoning, are introduced in Lessons 13-2 through 13-4. A student who knows the content of Lessons 13-1 through 13-4 has enough knowledge to follow the logic in most mathematical proofs.

Lesson 13-5 applies the Laws of the Contrapositive and Indirect Reasoning to deduce properties of tangents to circles and spheres.

Playfair's Parallel Postulate is covered in Lesson 13-6 and is contrasted with Euclid's approach. The presentation is a more advanced look at ideas about mathematical systems first introduced in Chapter

1. The Parallel Postulate enables unique parallels to be drawn, and is presented in conjunction with the question of when lines and other figures are uniquely determined.

The chapter ends with a discussion of exterior angles in triangles (Lesson 13-7) and in polygons and related inequalities (Lesson 13-8). The content of these two lessons is needed for certain problems and proofs in the last two chapters.

Be careful not to spend too much time on the logic puzzles first introduced in Lesson 13-3. They are interesting for many students and teachers but are best treated as a recreational application.

PERSPECTIVES ■ CHAPTER 13

The Perspectives provide the rationale for the inclusion of topics or approaches, provide mathematical background, and make connections with other lessons and within UCSMP.

13-1

THE LOGIC OF MAKING CONCLUSIONS

Two laws of logic are discussed in this lesson, namely, the Law of Detachment (If p and $p \Rightarrow q$, then q) and the Law of Transitivity (if $p \Rightarrow q$ and $q \Rightarrow r$, then $p \Rightarrow r$).

In typical two-column proofs, the Law of Detachment is found in almost every line. In them, q is the "conclusion," while $p \Rightarrow q$ is the "justification" for q. It is p, the given, that is sometimes lost when thinking about each line. In this book, p is often stated parenthetically next to the justification.

Without the Law of Transitivity, it would not be possible to say that the last statement deduced follows from the original given. Conclusions can also be used to make other conclusions. The important point is that a conclusion made from a conclusion is just as true as the first conclusion.

13-2

NEGATIONS

The negation of p, called *not-p*, is the statement that is false when p is true, and true when p is false. This lesson discusses the writing of negations and the following three statements, given that $p \Rightarrow q$ is the original statement.

$q \Rightarrow p$	converse
not-p $\Rightarrow$ *not-q*	inverse
not-q $\Rightarrow$ *not-p*	contrapositive

The Law of the Contrapositive states that when $p \Rightarrow q$ is true, then its contrapositive is true. If the converse $q \Rightarrow p$ is true, then the biconditional $p \Leftrightarrow q$ is true, and all four of the above statements are true. There can never be an odd number of true statements within this group of four.

13-3

RULING OUT POSSIBILITIES

There are two reasons for this lesson. The mathematical reason is that the idea of ruling out possibilities forms the basis for indirect reasoning, the focus of Lesson 13-4. The pedagogical reason is that logic puzzles of the type given in the lesson are very motivating for students.

13-4

INDIRECT PROOF

Many students have difficulty understanding the logic of indirect proofs. Stress that an indirect proof begins by reasoning from a statement whose truth value is not known and not from a false statement. If the reasoning started from a false statement, the conclusions could either be true or false. However, if valid reasoning from a statement of unknown truth value leads to a false conclusion, then the original statement must be false.

Do not require that an indirect proof be placed in two-column format. This format does not work well because some of the justifications are logical laws.

13-5
TANGENTS TO CIRCLES AND SPHERES

Some theorems about circles and spheres, such as the Radius-Tangent Theorem, are important for future work in mathematics. This theorem states that a line is tangent to a circle if and only if it is perpendicular to a radius at the endpoint of the radius on the circle. The "if" part of this theorem is deduced with the help the Law of Indirect Reasoning. The "only if" part of the theorem is proved with the help of the Law of Contrapositive. Thus, this lesson applies the logic of the previous lessons.

13-6
UNIQUENESS

In Chapter 4, auxilliary lines (angle bisector symmetry lines) were needed for some proofs with reflections. In Chapter 5, a parallel was drawn (using the Corresponding Angles Postulate and Angle Measure Postulate) to help deduce the Triangle-Sum Theorem. In Chapter 6, perpendiculars were drawn from points to lines. These auxiliary lines and parts of lines could only be drawn because they were unique.

The importance of the idea of auxiliary lines is demonstrated by how little could be proved without them. Virtually any nonobvious theorem requires the use of an auxiliary line. The new idea in this lesson is the justification for an auxiliary line, not the drawing of one.

In Euclidean geometry, there is a unique line parallel to a given line through a point not on it. This justification for parallels is not the original statement as given by Euclid but is Playfair's version. It is called Playfair's Parallel Postulate, although it is listed as a theorem in this book. Euclid's statement is the 5th postulate on page 661.

13-7
EXTERIOR ANGLES

There are four theorems deduced in this lesson. The Exterior Angle Theorem (the measure of an exterior angle equals the sum of the measures of the two nonadjacent interior angles) is a simple consequence of the Triangle-Sum Theorem. The Exterior Angle Inequality (the measure of an exterior angle of a triangle is greater than the measure of either nonadjacent interior angle) follows as a corollary by using the Equation to Inequality Property. This inequality aids in deducing the Unequal Sides Theorem (in a triangle, larger sides are opposite larger angles), which in turn leads (through an indirect argument) to the Unequal Angles Theorem (in a triangle, larger angles are opposite larger sides).

13-8
EXTERIOR ANGLES OF POLYGONS

This lesson has two parts. The first part is devoted to exterior angles of polygons. The fact that the sum of the measures of the exterior angles is constant is such a surprise to students that it seems like a trick. The second part of the lesson explains why the surprising fact is not a trick. This is done by connecting the exterior angle sum with rotations and particularly with the number of degrees in a circle. LOGO provides a concrete example of how these properties are related. To draw a polygon in LOGO, a turn of 360° is necessary.

CHAPTER 13

We recommend 11 to 14 days for this chapter: 8 to 10 on the lessons and quizzes; 1 for the Progress Self-Test; 1 or 2 for the Chapter Review; and 1 for a Chapter test. (See the Daily Pacing Chart on page 628A.)

CHAPTER 13

Logic and Indirect Reasoning

13-1: The Logic of Making Conclusions

13-2: Negations

13-3: Ruling Out Possibilities

13-4: Indirect Proof

13-5: Tangents to Circles and Spheres

13-6: Uniqueness

13-7: Exterior Angles

13-8: Exterior Angles of Polygons

628

The 15 clues below are from a famous puzzle called "Who Owns the Zebra?" (This puzzle dates from the 1950s, before the dangers of smoking were widely recognized.)

1. There are five houses, each of a different color and inhabited by men of different nationalities, with different pets, drinks, and cigarettes.
2. The Englishman lives in the red house.
3. The Spaniard owns the dog.
4. Coffee is drunk in the green house.
5. The Ukranian drinks tea.
6. The green house is immediately to the right (*your* right) of the ivory house.
7. The Old Gold smoker owns snails.
8. Kools are smoked in the yellow house.
9. Milk is drunk in the middle house.
10. The Norwegian lives in the first house on the left.
11. The man who smokes Chesterfields lives in the house next to the man with the fox.
12. Kools are smoked in the house next to the house where the horse is kept.
13. The Lucky Strike smoker drinks orange juice.
14. The Japanese man smokes Parliaments.
15. The Norwegian lives next to the blue house.

Now, who drinks water? And who owns the zebra?

Answers:
water–Norwegian
zebra–Japanese

"Who Owns the Zebra?" is famous partially because nothing in the clues seems to have anything to do with water or zebras. Consequently, it doesn't seem like there is enough information to figure out the answer to the question. However, by carefully using logic and ruling out possibilities, the owner of the zebra can be determined.

The logic in these puzzles is the same as the logic used in mathematics. Instead of reasoning from clues, mathematicians reason from postulates. Instead of finding out who owns the zebra or who drinks water, mathematicians try to find out what is true about figures or numbers or other mathematical ideas.

In the first ten chapters of this book, you were introduced to all of the postulates that are needed in Euclidean geometry. You may not have realized that there were no new postulates, no new assumptions in Chapters 11 and 12. Nor are there any new assumptions in the remainder of this book. The postulates you have seen are sufficient to deduce any theorem of Euclidean geometry.

However, there are two types of proofs in mathematics—direct and indirect—and thus far you have been asked only to write direct proofs. In this chapter, you will learn about the logic of indirect reasoning and see and write some indirect proofs. Indirect reasoning is used to solve logic puzzles like "Who Owns the Zebra?" and also to prove many theorems. You may find some indirect proofs easier to write than direct proofs.

CHAPTER 13   Logic and Indirect Reasoning   **629**

USING PAGES 628-629
The origin of "Who Owns the Zebra?" is unknown to the authors. It is one of those puzzles that is attractive enough to cause teachers to hand it down from one to another. It is quite difficult to solve, even if you have experience with these kinds of logic puzzles. The solver must go through the clues again and again, each time checking to see if the little bit of information added the last time is enough to add a little more information this time. Do not make solving this puzzle a requirement; it should be pure fun and/or extra credit.

RESOURCES
■ Lesson Master 13-1
▣ Visual for Teaching Aid
79 can be used with
Examples 2 and **3**.

OBJECTIVES

D Follow the basic laws of reasoning to make conclusions.
J Apply laws of reasoning in real situations.

TEACHING NOTES

There are three major reasons for stating laws such as the Law of Detachment and the Law of Transitivity. The first is to catalog the ways in which conclusions are made. The Law of Detachment is the simplest. Second, these laws characterize the reasoning used in mathematical proofs. And third, some laws of reasoning, such as the Law of Indirect Reasoning, are not so obvious.

There are three types of examples given in the lesson. **Example 1** involves a real-life situation and the use of algebra. **Example 2** is a geometric example, and **Example 3** is a puzzle. Since students have made conclusions in algebra before, you might want to give **Example 1** the most attention.

The Logic of Making Conclusions

The battle of Waterloo is one of the subjects in logic puzzles by Charles Dodgson. See Example 3 on page 632.

To begin the study of logic, we examine a proof similar to some you have written before. In this case, however, we have identified each statement with a letter so that the logic becomes clearer.

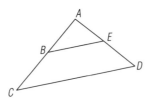

Given: $\overline{BE} \parallel \overline{CD}.$ p
Prove: $\triangle ABE \sim \triangle ACD.$ r

Conclusions	Justifications
1. $\angle ABE \cong \angle ACD,$ $\angle AEB \cong \angle ADC$ q	$\parallel$ lines $\Rightarrow$ corr. $\angle$s = $p \Rightarrow q$
2. $\triangle ABE \sim \triangle ACD$ r	AA Similarity Theorem $q \Rightarrow r$

Recall that a justification for a conclusion is a true if-then statement with the conclusion as the consequent. Notice how this idea is used in step 1 of the above proof. $p \Rightarrow q$ is the justification for concluding q from the given p. The general logical principle is called the *Law of Detachment* because q is "detached" from $p \Rightarrow q$. It is a generalization of the common sense idea that when $p \Rightarrow q$ is a true statement and p is true, q follows.

Law of Detachment:

> If you have a statement or given information p and a justification of the form $p \Rightarrow q$, you may conclude q.

Conclusions can be antecedents for making other conclusions. In step 2, from the conclusion q and the justification $q \Rightarrow r$, the conclusion r follows. Having steps 1 and 2, you can conclude that $p \Rightarrow r$. The proof can be diagrammed as follows:

$$p \Rightarrow q$$
$$q \Rightarrow r$$

from which you can conclude $p \Rightarrow r.$

The logical idea is the *Law of Transitivity*. (It is sometimes called the *Transitive Property of Implication*.)

Law of Transitivity:

If $p \Rightarrow q$ and $q \Rightarrow r$, then $p \Rightarrow r$.

Logical principles can be applied to everyday thinking.

■ ■ ■ ■ ■ ■ ■ ■ ■

Example 1 A commercial states:
> If you want to be popular, you should dress well.
> If you dress well, you should wear brand X jeans.

What conclusion is desired?

Solution Assign variables for the statements.
> *p:* You want to be popular.
> *d:* You dress well.
> *j:* You wear brand X jeans.

The commercial states:
> If *p*, then *d*. If *d*, then *j*. Using the symbol for $\Rightarrow$,
> you can write $p \Rightarrow d$ and $d \Rightarrow j$.

By the Law of Transitivity, you can conclude $p \Rightarrow j$. In words:
> If you want to be popular, you should wear brand X jeans.

Of course, the commercial wants you to believe that $p \Rightarrow d$ and $d \Rightarrow j$ are true statements. Many people would *not* accept these statements as true. Recall from Chapter 2 that if an antecedent is not true, you cannot trust any conclusion made from it. If either $p \Rightarrow d$ or $d \Rightarrow j$ is false, you have no reason to automatically conclude $p \Rightarrow j$.

The Law of Transitivity is used often in algebra. Each step in many algebra problems is a conclusion based on the previous step. The end result (*r*) is often not obvious from the given information (*p*).

p	$3n + 18 > 16$	Given
$\Rightarrow q$	$3n > -2$	Addition Property of Inequality ($p \Rightarrow q$)
$\Rightarrow r$	$n > -\frac{2}{3}$	Multiplication Property of Inequality ($q \Rightarrow r$)

Because of the Law of Transitivity, you can conclude $p \Rightarrow r$:
> If $3n + 18 > 16$, then $n > -\frac{2}{3}$.

In Example 1, the justifications were properties of inequality and operations and the logic was "behind the scenes." But sometimes the justifications you might use are part of the given information. Then the logical laws themselves become the justifications. This is shown in Example 2, in which the given statements (1) and (2) are used as justifications.

LESSON 13-1 The Logic of Making Conclusions   **631**

Alternate Approach
Venn diagrams can represent some of the less complicated logic patterns. Here is a diagram for statement 1 of **Example 2**.

K = set of kites
R = set of rhombuses

Here is a diagram for statement 2.

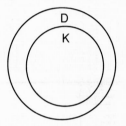

P = set of figures with perpendicular diagonals
K = set of kites

Statement 3 is represented as a dot in the R circle.

Combining the diagrams shows possible conclusions. The dot being in circle P means the diagonals of *BUSM* are perpendicular.

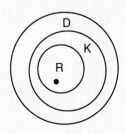

Error Analysis A common incorrect pattern students use when reasoning is "if $p \Rightarrow q$ and *q*, therefore *p*." Caution students that this is an invalid pattern and should not be confused with the Law of Detachment.

ADDITIONAL EXAMPLES

1. A camp brochure states: "The registration deadline is May 1st." Jack registered on April 29th.

a. How are these two facts related to the Law of Detachment?

The first statement is: If a person registers by May 1st, then he or she meets the deadline. The second statement is: Jack registered by May 1st.

b. What conclusion is desired?

Jack met the deadline.

2. Make a conclusion from these statements.

(1) A little learning is a dangerous thing. (Alexander Pope)

(2) If a little knowledge is dangerous, then no one is out of danger. (Thomas Huxley)

No one is out of danger.

3. What conclusions can be made from the following three statements?

(1) Every rectangle is an isosceles trapezoid.

(2) ABCD is a rectangle.

(3) The perpendicular bisector of the bases of an isosceles trapezoid is a symmetry line for the isosceles trapezoid.

From (1) and (2), ABCD is an isosceles trapezoid; from (1) and (3), every rectangle has a symmetry line, the perpendicular bisector of its bases; from (1), (2), and 3), the perpendicular bisector of the bases of ABCD is a symmetry line for ABCD.

NOTES ON QUESTIONS

Question 1: The difficulty of "Who Owns the Zebra?" is another reason for its fame.

Question 13: Arthur Ashe did win Wimbledon in 1975.

Question 14: Draw an isosceles △ABC that is not equilateral to show that the answer is correct.

Example 2
What conclusions can be made from the following?

(1) Every rhombus is a kite.

(2) The diagonals of a kite are perpendicular.

(3) *BUSM* is a rhombus.

Solution First put the conditionals in if-then form. Call (3) *r*, for the special instance of figure *BUSM*.

(1) $r \Rightarrow k$: If a figure is a rhombus, then it is a kite.

(2) $k \Rightarrow p$: If a figure is a kite, then its diagonals are perpendicular.

From (1) and (2), using the Law of Transitivity, you can conclude $r \Rightarrow p$: If a figure is a rhombus, then its diagonals are perpendicular.

From *r* and $r \Rightarrow p$, using the Law of Detachment, you can conclude *p*:
The diagonals of *BUSM* are perpendicular.

Since the given statements (1)–(3) are true, the conclusion should be true.

Check Statements (1) and (2) are theorems we have proved, so they are true. Now draw a situation in which (3) is true also. That is, draw a picture of a rhombus *BUSM*. Don't make it special. Do its diagonals seem perpendicular? Yes, the conclusion checks.

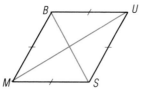

Lewis Carroll, the Englishman [1832-1898] best known for writing *Alice in Wonderland,* was a logician. That is, he studied the process of reasoning. Under his given name, Charles L. Dodgson, he wrote books on logic. Here is a puzzle from one of his books.

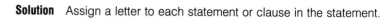

Example 3
Given these statements, what can you conclude using all the statements?

(1) My gardener is well worth listening to on military subjects.

(2) No one can remember the battle of Waterloo, unless he is very old.

(3) Nobody is really worth listening to on military subjects, unless he can remember the battle of Waterloo.

Solution Assign a letter to each statement or clause in the statement.

p: A person is worth listening to on military subjects.

q: A person can remember Waterloo.

r: A person is very old.

Now analyze the givens.

(1) is merely *p*, for the special instance of the gardener.

(2) is $q \Rightarrow r$.

(3) is $p \Rightarrow q$.

From (2) and (3), using the Law of Transitivity, you get $p \Rightarrow r$.

Together with (1), using the Law of Detachment, you get *r* as applied to the gardener. Lewis Carroll's desired conclusion: My gardener is very old.

Charles Dodgson (1832-1898)

632

Covering the Reading

1. Why is "Who Owns the Zebra?" famous?
   Nothing in the clues seems to deal with zebras.
2. What two kinds of proofs are there in mathematics?
   direct and indirect
3. Which two logical principles are used in the proof which begins this lesson? Law of Detachment, Law of Transitivity

4. If p is given and $p \Rightarrow q$ is true, then __?__ can be concluded. q

In 5–8, what can be concluded from the given statements?

5. (1) Every square is a rectangle.
   (2) Every rectangle is a parallelogram.
   Every square is a parallelogram.
6. (1) Every triangle with two congruent sides has at least two congruent angles.
   (2) If a triangle is isosceles, then it has two congruent sides.
   If a triangle is isosceles, then it has at least two congruent angles.
7. (1) Your teeth will be whiter if you use Toothdazzle.
   (2) The whiter your teeth are, the more popular you will be with the opposite sex. If you use Toothdazzle, the more popular you will be with the opposite sex.
8. (1) If a figure is a prism, then the figure is a polyhedron.
   (2) A figure is a polyhedron if it is a pyramid.
   No conclusion can be made.
9. Explain how the Law of Transitivity is used when solving the sentence $7(x - 12) < 70$.
   See margin.

Applying the Mathematics

In 10–13, assume this statement is true: If a tennis player has won Wimbledon, then the player is world class. Using the Law of Detachment only, what (if anything) can you conclude if you also know the given statement is true?

10. Martina Navratilova has won Wimbledon.
    Martina Navratilova is world class.
11. Boris Becker has won Wimbledon. Boris Becker is world class.

12. Gabriela Sabatini has not won Wimbledon (as of 1989).
    No conclusion can be made.
13. Arthur Ashe won the U.S. Open Tennis Tournament in 1968.
    No conclusion can be made.
14. What can you conclude from these two statements?
    (1) A triangle has two congruent angles if it is equilateral.
    (2) $\triangle ABC$ has two congruent angles.
    Nothing can be concluded.

In 15–18, in some states if a person has a driver's license, then the person's age is greater than or equal to 16. Tell what you can conclude in these states from this statement if you also know the following:

15. Joe has a driver's license.
    Joe is 16 or older.
16. Jamie drives a car legally.
    Jamie is 16 or older.
17. Florence is 18 years old.
    Nothing can be concluded.
18. Isabel does not drive a car.
    Nothing can be concluded.

Martina Navratilova won the singles title at Wimbledon, England, July 6, 1985.

LESSON 13-1 The Logic of Making Conclusions **633**

MORE PRACTICE
For more questions on SPUR Objectives, use *Lesson Master 13-1*, shown below.

ADDITIONAL ANSWERS
9. See the margin on p. 634.

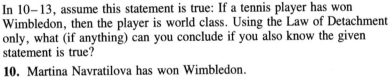

NAME _____

LESSON **MASTER 13–1**
QUESTIONS ON **SPUR** OBJECTIVES

■ **PROPERTIES** *Objective D (See pages 678–681 for objectives.)*
In 1–4, given the statements, a. what (if anything) can you conclude?
b. What reasoning laws have you used?

1. (1) If a figure is a rhombus, then it is a parallelogram.
   (2) *NOVA* is a rhombus.
   a. *NOVA* is a parallelogram.
   b. Law of Detachment

2. (1) If $x = 12$, then $y = 10$.
   (2) If $z = 4$, then $x = 12$.
   (3) $z = 4$
   a. $y = 10$
   b. Laws of Detachment and of Transitivity

3. (1) Someone got out of a car.
   (2) Whenever someone gets out of a car, a sound is made.
   a. A sound is made.
   b. Law of Detachment

4. (1) If $x = 22$, then $y = 4$.
   (2) $y = 4$
   a. Nothing can be concluded.
   b. _____

Geometry © Scott, Foresman and Company   *Continued* 119

NAME _____
Lesson MASTER 13–1 (page 2)

■ **USES** *Objective J*
In 5–8, given the statements, a. what (if anything) can you conclude?
b. What laws of logic have you used?

5. (1) I go to bed if I finish my lessons.
   (2) I fall asleep if I go to bed.
   (3) I finished my lessons last night.
   a. I fell asleep last night.
   b. Laws of Detachment and of Transitivity

6. (1) I had a good day today.
   (2) When it is payday, I have a good day.
   a. Nothing can be concluded.
   b. _____

7. (1) If you want to be happy, you must make a lot of money.
   (2) If you want to make a lot of money, you have to go to graduate school.
   a. If you want to be happy, you have to go to graduate school.
   b. Law of Transitivity

8. (1) Catfish cannot breathe air.
   (2) If an animal cannot breathe air, it must live in the ocean.
   a. Catfish live in the ocean.
   b. Law of Detachment

120   Geometry © Scott, Foresman and Company

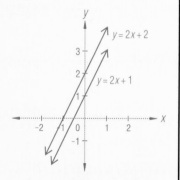
19. Use the drawing at the right.
  a. Make a conclusion using the Law of Detachment. Justify your conclusion.
  b. Make a second conclusion using the Law of Transitivity. See margin.

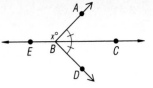

20. Lewis Carroll asked if this reasoning is correct. Is it?
  (1) Dictionaries are useful.
  (2) Useful books are valuable.
  Conclusion: Dictionaries are valuable. Yes

21. Use the drawing at the left. $HI = 4$, $EF = 6$, $EI = 8$, and $FG = 10$.
  a. Find FI. 10   **b.** Find FH. $\sqrt{116}$ **c.** Find GH. $\sqrt{216}$
  d. *Multiple choice.* Which of the following has *not* been used in finding GH?
  (i) Law of Detachment   (ii) Law of Transitivity
  (iii) Pythagorean Theorem   (iv) All of these are used. (iv)

22. Use the drawing for Question 21.
  Explain why $GH^2 = FG^2 + HI^2 + IE^2 + EF^2$. See margin.

Review

23. The height of a pyramid is doubled and the dimensions of its rectangular base are tripled. What happens to its volume?
  (*Lesson 10-6*) It is multiplied by 18.

24. The height of a cylinder is doubled and the diameter of its circular base is tripled. What happens to its volume? (*Lesson 10-5*)
  It is multiplied by 18.

25. What is the sum of the measures of the angles of a convex pentagon?
  (*Lesson 5-7*) 540

26. Give the definition of trapezoid. (*Lesson 5-2*) A quadrilateral is a trapezoid if and only if it has at least one pair of parallel sides.

27. Draw a counterexample to this statement: If a quadrilateral has two consecutive sides congruent, then it is a kite. (*Lessons 5-2, 2-2*)
  See margin.

28. a. Graph the lines with equations $y = 2x + 1$ and $y = 2x + 2$.
  b. Are these lines parallel or intersecting? parallel
  c. Are these lines horizontal, vertical, or oblique? oblique
  (*Lessons 3-4, 1-3*) a) See margin.

29. Expand: **a.** $(x - y)^2$; **b.** $(a - (-a))^2$. (*Previous course*)
  a) $x^2 - 2xy + y^2$; b) $4a^2$

Exploration

30. Let p be the statement "$ABCD$ is a rectangle." Find as many theorems as you can of the form $p \Rightarrow q$, and for each tell what q means for rectangle $ABCD$. See margin.

31. Examine the clues in "Who Owns the Zebra?" Make a conclusion that is not given in the clues.
  Sample: The Norwegian lives in the yellow house.

634

13-2

Negations

Jane is studying for the next test.

Indirect reasoning is based on the idea of *negation*. The **negation** of a statement *p*, called **not-p,** is a statement that is true whenever statement *p* is false and is false whenever statement *p* is true.

Statement: You study for the next test.
Negation: You do not study for the next test.

The above example shows that you can often write the negation by changing the verb. If the verb is negative, then the negation has a positive verb.

p: The quadrilateral *ABCD* is not a parallelogram.
not-p: The quadrilateral *ABCD* is a parallelogram.

Changing something other than the verb will not necessarily give the negation. But the word "not" can be avoided by considering all alternatives.

p: $\triangle ABC$ is isosceles.
not-p: $\triangle ABC$ is scalene.

t: $\angle A$ is a right angle.
correct *not-t:* $\angle A$ is acute or $\angle A$ is obtuse.
incorrect *not-t:*   m$\angle A = 45$.

The negation of a negation is the original statement. The statements *p* and *not-(not-p)* are identical.

Recall that from any conditional $p \Rightarrow q$, you can form its converse $q \Rightarrow p$. Let *p* = "a triangle is equilateral" and *q* = "a triangle has three acute angles."

Original $p \Rightarrow q$: If a triangle is equilateral,
                then it has three acute angles.
Converse $q \Rightarrow p$: If a triangle has three acute angles,
                then it is equilateral.

Here the original is true, the converse false.

LESSON 13-2   Negations   **635**

RESOURCES
■ Lesson Master 13-2

OBJECTIVES

C Write the converse, inverse, or contrapositive of a conditional.
D Follow the basic laws of reasoning to make conclusions.
J Apply laws of reasoning in real situations.

TEACHING NOTES

You might wish to point out to students that the inverse and converse of a statement are either both true or both false. This is because the inverse is the contrapositive of the converse.

Making Connections
The Law of the Contrapositive is discussed in most geometry books, although it is not always named. In this lesson, the law is applied to logic puzzles. In Lesson 13-5, it is applied in the proof that a tangent to a circle is perpendicular to the radius drawn at the point of contact.

Surprisingly, the Law of the Contrapositive is not used more often in proofs. Many theorems that seem to require an indirect proof can be understood more easily if the law is used. For instance the theorem that $\sqrt{2}$ is irrational can be stated as follows: If $\frac{a}{b}$ is in lowest terms and *a* and *b* are positive integers, then $\sqrt{2} \neq \frac{a}{b}$. The usual indirect proof really proves the contrapositive directly, that is, if $\sqrt{2} = \frac{a}{b}$ and *a* and *b* are positive integers, then $\frac{a}{b}$ cannot be in lowest terms.

Reading As students read the lesson, ask them to consider grammar and English usage when negating a statement, or finding the converse, inverse, or contrapositive of a statement. The result should not be an awkward statement. Ask them to read the statements very carefully and to try to make up some of their own examples.

ADDITIONAL EXAMPLES

1. Give the converse, inverse, and contrapositive of the following statement: If you live in an air-conditioned place, you have the opportunity to be cool in the summer.
Converse: If you have the opportunity to be cool in the summer, then you live in an air-conditioned place.
Inverse: If you do not live in an air-conditioned place, you do not have the opportunity to be cool in the summer.
Contrapositive: If you do not have the opportunity to be cool in the summer, then you do not live in an air-conditioned place.

2. Make a conclusion from the two statements.
(1) Bill cannot become an eagle scout.
(2) If a person is a boy scout, he can become an eagle scout.
Bill is not a boy scout.

3. Make a conclusion using all three statements.
(1) If we hang an Escher drawing on this wall, people will smile as they enter the room.
(2) If we do not put up an Escher drawing on this wall, I will be bothered.
(3) I will not be bothered if we remove these paintings from this wall.
If we remove paintings from this wall, then people will smile as they enter the room.

Negating *both* parts of the original conditional gives a new conditional of the form *not-p* ⇒ *not-q*, called the **inverse** of the original.

Inverse *not-p* ⇒ *not-q*: If a triangle is not equilateral, it does not have three acute angles.

This inverse is false. There are triangles which are not equilateral but do have three acute angles.

However, if both parts of the original are negated and the antecedent and consequent are switched, a second *true* statement appears. This statement, of the form *not-q* ⇒ *not-p*, is called the **contrapositive** of the original.

Contrapositive *not-q* ⇒ *not-p*: If a triangle does not have three acute angles, it is not equilateral.

Example 1 Given the conditional "If you live in California, then you need a mountain bicycle," write the converse, contrapositive, and inverse.

Solution Converse $q \Rightarrow p$: If you need a mountain bicycle, then you live in California.
Contrapositive *not-q* ⇒ *not-p*: If you do not need a mountain bicycle, then you do not live in California.
Inverse *not-p* ⇒ *not-q*: If you do not live in California, then you do not need a mountain bicycle.

The given and all three statements in the solution of Example 1 are false. Both Example 1 and the equilateral triangle example preceding it verify the following law of logic.

Law of the Contrapositive:
A statement ($p \Rightarrow q$) and its contrapositive (*not-q* ⇒ *not-p*) are either both true or both false.

To summarize: If a given statement is true, you may conclude that its contrapositive is true, but its converse and inverse may be either true or false. The Law of the Contrapositive used along with the Law of Detachment and the Law of Transitivity allows you to make many more conclusions.

Example 2 Given are two statements.
(1) Every square is a kite.
(2) Quadrilateral *POTS* is not a kite.
What conclusion can be made using both statements?

Solution In if-then form, (1) is: If a figure is a square, then it is a kite. This is a true statement; thus, the contrapositive is also true and may be stated as follows: If a figure is not a kite, then it is not a square. Now, since (2) *POTS* is not a kite, you can use the Law of Detachment to conclude that *POTS* is not a square.

You have now studied enough laws of logic to figure out many logic puzzles. Here is a version of another one of Lewis Carroll's puzzles. Notice how the Law of the Contrapositive and the Law of Transitivity are both used.

■ ■ ■ ■ ■ ■ ■ ■

Example 3 Given these statements, what can you conclude?
(1) Babies are illogical.
(2) Any person who can manage a crocodile is not despised.
(3) Illogical persons are despised.

Solution First translate as many statements as possible into if-then form. To avoid lots of writing, use variables to name the parts of the statements.
Let   *B:*   A person is a baby.
         D: A person is despised.
         C: A person can manage a crocodile.
         I: A person is illogical.
Now   (1) becomes $B \Rightarrow I$.
         (2) becomes $C \Rightarrow not\text{-}D$.
         (3) is $I \Rightarrow D$.
From (1) and (3) you can conclude (using transitivity) $B \Rightarrow D$. The contrapositive of (2) is $D \Rightarrow not\text{-}C$. So, using transitivity again, the conclusion is $B \Rightarrow not\text{-}C$. A baby cannot manage a crocodile.

Questions

In 1–4, give the negation of the statement.
1. The perimeter of an *n*-gon with side *s* is *ns*.
   The perimeter of an *n*-gon with side *s* is not *ns*.
2. ∠*A* is acute. **∠*A* is not acute; or ∠*A* is either right or obtuse.**
3. You were not late for school today. **You were late for school today.**
4. △*GHI* is scalene. **△*GHI* is isosceles; or △*GHI* is not scalene.**

LESSON 13-2 Negations   **637**

NOTES ON QUESTIONS
Question 6: Ask students which statements are true. (original and contrapositive only)

Question 8: When a step in an equation and its converse are both true, the step is called reversible. Adding the same number to both sides of an equation is reversible. However, squaring both sides of an equation is not reversible.

Question 14: In this question and elsewhere, when statements are numbered, it is assumed that students will try to use all the statements in making their conclusions. One could conclude (from (1) by using the Law of the Contrapositive) that if a network is not traversable, then it does not have only even vertices. This is not the best response, however, because it does not use (2).

Question 15: You might want students to give other examples from mathematics.

Question 18: Here the advertisers want the listener to think the inverse: If I do not try the product, I will be sorry. Even if the original ad is true, the inverse does not have to be true. Advertisements usually are technically true, but they often want the listener or reader to reason that the converse or inverse is true.

Question 29: You might wish to give students a few days to do this question, or give a prize for the best or funniest puzzle. One possible criterion for *best* is that the given statements are saying that people usually take as true while the conclusion is surprising.

5. The negation of a statement *p* is written __?__ . *not-p*

In 6–9, give **a.** the converse; **b.** the contrapositive; and **c.** the inverse of the given statement.

6. If m∠T = 45, then ∠T is acute. See margin.

7. *p* ⇒ *q* See margin.

8. If *ax* + *by* = *c*, then *ax* = *c* − *by*. See margin.

9. You can get $10 for that old tape recorder when you bring it in Saturday. See margin.

In 10–12, *multiple choice*. The four choices are:
(a) negation
(b) converse
(c) inverse
(d) contrapositive.

10. If a statement is true, its __?__ must be true. **(d)**

11. If a statement is true, its __?__ is false. **(a)**

12. If a statement is false, its __?__ is false. **(d)**

13. Give the contrapositive: If △ABC is not a right triangle, then the Pythagorean Theorem does not hold for △ABC. See margin.

14. Make a conclusion using both of the following true statements.
(1) If a network has only even vertices, it is traversable.
(2) The network below is not traversable.
The network below does not have only even vertices.

Applying the Mathematics

15. a. Make a conclusion using both these statements.
(1) If *x* = 3, then *y* = 4.
(2) *y* = 5 *x* ≠ 3
b. Which two of the three laws—Detachment, Transitivity, or Contrapositive—are needed to make your conclusion?
Detachment and Contrapositive

16. If these three statements are true, what can be concluded using all of them?
(1) *p* ⇒ *q*
(2) *q* ⇒ *r*
(3) *not-r not-p*

17. Joanne had a date, but her mother truthfully told her, "If you don't apologize to your brother for the way you treated him, then you're not going out tonight." Joanne went on her date. Is it true that she apologized to her brother? Yes

638

18. José heard the ad "If you try our product, you won't be sorry." Later on, José was not sorry. Does that mean he tried the product? **No**

19. Make a conclusion from all these statements, adapted from Lewis Carroll.
(1) All unripe fruit is unwholesome.
(2) All these apples are wholesome.
(3) No fruit grown in the shade is ripe.
None of these apples was grown in the shade.

20. Make a conclusion using both these statements.
(1) All equilateral triangles have three 60° angles.
(2) $m\angle ABC = 59$ **△ABC is not equilateral.**

21) From a statement or given information p and a justification of the form $p \Rightarrow q$, you may conclude q.

Review

21. State the Law of Detachment. *(Lesson 13-1)*

22. Fill in the blank. Then make a conclusion from all the statements. *(Lessons 13-1, 5-2)*
(1) *ABCD* is a rhombus.
(2) If a figure is a rhombus, then it is a(n) __?__ .
(3) Opposite sides of a parallelogram are parallel.
parallelogram; The opposite sides of *ABCD* are parallel.

23. Given: $\overline{AD} \parallel \overline{BC}$;
$\overline{AB} \parallel \overline{CD}$.
Prove: $\overline{AB} \cong \overline{CD}$. *(Lesson 7-6)* **See margin.**

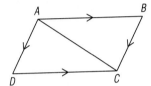

24. *Multiple choice.* In Question 23, what have you proved?
(a) In a parallelogram, opposite sides are parallel.
(b) In a parallelogram, opposite sides are congruent.
(c) If opposite sides of a quadrilateral are congruent, the figure is a parallelogram.
(d) If opposite sides of a quadrilateral are parallel, the figure is a parallelogram.
(Lesson 7-6) **(b)**

In 25–28, solve. *(Previous course)*

25. $5x - 13 = 19x + 15$ **-2**

26. $8(y - 3) = 7(3y + 1)$ $\frac{-31}{13} \approx$ **-2.38**

27. $6z^2 = 150$ **5, -5**

28. $(w + 5)^2 = 289$ **12,-22**

Exploration

29. Make up your own logic puzzle like Example 3.
Sample: **Anything that squips isn't a wozzle.**
Only wozzles tibble.
Everything is red unless it tibbles.
Ip is green.

Conclusion: **Ip doesn't squip.**

FOLLOW-UP

MORE PRACTICE
For more questions on SPUR Objectives, use *Lesson Master 13-2,* shown below.

NAME _____

LESSON **MASTER 13–2**
QUESTIONS ON **SPUR** OBJECTIVES

■**PROPERTIES** *Objective C (See pages 678–681 for objectives.)*
In 1–4, write: a. the converse, b. the inverse, and c. the contrapositive of the statement. d. Which of these are true?

1. If $y = 4$, then $y^2 = 16$.
a. If $y^2 = 16$, then $y = 4$. _____
b. If $y \neq 4$, then $y^2 \neq 16$. _____
c. If $y^2 \neq 16$, then $y \neq 4$. _____
d. **original and contrapositive** _____

2. If a figure is a quadrilateral, then it is a parallelogram.
a. If a figure is a parallel., then it is a quad. _____
b. If a figure is not a quad., then it is not a parallel. _____
c. If a figure is not a parallel., then it is not a quad. _____
d. **converse and inverse** _____

3. All integers are rational numbers.
a. **All rational numbers are integers.** _____
b. If a number is not an integer, then it is not **a rational number.** _____
c. If a number is not a rational number, then it **is not an integer.** _____
d. **original and contrapositive.** _____

4. Use the figure at the right.
If $a = 50$, then $m\angle Z = 75$.

a. If $m\angle Z = 75$, then $a = 50$. _____
b. If $a \neq 50$, then $m\angle Z \neq 75$. _____
c. If $m\angle Z \neq 75$, then $a \neq 50$. _____
d. **None of these is true.** _____

Geometry © Scott, Foresman and Company *Continued* **121**

NAME _____
Lesson MASTER 13–2 (page 2)

■**USES** *Objective J*
In 5–8, given the statements, a. what (if anything) can you conclude using the laws of logic? b. What laws of logic have you used?

5. (1) If you can answer this question, then your teacher will give you a good grade.
(2) Your teacher did not give you a good grade.
a. **You did not answer this question.** _____
b. **Laws of the Contrapositive and of Detachment** _____

6. (1) All people are mortal.
(2) The world will never die.
(3) If something is mortal, then it will die.
a. **The world is not a person.** _____
b. **Laws of the Contrapositive and of Transitivity** _____

7. (1) I drew a circle.
(2) If something is a square, it is not a circle.
a. **I did not draw a square.** _____
b. **Laws of the Contrapositive and of Detachment** _____

8. (1) If $x = 4$, then $y = 11$.
(2) $y = 8$
a. **$x \neq 4$** _____
b. **Laws of the Contrapositive and of Transitivity** _____

122 Geometry © Scott, Foresman and Company

RESOURCES
- Lesson Master 13-3
- Quiz for Lesson 13-1 Through 13-3
- Visual for Teaching Aid 80 can be used with **Example 1**.
- Visual for Teaching Aid 81 can be used with **Question 11**.
- Visual for Teaching Aid 82 can be used with **Question 12**.

OBJECTIVES

D Follow the basic laws of reasoning to make conclusions.

J Apply laws of reasoning in real situations.

TEACHING NOTES

Mathematics can be fun, as this lesson demonstrates. It also sets up the logic of indirect reasoning in the next lesson.

Remind students that when starting with a few statements, many others can be deduced. Indeed, this is a major attraction of logic puzzles.

However, also remind students that sometimes it is not clear how to solve a problem at first glance. By reading over the clues and looking at the grid, a useful fact may be found. Thus, this lesson deals with some important problem-solving strategies such as *reading carefully* and *making a diagram*.

LESSON

13-3

Ruling Out Possibilities

Indirect reasoning is based on the idea of ruling out possibilities. It is used even by animals or babies. If a baby knows that a toy is in either a parent's right hand or the parent's left hand, and the right hand is opened and found empty, the baby will know to look in the left hand for the toy. This innate principle of reasoning is called the *Law of Ruling Out Possibilities*.

Law of Ruling Out Possibilities:

When *p or q* is true and *q* is not true, then *p* is true.

You know every angle in a triangle is either acute, right, or obtuse. So if an angle in a triangle is not acute or right, then it is obtuse. There is no other possibility.

In real life, if words are not carefully defined, you may not be able to rule out possibilities so easily. For example, if a person is not young, that does not necessarily mean the person is old.

In the questions for this lesson, you are asked to solve some logic puzzles. These puzzles use the idea of ruling out possibilities again and again. Notice how little information is given. Yet you can deduce a great deal. The same happens in geometry.

Here are some hints for doing these puzzles: (1) Logic puzzles take a lot of time and analysis, so do not hurry. (2) Construct a grid and place an X in a square whenever something cannot occur. Place an O in the square when the situation *must* occur.

640

Example 1   Carol, Sue, Jill, Dave, and Jim each play a different instrument in the school band. The instruments they play are clarinet, cornet, flute, trombone, and tuba. From the clues below determine which instrument each student plays.
(1) Carol plays either the clarinet, cornet, or tuba.
(2) Sue does not play the flute.
(3) Dave does not play any of these instruments: trombone, cornet, flute, or clarinet.
(4) Jim plays either the tuba or the cornet.

Solution   To solve this puzzle the grid below can be used. The first clue tells you that Carol does not play the flute and that Carol does not play the trombone. Two X_1s in the first row of the grid show this. (We call it X_1 so you can tell it comes directly from clue (1).) The third clue tells you four instruments Dave does not play. The four X_3s in the fourth row show this. Of course, this means that Dave must play the tuba. We show this with an O. Now we know that no one else plays the tuba, so we place four Xs in the column labeled "tuba."

	Clarinet	Cornet	Flute	Trombone	Tuba
Carol			X_1	X_1	X
Sue					X
Jill					X
Dave	X_3	X_3	X_3	X_3	0
Jim					X

You are asked to complete this puzzle in Question 7 at the end of this section.

Sometimes a single piece of given information may yield many conclusions, as in the following example.

Example 2   In Question 12 at the end of this lesson, clue (4) is "Neither Edgar nor the person named Voila is the guard or the teller." What can be concluded from that?

Solution   At least five things can be concluded.
Edgar's last name is not Voila.
Edgar is not the guard.
Edgar is not the teller.
Voila is not the guard.
Voila is not the teller.

A number of logic puzzles by Wayne Williams were selected for this lesson. Other logic puzzles written by him are in the books *Quizzles* and *More Quizzles,* which are distributed by Dale Seymour Publications of Palo Alto, California, in a blackline master form for duplicating. Each puzzle is on a separate page and the grid is drawn. You are also certain to have some students become very interested in these puzzles, and all students will remember that they did some in their geometry class. **Small groups** are appropriate for working out the more complicated puzzles.

Reading   You might need to read this lesson aloud with students. Discuss in detail how the grid is constructed in **Example 1** and how the X's and O's are determined. Encourage students to give some of their own valid conclusions from the statements in the Examples and ask them to show how they relate to the grids that have been set up.

ADDITIONAL EXAMPLES
1. Presidents Buchanan, Grant, Johnson, and Lincoln were four consecutive presidents of the United States. From the clues below, determine the order in which they served.
(1) Buchanan served before Johnson, who became president when the president was assassinated.
(2) Grant won the election because of his popularity during the Civil War.
(3) Lincoln served during almost the entire Civil War and was the only of these presidents to die in office.
Buchanan, Lincoln, Johnson, Grant

2. I am thinking of a one-digit number from 0 through 9. From the clues, determine my number.
(1) It is not prime.
(2) It cannot be the last digit of the square of an integer.

641 [8]

NOTES ON QUESTIONS

Question 7: This question should be discussed in detail. There will be students who do not know where to begin, even with the start given on page 641.

Question 10: The Trichotomy Law is sometimes used as the justification for the statement that either $a = b$ or $a \neq b$. If you wish to use this justification, be certain to review this question in class. The Trichotomy Law is used in some of the indirect proofs in the next lesson.

Questions 11 and 12: It will take some time to review these questions.

Small Group Work for Questions 13-16: It might be helpful if students go over these questions in groups. Ask them to list all correct answers for each question.

ADDITIONAL ANSWERS

5. Sample: The teller is male, either Farmer or Guinness; Shirley is Ms. Edwards.

7. Carol plays the clarinet, Sue plays the trombone, Jill plays the flute, Dave plays the tuba, Jim plays the cornet.

11. Mike - chemist, Darlene - dentist, Gary - teacher, Wanda - car dealer, Ken - farmer, Brad - doctor, Joyce - lawyer

12. Catherine Viola - secretary, Edgar Guinness - manager, Wilbur Farmer - teller, Marjorie Landis - guard, Shirley Edwards - bookkeeper

For Question 12 and other logic problems like it, a complicated grid is often very helpful. The grid should have a space for each *last name-first name* pair, for each *first name-bank job* pair, and for each *bank job-last name* pair. The grid below will do.

On this grid we have noted the possibilities which can be ruled out by clue (4).

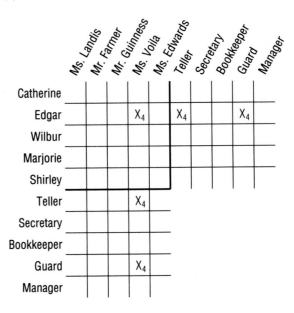

Questions

Covering the Reading

1. Marilyn tosses a coin. The face that shows up is not "heads." You conclude that the face that shows up is "tails." What principle of reasoning have you used? **Law of Ruling Out Possibilities**

2. If statement m or statement n is true and m is not true, then __?__ must be true. n

3. Two different lines s and t in the same plane are not parallel. What can be concluded about s and t?
   s and t have exactly one point in common.

In 4–6, refer to Question 12 on the next page.

4. From clue (3) alone, who is known *not* to be the secretary?
   Edgar, Wilbur, Mr. Farmer, and Mr. Guinness

5. Write at least two conclusions that follow from clue (1). **See margin.**

6. Write at least two conclusions that follow from clue (5).
   Sample: Edgar is not the bookkeeper; Wilbur is Mr. Farmer.

7. Finish Example 1 of this lesson. **See margin.**

642

In 8 and 9, make a conclusion from the given information.

8. Line *m* is not parallel to plane *X* and *m* is not in plane *X*.
Line *m* and plane *X* have exactly one point in common.

9. *ABCD* is a trapezoid with $\overline{AB} \parallel \overline{CD}$, but *ABCD* is not a parallelogram.
Sample: $\overline{BC}$ is not parallel to $\overline{AD}$.

10. The **Trichotomy Law** for real numbers is: Of two real numbers *a* and *b*, either *a* < *b*, *a* = *b*, or *a* > *b*, and no two of these can be true at the same time. Suppose you know that $\sqrt{2} \neq \frac{41}{29}$. What can you conclude by using the Trichotomy Law? $\sqrt{2} < \frac{41}{29}$ or $\sqrt{2} > \frac{41}{29}$

11. Seven seniors, Joyce, Mike, Darlene, Gary, Wanda, Ken, and Brad, were asked about their career plans. These occupations were mentioned: lawyer, farmer, teacher, doctor, dentist, car dealer, and chemist. No occupation was selected by more than one student. Using the following clues, find out who mentioned which occupation.
(1) Joyce doesn't want to be a doctor, car dealer, or chemist.
(2) Mike doesn't want to be a doctor or car dealer either.
(3) Gary wants to be either a teacher, dentist, or farmer.
(4) Ken wants to be either a dentist or farmer.
(5) Brad doesn't want to be a car dealer.
(6) Darlene wants to be a dentist. See margin.

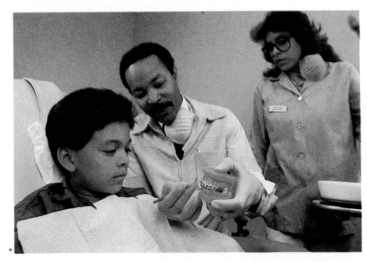

12. The Smalltown Bank has a teller, secretary, bookkeeper, guard, and manager named Mr. Farmer, Mr. Guinness, Ms. Landis, Ms. Voila, and Ms. Edwards, though not necessarily in that order. The two men are Edgar and Wilbur, while the three women are Catherine, Marjorie, and Shirley. From the clues below, determine the first and last names of each person and his or her position at the bank. (Hint: Use the grid on the previous page.)
(1) Neither Catherine nor Marjorie is the teller and neither is Ms. Edwards.
(2) Shirley is not the guard.
(3) The secretary is either Catherine or Ms. Landis.
(4) Neither Edgar nor the person named Voila is the guard or teller.
(5) Mr. Farmer, Edgar, and the bookkeeper have all worked at the bank for more than five years. See margin.

LESSON 13-3 Ruling Out Possibilities **643**

MORE PRACTICE
For more questions on SPUR Objectives, use *Lesson Master 13-3,* shown on page 643.

EXTENSION
You might want to extend **Question 19** by asking students to give some suggestions on how to write a logic puzzle. These might include statements like the following: Pick an interesting topic and construct a grid for related items. Put O's in the grid and start making up sentences to go along with what "aren't O's" and so on.

EVALUATION
A quiz covering Lessons 13-1 through 13-3 is provided in the Teacher's Resource

ADDITIONAL ANSWERS
13. a. If I eat my hat, then Jackie is a good cook.
b. If Jackie is not a good cook, I will not eat my hat.
c. If I don't eat my hat, then Jackie is not a good cook.

17.

Conclusions	Justifications
1. *AC = BC,* *DC = EC*	def. of isosceles Δ (meaning)
2. ∠*ACD* ≅ ∠*BCE*	Vertical Angle Thm.
3. △*ACD* ≅ △*BCE*	SAS Congruence Thm. (steps 1 and 2)

Review

13. Consider this statement: "If Jackie is a good cook, I'll eat my hat!" Give the **a.** converse; **b.** inverse; and **c.** contrapositive. *(Lesson 13-2)* See margin.

In 14 and 15, make a conclusion from these three statements. *(Lessons 13-2, 13-1)*

14. (1) Every integer is a real number.
(2) Every natural number is an integer.
(3) The complex number i is not a real number.
The complex number *i* is not a natural number.

15. (1) Every square is a rhombus.
(2) Diagonals in a kite are perpendicular.
(3) A figure is a kite if it is a rhombus.
Diagonals in a square are perpendicular.

16. Write the negation of this statement in two different ways: △*ABC* is isosceles. *(Lessons 13-2, 2-7)*
△*ABC* is not isosceles, or △*ABC* is scalene.

17. Refer to the figure below.
Given: Diagonals of quadrilateral *ABED* intersect at *C*.
△*ABC* and △*DCE* are isosceles, both with vertex angle *C*.
Prove: △*ACD* ≅ △*BCE*. *(Lesson 7-3)* See margin.

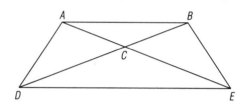

18. Given $A = (5, 3)$, $B = (-6, 3)$, $C = (-6, -2)$, $D = (5, -2)$.
a. What kind of figure is *ABCD*? rectangle
b. Show that $AC = BD$. *(Lessons 11-2, 5-2)*
$$AC = \sqrt{(5 - -6)^2 + (3 - -2)^2} = \sqrt{11^2 + 5^2} = \sqrt{146}$$
$$BD = \sqrt{(-6 - 5)^2 + (3 - -2)^2} = \sqrt{(-11)^2 + 5^2} = \sqrt{146}$$

Exploration

19. Question 12 and Example 1 are adapted from puzzles found in *Pencil Puzzle Treasury,* by Wayne Williams, Grosset and Dunlap publishers, New York, 1978. Logic puzzles of this type can be found in *Games* magazine or magazines by Dell Publishing Co. and other places. Find an example of a logic puzzle different from the ones given in this lesson, or write one yourself!

Sample: From *The Dell Book of Logic Problems* is the following entitled "The Golden-Agers": The GoldenAge Retirement Home has a remarkable group of five women—one is named Louise—who are more than 90 years of age. No two are the same age, and none has reached 100 (all ages are considered to be in whole numbers). With the aid of the following clues you should be able to decide the full name and age of each.
1. Jenny's age is halfway between Mrs. Bowen's and Mrs. Jones's.
2. Sarah is older than Mrs. Jones, but younger than Jenny.
3. All the women's ages are in even numbers, except Mrs. Wall's.
4. Susan is neither the oldest nor the youngest.
5. Mrs. King is as much older than Anna as Mrs. Walker is older than Mrs. King.
Solution: Louise Bowen is 98, Susan Walker is 96, Jenny Wall is 95, Sarah King is 94, and Anna Jones is 92.

644

13-4

Indirect Proof

RESOURCES
- Lesson Master 13-4
- Visual for Teaching Aid 83 displays the Laws of Reasoning.
- Computer Master 27

A lawyer, summing up a case for a jury, says, "The prosecutors assume the defendant–my client–committed the crime. Then my client would have been at the scene of the crime. But remember that we brought in witnesses and telephone records. These extra people and records demonstrate my client was on a farm 15 miles away. A person can't be in two places at one time! My client could not have been both on the farm and at the scene of the crime at the same time. So the assumption my client did the crime cannot be true. So it must be false. Ladies and gentlemen of the jury, the defendant is not guilty."

In this summing up, the lawyer has used indirect reasoning.

In **direct reasoning,** a person begins with given information known to be true. The Laws of Detachment and Transitivity are used to reason from that information to a conclusion. The proofs you have written so far in this book have been **direct proofs.**

In **indirect reasoning,** a person tries to rule out all the possibilities except the one thought to be true. This is exactly what you did in solving the logic puzzles of the last lesson. You marked Xs in boxes to show that certain possibilities could not be true. When you had enough Xs, you knew that only the possibility left could be correct.

You can rule out a possibility if you know it is false. But how can you tell that a statement is false? One way to tell is if you know its negation is true. For instance, suppose you know $y = 5$ is true. Then $y \neq 5$ is false. Suppose you know $\triangle ABC$ is isosceles. Then it is false to say it is scalene.

You also know a statement is false if it contradicts another statement known to be true. For instance, if your friend Lillian is a senior, then she cannot be a junior. If you know 5 is a solution to an equation, and there is only one solution to that equation, then 3 cannot be a solution. If one statement contradicts another, they are called *contradictory*.

LESSON 13-4 Indirect Proof **645**

OBJECTIVES

D Follow the basic laws of reasoning to make conclusions.
E Write indirect proofs.
J Apply laws of reasoning in real situations.

TEACHING NOTES

Ask students how they know a statement is false. Point out that one way to know that a statement is false is if it contradicts another statement known or assumed to be true. At the beginning of the lesson, the lawyer points out that a person being in one place contradicts the possibility that the person could be in another place. In **Example 3**, the true statement $12 \neq 6$ is contradicted. In **Example 4**, the statements $149^2 = 22,200$ and $149^2 = 22,201$ contradict each other. In **Example 5**, the reasoning leads to a statement contradicting the Triangle-Sum Theorem. Generally, it is easier to understand an indirect proof if a well-known statement is contradicted.

Stress that indirect reasoning is just as valid as direct reasoning. Point out that indirect reasoning was used earlier in the course. One of the first indirect arguments was in Lesson 1-7. It was explained in that lesson that two lines could not intersect in two different points A and B. If that were the case, then there would be two lines through A and B which would contradict a postulate.

Review **Examples 4** and **5** carefully as they show students what can be written in order to have a valid proof. Students seldom have had to write a careful argument of any kind so the task here is as much a writing task as it is a mathematical task. The three steps are given simply to organize the task and should not be considered as the only way to do the work.

All the laws of reasoning that are needed in this course have now been discussed. They are summarized on *Visual for Teaching Aid 96*.

Alternate Approach
Some students may feel more comfortable writing paragraph proofs. You can have them rewrite the proofs to **Examples 3** and **4** in paragraph form for practice, but make sure they incorporate all the steps listed. Since the proofs can be worded differently, you might want students to discuss them in **small groups.**

Definition:

Two statements p and q are **contradictory** if and only if they cannot both be true at the same time.

Example 1   Let p be the statement: $\angle V$ is acute. Let q be: $\angle V$ is right. Are p and q contradictory?

Solution   Yes. An acute angle has measure less than 90. A right angle has measure 90. A number cannot be both less than 90 and 90 at the same time, so an angle cannot be both acute and right at the same time.

Example 2   Let p: ABCD is a rhombus. Let q: ABCD is a rectangle. Are p and q contradictory?

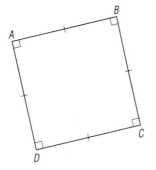

Solution   No. p and q can be true at the same time. Square ABCD at the left is both a rhombus and a rectangle.

A **contradiction** is a situation in which two contradictory statements p and q are both asserted as true. Contradictions are false statements. In Example 1, the statement p *and* q ($\angle A$ is acute *and* $\angle A$ is right) is false, because p and q are contradictory. However, in Example 2, the statement p *and* q (ABCD is a rhombus *and* ABCD is a rectangle) is not necessarily false.

Sometimes it isn't so easy to tell whether a statement is true or false. Then you can employ the logic used by the lawyer in the situation described at the beginning of this lesson.

Step 1. If you think a statement is false, start by assuming it *for the moment* and reason from it. (The prosecutors thought the defendant was at the spot the crime was committed. The lawyer started with this assumption.)
Step 2. Using valid logic, try to make the reasoning lead to a contradiction or other false statement. (The lawyer argued that the defendant would then have had to be in two places at the same time.)
Step 3. Since the reasoning leads to a contradiction or other false statement, the assumed statement must be false. (The lawyer concluded that the defendant could not be at the scene of the crime.)

646

This logic exemplifies the *Law of Indirect Reasoning*. It is the fifth and last law of logic discussed in this book.

Law of Indirect Reasoning:

If valid reasoning from a statement *p* leads to a false conclusion, then *p* is false.

Example 3 Show that the statement $3(4 + 2x) = 6(x + 1)$ is never true.

Solution
Step 1.   Begin with the equation and reason from it as you would any normal equation to see what happens. First use the Distributive Property.
$$12 + 6x = 6x + 6$$
Step 2.   Add $-6x$ to each side. This leads to the conclusion $12 = 6$.
Step 3.   Since "$12 = 6$" is a false conclusion, by the Law of Indirect Reasoning, the original statement $3(4 + 2x) = 6(x + 1)$ is not true.

A proof using the Law of the Contrapositive, the Law of Ruling Out Possibilities, or the Law of Indirect Reasoning is called an **indirect proof.** The next two Examples suggest how to write indirect proofs.

Example 4 Use an indirect proof to show that $\sqrt{22200} \neq 149$.

Solution No drawing is needed, so begin by analyzing the problem. There are only two possibilities here. Either $\sqrt{22200} = 149$ or $\sqrt{22200} \neq 149$. To show that the first possibility is false, reason from it to produce a contradiction. Write:

Either $\sqrt{22200} = 149$ or $\sqrt{22200} \neq 149$.
1. Assume $\sqrt{22200} = 149$.
2. Then, squaring both sides: $22200 = 149^2$.
However, by the definition of power,
$149^2 = 149 \cdot 149 = 22201$.
3. The two statements in step 2 are contradictory.
The assumption of step 1 has led to a false conclusion.
By the Law of Indirect Reasoning, the assumption of
step 1 is false. Thus $\sqrt{22200} \neq 149$.

Notice the steps in the proof. Start by stating all possibilities. Then pick an option you think is not true and make conclusions from it. Reason until you get a false conclusion. Then apply the Law of Indirect Reasoning to rule out that possibility. Rule out all possibilities until the statement you desire is the only one left.

1. Are the statements contradictory?
a. *ABCD* is a square. *ABCD* is a trapezoid.
No
b. Billy is 15. Billy has an airplane pilot's license.
No
c. $|x| = -4$. $|x| = 4$.
Yes
d. $m = 5$. $m \leq 5$.
No

2. What statement is contradicted by each statement below?
a. $m\angle ABC + m\angle BCA + m\angle CAB = 360$.
Triangle-Sum Theorem
b. *M* is the midpoint of $\overline{AB}$, $AM = 50$, and $BM = 40$.
definition of midpoint

3. Prove that $\sqrt[3]{9} \neq 2$.
Either $\sqrt[3]{9} \neq 2$ or $\sqrt[3]{9} = 2$. Suppose $\sqrt[3]{9} = 2$. Then by substitution, $(\sqrt[3]{9})^3 = 2^3$, from which $9 = 8$. This contradicts the known fact that $9 \neq 8$. By the Law of Indirect Reasoning, the supposition is false, and thus $\sqrt[3]{9} \neq 2$.

4. Prove that a convex pentagon cannot have four acute angles.
Let *ABCDE* be the pentagon. Either *ABCDE* has or does not have four acute angles. Suppose it has and that the angles are *A*, *B*, *C*, and *D*. Then, adding their measures, $m\angle A + m\angle B + m\angle C + m\angle D < 360$. But the sum of the measures of all five angles is 540. This means that $\angle E$ has measure greater than 180, which contradicts the Angle Measure Postulate. Thus, by the Law of Indirect Reasoning, the supposition is false and the pentagon does not have four acute angles.

648

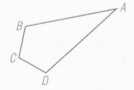
Example 5 Use an indirect proof to show that no triangle has two obtuse angles.

Solution First rewrite in if-then form: If a figure is a triangle, then it does not have two obtuse angles. Now draw a representative triangle.

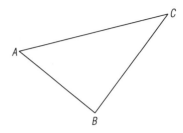

Either $\triangle ABC$ has two obtuse angles, say $\angle A$ and $\angle B$, or it does not.
1. Assume both $\angle A$ and $\angle B$ are obtuse.
2. Then, by definition of obtuse, $m\angle A > 90$ and $m\angle B > 90$. By the Addition Property of Inequality, $m\angle A + m\angle B > 180$. Then, because $m\angle C > 0$ for any angle in a triangle, $m\angle A + m\angle B + m\angle C > 180$. But the Triangle-Sum Theorem says that $m\angle A + m\angle B + m\angle C = 180$.
3. The last two statements in step 2 are contradictory. A false conclusion has been reached. By the Law of Indirect Reasoning, the assumption of step 1 is false. $\angle A$ and $\angle B$ cannot both be obtuse.

In Example 5, the following statement has been proved: (1) If a figure is a triangle, then it does not have two obtuse angles. Its contrapositive is: (2) If a figure has two obtuse angles, then it is not a triangle. By the Law of the Contrapositive, statement (2) is also true.

Questions

Covering the Reading

1. What kind of reasoning has the lawyer in this lesson used? indirect

2. Beginning with $2 + 5x = 5x - 8$, a student added $-5x$ to each side and ended up with $2 = -8$. What should the student conclude?
$2 + 5x = 5x - 8$ is never true.

3. Beginning with $\sqrt{2400} = 49$, a student squared both sides and wound up with $2400 = 2401$. What should the student conclude?
$\sqrt{2400} \neq 47$

4. State the Law of Indirect Reasoning. If valid reasoning from a statement p leads to a false conclusion, then p is false.

5. *Multiple choice.* Consider the equation $3(x - 2) = 3x - 2$. Which is true?
(a) The equation has no solution (is never true).
(b) The equation has one solution, 0.
(c) The equation is true for all real numbers. (a)

6. When are two statements contradictory?
if and only if they cannot both be true at the same time

7. By indirect reasoning, show that $\sqrt{9800} \neq 99$. *See margin.*

8. a. Draw a quadrilateral with three obtuse angles.
   b. By indirect reasoning, show that a quadrilateral cannot have all four angles obtuse.
   See margin.

In 9 and 10, give a statement contradictory to the given one.

9. $\triangle ABC$ is isosceles. $\triangle ABC$ **is scalene.**

10. Coplanar lines m and n are parallel.
   Lines m and n have exactly one point in common.

In 11–13, determine whether the statements are contradictory.

11. $m\angle A = 85$ and $\angle A$ is obtuse. **contradictory**

12. *GHIJ* is a trapezoid and *GHIJ* is a square. **not contradictory**

13. Phil is older than 25 and Phil attends high school. **not contradictory**

14. Either a triangle can have two right angles or it cannot.
   a. Show that one of these possibilities leads to a contradiction.
   b. Using the Law of Ruling Out Possibilities, what can you conclude? **a) See margin. b) A triangle cannot have two right angles.**

15. a. Solve $-12x > 252$. **x < -21**
   b To do part **a**, did you use direct or indirect reasoning?
   direct reasoning

16. Refer to $\triangle ABC$ below.
   Given: $m\angle A > m\angle B > m\angle C$.
   Prove: $\triangle ABC$ is scalene. **See margin.**

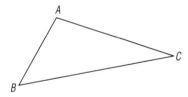

17. (This puzzle is taken from *Quizzles*, by Wayne Williams, published by Grosset and Dunlap, 1976.) Mary, Isobel, Marcia, Grace, and Ruth are on the Grand Avenue School basketball team. Each girl has a different hair color. The hair colors are blond, red, auburn, black, and brunette. As it happens, no two girls on the team are the same height: they are 5'11", 5'10", 5'8", 5'7", and 5'6". From the clues given, try to determine the hair color and height of each of the girls on the team. (Hint: Use a grid like that shown in Lesson 13-3.)
   (1) Mary is taller than Ruth who is two inches taller than the redhead.
   (2) The brunette is not 5'8" tall.
   (3) Marcia and Mary are neither the tallest nor the shortest.
   (4) The girl with black hair is two inches taller than Ruth.
   (5) Isobel is taller than the blond, who is one inch taller than Grace.
   (Lesson 13-3) **Isobel−5'11"−brunette; Mary−5'10"−black; Ruth−5'8"−auburn; Marcia−5'7"−blond; Grace−5'6"−red**

Margin notes (right column):

14. a. If a triangle has two right angles, then the third angle must either have zero measure, which is impossible, or the sum of the angles is greater than 180°. This contradicts the Triangle-Sum Theorem.

16. Either $\triangle ABC$ is scalene or $\triangle ABC$ is isosceles. Suppose $\triangle ABC$ is isosceles. Then by the definition of isosceles triangle (meaning), two of its sides will be congruent. The angles opposite those sides will then be congruent by the Isosceles Triangle Theorem. This contradicts the given. So, by the Law of Indirect Reasoning, the assumption that $\triangle ABC$ is isosceles is false, and thus $\triangle ABC$ is scalene.

18. Give the negation of this statement: $\triangle ABC \sim \triangle DEF$. *(Lesson 13-2)*
$\triangle ABC$ is not similar to $\triangle DEF$.

19. For the statement "If $\triangle ABC \sim \triangle DEF$, then $\angle A \cong \angle D$," write the
 a. contrapositive, **b.** converse, and **c.** inverse.
 d. which of these three statements is (are) true? *(Lesson 13-2)*
 See below.

In 20 and 21, use the figure
at the right. $\overline{WV} \parallel \overline{ZY}$.

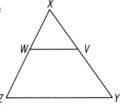

20. If $XW = 7$, $XV = 9$, and $VY = 11$, find WZ. *(Lesson 12-10)* $\frac{77}{9} \approx 8.56$

21. If $XW = 6$, $WZ = 3$, and $WV = 8$, find YZ. *(Lesson 12-3)* 12

22. Below, a rectangle is placed conveniently on a coordinate plane. Use
the placement to prove: In any rectangle, the diagonals have the same
length. *(Lesson 11-5)* See below.

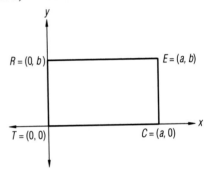

23. In everyday life, indirect reasoning is often used as follows. If you do
A, then B will happen. B is horrible (or dangerous or some other bad
thing). Therefore you should not do A. Give two examples of possible
As and Bs. samples:
 A: drive too fast; *B:* have an accident
 A: run without stretching first; *B:* pull a muscle

---

19) a) If $\angle A$ is not congruent to $\angle D$, then $\triangle ABC$ is not similar to $\triangle DEF$.
 b) If $\angle A \cong \angle D$, then $\triangle ABC \sim \triangle DEF$.
 c) If $\triangle ABC$ is not similar to $\triangle DEF$, then $\angle A$ is not congruent to $\angle D$.
 d) The contrapositive is true.

22) 1. $TE = \sqrt{(a - 0)^2 + (b - 0)^2} = \sqrt{a^2 + b^2}$ **Distance Formula**
 $RC = \sqrt{(0 - a)^2 + (b - 0)^2} = \sqrt{(-a)^2 + b^2}$
 $= \sqrt{a^2 + b^2}$

 2. $TE = RC$ **Transitive Property
 of Equality**

650

13-5

Tangents to Circles and Spheres

This solar eclipse was photographed in space from an Apollo spacecraft. A solar eclipse observed from Earth is discussed on page 654.

RESOURCES
■ Lesson Master 13-5
▣ Computer Master 28

OBJECTIVE

F Make deductions from properties of radii perpendicular to tangents.

TEACHING NOTES

Students should finish this lesson knowing two relationships involving tangents. (1) A segment from a point outside a circle to the circle is a tangent if and only if it is perpendicular to the radius drawn to the point of intersection with the circle. The proof of this if-and-only-if statement is given in two parts. Do not expect students to be able to replicate these indirect proofs. (2) When the two tangents from an external point are drawn, and the radii are drawn to the points of tangency, a kite is formed. This is **Question 14.** The proof is easy and should be discussed.

Indirect reasoning has been used at least since the time of Euclid to deduce theorems. Early in this century, some mathematicians tried to see what could be deduced without indirect reasoning. These mathematicians allowed themselves to use only direct proofs. They were unable to find direct proofs for many important theorems for which there were indirect proofs. These attempts point out that indirect reasoning is necessary.

In this lesson, indirect reasoning is used to deduce two theorems about *tangents*. The word "tangent" comes from the Latin word meaning "touching." Think of a wheel (a circle) as tangent to a ramp (a line) as it rolls up or down the ramp. If the wheel and ramp are very hard, they are thought to have only one point in common.

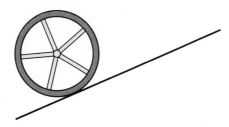

Definition

A **tangent to a circle** is a line which intersects the circle in exactly one point.

The point of intersection of a circle and the line is called the **point of tangency.**

Tangents to circles can be constructed easily, due to the following theorem. Notice how short its (indirect) proof is.

LESSON 13-5 Tangents to Circles and Spheres **651**

In the figure below, you may wish to call quadrilateral *XOYP* the *tangent kite*. It is special. Its congruent angles are right angles, and the symmetry diagonal is the distance from the point to the center. If the vertices of the right angles are connected, a *chord triangle* is formed, and the triangle and kite have the same symmetry line. This triangle is studied further in Lesson 15-1.

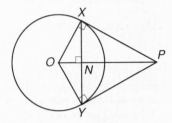

tangent kite XOYP
chord triangle OXY

Tangents occur often in applications. Disks and solid spheres may not allow themselves to be broken by secants, but they can be supported by tangent lines and planes. The bicycle wheel on page 651 touches the ramp not at its bottom but at the foot of the perpendicular from its center to the ramp. The **Example** shows how tangents to the sun and moon can help to determine the radius of the sun.

Making Connections At this point, students do not have the background to understand the importance of tangents to the graph of a function at a particular point on that graph. Nor can they understand the relationship of the tangent to the derivative. However, you still might draw a parabolic path of a projectile and point out that the slope of a tangent to that parabola is positive as the ball goes up, zero when it hits its peak, and negative when it comes down. Conclude therefore that the slope tells quite a bit about the path of a projectile.

Theorem:

If a line is perpendicular to a radius of a circle at the radius's endpoint on the circle, then it is tangent to the circle.

Proof

Draw Here is a figure and the theorem restated.
Given: $\odot O$, $\overline{OP} \perp \ell$.
Prove: ℓ is tangent to the circle.

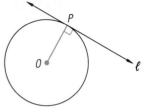

Analyze It needs to be shown that no other point of ℓ is on the circle. Assume another point of ℓ is on the circle. This will lead to a contradiction.

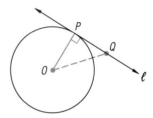

Write Assume *Q* is another point on ℓ and on the circle. Since *Q* is on ℓ, $\triangle OPQ$ is a right triangle with hypotenuse $\overline{OQ}$. So $OQ > OP$. But since *Q* is on the circle, $OQ = OP$. The statement $OQ > OP$ *and* $OQ = OP$ is a contradiction. By the Law of Indirect Reasoning, the assumption must be false. So ℓ intersects the circle at exactly one point. By the definition of tangent (sufficient condition), ℓ is tangent to $\odot O$.

The converse of this theorem is true, but its proof is longer. The proof uses the Law of the Contrapositive.

Theorem:

If a line is tangent to a circle, then it is perpendicular to the radius drawn to the point of tangency.

652

Proof

Draw   Below is a figure.
Restate the given and prove in terms of the figure.
Given: *m* is tangent to ⊙*O* at point *P*.
Prove: $\overline{OP} \perp m$.

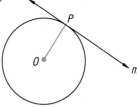

Analyze   The contrapositive is as follows:
Given: $\overline{OP}$ is not ⊥ to *m*.
Prove: *m* is not tangent to ⊙*O* at point *P*.

If the contrapositive is proven true, then the original statement is true.

Write   Since $\overline{OP}$ is not ⊥ to *m*, a different segment, $\overline{OQ}$, can be drawn from *O* perpendicular to *m*. Locate *R* on *m* so that *Q* is between *R* and *P* and *QR* = *QP*. Then △*OQR* ≅ △*OQP* because of the SAS Congruence Theorem. So *OR* = *OP*. This means *R* is on ⊙*O* (it is the same distance from *O* as *P*). So *m* contains two points on the circle. Thus *m* is not a tangent.

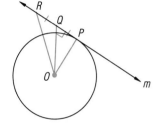

The contrapositive has been proved. By the Law of the Contrapositive, the original statement is true.

The two theorems of this lesson can be written as one if-and-only statement:

Radius-Tangent Theorem:

A line is tangent to a circle if and only if it is perpendicular to a radius at the radius's endpoint on the circle.

As you have learned, many properties of two-dimensional figures extend to three-dimensional figures. The idea of tangency extends very easily to spheres. A **tangent to a sphere** is a line or plane which intersects the sphere in exactly one point. That point is called the **point of tangency.** A common example of a plane tangent to a sphere is a ball resting on a ramp.

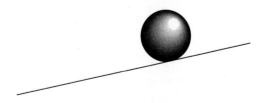

Alternate Approach
You may wish to summarize the terminology relating to circles while doing this lesson. Either draw a large circle on the chalkboard with appropriate lines and segments labeled and named, or prepare a worksheet with several circles that students can label and name themselves.

ADDITIONAL EXAMPLES
1. Describe how to construct a tangent to a circle *O* at a given point *T* on it.
Step 1: $\overline{OT}$ (Straightedge postulate); Step 2: Subroutine: ⊥ to $\overline{OT}$ at *T*. The construction works because the perpendicular to a radius at its endpoint is tangent to the circle.

2. Circle *O* has radius 5 and *OP* = 12. How long are the sides of the tangent kite *OXPY*?
5, 5, $\sqrt{119}$, and $\sqrt{119}$

You can approximate the shape of the earth, moon, and sun with spheres. When the moon comes directly between the sun and a part of the earth, that part witnesses a *solar eclipse*. The figure here shows this but is misleading. The sun is relatively *much* bigger and these objects are *much* farther from each other.

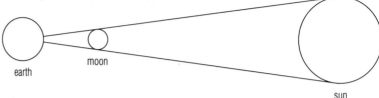

The lines in the above drawing are *common tangents* to the spheres of the moon and the sun. The tangent lines come very close to intersecting on the earth; at most only a small part of the earth sees a solar eclipse when it happens. If you ignore the earth in the drawing, then the drawing looks somewhat like a sphere and its size-change image. This means that there are proportions. These proportions can be used to calculate the radius of the sun.

Example It is known that the moon is about 240,000 miles from the earth, the sun about 93,000,000 miles from the earth, and the moon's radius is 1080 miles. Estimate the radius of the sun.

Solution First draw a picture. Here M and S are the centers of the sun and moon. N and T are points of tangency of a common tangent. The distances $EM = 240{,}000$, $ES = 93{,}000{,}000$, and $MN = 1080$ are known. ST is the radius of the sun.

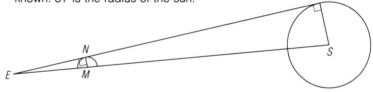

Because $\overline{MN}$ and $\overline{ST}$ are radii, they are perpendicular to $\overleftrightarrow{ET}$. Since $\angle E$ is common to $\triangle EMN$ and $\triangle EST$, by AA Similarity, $\triangle EMN \sim \triangle EST$. And so,

$$\frac{EM}{ES} = \frac{MN}{ST}.$$

Substituting for these lengths,

$$\frac{240000}{93000000} = \frac{1080}{ST}.$$

Simplify the fraction at the left to $\frac{24}{9300}$ before using your calculator! Solving this proportion, $ST = 418{,}500$ miles, quite close to the actual value of about 432,000 miles.

The earth's radius is only about 3960 miles, so the sun is well over 100 times bigger than the earth in its linear dimensions.

654

Covering the Reading

1. a. By definition, when is a line tangent to a circle?
   b. Give another condition sufficient for a line to be tangent
      to a circle.
      a, b) See margin.

2. ℓ is tangent to $\odot O$ below at P. Must ℓ be perpendicular to $\overline{OP}$?
   Yes

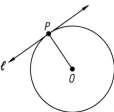

3. In the proof of the first theorem of this lesson, what contradiction
   is reached? $OQ > OP$ and $OQ = OP$.

4. *Multiple choice.* The first two theorems of this lesson are
   (a) converses   (b) inverses
   (c) contrapositives   (d) negations. **(a)**

5. To prove the second theorem in this lesson, what logical principle
   was applied? **Law of the Contrapositive**

6. a. About how many times larger than the moon is the sun?
   b. About how many times farther away from the earth is the sun
      than the moon?
      a, b) See margin.

7. $\overleftrightarrow{CA}$ below is a common tangent to circles P and Q at points A and B.
   If $CB = 5$, $AB = 10$, and the radius of circle Q is 3, what is the
   radius of circle P? **9**

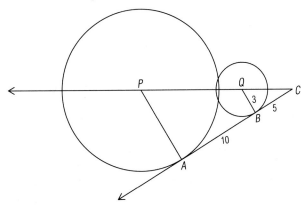

Applying the Mathematics

In 8–10, give a real-world example of the given mathematical idea.

8. a line tangent to a circle **a wheel on a ramp**

9. a plane tangent to a sphere **a ball on a floor**

10. a line tangent to a sphere **a ball on a wire**

LESSON 13-5   Tangents to Circles and Spheres   **655**

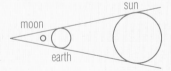

11. Use the given and the figure of Question 7. What is the length of $\overline{PQ}$? $\sqrt{136} \approx 11.7$

12. a. Extend the if-and-only-if theorem of this lesson to apply to spheres. **See margin.**
    b. Is the extension true? **Yes**

13. In the figure below at the left, $\overline{IZ}$ is tangent to sphere P at point I.
    a. Is $\overline{ZI} \perp \overline{IP}$? **Yes**
    b. How many other tangents are there from point Z to sphere P? **infinitely many**

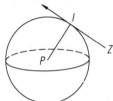
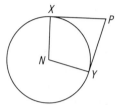

14. Refer to the figure above at the right.
    Given: Point P is outside $\odot N$;
    $\overline{PX}$ and $\overline{PY}$ are tangents to $\odot N$ at points X and Y.
    Prove: $PXNY$ is a kite. (You will have proved that the two tangents to circle N from point P have the same length. This is a theorem you should remember.) **See margin.**

15. Copy the figure below and draw the *four* common tangents to circles O and P.

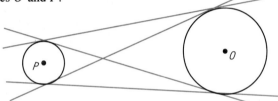

16. $\overline{PT}$ is tangent to $\odot O$ below at T. $PT = 12$ and $PO = 15$.
    a. What is the area of the circle? $81\pi \approx 254.5$ units^2
    b. What is the distance from P to N, the point on the circle nearest to P? **6 units**

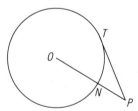

17. *Multiple choice.* Use the information in this lesson and assume that the earth and the sun have similar shape. Then the volume of the sun is about how many times the volume of the earth?
    (a) one thousand   (b) one million
    (c) one billion   (d) one trillion *(Lessons 12-6, 10-8)* **(b)**

18. Give an indirect proof to show that $\sqrt{39,600} \neq 199$. *(Lesson 13-4)*
See margin.

In 19 and 20, given the statements, **a.** what (if anything) can you conclude? **b.** What reasoning laws have you used?

19. (1) Either Julie walks to school or she rides her bicycle to school.
(2) Julie's bicycle is being repaired. *(Lesson 13-3)* a) **Julie walks to school.**
b) **The Law of Ruling Out Possibilities**

20. (1) All people who grew up in Mississippi have a southern accent.
(2) If you did not grow up in Mississippi, then you do not know the Ole Miss fight song.
(3) Murray does not have a southern accent. *(Lesson 13-2)*
See margin.

21. a. Write the contrapositive of the statement: If a figure is a rectangle, then its diagonals are congruent.
b. Is the contrapositive true? *(Lesson 13-2)*
See margin.

22. Draw the reflection line of the glide reflection mapping $\triangle ABC$ onto $\triangle XYZ$. *(Lesson 6-6)*

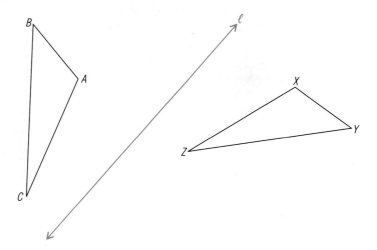

23. The drawing of the earth, sun, and moon in this lesson is nowhere near scale. 23.a. See below.
a. Draw a figure of the earth and the moon to scale using a tracing of the circle drawn at the left as the earth.
b. How far away would the sun be on the scale of your drawing and what would be its diameter?
23.b. about 310 feet away with a diameter of about 35 inches

24. Draw the relative positions of the moon, earth, and sun during an eclipse of the moon. See margin.

25. What is an annular eclipse? **an eclipse of the sun in which the moon covers the sun incompletely, leaving a narrow uneclipsed ring which surrounds the dark moon**

23a)

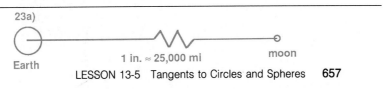

1 in. ≈ 25,000 mi
Earth   moon

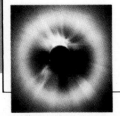

Total solar eclipse   2/26/79

LESSON 13-5   Tangents to Circles and Spheres   **657**

FOLLOW-UP

MORE PRACTICE
For more questions on SPUR Objectives, use *Lesson Master 13-5*, shown below.

EXTENSION
Planes can be tangent to spheres. Discuss whether the theorems of this lesson are true if the word *line* is replaced by *plane* and the word *circle* is replaced by *sphere*.
Yes
How many planes are there that are tangent to a sphere and contain a point outside the sphere?
infinitely many

NAME _____

LESSON **MASTER   13–5**
QUESTIONS ON **SPUR** OBJECTIVES

■ **PROPERTIES** *Objective F (See pages 678–681 for objectives.)*
In 1–3, $\overline{XY}$ and $\overline{XZ}$ are tangents to $\odot C$.

1. a. What is the measure of $\angle CYX$?   **90**
b. What type of figure is $WYCZ$?   **kite**

2. If $XZ = 12$ and $ZC = 5$, find the area of $XYCZ$.   **60 units²**

3. If $XY = 16$ and $XC = 20$, find the circumference of $\odot C$. $24\pi \approx$ **75.4 units**

In 4–6, $\overline{AB}$ is a common tangent to $\odot X$ and $\odot Y$.

4. If $AM = 10$, $MB = 10$, and $AY = 24$, then
a. $AX =$ **12**, **b.** $BY = \sqrt{176}$ or $2\sqrt{44} \approx 13.26$, **c.** $MX = \dfrac{\sqrt{44}}{6.63}$

5. If $BY = 1.3 MX$, $\dfrac{AB}{AM} =$ **1.3**.

6. If the circumference of $\odot X$ is 2π, $AM = 4$, and $AB = 6$, what is the area of $\odot Y$? $2.25\pi \approx 7.07$ **units²**

7. How many tangents can be drawn through a point outside a given circle to that circle?   **2**

8. In another solar system, the Mune is about 120,000 km from the Urth, the Son is about 47,500,000 km from the Urth, and the Mune's radius is 540 km. Estimate the radius of the Son.   **≈213,750 km**

126   *Geometry © Scott, Foresman and Company*

OBJECTIVES

G Justify auxiliary lines.
K Know the history and impact of Playfair's Parallel Postulate on the development of geometry.

TEACHING NOTES

Given the uniqueness of perpendiculars, it is natural to wonder about the uniqueness of parallels. One of the greatest discoveries in mathematics is that one can assume non-uniqueness of parallels and still get a consistent geometry. The mathematicians Lobachevsky and Bolyai both made this discovery in the late 1820s.

Lobachevsky and Bolyai wanted to prove Euclid's fifth postulate from the other four. They began with indirect reasoning, assuming a negation of Playfair's Postulate. Instead of arriving at a contradiction, they were able to deduce many theorems. Other mathematicians had followed the same approach but thought that they had not reasoned long enough to get a contradiction. The brilliance of Lobachevsky and Bolyai was to realize that there was no contradiction to be found. Other mathematicians later verified that Lobachevsky and Bolyai were correct by describing planes (recall that *plane* is undefined) that satisfied the contradiction of Playfair's Parallel Postulate.

LESSON

13-6

Uniqueness

There is exactly one original Mona Lisa painting. It hangs in the Louvre in Paris.

When some people think of mathematics, they think of exactness. They think every question has exactly one answer. You know that isn't always the case. Some equations, like $x^2 = 49$, have more than one solution. Any proof can be done in many different ways. Estimation is one important part of mathematics. Probability and statistics are not exact.

Still, at times it is quite helpful to know there is exactly one of something, because then there is no possible confusion. It is said that the thing is **uniquely determined.**

In proofs, when a line or a circle or something else is uniquely determined, then it can be added to a given figure. It is called an **auxiliary** line or auxiliary circle, etc. Auxiliary lines were used in both proofs in the previous lesson.

For instance, if you are given a parallelogram, either diagonal is uniquely determined and can be an auxiliary line segment. The justification for this is part of the Point-Line-Plane Postulate studied in Chapter 1: Through two points, there is exactly one line. The phrase "exactly one" tells you that the line is uniquely determined.

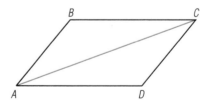

Parallelogram *ABCD* with
auxiliary segment $\overline{AC}$

658

If a figure is not uniquely determined, there are two possibilities. The first possibility is that there may be no such figure satisfying all the conditions. For instance, suppose you are given a parallelogram *ABCD* and want to draw a diagonal that bisects an angle. Although its angle bisectors are uniquely determined and diagonals are uniquely determined, you cannot be certain that a diagonal also is an angle bisector. They could be different lines. So you cannot add to this figure "a diagonal which is an angle bisector."

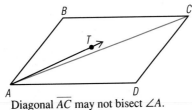

Diagonal $\overline{AC}$ may not bisect $\angle A$.
Angle bisector $\overrightarrow{AT}$ may not go through point C.

The second possibility is that many figures satisfy the condition(s). For instance, a segment has many bisectors. You could use a bisector of a segment in a proof but which bisector do you want?

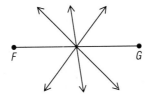

There are many bisectors of $\overline{FG}$.

A segment has exactly one midpoint. No one could speak of *the* midpoint unless there were only one. But uniqueness is not always so obvious. What about the number of lines parallel to a given line through a point not on it?

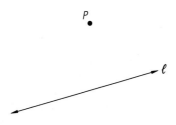

With algebra, it is easy to see that there is at least one parallel. It is the line through *P* with the same slope as ℓ. But is there more than one parallel? An indirect proof helps to deduce the answer, which is found in the next theorem.

You may wish to emphasize the following facts: (1) The theorems in a mathematical system depend on the postulates chosen. (2) The applicability of a mathematical system depends on the postulates chosen. (3) Changing the postulates *may* change the set of possible theorems that can be proved and the applicability of the theorems.

Alternate Approach
You might want to write down a list of those figures that are uniquely determined and the reason why they are.

given two points, the segment joining them (Point-Line-Plane Postulate, part b)

given a ray and a distance *x,* the point on the ray at that distance from the endpoint (Point-Line-Plane Postulate, parts a and d)

given a segment, its midpoint (definition of midpoint)

given a ray and a measure *x* between 0 and 180, an angle with the ray as one side on a given half-plane of the ray, and with measure *x* (Angle Measure Postulate)

given an angle, its bisector (definition of angle bisector)

given a line and a point, the perpendicular to that line through that point (from uniqueness of angle, definition of perpendicular, and Linear Pair Theorem)

given a segment, its perpendicular bisector (definition of perpendicular bisector)

given a point and a line, the reflection image of that point (Reflection Postulate, part a)

given a point *P* and a transformation T, the image point T(*P*) (definition of transformation)

given a point and a line, the perpendicular to that line from that point (from Reflection Postulate)

Uniqueness of Parallels Theorem (Playfair's Parallel Postulate):

Through a point not on a line, there is exactly one parallel to
the given line.

Proof

Since there is at least one parallel, the only other possibility is that
there is more than one parallel. This is the situation to draw and
the statement to reason from. A figure is drawn below.

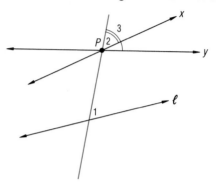

1. Assume there are two different lines x and y through P parallel
to line ℓ.
2. Then angles 1 and 2 are corresponding angles, and
so are angles 1 and 3. So, since // lines $\Rightarrow$ corr. $\angle$s =,
$m\angle 1 = m\angle 2$ and also $m\angle 1 = m\angle 3$.
3. This means $m\angle 2 = m\angle 3$. But then the angle between lines x
and y must have measure 0, which means the
lines x and y are identical.
4. The last conclusion in step 3 contradicts the assumption of step 1.
So we have reached a false conclusion. By the Law of Indirect
Reasoning, the assumption of step 1 is false, so there is not more
than one line through P parallel to ℓ. Since there is at least one
such line, we can conclude that there is exactly one line through P
parallel to ℓ.

Recall that a glide reflection is the composite of a reflection r_ℓ and a
translation T in a direction parallel to ℓ. Here is a drawing of a point
A and its image C under a glide reflection with reflecting line ℓ.

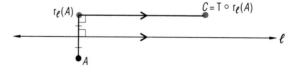

660

Notice how the Uniqueness of Parallels Theorem is used in the proof of the following theorem which was first stated in Lesson 6-6. This theorem, you may recall, helps to draw the reflecting line for a glide reflection if you know the location of a figure and its image.

Theorem:

In a glide reflection, the midpoint of the segment connecting a point to its image lies on the glide-reflection line.

Proof

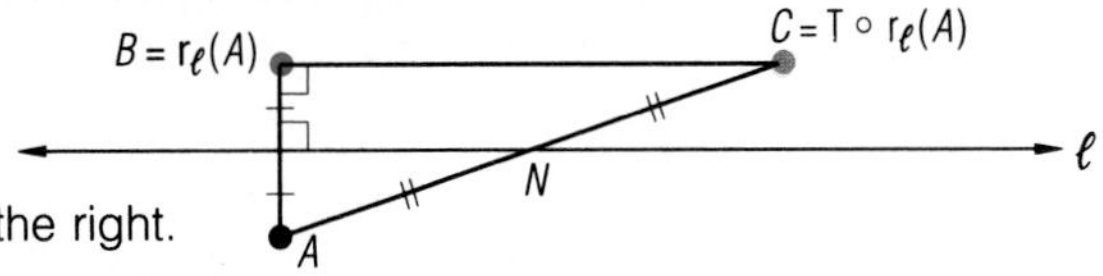

Use the figure at the right.

Given: $C = T \circ r_\ell (A)$,
where T is a translation parallel to ℓ.
N is the midpoint of $\overline{AC}$.

Prove: ℓ contains N.

Let $B = r_\ell (A)$ and let M be the midpoint of $\overline{AB}$. Now mark the figure.

From the Midpoint Connector Theorem, $\overleftrightarrow{MN}$ is parallel to $\overline{BC}$. But, from the definition of reflection, ℓ contains M, and because the translation T is parallel to ℓ, ℓ is parallel to $\overline{BC}$. Thus both ℓ and $\overleftrightarrow{MN}$ are parallel to $\overline{BC}$ through M. By the Uniqueness of Parallels Theorem, ℓ and $\overleftrightarrow{MN}$ must be the same line. Thus ℓ contains N.

The uniqueness of parallels statement is important in the history of mathematics. In fact, it ultimately changed the entire nature of mathematics.

Euclid began his geometry with ten assumptions, which today are called postulates, and with a number of definitions. Five of the postulates were algebraic in nature and caused no argument among mathematicians. The other five postulates were geometric and are given here in free translation.

Postulates of Euclid:

1. Two points determine a line segment.
2. A line segment can be extended indefinitely along a line.
3. A circle can be drawn with any center and any radius.
4. All right angles are congruent.
5. If two lines are cut by a transversal, and the interior angles on the same side of the transversal have a total measure of less than 180, then the lines will intersect on that side of the transversal.

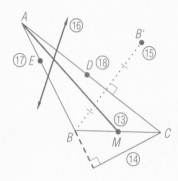
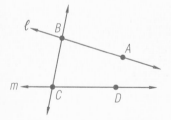
You can see that the fifth postulate is much longer and more complex than the others. This bothered mathematicians, who felt that such a complicated statement should not be assumed true. For 2000 years they tried to prove the fifth postulate from Euclid's other assumptions.

Being unable to prove it, some mathematicians substituted simpler statements for it. The uniqueness of parallels property was first suggested by the Greek mathematician Proclus about A.D. 450, but it is known as *Playfair's Parallel Postulate* because it was used by the British mathematician John Playfair in the year 1795. The statement is proved as a theorem in this lesson based on assuming the Parallel Lines Postulate (// lines ⇒ corr. ∠s =).

Other mathematicians substituted different statements for Playfair's Parallel Postulate. When they assumed there were no parallels to a line through a point not on it, they were able to develop a spherical geometry that could apply to the surface of the earth. When they assumed there was more than one parallel to a line through a point not on it, they developed types of geometry for other surfaces. These geometries are called *non-Euclidean*.

The works of these mathematicians greatly influenced *all* later mathematics. For the first time, postulates were viewed as statements *assumed* true instead of statements definitely true. After them, mathematicians experimented with a variety of algebras and geometries formed by modifying or changing postulates. Their experiments were at first thought to be merely a game, but are now considered quite important. Non-Euclidean geometries are important in physics in the theory of relativity. A useful algebra, different from what you have studied, is applied in the construction of computers.

Questions

Covering the Reading

In 1–3, tell whether the auxiliary figure is or is not uniquely determined.

1. a line through two points uniquely determined

2. a line parallel to a given line through a point not on it
uniquely determined

3. a diagonal bisecting an angle of a quadrilateral
not uniquely determined

In 4 and 5, draw the reflecting line of the glide reflection mapping one figure onto the other.

4.  **5.**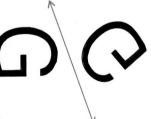

662

6. State Playfair's Parallel Postulate. **Through a point not on a line, there is exactly one parallel to the given line.**

7. How many postulates were in Euclid's geometry? **ten**

8. How many of Euclid's postulates were geometric in nature? **five**

9. Which of Euclid's postulates listed in the lesson most troubled mathematicians? **number 5**

10. Can Playfair's Parallel Postulate be proved from the first four postulates of Euclid? **No**

11. Geometries in which Playfair's Parallel Postulate is not true are called __?__. **non-Euclidean geometries**

12. Since the discovery of non-Euclidean geometries, postulates have been viewed as __?__ rather than as statements which are definitely true. **statements which are assumed true**

Applying the Mathematics

In 13–18, use a ruler, compass, and protractor or an automatic drawer. Copy the drawing of △*ABC* for each question, then draw the given auxiliary figure. Tell whether the auxiliary figure is uniquely determined. **See margin for 13-18.**

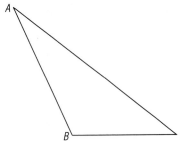

13. segment connecting *A* to the midpoint of $\overline{BC}$ (a median of the triangle)

14. perpendicular to $\overleftrightarrow{AB}$ through *C* (an altitude of the triangle)

15. reflection image of *B* over the line $\overleftrightarrow{AC}$

16. bisector of $\overline{AB}$

17. point *E* between *A* and *B*

18. point *D* on $\overrightarrow{AC}$ so that *AD = BC*

19. Draw a figure describing Euclid's fifth postulate. State the antecedent and consequent of that postulate in terms of your figure. **See margin.**

20. Euclid's first postulate is like what postulate in this book? **Point-Line-Plane Postulate**

21. Euclid's third postulate is like what property of constructions? **Compass Rule**

22. *Multiple choice.* Which of these lines is parallel to the line with equation $3x + 2y = 5$ and contains the point (10, 13)?
    (a) $3x + 2y = 23$ (b) $2x - 3y = 23$
    (c) $3x + 2y = 56$ (d) $2x - 3y = 56$ **(c)**

LESSON 13-6 *Uniqueness* **663**

23. $\overline{PT}$ is tangent to $\odot O$ at point T. If $PO = 20$ and $PT = 16$, what is the radius of $\odot O$? *(Lesson 13-5)* **12 units**

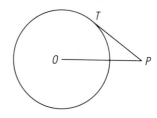

24. Show by indirect reasoning that a quadrilateral cannot have four acute angles. *(Lesson 13-4)* **See margin.**

In 25 and 26, given the statements, what (if anything) can you conclude using all the given statements and the rules of logic? *(Lessons 13-3, 13-2, 13-1)*

25. (1) You are elected President of the U.S. if you win the majority of electoral votes.
(2) In 1960, Richard Nixon was not elected President.
In 1960, Richard Nixon did not win the majority of electoral votes.

Richard Nixon delivered a campaign address at Dallas Memorial Auditorium.

26. (1) Miami won the football game 6–3.
(2) You can score six points in football by three safeties, two field goals, or one touchdown.
(3) Miami did not have any safeties or touchdowns.
Miami scored two field goals.

In 27 and 28, consider kites, trapezoids, parallelograms, rhombuses, and rectangles. Name the types of quadrilaterals for which the property is always true. *(Lessons 5-5, 5-4, 5-2)*

27. The diagonals are congruent. **rectangles**

28. There is a pair of congruent sides.
kites, parallelograms, rhombuses, rectangles

29. What does the word *auxiliary* mean outside of mathematics?
assisting; supplementing

30. **a.** Name five things outside of mathematics which are unique.
b. Name five things which are not unique.
See margin.

31. Who owns the zebra? **the Japanese man**

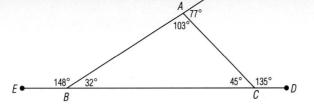

LESSON 13-7

Exterior Angles

Above is pictured a triangle. At each vertex, one of its sides has been extended. The angles formed in this way are the *exterior angles* of the triangle. In this lesson and the next one, various techniques are applied to determine properties of exterior angles of triangles and other polygons.

Definition:

An angle is an **exterior angle** of a polygon if and only if it forms a linear pair with one of the angles of the polygon.

Above, the exterior angles are $\angle ABE$, $\angle ACD$, and $\angle FAC$. To distinguish exterior angles of a polygon from the polygon's own angles, the angles of the polygon are called **interior angles.** Measures of exterior angles in triangles are quite nicely related to the measures of the triangle's interior angles. Notice above that each exterior angle measure is the sum of the measures of two of the triangle's interior angles: $148 = 103 + 45$; $77 = 45 + 32$; and $135 = 103 + 32$. The general property is quite easy to prove using algebra.

Exterior Angle Theorem:

In a triangle, the measure of an exterior angle is equal to the sum of the measures of the two nonadjacent interior angles.

Proof

Draw   A triangle is shown here.

Given: $\triangle ABC$, exterior $\angle 4$.
Prove: $m\angle 4 = m\angle 2 + m\angle 3$.
Write   **By the Triangle-Sum Theorem,**
   $m\angle 1 + m\angle 2 + m\angle 3 = 180.$
Since $\angle ACB$ and $\angle ACD$ form a linear pair,
   $m\angle 1 + m\angle 4 = 180.$
So these sums of angle measures are equal to each other:
   $m\angle 1 + m\angle 4 = m\angle 1 + m\angle 2 + m\angle 3.$
Subtracting $m\angle 1$ from each side,
   $m\angle 4 = m\angle 2 + m\angle 3.$

LESSON 13-7   *Exterior Angles*   **665**

RESOURCES
■ Lesson Master 13-7
▣ Computer Master 29

OBJECTIVES

H From given information, deduce which sides or angles of triangles are smallest or largest.
I Use the Exterior Angle Inequality to determine angle measures.

TEACHING NOTES

The Exterior Angle Theorem and Exterior Angle Inequality are often combined into one statement: The measure of an exterior angle to a triangle is equal to the sum of the measures of the two nonadjacent interior angles and greater than either one of them.

The two theorems mentioned above could have been proved as soon as the Triangle-Sum Theorem was available, but they were not needed then. The Exterior Angle Inequality is needed to prove the Unequal Sides Theorem. The proof of the Unequal Sides Theorem is not difficult but requires attention if it is to be understood. It should be discussed in detail. This theorem is used with an indirect proof to prove the Unequal Angles Theorem.

After **Example 1,** a triangle, whose sides and angle measures are given, is presented. Have students verify that the given measures are reasonably accurate. Also, have students try to draw an equilateral triangle using just

There is a conclusion which directly follows from this theorem. Since $m\angle 4 = m\angle 2 + m\angle 3$, use the Equation to Inequality Property to conclude

$$m\angle 4 > m\angle 2$$
and $\quad m\angle 4 > m\angle 3.$

The result is called the *Exterior Angle Inequality*.

Exterior Angle Inequality:

In a triangle, the measure of an exterior angle is greater than the measure of either nonadjacent interior angle.

Example 1 Refer to the figure below. If $m\angle APE = 35$, what can be concluded about the other angle measures?

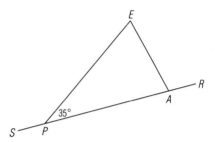

Solution You can actually conclude something about each angle in the figure. $m\angle SPE = 145$ by the Linear Pair Theorem.
Now, applying the Exterior Angle Inequality,
$$m\angle E < 145$$
and $m\angle EAP < 145$.
The Exterior Angle Inequality also shows that $m\angle EAR > 35$.

The Exterior Angle Inequality enables some properties of interior angles to be deduced. Below is a scalene triangle with sides and angles measured to the nearest millimeter and degree. Notice the smallest angle is opposite the smallest side; the largest angle is opposite the largest side. This important result is true in any triangle.

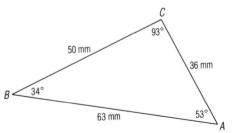

Unequal Sides Theorem:

If two sides of a triangle are not congruent, then the angles opposite them are not congruent, and the larger angle is opposite the longer side.

Proof

First we draw a figure and state the given and to prove in terms of that figure.

Given: $\triangle ABC$ with $BA > BC$.
Prove: $m\angle C > m\angle A$.

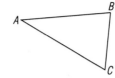

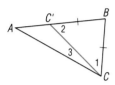

Angles opposite sides have already been explored in isosceles triangles. To use these results, draw an isosceles triangle as at the left by locating C' on $\overrightarrow{BA}$ so that $BC' = BC$. Then C' is between A and B because $BA > BC'$.

Conclusions	Justifications
1. Identify point C' on $\overrightarrow{BA}$ with $BC' = BC$.	On a ray, there is exactly one point at a given distance from an endpoint.
2. $m\angle 1 = m\angle 2$	Isosceles Triangle Theorem
3. $m\angle 2 > m\angle A$	Exterior Angle Inequality (with $\triangle CC'A$)
4. $m\angle 1 > m\angle A$	Substitution (step 2 into step 3)

[Comment: Now all that is left to show is that $m\angle BCA > m\angle 1$.]

5. $m\angle 1 + m\angle 3 = m\angle BCA$	Angle Addition Postulate
6. $m\angle BCA > m\angle 1$	Equation to Inequality Property
7. $m\angle BCA > m\angle A$	Transitive Property of Inequality (steps 4 and 6)

The contrapositive of any theorem is true, as you know. The contrapositive of the Isosceles Triangle Theorem is: If two angles in a triangle are not congruent, then the sides opposite them are not congruent. But which side is opposite the larger angle? Because of the Unequal Sides Theorem, the larger side cannot be opposite the smaller angle. All possibilities but one have been ruled out. The larger side must be opposite the larger angle.

Unequal Angles Theorem:

If two angles of a triangle are not congruent, then the sides opposite them are not congruent, and the longer side is opposite the larger angle.

1. In $\triangle ABC$, $AB = 10$, $BC = 11$, and $AC = 12$. Order the angles from smallest to largest.
C, A, and B

2. An exterior angle of $\triangle DEF$ at E has measure 175. What can you conclude from this about the nonadjacent interior angles?
$m\angle EDF + m\angle DFE = 175$ and each of these angles has measure less than 175.

3. Is the Unequal Sides Theorem true for pentagons? Verify your answer.
No. In the figure below, $\overline{CD}$ is the side opposite $\angle A$ and $\overline{BC}$ is the side opposite $\angle E$. $BC > CD$, but $m\angle A > m\angle E$.

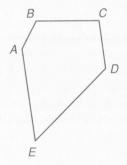

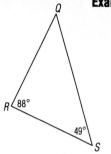

Example 2 In △*QRS* at the left, arrange the sides in order from shortest to longest.

Solution From the Triangle-Sum Theorem,
$$m\angle Q + 88 + 49 = 180$$
so
$$m\angle Q = 43$$
Since m∠*Q* is the smallest angle measure, $\overline{RS}$ is the shortest side. Since m∠*R* is the largest, $\overline{QS}$ is the longest side. Thus the sides of △*QRS* from shortest to longest are: $\overline{RS}, \overline{RQ}, \overline{QS}$.

Questions

Covering the Reading

In 1 and 2, use the figure below.

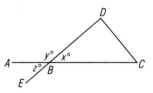

1. If m∠*C* = 50 and m∠*D* = 90, find
  a. *x* 40   **b.** *y* 140   **c.** *z*. 40

2. How is m∠*ABD* related to m∠*C* and m∠*D*? m∠*ABD* = m∠*C* + m∠*L*

In 3–5, sides of △*FGI* have been extended in the drawing below. For the named angle, give two angles with less measure.

3. ∠4 ∠2 and ∠1

4. ∠5 ∠3 and ∠1

5. ∠6 ∠2 and ∠3

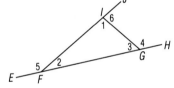

6. a. State the Exterior Angle Theorem.
  b. State the Exterior Angle Inequality.
  See margin.

In 7–10, use the triangles below.

7. Name the largest angle of △*ABC*. ∠*B*

8. Name the smallest angle of △*ABC*. ∠*C*

9. Name the longest side of △*DEF*. $\overline{FE}$

10. Name the shortest side of △*DEF*. $\overline{DE}$

668

11. *True or false?* In an obtuse triangle, the longest side is opposite the obtuse angle. **True**

12. In $\triangle LUV$, $LU > UV > LV$ and one angle has measure 60. Which angle is it? **∠L**

13. Name the shortest segment in the figure below. (The figure is not necessarily drawn accurately.) **GJ**

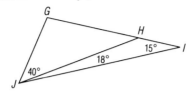

In 14 and 15, segments $\overline{PS}$ and $\overline{PR}$ trisect $\overline{QT}$ in right triangle PQT below.

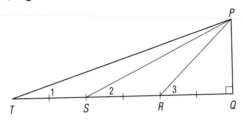

14. Prove: $m\angle 3 > m\angle 1$. **See margin.**

15. Prove: $PQ < PS$. **See margin.**

16. In $\triangle UVW$, X is between U and V. If $m\angle WXU = 70$, what can be concluded about
    a. $m\angle V$ **m∠V < 70**
    b. $m\angle U$ **m∠U < 110**
    c. $m\angle UWX$? **m∠UWX < 110**

17. Below, $\overrightarrow{CB}$ bisects $\angle ACD$. In terms of x and y, find:
    a. $m\angle ACB$ **x**
    b. $m\angle CBD$ **x + y**
    c. $m\angle D$. **180 − 2x − y**

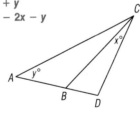

18. In $\triangle PQR$, a student wanted to draw the line from P perpendicular to $\overline{QR}$ at its midpoint. **a.** Is this auxiliary line uniquely determined? **b.** If so, give the justification. If not, tell why not.
    (Lesson 13-6) **a) No; b) The ⊥ from P to QR may not intersect QR at its midpoint.**

19. State Playfair's Parallel Postulate. *(Lesson 13-6)* **Through a point not on a line, there is exactly one line parallel to the given line.**

20. Are postulates definitely true? *(Lesson 13-6)* **No**

21. How many postulates did Euclid use that are geometric? *(Lesson 13-6)* **5**

ADDITIONAL ANSWERS
6. a. In a triangle, the measure of an exterior angle is equal to the sum of the measures of the two nonadjacent interior angles.
b. In a triangle, the measure of an exterior angle is greater than the measure of either nonadjacent interior angle.

14. ∠3 is an exterior angle of △PRT. Therefore, by the Exterior Angle Inequality, m∠3 > m∠1.

15. Sample: m∠Q = 90 (given). m∠2 < 90, since m∠2 + m∠SPQ = 90. Therefore, m∠2 < m∠Q by substitution. So PQ < PS by Unequal Angles Theorem.

EXTENSION
Computer You may wish
to have students determine
whether each of the following
statements about triangles is
true or false by using an automatic drawer.
(1) An exterior angle can be
complementary to an interior
angle.
True
(2) An exterior angle can be
supplementary to a remote
interior angle.
False
(3) An exterior angle is always obtuse.
False
(4) The measure of an ex-
terior angle can be less than
the measure of an interior
angle.
True
(5) An exterior angle of an
obtuse triangle can be acute.
True
(6) The measure of an exterior angle can equal the measure of a remote interior
angle.
False

EVALUATION
Alternative Assessment
At this point, you might want
students to summarize the
algebraic relationships they
know about triangles by doing the following activities:
(1) draw and label acute, obtuse, and right triangles (include some exterior angles),
(2) list all equality relationships they know about the
triangles, and (3) list all inequality relationships they
know. Encourage them to
use their textbooks for reference.

22. Prove: The tangent lines to the endpoints of a diameter are parallel.
(Lesson 13-5) See below.

23. $\overrightarrow{AC}$ is a common tangent to $\odot O$ and $\odot P$ below. The radius of $\odot O$ is
3 cm and the radius of $\odot P$ is 8 cm. If $AB = 12$ cm, find AC.
(Lesson 13-5) 32 cm

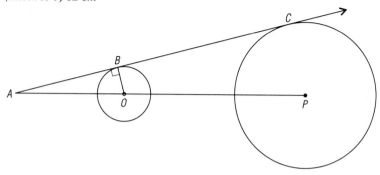

24. Solve $15(x - 7) = 3(19 + 5x)$. *(Lesson 13-4, Previous course)*
no solution

Exploration

25. a. Show that the Exterior Angle Inequality is not true for pentagons.
b. Is the Exterior Angle Inequality true for quadrilaterals? No

---

25a) The exterior angle $\angle DEX$ is not greater than the interior angles $\angle A$,
$\angle B$, or $\angle D$.

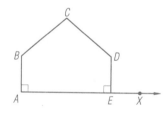

22) Draw:
Given: $\overline{RS}$ is a diameter of $\odot O$;
$\overleftrightarrow{RT}$ is tangent to $\odot O$ at R;
$\overleftrightarrow{SU}$ is tangent to $\odot O$ at S.
Prove: $\overleftrightarrow{RT} \parallel \overleftrightarrow{SU}$.
$\overleftrightarrow{RT}$ is $\perp \overrightarrow{RO}$ and $\overleftrightarrow{SU} \perp \overrightarrow{SO}$, by the Radius-Tangent Theorem.
So $\overleftrightarrow{RT} \parallel \overleftrightarrow{SU}$, by the Two Perpendiculars Theorem.

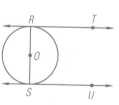

LESSON 13-8

Exterior Angles of Polygons

RESOURCES
■ Lesson Master 13-8

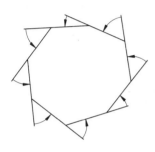

Think of walking around a convex polygon. At each vertex, you must change direction. The amount of the change in direction is measured by an exterior angle at that vertex.

The total amount of change in direction, as you walk around, is the *sum of the measures of the exterior angles of the polygon,* where one exterior angle is picked at each vertex.

Since the sum of the *interior* angle measures gets larger as the number of sides of the polygon increases, you might think that the sum of exterior angle measures also increases. What is surprising is that the sum of the exterior angle measures does not increase. The sum is constant. It is the same as one revolution, 360°. It is the same amount as you turn in going around a circle.

OBJECTIVES

A Draw regular polygons using LOGO programs.
B Determine measures of exterior angles in polygons.

TEACHING NOTES

There are two results that students find surprising in this lesson. The first is that the sum of the measures of the exterior angles of any convex polygon, one at each vertex, is 360 *regardless of the number of sides of the polygon.* This fact was known to the ancient Greeks.

Exterior Angles of a Polygon Sum Theorem:

In any convex polygon, the sum of the measures of the exterior angles, one at each vertex, is 360.

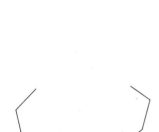

Proof

Consider any convex *n*-gon. It has *n* vertices. At each vertex, the measures of the interior angle and one exterior angle add to 180. So the sum of the interior and exterior angles at the *n* vertices is (180*n*). But we know the sum of the interior angle measures is 180(*n* − 2) degrees. So form this equation (all measures are in degrees):

Sum of interior angles	+	sum of exterior angles	=	sum of all interior-exterior pairs.
180(*n* − 2)	+	*x*	=	180*n*

Solving this equation for *x*,

$$180n − 360 + x = 180n$$
$$-360 + x = 0$$
$$x = 360.$$

The previous theorem gives an alternate way of finding the number of degrees in each angle of a regular polygon.

The second surprising result is that this ancient fact has applications in today's LOGO computer language. LOGO uses exterior angles to draw polygons, and it is necessary to turn through 360° (or some multiple) in order to complete any polygon.

In LOGO, turns to the right are clockwise; turns to the left are counterclockwise. If the polygon to be drawn is not convex, the sum of the angle measures (with clockwise considered as negative and counterclockwise as positive) will be 360°. Nothing can demonstrate the concept of the Exterior Angles of a Polygon Sum Theorem more nicely than a LOGO demonstration.

LESSON 13-8 *Exterior Angles of Polygons* **671**

Example The regular polygon at the left has 18 sides.

a. How many degrees are in each exterior angle?
b. How many degrees are in each interior angle?

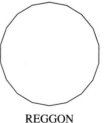

Solution

a. The sum of the exterior angles is 360. Since the polygon is regular, all of the interior angles have the same measure. So all the exterior angles do also. There are 18 exterior angles, so each must have measure 20.

b. Each interior angle forms a linear pair with an exterior angle. Thus each interior angle has measure 160.

The idea of the Example is used in the computer language Logo to create regular polygons. In Logo, the command FORWARD traces a segment on a screen of a particular length. The command RIGHT turns the arrow clockwise the number of degrees you specify.

REPEAT simply does it as many times as indicated. Here is a Logo program for drawing a regular 18-gon in which each side has length 7. A side of length 7 is drawn, the tracer turns 20° clockwise for the exterior angle, and this is repeated 17 more times. Call the polygon REGGON. (If you stored REGGON in the machine, then you could call upon it later in some more complicated program.) Notice how short the program is.

```
TO REGGON
  REPEAT 18 [FORWARD 7 RIGHT 20]
END
```

To draw something that looks more like a circle, make the length of the segment smaller and the angle smaller. The following will look very much like a circle. Make the length 3, the turn 2°. This must be repeated 180 times to get all the way around.

```
TO 180GON
  REPEAT 180 [FORWARD 3 RIGHT 2]
END
```

The results of these programs are shown here.

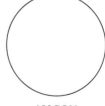

REGGON   180GON

1. A pentagon with some sides extended is drawn below.
 a. Find *a*. 85
 b. Find *a* + *b* + *c* + *d* + *e*. 360

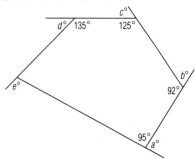

2. a. In a hexagon, the sum of the measures of the interior angles is ___?___ . 720
 b. The sum of the measures of the exterior angles is ___?___ . 360

3. In an *n*-gon, give:
 a. the sum of the measures of the interior angles; (*n* − 2) · 180
 b. the sum of the measures of the exterior angles. 360

4. Below is regular polygon *CONSIDERABLY*.
 a. What is m∠*SIX*? 30   **b.** m∠*SID* = ___?___ 150

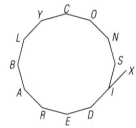

5. Write a Logo program that will draw a regular octagon with sides of length 12. See margin.

6. Write a Logo program that will draw a regular decagon with sides of length 5. See margin.

7. What will this Logo Program draw?
```
TO OBJECT
  REPEAT 30 [FORWARD 4 RIGHT 12]
END
```
a regular 30-gon with sides of length 4

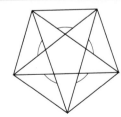

8. A regular pentagon and its diagonals is drawn at the left. Five angles are marked in the figure. What is the sum of their measures? 540

9. Using an indirect proof, prove that no convex decagon has four right interior angles. See margin.

LESSON 13-8   Exterior Angles of Polygons   **673**

Question 8: The problem has a surprise elegant solution. Consider the angles vertical to those marked.

ADDITIONAL ANSWERS
5.
TO OCT
 REPEAT 8 [FORWARD 12
  RIGHT 45]
END

6.
TO DEC
 REPEAT 10 [FORWARD 5
  RIGHT 36]
END

9. Assume figure *F* is a convex decagon with 4 right interior angles. The corresponding exterior angles also would be right angles, and so the sum of their measures would be 360°. So the sum of the measures of all 10 exterior angles would exceed 360°, which contradicts the Exterior Angles of a Polygon Sum Theorem. Therefore, the assumption is false. Thus, no convex decagon can have 4 right interior angles.

MORE PRACTICE

For more questions on SPUR Objectives, use *Lesson Master 13-8,* shown on page 673.

ADDITIONAL ANSWERS

11. ∠3 is an exterior angle of △*XYV*, so m∠3 > m∠2 (from Exterior Angles Inequality Theorem). Similarly, ∠2 is an exterior angle of △*WXV*, so m∠2 > m∠1. Transitivity gives m∠3 > m∠2 > m∠1. So ∠1 is the smallest.

12. not uniquely determined

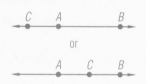

13. not uniquely determined; sample:

14. not uniquely determined

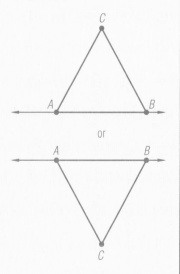

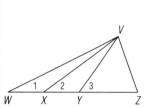

10. Refer to the figure at the right. If m∠*CBD* = 71, what can be concluded about

  a. m∠*ABD* m∠*ABD* = 109
  b. m∠*C* m∠*C* < 109
  c. m∠*D*? *(Lesson 13-7)* m∠*D* < 109

11. Refer to the figure at the left. Which angle is the smallest: 1, 2, or 3? Justify your conclusion. *(Lesson 13-7)* See margin.

In 12–14, *A* and *B* are given points. Draw the indicated figure. Tell whether the figure is uniquely determined. *(Lessons 13-6, 4-5, 2-5)*

12. point *C* on $\overleftrightarrow{AB}$ such that $AC = \frac{1}{2}AB$ See margin.

13. point *C* such that *AC* = *CB* See margin.

14. point *C* such that △*ABC* is equilateral See margin.

15. A square and a circle each have area 400 square meters. Which has the larger perimeter? *(Lessons 8-3, 8-1)* the square

16. Where should you aim on wall *x* below to shoot a golf ball *G* off sides *x*, *y*, and *z* and into the hole at *H*? *(Lesson 6-4)*

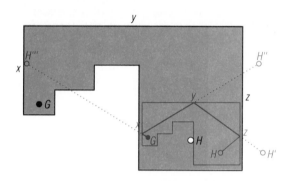

17. $\overline{AC}$ is a diagonal of rectangle *ABCD* below. $\overline{AC} \perp \overline{PB}$. Name all angles with the same measure as ∠*CAB*. *(Lesson 5-7)* ∠*ACD*, ∠*CBP*

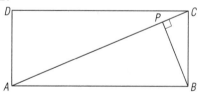

18. a. Run the Logo program for REGGON in this lesson. (You will need to find Logo software to do this.) Bring in a printout of what you get. Answers will vary.

  b. Make up a Logo program of your own. Answers will vary.

674

Summary

Every mathematical argument follows rules of logic. In this chapter, five rules are stated.

Law of Detachment: If you have a statement or given information p and a justification of the form $p \Rightarrow q$, you may conclude q.

Law of Transitivity: If $p \Rightarrow q$ and $q \Rightarrow r$, then $p \Rightarrow r$.

Law of the Contrapositive: A statement $p \Rightarrow q$ and its contrapositive $not\text{-}q \Rightarrow not\text{-}p$ are either both true or both false.

Law of Ruling Out Possibilities: When p or q is true and q is not true, then p is true.

Law of Indirect Reasoning: If valid reasoning from a statement p leads to a false conclusion, then p is false.

The last three of these laws are the logic used in indirect proofs. If you can prove that the contrapositive of a statement is true, then the statement is true. If you can rule out all possibilities but one, then the possibility left is true. If you reason from the negation of what you want to prove and arrive at a contradiction, then the negation is false. Thus what you want to prove must be true.

Indirect reasoning is used in everyday life, in puzzle problems, and throughout mathematics. In this chapter, indirect reasoning was applied in the proof of Playfair's Parallel Postulate, a very important postulate in the history of mathematics, and to prove theorems about tangents to circles and angles in triangles and polygons.

Vocabulary

Below are the most important terms and phrases for the chapter.
For the starred (*) terms you should be able to give a definition of the term.
For the other terms you should be able to give a general description and a specific example of each.

Lesson 13-1
Law of Detachment
Law of Transitivity (Transitive
  Property of Implication)

Lesson 13-2
negation, *not-p*
inverse
contrapositive
Law of the Contrapositive

Lesson 13-3
Law of Ruling Out Possibilities
Trichotomy Law

Lesson 13-4
direct reasoning, direct proof
indirect reasoning, indirect proof
*contradictory, *contradiction
Law of Indirect Reasoning

Lesson 13-5
*tangent to a circle
point of tangency
Radius-Tangent Theorem
tangent to a sphere, tangent
common tangents

Lesson 13-6
uniquely determined
auxiliary
Uniqueness of Parallels Theorem
  (Playfair's Parallel Postulate)
Postulates of Euclid
non-Euclidean

Lesson 13-7
*exterior angle
Exterior Angle Theorem
Exterior Angle Inequality
Unequal Sides Theorem
Unequal Angles Theorem

Lesson 13-8
Exterior Angles of a Polygon
  Sum Theorem
Logo

SUMMARY

The Summary gives an overview of the entire chapter and provides an opportunity for students to consider the material as a whole. Thus, the Summary can be used to help students relate the various concepts presented in the chapter.

VOCABULARY

Terms, symbols, and properties are listed by lesson to provide a checklist of concepts a student must know. Emphasize to students that they should read the vocabulary list carefully before starting the Progress Self-Test. If students do not remember the meaning of a term, a statement of a theorem, or the five rules of reasoning, they should refer back to the individual lesson.

Progress Self-Test

See margin for answers not shown below.

Directions: Take this test as you would take a test in class. Then check your work with the solutions in the Selected Answers section in the back of the book.

1. Consider the statement: If a figure is a hexagon, then it is a polygon.
   a. Is the statement true? **Yes**
   b. Write the inverse of this statement.
   c. Show that the inverse is false by drawing a counterexample.

2. Consider the statement: If two angles are adjacent, then they form a linear pair.
   a. Write the contrapositive of the statement.
   b. Is the contrapositive true? **No**

3. $\angle A$ in $\triangle ABC$ is neither acute nor obtuse.
   a. What can you conclude?
   b. What law of logic have you used?

4. Write an argument to show why no triangle can have three angles all with measures under 50°.

5. Write an indirect proof to show that $\sqrt{80} \neq 40$.

6. What is the measure of an exterior angle of a regular duodecagon? **30**

7. Write a Logo program that will draw a regular octagon with sides of length 6.

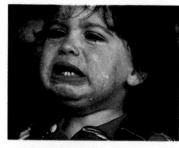

8. What (if anything) can you conclude using all the following statements?
   (1) All babies are happy.
   (2) If someone is teething, then that person is a baby.
   (3) Nate is sad. **Nate is not teething.**

9. *Multiple choice.* In the figure below, Y is between X and Z but the figure is not necessarily drawn accurately. Which is the shortest segment?
   (a) WX (b) WY (c) WZ
   (d) XY (e) XZ (f) YZ (f)

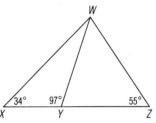

10. In the figure below, suppose $m\angle ABD = 120$. What can be concluded about
    a. $m\angle CBD$
    b. $m\angle C$
    c. $m\angle D$?

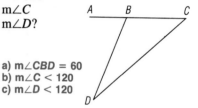

    a) $m\angle CBD = 60$
    b) $m\angle C < 120$
    c) $m\angle D < 120$

11. Until the discovery of non-Euclidean geometries, postulates were thought to be __?__ true. Now it is realized that they are only __?__ true. **definitely, assumed**

In 12 and 13, give a justification for drawing the auxiliary line in this figure, or indicate that it cannot be justified.

12. the line through C parallel to $\overleftrightarrow{AB}$
13. the bisector of $\angle B$ containing the midpoint of $\overline{AC}$ **cannot be justified**

676

14. $\overline{PU}$ and $\overline{PT}$ are tangents to $\odot O$ below. If $\angle P$ is a right angle, what kind of quadrilateral is $OUPT$? **square**

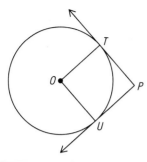

15. $\overrightarrow{CE}$ is a common tangent to $\odot A$ and $\odot B$. If $BD = 9$, $CD = 20$, and $CE = 50$, find the radius of $\odot A$. **22.5 units**

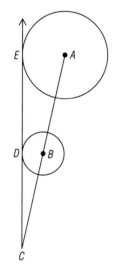

16. Four cards, the Jack, Queen, King, and Ace, are from four different centuries, the seventeenth, eighteenth, nineteenth, and twentieth. From the clues below, match each card to its century. (Note: the seventeenth century covers the years from 1601–1700; the eighteenth: 1701–1800; the nineteenth: 1801–1900; the twentieth: 1901–2000.)
1. The Queen is older than the King.
2. The Jack is exactly 100 years older than the Queen.
3. The Ace is older than the Jack.

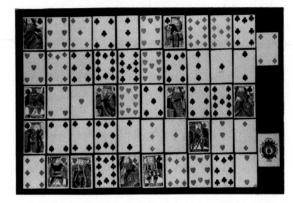

CHAPTER REVIEW

The main objectives for the chapter are organized here into sections corresponding to the four main types of understanding emphasized in this chapter: Skills, Properties, Uses, and History.

The four types of understanding are not in increasing order of difficulty. There may be hard skills and easy representations; some uses may be easier than anything else; and so on.

USING THE CHAPTER REVIEW
Students should be able to answer questions like these with about 85% accuracy by the end of the chapter.

You may assign these questions over a single night to help students prepare for a test the next day, or you may assign the questions over a two-day period.

If you assign the questions over two days, then we recommend assigning the *evens* for homework the first night so that students get feedback in class the next day. Then assign the *odds* for the second night (the night before the test) so that students can use the answers provided in the book as a study aid.

ADDITIONAL ANSWERS
1.
TO HEXAGON
  REPEAT 6 [FORWARD 10
    RIGHT 60]
END

2.
TO NGON
  REPEAT 360 [FORWARD
    .5 RIGHT 1]
END

See margin for answers not shown below.

Chapter Review

Questions on SPUR Objectives

SPUR stands for **S**kills, **P**roperties, **U**ses, and **R**epresentations.
The Chapter Review questions are grouped according to the
SPUR Objectives for this chapter.

SKILLS deal with the procedures used to get answers.

■ **Objective A:** *Draw regular polygons using Logo programs.* *(Lesson 13-8)*

In 1 and 2, write a Logo program which will draw the following figures.
1. a regular hexagon with sides of length 10
2. a regular 360-gon with sides of length $\frac{1}{2}$

■ **Objective B:** *Determine measures of exterior angles in polygons.* *(Lesson 13-8)*

3. Refer to $\triangle XYZ$ below.
  a. Find m$\angle X$. **46**
  b. Find m$\angle Y$. **92**

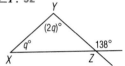

4. a. The sum of the measures of the exterior angles in a regular octagon is __?__. **360**
  b. The measure of each interior angle in a regular octagon is __?__. **135**

PROPERTIES deal with the principles behind the mathematics.

■ **Objective C:** *Write the converse, inverse, or contrapositive of a conditional.* *(Lesson 13-2)*

In 5–8, write **a.** the converse, **b.** the inverse, and **c.** the contrapositive of the statement. **d.** Tell which of these is (are) true.
5. If $x = 3$, then $x^2 = 9$.
6. If a figure is a rectangle, then it is a square.
7. All New Yorkers live in the U.S.

Times Square, New York City

8. Use the figure below. If m$\angle ABC = 40$, then m$\angle DBC = 140$.

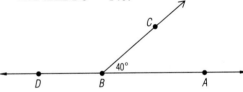

■ **Objective D:** *Follow the basic laws of reasoning to make conclusions.* *(Lessons 13-1, 13-2, 13-3, 13-4)*

In 9–15, using all the statements,
a. what (if anything) can you conclude?
b. What laws of reasoning have you used?

9. (1) If a figure is a rectangle, then it is a trapezoid.
  (2) *LOVE* is a rectangle.

678

10. (1) If corresponding angles formed by a transversal are congruent, then two lines are parallel.
(2) If alternate interior angles formed by a transversal are congruent, then so are corresponding angles.

11. (1) If $x = 11$, then $y = 10$.
(2) $y = 7$

12. (1) $x = 11$ or $y = 10$.
(2) $y = 7$

13. (1) If $\ell \perp m$, then m$\angle A = 90$.
(2) m$\angle A = 75$

14. (1) If you answer this correctly, you will make me feel good.
(2) I will give you a hug if you make me feel good.
(3) You answer this correctly.

15. The following is from Lewis Carroll.
(1) No name in this list is unsuitable for the hero of a romance.
(2) Names beginning with a vowel are always melodious.
(3) No name is suitable for the hero of a romance, if it begins with a consonant.

16. Solving
$(2x - 5)(3x + 4) = (x - 1)(6x - 1)$,
Nella came up with the equation -20 = 1.
a. What should Nella conclude?
b. What law of logic is being used?

17. The area of a square is 48 mm². A certain teacher claims that the perimeter of that same square is 144 mm.
a. What can you conclude?
b. What rule of logic is being applied to answer part **a**?

18. a, b, c, d, and e are the numbers 1, 2, 3, 4, and 5 but not necessarily in that order. From the clues, match each of the variables and numbers.
(1) d is not odd.
(2) e is larger than c.
(3) c and b are not primes.
(4) d is larger than b.
$a = 3$, $b = 1$, $c = 4$, $d = 2$, $e = 5$

■ **Objective E:** *Write indirect proofs.* (Lesson 13-4)

19. Explain why a quadrilateral cannot have four acute angles.

20. Give an indirect proof to show $\sqrt{2400} \neq 49$.

21. Give an indirect proof to show that $\sqrt{2} \neq \frac{239}{169}$.

■ **Objective F:** *Make deductions from properties of radii perpendicular to tangents.* (Lesson 13-5)

22. $\overline{AB}$ and $\overline{AC}$ are tangents to $\odot D$.
a. What kind of figure is *ABDC*? kite
b. What kind of figure is *ABD*?
right triangle

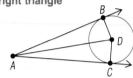

23. Use the figure above. If $AD = 41$ and $AC = 40$, find the circumference of $\odot D$.
$18\pi \approx 56.5$ units

In 24 and 25, $\overleftrightarrow{XZ}$ is a common tangent to $\odot O$ and $\odot P$ below.

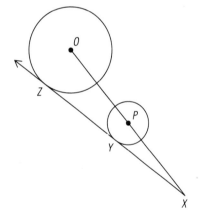

24. If $XY = 10$, $OZ = 8$, and $PY = 4$, find ZY. 10 units

25. If the radius of $\odot P$ is 15 mm, $XZ = 165$ mm, and $XY = 45$ mm, find the area of $\odot O$.
$3025\pi \approx 9503.3$ mm²

---

5. a. If x² = 9, then x = 3.
b. If x ≠ 3, then x² ≠ 9.
c. If x² ≠ 9, then x ≠ 3.
d. original, contrapositive

6. a. If a figure is a square, then it is a rectangle.
b. If a figure is not a rectangle, then it is not a square.
c. If a figure is not a square, then it is not a rectangle.
d. converse, inverse

7. a. All people in the U.S. live in New York.
b. If a person is not a New Yorker, then that person does not live in the U.S.
c. If a person does not live in the U.S., then that person is not a New Yorker.
d. original, contrapositive

8. a. If m∠DBC = 140, then m∠ABC = 40.
b. If m∠ABC ≠ 40, then m∠DBC ≠ 140.
c. If m∠DBC ≠ 140, then m∠ABC ≠ 40.
d. All are true.

9. a. *LOVE* is a trapezoid.
b. Law of Detachment

10. a. If alternate interior angles formed by a transversal are congruent, then two lines are parallel.
b. Law of Transitivity

11. a. x ≠ 11
b. Law of Contrapositive and Law of Detachment

12. a. x = 11
Law of Ruling Out Possibilities

13. a. ℓ is not perpendicular to *m*.
b. Law of Contrapositive and Law of Detachment

14. a. I will give you a hug.
b. Law of Detachment and Transitivity

15., 16., 17., 19., 20., 21.
See the margin on p. 680.

■ **Objective G:** *Justify auxiliary lines.* (Lesson 13-6)

In 26–29, give a justification for drawing the auxiliary line in this figure, or indicate that it cannot be justified.

26. diagonal $\overline{AC}$
27. line $\overleftrightarrow{CE}$ parallel to $\overline{AD}$
28. the bisector of ∠*B* Angle Measure Postulate
29. the ⊥ bisector of $\overline{AB}$ and $\overline{CD}$
 cannot be justified

■ **Objective H:** *From given information, deduce which sides or angles of triangles are smallest or largest.* (Lesson 13-7)

In 30 and 31, refer to △*ABC* below.

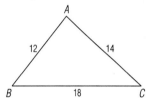

30. Name the largest angle. ∠*A*
31. Name the smallest angle. ∠*C*

In 32 and 33, the figures are not drawn accurately.

32. Name the sides of △*DEF* below in order from shortest to longest. $\overline{EF}, \overline{DE}, \overline{DF}$

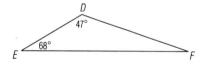

33. Refer to the figure *GHIJ* at the right. Name the shortest segment in the figure. $\overline{HI}$

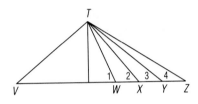

■ **Objective I:** *Use the Exterior Angle Inequality to determine angle measures.* (Lesson 13-7)

34. In △*QRS* below, if m∠*QST* = 132, what can be concluded about
a. m∠*QSR* m∠*QSR* = 48
b. m∠*Q* m∠*Q* < 132
c. m∠*R*? m∠*R* < 132

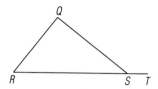

35. Refer to the figure below. Which angle is largest: 1, 2, 3, or 4? Explain your reasoning.

680

USES deal with applications of mathematics in real situations.

■ **Objective J:** *Apply laws of reasoning in real situations. (Lessons 13-1, 13-2, 13-3, 13-4)*

In 36–38, given the statements, what (if anything) can you conclude using the rules of logic?

36. (1) I am allowed to watch TV at 8 pm if I finish my homework.
    (2) I am not allowed to watch TV at 8 pm.

37. (1) Either Mary is too old for camp or she can go to camp.
    (2) Mary cannot go to camp.

38. (1) All bats are mammals.
    (2) No mammal can live without air.
    (3) Air is not found on the moon.
    No bat can live on the moon.

39. Ted is looking for his lost homework paper. It isn't in his notebook. It isn't in his school locker. So he concludes that it is at home.
    a. What reasoning law has he used?
    b. What is wrong with his reasoning?

REPRESENTATIONS deal with pictures, graphs, or objects that illustrate concepts.

There are no representations objectives in this chapter.

HISTORY deals with the development of mathematics.

■ **Objective K:** *Know the history and impact of Playfair's Parallel Postulate on the development of geometry. (Lesson 13-6)*

40. How many geometric postulates were in Euclid's *Elements*? **five**

41. State Playfair's Parallel Postulate.
    Through a point not on a line, there is exactly one line parallel to the given line.

42. How did the development of non-Euclidean geometry change the view of the truth of Euclid's postulates?
    Postulates are now viewed as statements assumed true instead of statements definitely true.

CHAPTER 14 ■ TRIGONOMETRY AND VECTORS

DAILY PACING CHART ■ CHAPTER 14

Every chapter of UCSMP *Geometry* includes lessons, a Progress Self-Test, and a Chapter Review. For optimal student performance, the self-test and review should be covered. (See *General Teaching Suggestions: Mastery* on page T36 of the Teacher's Edition.) By following the pace of the Full Course given here, students can complete the entire text by the end of the year. Students following the pace of the Minimal Course spend more time when there are quizzes and on the Chapter Review and will generally not complete all of the chapters in this text.

When all lessons are covered from the beginning (the recommendation of the authors), then students in the Minimal Course can cover through Lesson 13-4 and will cover all they need for future courses. For more information on pacing, see *General Teaching Suggestions: Pace* on page T35 of the Teacher's Edition.

DAY	MINIMAL COURSE	FULL COURSE
1	14-1	14-1
2	14-2	14-2
3	14-3	14-3
4	14-4	14-4
5	Quiz (TRF); Start 14-5.	Quiz (TRF); 14-5
6	Finish 14-5.	14-6
7	14-6	14-7
8	14-7	Progress Self-Test
9	Progress Self-Test	Chapter Review
10	Chapter Review	Chapter Test (TRF)
11	Chapter Review	
12	Chapter Test (TRF)	

TESTING OPTIONS
■ Quiz for Lessons 14-1 Through 14-4   ■ Chapter 14 Test, Form A   ■ Chapter 14 Test, Cumulative Form
■ Chapter 14 Test, Form B

PROVIDING FOR INDIVIDUAL DIFFERENCES
The student text has been written for, and tested with, average students. It also has been used successfully with better and more poorly prepared students.

The Lesson Notes often include Error Analysis and Alternate Approach features to help you with those students who need more help. A blackline Lesson Master (in the Teacher's Resource File), keyed to the chapter objectives, is provided for each lesson to allow more practice. (However, since it is very important to keep up with the daily pace, you are not expected to use all of these masters. Again, refer to the suggestions for pacing on page T35.) Extension activities are provided in the Lesson Notes for those students who have completed the particular lesson in a shorter amount of time than is expected, even in the Full Course.

OBJECTIVES ■ CHAPTER 14

The objectives listed here are the same as in the Chapter 14 Review on pages 728-731 of the student text. The Progress Self-Test on pages 726-727 and the tests in the Teacher's Resource File cover these objectives. For recommendations regarding the handling of this end-of-chapter material, see the notes in the margin on the corresponding pages of the Teacher's Edition.

OBJECTIVES FOR CHAPTER 14 (Organized into the SPUR Categories—Skills, Properties, Uses, and Representations)	Progress Self-Test Questions	Chapter Review Questions	Lesson Master from Teacher's Resource File*
SKILLS			
A Calculate lengths of sides in isosceles right triangles and in 30-60-90 triangles.	8-10	1 through 7	14-1
B Determine sines, cosines, and tangents from drawings.	1, 2	8 through 12	14-3, 14-4
C Calculate sines, cosines, and tangents of angles in right triangles.	11-14	13 through 23	14-3, 14-4
D Calculate lengths using the Right Triangle Altitude Theorem.	4-6	24 through 28	14-2
PROPERTIES			
E Draw the sum of two or more vectors.	18, 19	29 through 36	14-5, 14-6
F Know the definitions of sine, cosine, and tangent.	3	37 through 43	14-3, 14-4
G Recognize and derive the geometric mean properties in right triangles.	7	44 through 47	14-2
H Identify the properties of vector addition.	20	48 through 51	14-6
USES			
I Use sines, cosines, and tangents to determine unknown lengths in real situations.	16, 17	52 through 55	14-3, 14-4
J Use vectors for forces to determine combinations of forces.	24, 25	56 through 61	14-5, 14-7
REPRESENTATIONS			
K Graph sums and scalar multiples of vectors represented as ordered pairs.	21	62 through 65	14-6
L Convert directed segments to ordered pairs, and vice versa.	22, 23	66 through 69	14-7

*The masters are numbered to match the lessons

OVERVIEW ■ CHAPTER 14

This chapter covers the trigonometry and vector ideas that every student should know.

Trigonometry is needed for the study of physics by college-bound students. However, many other students also can benefit from studying some basic trigonometry. An examination of books for the trades (which use essentially arithmetic skills) will show that these books contain a reasonable amount of trigonometry. Most often, it is the trigonometry presented in this book: some right triangle trigonometry needed to find the lengths of sides given angle measures and a side, and some instruction on how to find angle measures.

Students who will study the physical sciences also need to know vector ideas. The study of business and economics today requires the use of vectors, and a knowledge of how physical forces combine should be a part of every person's education.

The mathematical idea joining trigonometry and vectors is the right triangle. The chapter begins with a discussion of 30-60-90 and 45-45-90 triangles in Lesson 14-1. Lesson 14-2 discusses the consequences of the similar triangles formed by the altitude to the hypotenuse.

It is easier to examine one trigonometric function first and then to introduce the others. Accordingly, only the tangent ratio, the easiest one to understand and the one most connected with slope, is introduced in Lesson 14-3. Lesson 14-4 covers the sine and cosine of an angle.

Vectors as directed line segments are introduced in Lesson 14-5. The sum of two vectors is defined using the parallelogram rule. In Lesson 14-6, the same ideas are repeated with coordinates, and properties of the addition of vectors are discussed. Lesson 14-7 shows how to translate from directed segments to ordered pairs by using trigonometry.

The use of scientific calculators is essential in this chapter.

PERSPECTIVES ■ CHAPTER 14

The Perspectives provide the rationale for the inclusion of topics or approaches, provide mathematical background, and make connections with other lessons and within UCSMP.

14-1

SPECIAL RIGHT TRIANGLES

There are no precise characteristics for making a triangle special. Some triangles are special because of the ratios of the lengths of their sides. For instance, there are the 3-4-5 right triangles, with sides $3x$, $4x$, and $5x$. Some triangles are special because of the ratios of their angles. The two special triangles in this lesson have angle ratios 1:2:3 (that is, 30-60-90) and 1:1:2 (that is, 45-45-90). The special triangle in the Exploration, called the *heptagonal triangle,* has angles in the ratio 1:2:4.

The 30-60-90 and 45-45-90 triangles are special for at least two reasons. First, each occurs in conjunction with at least two regular polygons, the 30-60-90 triangle with the equilateral triangle and regular hexagon, and the 45-45-90 triangle with the square and regular octagon. Second, the sines, cosines, and tangents of the acute angles in these triangles are either rational (0, $\frac{1}{2}$, or 1) or rational multiples of square roots of integers ($\frac{\sqrt{2}}{2}$, $\frac{\sqrt{3}}{3}$, or $\sqrt{3}$). The second fact is unique among acute angles with integral degree measures. The goal of the lesson is to determine the extended ratio of the sides in each of the special triangles.

14-2

LENGTHS IN RIGHT TRIANGLES

When the altitude to a right triangle is drawn, the resulting figure has two triangles, each similar to the original and to each other. The result from this splitting is that segments have some very nice relationships, all connected with geometric means and summarized in the Right Triangle Altitude Theorem. This theorem has two parts but gives rise to three relationships in any triangle because there are two legs.

The Right Triangle Altitude Theorem provides an alternate way to deduce the Pythagorean Theorem. Since the Pythagorean Theorem was proved in Chapter 8, the alternate proof is relegated to the questions.

14-3

THE TANGENT RATIO

After showing that the ratio of the opposite side to the adjacent side is constant for an angle in a right triangle of a fixed measure, and then defining the tangent as that ratio, Lesson 14-3 provides three ways to calculate or estimate tangents of angles. (1) When the angle measure is given, estimate the tangent by drawing a right triangle with an acute angle of the given measure and then calculate the tangent ratio. (2) When the angle measure is given, estimate the tangent by pressing the appropriate keys on a scientific calculator. (3) When the lengths of the sides in a right triangle are given or can be determined, the tangent can be calculated as an appropriate ratio. Students should be able to use all three methods.

14-4
THE SINE AND COSINE RATIOS
This lesson contains a standard treatment of the sine and cosine ratios. Students are expected to calculate the ratios and to use them to calculate unknown lengths in right triangles.

14-5
VECTORS
For the reasons given in the Overview, many reports recommend that all students be introduced to vectors. We put vectors here because they are essentially geometric ideas and provide a nice simple application of coordinates, parallelograms, transformations, and trigonometry.

A vector is a quantity that has a magnitude and a direction. There are two equivalent ways of describing vectors. The synthetic description using directed line segments is given in this lesson. With this de-scription, vectors are represented as arrows, and two vectors are equivalent if and only if they are translation images of each other.

Vector addition is used to obtain the result of two forces that are simultaneously applied to an object, such as the force of a motor-boat and the force of the current of the water on which it is being driven. The sum of two vectors is given by the parallelogram rule.

14-6
PROPERTIES OF VECTORS
The analytic description of a vector is given in this lesson. A two-dimensional vector is an ordered pair (a, b). In higher dimensions, the vector is an ordered n-tuple.

The vector (a, b) can be represented either as a point (a, b) or as the directed line segment joining $(0, 0)$ to (a, b). The latter was cho-sen in this lesson because it fits so well with the synthetic description. The sum of (a, b) and (c, d) is $(a + c, b + d)$, which is the fourth vertex of the parallelogram with consecutive vertices (a, b), $(0, 0)$, and (c, d).

It is relatively easy to show that vector addition satisfies many of the properties of real number addi-tion. For example, it is commutative and associative, it has an identity $(0, 0)$, and each element has an additive inverse $(-a, -b)$.

Scalar multiplication of vectors is also introduced in this lesson. Since scalar multiplication is re-lated to size changes, the concept of vector serves as an example that illustrates the connection of mathematical ideas.

14-7
ADDING VECTORS USING TRIGONOMETRY
Suppose a vector is described by giving its magnitude r and direction ø. An interesting question to ask is: What is its ordered pair descrip-tion? This question can be an-swered by using sines and cosines. Its ordered pair description is (r cos ø, r sin ø).

Suppose a vector is given as an ordered pair (a, b). Another ques-tion to consider is: What is its mag-nitude and direction? Answering this question requires knowing the tangent ratio; the magnitude is one of $\pm\sqrt{a^2 + b^2}$, and its direction is the angle whose tangent is $\frac{b}{a}$.

These questions are asked in this lesson, and serve as a nice review of many of the ideas in the chapter.

We recommend 10 to 12 days for this chapter: 7 to 8 on the lessons and quiz; 1 for the Progress Self-Test; 1 or 2 for the Chapter Review; and 1 for a Chapter test. (See the Daily Pacing Chart on page 682A.)

CHAPTER 14

Trigonometry and Vectors

14-1: Special Right Triangles

14-2: Lengths in Right Triangles

14-3: The Tangent Ratio

14-4: The Sine and Cosine Ratios

14-5: Vectors

14-6: Properties of Vectors

14-7: Adding Vectors Using Trigonometry

A ship, animal, or projectile that goes through the water or air is subject to two basic forces. There is the movement due to the ship's motor, the animal's muscles, or the projectile's initial impetus. There is also the force of the air or water currents. The mathematics that explains how these or other forces combine is the mathematics of *vectors*.

The height of the mast of a ship can be calculated without having to climb the mast. The finding of unknown distances like this is one of the basic applications of *trigonometry*. In the age before man-made satellites could map the earth (that is, before 1957), trigonometry enabled people to determine the locations of mountain peaks and other landmarks so that accurate maps could be made.

A knowledge of trigonometry and vectors is necessary to understand the physical world around us. Sometimes a full semester course is devoted to studying trigonometry. Similarly, there are full semester courses which cover vector ideas.

In this chapter, you are not expected to become expert in either of these areas of mathematics. Your goal should be to understand the meaning and applications of such things as sines, cosines, tangents, components of vectors, and addition of vectors, so that when you encounter these ideas in later courses they will not be totally new to you.

The study of both trigonometry and vectors utilizes properties of right triangles. Consequently, this chapter begins with a more in-depth look at these triangles.

USING PAGES 682-683
Students probably have heard of the words *trigonometry* and *vector* and may associate them with advanced courses. Consequently, your first task may be to convince students that these words do not refer to mathematics that is any more difficult than that seen in previous chapters.

Explain the origin of the word *trigonometry*. From the Latin, *tri* means three, *gon* means side, and *metry* means measure. Trigonometry literally means "measuring triangles," and students will learn how to find the lengths of sides of triangles and their angle measures.

Some students may know that an airplane comes in on a *vector,* which is an arrow describing the airplane's position relative to an airport. This is one application of vectors that students will learn about in this chapter.

OBJECTIVE

A Calculate lengths of sides in isosceles right triangles and in 30-60-90 triangles.

TEACHING NOTES

This is a difficult lesson for some students. You could begin this class by drawing the diagram below on the chalkboard and asking how many squares of different sizes are shown, and what are their areas?

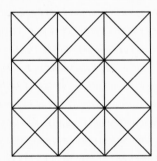

There are 9 unit squares. The next larger size is the square whose area is 2, and thus the side length is $\sqrt{2}$. There are five such squares. There are also four squares whose area is 4, and there is one square whose area is 9. But the smallest squares are the 12 with area $\frac{1}{2}$. Their sides must be $\sqrt{\frac{1}{2}}$, but that is also equal to half of a diagonal of the unit square, or $\frac{\sqrt{2}}{2}$. In this way, the lengths of the sides of many 45-45-90 right triangles were found.

14·1

Special Right Triangles

The diagonal from home plate to second base or from first base to third divides the baseball diamond into two isosceles right triangles. See Example 1.

Certain right triangles have such relationships among their sides and angles that they are considered special. These triangles occur in many situations that involve other polygons. By drawing the diagonals of a square, eight isosceles right triangles are formed. (Can you find all eight?) Suppose the congruent sides have length x and the hypotenuse has length c, as in the triangle at the right below.

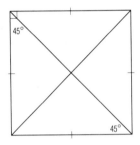 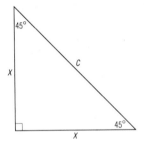

By the Pythagorean Theorem, $\quad c^2 = x^2 + x^2$.
So $\qquad\qquad\qquad\qquad\qquad c^2 = 2x^2$.
Taking the positive square root, $\quad c = x \cdot \sqrt{2}$.

The result is a relationship among the sides of any isosceles right triangle.

Isosceles Right Triangle Theorem:

In an isosceles right triangle, if a leg is x then the hypotenuse is $x\sqrt{2}$.

Notice that all isosceles right triangles are similar, because they all have the same angles: 45°, 45°, and 90°. Sometimes they are called **45-45-90 triangles.**

Example 1   A major league baseball diamond is a 90-ft square. In baseball, how far is it from home plate to second base?

Solution

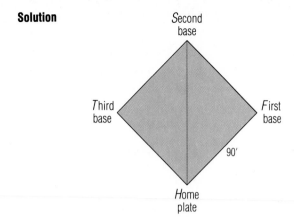

Triangle *HFS* is an isosceles right triangle with $\overline{HS}$ as its hypotenuse.
$$HS = 90\sqrt{2} \text{ feet}$$
$$\approx 127.3 \text{ feet}$$

Another special right triangle is the **30-60-90 triangle.** It can be formed by any altitude of an equilateral triangle or by drawing diagonals in a regular hexagon. How many 30-60-90 triangles are in the drawing below at the right?

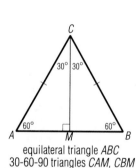

equilateral triangle *ABC*
30-60-90 triangles *CAM, CBM*

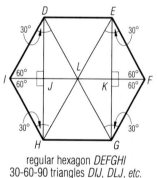

regular hexagon *DEFGHI*
30-60-90 triangles *DIJ, DLJ, etc.*

Again the lengths have a simple relationship.

30-60-90 Triangle Theorem:

In a 30-60-90 triangle, if the short leg is *x* then the longer leg is $x\sqrt{3}$ and the hypotenuse is 2*x*.

To emphasize the relationship between hexagons and equilateral triangles, show that a tessellation of equilateral triangles contains a tessellation of regular hexagons.

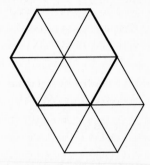

Another way of stating the Isosceles Right Triangle Theorem is as follows: The sides of an isosceles right triangle are in the extended ratio $1:1:\sqrt{2}$. Likewise, the 30-60-90 Triangle Theorem can be stated in the following way: The sides of a 30-60-90 triangle are in the extended ratio $1:\sqrt{3}:2$.

Make sure students understand the new way of referring to a triangle, namely by using its angles or sides as a label, as is done for the 30-60-90 triangle, the 3-4-5 triangle, and others in this lesson. Point out that although the new angle description refers to the actual angle measures, the new description by sides only refers to the ratio of the side lengths, not the actual lengths of the sides.

There are also special triangles that are not right triangles. One example is the triangle in **Question 22** (see notes below); another is the 36-72-72 angle-measured isosceles triangle, which occurs when the diagonals of a regular pentagon are drawn.

Proof

Here is a figure with the given and what is to be proved in terms of the figure.

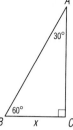

Given: $\triangle ABC$ with m$\angle A$ = 30, m$\angle B$ = 60, m$\angle C$ = 90. The shorter leg is opposite the smaller acute angle, so let $BC = x$.
Prove: (1) $AB = 2x$;
(2) $AC = x\sqrt{3}$.

The idea is to think of $\triangle ABC$ as half an equilateral triangle and use the Pythagorean Theorem.

(1) Reflect $\triangle ABC$ over $\overleftrightarrow{AC}$. Let $D = r_{\overleftrightarrow{AC}}(B)$. Reflections preserve distance, so $CD = x$. Since reflections preserve angle measure, the image $\triangle ADC$ is a 30-60-90 right triangle, with m$\angle ACD$ = 90, m$\angle ADC$ = 60, and m$\angle CAD$ = 30. Thus, B, C, and D are collinear, and the big triangle ABD has three 60° angles making it equilateral with $AB = BD = 2x$.

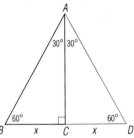

(2) Now, using $AB = 2x$, we can apply the Pythagorean Theorem to $\triangle ABC$ and get AC.

$$AC^2 + BC^2 = AB^2$$
$$AC^2 + x^2 = (2x)^2$$
$$AC^2 + x^2 = 4x^2$$
$$AC^2 = 3x^2$$

Taking the positive square root of each side,
$$AC = x\sqrt{3}.$$

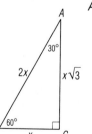

686

Example 2 A zoologist measured the length of a side of a cell in a natural beehive (a tessellation of regular hexagons) as 8.0 mm but forgot to measure the height h of each cell. Approximate the height to the nearest 0.1 mm.

Solution The figure below isolates one cell. DH is the desired height. $m\angle DIH = 120$ and $DI = IH$ from properties of a regular hexagon, so $\triangle DIJ$ is a 30-60-90 right triangle with hypotenuse 8.0. Let IJ, the shortest side, be x. Then, using the 30-60-90 Triangle Theorem, the hypotenuse $DI = 2x = 8.0$, so $x = 4.0$. Longer leg $DJ = x\sqrt{3} = 4\sqrt{3}$.

So
$$DH = 2 \cdot 4\sqrt{3}$$
$$= 8\sqrt{3}$$
$$\approx 13.9 \text{ mm}.$$

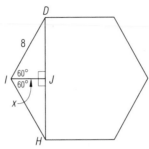

With these theorems, lengths can be found in some non-right triangles that contain 30, 45, or 60 degree angles.

Example 3 In $\triangle XYZ$, $m\angle Z = 45$, $m\angle Y = 30$, and $XY = 8$. Find XZ and YZ.

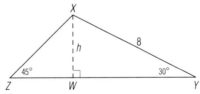

Solution Right triangles are needed, so an auxiliary line is drawn, the altitude from X to $\overline{YZ}$. This forms 45-45-90 right triangle XZW and 30-60-90 right triangle XYW. Now apply the theorems of this lesson. h, opposite the 30° angle in $\triangle XYW$, is half of 8, so $h = 4$. $YW = h\sqrt{3} = 4\sqrt{3}$. Since the left triangle is isosceles, $ZW = h = 4$. Adding, $YZ = 4 + 4\sqrt{3} \approx 10.93$. $XZ = h \cdot \sqrt{2} = 4\sqrt{2} \approx 5.66$

Check An accurate picture verifies these lengths.

Of course, you could always measure to get approximate lengths and angle measures in a triangle. One advantage of having the theorems of this lessson is that for these common triangles you do not have to measure. Another advantage is that they give exact values.

1. An airport is to be built on a piece of land one mile square. (Midway Airport in Chicago is such an airport.) Approximate the length of the longest runway that the airport can have to the nearest 50 feet.
$5280\sqrt{2} \approx 7450$ feet

2. What are the lengths of the legs of a 30-60-90 right triangle whose hypotenuse has length 50?
25 and $25\sqrt{3}$

3. Triangle ABC is an isosceles right triangle and $m\angle DAC = 30$. If $AC = 4$, what is the length of BD?

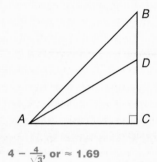

$4 - \frac{4}{\sqrt{3}}$, or ≈ 1.69

Covering the Reading

1. In an isosceles right triangle, each acute angle measures __?__ .
   45

2. In a right triangle in which the hypotenuse is double one leg, the acute angles have measures of __?__ and __?__ . 30, 60

3. In the drawing of regular hexagon *DEFGHI* near the start of this lesson, name some of its diagonals and all the 30-60-90 triangles. **See margin.**

4. *True* or *false*?
   a. All right triangles are similar. **False**
   b. All right triangles with a 60° angle are similar. **True**
   c. All isosceles right triangles are similar. **True**

5. In Example 3, what is the measure of $\angle ZXY$? 105

6. In Example 3, what is the perimeter of $\triangle XYZ$?
   $12 + 4\sqrt{2} + 4\sqrt{3} \approx 24.59$ units

7. If one leg of an isosceles right triangle has length 10 cm, the hypotenuse has length __?__ . $10\sqrt{2} \approx 14.14$ cm

8. A square has side s. What is the length of its diagonals? $s\sqrt{2}$ units

9. If the shortest side of a 30-60-90 triangle is 6 cm, what are the lengths of the other two sides (to the nearest 0.1 cm)?
   10.4 cm, 12.0 cm

10. In Major League baseball, how far is it from first base to third base?
    $90\sqrt{2} \approx 127.3$ ft

Applying the Mathematics

11. An equilateral triangle has a side of length E units. What is the length of one of its altitudes? $\frac{E\sqrt{3}}{2}$ units

12. Suppose the cell of a natural beehive is a regular hexagon with a side of length 5 mm. What is the width of each cell? (The width is the distance between parallel sides.) $5\sqrt{3} \approx 8.66$ mm

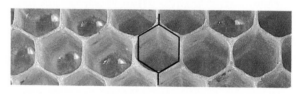

13. The hypotenuse of an isosceles right triangle is 100 feet. Find the dimensions of the other sides of the triangle. $\frac{100}{\sqrt{2}} \approx 70.71$ ft

14. Use the figure below. If $OL = h$, find the perimeter of $\triangle BLT$ in terms of h. $3h + h\sqrt{2} + h\sqrt{3} \approx 6.15h$

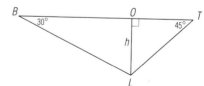

688

15. $\overline{BP} \perp \overline{AC}$ in rectangle *ABCD* below. All triangles in the figure are similar to $\triangle ADC$. Name them with vertices in the correct order. *(Lesson 12-9)* $\triangle CBA, \triangle BPA, \triangle CPB$ (and also $\triangle ADC$)

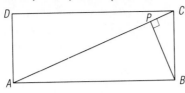

16. These triangles, all similar to each other, are not drawn very accurately. Find the values of *a*, *b*, and *c*. *(Lessons 12-5, 8-7)*

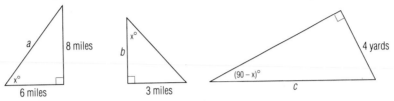

a = 10 miles, $b = 2\frac{1}{4}$ miles, c = 6 yards, 2 feet

17. Solve for length *DE*. $\frac{30}{DE} = \frac{DE}{5}$ *(Lesson 12-4)* $\sqrt{150} \approx 12.25$

18. The fraction $\frac{4}{\sqrt{3}}$ equals $\frac{4}{\sqrt{3}} \cdot \frac{\sqrt{3}}{\sqrt{3}}$, or $\frac{4\sqrt{3}}{3}$. This last form is easier to add to other multiples of $\sqrt{3}$, and is sometimes thought to be simpler. In this way, simplify:

a. $\frac{5}{\sqrt{3}}$ **b.** $\frac{1}{\sqrt{2}}$ **c.** $\frac{3}{\sqrt{6}}$. *(Previous course)* See margin.

19. *Multiple choice.* $\sqrt{75}$ =
(a) $5\sqrt{3}$ (b) $25\sqrt{3}$ (c) $3\sqrt{5}$ (d) $3\sqrt{25}$ *(Previous course)*
(a)

20. *Multiple choice.* $\sqrt{16 + 16}$ =
(a) $2\sqrt{16}$ (b) $16\sqrt{2}$ (c) $4\sqrt{2}$ (d) 8 *(Previous course)* (c)

21. A square and a circle each has area 400 square meters. Which has the larger perimeter? *(Lessons 8-9, 8-8, 8-3, 8-1)* square

22. There are many triangles that could be considered special. One such triangle is formed by the side *a*, a shorter diagonal *b*, and a longer diagonal *c* of a regular heptagon.

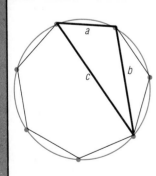

a. Draw, as accurately as you can, a regular heptagon. A good way is to draw seven equally spaced points on a circle, as has been done at the left.

b. Measure *c*, *a*, and *b* for your regular heptagon.

Calculate $\left(\frac{c}{a}\right)^2 + \left(\frac{a}{b}\right)^2 + \left(\frac{b}{c}\right)^2$.

Your answer should be very close to a whole number. Which whole number? 6

c. Measure the three angles of this triangle. How do they seem to be related? The angles have measures x, 2x, and 4x, where $x = \frac{180}{7}$.

MORE PRACTICE

For more questions on SPUR Objectives, use *Lesson Master 14-1,* shown below.

EXTENSION

You may wish to have students describe as many ways as possible to construct 30-60-90 and 45-45-90 triangles. Encourage them to be creative. For example, the diagram for **Example 2** may give them an idea for constructing a 30-60-90 triangle and the diagram for **Example 1** may give them an idea for a 45-45-90 triangle.

EVALUATION
Alternative Assessment

Ask several students to summarize the Isosceles Right Triangle and the 30-60-90 Triangle Theorems by stating them, giving specific instances of each, and by showing how the shorter sides can be calculated from the known longer sides.

NAME _____

LESSON **MASTER 14–1**
QUESTIONS ON **SPUR** OBJECTIVES

■ **SKILLS** *Objective A (See pages 728–731 for objectives.)*

1. A square has sides of length 4. What is the length of either diagonal? $4\sqrt{2} \approx 5.66$ units

2. In $\triangle ABC$ at the right, find *AC* and *BC*.
$AC =$ ___ 5
$BC =$ ___ $5\sqrt{3} \approx 8.66$

3. In $\triangle XYZ$, find *XZ* and *XY*.
$XZ =$ ___ q
$XY =$ ___ $q\sqrt{2}$

4. In $\triangle MNO$ below, find *MO*. $5\sqrt{3} \approx 8.66$

In 5 and 6, use the figure at the right below.

5. If *KM* = 10, then
$KL =$ ___ $10\sqrt{2} \approx 14.14$,
$JM =$ ___ $10\sqrt{3} \approx 17.32$,
$LM =$ ___ 10,
$JK =$ ___ 20.

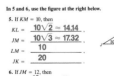

6. If *JM* = 12, then
$KM =$ ___ $\frac{12}{\sqrt{3}}$ or $4\sqrt{3} \approx 6.93$,
$LM =$ ___ $\frac{12}{\sqrt{3}}$ or $4\sqrt{3} \approx 6.93$,
$JK =$ ___ $\frac{24}{\sqrt{3}}$ or $8\sqrt{3} \approx 13.86$.

130

RESOURCES
■ Lesson Master 14-2

OBJECTIVES

D Calculate lengths using the Right Triangle Altitude Theorem.
G Recognize and derive the geometric mean properties in right triangles.

TEACHING NOTES

If a right triangle is drawn like the one in **Example 2**, it is easier to remember the relationships of the Right Triangle Altitude Theorem. Any one of the three segments emanating from the vertex *C* can be the geometric mean of two other segments in the figure. If the endpoint of the geometric mean segment is *X*, then the two other segments are those segments of the hypotenuse with endpoint *X*. For example, if *X* is *D*, then *CD* is the geometric mean of *AD* and *BD*. If *X* is *A*, then *CA* is the geometric mean of *DA* and *BA*.

Stress the similarity relationship between the triangles formed by the altitude to the hypotenuse of a right triangle and show students how the proportions are derived. The algebraic relationships in the Right Triangle Altitude Theorem are then based on these proportions.

Point out that geometric means have applications outside of geometry. The common average, the arithmetic mean, likewise has applications in geometry. For example, the coordinate of the midpoint of a segment on a

LESSON

14-2

Lengths in Right Triangles

Constructing these house frames involves forming right triangles.

Occasionally the two means in a proportion are equal, as in
$$\frac{2}{10} = \frac{10}{50}.$$

When this happens, the number that appears twice is called a *geometric mean* of the other two numbers. Above, the truth of the proportion signifies that 10 is a geometric mean of 2 and 50.

Definition:

Let *a*, *b*, and *g* be positive numbers. *g* is a **geometric mean** of *a* and *b* if and only if
$$\frac{a}{g} = \frac{g}{b}.$$

The definition provides a way of calculating the geometric mean of any pair of positive real numbers.

Example 1 Find the geometric mean of 7 and 12.

Solution Let *g* be the geometric mean. From the definition of geometric mean,
$$\frac{7}{g} = \frac{g}{12}.$$
Using the Means-Extremes Property,
$$g^2 = 84.$$
So
$$g = \pm\sqrt{84}.$$
From the definition of geometric mean, *g* is positive; so the geometric mean of 7 and 12 is $\sqrt{84}$.

Check $\sqrt{84}$ is about 9.17. Is $\frac{7}{9.17} \approx \frac{9.17}{12}$? Yes, 0.7634 ≈ 0.7642.

From the definition of geometric mean, if $\frac{a}{g} = \frac{g}{b}$ then $g^2 = ab$; thus $g = \sqrt{ab}$. This shows:

690

Geometric Mean Theorem:

The geometric mean of the positive numbers a and b is $\sqrt{ab}$.

The geometric mean $\sqrt{ab}$ is always a number between a and b. As you will explore in Question 21, it is always closer to the smaller of a or b.

You may recall that the average of two numbers is called their **arithmetic mean.** The arithmetic mean is exactly midway between the numbers. Both kinds of means have applications in arithmetic, algebra, and geometry. The name "geometric mean" comes from relationships among lengths in any right triangle, relationships that were discovered by the ancient Greeks and are in Euclid's *Elements*.

As usual, the small letters a and b are used for the lengths of the legs of a right triangle, and c for the hypotenuse. The letter h is for the altitude to the hypotenuse, which splits c into two lengths, x and y, so $x + y = c$.

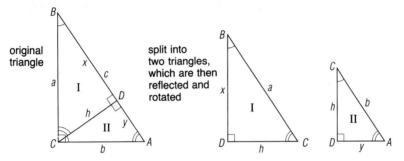

original triangle

split into two triangles, which are then reflected and rotated

$m\angle A = m\angle BCD$ since both equal $90 - m\angle B$. So $\triangle I$, $\triangle II$, and $\triangle ABC$ are all right triangles and each includes an angle equal in measure to $\angle A$. Thus all three triangles are similar: $\triangle ABC \sim \triangle CBD \sim \triangle ACD$. Since the triangles are similar, corresponding sides are proportional. Now look for proportions where the same quantity appears twice.

Consider triangles I and II. A length of a side in both is h.

$$\frac{x}{h} = \frac{h}{y}$$

For triangle I and the original (biggest) triangle, a is a side in both, and for triangle II and the original triangle, b is a side in both.

$$\frac{x}{a} = \frac{a}{c} \quad \text{and} \quad \frac{y}{b} = \frac{b}{c}$$

Thus the altitude h and the legs a and b are geometric means of other lengths. Almost everyone remembers these lengths by their positions in the original triangle, as stated in the following theorem.

LESSON 14-2   Lengths in Right Triangles   **691**

number line is the arithmetic mean of the coordinates of the endpoints. The names of these means derive from the first applications of them to be discovered. The *harmonic mean* (**Question 20**) comes from music: if a, b, and c are three equally spaced notes on a piano with b between a and c, then the period of vibration of b equals the harmonic mean of the periods of vibration of a and c.

After drawing the altitude to the hypotenuse, demonstrate that if an altitude of one of the smaller triangles is drawn, then the original triangle has been split into three similar triangles. By drawing more altitudes, a right triangle can be split into any number of similar triangles.

All triangles can be split into four similar triangles by connecting the midpoints of the sides. By connecting the midpoints of one of the smaller triangles, the original triangle can be split into 7 similar triangles, and by continuing the process, you can get 10, 13, 16, . . . similar triangles.

The only triangles that can be split into two or three triangles similar to themselves and the original are right triangles. (The proof is not difficult but is by no means trivial; one must consider all possible ways in which a triangle can be split.) And there is only one triangle other than a right triangle that can be split into *five* triangles similar to itself, the 30-30-120 triangle. You might wish to ask students if they can find out how to do the splitting. The answer is below.

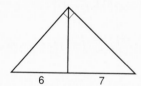
Right Triangle Altitude Theorem:

In a right triangle,
a. the altitude to the hypotenuse is the geometric mean of the segments into which it divides the hypotenuse; and
b. each leg is the geometric mean of the hypotenuse and the segment of the hypotenuse adjacent to the leg.

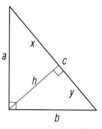

In the figure above, $h = \sqrt{xy}$, $a = \sqrt{cx}$, and $b = \sqrt{cy}$.

Example 2 $\overline{CD}$ is the altitude to the hypotenuse of right triangle ABC, as shown below. If $AD = 3$, $DB = 12$, find CD, CA, and CB.

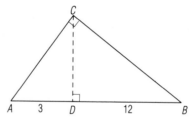

Solution CD is the geometric mean of AD and BD.
So $\qquad CD = \sqrt{3 \cdot 12} = \sqrt{36} = 6$.
CA is the geometric mean of BA and DA.
So $\qquad CA = \sqrt{15 \cdot 3} = \sqrt{45} = 3\sqrt{5}$.
CB is the geometric mean of AB and DB.
So $\qquad CB = \sqrt{15 \cdot 12} = \sqrt{180} = 6\sqrt{5}$.

Questions

Covering the Reading

In 1 and 2, find the geometric mean of the given numbers to the nearest hundredth.

1. 2 and 50 10.00   **2.** 9 and 12 10.39

3. *True* or *false*? If g is the geometric mean of a and b, and $a < b$, then g is closer to a than to b. True

692

In 4–6, use the figure below.

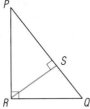

4. a. $m\angle P = m\angle \underline{\quad?\quad}$ QRS
   b. $\triangle PRQ \sim \underline{\quad?\quad} \sim \underline{\quad?\quad}$ $\triangle RSQ$, $\triangle PSR$

   c. $\dfrac{QS}{RQ} = \dfrac{RQ}{\underline{\quad?\quad}}$ PQ

   d. $\dfrac{QS}{\underline{\quad?\quad}} = \dfrac{RS}{PS}$ RS

   e. RP is the geometric mean of $\underline{\ ?\ }$ and $\underline{\ ?\ }$. PQ, PS
   f. RS is the geometric mean of $\underline{\ ?\ }$ and $\underline{\ ?\ }$. PS, SQ
   g. RQ is the geometric mean of $\underline{\ ?\ }$ and $\underline{\ ?\ }$. PQ, SQ

5. If $RS = 6$ and $PS = 9$, then $QS = \underline{\ ?\ }$. 4

6. If $RS = 6$ and $SQ = 4$, then $QR = \underline{\ ?\ }$. $\sqrt{52} \approx 7.21$

7. Using the diagram at the right, find the lengths of
   a. NS 13
   b. SE $\frac{25}{13} \approx 1.92$
   c. IE. $\frac{60}{13} \approx 4.62$

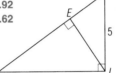

Applying the Mathematics

8. Below is the famous 3-4-5 right triangle. The altitude to the hypotenuse has been drawn. Find the lengths of x, y, and h.
   $x = \frac{16}{5} = 3.2$, $y = \frac{9}{5} = 1.8$, $h = \frac{12}{5} = 2.4$

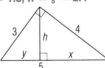

9. Refer to the figure below.
   a. Is $\triangle QRT \sim \triangle RST$? Yes
   b. True or false? $m\angle QRS = 90$ True

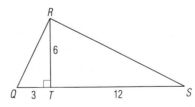

NOTES ON QUESTIONS
Small Group Work for
Question 4-6: You might want to have students go over these questions in a group environment. They should pay careful attention to the correspondences between vertices and then set up all the ratios using segments in the proportions.

Computer for Question 8: You might ask students to verify their answers with an automatic drawer.

Question 11: Three proofs of the Pythagorean Theorem are found or suggested in this book. The first, using area, is in Lesson 8-7. The second is President Garfield's proof, in the Additional Examples in the margin for Lesson 8-7. The third is in this question. It is the only one of the proofs that uses results about similar figures.

The Right Triangle Altitude Theorem can be deduced from the Pythagorean Theorem as follows:

Use the figure on page 692.
$$a^2 + b^2 = c^2$$
$$h^2 + x^2 = a^2$$
$$h^2 + y^2 = b^2$$
$$x + y = c$$
Square the last equation.
$$x^2 + 2xy + y^2 = c^2$$
Add the middle two equations.
$$2h^2 + x^2 + y^2 = a^2 + b^2$$
Substitute using the first equation.
$$2h^2 + x^2 + y^2 = c^2$$
Equate the two expressions for c^2 and subtract $x^2 + y^2$.
$$2h^2 + x^2 + y^2 = x^2 + 2xy + y^2$$
$$2h^2 = 2xy$$
$$h^2 = xy$$
(This is part a.) Now substitute for h^2 in the second equation.
$$xy + x^2 = a^2$$
$$x(y + x) = a^2$$
$$xc = a^2$$
(This is part b.)

10. Nancy Weintraub taught the members of Girl Scout Troop 715 that they could use a notebook to estimate distances. To show them how, she used the lifeguard tower at Henson Beach. She held her notebook near her eye (5 feet off the ground) and moved back from the tower until she could sight both the top and bottom of the tower. Then she asked Amy Finch to estimate her (Nancy's) distance from the tower by pacing. Amy estimated 8 feet.
  a. Which part of the right triangle altitude theorem could Nancy now use to find the height of the lifeguard tower? **part a**
  b. How tall is the tower? $\approx$17.8 feet

5 ft

11. Provide the missing justifications in this argument verifying the Pythagorean Theorem.

Conclusions	Justifications See margin.
1. a is the geometric mean of c and x. b is the geometric mean of c and y.	**a.** ?
2. $a = \sqrt{cx}$, $b = \sqrt{cy}$	**b.** ?
3. $a^2 = cx$, $b^2 = cy$	Multiplication Property of Equality
4. $a^2 + b^2 = cx + cy$	**c.** ?
5. $a^2 + b^2 = c(x + y)$	**d.** ?
6. $x + y = c$	Betweenness Theorem
7. $a^2 + b^2 = c^2$	**e.** ?

Review

12. In Question 11, why is it inappropriate to use the Pythagorean Theorem as the justification for conclusion 7? *(Lesson 3-3)* See margin.

13. The sides of an equilateral triangle have length 5.
  a. Find the length of an altitude of this triangle.
  b. Find its area. *(Lesson 14-1)*
    a) $\frac{5\sqrt{3}}{2} \approx 4.33$ units; b) $\frac{25\sqrt{3}}{4} \approx 10.83$ units²

14. The diagonal of a square field has length 50 meters. What is the length of a side? *(Lesson 14-1)* $\frac{50}{\sqrt{2}} \approx 35.36$ meters

15. A prism has the same base as a pyramid but twice the height. How do their volumes compare? *(Lessons 10-7, 10-5)* **See margin.**

16. In the box below, if *all* pairs of vertices are connected, __
  a. how many of the segments have the same length as $\overline{AC}$? **4**
  b. How many of the segments have the same length as $\overline{AG}$? **4**
  (Lesson 9-2)

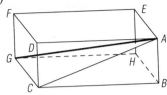

17. Refer to the figure at the right.
  Given: $BD = CE$;
          $MB = CM$;
          M is the midpoint of $\overline{DE}$.
  Prove: $ABMC$ is a kite.
  (Lesson 7-3) **See margin.**

18. a. Find a fraction equal to $\frac{1}{\sqrt{3}}$ with no radical sign in its denominator.
  b. Find $\frac{1}{\sqrt{3}}$ to the nearest millionth. *(Previous course)* a) $\frac{\sqrt{3}}{3}$; b) **0.577350**

19. Solve for y: $3y - 2 = y^2$. *(Previous course)* **2 or 1**

Exploration

20. If a racer averages 120 mph for one lap and 200 mph for a second lap, the average speed for the two laps is not 160 mph, but 150 mph, the *harmonic mean* of 120 and 200.

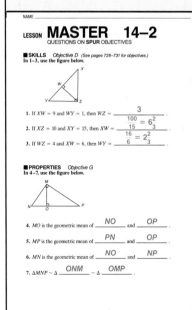

  a. Look in a dictionary, or generalize this example, to find a formula for the harmonic mean of x and y. $\frac{2xy}{x+y}$
  b. Using examples of the harmonic mean and the geometric mean of two positive numbers a and b, with $b < a$, is one always greater than the other? If so, which one is greater? **The geometric mean is greater than the harmonic mean.**

21. Which is larger, the geometric mean of two positive numbers or their arithmetic mean? Are the geometric and arithmetic means of two numbers ever equal? **If the two given numbers are unequal, the geometric mean is less than the arithmetic mean. If the given numbers are equal, both means equal the given number.**

LESSON 14-2   Lengths in Right Triangles   **695**

LESSON

14-3

The Tangent Ratio

In Example 3 of Lesson 14-1, measures of two angles and a non-included side in a triangle were given. That is the AAS condition. From this information, measures of all other angles and sides could be computed. In general, using trigonometry *all* sides and angles can be found whenever enough information is given for a triangle congruence condition. In this book you will learn how to do this with right triangles.

Consider two right triangles *ABC* and *XYZ* with a pair of congruent acute angles. The triangles might be formed by figures and shadows at the same time of day. Following custom, in the drawing at the right the side opposite angle *A* is called *a,* the side opposite angle *B* is called *b,* and so on. You should be careful to write small letters differently from capital letters.

The triangles are similar because of AA Similarity.

Since corresponding sides are proportional, $\dfrac{a}{x} = \dfrac{b}{y}$.

By the Means-Exchange Property,

$$\frac{a}{b} = \frac{x}{y}.$$

The legs *a* and *x* are **opposite** the congruent angles *A* and *X*. The legs *b* and *y* are **adjacent to** angles *A* and *X*. This argument shows that in every right triangle, the ratio of lengths

$$\frac{\text{leg opposite angle } A}{\text{leg adjacent to angle } A}$$

is the same for the angle congruent to *A*. This ratio is called the *tangent of angle A.*

696

Definition:

In right triangle ABC with right angle C,

the **tangent of** $\angle A$, written **tan A**, is $\dfrac{\text{leg opposite } \angle A}{\text{leg adjacent to } \angle A}$.

Tangents can be estimated by measuring.

Example 1   Estimate the tangent of an angle of 25°.

Solution   Draw a right triangle with a carefully measured 25° angle. Measure the leg opposite that angle. Using the triangle below, that leg is 24 mm. Then measure the leg adjacent to the angle; it is about 52 mm. The ratio of these lengths, $\frac{24}{52}$, is an estimate of the tangent of 25°.

The estimate can be converted to a decimal: $\frac{24}{52} \approx 0.46$.

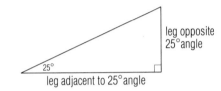

leg opposite 25° angle

25°

leg adjacent to 25° angle

You can write $\tan 25° \approx \frac{24}{52}$

or $\tan 25° \approx 0.46$.

Today, most people use calculators to approximate values of tangents. Every scientific calculator contains a $\boxed{\text{tan}}$ key. To use this key, make sure your calculator is measuring angles in degrees (there are other ways, but they are not discussed in this text). To find the approximate value of tan 25°, use the following key sequence.

25 $\boxed{\text{tan}}$

Your calculator may display 0.4663077. That means $\tan 25° \approx 0.4663077$.

When the measure of an angle and one leg are known, the tangent enables you to find the length of the other leg.

The origin of the name *tangent* is found in the diagram below. The length of the segment of the tangent to the unit circle from point P is tan A.

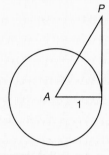

Making Connections   An application of tangents that is not covered in this book is the slope of lines. Specifically, the slope of an oblique line is the tangent of the angle the upward part of the line makes with the positive ray of the x-axis.

Example 2 At a location 50 m from the base of a tree, the *angle of elevation* of the tree is 33°. Determine the height of the tree.

Solution The angle of elevation is ∠A in the figure below.

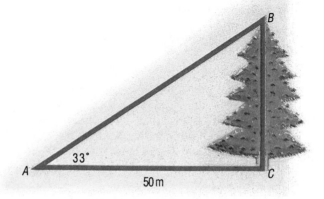

$$\tan 33° = \frac{\text{leg opposite } \angle A}{\text{leg adjacent to } \angle A}$$

$$\tan 33° = \frac{BC}{50}$$

Multiplying both sides by 50,
$$BC = 50 \cdot \tan 33°$$
$$= 50 \; \boxed{x} \; 33 \; \boxed{\text{tan}} \; \boxed{=}$$
$$\approx 32.47038$$
$$\approx 32 \text{ meters.}$$

The exact value of a tangent of an acute angle can be determined if you know the lengths of the two legs in a right triangle with that angle.

Example 3 In the right triangle below, find tan D.

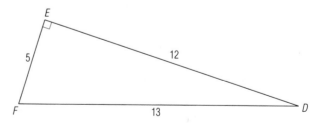

Solution $\tan D = \dfrac{\text{leg opposite } \angle D}{\text{leg adjacent to } \angle D} = \dfrac{EF}{ED} = \dfrac{5}{12}$

Tangents of angles in special triangles can be found exactly.

698

Example 4 Give an exact value for tan 60°.

Solution Draw a 30-60-90 triangle.

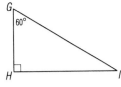

In △GHI, tan 60° = tan G = $\dfrac{\text{leg opposite } \angle G}{\text{leg adjacent to } \angle G} = \dfrac{HI}{GH}$.

GH is the shorter leg. Call it x. Then $HI = x\sqrt{3}$.

Substituting, tan 60° = $\dfrac{x\sqrt{3}}{x} = \sqrt{3}$.

Check Press 60 [tan] on your calculator. You should get 1.732...,
which is approximately $\sqrt{3}$.

The tangent of an angle is an example of a **trigonometric ratio.**
Almost all scientific calculators have buttons for calculating three
trigonometric ratios. You will study the other two of these ratios in
the next lesson.

Questions

Covering the Reading

1. Draw a right triangle with a 40° angle, measure its sides, and use
those measurements to estimate tan 40°. **See margin.**

2. By measuring sides of △ABC below, estimate tan A.
between .4 and .5

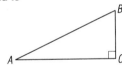

3. Using a calculator, approximate tan 73° to the nearest thousandth.
3.271

4. When the sun is 32° up from the horizon, the wall of a store casts a
shadow 25 meters long. How high is the wall?
25 tan 32° ≈ 15.62 meters

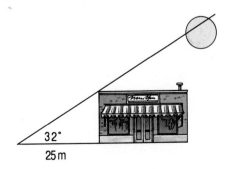

Question 1: A good estimate is within 5%, that is, between about .80 and .88. Remind students that larger drawings tend to yield better estimates, and it is easier to divide with lengths given in metric units.

Questions 5 and 6: In general, the tangents of complementary angles are reciprocals, as these questions show.

Questions 11 and 12: You might want to have students use their calculators to make some conjectures about the values of tangents.

Question 13: You might ask students to substitute values for the sides of △ABC and verify the Right Triangle Altitude Theorem using tangents.

Question 19: This exercise allows students to practice calculating tangents with a calculator. It also demonstrates an amazing theorem that is not well known: In any △ABC, tan A · tan B · tan C = tan A + tan B + tan C. The proof requires the identity for tan (A + B) and is beyond the scope of this course.

ADDITIONAL ANSWERS
1. sample: tan 40° ≈ $\frac{30}{36}$ = .8$\overline{3}$

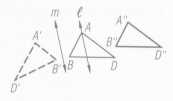
In 5 and 6, use $\triangle DEF$ below.

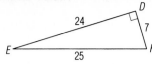

5. Calculate tan E. $\frac{7}{24} \approx .292$

6. Calculate tan F. $\frac{24}{7} \approx 3.43$

7. Give an exact value for tan $30°$. $\frac{1}{\sqrt{3}}$ or $\frac{\sqrt{3}}{3}$

8. Give an exact value for tan $45°$. 1

9. Draw a right triangle with legs of 4 units and 6 units. Use this triangle to estimate answers to the following questions.
a. What is $m\angle A$ if tan $A = \frac{2}{3}$? between 30° and 35°
b. What is $m\angle A$ if tan $A = \frac{3}{2}$? between 55° and 60°

10. From eye level 5′ off the ground and 20′ away from a flagpole, a person has to look up at a 40° angle to see the top of the pole. How high is the pole? 5 + 20 tan 40° ≈ 22 ft

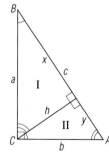

11. Use the figure below. Of angles 1, 2, 3, and 4:
a. Which has the largest tangent? $\angle 4$
b. Which has the smallest tangent? $\angle 1$

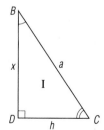

12. Without calculating, explain why tan $75° >$ tan $74°$. See margin.

13. Use the figure below.
a. Find tan BCD in triangle I. $\frac{x}{h}$
b. Find tan A in triangle II. $\frac{h}{y}$
c. Since $m\angle BCD = m\angle A$, tan $BCD =$ tan A. Substitute in your answers from parts **a** and **b** into the equation tan $BCD =$ tan A. $\frac{x}{h} = \frac{h}{y}$
d. What part of the Right Triangle Altitude Theorem have you proved? part a

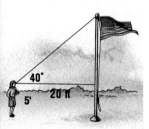

In 14 and 15, refer to the figure below.

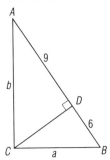

14. The altitude $\overline{CD}$ of a right triangle *ABC* splits the hypotenuse into segments of lengths 6 and 9. Find the lengths of the altitude and the two legs. *(Lesson 14-2)*
altitude $= \sqrt{54} \approx 7.35$, $a = \sqrt{90} \approx 9.49$, $b = \sqrt{135} \approx 11.62$

15. $\triangle ABC \sim \underline{\;?\;} \sim \underline{\;?\;}$ *(Lesson 14-2)* $\triangle ACD, \triangle CBD$

16. *ZONK* is a trapezoid. $m\angle Z = m\angle O = 45$, $ZO = 24$, and $NK = 9$. Find the area of *ZONK*. *(Lesson 14-1)* 123.75 units²

17. About how long a straw can fit into a box 3″ by 4″ by 8″ in the way shown at the left? *(Lesson 11-6)*
$\sqrt{89} \approx 9.43″$

18. Trace the figure below, in which $\ell \parallel m$.
  a. Draw $r_\ell \circ r_m(DAB)$.
  b. Describe this transformation. *(Lesson 6-2)*
  See margin.

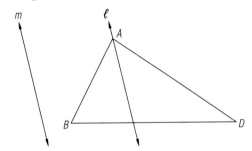

19. Choose three angle measures (other than 90) whose sum is 180. (For example, you could choose 25, 97, and 58.) See margin.
  a. Using a calculator, find the sum of the tangents of the numbers you have chosen.
  b. Calculate the product of the tangents of the numbers you have chosen.
  c. Repeat parts **a** and **b** with a different three numbers.
  d. Make a conjecture based on what you find.

LESSON 14-3   The Tangent Ratio   **701**

FOLLOW-UP

MORE PRACTICE
For more questions on SPUR Objectives, use *Lesson Master 14-3*, shown below.

EXTENSION
Show students how to use their 2nd Function or Inverse keys to find the acute angles of a right triangle with given side lengths. You can also emphasize that knowing the trigonometric ratios allows them to *completely* find the measures of all angles and sides in a right triangle from the length of one side and the measure of one of the acute angles.

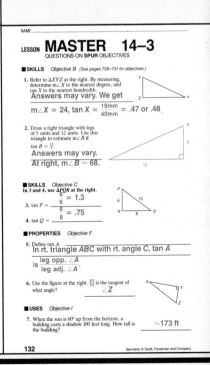

NAME

LESSON **MASTER   14–3**
QUESTIONS ON **SPUR** OBJECTIVES

■ **SKILLS** *Objective B* *(See pages 728–731 for objectives.)*

1. Refer to $\triangle XYZ$ at the right. By measuring, determine $m\angle X$ to the nearest degree, and $\tan X$ to the nearest hundredth.
Answers may vary. We get

$m\angle X = 24$, $\tan X = \frac{19mm}{40mm} = .47$ or $.48$

2. Draw a right triangle with legs of 5 units and 12 units. Use this triangle to estimate $m\angle B$ if $\tan B = \frac{12}{5}$.
Answers may vary.
At right, $m\angle B \approx 68$.

■ **SKILLS** *Objective C*
In 3 and 4, use $\triangle PQR$ at the right.

3. $\tan P = \dfrac{6}{6} = 1.3$

4. $\tan Q = \dfrac{6}{8} = .75$

■ **PROPERTIES** *Objective F*

5. Define $\tan A$. In rt. triangle *ABC* with rt. angle *C*, $\tan A$ is $\dfrac{\text{leg opp. } \angle A}{\text{leg adj. } \angle A}$.

6. Use the figure at the right. $\frac{XY}{YZ}$ is the tangent of what angle? $\angle Z$

■ **USES** *Objective I*

7. When the sun is 60° up from the horizon, a building casts a shadow 100 feet long. How tall is the building? ≈ 173 ft

132   Geometry © Scott, Foresman and Company

RESOURCES
■ Lesson Master 14-4
■ Quiz for Lessons 14-1
Through 14-4

OBJECTIVES

B Determine sines, cosines, and tangents from drawings.
C Calculate sines, cosines, and tangents of angles in right triangles.
F Know the definitions of sine, cosine, and tangent.
I Use sines, cosines, and tangents to determine unknown lengths in real situations.

TEACHING NOTES

You may have found in the last lesson that understanding the keys on a calculator is a great motivator for learning mathematical ideas. This lesson should be even more motivating, because two keys are explained and because the words *sine* and *cosine* are associated exclusively with trigonometry.

As with tangents, students should be able to obtain exact or approximate values of sines and cosines given sides of a right triangle (**Example 1**), in special triangles (**Example 2**), by using a calculator or by drawing (as shown in **Example 3**). Nothing is better than an actual drawing.

LESSON

14-4

The Sine and Cosine Ratios

The tangent is the ratio of the lengths of two legs in a right triangle. When a leg is compared to the hypotenuse, the *sine* or *cosine* ratio results.

Definitions:

In right triangle ABC with right angle C,

the **sine of** $\angle A$, written **sin A**, is $\dfrac{\text{leg opposite } \angle A}{\text{hypotenuse}}$;

the **cosine of** $\angle A$, written **cos A**, is $\dfrac{\text{leg adjacent to } \angle A}{\text{hypotenuse}}$.

In the above triangle, $\sin A = \dfrac{a}{c}$ and $\cos A = \dfrac{b}{c}$.
For any angle congruent to A, these sine and cosine ratios are the same because the angles would be in similar right triangles.

Example 1 Right triangle ABC has side lengths as indicated. Find each value.

a. $\sin A$ **b.** $\cos A$
c. $\sin B$ **d.** $\cos B$

Solution

a. $\sin A = \dfrac{\text{leg opposite } \angle A}{\text{hypotenuse}} = \dfrac{5}{13} \approx 0.3846$

b. $\cos A = \dfrac{\text{leg adjacent to } \angle A}{\text{hypotenuse}} = \dfrac{12}{13} \approx 0.9231$

c. $\sin B = \dfrac{\text{leg opposite } \angle B}{\text{hypotenuse}} = \dfrac{12}{13} \approx 0.9231$

d. $\cos B = \dfrac{\text{leg adjacent to } \angle B}{\text{hypotenuse}} = \dfrac{5}{13} \approx 0.3846$

In Example 1, notice that $\sin A = \cos B$ and $\sin B = \cos A$. This is because the leg opposite either angle is the leg adjacent to the other. Angles A and B are also complementary. This is the origin of the term "cosine"; *cosine* is short for *complement's sine*.

702

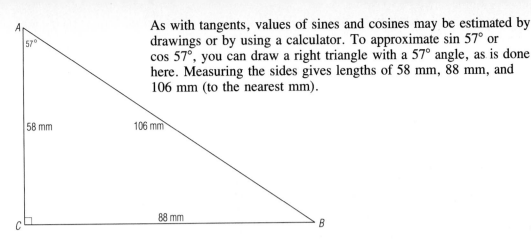

As with tangents, values of sines and cosines may be estimated by drawings or by using a calculator. To approximate sin 57° or cos 57°, you can draw a right triangle with a 57° angle, as is done here. Measuring the sides gives lengths of 58 mm, 88 mm, and 106 mm (to the nearest mm).

To two decimal places, $\sin 57° = \frac{BC}{AB} \approx \frac{88}{106} \approx .83$ and $\cos 57° = \frac{AC}{AB} \approx \frac{58}{106} \approx .55$. A calculator gives greater accuracy.

For sin 57°, press 57 [sin].
An 8-digit display will show 0.8386706. So sin 57° ≈ .8387.
For cos 57°, press 57 [cos].
The display may show 0.544639. So cos 57° ≈ 0.5446.

Drawings and calculators usually give approximate values of sines and cosines. Exact values occur only when the lengths of sides are known exactly.

In special triangles, the exact values of sines, cosines, and tangents can be obtained because the sides are known exactly.

Example 2   Find exact values of sin 30° and cos 30°.

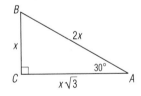

Solution   Sketch a triangle as shown at the left. This is a 30-60-90 triangle, so the legs are x and $x\sqrt{3}$ and the hypotenuse is $2x$.

$$\sin 30° = \frac{x}{2x} = \frac{1}{2}$$
$$\cos 30° = \frac{x\sqrt{3}}{2x} = \frac{\sqrt{3}}{2}$$

Sines and cosines have a great number and variety of applications. The ancient Babylonians and Greeks measured triangles carefully, needing such measurements for navigation, surveying, and astronomy. The first table of trigonometric values was constructed by Claudius Ptolemy in the 2nd century A.D. Values like our present sine, cosine, and tangent values were first obtained by the German astronomer Regiomontanus (1436–1476). The abbreviations *sin,* *cos,* and *tan* are due to Euler.

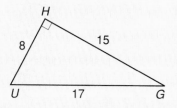
Example 3 Suppose a particular type of ladder is safe if the angle it makes with the ground is from 65° to 80°.

a. How far up on a vertical wall can a 30-foot ladder of this type reach?
b. How far, at minimum, should it be placed from the base of the wall?

Solution First draw a picture.

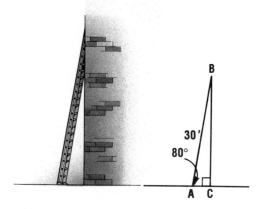

In the figure drawn, part **a** needs *BC* and part **b** needs *AC*.

a. The leg opposite 80° is desired. The hypotenuse is known. So the sine should be used.
$$\sin 80° = \frac{\text{leg opposite 80° angle}}{\text{hypotenuse}}$$
A calculator shows sin 80° ≈ 0.985.

Substituting: $0.985 \approx \frac{BC}{30}$.

Solve for *BC*. $BC \approx 30 \cdot 0.985 \approx 29.6$ feet
The ladder will reach about 29.6 feet high on the wall.

b. $\overline{AC}$ is the leg adjacent to the 80° angle. This suggests using the cosine.
$$\cos 80° = \frac{\text{leg adjacent to 80° angle}}{\text{hypotenuse}}$$
A calculator shows cos 80° ≈ 0.174. Substituting:
$$0.174 \approx \frac{AC}{30}$$
$$AC \approx 30 \cdot 0.174 \approx 5.2 \text{ feet.}$$

5.2 feet is 5 feet, 2.4 inches. You should place the ladder at least 5′ 3″ away from the wall. Otherwise the ladder is too close to perpendicular to be used safely.

Check   The Pythagorean Theorem can check both answers at once.
Does $AC^2 + BC^2 = AB^2$?
Does $(5.2)^2 + (29.6)^2 = 30^2$?
The left side is 903.2, the right side is 900. This is close enough, given the approximations used for sin 80° and cos 80° and the rounding done to get 5.2 and 29.6.

704

NOTES ON QUESTIONS
Questions 4 and 5:
Students should not use their calculators (unless they want to check calculations) when they are asked to find exact values. Answers should be reduced ratios.

Question 6: Students can use their calculators to find the approximations directly or to check the decimal values of the ratios for the triangle.

ADDITIONAL ANSWERS
1. a. In right triangle ABC with right angle C, the sine of $\angle A = \frac{\text{leg opposite } \angle A}{\text{hypotenuse}}$.
b. The cosine of $\angle A = \frac{\text{leg adjacent to } \angle A}{\text{hypotenuse}}$.

Covering the Reading

1. Define: **a.** $\sin \angle A$, **b.** $\cos \angle A$. **See margin.**

2. In $\triangle MNO$ below, identify each segment.
   a. leg opposite $\angle N$ $\overline{MO}$
   b. hypotenuse $\overline{MN}$
   c. leg adjacent to $\angle M$ $\overline{MO}$
   d. leg adjacent to $\angle N$ $\overline{NO}$

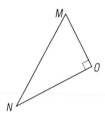

3. In $\triangle FGH$ below, find:
   a. $\sin F$ $\frac{2}{2\sqrt{5}} = \frac{1}{\sqrt{5}} \approx .447$
   b. $\cos F$ $\frac{4}{2\sqrt{5}} = \frac{2}{\sqrt{5}} \approx .894$
   c. $\tan G$ 2
   d. $\sin G.$ $\frac{4}{2\sqrt{5}} = \frac{2}{\sqrt{5}} \approx .894$

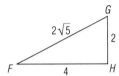

4. Give exact values of: **a.** $\sin 60°$ **b.** $\cos 60°$ **c.** $\tan 60°$.
   a) $\frac{\sqrt{3}}{2}$; b) $\frac{1}{2}$; c) $\sqrt{3}$

5. Give exact values of: **a.** $\sin 45°$ **b.** $\cos 45°$ **c.** $\tan 45°$.
   a) $\frac{1}{\sqrt{2}}$ or $\frac{\sqrt{2}}{2}$; b) $\frac{1}{\sqrt{2}}$ or $\frac{\sqrt{2}}{2}$; c) 1

6. The figure below shows approximate lengths of the sides in a right triangle with angles of 42° and 48° and hypotenuse 15. Use these lengths to fill in the blanks.
   a. $\sin 48° \approx$ __?__ .73
   b. $\cos 48° \approx$ __?__ .67
   c. $\tan 42° \approx$ __?__ .91
   d. $\cos 42° \approx$ __?__ .73

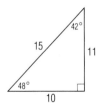

7. Estimate to the nearest thousandth: **a.** $\sin 13.2°$ **b.** $\cos 13.2°$.
   a) .228; b) .974

8. **a.** How far up on a vertical wall can a 20′ ladder of the type in Example 3 safely reach? $\approx$ **19.7 ft**
   b. How far, at minimum, should the bottom be placed from the wall? $\approx$ **3.5 ft**

9. What is the farthest that the ladder of Example 3 should be placed from the wall? $\approx$ **8.5 ft**

Question 14: Note that the angle of depression from the top of the building has the same measure as the angle of elevation from the bottom of the building. Ask students to explain why. (If parallel lines are cut by a transversal, then alternate interior angles have the same measure.)

Question 16: You might also want students to estimate the sine and cosine by measuring the hypotenuse as well.

Question 22: Many patterns can be seen in this table. Students should notice that as angle measures increase the sine and tangent increase, but the cosine decreases, and that the cosine of an angle equals its *complement's* sine (thus the origin of the term cosine). The origin of the word *sine* is given in the notes for Lesson 15-1.

ADDITIONAL ANSWERS
10. b. The right triangle with an 89° angle and a 90° angle is close to isosceles, so the length of the leg opposite the 89° angle is almost the same as the hypotenuse.

11. a. sample: sin B ≈ $\frac{25}{46}$ ≈ .543; sin B' ≈ $\frac{17}{32}$ ≈ .531.
b. They probably will not be equal, due to measurement error, but very close.

FOLLOW-UP

MORE PRACTICE
For more questions on SPUR Objectives, use *Lesson Master 14-4,* shown on page 707.

EXTENSION
You might want to use the table of values calculated in Exploration **Question 22** to

Applying the Mathematics

10. **a.** Use a calculator to estimate sin 89° to the nearest ten-thousandth.
    b. Give a geometric reason why the value is so near 1.
    a) .9998; b) See margin.

11. In the triangles below, $\angle B \cong \angle B'$.
    a. By measuring, estimate sin B and sin B'.
    b. Are the results as expected?
    See margin.

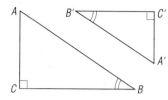

12. **a.** Of the angles 1, 2, 3, 4, and 5 pictured at the left, which angle has the largest sine? ∠5
    b. Which angle has the largest cosine? ∠1

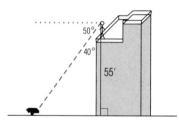

13. What length wire is needed as a brace for a 20-foot pole, if the brace is to make an angle of 85° with the ground? ≈ 20.1 ft

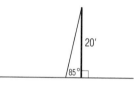

14. From the top of a building you look down at an object on the ground. If your eyes are 55 feet above the ground, and the angle of sight, called the *angle of depression*, is 50° below the horizontal, how far is the object from you? ≈ 72 ft

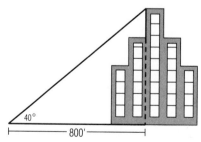

Review

15. How tall is this building? *(Lesson 14-3)* ≈ 670 ft

16. Refer to △*LMN* below. Estimate tan *N* by measuring *LM* and *LN* to the nearest mm. *(Lesson 14-3)* ≈ $\frac{14}{26}$ ≈ **0.538**

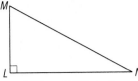

17. Find the geometric mean of 75 and 100 to the nearest hundredth. *(Lesson 14-2)* ≈ **86.60**

18. Refer to the figure below. *(Lesson 14-2)*
  a. *RQ* is the geometric mean of __?__ and __?__. **TQ, SQ**
  b. *RT* is the geometric mean of __?__ and __?__. **QT, ST**
  c. *RS* is the geometric mean of __?__ and __?__. **TS, QS**

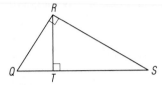

19. a. Write the converse, the inverse, and the contrapositive of the following statement:
    If *M* is between *P* and *Q*, then *PM* + *MQ* = *PQ*. **See below.**
  b. Which of the statements you have written in part **a** are true? *(Lessons 13-2, 1-9, 1-8)* **All are true.**

20. Isosceles △*ABC* has vertex angle *A*. If its sides are 7, 7, and 12, find the length of the altitude from *A*. *(Lessons 8-7, 5-1)*
  $\sqrt{13}$ ≈ **3.6 units**

21. Rewrite without fractions or converting to decimals.
  a. $\dfrac{100}{\sqrt{2}}$; **50√2**   **b.** $\dfrac{100}{\sqrt{2}}$ + 8√2 *(Previous course)* **58√2**

Exploration

22. a. Fill in this table of values of the sine and cosine using your calculator.

x	sin *x*	cos *x*	*x*	sin *x*	cos *x*	*x*	sin *x*	cos *x*
0	0.0	1.0	30	.5	.866	60	.866	.5
5	.087	.996	35	.574	.819	65	.906	.423
10	.174	.985	40	.643	.766	70	.940	.342
15	.259	.966	45	.707	.707	75	.966	.259
20	.342	.940	50	.766	.643	80	.985	.174
25	.423	.906	55	.819	.574	85	.996	.087
						90	1.0	0.0

  b. For which values of *x* does $(\sin x)^2 + (\cos x)^2 = 1$? **all**

19a) converse: If *PM* + *MQ* = *PQ*, then *M* is between *P* and *Q*.
    inverse: If *M* is not between *P* and *Q*, then *PM* + *MQ* ≠ *PQ*.
    contrapositive: If *PM* + *MQ* ≠ *PQ*, then *M* is not between *P* and *Q*.

LESSON 14-4   The Sine and Cosine Ratios   **707**

---

ask students to make some generalizations about the value of the sine and cosine function as the angle increases or decreases. Ask the following questions:
(1) What happens to the value of the sine as the angle increases from 0 to 90?
The sine increases from 0 to 1.
(2) What happens to the value of the cosine in the same interval?
The value of the cosine decreases from 1 to 0.
(3) What is the maximum value for the sine or cosine?
one
(4) Justify your answer to (3) above by considering the possible lengths of the sides of a right triangle.
Since the hypotenuse is the longest side and is the denominator, the ratios are always less than one (the angle and therefore the ratio is never 0).

EVALUATION
A quiz covering Lessons 14-1 through 14-4 is provided in the Teacher's Resource File.

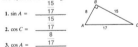

RESOURCES
■ Lesson Master 14-5
■ Computer Master 32

OBJECTIVES

E Draw the sum of two or more vectors.
J Use vectors for forces to determine combinations of forces.

TEACHING NOTES

The first use of vectors and the discovery of the Parallelogram Law was made in 1586 by Simon Stevin, the Flemish mathematician who is better known for his invention of decimal notation for fractions.

Many students have difficulty in thinking of one object, the vector, as representing two things: magnitude and direction. You might mention that if an artist wants to express fast motion of a car, lines are often drawn behind the car; and if the car goes still faster, the lines are longer.

Examples 3 and **4** use motorboats in waters with currents to motivate vector addition. To make this intuitive, you might have students imagine a river in which there are two piers A and B, with B directly north of A.

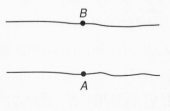

LESSON 14-5

Aircraft departing from Los Angeles International Airport

Vectors

The air distance between Dallas/Fort Worth International Airport (DFW) and the Los Angeles International Airport (LAX) is the same in both directions. But if you look at the airline schedule, you will find that the scheduled time from LAX to DFW is less than the scheduled time from DFW to LAX. For instance, in 1989, American Airlines scheduled an average of 2 hours, 59 minutes for its flights from LAX to DFW, but 3 hours, 10 minutes from DFW to LAX. The difference is due to winds in the upper atmosphere which, in the United States, almost always go from west to east. These winds speed up planes going east (the approximate direction from LAX to DFW) and slow down planes going west. The mathematics of *vectors* helps to explain this idea.

A **vector** is a quantity that has both **magnitude** and **direction.** Here are some examples.

vector	its magnitude	its direction
northeast wind at 40 mph	40 mph	northeast
gravity on the surface of the earth	9.8 meters per second per second	downward
person pushing a refrigerator south with a force of 100 pounds	100 pounds	south

Vectors are represented by **directed line segments.** A directed line segment is drawn like a normal line segment, except that it has an arrow at one endpoint. For instance, drawn below is the directed line segment $\overrightarrow{OA}$ representing a northeast wind of 20 mph. Point O is the **initial point** of the vector and A is its **terminal point.** Its direction is 50° north of east (or 40° east of north) and its magnitude is 20, the distance OA. *Caution: Although a directed line segment is pictured like a ray, it is not a ray. It has a finite length; it does not continue forever.*

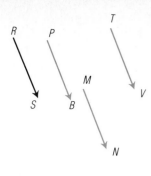

Two vectors are **equal vectors** if and only if they have the same direction and magnitude. You can draw a specific vector wherever you wish as long as it has the proper direction and magnitude. The vector $\overrightarrow{OA}$ started at the origin of a coordinate system, but a vector can start anywhere. The four vectors drawn at the left are equal: $\overrightarrow{RS} = \overrightarrow{PB} = \overrightarrow{MN} = \overrightarrow{TV}$.

Vectors are closely related to translations. Like a vector, a translation or slide is determined by its magnitude and direction. In a given translation, the segments connecting preimage to image points have the same direction and magnitude. This result can be stated in terms of vectors.

Theorem:

Two vectors are equal if and only if their initial and terminal points are preimages and images under the same translation.

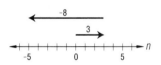

Remember when you learned to add positive and negative numbers? You were probably told you could picture the numbers by arrows. For instance, in adding 3 and -8, you drew arrows whose lengths were 3 and 8, but in opposite directions, as shown at the left. These arrows are, in fact, directed segments. You were adding vectors! Notice that you started the second arrow at the endpoint of the first. The sum was indicated by the endpoint of the second arrow. This is exactly the rule for adding vectors.

Definition:

The **sum** or **resultant** of two vectors $\overrightarrow{AB}$ and $\overrightarrow{BC}$, written $\overrightarrow{AB} + \overrightarrow{BC}$, is the vector $\overrightarrow{AC}$.

■ ■ ■ ■ ■ ■ ■ ■ ■

Example 1 Given are two vectors $\overrightarrow{AB}$ and $\overrightarrow{BC}$. Draw their sum.

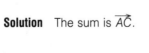

Solution The sum is $\overrightarrow{AC}$.

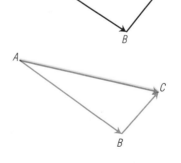

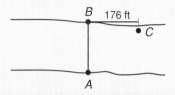

If any student has tried to row a boat or paddle a canoe against a current, have him or her recall and discuss the experience with the class, and relate it to vectors.

Error Analysis Students sometimes make errors in application problems involving vector sums because they do not understand the parallelogram rule. Point out that normally vector addition can be represented with the initial point of one vector as the terminal point of the other vector. With the parallelogram rule, the initial points coincide, making it easy to complete the parallelogram and therefore calculate the length and magnitude of the vectors.

Making Connections In this lesson, students are expected to picture the sum of two vectors. In Lessson 14-6, they will learn how to represent the sum if the vectors are given as ordered pairs. In Lesson 14-7, they learn the means of describing the sum if the vectors are given by magnitude and direction.

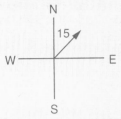
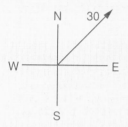
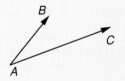
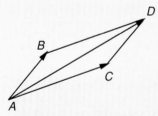
When the initial point of one given vector is not the terminal point of the other, you can still find the sum. Merely replace the second vector by an equal vector that *does* start at the terminal point of the first. In Example 2, the vectors are described by single boldface letters. The most common letters used are **u**, **v**, and **w**.

Example 2 With **u** and **v** as given, draw **u** + **v**.

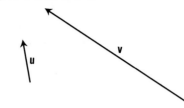

Solution Use the directed segment for **v** that starts at the terminal point of **u**.

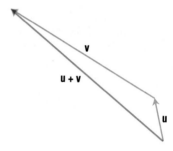

The significance of vector addition is that it models the way many physical forces in the world combine.

Example 3 A motorboat is traveling up a river at a speed that would be 25 miles an hour in still water. There is a current of 15 miles an hour coming down the river. How far will the motor boat travel in an hour?

Solution Possible vectors are drawn here. The resultant is a vector that represents a speed of 10 mph up the river.

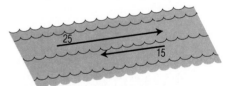

So, in a single hour, the boat will travel 10 miles up the river. (If the boat were traveling down the river, it would be with the current. So the resultant speed of the boat would be 25 + 15, or 40 mph down the river.)

Even when the current is in an oblique direction relative to the boat, the path and ground speed of the boat can be found by adding vectors.

Example 4

A motorboat is traveling due east at 20 miles an hour. There is a 5 mph current in the direction 40° west of south. In what direction will the motorboat move?

Solution Draw a directed segment for each vector.

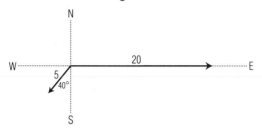

To find the sum, slide one of the vectors so its initial point is the terminal point of the other. Below, we moved the vector $\overrightarrow{OB}$ to have A as its initial point.

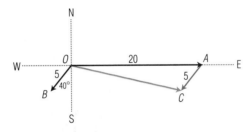

The resultant, which is the path of the boat, is in the direction of the vector $\overrightarrow{OC}$. The speed of the motorboat is indicated by the length of that vector. (Notice that the length of $\overrightarrow{OC}$ is less than the length of $\overrightarrow{OA}$. This is as you might expect, since the current is "fighting" the boat. In the last lesson of this chapter, you will learn how to determine the precise direction and magnitude of $\overrightarrow{OC}$.)

In Example 4, since $\overrightarrow{AC}$ and $\overrightarrow{OB}$ are of equal length and parallel, $OACB$ is a parallelogram. For this reason, the addition of vectors is said to follow the **parallelogram rule.** That is, the sum of two noncollinear vectors $\overrightarrow{OA}$ and $\overrightarrow{OB}$ is the vector $\overrightarrow{OC}$ such that $OACB$ is a parallelogram.

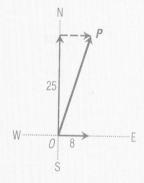

13.

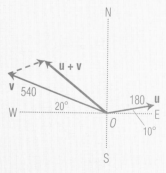

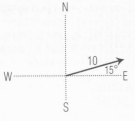
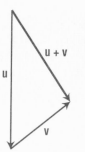
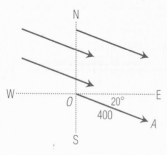
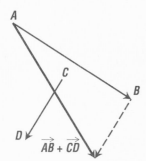
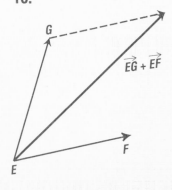
Questions

1. **a.** Why is the time scheduled for an airplane to travel from Los
Angeles to Dallas/Fort Worth not the same as the time scheduled
to travel from Dallas/Forth Worth to Los Angeles?
   b. Which trip usually takes longer?
   a) See margin. b) The trip east to west usually takes longer.

2. Suppose a motorboat can travel at a maximum speed of 20 mph in
still water. What is its maximum ground speed
   a. against a 4 mph current? **16 mph**
   b. with a 5 mph current? **25 mph**

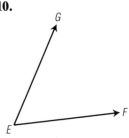

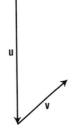

3. Name the initial point, terminal point, magnitude, and direction of the
vector $\overrightarrow{OA}$, as shown at the left. **initial point: O; terminal point: A;
magnitude: 400; direction: 20° south of east**

4. Draw a vector with magnitude 10 and direction 15° north of East.
See margin.

5. By definition, when are two vectors equal?
if they have the same direction and magnitude

6. Draw three vectors equal to the vector of Question 3.
See margin.

7. What sum is pictured here?

-4 + -2 = -6

In 8–10, trace the vectors and then draw their sum.

8.   **9.** *A*   **10.**

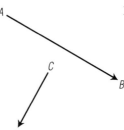

11. What is the parallelogram rule for adding vectors? **The sum of two
noncollinear vectors, $\overrightarrow{OA}$ and $\overrightarrow{OB}$, is the vector $\overrightarrow{OC}$ such that OACB is a
parallelogram.**

12. A motorboat is traveling north at a speed of 25 kilometers per hour in
still water. There is a current going due east at 8 kilometers per hour.
Draw a picture showing the direction in which the boat will move.
See margin.

13. An airplane is traveling at a speed and direction that would be
540 mph in the direction 20° north of west in still air. The jet stream
is pushing the plane at 180 mph in the direction 10° north of east.
Draw a picture of these velocity vectors and show the direction in
which the plane will move.
See margin.

712

In 14–16, draw the possible vector. **See margin.**

14. the force of gravity (9.8 meters per second per second)

15. a person pushing a sofa in a direction 37° west of north with a force of 150 pounds

16. a person pushing a sofa in a direction 37° east of south with a force of 150 pounds

17. Draw **u** + **v** + **w**. **See margin.**

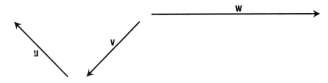

Review

18. In △XYZ, give the value of:
a. sin X $\frac{56}{65} \approx .862$
b. tan X $\frac{56}{33} \approx 1.697$
c. cos Z. *(Lessons 14-4, 14-3)*
   $\frac{56}{65} \approx .862$

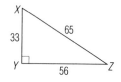

In 19 and 20, refer to △PQR at the left.

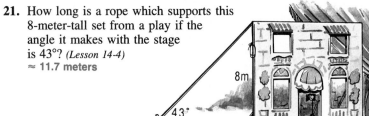

19. By measuring, determine tan R, sin R, and cos R (give answers to the nearest hundredth). *(Lessons 14-4, 14-3)*
tan R = $\frac{35 \text{ mm}}{15 \text{ mm}} \approx 2.33$; sin R = $\frac{35 \text{ mm}}{38 \text{ mm}} \approx 0.92$; cos R = $\frac{15 \text{ mm}}{38 \text{ mm}} \approx 0.39$

20. *Multiple choice.* Which equals p? *(Lesson 14-4)*
(a) q sin P   (b) q cos P   (c) r sin P   (d) r cos P **(a)**

21. How long is a rope which supports this 8-meter-tall set from a play if the angle it makes with the stage is 43°? *(Lesson 14-4)*
$\approx$ **11.7 meters**

22. What is the exact value of cos 30°? *(Lessons 14-4, 14-1)* $\frac{\sqrt{3}}{2}$

23. Find the surface area of a sphere with radius 12. *(Lesson 10-9)*
576π ≈ 1810 units²

24. Find the volume of a sphere with radius 12. *(Lesson 10-8)*
2304π ≈ 7238 units³

Exploration

25. a. Find out how long it takes by airplane to go from a nearby airport on a nonstop flight to some other location, and how long the return flight takes. **Answers will vary.**
b. Allowing some time for takeoff and landing (from 5 minutes at a smaller airport to 20 minutes at the largest airports), about how fast does the schedule assume the plane can travel? Is there any assumption about wind? **Answers will vary.**

FOLLOW-UP

MORE PRACTICE
For more questions on SPUR Objectives, use *Lesson Master 14-5*, shown below.

12.-17. See the margin on p. 711.

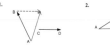
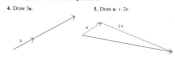

OBJECTIVES

E Draw the sum of two or
  more vectors.
H Identify the properties of
  vector addition.
K Graph sums and scalar
  multiples of vectors represented as ordered pairs.

TEACHING NOTES

By now, students should expect to see coordinate representations of ideas that are
first presented synthetically.
The coordinate view of vector
is particularly useful. Addition
is remarkably easy to de-
scribe, and there is a natural
extension to three dimen-
sions (see **Question 28**) and
even higher dimensions.

You might begin by reviewing
the convenient coordinate
placement for a parallelogram, namely (b, c), $(0, 0)$,
$(a, 0)$, and $(a + b, c)$. Use
slopes to verify that these
four vertices determine a parallelogram. Thus, if three
consecutive vertices of a parallelogram are (b, c), $(0, 0)$,
and $(a, 0)$, then the fourth
vertex is $(a + b, c)$. Now
consider a more difficult
question: If three consecutive
vertices of a parallelogram
are (a, b), $(0, 0)$, and (c, d),
what is the fourth vertex?
The answer is $(a + c,$
$b + d)$, and again the answer can be verified by using
slopes. (See **Question 14**.)

Properties of Vectors

A vector can describe the forces acting on a bullet.

Any vector can be placed so that its initial point is the origin. If its terminal point is (a, b), the vector is named $(\boldsymbol{a, b})$. The **horizontal component** of (a, b) is a; the **vertical component** is b. This is the **ordered pair description of a vector.**

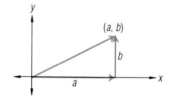

vector (a, b)
horizontal component a
vertical component b

The vector (a, b) can be interpreted as the resultant of a horizontal force a and a vertical force b. For instance, if a bullet is fired hori-zontally at an initial speed of 200 meters per second, gravity will pull it down about 10 meters per second, and its location after one second could be described by the vector $(200, -10)$. (It would have to be fired from an altitude of 10 meters or more, so as not to hit the ground before one second.)

When vectors are described as ordered pairs, they can be easily added.

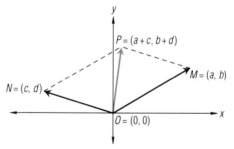

Vector Addition Theorem:

> The sum of the vectors (a, b) and (c, d) is the vector $(a + c, b + d)$.

714

Proof

The idea is to use the parallelogram rule. We let $O = (0, 0)$, $M = (a, b)$, $N = (c, d)$, and $P = (a + c, b + d)$. To show that $\overrightarrow{OP}$ is the sum of $\overrightarrow{OM}$ and $\overrightarrow{ON}$, it needs to be shown that $OMPN$ is a parallelogram. For this, all that is needed is to show that $\overrightarrow{MP}$ and $\overrightarrow{ON}$ are equal vectors. They are equal if they have the same direction (slope) and magnitude (length). This is left to you in Question 14.

The Vector Addition Theorem can be exemplified using forces. To combine two forces, add their horizontal components and add their vertical components. If the bullet mentioned above is fired from a plane going 300 meters per second (about 675 mph), in the direction of the plane, its location after one second is $(200, -10) + (300, 0)$ which is $(500, -10)$.

Vector addition is so named because it has many of the properties of ordinary real number addition. These real number properties, in fact, help to prove the corresponding properties for vectors.

Properties of Vector Addition Theorem:

(1) Vector addition is commutative.
(2) Vector addition is associative.
(3) $(0, 0)$ is an identity for vector addition.
(4) Every vector (a, b) has an additive inverse $(-a, -b)$.

Proof

All the parts use the strategy of adding appropriate vectors and using the corresponding real number property.
(1) It must be shown that $(a, b) + (c, d) = (c, d) + (a, b)$. That is left to you.

(2) It must be shown that
$((a, b) + (c, d)) + (e, f) = (a, b) + ((c, d) + (e, f))$.

$((a, b) + (c, d)) + (e, f) = (a + c, b + d) + (e, f)$	Vector Addition Theorem
$= ((a + c) + e, (b + d) + f)$	Vector Addition Theorem
$= (a + (c + e), b + (d + f))$	Associativity of real number addition
$= (a, b) + (c + e, d + f)$	Vector Addition Theorem
$= (a, b) + ((c, d) + (e, f))$	Vector Addition Theorem

(3) For any vector (a, b),

$(a, b) + (0, 0) = (a + 0, b + 0)$	Vector Addition Theorem
$= (a, b).$	0 is identity for real number addition.

Thus, $(0, 0)$ is an identity for vector addition.

(4) This is left to you.

The parallelogram law for adding vectors is very easy to describe if the vectors are given as ordered pairs. And since the major applications of vectors require adding them, the coordinate description is very popular. The only problem is to determine the coordinate description of a vector when it is given in some other form; this problem is studied in the next lesson.

Another way of thinking of the rule for the sum of two vectors is that each vector is itself the sum of a horizontal vector and a vertical vector. The horizontal component (first coordinate) of the sum is the sum of the horizontal vectors of the two vectors being added; the vertical component (second coordinate) is the sum of the vertical vectors.

Point out that the operation is called vector addition precisely because this operation satisfies many of the same properties of addition of numbers.

Alternate Approach
You might want to go over several examples of vector properties with students. You can make a list like the following for the vectors $(-6, 2)$, $(-12, 4)$, and $(3, 1)$:

Commutative:
$(-6, 2) + (-12, 4) = (-12, 4) + (-6, 2) = (-18, 6)$

Associative:
$((-6, 2) + (-12, 4)) + (3, 1) = (-6, 2) + ((-12, 4) + (3, 1)) = (-15, 7)$

Identity: $(0, 0)$
$(-6, 2) + (0, 0) = (-6, 2)$

Inverse:
Opposite Vectors:
$(-6, 2) + (6, -2) = (0, 0)$

Slope:
Slope of $(-6, 2) = \frac{2}{-6} = \frac{-1}{3}$

Parallelism: Equal slopes $\Rightarrow$ parallel
Slope of $(-6, 2)$ = slope of $(-12, 4) = \frac{-1}{3}$

Scalar Multiplication:
$3(-6, 2) = (-18, 6)$

715

Parts (1) and (2) of the Properties of Vector Addition Theorem are important because they imply that any number of vectors can be combined in any order. Part (2) of the Properties of Vector Addition Theorem is obvious when adding ordered pairs, but not so obvious with directed segments.

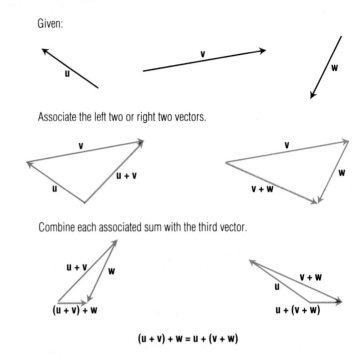

The vector (0, 0), called the **zero vector,** represents a force whose magnitude is zero. A helicopter is able to hover because the resultant of all the forces that act on it is the zero vector. The vectors (*a, b*) and (-*a, -b*), whose sum is the zero vector, are called **opposite vectors.** If two teams engage in a tug-of-war, and neither is moving the other, the forces they have applied are opposite vectors.

There are operations with vectors other than vector addition. Perhaps the simplest is multiplication of a vector by a real number, called *scalar multiplication*.

The idea of scalar multiplication is simple. If 3 people each push with the same force **v**, then the total force is **v + v + v**. This is the force 3**v**.

It is easiest to give the general definition of scalar multiplication in terms of ordered pairs.

Definition:

Let *k* be a real number and (*a*, *b*) be a vector. Then
***k*(*a*, *b*)**, the **scalar multiple** of *k* and (*a*, *b*), is the
vector (*ka*, *kb*).

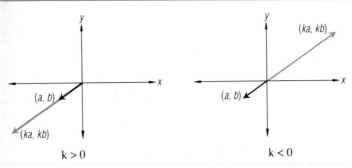

k > 0

k < 0

Recall that the point (*ka*, *kb*) is the image of (*a*, *b*) under a size
change of magnitude *k*. Thus, when *k* is positive, the vector (*ka*, *kb*)
has the same direction as (*a*, *b*) and *k* times the magnitude of (*a*, *b*).
When *k* is negative, the vectors (*a*, *b*) and (*ka*, *kb*) have opposite
directions.

Scalar multiplication has many properties, some of which are
touched upon in the Questions.

Questions

Covering the Reading

1. Name the horizontal and vertical components of the vector (2, 3).
   horizontal: 2; vertical: 3

In 2–5, add the vectors.

2. (300, 15) + (100, 212) (400, 227)

3. (*a*, *b*) + (*c*, *d*) (a + c, b + d)

4. (-9, 6) + (9, -6) (0, 0)

5. (0, 0) + $(\frac{1}{2}, -\frac{\sqrt{3}}{2})$ $(\frac{1}{2}, -\frac{\sqrt{3}}{2})$

6. Which of the vectors in Questions 2–5 are opposite vectors?
   (-9, 6) and (9, -6)

7. What vector is the additive identity? (0, 0)

8. A plane is traveling east at 250 meters per second. A bullet is fired
   backwards from the plane at 175 meters per second. Gravity pulls the
   bullet down 10 meters per second.
   a. What vector describes the effect of gravity in one second? (0, -10)
   b. What vector would describe the location of the bullet after one
      second if the plane were standing still? (-175, -10)
   c. What vector describes the location of the bullet after one second
      taking into account the moving plane? (75, -10)

LESSON 14-6 Properties of Vectors   **717**

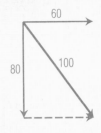
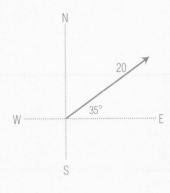
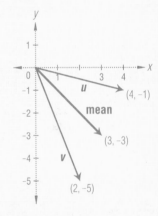

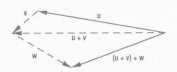
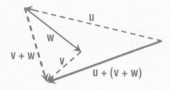
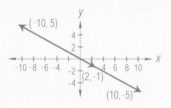

9. Below are 3 vectors **u**, **v**, and **w**.
  a. Draw $(\mathbf{u} + \mathbf{v}) + \mathbf{w}$. See margin.
  b. Draw $\mathbf{u} + (\mathbf{v} + \mathbf{w})$. See margin.
  c. What property is verified by the results of parts **a** and **b**?
    vector addition
    is associative.

10. Write $2 (-9, 5)$ as a single vector. (-18, 10)

11. Draw the vectors $(2, -1)$, $5 (2, -1)$, and $-5 (2, -1)$. See margin.

12. The operation in Questions 10 and 11 is called __?__.
  scalar multiplication

13. Given the vector $\overrightarrow{AB}$ as shown at the left, draw $4 \overrightarrow{AB}$. See margin.

Applying the Mathematics

14. Finish the proof of the Vector Addition Theorem by showing that $\overrightarrow{MP}$ and $\overrightarrow{ON}$:
  a. are parallel;
  b. have the same length.
  See margin.

15. Prove that vector addition is commutative. See margin.

16. Prove that (a, b) and $(-a, -b)$ are opposite vectors. See margin.

17. A plane is traveling at a ground speed (horizontally) of 350 mph and is descending at 1000 feet per minute. Convert these quantities to the same unit to find the slope of the vector describing the plane's path.
  $\approx -.032$

18. a. Determine whether this statement is true for all vectors (a, b) and (c, d) and scalar multiple k:
    $k[(a, b) + (c, d)] = k(a, b) + k(c, d)$. True
  b. What property have you proved or disproved in part **a**?
    Scalar multiplication distributes over vector addition.

19. A vector has magnitude 2 and direction 30° north of east. What are its components? horizontal: $\sqrt{3}$; vertical: 1

Review

20. Here is a view of a refrigerator and wall from the top.

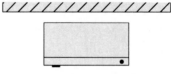

You pull on the refrigerator with a force of 80 lb perpendicular to and away from the wall. A friend pushes with a force of 60 lb parallel to the wall from left to right. Draw the two force vectors and their sum. *(Lesson 14-5)* See margin.

21. Draw the vector representing the velocity of a tornado traveling at 20 mph in the direction 35° north of east. *(Lesson 14-5)* See margin.

718

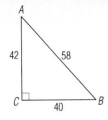

In 22 and 23, refer to $\triangle ABC$ at the left.

22. Give exact values for
  a. $\cos A$ $\frac{42}{58} = \frac{21}{29}$
  b. $\tan B$; $\frac{42}{40} = \frac{21}{20}$
  c. $\sin A$. *(Lessons 14-4, 14-3)* $\frac{40}{58} = \frac{20}{29}$

23. *True* or *false*? $m\angle A > m\angle B$. *(Lesson 13-7)* **False**

24. Refer to $\triangle DEF$ below. By measuring, estimate:
  a. $\cos D$
  b. $\tan D$. *(Lessons 14-4, 14-3)*
      Answers will vary. Samples: a) $\approx \frac{17 \text{ mm}}{35 \text{ mm}} \approx .5$; b) $\approx \frac{31 \text{ mm}}{17 \text{ mm}} \approx 1.8$

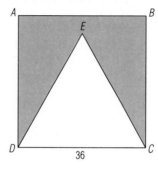

25. Without a calculator, give the value of $\tan 45°$. *(Lessons 14-3, 14-1)* **1**

26. Find the area of the shaded region between square $ABCD$ and equilateral triangle CDE. *(Lessons 14-1, 8-5)* $1296 - 324\sqrt{3} \approx 734.8$ units²

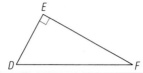

Exploration

27. a. Draw a pair of vectors **u** and **v** and calculate their mean $\frac{1}{2}(\mathbf{u} + \mathbf{v})$. Then draw the mean.
  b. Do this with other pairs of vectors. Describe the mean geometrically.
      See margin.
28. The vectors in this lesson are two-dimensional. Suggest how three-dimensional vectors might be described and added.
      sample: $(a, b, c) + (d, e, f) = (a + d, b + e, c + f)$

FOLLOW-UP

MORE PRACTICE
For more questions on SPUR Objectives, use *Lesson Master 14-6,* shown below.

EXTENSION
Students may be interested in trying to do a vector proof using coordinates.
Prove: If $\overrightarrow{AM} = \overrightarrow{MB}$ then M is the midpoint of $\overrightarrow{AB}$.
Proof: Let (a, b) be the coordinates of A, (m, n) be the coordinates of M, and (c, d) be the coordinates of B. Then $\overrightarrow{AM} = (m - a, n - b)$ and $\overrightarrow{MB} = (c - m, d - n)$ by the definition of a vector. Since $\overrightarrow{AM} = \overrightarrow{MB}$, $m - a = c - m$ and $n - b = d - n$ by the definition of equal vectors. Therefore, by algebra, $m = \frac{a + c}{2}$ and $n = \frac{b + d}{2}$. Since this is the same as the Midpoint Formula (Lesson 11-4), M is the midpoint of $\overrightarrow{AB}$.

20., 21., 27. See the margin on p. 717.

TEACHING NOTES

Making Connections
The magnitude-direction description of vector is akin to describing a point by its polar coordinates. Thus, the work in this lesson, to convert between magnitude direction and ordered-pair descriptions of vectors, is very much like converting between rectangular and polar coordinates, a subject students will study in a later course.

Due to the use of the trigonometric ratios, students are often surprised by the ease with which the conversion between the two descriptions of a vector can be done. Some practice is needed, however. Notice that the (inv) or (2nd) keys, in consort with a (sin), (cos), or (tan) key, cause the trigonometric operation to be undone. At this point, it is not necessary to speak of inverse functions.

Examples 1 and **2** convert from a direction-magnitude to an ordered-pair description. **Example 3** converts an ordered pair to its direction and magnitude. **Example 4** requires conversion in both directions—one way in order to add the vectors, the other

Adding Vectors Using Trigonometry

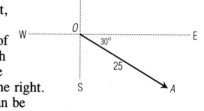

You have seen vectors described in two ways in this chapter. First, they were described as directed segments. For instance, a wind of 25 mph in the direction 30° south of east could be described by the directed segment $\overrightarrow{OA}$ shown at the right. As directed segments, vectors can be added geometrically, by putting one segment at the end of the other.

Second, vectors were described by ordered pairs. The ordered pair $(8, 2)$ stands for the vector connecting $(0, 0)$ to the point $(8, 2)$. The sum of vectors (a, b) and (c, d) is the vector $(a + c, b + d)$. The properties of vectors are quite easily deduced from the description of vectors as ordered pairs.

Because it is so easy to add vectors as ordered pairs, it is natural to want to translate from directed segments to ordered pairs. This can be done using trigonometry.

■ ■ ■ ■ ■ ■ ■ ■

Example 1 Describe the vector $\overrightarrow{OA}$ above with an ordered pair.

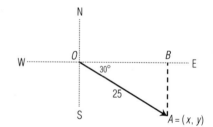

Solution The desired ordered pair contains the coordinates of point A. Let $A = (x, y)$ as shown at the right. From the graph you can see that x is positive and y is negative. The absolute values of x and y are OB and BA. Now use trigonometry.

Since $\dfrac{OB}{OA} = \cos 30°$,

$$OB = OA \cos 30°$$
$$= 25 \cos 30°.$$

Similarly, because $\dfrac{BA}{OA} = \sin 30°$,

$$BA = OA \sin 30°$$
$$= 25 \sin 30°.$$

Now remember that the first coordinate of A is positive and the second coordinate is negative. Thus $A = (25 \cos 30°, -25 \sin 30°)$. With a calculator, you can find that $\cos 30° \approx 0.866$ and $\sin 30° = 0.5$, so $A \approx (21.65, -12.5)$.

720

In Example 1, because 30° is a special angle, you can find exact coordinates for point A. Because $\cos 30° = \frac{\sqrt{3}}{2}$ and $\sin 30° = \frac{1}{2}$, so $A = (12.5\sqrt{3}, -12.5)$. Usually you cannot find exact coordinates.

■ ■ ■ ■ ■ ■ ■ ■

Example 2   Find the components of the vector whose magnitude is 150 and whose direction is 10° south of west.

Solution   Draw a picture. The components of the vector are the coordinates of point C below. The picture includes a right triangle whose sides will give the coordinates of C.

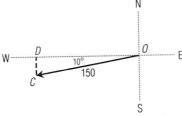

First notice that both coordinates of C are negative. Their absolute values are OD and DC.

Since $\cos 10° = \dfrac{OD}{OC}$,

$$OD = OC \cos 10°.$$

Since $\sin 10° = \dfrac{DC}{OC}$

$$DC = OC \sin 10°.$$

The x-component of C is $-OC \cos 10°$ and the y-component is $-OC \sin 10°$. With a calculator, you can get decimal approximations: $\overrightarrow{OC} \approx (-147.72, -26.05)$.

From Examples 1 and 2 you can see that one component of a vector is found using the sine of the given angle. The other component is found using the cosine. However, instead of memorizing formulas, it is usually easier to draw a picture each time and use the definitions of sine and cosine.

To go from the ordered pair description to one in terms of direction and magnitude, the tangent is required.

---

way to interpret the result. If a student can follow **Example 4** and do **Questions 9-11**, then the student has learned all of the ideas in this lesson.

You may wish to go over the reading and Examples very carefully with students. Have them verify the steps shown in the Examples with their calculators as you are explaining them, and emphasize the use of positive angles only. (Although calculators can handle negative angles, it involves more trigonometry than can be taught here.) You might need to spend some extra time in showing students how to use their Inverse or 2nd Function key to determine the angles for the triangles formed.

Since this lesson has many ideas and is the last lesson of the chapter, do not expect great mastery.

ADDITIONAL EXAMPLES
1. Give the horizontal and vertical components of a force of 50 pounds in a direction 10° north of east.
(50 cos 10°, 50 sin 10°) ≈ **(49.24, 8.68)**

2. Find the direction and magnitude of the vector (-7, 11).
direction 58° north of west (or 32° west of north); magnitude $\sqrt{170}$ ≈ 13.04

3. A plane is flying at a speed and direction which, in still air, would be 360 mph and 30° south of east. There is a wind of 75 mph in the direction 40° north of east. What is the resultant ground speed and direction of the plane?
The vector is (180$\sqrt{3}$ + 75 cos 40°, -180 + 75 sin 40°) ≈ (369, -132), which translates into a ground speed of about 392 mph in the direction about 20° south of east.

Example 3   Find the direction and magnitude of the vector (3, 5).

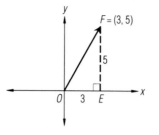

Solution   Again, draw a picture. A sample is on the left.

The magnitude of the vector is *OF*. Using the Pythagorean Theorem,
$$OF = \sqrt{3^2 + 5^2} = \sqrt{34} \approx 5.83.$$

The direction can be found from m∠*FOE*. What we know is that
$$\tan∠FOE = \tfrac{5}{3}.$$

To determine m∠*FOE*, press
$$5 \boxed{÷} 3 \boxed{=} \boxed{\text{INV}} \boxed{\text{tan}}.$$

(Pressing the $\boxed{\text{INV}}$ key just prior to the $\boxed{\text{tan}}$ key gives you the measure of the angle whose tangent is $\tfrac{5}{3}$.)

You should see 59.0362... displayed. This means that m∠*FOE* ≈ 59. So the direction of this vector is about 59° north of east, or you could say about 31° east of north.

The above examples provide algebraic tools to combine forces given their magnitudes and directions. Notice how many of the ideas of this chapter are applied in the next Example.

Example 4   To move a heavy box, one person pushes north with a force of 125 lb. A second person pushes northwest with a force of 100 lb. What is the magnitude and direction of the combined force?

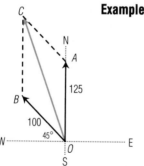

Solution   The force vectors are $\overrightarrow{OA}$ and $\overrightarrow{OB}$ as pictured at the left. The combined force is given by $\overrightarrow{OC}$, where $\overrightarrow{OC} = \overrightarrow{OA} + \overrightarrow{OB}$. *OACB* is a parallelogram.

It is easy to see that $\overrightarrow{OA} = (0, 125)$. Using the ideas of Examples 1 and 2, $\overrightarrow{OB} = (-100 \cos 45°, 100 \sin 45°) \approx (-70.7, 70.7)$. So $\overrightarrow{OC} = \overrightarrow{OA} + \overrightarrow{OB} \approx (0 + -70.7, 125 + 70.7) = (-70.7, 195.7)$.

The magnitude of $\overrightarrow{OC}$ is *OC*; $OC \approx \sqrt{(-70.7)^2 + 195.7^2} \approx 208.1$.

From the definition of tangent, $\tan∠COD \approx \tfrac{195.7}{70.7} \approx 2.768$, so   m∠*COD* ≈ 2.768 $\boxed{\text{INV}}$ $\boxed{\text{tan}}$
$$\approx 70.1°.$$

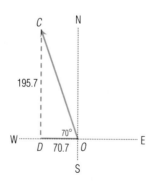

The combined force is about 208 pounds in a direction 70° north of west (or 20° west of north).

Covering the Reading

1. What are two ways of describing vectors?
directed segments, ordered pairs

In 2–5, find the components of the vector.

2. See margin.

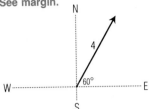

3. See margin.

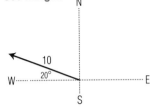

4. See margin.

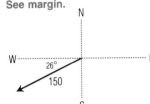

5. x = 0, y = -3

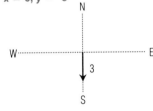

6. If tan A = 0.532 and A is an acute angle, estimate m∠A to the nearest degree. **28**

In 7 and 8, give the direction and magnitude of the vector. See margin.

7.

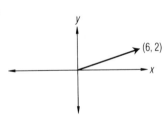

8.

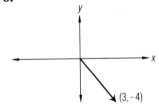

Applying the Mathematics

9. To move a crate, one person pushes east with a force of 130 pounds. A second person pushes 50° south of east with a force of 70 pounds. What is the magnitude and direction of the combined force?
magnitude: ≈183 lbs; direction: ≈ 17° S of E (or 73° E of S)

10. A plane is flying at a speed and direction which, in still air, would be 550 mph, 25° north of west. There is a wind of 80 mph, 10° south of east. Give the resultant ground speed and direction of the plane.
speed: ≈ 473 mph; direction: ≈ 27.5° N of W (or 62.5° W of N)

11. From the top of a roof, a person throws a ball horizontally at 88 feet per second. The force of gravity pulls it down 32 feet in the first second. After one second, how far and in what direction from the person will the ball be? **≈ 93.7 ft away; ≈ 20° below horizontal**

LESSON 14-7 Adding Vectors Using Trigonometry **723**

MORE PRACTICE
For more questions on SPUR Objectives, use *Lesson Master 14-7*, shown below.

EXTENSION
You may want students to verify another property of vectors (see **Question 21**): two nonvertical vectors are perpendicular if the products of their slopes is -1. You can use the last two vectors (-12, 4) and (3, 1) as an example, and then have students make up their own examples. Include an example such as the following: What vectors (*a*, *b*) would be perpendicular to (4, 2)?

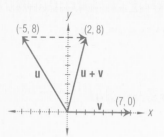
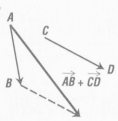
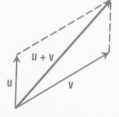
12. Give the inverse of the vector (-7, 13). *(Lesson 14-6)* (7, -13)

13. Graph **u**, **v**, and **u** + **v** where **u** = (-5, 8) and **v** = (7, 0).
(Lesson 14-6) **See margin.**

In 14 and 15, trace the given vectors. Then draw their sum. *(Lesson 14-5)*

14.

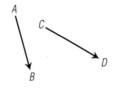

15. **See margin.**

16. In a 5-12-13 right triangle, find the length of the altitude to the hypotenuse and the lengths of the segments into which the altitude splits the hypotenuse. *(Lesson 14-2)*
alt $= \frac{60}{13}$, segments of hypotenuse are $\frac{25}{13}$ and $\frac{144}{13}$

17. What is the area of $\triangle STU$ below? *(Lessons 14-1, 8-5)*
$\frac{225\sqrt{3}}{4} \approx 97.4$ units²

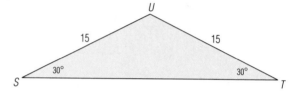

18. Make a conclusion using all of the following statements.
 a. No x is a y.
 b. If an animal is not a y, then the animal is not a z.
 c. Rudolph is a z. *(Lesson 13-4)* Rudolph is not an x.

19. Young children who play string instruments like the violin or cello often use instruments that are similar to, but smaller than, the adult-size instrument. An $\frac{1}{8}$-size cello is $\frac{1}{8}$ the volume of a full-size cello. How do the heights of these cellos compare? *(Lesson 12-6)*
The $\frac{1}{8}$-size cello is $\frac{1}{2}$ the height of a full-size cello.

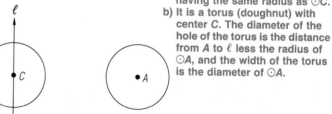

20. a. Describe the figure formed by rotating circle C in space about line ℓ.
 b. Describe the figure formed by rotating circle A in space about line ℓ. *(Lesson 9-4)*

 a) It is a sphere with center C and having the same radius as $\odot C$.
 b) It is a torus (doughnut) with center C. The diameter of the hole of the torus is the distance from A to ℓ less the radius of $\odot A$, and the width of the torus is the diameter of $\odot A$.

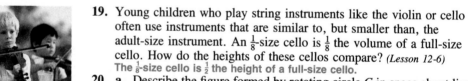
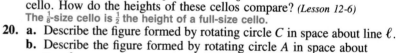

21. There is an operation on vectors called the *dot product*. Find out what the dot product of (a, b) and (c, d) is. The dot product of two vectors (a, b) and (c, d) is the real number $ac + bd$.

724

Summary

Right triangles are important because any triangle and thus any polygon can be split up into them, and because knowing only one acute angle and one side, all lengths are determined. Certain right triangles occur so often that they are special. The isosceles right triangle has angles of 45°, 45°, and 90° and sides of lengths x, x, and $x\sqrt{2}$. Any equilateral triangle can be split into two right triangles with angles of 30°, 60°, and 90° and sides with lengths x, $x\sqrt{3}$, and $2x$.

When the altitude to the hypotenuse of a right triangle is drawn, two triangles are formed, each similar to the original. Three of the resulting proportions involve a geometric mean, as one length appears as both means in the proportion. The altitude itself is the geometric mean of the segments into which it divides the hypotenuse. Either leg is the geometric mean of the hypotenuse and the segment of the hypotenuse closest to it.

When right triangles have congruent angles, they are similar and the ratios of corresponding sides in the triangles are equal. These ratios are called trigonometric ratios; three of them are the tangent, sine, and cosine of any angle. The trigonometric ratios can be estimated using an accurate drawing, or a scientific calculator, or calculated exactly if you are given lengths of sides in the triangle or are dealing with one of the two special triangles.

A vector is a quantity with a magnitude and a direction. Vectors may be described geometrically as directed line segments, or algebraically as ordered pairs. It is useful to be able to convert from either description to the other. Vectors can stand for forces, velocities, pressures, acceleration, and other physical quantities. Vector addition gives the result of combining forces or other quantities. The operation of vector addition has many of the properties of ordinary real number addition: commutativity, associativity, an identity, and inverses. Scalar multiplication yields vectors with the same or opposite directions but different magnitudes.

Vocabulary

Below are the most important terms and phrases for this chapter.
For the starred (*) items you should be able to give a definition of the term.
For the other items you should be able to give a general description and a specific example of each.

Lesson 14-1
45-45-90, 30-60-90 triangles
Isosceles Right Triangle Theorem
30-60-90 Triangle Theorem

Lesson 14-2
*geometric mean
arithmetic mean
Geometric Mean Theorem
Right Triangle Altitude Theorem

Lesson 14-3
leg adjacent to an angle
leg opposite an angle
*tangent of an angle
tan A, [tan]
trigonometric ratio

Lesson 14-4
*sine of an angle, sin A, [sin]
*cosine of an angle
cos A, [cos]

Lesson 14-5
vector, $\overrightarrow{AB}$, **v**
directed line segment
direction of vector
magnitude of vector
initial point, terminal point
equal vectors
*sum of two vectors
resultant of two vectors, **u** + **v**
parallelogram rule

Lesson 14-6
ordered pair description of a
    vector
horizontal component
vertical component
Vector Addition Theorem
Properties of Vector Addition
    Theorem
zero vector
opposite vectors
*scalar multiplication
*scalar multiple
*k (a, b)

Lesson 14-7
[INV] [tan]

Whereas end-of-chapter materials may be considered optional in some texts, they should not be considered optional in UCSMP *Geometry*. The Progress Self-Test provides the opportunity for feedback and correction; the Chapter Review provides additional opportunities for practice. It is at this point that the material "gels" for many students, allowing them to solidify skills and concepts before a test. In general, student performance is markedly improved after these pages.

USING THE PROGRESS SELF-TEST

Assign the Progress Self-Test as a one-night assignment. Worked-out *solutions* for all questions are in the Selected Answers section of the student text. Encourage students to take the Progress Self-Test honestly, grade themselves, and then be prepared to discuss the test in class.

Advise students to pay special attention to those Chapter Review questions (pages 728-731) which correspond to questions missed on the Progress Self-Test. A chart provided with the Selected Answers keys the Progress Self-Test questions to the lettered SPUR Objectives in the Chapter Review or to the Vocabulary. It also keys the questions to the corresponding lessons where the material is covered.

Progress Self-Test

See margin for answers not shown below.

Directions: Take this test as you would take a test in class. Use a ruler and calculator. Then check your work with the solutions in the Selected Answers section in the back of the book.

1. In right triangle *XYZ* below, estimate cos *Y* by measuring two sides. Give an answer to the nearest hundredth.

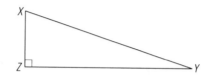

2. Refer to the figure below. Of the numbered angles, which has the smallest tangent? ∠3

3. In right triangle *ABC* below, if sin $B = \frac{9}{11}$, find cos *A*. $\frac{9}{11}$

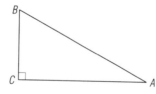

In 4 and 5, refer to the figure below. Suppose *XY* = 60, *XZ* = 45, and *ZY* = 75.

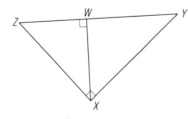

4. Find *WZ*. 27   **5.** Find *WY*. 48

726

In 6 and 7, use the figure below.

6. If *BC* = 6 and *BD* = 2, find *AB*. 18

7. *CD* is the geometric mean of __?__ and __?__. *AD, DB*

In 8–10, use the figure below. If *AB* = 7, find:

8. *BC*   **9.** *AC*   **10.** *AD*.
   7              $7\sqrt{2} \approx 9.9$ $14\sqrt{2} \approx 19.8$

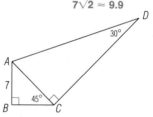

In 11 and 12, use triangle *DEF* below.

11. Find tan *D*. $\frac{48}{14} \approx 3.43$ **12.** Find cos *E*. $\frac{48}{50} = .96$

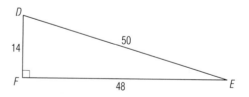

In 13 and 14, give the exact value.

13. sin 60° $\frac{\sqrt{3}}{2}$ **14.** tan 45° 1

15. Find the geometric mean of 18 and 30 to the nearest hundredth. **23.24**

726

16. From eye level 5 ft above the ground, a person has to look up at an angle of 35° to see the top of a tree 40 ft away. How tall is the tree? **≈ 33 ft**

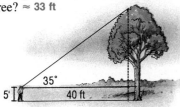

17. How far up on a vertical wall can a 15-foot ladder reach if the angle it makes with the ground is 80°? **≈ 14.77 ft**

18. Trace the vectors below. Then draw their sum.

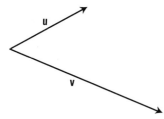

19. Use the vectors above.
  a. Draw 2 **v** + **u**.   **b.** Draw 2 (**v** + **u**).
20. Draw an opposite of vector $\overrightarrow{AB}$ below.

21. Graph **u**, **v**, and **u** + **v**, where **u** = (-4, 2) and **v** = (0, -6).

22. Give the components of vector $\overrightarrow{OA}$ below.
horizontal: ≈ -41
vertical: ≈ -28.7

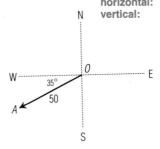

23. Give the direction and magnitude of the vector (30, -16).

24. An airplane can travel at 700 kilometers per hour in still air. With a head wind of 150 kilometers per hour, how far could it travel in $3\frac{1}{2}$ hours? **1925 kilometers**

25. A kayak is moved by a 4 mph current 25° west of north, and the kayaker is paddling at a speed of 8 mph in the direction 50° east of north. With a picture, show what direction the boat will move.

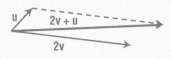

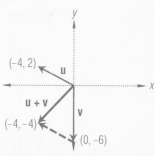

Chapter Review

Questions on SPUR Objectives

SPUR stands for **S**kills, **P**roperties, **U**ses, and **R**epresentations.
The Chapter Review questions are grouped according to the
SPUR Objectives for this chapter.

CHAPTER REVIEW

The main objectives for the chapter are organized here into sections corresponding to the four main types of understanding this book promotes: Skills, Properties, Uses, and Representations. We call these the SPUR objectives. The four types of understanding are not in increasing order of difficulty. There may be hard skills and easy representations; some uses may be easier than anything else; and so on.

USING THE CHAPTER REVIEW

Students should be able to answer questions like these with about 85% accuracy by the end of the chapter.

You may assign these questions over a single night to help students prepare for a test the next day, or you may assign the questions over a two-day period.

If you assign the questions over two days, then we recommend assigning the *evens* for homework the first night so the students get feedback in class the next day. Then assign the *odds* for the second night (the night before the test) so that students can use the answers provided in the book as a study aid.

SKILLS deal with the procedures used to get answers.

■ **Objective A:** *Calculate lengths of sides in isosceles right triangles and in 30-60-90 triangles.* *(Lesson 14-1)*

1. In △ABC below, find AC and BC.

 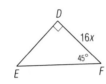

2. In △DEF above, find DE and EF.

3. A square has sides of length 12. What is the length of a diagonal? 12√2

4. An equilateral triangle has sides of length q. Find the length of an altitude. $\frac{q\sqrt{3}}{2}$

In 5 and 6, use the figure below.

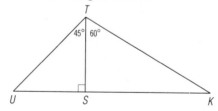

5. If ST = 7, find **a.** TU **b.** US **c.** SK and **d.** TK. a) 7√2; b) 7; c) 7√3; d) 14

6. If SK = 13, find **a.** ST **b.** SU and **c.** TK.

7. Refer to △XYZ at the right with measures as marked. Find YZ. (Hint: Draw an altitude from X.) 25√3 ≈ 43.30 units

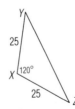

■ **Objective B:** *Determine sines, cosines, and tangents from drawings.* *(Lessons 14-3, 14-4)*

8. Refer to △ABC below. By measuring, determine m∠A (to the nearest degree), and tan A, sin A, and cos A (to the nearest hundredth).

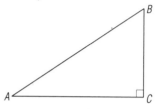

9. Refer to △DEF below. By measuring, determine m∠E to the nearest degree, and sin E, cos E, and tan E to the nearest hundredth.

10. Draw a right triangle with legs of 3 units and 5 units. Use this triangle to estimate m∠A if tan A = $\frac{3}{5}$.

In 11 and 12, use the figure below. Choose from the numbered angles.

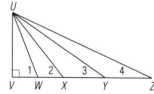

11. Which angle has the largest tangent? ∠1
12. Which angle has the largest sine? ∠1

728

■ Objective C: *Calculate sines, cosines and tangents of angles in right triangles.* *(Lessons 14-3, 14-4)*

In 13–16, use △*ABC* below. Give exact values for each.

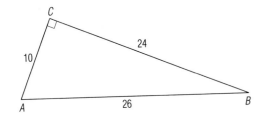

13. $\sin A \frac{24}{26} = \frac{12}{13}$
14. $\cos B \frac{24}{26} = \frac{12}{13}$
15. $\tan B \frac{10}{24} = \frac{5}{12}$
16. $\cos A \frac{10}{26} = \frac{5}{13}$

In 17–19, estimate to the nearest thousandth.

17. $\sin 57.5°$ .843
18. $\tan 22.1°$ .406
19. $\cos 1°$ 1.000

In 20–23, give exact values.

20. $\sin 30°$ $\frac{1}{2}$
21. $\tan 60°$ $\sqrt{3}$
22. $\tan 45°$ 1
23. $\cos 45°$ $\frac{1}{\sqrt{2}} = \frac{\sqrt{2}}{2}$

■ Objective D: *Calculate lengths using the Right Triangle Altitude Theorem.* *(Lesson 14-2)*

In 24–26, refer to the figure at the right below.

24. If $AD = 9$ and $DB = 4$, then $CD = \underline{\ ?\ }$. 6
25. If $AC = 7$ and $AB = 12$, then $AD = \underline{\ ?\ }$. $\frac{49}{12} \approx 4.08$
26. If $DC = 12$ and $AD = 18$, then $BC = \underline{\ ?\ }$. $\sqrt{208} \approx 14.42$

27. At the right is a 7-24-25 right triangle. Find the length of x, y, and z.

$x = \frac{49}{25} = 1.96$

$y = \frac{168}{25} = 6.72$

$z = \frac{576}{25} = 23.04$

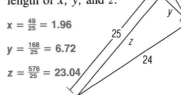

28. In △*RQS* below, $\overline{QR} \perp \overline{RS}$ and $\overline{RT} \perp \overline{QS}$. If $RT = 4$ and $TS = 8$, find
   a. QT 2
   b. QR $\sqrt{20} \approx 4.47$
   c. RS $\sqrt{80} \approx 8.94$
   d. QS. 10

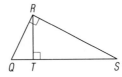

PROPERTIES deal with the principles behind the mathematics.

■ Objective E: *Draw the sum of two or more vectors.* *(Lessons 14-5, 14-6)*

In 29–34, trace the given vectors. Then draw their sum.

29.
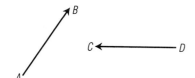

30.

31.
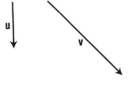

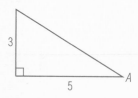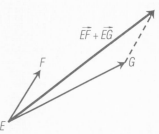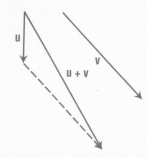

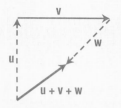
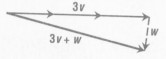
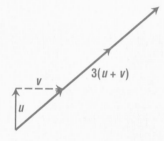
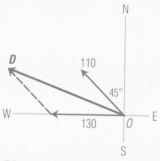
32.

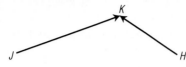

33.

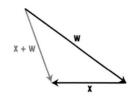

34.

35. Trace the vectors and draw **u + v + w**.

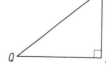

36. Use the vectors from Question 35.
 a. Draw 3 **v** + **w**. **b.** Draw 3 (**u** + **v**).

■ **Objective F:** *Know the definitions of sine, cosine, and tangent.* (*Lessons 14-3, 14-4*)

In 37–39, △*ABC* is a right triangle with right angle *C*. Define each expression.

37. cos *A*   **38.** sin *A*   **39.** tan *A*

In 40 and 41, use the figure below.

40. $\frac{MP}{MQ}$ is the tangent of which angle? ∠**Q**

41. $\frac{MQ}{PQ}$ is the ___?___ of angle *P*. **sine**

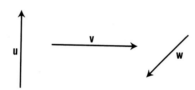

In 42 and 43, use right triangle △*ABC* below.

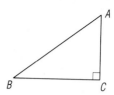

42. Write a ratio for tan *B*. $\frac{AC}{BC}$

43. If cos *A* = *x*, find sin *B*. **x**

■ **Objective G:** *Recognize and derive the geometric mean properties in right triangles.* (*Lesson 14-2*)

In 44–47, use the figure below.

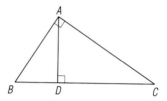

44. *AB* is the geometric mean of ___?___ and ___?___. **BC, BD**

45. *AD* is the geometric mean of ___?___ and ___?___. **BD, DC**

46. *AC* is the geometric mean of ___?___ and ___?___. **BC, DC**

47. △*ABC* ~ △___?___ ~ △___?___ **DBA, DAC**

■ **Objective H:** *Identify the properties of vector addition.* (*Lesson 14-6*)

48. What vector is the additive identity? **(0, 0)**

49. Draw the inverse of the vector $\overrightarrow{AB}$.

50. Give the inverse of the vector (2, 9). **(-2, -9)**

51. Using the vectors of Question 35, is it true that **u + v = v + u**? **Yes**

USES deal with applications of mathematics in real situations.

■ **Objective I:** *Use sines, cosines, and tangents to determine unknown lengths in real situations.* *(Lessons 14-3, 14-4)*

52. From eye level 2 meters off the ground and 25 meters from a sculpture, a person has to look up at an angle of 20° to see the top of it. How high is the sculpture (including the base)? ≈11.1 m

53. When the sun is 57° up from the horizon, a tree casts a shadow 14 yards long. How tall is the tree? ≈21.56 yards

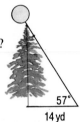

57°
14 yd

54. How far up a vertical wall does a 4-meter ladder reach if the angle it makes with the ground is 75°? ≈ 3.86 meters

55. From the window of a building you look down at a clown in a parade. If your eyes are 60 feet above the clown, and the angle of sight, measured from the building, is 25°, how far is the clown from you? ≈ 66 feet

25'
60 ft

■ **Objective J:** *Use vectors for forces to determine combinations of forces.* *(Lesson 14-5, 14-7)*

56. A motorboat is traveling with a speed which, in still water, would be 30 mph, against a current of 10 mph. How far will the boat travel in 15 minutes? 5 miles

57. An airplane can travel at 600 kilometers per hour in still air. With a tail wind of 100 kilometers per hour, how far could it travel in $2\frac{1}{2}$ hours? 1750 km

In 58–59, Show the answer with a picture.

58. Two people are pushing a heavy crate. One exerts a force of 130 pounds in a westerly direction, the other 110 pounds in a northwesterly direction. In what direction will the crate move?

59. A rowboat is moved by a 6 mph current 30° south of east and by rowers, who row at 3 mph in the direction 40° west of south. In what direction will the boat travel?

60. In the situation of Question 58, give the magnitude and direction of the combined force.

61. In the situation of Question 59, give the magnitude and direction of the combined force.

REPRESENTATIONS deal with pictures, graphs, or objects that illustrate concepts.

■ **Objective K:** *Graph sums and scalar multiples of vectors represented as ordered pairs.* *(Lesson 14-6)*

In 62 and 63, graph **u**, **v**, and **u + v**.
62. **u** = (2, 1), **v** = (3, 2)
63. **u** = (-4, -3), **v** = (5, 0)
64. If **w** = (-9, 5), graph **w** and 2**w**.
65. Graph **v** and 3**v** when **v** = (6, 1).

■ **Objective L** *Convert directed segments to ordered pairs, and vice-versa.* *(Lesson 14-7)*

66. Give the components of the vector $\overrightarrow{OA}$ at the right.

67. Describe $\overrightarrow{OB}$ below as an ordered pair.
68. Give the direction and magnitude of the vector (1, 10).
69. Give the direction and magnitude of the vector (-31, -26).

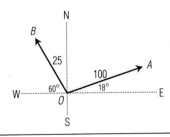

EVALUATION
Three forms of a Chapter Test are provided in the Teacher's Resource File. Chapter 14 Test, Forms A and B cover just Chapter 14. The third test is Chapter 14 Test, Cumulative Form. About 50% of this test covers Chapter 14, 25% covers Chapter 13, and 25% covers previous chapters. For information on grading, see *General Teaching Suggestions: Grading* on page T44 in the Teacher's Edition.

ASSIGNMENT RECOMMENDATION
We strongly recommend that you assign the reading and questions from Lesson 15-1 for homework the evening of the test. It gives students work to do if they complete the test before the end of the period and keeps the class moving.

61. magnitude ≈ 6.2 mph direction: ≈ 32° E of S (or 58° S of E)

62.

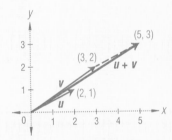

63., 64., 65. See Additional Answers in the back of this book.

66. horizontal: ≈ 95.1 vertical: ≈ 30.9

67. ≈ (-12.5, 21.65)

68. magnitude = $\sqrt{101}$ ≈ 10.05 direction: ≈ 84° N of E (or 6° E of N)

69. magnitude = $\sqrt{1637}$ ≈ 40.5 direction: ≈ 50° W of S (or 40° S of W)

CHAPTER 15 ■ FURTHER WORK WITH CIRCLES

DAILY PACING CHART ■ CHAPTER 15

Every chapter of UCSMP *Geometry* includes lessons, a Progress Self-Test, and a Chapter Review. For optimal student performance, the Self-Test and Review should be covered. (See *General Teaching Suggestions: Mastery* on page T36 of the Teacher's Edition.) By following the pace of the Full Course given here, students can complete the entire text by the end of the year. Students following the pace of the Minimal Course spend more time when there are quizzes and on the Chapter Review and will generally not complete all of the chapters in this text. For more information on pacing, see *General Teaching Suggestions: Pace* on page T35 of the Teacher's Edition.

DAY	MINIMAL COURSE	FULL COURSE
1	15-1	15-1
2	15-2	15-2
3	15-3	15-3
4	Quiz (TRF); Start 15-4.	Quiz (TRF); 15-4.
5	Finish 15-4.	15-5
6	15-5	15-6
7	15-6	Quiz (TRF); 15-7
8	Quiz (TRF); Start 15-7.	15-8
9	Finish 15-7.	15-9
10	15-8	Progress Self-Test
11	15-9	Chapter Review
12	Progress Self-Test	Chapter Test (TRF)
13	Chapter Review	Comprehensive Test (TRF)
14	Chapter Review	
15	Chapter Test (TRF)	
16	Comprehensive Test (TRF)	

TESTING OPTIONS
- ■ Quiz for Lessons 15-1 Through 15-3
- ■ Quiz for Lessons 15-4 Through 15-6
- ■ Chapter 15 Test, Form A
- ■ Chapter 15 Test, Form B
- ■ Chapter 15 Test, Cumulative Form
- ■ Comprehensive Test for Chapters 1-15

PROVIDING FOR INDIVIDUAL DIFFERENCES

The student text has been written for, and tested with, average students. It also has been used successfully with better and more poorly prepared students.

The Lesson Notes often include Error Analysis and Alternate Approach features to help you with those students who need more help. A blackline Lesson Master (in the Teacher's Resource File), keyed to the chapter objectives, is provided for each lesson to allow more practice. (However, since it is very important to keep up with the daily pace, you are not expected to use all of these masters. Again, refer to the suggestions for pacing on page T35.) Extension activities are provided in the Lesson Notes for those students who have completed the particular lesson in a shorter amount of time than is expected, even in the Full Course.

OBJECTIVES ■ CHAPTER 15

The objectives listed here are the same as in the Chapter 15 Review on pages 788-791 of the student text. The Progress Self-Test on pages 786-787 and the tests in the Teacher's Resource File cover these objectives. For recommendations regarding the handling of this end-of-chapter material, see the notes in the margin on the corresponding pages of the Teacher's Edition.

OBJECTIVES FOR CHAPTER 15 (Organized into the SPUR Categories—Skills, Properties, Uses, and Representations)	Progress Self-Test Questions	Chapter Review Questions	Lesson Master from Teacher's Resource File*
SKILLS			
A Calculate lengths of chords of arcs.	4	1 through 6	15-1
B Calculate measures of inscribed angles from measures of intercepted arcs, and vice versa.	5	7 through 11	15-3
C Calculate measures of angles between chords, secants, or tangents, from measures of intercepted arcs, and vice versa.	6, 7	12 through 17	15-3, 15-5, 15-6
D Locate the center of the circle given sufficient information using the right angle or perpendicular bisector method.	1	18 through 23	15-4
E Apply the Secant Length Theorem.	9, 10	24 through 27	15-7
PROPERTIES			
F Make deductions from properties of radii perpendicular to chords, and know sufficient conditions for radii to be perpendicular to them.	3	28 through 31	15-1
G Make deductions from properties of inscribed angles formed by chords, tangents, or secants.	8	32 through 34	15-3, 15-5, 15-6
H Apply the Isoperimetric Inequalities to determine which figures have the most or least area, perimeter, or volume.	12	35 through 40	15-8, 15-9
USES			
I Given the angle width of a lens and the width of an object, determine the set of points from which the object will fit in the picture.	13, 14	41 through 42	15-4
J Apply the Isoperimetric Inequalities in real situations.	11	43 through 46	15-8, 15-9
REPRESENTATIONS			
K Make a schedule for a round-robin tournament.	2	47 through 49	15-2

*The masters are numbered to match the lessons.

OVERVIEW ■ CHAPTER 15

Although this chapter is devoted to circles, it brings together ideas from many earlier chapters of the book. Measurement of arcs and relations with central angles and chord length are discussed in Lesson 15-1. In Lesson 15-2, rotations, regular polygons, and points as nodes of a network are combined in a wonderful application of geometry to scheduling teams. In Lesson 15-3, the relationship of an inscribed angle to its intercepted arc is proved, and this relationship is applied in Lesson 15-4 to show

another way of finding the center of a circle. Trigonometry helps to locate the distance of the center from an object.

Lessons 15-5 through 15-7 present the theorems that relate the lengths of chords, secants, and tangents in circles, and the measures of angles formed by these segments, with the arcs they intercept. Lessons 15-8 and 15-9 discuss the Isoperimetric Theorems and Inequalities. The theorems in these lessons cannot be proved at this level because they require

ideas from advanced calculus.

As the chapter opener pages indicate, circles have a variety of applications. Two interesting and useful applications studied in this chapter are the scheduling of teams and locating the position for a photographer so that an entire object lies in the field of vision. These applications are likely to be used by students, and should be studied in detail.

It is advisable for students to have compasses available for every lesson in this chapter.

PERSPECTIVES ■ CHAPTER 15

The Perspectives provide the rationale for the inclusion of topics or approaches, provide mathematical background, and make connections with other lessons and within UCSMP.

15-1

CHORD LENGTH AND ARC MEASURE

Since the endpoints of a chord and the center of its circle form the vertices of an isosceles triangle, certain properties of the isosceles triangle can be restated in terms of chords and circles. These properties are summarized in the Chord-Center Theorem. Properties of rotations and the definition of congruence lead to the fact that minor arcs in a circle are congruent if and only if their chords are congruent.

Using properties of special triangles, students can calculate lengths of chords for arcs of 60°, 90°, and 120°. Using the trigonometry of the previous chapter, the length of a chord for any arc can be calculated.

15-2

REGULAR POLYGONS AND SCHEDULES

This lesson explains an algorithm by using regular polygons and rotations to schedule any number of teams in a round-robin tournament.

At the same time, the algorithm yields more information about regular polygons than students customarily learn in geometry; for instance, the numbers of diagonals of each length, the parallel diagonals, and the rotation symmetry of the polygon.

The points in the application of this lesson stand for teams and segments stand for games. The schedule is in fact a network. But symmetry requires that the points be viewed as locations. Thus, in an elegant way, the application combines the notions of Euclidean geometry with those of networks.

15-3

THE INSCRIBED ANGLE THEOREM

The theorem of the lesson states that the measure of an inscribed angle is half the measure of its intercepted arc. The theorem is motivated by the problem of deciding where a photographer can stand in order to fit an entire building in a picture. The proof of the theorem is

the standard one involving consideration of three cases.

15-4

LOCATING THE CENTER OF A CIRCLE

In Lesson 4-5, students learned how to find a circle through any three given points. The method used to do this, namely the perpendicular bisector method, has the advantage of not requiring an entire circle. One can find the center of an arc, or the circle through just three points. The method is justified by using the theorem that the perpendicular bisector of a chord contains the center of a circle.

In this lesson, a second method for locating the center of a circle, the right angle method, is described and justified. Carpenters use the right angle method to locate centers of circles. It requires drawing a few lines and does not require a compass.

The photographer's problem in Lesson 15-4 can now be solved

both in theory and in practice. That is, the set of points where the photographer can stand to fit an object in the picture is an arc. The center of that arc can be located, and the distance from the object to the center can be calculated.

15-5

ANGLES FORMED BY CHORDS OR SECANTS

The two theorems in this lesson, the Angle-Chord Theorem and the Angle-Secant Theorem, can be viewed as special cases of one general theorem. Think of standing at the vertex of an angle and simultaneously looking down its interior and back at its vertical angle. Suppose there is a single circle that has two arcs passing through this interior. Measure an arc as positive if you are inside of it and negative if you are outside of it. Then the measure of your angle is the average of the measures of the arcs.

The importance of these theorems is as an application of the Inscribed Angle Theorem. Since the theorems are seldom applied outside of secondary school geometry, the lesson can be skipped if time is short.

15-6

ANGLES FORMED BY TANGENTS

This lesson extends the results of the previous lesson to tangents. It enables students to have a second day to assimilate the relationships between arc and angle measures.

15-7

LENGTHS OF CHORDS, SECANTS, AND TANGENTS

The major theorem of this lesson is the Secant Length Theorem. In some books, this theorem is considered as two unrelated theorems. (1) In a circle, if two chords intersect, the product of the segments of one chord equals the product of the segments of the other. (2) In a circle, if two secants intersect *outside* a circle, the product of one secant and its external segment equals the product of the other secant and its external segment. Considering the Secant Length Theorem as two unrelated theorems disguises the fact that they are two cases of the same theorem.

A special case of the Secant Length Theorem is that the square of the length of a tangent to a circle equals the product of the length of a secant from that point and its external segment. Quadratic equations arise frequently in situations that apply this theorem.

15-8

THE ISOPERIMETRIC INEQUALITY

The Isoperimetric Inequality is not discussed in many secondary school geometry books for two reasons: It was not in Euclid's development of geometry and its proof requires the use of advanced calculus. However, the theorem for the plane probably was known to

the ancient Carthaginians. The problem of finding the maximum area for a given perimeter is attributed to Dido, the founder of Carthage, and is called *Dido's Problem.*

A topic often covered in secondary school mathematics (and seldom in geometry) is that of all rectangles with the same perimeter, the square has the most area. (See Question 12.) From this result, some students get the impression that the square is best of all figures.

The purpose of this lesson and the next is three-fold. First, the results are important. Second, the results can be used to explain a variety of natural phenomena. For instance, the plane version explains why the water level in a paper cup goes up if the cup is squeezed (the circular cross-sections become noncircular and lose area; the lost areas add up in lost volume, so the water has no place to go but up and out of the cup). Third, the inequality continues to reinforce the idea that area and perimeter are different concepts.

15-9

THE ISOPERIMETRIC THEOREMS IN SPACE

Analogous to the plane version, the space version of the Isoperimetric Inequality reinforces the idea that the surface area and volume measures of physical objects are very different concepts.

We recommend 13 to 16 days for this chapter: 9 to 11 on the lessons and quizzes; 1 for the Progress Self-Test; 1 or 2 for the Chapter Review; 1 for a Chapter test; and 1 for the Comprehensive Test. (See the Daily Pacing Chart on page 732A.)

Further Work with Circles

15-1: Chord Length and Arc Measure
15-2: Regular Polygons and Schedules
15-3: The Inscribed Angle Theorem
15-4: Locating the Center of a Circle
15-5: Angles Formed by Chords or Secants

15-6: Angles Formed by Tangents
15-7: Lengths of Chords, Secants, and Tangents
15-8: The Isoperimetric Inequality
15-9: The Isoperimetric Theorems in Space

732

Circles have been important figures since antiquity. The ancient Greeks believed that the sun, planets, and other celestial objects went around the earth in circles. The great scientist Galileo Galilei wrote in 1623:

> *. . . the universe . . . is written in the language of mathematics, and its characters are triangles, circles, and other geometrical figures, without which it is humanly impossible to understand a single word of it; without these, one is wandering about in a dark labyrinth.*

Already in this book you have seen circles arise from rather different sources:

as cross-sections of cylinders, cones, spheres, and other surfaces made by rotating a figure in three-dimensions;

as a limit of regular polygons;

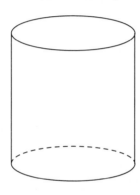

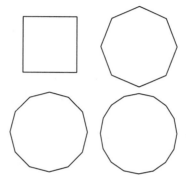

as containing shortest paths on the surface of a sphere;

as sets of points the same distance from a center.

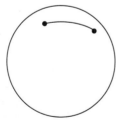

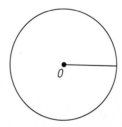

With these properties, the circle or arc is viewed as a whole. In this chapter, the measures of angles and segments associated with circles are examined in some detail. The results are very pretty and often quite surprising, and are related to further applications of this simple figure.

USING PAGES 732-733
The point of Galileo's quote is quite simple: *Every* physical object is geometric, because every physical object has a shape.

Students have been familiar with circles from the time they were very young, so instances of circles do not need to be reviewed. Four sources for the origin of circles are given along with the pictures on this page. A fifth source of circles is found in wheels or cylinders that support a rolling object.

CHAPTER 15   Further Work with Circles   **733**

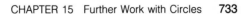

LESSON 15-1

RESOURCES
■ Lesson Master 15-1
▣ Computer Master 33

OBJECTIVES

A Calculate lengths of chords of arcs.
F Make deductions from properties of radii perpendicular to chords, and know sufficient conditions for radii to be perpendicular to them.

TEACHING NOTES

You might begin this lesson by writing down the four parts of the Chord-Center Theorem. Have students match the statements with statements that they know about isosceles triangles.

Throughout this chapter, angles, chords, and arcs in circles are drawn with various tilts. This can be done because in a circle all directions are the same. The Arc-Chord Congruence Theorem can be thought of as a restatement of this property.

Whereas two arcs with measure $x°$ in the same circle or in circles with the same radius are congruent, two arcs with measure $x°$ in circles with different radii are similar. (See the Extension on page 739.) These properties can help students to distinguish between arc length and arc measure. An arc's length changes if the size of the circle changes, but its measure stays the same if the central angle of the arc does not change.

Chord Length and Arc Measure

Recall some information about angles and circles. An angle with its vertex at the center of a circle is a **central angle** of the circle. The arc of the circle on and in the interior of the angle is said to be **intercepted** by the angle. The **measure of the intercepted arc** is defined as the measure of its central angle.

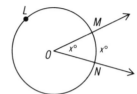

central angle MON and its intercepted arc $\widehat{MN}$.
$m\angle MON = x°$
$m\widehat{MN} = x°$

Above, $m\angle MON$ seems to be about 45, and arc $\widehat{MN}$ also measures 45°. Since $45 = \frac{1}{8} \cdot 360$, the arc is about $\frac{1}{8}$ of the circle. $\widehat{MN}$ is a **minor arc** because its measure is less than 180°. The **major arc** $\widehat{MLN}$ has measure $360° - 45°$, or 315°. An arc with measure 180° is a **semicircle.**

If $\widehat{AB}$ is an arc of a circle, the segment $\overline{AB}$ is called the **chord of the arc** $\widehat{AB}$. When $\widehat{AB}$ is not a semicircle, the triangle determined by A, B, and center O is isosceles.

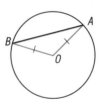

$\overline{AB}$ is the chord of $\widehat{AB}$.

You have learned that, in an isosceles triangle, the bisector of the vertex angle, the perpendicular bisector of the base, the altitude from the vertex, and the median from the vertex all lie on the same line. (See Lesson 5-1 if you have forgotten.) In the language of circles and chords, this leads to the following theorem.

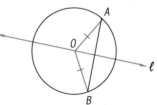

734

Chord-Center Theorem:

a. The line containing the center of a circle perpendicular to a chord bisects the chord.

b. The line containing the center of a circle and the midpoint of a chord bisects the central angle determined by the chord.

c. The bisector of the central angle of a chord is perpendicular to the chord and bisects the chord.

d. The perpendicular bisector of a chord of a circle contains the center of the circle.

Proof

Each part is only a restatement of a property of isosceles triangles.
a. This says the altitude to the base is a median.
b. This says the __?__ is also a(n) __?__ .
c. This says the __?__ is also a(n) __?__ .
d. This says the __?__ is also a(n) __?__ .

If two circles $\odot X$ and $\odot Y$ have equal radii, then one can be mapped onto the other by the translation mapping X to Y. So they are congruent. Of course, if they do not have equal radii, since isometries preserve distance, no isometry will map one onto the other.

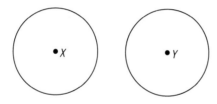

This proves that circles are congruent if and only if they have equal radii.

If two arcs in the same or congruent circles have the same measure, then they are congruent. In the circle below, you can rotate $\overset{\frown}{AB}$ about O by the measure of $\angle AOC$ to the position of $\overset{\frown}{CD}$. Then the chord $\overline{AB}$ rotates to $\overline{CD}$ also, and $\overline{AB} \cong \overline{CD}$. Thus, in a circle, arcs of the same measure are congruent and have congruent chords. This proves part **a** of the next theorem. The proof of part **b** is left for you as Question 14.

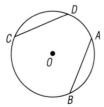

LESSON 15-1   Chord Length and Arc Measure   **735**

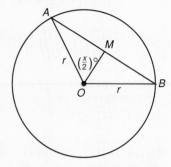

The following is the general way to find the length of a chord of any arc. Suppose the arc has measure $x°$. Then its central angle has measure $x°$. Draw the chord connecting the endpoints of the arc; draw the radii to the endpoints of the arc; and draw the perpendicular bisector of the chord (containing the center of the circle).

AB is the length of the chord. Now, m$\angle AOM = \frac{x}{2}$, so $AM = r \sin \frac{x}{2}$. Thus, $AB = 2r \sin \frac{x}{2}$. This application of sines to chords was the first use of sines historically. The Greek mathematician Ptolemy calculated lengths of chords in this way. The word *sine* comes from the Latin *sinus,* meaning *bridge* (with sinuses being under the bridge of the nose), and derives from the fact that when $\overline{AB}$ is horizontal and above the center, $\triangle ABO$ with $\overline{OM}$ drawn looks like a nose.

The term *inscribed polygon* is important to discuss because it is used in later lessons. The term *circumscribed polygon* is defined in **Question 24**.

You may want to emphasize the notations used for chords, arcs, central angles, and major versus minor arcs. Chords are segments and therefore use the same notation as before, but arcs are used to designate the arc connecting the chord between two points. Central angles are named as angles normally are, but notice the use of three points to name a major arc. Arcs named with two letters are minor arcs unless the word "major" is included in the description.

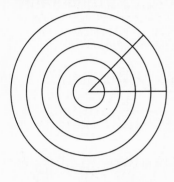

Arc-Chord Congruence Theorem:

In a circle or in congruent circles:
a. If two arcs have the same measure, they are congruent and their chords are congruent.
b. If two chords have the same length, their minor arcs have the same measure.

In circles with *different* radii, however, arcs of the same measure are not congruent. They are *similar*. And their chords are not congruent. This is pictured below.

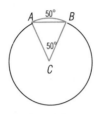
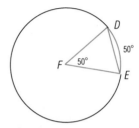

$m\ \widehat{AB} = m\ \widehat{DE}$
and $\ \widehat{AB} \sim \widehat{DE}$,
but $\ \overline{AB} \not\equiv \overline{DE}$.

A natural question to ask is: Given the measure of an arc, can the length of its chord be found? This can always be done using trigonometry if the radius of the circle is known. If the arc measure is 60°, 90°, or 120°, it can be done without trigonometry.

Example 1 A circle has a radius of 10″. Find the length of a chord of
a. a 60° arc; **b.** a 90° arc; **c.** a 120° arc.

Solution Always draw a picture.

a. △*AOB* is an isosceles triangle with a 60° vertex angle, so it is equilateral. So *AB* = 10″.

b. △*COD* is an isosceles right triangle. So *CD* = $10\sqrt{2}$″ ≈ 14.14″.

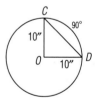

c. Draw the altitude $\overline{OG}$ to the base of △*OEF*. The two triangles formed are 30-60-90 triangles. *OE* = 2 · *OG*, so *OG* = 5″. *GE* = $\sqrt{3}$ · *OG*, so *GE* = $5\sqrt{3}$″, from which *FE* = $10\sqrt{3}$″ or *FE* ≈ 17.32″.

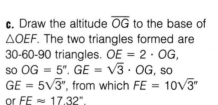

736

Example 1 provides a way of finding the length of a side of a regular hexagon, square, or equilateral triangle whose vertices are on a circle. Any polygon whose vertices lie on a given circle is called an **inscribed polygon.** The center of an inscribed regular polygon is the center of the circle.

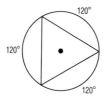 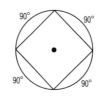 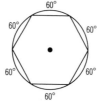

Using trigonometry, you can always find the length of a chord if you know its arc measure and the radius of the circle.

■ ■ ■ ■ ■ ■ ■ ■ ■ ■

Example 2 Find the length of a chord of a 103° arc in a circle of radius 20 cm.

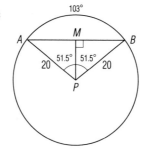

Solution A picture is drawn at the right. The length of $\overline{AB}$ is desired.

Because $\triangle PAB$ is isosceles with vertex angle P, if M is the midpoint of $\overline{AB}$, then $\overline{PM} \perp \overline{AB}$ and $\overline{PM}$ bisects $\angle APB$. Thus $\triangle APM$ is a right triangle and $m\angle APM = \frac{103}{2} = 51.5$. To find AM, use trigonometry.

$$\sin 51.5° = \frac{AM}{20}$$
$$AM = 20 \cdot \sin 51.5° \approx 15.65$$

Since M is a midpoint, $AB = 2 \cdot AM \approx 31.30$ cm.

Questions

Covering the Reading

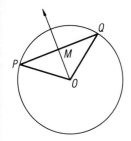

1. The measure of a minor arc of a circle is between __?__ and __?__.
   0, 180
2. The measure of a major arc of a circle is between __?__ and __?__.
   180, 360

In 3–6, use ⊙O pictured at the left.

3. If m∠POQ = 98, then m $\overparen{PQ}$ = __?__. 98°

4. Explain why △OPQ is isosceles. **See margin.**

5. If $\overline{OM} \perp \overline{PQ}$, then $\overline{OM}$ __?__ $\overline{PQ}$. **bisects**

6. If $\overrightarrow{OM}$ bisects ∠POQ, then $\overrightarrow{OM}$ __?__ $\overline{PQ}$.
   bisects or is the ⊥ bisector of

LESSON 15-1 Chord Length and Arc Measure   **737**

circle route) from Washington, D.C., to Beijing is about 6950 miles.
The arc measures about 100.5°; its chord has a length of about 6090 miles.

NOTES ON QUESTIONS
Questions 1 and 2: The phrase "between ___ and ___" is used when the endpoints of an arc are excluded, and "from ___ to ___" when the endpoints are included.

Question 9: The drawing confirms the answer, but some students may not realize that.

Questions 10-13: Encourage students always to draw a picture. Notice that although the problems look quite similar, the method of solution is not necessarily the same. It depends on the type of triangle drawn.

Question 15: There are many other questions of this type in the review sets of later lessons.

Computer for Question 24: Using an automatic drawing program may help students make these conjectures. For example, for part **a** you could draw various types of quadrilaterals and ask the computer to inscribe circles in the quadrilaterals (this is equivalent to the quadrilateral being circumscribed). Then test the conjectures with the measure features of the program.

ADDITIONAL ANSWERS
4. OP = OQ by the definition of circle, and △OPQ is isosceles by the definition of isosceles triangle (sufficient condition).

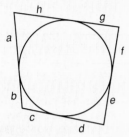
Applying the Mathematics

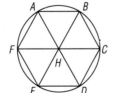

7. Fill in the blanks in the proof of the Chord-Center Theorem. See margin.

8. *Multiple choice.*
Two circles are congruent if and only if their radii are
(a) parallel
(b) perpendicular
(c) equal in length
(d) none of these. (c)

9. Refer to $\odot Z$ and $\odot A$ below.
True or false? If $m\angle Z = m\angle A$, then $XY = BC$. False

In 10–13, $\odot O$ at the right has radius 25 m.

10. Find the length of a chord of a 60° arc.
25 m

11. Find the length of a chord of a 90° arc.
$25\sqrt{2} \approx 35.4$ m

12. Find the length of a chord of a 120° arc.
$25\sqrt{3} \approx 43.3$ m

13. Find the length of a chord of a 53° arc.
≈ 22.3 m

14. Complete this proof of part **b** of the Arc-Chord Congruence Theorem.

Given: $AB = CD$ in $\odot O$ as shown below.
Prove: $m\overset{\frown}{AB} = m\overset{\frown}{CD}$.
(Hint: The measure of an arc equals the measure of its central angle.)
See margin.

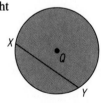

15. The circular hole with center Q shown at the right has a radius of 3 ft. A 5-foot board $\overline{XY}$ is to be wedged into the hole. What will be the distance from Q to $\overline{XY}$? (Hint: Draw some auxiliary radii and perpendiculars.)
$\sqrt{2.75} \approx 1.66$ ft

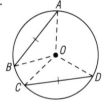

16. Regular hexagon $ABCDEF$ is inscribed in $\odot H$.
Suppose $HA = 13$.
a. Find $m\angle AHB$. 60
b. Find the perimeter of $ABCDEF$. 78 units

17. $LMNP$ is a square inscribed in $\odot O$ at the right. The radius of the circle is $6\sqrt{2}$. Find the length of a side of the square. 12 units

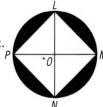

Review

In 18 and 19, use ⊙Q at the right.

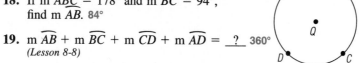

18. If m $\overset{\frown}{ABC}$ = 178° and m $\overset{\frown}{BC}$ = 94°, find m $\overset{\frown}{AB}$. **84°**

19. m $\overset{\frown}{AB}$ + m $\overset{\frown}{BC}$ + m $\overset{\frown}{CD}$ + m $\overset{\frown}{AD}$ = __?__ **360°**
(Lesson 8-8)

20. In the figure below, find m∠A. *(Lesson 13-7)* **94**

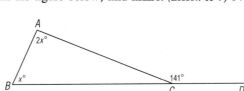

21. A square pyramid has a base with sides 2 m and height 1.4 m. What is its volume? *(Lesson 10-7)* $\frac{28}{15}$ ≈ **1.87 m³**

22. To rotate a figure -120°, you could reflect the figure over two lines where the acute angle between the lines has measure __?__. *(Lesson 6-3)* **60**

23. a. The measure of an angle of a regular *n*-gon is __?__.
  b. The measure of an angle of a regular octagon is __?__. *(Lesson 5-7)*
  a) $\frac{(n-2) \cdot 180}{n}$; b) **135**

Exploration

24. A polygon is **circumscribed** about a circle if each of its sides is tangent to the circle. At the right, a quadrilateral has been circumscribed about circle *O*.

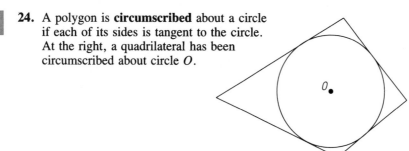

Experiment with various circles and polygons. Tell whether you think these conjectures are *true* or *false*.

  a. If a quadrilateral is circumscribed about a circle, then at least two of its sides are congruent.
  b. If a rectangle is circumscribed about a circle, then it is a square.
  c. If an isosceles trapezoid is circumscribed about a circle, then it is a rectangle.
  d. A polygon with an odd number of sides greater than 3 cannot be circumscribed about a circle.
  Answers will vary.
  a), c), and d) happen to be false; b) can be proved true.

LESSON 15-1 Chord Length and Arc Measure **739**

FOLLOW-UP

MORE PRACTICE
For more questions on SPUR Objectives, use *Lesson Master 15-1*, shown below.

EXTENSION
Have students explore the proof of the Arc-Chord Similarity Theorem which states that in any circle or congruent circles, if two arcs have the same measure, then they are similar. The proof is typical of similarity proofs. If the radii of the circles of the arcs are *a* and *b*, change the size of the circle with radius *a* by magnitude $\frac{b}{a}$. The image of the arc will have the same measure (since the measure of the central angle is preserved under a size change), and the image circle will be congruent to the other circle. So the image arc and the arc in the circle of radius *b* are congruent. Therefore, one arc can be mapped onto the other by the composite of an isometry and a size change, and they are similar.

NAME _____

LESSON **MASTER 15–1**
QUESTIONS ON **SPUR** OBJECTIVES

■ **SKILLS** *Objective A (See pages 788–791 for objectives.)*
In 1–3, a circle has a radius of 2 cm. What is the length of a chord of

1. a 60° arc ___**2 cm**___.

2. a 120° arc ___**2√3 ≈ 3.46 cm**___.

3. an 84° arc ___**4 sin 42°**___
___**≈ 2.68 cm**___.

In 4 and 5, ABCD is a square inscribed in ⊙O below.
AB = 10√2.

4. Find OC.
___**10**___

5. Find the area of the shaded region.
___**100π − 200 ≈ 114 units²**___

■ **PROPERTIES** *Objective F*
In 6–8, given ⊙O, $\overline{XY} \perp \overline{WZ}$, and $\overline{OX} \perp m$. Justify each statement, if possible.

6. m ∥ $\overline{WZ}$
Two Perpendiculars
Theorem

7. WV = VZ
Chord-Center Theorem

8. OV = YV
cannot be justified

138   Geometry © Scott, Foresman and Company

RESOURCES
■ Lesson Master 15-2

OBJECTIVE

K Make a schedule for a round-robin tournament.

TEACHING NOTES

Allow your students the joy of discovery. Do not discuss the lesson before students have read it and completed the questions independently.

Certain ideas are so surprising and interesting that they are almost always remembered. Scheduling is one of those ideas. The conceptualization of scheduling by using regular polygons yields an automatic algorithm. Students will be surprised that geometry has an application to a situation that is not geometric at all.

The point to be emphasized in a class discussion is that the algorithm could be employed in scheduling any number of teams. With a larger number of teams, the advantage of the geometric method becomes even greater.

Making Connections
Students who have taken UCSMP *Transition Mathematics* have studied how to use the vertices of a polygon to help them do simple scheduling.

15-2

Regular Polygons and Schedules

In many competitions, from baseball to chess to soccer to bowling, each competitor plays all the others. When each competitor (or team) plays each other competitor exactly once, it is called a **round-robin** tournament. Scheduling this, as you know if you have ever tried it, can be tricky. Suppose there are seven teams to be scheduled so that each plays the other six. The first thing you might do is number the teams 1 through 7. Now schedule a first week. One team doesn't play. That team gets a **bye.**

1 plays 2	3 plays 4	5 plays 6	7 bye

What about a second week? Try 1 playing 3. Perhaps 2 plays 4? Here's a possibility.

1 plays 3	2 plays 4	5 plays 7	6 bye

Now a third week. We just try to have teams play teams they haven't.

1 plays 4	2 plays 5	6 plays 7	3 bye

It seems easy. Here is a fourth-week schedule.

1 plays 5	2 plays 6	3 plays 7	4 bye

Another week. It's starting to get complicated. We keep looking back so as not to repeat.

1 plays 6	2 plays 3	4 plays 7	5 bye

How many weeks to go? Team 1 still has to play 7. So does 2. We make 2 the bye.

1 plays 7	3 plays 6	4 plays 5	2 bye

There's only one week left. Can you see what it should be?

_?_	_?_	_?_	_?_

It doesn't seem hard. But perhaps we were lucky. What if there were more teams? It would be nice if there was some algorithm that automatically created the schedule. The algorithm described here is surprising in that it uses rotation and properties of regular polygons and circles.

740

Step 1   Let the 7 teams be vertices of an inscribed
regular 7-gon (heptagon).

Step 2   (the first week) Draw a chord and all chords parallel to it.
Because the polygon has an odd number of sides, no two
chords have the same length. This is the first week's schedule

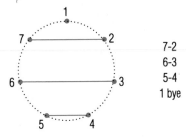

7-2
6-3
5-4
1 bye

Since the top chord joins 7 and 2, team 7 plays team 2 the first
week. This is called a **pairing,** and is written 7-2. Also in the first
week, team 6 plays team 3, team 5 plays team 4, and team 1
gets a bye. The full schedule will be completed when all sides
and diagonals of the heptagons have been drawn.

Step 3   (the second week) Rotate the chords $\frac{1}{7}$ of a revolution. For
example, the first week pairing 7-2 rotates into the pairing 1-3.

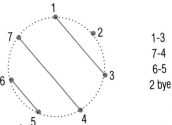

1-3
7-4
6-5
2 bye

Step 4   Continue rotating $\frac{1}{7}$ of a revolution for each week. Because in a
week no two chords have the same length, no pairing repeats. In
a total of seven weeks, the schedule is complete.

3rd week:	2-4	1-5	7-6	3 bye
4th week:	3-5	2-6	1-7	4 bye
5th week:	4-6	3-7	2-1	5 bye
6th week:	5-7	4-1	3-2	6 bye
7th week:	?	?	?	?

Again we leave the 7th week for you to figure out. It is easier
this time.

LESSON 15-2 Regular Polygons and Schedules   **741**

The same procedure will not work with an even number of teams. If parallel chords are drawn using the vertices of a regular octagon, some will have the same length. So, as you rotate, you will repeat pairings.

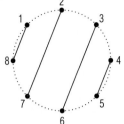

However, instead of putting the 8th team on the circle, it can be placed at the center of the circle. The radius joins team 8 and the bye in the above schedule. As you rotate the chords to make the schedule, rotate the radius too! This shows the surprising result: It takes as many weeks for a schedule of 7 teams as it does for a schedule of 8 teams. In general, it takes as many weeks for a schedule of $2n - 1$ teams as for a schedule of $2n$ teams.

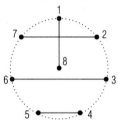

With 7 teams there are 3 games for each of 7 weeks, or 21 pairings. Of these, 7 are sides of the regular heptagon, 7 are congruent shorter diagonals, and 7 are congruent longer diagonals. Scheduling a league of 7 or 8 teams thus has revealed some properties of the regular heptagon!

In the Questions, you should assume that all schedules are round-robin.

Questions

Covering the Reading

1. Complete the last week of pairings in the first schedule discussed in this lesson. *2 plays 7, 3 plays 5, 4 plays 6, 1 bye*

In 2–7, refer to the use of the regular heptagon to schedule teams.

2. How is a game between teams 4 and 6 pictured? *as a chord connecting 4 and 6*

3. To find the pairings for the first week, all chords ___?___ to a given chord are drawn. *parallel*

742

4. How are the chords for one week related to the chords for the next week? They are rotated $\frac{1}{7}$ of a revolution.

5. Complete the last week of pairings. 6-1, 5-2, 4-3, 7 bye

6. Where is an 8th team pictured to use this idea to schedule 8 teams? in the center of the circle

7. Write a complete schedule for 8 teams. See margin.

8. A regular heptagon has diagonals of how many different lengths? two

9. *True* or *false*? It takes as many weeks for a schedule of 9 teams as it does for a schedule of 10 teams. True

10. a. To schedule 9 teams, what should be done first? a-c) See margin.
    b. Give the first two weeks of a schedule for 9 teams.
    c. Complete a schedule for 9 teams.
    d. How many diagonals does a nonagon have? 27
    e. Indicate what you can do to convert the schedule in c for 10 teams. Replace each bye with team 10.

11. Explain why the algorithm of this lesson will not work for scheduling 6 teams. (Begin with the diagram at the left.) Two chords have the same length, so after 3 weeks, the pairings will be repeated.

12. Make a complete schedule for a tournament with 6 teams. See margin.

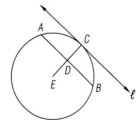

13. Which two of the following descriptions of a point are used in the idea of scheduling?
    (a) dot
    (b) ordered pair
    (c) location
    (d) node of network (c) and (d)

14. $\overline{IB}$ is a chord in circle G. If $IB = 12$ and $IG = 10$, find the shortest distance from G to $\overline{IB}$. *(Lesson 15-1)* 8 units

15. Find the length of a chord of a 120° arc in a circle of radius 45 mm. *(Lesson 15-1)* $45\sqrt{3} \approx 77.9$ mm

16. Find the length of a chord of a 160° arc in a circle of radius 45 mm. *(Lesson 15-1)*. ≈ 88.6 mm

17. Given: ℓ is tangent to $\odot E$ at C;
    $AD = DB$.
    Prove: $\overline{AB} \parallel \ell$. *(Lesson 15-1)*
    See margin.

---

10. a. Let the 9 teams be vertices of a regular 9-gon.
b. sample:
wk 1: 9-2, 8-3, 7-4, 6-5, 1 bye
wk 2: 1-3, 9-4, 8-5, 7-6, 2 bye
c.
wk 3: 2-4, 1-5, 9-6, 8-7, 3 bye
wk 4: 3-5, 2-6, 1-7, 9-8, 4 bye
wk 5: 4-6, 3-7, 2-8, 1-9, 5 bye
wk 6: 5-7, 4-8, 3-9, 2-1, 6 bye
wk 7: 6-8, 5-9, 4-1, 3-2, 7 bye
wk 8: 7-9, 6-1, 5-2, 4-3, 8 bye
wk 9: 8-1, 7-2, 6-3, 5-4, 9 bye

12. sample:
wk 1: 2-5, 3-4, 1-6
wk 2: 3-1, 4-5, 2-6
wk 3: 4-2, 5-1, 3-6
wk 4: 5-3, 1-2, 4-6
wk 5: 1-4, 2-3, 5-6

17.

Conclusions	Justifications
1. $\ell \perp \overline{CE}$	Tangent to Circle Thm.
2. $\overline{AB} \perp \overline{CE}$	Chord-Center Thm. (parts b and c)
3. $\overline{AB} \parallel \ell$	Two Perpendiculars Thm.

MORE PRACTICE
For more questions on SPUR
Objectives, use *Lesson Mas-
ter 15-2,* shown on page 743.

EXTENSION
Use the Exploration **Question 23** as a guide to having
students make up a schedule
for a team or league with
which they are familiar. Is it
round-robin? Is it double
round-robin so each team
plays every other at home?
Are there divisions? Determine how many games are
played in all.

ADDITIONAL ANSWERS
21. (Art is reduced in size.)

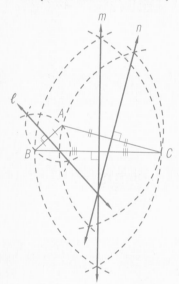

18. Square *WHUN* is inscribed in circle *Q* at the left. If the radius is $\sqrt{13}$ cm, find the perimeter of *WHUN*. *(Lesson 15-1)* $4\sqrt{26} \approx 20.4$ cm

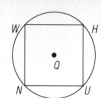

19. Willow, Lake, and Central are east-west streets. Greenwood and Landwehr are north-south streets. Milwaukee is oblique. What is the distance on Milwaukee from Lake to Willow? *(Lesson 12-8)* 1.8 miles

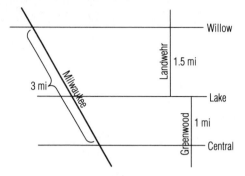

20. Trace the drawing at the left. Draw line *m* so that $r_m \circ r_\ell(A) = B$. *(Lesson 6-3)*

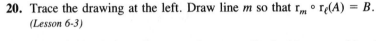

21. Trace $\triangle ABC$ below. Construct the perpendicular bisectors of its sides. *(Lesson 3-6)* See margin.

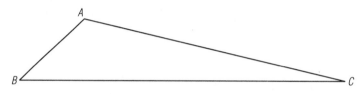

22. Solve for *x:* $100n - 200 + x = 100n$. *(Previous course)* x = 200

Exploration

23. **a.** Find a schedule for teams in a league involving your school or community. Answers will vary.
    b. What factors affect schedules that this lesson does not mention?
    samples: where game is played; dates and times can be affected by holidays or travel schedules; certain pairings may be saved for the final games of the season

744

15-3

The Inscribed Angle Theorem

LESSON 15-3

RESOURCES
- Lesson Master 15-3
- Quiz for Lessons 15-1 Through 15-3
- Visual for Teaching Aid 85 shows the diagram on page 745.

The **picture angle** of a camera lens is a measure indicating how wide a field of vision can be captured in one photo. A normal camera lens in a Nikon 35 mm camera has a picture angle of 46°. A wide-angle lens may have a picture angle as large as 118°. A telephoto lens has a smaller picture angle, perhaps 18°.

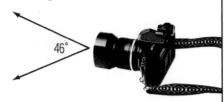

Here is a situation in photography. You want to take a picture of a building, and you want to get the entire front of the building in your picture. (Assume the height of the building is not a problem.) Suppose you have only one normal lens with a 46° field. The diagram pictures the situation as seen from above.

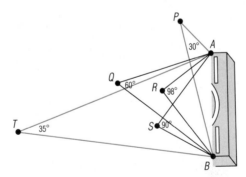

Let *A* and *B* be the endpoints of the building. If you stand at *Q*, m∠*AQB* is larger than 46, so the picture cannot include the entire front. The same is true for points *R* and *S*. But at points *P* and *T*, the whole front can be in the picture. There is a natural question: where are all the vertex points that make a 46° angle with points *A* and *B*? The answer is surprising. It is found by considering *inscribed angles* in a circle.

OBJECTIVES

B Calculate measures of inscribed angles from measure of intercepted arcs, and vice versa.

C Calculate measures of angles from measures of intercepted arcs, and vice versa.

G Make deductions from properties of inscribed angles.

TEACHING NOTES

Begin the lesson by drawing a circle and three angles *A*, *B*, and *C* that inscribe the same arc.

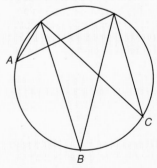

The angles do not look congruent because their sides are not the same lengths. If you look near the vertices, however, the openings are the same. This suggests the angles are congruent. The proof of the theorem may be difficult because it is done in cases. Point out that a proof is not complete if all possibilities are not considered.

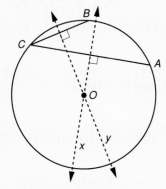
Definition:

> An angle is an **inscribed angle** in a circle if and only if (a) the vertex of the angle is on the circle and (b) each side of the angle intersects the circle at a point other than the vertex.

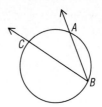

Inscribed angle ABC intercepts arc $\widehat{AC}$.

Consider <u>some</u> inscribed angles A, B, and C which intercept the same arc $\widehat{MN}$. You should measure these angles and then measure $\angle MON$ to determine $m\ \widehat{MN}$.

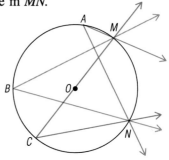

Ab<u>ove</u>, you should find that $m\angle A = m\angle B = m\angle C \approx 37$, and $m\ \widehat{MN} \approx 74°$. These are instances of a surprising relationship which is true of all inscribed angles and their intercepted arcs.

Inscribed Angle Theorem:

> In a circle, the measure of an inscribed angle is one-half the measure of its intercepted arc.

The steps of the proof depend on the position of the center O relative to the inscribed $\angle ABC$. There are three possibilities. They are referred to as Case I, Case II, and Case III.

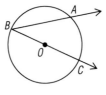 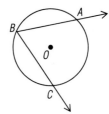 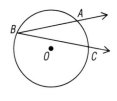

Case I: O lies on a side of $\angle ABC$.

Case II: O is in the interior of $\angle ABC$.

Case III: O is in the exterior of $\angle ABC$.

746

Proof

For all three figures the given and to prove are the same.

Given: ∠ABC inscribed in ⊙O.

Prove: m∠ABC = ½ · m$\widehat{AC}$.

Case I: The auxiliary segment $\overline{OA}$ is required. Since △AOB is isosceles, m∠B = m∠A. Call this measure x. By the Exterior Angle Theorem, m∠AOC = 2x.

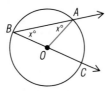

Because the measure of an arc equals the measure of its central angle,

m$\widehat{AC}$ = 2x = 2 · m∠B.

Solving for m∠B, m∠B = ½ m$\widehat{AC}$.

Case I proves that m∠B = ½ m$\widehat{AC}$ when one ray of ∠B contains point O. This result is used in the proofs of Case II and Case III.

Case II: The auxiliary ray $\overrightarrow{BO}$ is needed.

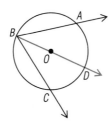

$$m\angle ABC = m\angle ABD + m\angle DBC \quad \text{(Angle Addition Postulate)}$$
$$= \tfrac{1}{2}m\widehat{AD} + \tfrac{1}{2}m\widehat{DC} \quad \text{(by the result of Case I)}$$
$$= \tfrac{1}{2}(m\widehat{AD}+m\widehat{DC}) \quad \text{(Distributive Property)}$$
$$= \tfrac{1}{2}m\widehat{AC} \quad \text{(Arc Addition, substitution)}$$

Case III: The proof is like that for Case II.
For Case III, m∠ABC = m∠ABD − m∠CBD.

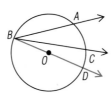

You are asked to finish the steps in Question 11.

1. The three angles of △ABC have measures 40, 60, and 80. If the circle through A, B, and C is drawn, what are the measures of the three minor arcs formed by the points? **80°, 120°, and 160° (The check is that they add to 360°.)**

2. ABCDEF is a regular hexagon. Find m∠BFE. **Inscribe the regular hexagon in a circle, as shown below.**

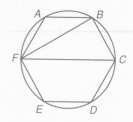

∠**BFE intercepts an arc of 180°, so it is a right angle.**

The Inscribed Angle Theorem is easy to apply.

Example 1 Four points, A, B, C, and D, split a circle into arcs with measures as shown. Find the measures of the angles of $ABCD$.

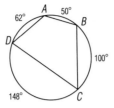

Solution

$m\angle A = \frac{1}{2} m\widehat{BCD} = \frac{1}{2}(100° + 148°) = 124$

$m\angle B = \frac{1}{2} m\widehat{ADC} = \frac{1}{2}(62° + 148°) = 105$

$m\angle C = \frac{1}{2} m\widehat{DAB} = \frac{1}{2}(62° + 50°) = 56$

$m\angle D = \frac{1}{2} m\widehat{ABC} = \frac{1}{2}(50° + 100°) = 75$

Check The four angle measures add up to 360° as they should for a quadrilateral. Furthermore, the measures look correct.

The next Example demonstrates a surprising consequence of the Inscribed Angle Theorem.

Example 2 Let $\widehat{PQR}$ be a semicircle. Find $m\angle PQR$.

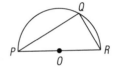

Solution Complete the circle.

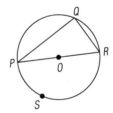

From the inscribed Angle Theorem, $m\angle PQR = \frac{1}{2}\widehat{PSR}$. Since $\widehat{PSR}$ is also a semicircle, $m\widehat{PSR} = 180°$. Thus $m\angle PQR = \frac{1}{2} \cdot 180 = 90$.

Example 2 proves the following.

Theorem:

An angle inscribed in a semicircle is a right angle.

What about the camera problem? The answer is given in Example 1 of the next lesson.

748

Covering the Reading

1. What is the picture angle of a camera lens? a measure indicating how wide a field of vision can be captured in one photo

2. Use the diagram at the right. A person stands at point P to take a picture of the house. Will the entire front of the house be in the picture:
   a. if the person uses a normal camera lens? Yes
   b. if the person uses a telephoto lens? No
   c. if the person uses a wide-angle lens? Yes

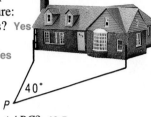

3. Use the circle below at the left. What is m∠ABC? 48.5

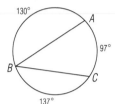 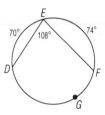

4. In the circle above at the right, what is m $\overarc{DGF}$? 216°

5. An angle inscribed in a semicircle has what measure? 90

In 6 and 7, $\overline{MN}$ is a diameter of ⊙O, as pictured at the right below.

6. a. m $\overarc{ML}$ = _?_ 130°
   b. m $\overarc{MPN}$ = _?_ 180°

7. a. m∠M = _?_ 25
   b. m∠N = _?_ 65
   c. m∠L = _?_ 90
   d. △LMN is a(n) _?_ triangle. right

8. Use the figure at the left.
   a. △TUV is _?_ in the circle. inscribed
   b. m∠U = _?_ 127.5

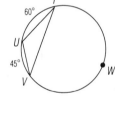

9. In the figure at the right, $\overline{YW}$ and $\overline{XZ}$ are diameters.
   a. m∠WOZ = _?_ n
   b. m∠Y = _?_ $\frac{n}{2}$

 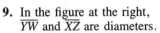

10. The proof of the Inscribed Angle Theorem has three cases. How do the cases differ?
    The center is either on, interior to, or exterior to the angle.

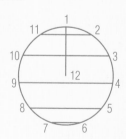
11. Write a proof for Case III of the Inscribed Angle Theorem.
See margin.

12. Use the figure below. Find the measures of the four angles of the quadrilateral. m∠A = 90, m∠B = 70, m∠C = 90, m∠D = 110

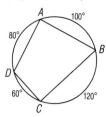

13. $\overline{AC}$ contains the center of the circle at the right. Calculate the measures of as many angles as you can.
m∠D = 90, m∠DCA = 60,
m∠ACB = 45, m∠B = 90
m∠DCB = 105, m∠BAC = 45,
m∠BAD = 75

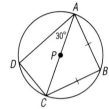

14. In ⊙O below, m∠M = 35 and m∠P = 92. If MP = NQ, find m $\overset{\frown}{MP}$. 53°

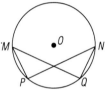

15. Fill in the justifications in this proof that in a circle, if two inscribed angles intercept the same arc, then they have the same measure.

Given: Inscribed angles *AMB* and *ANB*.
Prove: m∠*AMB* = m∠*ANB*.

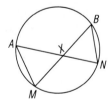

Conclusions		Justifications
1. m∠AMB = $\frac{1}{2}$ m$\overset{\frown}{AB}$	**a.** _?_	Inscribed Angle Theorem
2. m∠ANB = $\frac{1}{2}$ m$\overset{\frown}{AB}$	**b.** _?_	Inscribed Angle Theorem
3. m∠AMB = m∠ANB	**c.** _?_	Transitive Property of Equality (steps 1 and 2)

16. Use the given of Question 15.
Prove: △*AXM* ~ △*BXN*. See margin.

17. Twelve teams are in a league. Each team is to play each other once. Make up a schedule for the first week that can be rotated into a schedule for every other week. *(Lesson 15-2)* **See margin.**

18. Find the perimeter of an equilateral triangle inscribed in a circle of radius 24. *(Lesson 15-1)* $72\sqrt{3} \approx 124.71$ **units**

19. Regular pentagon *VWXYZ* is inscribed in ⊙*P* at the right.
   a. What is m$\widehat{WX}$? **72°**
   b. If *PW* = 50, find the perimeter of the pentagon. *(Lesson 15-1)*
   500 sin 36° ≈ 294 units

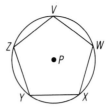

20. Square *ABCD* is inscribed in circle *O*. Square *EFGH* is circumscribed around circle *O*. In terms of *r*, the radius of circle *O*, express:
   a. the area between the circle and *EFGH*; $4r^2 - \pi r^2 = (4 - \pi)r^2$
   b. the area between *ABCD* and the circle. $\pi r^2 - 2r^2 = (\pi - 2)r^2$
   c. Which is larger, the area in part **a** or the area in part **b**?
   (Lessons 15-1, 8-9) **the area in part b**

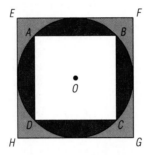

21. The length of a ballroom is twice its width and its area is 280 square yards. How long is it from one corner of the ballroom to the opposite corner? *(Lessons 8-7, 8-3, 8-1)* $\sqrt{700} \approx$ **26.46 yards**

22. In the figure below, *STICKEMUP* is a regular nonagon. *S* is the midpoint of $\overline{NT}$. What is m∠*PSN*? *(Lesson 5-7)* **40**

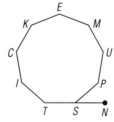

23. Examine a camera in your household or in a store. What is its normal picture angle? (You may need to refer to the instruction manual.)
   Answers will vary.

LESSON 15-3 The Inscribed Angle Theorem   **751**

FOLLOW-UP

MORE PRACTICE
For more questions on SPUR Objectives, use *Lesson Master 15-3*, shown below.

EXTENSION
You might want students to prove another interesting result of the Inscribed Angle Theorem: If a quadrilateral is inscribed in a circle, its opposite angles are supplementary.
Since the opposite angles of a quadrilateral intercept the total circle between them, their sum is equal to half a circle, or 180°.

EVALUATION
A quiz covering Lessons 15-1 through 15-3 is provided in the Teacher's Resource File.

OBJECTIVES

D Locate the center of the circle given sufficient information using the right angle or perpendicular bisector method.
I Given the angle width of a lens and the width of an object, determine the set of points from which the object will fit in the picture.

TEACHING NOTES

When there are two methods for solving a problem, the good problem solver may wonder when one method is to be preferred over the other. Ask students this question: When would the right angle method be preferred? If necessary, point out that if a circle already is drawn, for instance, by outlining a can or other cylinder, and a right angle is available, then this method is faster. Then ask: When would the perpendicular bisector method be preferred? Lead students to see that if only a part of a circle is given or if only three points are given, then this is the preferred method.

Although the example of a photographer is given in this lesson, in practice a photographer would usually back up until the building is in the field of vision. The ideas of the lesson would more likely be used by a motion picture team, because the location of the camera (a far more complicated piece of equipment)

15-4

Locating the Center of a Circle

Suppose you bought a circular coffee table and wished to place it on its base so that it balanced properly. To do this you need to find the center of the table. In Lesson 3-6 you learned how to do this by drawing perpendicular bisectors of chords. That method for locating the center of a circle is called the *perpendicular bisector method*.

There is a second method which relies on a theorem proved in the previous lesson: If an inscribed angle is a right angle, then its arc is a semicircle. So the segment connecting its endpoints is a diameter. Draw two diameters and you have the center.

The *right angle method* for locating the center of the circle:

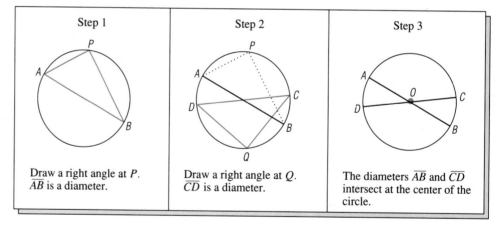

Step 1	Step 2	Step 3
Draw a right angle at P. $\overline{AB}$ is a diameter.	Draw a right angle at Q. $\overline{CD}$ is a diameter.	The diameters $\overline{AB}$ and $\overline{CD}$ intersect at the center of the circle.

This method is often used by people in drafting; the right angles are drawn with T-squares or metal ells. You can also use the corner of a piece of typing paper.

You can apply the construction of the center of a circle to the camera problem of Lesson 15-3.

752

Example 1   A camera has a 46° field of vision. Where can a person stand to get the entire front of the building in one picture?

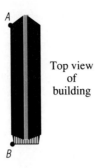

Top view
of
building

Solution   Consider a point *P* so that m∠*APB* = 46. The front of the building will just be in the picture if you stand at point *P*. Think of $\overline{AB}$ as a chord of an arc in a circle also containing *P*.

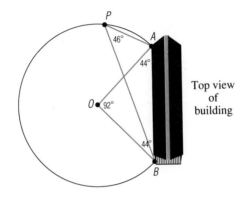

Top view
of
building

Step 1.   Determine m$\widehat{AB}$.

Since m∠*P* = $\frac{1}{2}$ m$\widehat{AB}$,

m$\widehat{AB}$ = 2 · m∠*P* = 92°.

Step 2.   Find the center *O* of this circle.
The center is the point *O* so that m∠*AOB* = 92. Since △*AOB* is isosceles, m∠*OAB* = m∠*OBA* = 44. Draw the 44° angles at *A* and *B*. Their sides intersect at *O*.

Step 3.   Draw ⊙*O* with radius *OA*.
Any point *P* on the major arc $\widehat{AB}$ of the circle will satisfy m∠*APB* = 46.

If you stand anywhere on major arc $\widehat{AB}$, the front of the building will exactly fit into the picture. Inside the circle you will only get part of the building. Outside the circle you will get more than the building.

is often mapped out in advance and away from the actual set.

Alternate Approach
With paper circles, there is a third way to find the center. Can students find it? (Fold the circle onto itself over two different diameters. Where they intersect is the center.)

ADDITIONAL EXAMPLES
1. Consider the situation of **Example 1**. If the building is 60 meters across, how far from the center of the circle is the building?
$\frac{30}{\tan 46°}$ ≈ **29 meters**

2. Explain how to locate the center of an arc you know to be a semicircle.
The center is the midpoint of the segment joining the endpoints of the arc.

To determine the distance to the place to stand, you need to calculate the radius of the circle. This can be done using trigonometry.

■ ■ ■ ■ ■ ■ ■ ■ ■

Example 2   A photographer wishes to photograph a building 130′ long with a lens that has an 80° field of vision. If she stands in front of the middle of the building, at least how far from the building should she be?

Solution   Let $\overline{QS}$ be the front of the building, as shown below. R is the midpoint of $\overline{QS}$.

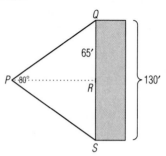

With the 80° lens, the photographer needs to stand at P. $\overline{PR} \perp \overline{QS}$ and PR is the minimum distance from the building. Since $\overleftrightarrow{PR}$ is the perpendicular bisector of $\overline{QS}$, $QR = 65′$ and $PQ = PS$. So $\triangle PQS$ is isosceles and $\overleftrightarrow{PR}$ bisects $\angle QPS$. So m$\angle RPQ = 40$. Now use trigonometry.

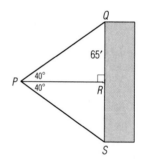

$$\frac{65}{PR} = \tan 40°$$

$$65 = PR \cdot \tan 40°$$

$$\frac{65}{\tan 40°} = PR$$

$$77.5′ \approx PR$$

If the photographer stands at least 77.5′ from the building, the picture will show the entire front.

Check $\angle Q$ is the larger acute angle in $\triangle PQR$, so PR should be greater than QR, which it is.

Covering the Reading

1. Trace the circle below at the left. Find its center using the right angle method.

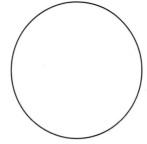

2. Trace the circle above at the right. Construct its center using the perpendicular bisector method. **See margin.**

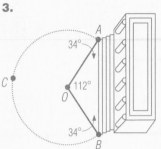

3. Suppose your camera lens has a 56° field of vision. Trace the building at the left and diagram where you could stand so that $\overline{AB}$, the building's front, just fits into your picture.

4. In Question 3, assume $AB = 60$ yards. If you wanted to stand in front of the middle of the building, at least how far from the building would you need to stand? **≈56.4 yards**

5. Each year, the classes at Emmy Noether H.S. take class pictures on the steps to the main entrance. The steps are 50 meters long.
   a. A photographer has an 88° wide-angle lens and wants to stand in front of the middle of the steps as close to the students as possible. Where should the photographer stand?
   b. At the same time other people want to take pictures of the class. If they all have 88° wide-angle lenses and want to be as close as possible, where can they stand? **See margin.**

2. (Art is reduced in size.)

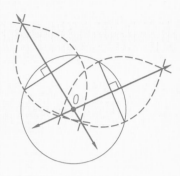

3.

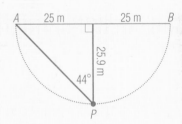

anywhere on $\overset{\frown}{ACB}$

5. a. The photographer should stand at point *P*, which is about 25.9 m from the steps.

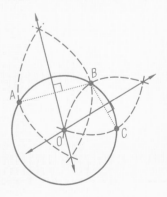

b. They can stand anywhere on $\overset{\frown}{APB}$, part of a circle with center *O*.

6. (Art is reduced in size.)

MORE PRACTICE
For more questions on SPUR Objectives, use *Lesson Master 15-4,* shown on page 757.

EXTENSION
Use **Question 10** to have students explain orally why a parallelogram inscribed in a circle must be a rectangle. **The measures of opposite angles add to 180°. Since the angles are congruent, they must be right angles.** Then go through all the special quadrilaterals and ask which ones can be inscribed and which ones cannot. **One general theorem is that an inscribed trapezoid must be an isosceles trapezoid.**

ADDITIONAL ANSWERS
6. See the margin on p. 755.

7. (Art is reduced in size.)

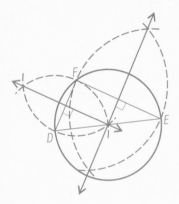

8. sample: (Art is reduced in size.)

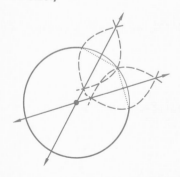

Applying the Mathematics

6. Trace points *A, B,* and *C* below. Use the perpendicular bisector method to construct the circle through points *A, B,* and *C*. (Hint: think of $\overline{AB}$ and $\overline{BC}$ as chords of the circle.) See margin.

7. Triangle *DEF* is inscribed in a circle. Draw that circle. See margin.

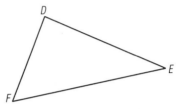

8. At the left is an arc of a circle. Trace the arc and locate the center of the circle. See margin.

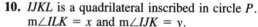

9. Draw a circle using the bottom of a can or bottle. Find the center of the circle using a sheet of paper and the right angle method. See margin.

Review

10. *IJKL* is a quadrilateral inscribed in circle *P*. m∠*ILK* = *x* and m∠*IJK* = *y*.
  a. Which arc measures $2x°$? $\widehat{IJK}$
  b. Which arc measures $2y°$? $\widehat{ILK}$
  c. What is $2x + 2y$? 360
  d. What is the sum of the measures of angles *ILK* and *IJK*? 180
  e. What is the sum of the measures of angles *LIJ* and *LKJ*? 180
  f. What does this prove about opposite angles in an inscribed quadrilateral? *(Lesson 15-3)* They are supplementary.

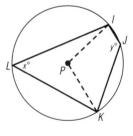

11. *BEHIVS* is a regular hexagon. The diagonals from *V* are drawn.
  a. Find the measures of the numbered angles. All are 30.
  b. *True* or *false?* △*BEV* is a right triangle. *(Lesson 15-3)* True

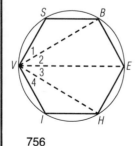

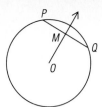

12. $\overline{PQ}$ at the left is a chord of $\odot O$.
  a. If M is the midpoint of $\overline{PQ}$, then __?__. $\overline{OM} \perp \overline{PQ}$.
  b. If $\overline{OM} \perp \overline{PQ}$, then __?__. $PM = MQ$
  c. If $\overrightarrow{OM}$ bisects $\angle POQ$, then __?__. *(Lesson 15-1)*
    $\overline{OM} \perp \overline{PQ}$ and $\overline{OM}$ bisects $\overline{PQ}$.

13. The __?__ of a chord of a circle contains the center of the circle.
  (Lesson 15-1) perpendicular bisector

14. In $\odot O$ at the right, $PQ = 12$ and
PQ is 8 units away from
the center. What is OQ?
(Lesson 15-1) 10 units

15. Use the figure below. $\overline{AB}$ is a diameter of $\odot C$. $\triangle BCD$ is equilateral.
  a. Find the measures of as many angles as you can. See below.
  b. If $BD = x$, then what is the length of $\overline{AC}$? x
  c. If $BD = 7$, what is the length of $\overline{AD}$? *(Lessons 15-3, 15-1)* $7\sqrt{3} \approx 12.12$

a) $m\angle A = m\angle CDA = 30$,
  $m\angle ACD = 120$,
  $m\angle ADB = 90$,
  $m\angle BCD = m\angle BDC$
  $= m\angle CBD = 60$

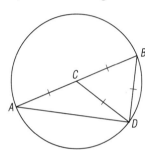

16. a. Give the contrapositive of this statement: If a figure is a rectangle,
  then its diagonals are congruent.
  b. Is the contrapositive true? *(Lesson 13-2)* Yes
  a) If the diagonals of a figure are not congruent, then it is not a rectangle.

17. Sod is to be put on a circular golf course putting green 50′ in
diameter. How much sod is needed? *(Lesson 8-9)*
$625\pi \approx 1963.5$ square feet

Exploration

18. Each of the three circles below overlaps the other two. The three
chords common to each pair of circles are drawn. They seem to have
a point in common. Experiment to decide whether this is always true.

Answers will vary.
(It is always true.)

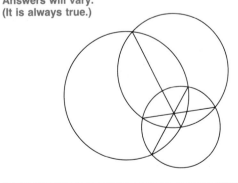

LESSON 15-4   Locating the Center of a Circle   **757**

NAME _____

LESSON **MASTER 15–4**
QUESTIONS ON **SPUR** OBJECTIVES

■ **SKILLS** *Objective D (See pages 788–791 for objectives.)*
In 1 and 2, find the center of the circle using the right angle method.

1.   2.

3. Draw the circle through the three points *X, Y,* and *Z* below.

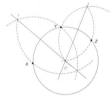

Construct the perpendicular bisectors of $\overline{XY}$ and
$\overline{YZ}$. These lines intersect in point *O*, which is
equidistant from *X, Y,* and *Z.* Draw the circle with
center *O* and radius *OX.* Since *OX = OY = OZ,* the
circle contains *X, Y,* and *Z.*

Geometry © Scott, Foresman and Company   *Continued* **141**

NAME _____
Lesson MASTER 15–4 (page 2)

■ **USES** *Objective I*
In 4–6, a photographer wants to take a picture of a billboard whose base $\overline{AB}$
is 50 feet long.

4. Locate all points where the photographer could stand to fit $\overline{AB}$ exactly in
the picture if the camera lens has a picture angle of 58°.
anywhere on the major arc *AB*

5. How far from *C,* the midpoint of $\overline{AB}$, will the
photographer have to be if he backs up
perpendicular to the billboard?   ≈45 ft

6. Another photographer's camera lens has a
picture angle of 62°. Will this photographer be
able to stand closer to the billboard than the
first?   Yes

7. In general, the smaller the picture angle, the __greater__ the
distance one must be to fit the object in question exactly in the picture.

142   Geometry © Scott, Foresman and Company

OBJECTIVES

C Calculate measures of angles between chords or secants from measures of intercepted arcs, and vice versa.
G Make deductions from properties of inscribed angles formed by chords or secants.

TEACHING NOTES

Beginning with a concrete example is always a good idea. You might have students draw a regular hexagon *ABCDEF* inscribed in a circle.

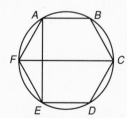

Note that each side of the polygon is a chord of a 60° arc. Now connect $\overline{AE}$ and $\overline{FC}$ as shown above. These segments are perpendicular (a result of the reflection symmetry of the regular polygon). But notice that m$\widehat{AF}$ = 60° and m$\widehat{CE}$ = 120°. Thus, the measure of the angle formed by the two intersecting chords is the average of the measures of the arcs intercepted by the angle and the vertical angle.

Angles Formed by Chords or Secants

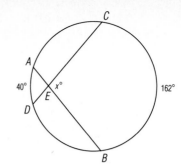

Each side of a central angle or an inscribed angle intersects the circle. In this lesson and the next one, other angles for which both sides intersect a circle will be discussed. The Inscribed Angle Theorem enables angle measures to be determined even for these angles. First, consider an angle whose vertex is in the interior of a circle. For instance, consider the situation pictured below at the left, where two chords $\overline{AB}$ and $\overline{CD}$ intersect at E. Given m$\widehat{AD}$ = 40° and m$\widehat{BC}$ = 162°, what is x?

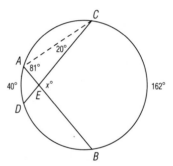

To find m$\angle CEB$, draw the auxiliary segment $\overline{AC}$, as done above. Now $\angle A$ and $\angle C$ are inscribed angles whose measures are half their arcs. So m$\angle A = 81$ and m$\angle C = 20$. $\angle CEB$ is an exterior angle of $\triangle ACE$. Its measure is the sum of these two angles. Thus, $x = 101$.

The argument can be generalized and proves the following startling theorem.

> **Angle-Chord Theorem:**
>
> The measure of an angle formed by two intersecting chords is one-half the sum of the measures of the arcs intercepted by it and its vertical angle.

Example 1 In ⊙O at the left, m$\widehat{XY}$ = 200° and m$\widehat{VW}$ = 66°. Find m∠XQY.

Solution m∠XQY = ½(m$\widehat{XY}$ + m$\widehat{VW}$)
$$= \tfrac{1}{2}(200 + 66)$$
$$= \tfrac{1}{2}(266)$$
$$= 133$$

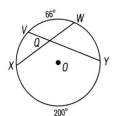

The measure of the angle between chords can be found even when the lines containing the chords intersect in the exterior of the circle. Such lines are called **secants.**

Definition:

A **secant** is a line that intersects a circle in two points.

Below at the <u>left</u>, ∠E is formed by two secants and ∠E intercepts the two arcs $\widehat{AC}$ and $\widehat{BD}$ with measures 84° and 26°. To find m∠E, draw $\overline{AD}$, as pictured below at the right.

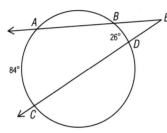 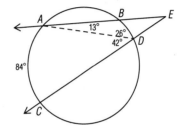

Again there are two inscribed angles, and one of them is ∠ADC, an exterior angle of △ADE. By the Exterior Angle Theorem,

$$m\angle A + m\angle E = m\angle ADC.$$
Solving for m∠E, $m\angle E = m\angle ADC - m\angle A$
$$= \tfrac{1}{2}\,m\widehat{AC} - \tfrac{1}{2}m\widehat{BD}.$$
Substituting, $= \tfrac{1}{2} \cdot 84 - \tfrac{1}{2} \cdot 26$
$$= 42 - 13$$
$$= 29.$$

Generalizing the argument proves the following theorem.

Angle-Secant Theorem:

The measure of an angle formed by two secants intersecting outside a circle is half the difference of the arcs intercepted by it.

Question 1 shows a procedure for finding the measure of an angle formed by two intersecting chords in general. The generalization of the procedure is the proof of the Angle-Chord Theorem.

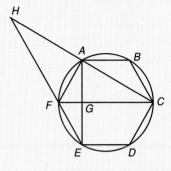

The chords $\overline{AC}$ and $\overline{EF}$ in the same figure can be extended to meet at H, as shown above. Have students verify that the measure of angle H is 30, half the difference of the measures of the arcs. The general theorem is the Angle-Secant Theorem.

As you are discussing this lesson with your students, you might want to point out that the theorems are generalized from examples rather than being proved first and then showing examples. Stress that much of mathematics was developed this way. That is, conjectures are made from observed results; then they are generalized and proved.

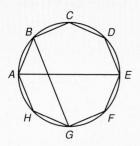
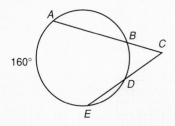
Example 2 In ⊙*R* below, m$\widehat{KTM}$ = 195° and m$\widehat{JL}$ = 51°. Find m∠*P*.

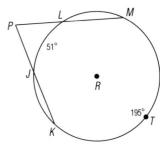

Solution From the Angle-Secant Theorem,

$$m\angle P = \tfrac{1}{2}(m\widehat{KTM} - m\widehat{JL})$$
$$= \tfrac{1}{2}(195 - 51)$$
$$= \tfrac{1}{2} \cdot 144$$
$$= 72.$$

In doing these problems, you have a choice between drawing the auxiliary segments and calculating, or memorizing a theorem. You should be able to do both.

Questions

Covering the Reading

1. Use the figure at the right. Find the measures of the numbered angles.
  a. m∠1 = __?__ **12.5**
  b. m∠2 = __?__ **48**
  c. m∠3 = __?__ **60.5**
  d. m∠4 = __?__ **119.5**

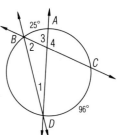

In 2 and 3, use the figure at the right.

2. What additional arc measure(s) do you need in order to find m∠1? **m$\widehat{XY}$ or m$\widehat{WX}$**

3. Suppose $\overline{XZ}$ is a diameter. Find m∠1. **100**

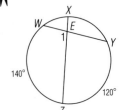

4. a. Using the diagram at the right, is enough information given to find m∠*F*? **Yes**
  b. If so, find m∠*F*. If not, what more do you need to know? **26**

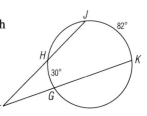

760

5. In the figure below, m$\widehat{LP}$ = 80° and m$\widehat{MO}$ = 50°.
Find:
  a. m∠MQO 65
  b. m∠N. 15

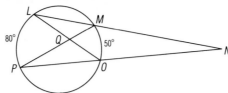

6. Define: secant.
A secant is a line that intersects a circle in two points.

Applying the Mathematics

7. A point P is outside ⊙O. How many secants of ⊙O contain P?
infinitely many

8. Use the circle below. Given: m$\widehat{RU}$ = 101° and $\overline{RS}$ ⊥ $\overline{TU}$. Find m$\widehat{ST}$.
79°

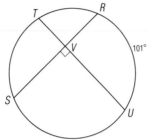

9. Rectangle VWXY is inscribed in the circle at the left. m$\widehat{WX}$ = 40°.
  a. What is the measure of the acute angle between the diagonals?
  b. What is m∠VYW? a) 40; b) 70

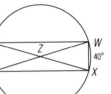

10. Use the figure below. If m$\widehat{BD}$ = 53° and m∠C = 45, what is m$\widehat{AE}$?
143°

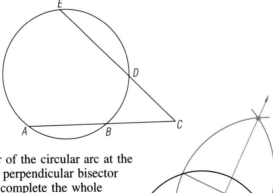

Review

11. Find the center of the circular arc at the right using the perpendicular bisector method. Then complete the whole circle. *(Lesson 15-4)*

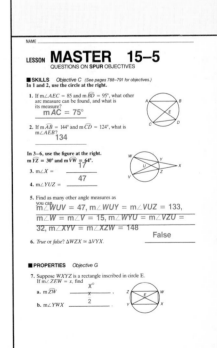

LESSON 15-5   Angles Formed by Chords or Secants   **761**

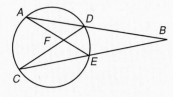
12. Suppose you have a camera with a picture angle of 118°. At least how far in front of the middle of the house shown would you need to stand to photograph the entire front? *(Lesson 15-4)* ≈15.6 ft

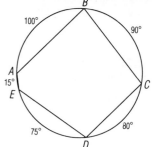

13. Find the measure of each angle of *ABCDE* at the right. *(Lesson 15-3)*
m∠*A* = 122.5, m∠*B* = 85,
m∠*C* = 95, m∠*D* = 102.5,
m∠*E* = 135

14. Create a round-robin schedule for ten teams. *(Lesson 15-2)*
See margin.

15. A chord is 7 inches away from the center of a circle with radius $12\frac{1}{2}$ inches. Find the length of the chord. *(Lesson 15-1)*
$2 \cdot \sqrt{107.25} \approx 20.71$ inches

16. **a.** State the Quadratic Formula.
b. Use the Quadratic Formula to solve $2x^2 + 5x - 1 = 0$.
(Previous course)
See below.

17. Solve for *x*: $x^2 - 30 = 34$. *(Previous course)* x = 8 or -8

18. Solve for *y*: $y + 12 > 21$. *(Previous course)* y > 9

Exploration

19. The sides of an inscribed pentagon *ABCDE* below are extended to form a **pentagram,** a five-pointed star.
a. What is the sum of the measures of angles, *F, G, H, I,* and *J*, if the pentagon is regular? 180
b. What is the largest and smallest this sum can be if the inscribed pentagon is not regular?
The sum is always 180.

16a) If $ax^2 + bx + c = 0$, then
$x = \frac{-b \pm \sqrt{b^2 - 4ac}}{2a}$.
b) $a = 2, b = 5, c = -1$, so
$x = \frac{-5 \pm \sqrt{33}}{4} \approx 0.19$ or -2.69.

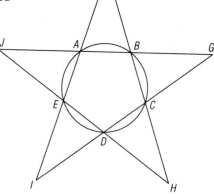

762

LESSON 15-6

Angles Formed by Tangents

In the previous lesson, angles were formed by chords or secants. In this lesson, angles which have at least one side tangent to a circle are explored. Recall that a tangent line intersects a circle at exactly one point, and a radius drawn to the point of tangency is perpendicular to the tangent line.

Consider first the angle formed by a tangent and a chord through the point of tangency. $\overleftrightarrow{BC}$ is tangent to $\odot O$ below at B and $m\overarc{AB} = 75°$.

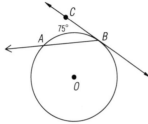

To find $m\angle ABC$, draw the diameter containing B and O. The semicircle $\overarc{BAD}$ has measure $180°$, so $m\overarc{AD} = 105°$.

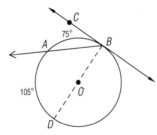

Thus $m\angle ABD = \frac{1}{2} \cdot 105 = 52.5$. Now, since $\overleftrightarrow{CB} \perp \overline{BD}$, $\angle CBA$ is complementary to $\angle ABD$. So $m\angle CBA = 37.5$. In general,

$$m\angle ABC = 90 - m\angle ABD$$
$$= \frac{1}{2} \cdot 180 - \frac{1}{2} \cdot m\overarc{AD}$$
$$= \frac{1}{2}(180 - m\overarc{AD})$$
$$= \frac{1}{2}m\overarc{AB}.$$

RESOURCES
- Lesson Master 15-6
- Quiz for Lessons 15-4 Through 15-6.
- Visual for Teaching Aid 87 can be used with **Questions 1-7**.
- Visual for Teaching Aid 88 can be used with **Questions 13**, **14**, and **15**.

OBJECTIVES

C Calculate measures of angles between chords, secants, or tangents, from measures of intercepted arcs, and vice versa.

G Make deductions from properties of inscribed angles formed by chords, tangents, or secants.

TEACHING NOTES

Point out to students that a tangent is the limit case of a secant; that is, a secant whose two points of intersection with the circle have become closer and closer until they are one. Thus, the angle relationships are not new: the measure of the angle formed by a tangent and a secant, or between two tangents, is just like the angle between two secants. The angle between a tangent and a chord is the limit of an inscribed angle.

Example 2 is a surprise to many students: one angle measure determines the measures of two arcs.

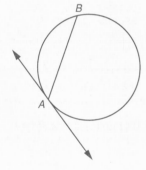
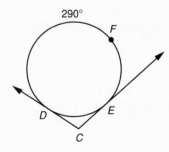
This proves the following theorem.

Tangent-Chord Theorem:

The measure of an angle formed by a tangent and a chord is half the measure of the intercepted arc.

Angles between tangents and secants are calculated just as angles between secants.

Tangent-Secant Theorem:

The measure of the angle between two tangents, or between a tangent and a secant, is half the difference of the intercepted arcs.

Proof

Consider secant $\overleftrightarrow{AB}$ and tangent $\overrightarrow{EC}$ at point C, forming ∠E, as below. Given m$\overset{\frown}{AC}$ = $x°$ and m$\overset{\frown}{BC}$ = $y°$, it needs to be shown that m∠$E = \frac{1}{2}(x - y)$.

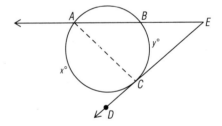

Draw $\overline{AC}$. Now m∠$DCA = \frac{1}{2}x$ and m∠$EAC = \frac{1}{2}y$. But ∠DCA is an exterior angle of △ACE. So

$$m\angle DCA = m\angle EAC + m\angle E.$$

Thus
$$m\angle E = m\angle DCA - m\angle EAC$$
$$= \frac{1}{2}x - \frac{1}{2}y$$
$$= \frac{1}{2}(x - y).$$

The proof for an angle between two tangents is similar. It is left to you as Question 6.

Example 1 Refer to the figure at the right. $\overrightarrow{AB}$ is tangent to the circle at B. Find $m\angle A$.

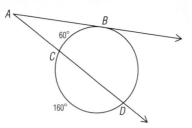

Solution The circle measures 360°, so $m\widehat{BD} = 140°$.

$$m\angle A = \tfrac{1}{2}(m\widehat{BD} - m\widehat{BC})$$
$$= \tfrac{1}{2}(140 - 60)$$
$$= 40$$

Example 2 Refer to the figure at the left. $m\angle P = 30$. What is $m\widehat{QSR}$?

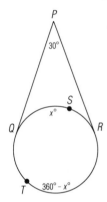

Solution Let $m\widehat{QSR} = x°$. Then $m\widehat{QTR} = 360° - x°$.
By the Tangent-Secant Theorem,
$$m\angle P = \tfrac{1}{2}(m\widehat{QTR} - m\widehat{QSR})$$
$$= \tfrac{1}{2}((360 - x) - x).$$
Substituting and solving for x,
$$30 = \tfrac{1}{2}(360 - 2x)$$
$$= 180 - x.$$
So $\qquad\qquad\qquad\qquad x = 150.$

Check When $x = 150$, $360 - x = 210$. Does $m\angle P$ equal half the difference of the two arcs? Yes, 30 is half of $210 - 150$.

Questions

Covering the Reading

1. $\overleftrightarrow{BC}$ is tangent to $\odot A$ below at B. If $m\widehat{BD} = 110°$, find:
   a. $m\angle ABC$ 90
   b. $m\angle DBC$. 55

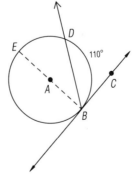

LESSON 15-6 *Angles Formed by Tangents* **765**

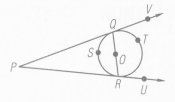
In 2–4, use the figure below. $\overrightarrow{PT}$ is tangent to circle O at point S.

2. m∠P = __?__ 20

3. m∠TSR = __?__ 54

4. *True* or *false*?
   m∠RSP = ½ m⌢RQS. **True**

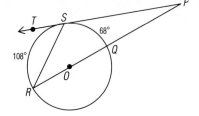

5. $\overline{AB}$ and $\overline{AC}$ are tangents to the circle at B and C. Find the measures of the indicated angles.
   a. ∠ABD **142.5**
   b. ∠CAB **60**
   c. ∠ACD **97.5**

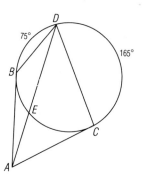

In 6 and 7, use the drawing below.

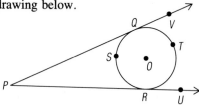

6. Prove that m∠P = ½ (m⌢QTR − m⌢QSR). (Hint: Draw $\overline{QR}$ and use an exterior angle of △PQR.) **See margin.**

7. If m∠P = 25, find the measures of arcs $\overset{\frown}{QSR}$ and $\overset{\frown}{QTR}$.
   m⌢QTR = 205°; m⌢QSR = 155°

8. Match the angles at the left with the ways to compute measures at the right.
   a. angle between two chords **(iii)**
   b. angle between two secants **(iv)**
   c. angle between two tangents **(iv)**
   d. angle between secant and tangent **(iv)**
   e. angle between chord and tangent **(ii)**
   f. inscribed angle **(ii)**
   g. central angle **(i)**

   (i) the intercepted arc
   (ii) ½ the intercepted arc
   (iii) ½ the sum of the intercepted arcs
   (iv) ½ the difference of the intercepted arcs

9. Given: $\overrightarrow{CB}$ and $\overrightarrow{CD}$ are tangent to ⊙A at B and D.
   Prove: m⌢BD = 180 − m∠C. **See margin.**

766

9. Draw $\overline{AB}$ and $\overline{AD}$. By the
Quadrilateral-Sum
Theorem, $m\angle A + m\angle B +$
$m\angle C + m\angle D = 360$, so
$m\angle A + 90 + m\angle C + 90 =$
360, so $m\angle A + m\angle C = 180$.
But $m\angle A = m\overparen{BD}$, so
$m\overparen{BD} + m\angle C = 180$, from
which $m\overparen{BD} = 180 - m\angle C$.

16. You can stand
anywhere on the part of
$\odot O$ drawn below.

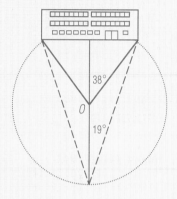

38°

O

19°

10. $\overrightarrow{PR}$ is tangent to $\odot O$ below at R. If $m\angle P = 41$, what is $m\overparen{QR}$? 49°

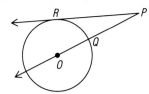

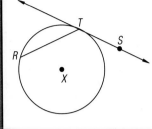

11. At the left, $\overleftrightarrow{ST}$ is tangent to $\odot X$ at T. If $m\angle RTS = 125$, find $m\overparen{TR}$. 110°

12. Refer to the figure at the right. Graph on a number line the possible measures of angle C.

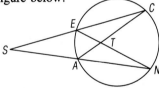

0   180

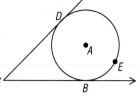

Review

13. Use the figure below. Find the measure of the indicated angle.
(Lessons 15-5, 15-3)
 a. 2 65
 b. 3 92.5
 c. 4 87.5
 d. E 22.5

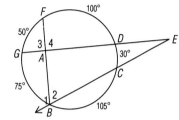

In 14 and 15, use the figure below.

14. If $m\angle S = 23$ and $m\overparen{CN} = 85°$, find $m\overparen{AE}$. 39°

15. a. Are triangles ANT and ECT similar? *(Lessons 15-3, 12-7)* Yes
 b. Are triangles ANT and ECT congruent? *(Lesson 7-2)*
 not necessarily

16. Suppose you have a camera with a picture angle of 38°. Trace the building below and diagram where you could stand so that the building's front just fits into your picture. *(Lesson 15-4)* See margin.

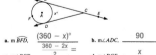

LESSON 15-6 Angles Formed by Tangents   **767**

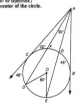

Question 21: This question should help prepare students for Lesson 15-9.

Question 22: The answer shows that the diameter of the moon occupies about a half degree of arc. The sun occupies about the same space, which is one reason why total eclipses are so rare.

ADDITIONAL ANSWERS

20. samples: $\frac{x}{4} = \frac{10}{q}$, $\frac{4}{q} = \frac{x}{10}$, $\frac{q}{4} = \frac{10}{x}$

FOLLOW-UP

MORE PRACTICE
For more questions on SPUR Objectives, use *Lesson Master 15-6*, shown on page 767.

EVALUATION
A quiz covering Lessons 15-4 through 15-6 is provided in the Teacher's Resource File.

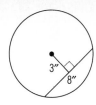

17. An 8″ chord is 3″ from the center of the circle at the left. What is the area of the circle? *(Lessons 15-1, 8-9)* $25\pi \approx 78.5$ in.²

18. The measures of the exterior angles of a quadrilateral are $4x$, $8x - 23$, $9x + 7$, and $5x - 40$.
   a. What is x? **16**
   b. What is the measure of each interior angle? *(Lesson 13-7)* **116, 75, 29, 140**

19. Below, $ABCD \sim JKHG$. Find as many missing lengths and angle measures as you can. *(Lesson 12-5)* **BC = 15; JG = 16; m∠G = 81**

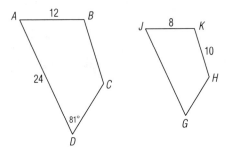

20. If $\frac{4}{x} = \frac{q}{10}$, write three other true proportions. *(Lesson 12-4)* **See margin.**

21. A sphere has diameter 24 mm.
   a. Find its volume. **2304π ≈ 7238.2 mm³**
   b. Find its surface area. *(Lessons 10-9, 10-8)* **576π ≈ 1809.6 mm²**

Exploration

22. Recall that from two to five times a year the moon comes between the earth and sun, with a situation like that diagrammed here. When that happens, an eclipse of the sun occurs for part of the earth.

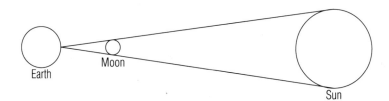

This picture is not to scale. The earth is roughly 7290 miles in diameter, the moon roughly 2160 miles. The moon is about 240,000 miles from the earth. The angle between the tangents is the angle of vision the moon and sun occupy in the sky. Find the measure of this angle. (You will need to use trigonometry.) **≈.51°**

Lengths of Chords, Secants, and Tangents

Usually if there are different-looking figures for a theorem, you would expect a different proof for each figure. In the theorem below, the surprise is that the same proof works, letter for letter, for two quite different figures. The theorem is simple, but amazing, and was known to Euclid.

Secant Length Theorem:

Suppose one secant intersects a circle at A and B, and a second secant intersects the circle at C and D. If the secants intersect at P, then
$$AP \cdot BP = CP \cdot DP.$$

Proof

Given: $\odot O$; secants $\overleftrightarrow{AB}$ and $\overleftrightarrow{CD}$ intersect at P.
Prove: $AP \cdot BP = CP \cdot DP$.

There are two figures, depending on whether P is inside or outside the circle.

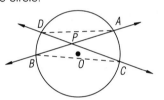   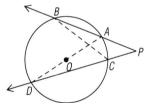

Analyze $AP \cdot BP$ will equal $CP \cdot DP$ if it can be proved that $\frac{AP}{CP} = \frac{DP}{BP}$. This suggests forming triangles and trying to prove them similar. Follow the conclusions and justifications, first for the left figure, then for the right figure.

Write	**Conclusions**	**Justifications**
	1. Draw $\overline{DA}$ and $\overline{BC}$.	Two points determine a line.
	2. $\angle BAD \cong \angle BCD$ $\angle ADC \cong \angle ABC$	In a $\odot$, inscribed angles intercepting the same arc are congruent.
	3. $\triangle DPA \sim \triangle BPC$	AA $\sim$ Theorem (steps 2 and 3)
	4. $\frac{AP}{CP} = \frac{DP}{BP}$	Corresponding sides of similar figures are proportional.
	5. $AP \cdot BP = CP \cdot DP$	Means-Extremes Property

LESSON 15-7

OBJECTIVE

E Apply the Secant Length Theorem.

TEACHING NOTES

Ask students to draw a circle with secants intersecting it and each other. Then measure the segments to verify the Secant Length Theorem. Surprisingly, few students ever measure to verify theorems. Then go through the proof. Student will understand how these theorems relate to previous ideas (inscribed angles, similar triangles, proportions) if they can repeat the proof. A third test of understanding comes through the numerical and algebraic questions involving the theorems.

The Tangent Square Theorem may be restated as follows: The length of the tangent to a circle from a point P is the geometric mean of the lengths of any secant from P to its points of intersection with the circle.

Error Analysis A common error students make when applying the Secant Length Theorem to the second figure shown in the proof is to use the chord lengths AB and CD for the calculations instead of PB and PD.

Computer An automatic drawing program might be helpful in verifying the theorems in this lesson.

■ ■ ■ ■ ■ ■ ■ ■

Example 1   Given chords $\overline{AB}$ and $\overline{CD}$ intersecting at P, with lengths as shown. Find PB.

Solution

$$PA \cdot PB = PC \cdot PD$$

Substituting,

$$3 \cdot PB = 5 \cdot 6$$
$$= 30.$$

So

$$PB = 10.$$

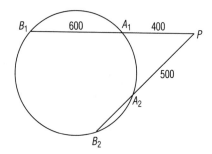

■ ■ ■ ■ ■ ■ ■ ■

Example 2   Given secants $\overleftrightarrow{A_1B_1}$ and $\overleftrightarrow{A_2B_2}$ intersecting at P, with lengths as shown. Find A_2B_2.

Solution A_2B_2 is found by first getting PB_2 and then subtracting PA_2 from it.

$$PA_1 \cdot PB_1 = PA_2 \cdot PB_2$$

Substituting,

$$400 \cdot 1000 = 500 \cdot PB_2$$

so

$$800 = PB_2.$$

Since

$$A_2B_2 = PB_2 - PA_2,$$
$$A_2B_2 = 800 - 500 = 300.$$

The Secant Length Theorem has a surprising application. Suppose a circle and point P are given. For any secant through P intersecting the circle in two points A and B, there is a product $AP \cdot BP$. This product is a number, and it is the *same* number for any secant through P which intersects the circle! In Example 2, it is the number 400,000.

$$PA_1 \cdot PB_1 = PA_2 \cdot PB_2$$
$$= PA_3 \cdot PB_3$$
$$= PA_4 \cdot PB_4$$

This is true for points P interior to the circle also. In Example 1, the product $PA \cdot PB$ is the number 30. The Swiss geometer

770

Jacob Steiner [1796–1863] called the product the **power of the point *P* for the circle *O*.**

The power of a point external to a circle is easily calculated if you know the length of a tangent from *P* to ⊙*O*.

> **Tangent Square Theorem:**
>
> The power of point *P* for ⊙*O* is the square of the length of a segment tangent to ⊙*O* from *P*.

Proof

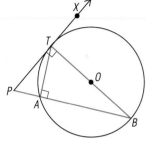

Draw   A figure is at the left.
Given: Point *P* outside ⊙*O* and $\overleftrightarrow{PX}$ tangent to ⊙*O* at *T*.
Prove: The power of point *P* for ⊙*O* is PT^2.
Write   Draw $\overrightarrow{TO}$ which intersects ⊙*O* at *B*. Let $\overline{PB}$ intersect ⊙*O* at *A* and *B*. Since $\overline{PT} \perp \overline{TB}$ and ∠*TAB* is inscribed in a semicircle, △*PTB* is a right triangle with altitude $\overline{TA}$. Thus $PT^2 = PA \cdot PB$ by the Right Triangle Altitude Theorem. Thus the power of point *P* for ⊙*O* is PT^2.

Since $PT^2 = PA \cdot PB$, $PT = \sqrt{PA \cdot PB}$. Thus the length of a tangent $\overline{PT}$ to a circle from a point is the geometric mean of the lengths of segments of a secant drawn from that point.

■ ▪ ▫ ▪ ▫ ▪ ▪ ■ ■ ■

Example 3 $\overleftrightarrow{AR}$ is tangent to the circle. If *AP* = 3 and *AR* = 6, find *AQ* and *PQ*.

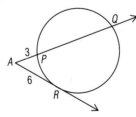

Solution   Use the Tangent Square Theorem: $AP \cdot AQ = AR^2$.
Substituting, $3 \cdot AQ = 6^2$
                                  $3 \cdot AQ = 36.$
So $AQ = 12.$
Then $PQ = AQ - AP$
                                     $= 12 - 3$
                                     $= 9.$

771

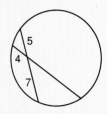
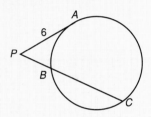

Some problems involving the power of a point require solving a quadratic equation.

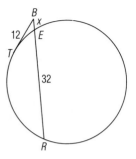

Example 4   Given that $\overleftrightarrow{BT}$ is tangent to the circle, $BT = 12$, and $ER = 32$, find BE.

Solution   From the Tangent Square Theorem,
$$BE \cdot BR = BT^2$$
$$BE \cdot (BE + ER) = BT^2.$$
Let $BE = x$. Substituting for BT, BE, and ER,
$$x(x + 32) = 144.$$
So
$$x^2 + 32x - 144 = 0.$$
Use the Quadratic Formula:
$$x = \frac{-32 \pm \sqrt{1024 + 576}}{2} = \frac{-32 \pm \sqrt{1600}}{2} = \frac{-32 \pm 40}{2}.$$
So $x = 4$ or $x = -36$. Ignoring the impossible negative value for BE, $BE = 4$.

Questions

Covering the Reading

1. In the figure at the right, $DP \cdot DT = \underline{\ ?\ }$. $DU \cdot DV$

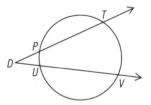

In 2 and 3, refer to the figure at the left.

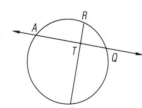

2. $AT \cdot TQ = \underline{\ ?\ }$ $PT \cdot TR$

3. If $AT = 6$, $TQ = 4$, and $TR = 3$, then $TP = \underline{\ ?\ }$. 8

4. Refer to the figure at the right. Let $TW = 3$, $WX = 3$, and $TU = 2$.
   a. Calculate TV. 9
   b. What is the power of point T for this circle? 18
   c. Calculate UV. 7

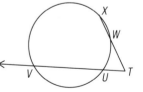

772

5. In Example 1, what is the power of point P? 30

In 6 and 7, refer to the figure at the left.

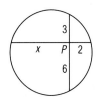

6. JQ is the geometric mean of __?__ and __?__ . JX, JY

7. If $JX = 2$ and $XY = 6$, then $JQ = $ __?__ . 4

8. Refer to the figure with two intersecting chords at the right.

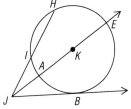

　a. $x = $ __?__ 9
　b. The power of P in this circle is __?__ . 18

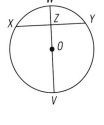

Applying the Mathematics

9. Use $\odot K$ below, with $\overleftrightarrow{JB}$ tangent to $\odot K$ at B. If $JI = 10$, $JA = 8$, and $AE = 12$, find HI. 6

10. In $\odot O$ at the left, diameter $WV = 16$. If $\overline{XY} \perp \overline{WV}$ and $XY = 10$, find WZ. $8 - \sqrt{39} \approx 1.76$

In 11 and 12, use the figure below. $\overline{BD}$ and $\overline{AC}$ intersect at P and $\overleftrightarrow{BA}$ and $\overleftrightarrow{CD}$ intersect at X. *True* or *false*? Carefully explain your response.

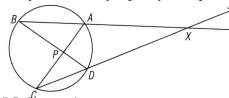

11. If $PA = PD$, then $PB = PC$. See margin.

12. It is impossible to have $m\widehat{BC} = m\widehat{AD}$. See margin.

13. Is the Secant Length Theorem true if the word "circle" in it is replaced by "sphere"? That is, if A, B, C, and D are points on a sphere, does $PA \cdot PB = PC \cdot PD$? Explain your answer.
See margin.

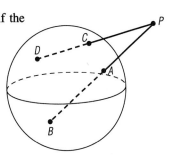

LESSON 15-7   Lengths of Chords, Secants, and Tangents   **773**

ADDITIONAL ANSWERS

11. True; $PA \cdot PC = PB \cdot PD$, so dividing by PA, $PB = PC$.

12. True; $\frac{1}{2}(m\widehat{BC} - m\widehat{AD}) = m\angle AXD$. If $m\widehat{BC} = m\widehat{AD}$, then $m\angle AXD = 0$, and then $\overleftrightarrow{BX}$ and $\overleftrightarrow{CX}$ are not different lines.

13. Yes; since D, C, and P are collinear, and B, A, and P are collinear, then D, C, P, B, and A are coplanar. Points D, C, A, and B lie on the circle which is the intersection of that plane and the sphere. Apply the Secant Length Theorem to this circle.

NAME _____

LESSON MASTER 15–7
QUESTIONS ON **SPUR** OBJECTIVES

■ **SKILLS**   *Objective E (See pages 788–791 for objectives.)*
In 1 and 2, use the figure below.

1. If $AE = 12$, $BE = 10$, and $CE = 20$, $DE = $ _____24_____ .

2. If $AE = 4$, $CE = 5$, and $DE = 6$, $BE = $ ___$\frac{20}{6} = 3.3$___ .

In 3 and 4, use the figure below.

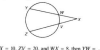

3. If $VX = 10$, $ZV = 20$, and $WX = 8$, then $YW = $ ___29.5___ .

4. If $WX = 4$, $YW = 5$, and $ZV = 6$, then $VX = $ ___≈3.71___ .

In 5 and 6, use the figure below. $\overrightarrow{AD}$ is tangent to $\odot Z$ at D.

5. If $AD = 6$ and $AB = 3$, find BC. ___9___

6. If $AB = 4$ and $BC = 5$, find AD. ___6___

Geometry © Scott, Foresman and Company   **145**

MORE PRACTICE

For more questions on SPUR Objectives, use *Lesson Master 15-7*, shown on page 773.

EXTENSION

Consider circle *O* below with tangents $\overline{PT}$ and $\overline{PS}$ and diameter $\overline{AB}$.

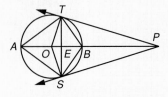

Identify all the segments that are geometric means of other segments.
PT and PS are geometric means of PB and PA. OT and OS are geometric means of OE and OP. TE and SE are geometric means of OE and PE. AT and AS are geometric means of AE and AB. BT and BS are geometric means of BE and AB. TE and SE are geometric means of AE and BE.
(Thus, OE · PE = AE · BE!)

ADDITIONAL ANSWERS
17.

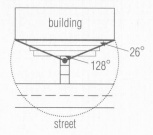

You can stand anywhere on the part of the circle drawn above.

Review

14. Find the measure of each angle in $\triangle BDC$ below. *(Lessons 15-6, 15-5)*
m∠B = 25, m∠CDB = 40, m∠DCB = 115

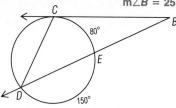

15. $\overrightarrow{XY}$ and $\overrightarrow{XZ}$ are tangent to $\odot O$ at the right at *Y* and *Z*. If m∠*X* = 45, find m$\overarc{YZ}$. *(Lesson 15-6)* **135°**

16. Find the measure of ∠*A* below. *(Lesson 15-5)* **42.5**

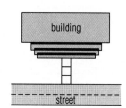

In 17 and 18, suppose you had a camera with a 64° picture angle. A top view of a building is shown at the left.

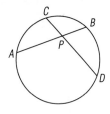

17. Draw where you can stand so that the entire front of the building will be seen in your picture. *(Lesson 15-4)* **See margin.**

18. If the building is 48 meters across, at least how far in front of the middle of the building would you need to stand? *(Lesson 15-4)*
≈38.4 m

19. In right triangle *ABC* at the right, find:
a. *AC*
b. tan *B*
c. sin *A*
d. cos *B*.
(Lessons 14-4, 14-3, 8-7)
a) 20 b) $\frac{20}{21} \approx .952$ c) $\frac{21}{29} \approx .724$ d) $\frac{21}{29} \approx .724$

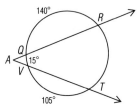

Exploration

20. a. Is the Secant Length Theorem true if the secants intersect *on* the circle? **Yes**
b. If true, prove it. If not true, show a counterexample.
PB = PC = 0, so PA · PB = 0 and PC · PD = 0, so PA · PB = PC · PD.

21. Is it possible for the lengths of the segments of two intersecting chords (*AP, BP, CP,* and *DP* in the figure at the left) to be four consecutive integers?
No. Let AP = x, CP = x + 1, DP = x + 2, and BP = x + 3.
Then x(x + 3) = (x + 1)(x + 2) ⇒ x² + 3x = x² + 3x + 2.
This yields 0 = 2, which is impossible.

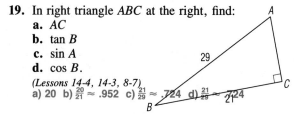

774

OBJECTIVES

H Apply the Isoperimetric
Inequalities to determine
which figures have the
most or least area or pe-
rimeter.

J Apply the Isoperimetric
Inequalities in real situations.

Suppose you have 100 feet of fencing. How can you arrange it to
provide the largest pen for the hogs? Here are some possibilities.

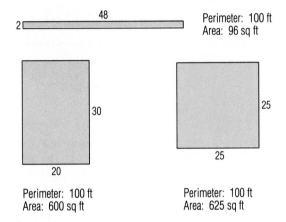

Of the figures above, the square has the most area. It is the best
quadrilateral shape for this purpose. But there is an even better
shape than the square. Consider making the play area circular.

If $\qquad C = 100$ ft,
then $\qquad 2\pi r = 100$ ft.
Thus, $\qquad r = \frac{100}{2\pi} = \frac{50}{\pi} \approx 15.92$ ft.

With the radius known, the area can
be calculated.

$$A = \pi r^2$$
$$\approx \pi(15.92)^2$$
$$\approx 796 \text{ sq ft}$$

Circumference: 100 ft
Area: 796 sq. ft.

The circle has about 171 sq ft more area than the square, even
though it has the same perimeter!

TEACHING NOTES

There are thousands of theorems involving figures that
can be proved from the postulates stated in this book.
However, some of the theorems we have stated require
concepts (such as limit)
whose detailed discussion is
beyond the scope of the
course. The theorems of this
lesson and the next lesson
are in the latter category.
Only numerical arguments
are given.

Making Connections
The use of figures on page
776 that are not normally
studied in geometry is a good
way to illustrate that geometric principles apply to many
subjects that are not discussed in a typical high
school geometry book.

The result, that the circle gives the most area, is the *Isoperimetric Theorem*. (The prefix "iso-" means "same.")

Isoperimetric Theorem:

Of all plane figures with the same perimeter, the circle has the most area.

The proof of this theorem requires advanced calculus, a subject usually not studied until college. The reason the proof is difficult is that it requires discussing all sorts of curves.

Pictured below are two such curves. At the left is an ellipse which is close to circular and thus encloses a good amount of area for its perimeter. At the right is a nonconvex curve with the same perimeter as the ellipse. As you can see, it encloses very little area for its perimeter.

Using the Isoperimetric Theorem, the maximal area for any perimeter p can be found. The steps in the proof are like those done above for the circle. The result is known as the *Isoperimetric Inequality*.

Isoperimetric Inequality:

If a plane figure has area A and perimeter p, then
$$A \le \frac{p^2}{4\pi}.$$

Proof

Suppose the figure is a circle. Then its radius is $\frac{p}{2\pi}$ and its area is $\pi(\frac{p}{2\pi})^2$. This expression simplifies to $\frac{p^2}{4\pi}$. So for a circle, $A = \frac{p^2}{4\pi}$. The area of any other figure must be less than $\frac{p^2}{4\pi}$, so $A \le \frac{p^2}{4\pi}$.

776

Example 1 Suppose a figure has perimeter 30 cm.

a. What is its largest possible area?

b. What is its smallest possible area?

Solution

a. The largest possible area is given by the Isoperimetric Inequality with $p = 30$.

$$A \leq \frac{30^2}{4\pi}$$

$$= \frac{900}{4\pi}$$

$$\leq 71.62 \text{ sq cm (approximately)}$$

The largest possible area, about 71.62 sq cm, occurs when the figure is a circle.

perimeter: 30
area: close to zero

perimeter: 30
area: $\frac{900}{4\pi} \approx 71.62$

b. The area can be as small as you want, but not zero. You can write, "The minimum is as close to zero as you like."

The inequality $A \leq \dfrac{p^2}{4\pi}$ can be solved for p.

Multiply both sides by 4π. $\qquad\qquad 4\pi A \leq p^2$

Rewrite the inequality to put p^2 on the left. $\qquad p^2 \geq 4\pi A$

Take the positive square root of each side. $\qquad p \geq \sqrt{4\pi A}$

Thus of all plane figures with a given area A, the perimeter p is at least $\sqrt{4\pi A}$. This result is a second way of stating the Isoperimetric Theorem.

Isoperimetric Theorem:

Of all plane figures with the same area, the circle has the least perimeter.

If the area of a circle is A, the perimeter (circumference) of a circle is $\sqrt{4\pi A}$. Any other figure with this area has a greater perimeter.

1. A square and an equilateral triangle each has perimeter 30 square meters. Which has the greater area?

The square has area 56.25 square meters and the equilateral triangle $25\sqrt{3}$ square meters; thus, the square has the greater area. (The square is more like a circle than the equilateral triangle.)

2. Describe the region of smallest perimeter that contains 100 square yards of ground.

a circle with radius $\sqrt{\frac{100}{\pi}} \approx$ 5.6 yards

Example 2 Suppose a square and a circle both have area 25 sq ft. Show that the perimeter (circumference) of the circle is smaller than the perimeter of the square.

Solution The square's area is 25 sq ft, so a side is 5 ft, and its perimeter is 20 ft. For the circle, $A = 25$, so $p = \sqrt{4\pi(25)} = \sqrt{100\pi}$, or about 17.72 ft. Since $17.72 < 20$, the circle needs less perimeter to enclose the same area. It is more efficient.

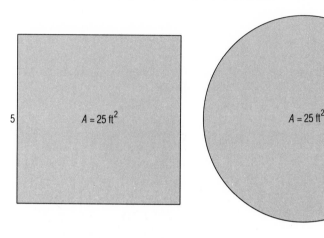

Questions

Covering the Reading

1. Of all rectangles with perimeter 100 ft, what are the dimensions of the one with the most area? **a square with side 10 ft**

2. **a.** Of all figures with perimeter 100 ft, which has the most area?
   b. What is that area?
   a) a circle; b) $\frac{2500}{\pi} \approx 796$ ft²

3. If a figure has perimeter 100 ft, what is its least possible area? **The minimum area is as close to zero as you like.**

4. Consider all figures with area 600 square meters. Which has the least perimeter? **circle**

5. Draw a non-polygonal figure that has a small area for its perimeter. **See margin.**

6. Draw a polygon with a small area for its perimeter. **See margin.**

7. A circle has area 9π sq cm. What is its circumference? $6\pi \approx 18.8$ cm

8. A square has area 9π sq cm. What is its perimeter? $12\sqrt{\pi} \approx 21.3$ cm

9. Which answer should be larger, that for Question 7 or that for Question 8? **Question 8**

10. Complete the statements.
    a. Of all figures with the same area, the _?_ has the _?_ perimeter.
    b. Of all figures with the same perimeter, the _?_ has the _?_ area.
    a) circle, least; b) circle, most

11. a. A fence encloses pentagonal region *ABCDE* at the right. Find the area of this region. **540 ft²**

    b. Find the area of the largest region that could be enclosed by this fence. $\frac{2025}{\pi} \approx$ **645 ft²**

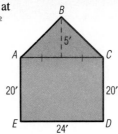

12. If a rectangle has perimeter 4*s*, then its sides can be called $s - t, s + t, s - t,$ and $s + t$.

    a. What is the area of this rectangle? $s^2 - t^2$

    b. For what value of *t* is the area the largest? **0**

13. Refer to $\odot O$ at the right. Suppose $XY = 8$, $YZ = 20$, and $XW = 10$.

    a. Find *WV*. **12.4 units**

    b. What is the power of point *X*?

    (Lesson 15-7) **224**

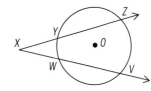

14. In the circle at the left, $AE = 16$, $BE = 14$, $CE = 18$. Find *DE*.

    (Lesson 15-7) $\frac{112}{9} \approx$ **12.4 units**

In 15 and 16, refer to $\odot O$ at the right. $\overrightarrow{AB}$ is tangent at point *B*.

15. If $m\angle A = 40$, find

    a. $m\widehat{BD}$ **130°**

    b. $m\widehat{BC}$. *(Lesson 15-6)* **50°**

16. Find $m\angle CBD$. *(Lesson 15-3)* **90**

17. In the figure at the left, find *x*. *(Lesson 15-5)* **64**

18. What is the measure of each interior angle of a regular decagon?

    (Lesson 13-8) **144**

19. State **a.** the converse, **b.** the inverse, and **c.** the contrapositive of the following statement: If we finish the next lesson, our class will have done every lesson in the book. *(Lesson 13-2)* **See margin.**

20. Calculate $\sqrt[3]{\pi}$ to the nearest hundredth. *(Lesson 10-3)* **1.46**

21. Give dimensions and draw a picture of a polygon whose perimeter is 100 feet and whose area is greater than 625 square feet. **See margin.**

MORE PRACTICE

For more questions on SPUR Objectives, use *Lesson Master 15-8*, shown below.

21. sample: a regular hexagon with perimeter 100 feet has area ≈ 722 ft².

$\frac{50}{3}$ ft

$A \approx 722$ ft²

NAME _____

LESSON **MASTER**   **15–8**
QUESTIONS ON **SPUR** OBJECTIVES

■ **PROPERTIES**   *Objective H (See pages 788–791 for objectives.)*

1. Consider all plane figures with perimeter of 10 inches.

    a. Which has the largest area?   circle

    b. What is this area?   ≈7.96 in.²

2. A circle and an equilateral triangle both have areas of 20 m². Which has the smaller perimeter?   circle

3. Of all quadrilaterals with a fixed perimeter, which has the most area?   square

4. Of all triangles with fixed area, which has the smallest perimeter?   equilateral

■ **USES**   *Objective J*

5. Draw a figure with a large area for its perimeter.

    sample:

6. Draw a figure with a large perimeter for its area.

    sample:

7. A carpenter wants to build a playpen with 20 feet of netting around it.

    a. What is the maximum area possible?   ≈31.8 ft²

    b. If a quadrilateral is desired, what is the maximum area possible?   25 ft²

RESOURCES
■ Lesson Master 15-9

LESSON

15-9

The Isoperimetric Theorems in Space

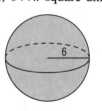

The role the circle plays in 2-dimensional relationships between area and perimeter is played by the sphere in 3-dimensional relationships between volume and surface area.

To emphasize the similarities, mathematicians use the same term, "isoperimetric," to indicate "same boundary." Again, a proof of the theorem requires advanced mathematics.

Isoperimetric Theorem (space version):

> Of all solids with the same surface area, the sphere has the most volume.

The theorem can be verified in different ways. First is with an example. Below, the sphere and the cylinder have the same surface area, 144π square units.

surface area
of sphere $= 4\pi r^2$
            $= 144\pi$ sq units

surface area
of cylinder $= L.A. + 2B$
            $= 2\pi rh + 2\pi r^2$
            $= 144\pi$ sq units

Which has the greater volume? Their volumes can be easily found from formulas.

volume
of sphere $= \frac{4}{3}\pi r^3$
          $= 288\pi$ units^3

volume
of cylinder $= Bh$
            $= \pi r^2 h$
            $= 224\pi$ units^3

The sphere has 64π cubic units more volume than the cylinder, almost 30% more volume. In fact, the sphere is the most efficient container. You would see spherical containers if they didn't roll!

A common experience provides a second verification. Suppose you blow air into a paper bag. The bag, being unable to stretch to change its surface area, will tend to assume a shape as close to a sphere as it can. If you blow in more air than the sphere can hold, the bag will burst.

Now, rather than a constant boundary, keep the interior constant. To do this, consider shapes with the same volume. The plastic container that holds a gallon of milk, but uses the least amount of plastic, would be shaped like a sphere. Soap bubbles consist of some soapy water and a fixed volume of air trapped inside. Because of surface tension, the bubble takes a shape to minimize the surface area surrounding the trapped air. That shape is a sphere.

Isoperimetric Theorem (space version):

> Of all solids with the same volume, the sphere has the least surface area.

The following example verifies the theorem numerically.

■ ■ ■ ■ ■ ■ ■ ■

Example A cube and a sphere have volume 1000 cubic meters. Calculate their surface areas.

Solution First draw figures and write down relevant formulas.

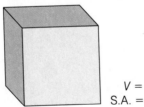
$V = s^3$
S.A. $= 6s^2$

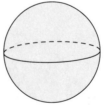
$V = \frac{4}{3}\pi r^3$
S.A. $= 4\pi r^2$

For the cube, $1000 = s^3$, so $s = \sqrt[3]{1000} = 10$.
The surface area of the cube $= 6s^2 = 600$ square meters.
For the sphere, $1000 = \frac{4}{3}\pi r^3$,
$\frac{750}{\pi} = r^3$
$238.7 \approx r^3$.
Take the cube root to find $r \approx 6.2$.
The surface area of the sphere $= 4\pi r^2 \approx 4 \cdot \pi \cdot 6.2^2 \approx 483$ square meters. The sphere has considerably less surface area than the cube. The cube "wastes" surface because of its flat faces and corners.

LESSON 15-9   The Isoperimetric Theorems in Space   **781**

ADDITIONAL EXAMPLES
1. A box with dimensions 3 in., 4 in., and 18 in. has a volume of 216 cubic in., the same as that of a cube with edge 6 in. Which has the greater surface area?
the box, 216 in.^{2} vs. 276 in.^{2}

2. Describe the solid of smallest surface area that can enclose a cubic meter.

a sphere with radius $\sqrt[3]{\frac{3}{4\pi}}$.

Just as a two-dimensional figure can have a large perimeter and a small area, so a three-dimensional figure can have a large surface area inside a very small volume. Think of sponges like the natural and artificial ones pictured here. The artificial sponge has the shape of a retangular solid with volume 12 cubic inches, whereas the natural sponge is more irregular. Both sponges are nonconvex curved surface with many nooks, and both sponges can be enclosed in a space whose volume is small. The nooks give the sponges a large surface area compared to space they occcupy. This large irregular surface enables sponges to hold a lot of water. Some water is held because in almost any position some of the surface is under it. Other water clings to the large surface just the way the inside of a glass remains wet after you pour out its contents.

The Isoperimetric Theorems involve square and cube roots, π, polygons, circles, polyhedra, and spheres. They explain properties of fences, soap bubbles, and sponges. They demonstrate the broad applicability of geometry and the unity of mathematics. Many people enjoy mathematics due to the way it connects diverse topics. Others like mathematics for its uses. Still others like the logical way mathematics fits together and grows. We have tried to provide all these kinds of experiences in this book and hope that you have enjoyed it.

Covering the Reading

1. Of all the figures with the same surface area, the ? has the most ? . **sphere, volume**

2. Of all the figures with the same volume, the ? has the least ? . **sphere, surface area**

3. Which statement, that of Question 1 or Question 2, explains the shape of a soap bubble? **Question 2**

4. The surface area of a solid is 600 square meters. To the nearest 100 cubic meters, what is the largest possible volume of the solid? **1400 m³**

5. In Question 4, what is the least possible volume? **The minimum volume is as close to zero as you like.**

6. A cube has volume 8 cubic units. What is its surface area? **24 units²**

7. Explain why sponges are able to hold so much water. **Some water has sponge surface area under it; other water clings to the sponge's surface area.**

Applying the Mathematics

8. The Water Pik company has claimed that its charcoal filter Instapure®, designed to be placed between a cigarette and a smoker's mouth, has over 6 acres of surface area.
   a. Can this claim possibly be true? **Yes**
   b. If so, why would anyone want to have so much surface area? If not, why can't the claim be true? **to filter as much smoke as possible**

9. a. A sphere has volume 36π cubic meters. What is its surface area?
   b. Give dimensions for a cylinder with volume 36π cubic meters. What is the surface area of the cylinder you identify?
   c. Give dimensions for a right cone with volume 36π cubic meters. What is its surface area?
   d. According to the Isoperimetric Inequality, the surface area in part **a** is ? than the surface area in parts **b** or **c**. **a) 36π ≈ 113 m²; b) See margin. c) See margin d) less**

10. The plastic milk container that would have the least material for a given amount of milk would be shaped like a sphere. Why are milk containers *not* spheres? **See margin.**

11. A sphere has surface area $x \cdot \pi$. Find its volume in terms of x.
    $\frac{\pi\sqrt{x^3}}{6}$ **units³**

Review

12. Consider all plane figures whose area is 12 square meters.
    a. Which has the smallest perimeter? **circle**
    b. What is the perimeter? *(Lesson 15-8)* $4\pi\sqrt{\frac{3}{\pi}} \approx 12.28$ **meters**

13. A circle and a square both have perimeters of 96 inches.
    a. Calculate their areas. **circle: $\frac{2304}{\pi} \approx 733$ in.²; square: 576 in.²**
    b. Which has the smaller area? *(Lesson 15-8)* **square**

FOLLOW-UP

MORE PRACTICE
For more questions on SPUR Objectives, use *Lesson Master 15-9,* shown below.

EVALUATION
Alternative Assessment
You might want several students to summarize orally the two- and three-dimensional isoperimetric relationships for the class.

ADDITIONAL ANSWERS
9. b. sample: radius of 2 m, height of 9 m; surface area: 44π ≈ 138 m²
c. sample: radius of 6 m, height of 3 m; surface area: 36π + 6π√45 ≈ 240 m²

10. sample: because they do not fit on a shelf or in a packing crate without rolling or wasting space

NAME _____

LESSON **MASTER   15–9**
QUESTIONS ON **SPUR** OBJECTIVES

■**PROPERTIES**   *Objective H (See pages 788–791 for objectives.)*

1. Consider all figures in space with a surface area of 10 square inches.
   a. Which has the largest volume?   **sphere**
   b. What is this volume?   **≈2.97 in.³**

2. A sphere and a cube each has volume of 20 m³. Which has the smaller surface area?   **sphere**

3. Of all rectangular prisms with a fixed surface area, which has the most volume?   **cube**

4. Of all tetrahedron with a fixed volume, which has the smallest surface area?
   regular tetrahedron or regular triangular pyramid

■**USES**   *Objective J*

5. Draw an object with a large volume for its surface area.
   sample:

6. Draw an object with a large surface area for its volume.
   sample:

7. Name a reason why the package with the least surface area for its volume might not be used.
   A spherical package would roll and does not stack well.

8. A farmer wants to build a holding tank for water. He has 100 ft² of material.
   a. What is the volume of the most efficient shape?   **≈94 ft³**
   b. What is the volume of the most efficient rectangular prism?   **≈68 ft³**

Geometry © Scott, Foresman and Company   **147**

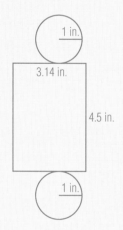
14. $\overrightarrow{QM}$ is tangent to $\odot X$ below at L. If $NQ = 6$ and $PN = 12$, find QL. *(Lesson 15-7)* $\sqrt{108} \approx 10.39$ units

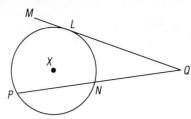

15. $\overline{DE}$ is a diameter of $\odot O$ below, and $\overline{AB} \perp \overline{DE}$. Prove that AC is the geometric mean of CD and CE. *(Lesson 15-7)* See margin.

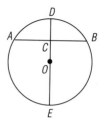

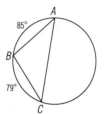

In 16 and 17, $\triangle ABC$ is inscribed in the circle at the left.

16. What are the measures of the angles of $\triangle ABC$? *(Lesson 15-3)*
m∠A = 39.5, m∠B = 98, m∠C = 42.5

17. What is the smallest side of $\triangle ABC$? *(Lesson 13-7)* $\overline{BC}$

18. Draw a net for a juice can. *(Lesson 9-7)* See margin.

19. It is 457 miles from Boston to Buffalo. It is 436 miles from Buffalo to New York City. From only this information, what can you say about the distance from Boston to New York City? *(Lesson 1-9)*
It is between 21 and 893 miles.

20. According to legend, the first person to use the Isoperimetric Inequality was Dido, the queen of Carthage.
a. Where is, or was, Carthage?
b. How did Dido use this inequality? (Hint: Look in an encyclopedia or dictionary under Dido.)
See margin.

21. Develop an Isoperimetric Inequality for space. That is, find a relationship between the volume V and surface area S.A. of any space figure.

Suppose a space figure has a surface area of S.A. If that figure is a sphere, then S.A. = $4\pi r^2$ and $V = \frac{4}{3}\pi r^3$. Solving each formula for r, $r = \sqrt{\frac{S.A.}{4\pi}}$ and $r = \sqrt[3]{\frac{3V}{4\pi}}$. Thus $\sqrt{\frac{S.A.}{4\pi}} = \sqrt[3]{\frac{3V}{4\pi}}$. Cubing both sides, $\frac{3V}{4\pi} = \left(\sqrt{\frac{S.A.}{4\pi}}\right)^3 = \frac{S.A.}{4\pi}\sqrt{\frac{S.A.}{4\pi}}$. So, $V = \frac{S.A.}{3}\sqrt{\frac{S.A.}{4\pi}} = \frac{S.A.}{6}\sqrt{\frac{S.A.}{\pi}}$. Now the sphere has the most volume for a given surface area, so for any figure, $V \leq \frac{S.A.}{6}\sqrt{\frac{S.A.}{\pi}}$.

784

Summary

The theorems and applications of this chapter are related to many of the ideas you have studied in earlier chapters. Scheduling using properties of circles and regular polygons utilizes networks, where points are nodes. For the places to take a photo so that an entire object fits into the photo, points are locations.

Perpendicular lines are important in circles. A line perpendicular to a chord bisects the chord if and only if it contains the center of the circle. If the sides of an inscribed angle are perpendicular, then the angle intercepts a semicircle. These theorems give ways of finding the center of a circle.

The chapter includes congruence and similarity also. In a circle or in congruent circles, arcs of the same measure are congruent if and only if they have congruent chords. Inscribed angles which intercept the same arc are congruent. If two chords $\overline{AB}$ and $\overline{CD}$ intersect at point E, $\triangle EAC$ and $\triangle EBD$ are similar. As a result, $AE \cdot BE = CE \cdot DE$. Amazingly, this theorem holds if the word "secant" is substituted for "chord" and A, B, C, and D are the points at which two secants intersect the circle.

Relationships between measures of angles and arcs are all derived from the definition that the measure of an arc is equal to the measure of its central angle. Other angles are measured by:

central angle—intercepted arc
inscribed angle—half the intercepted arc
angle between chords—
half the sum of the intercepted arcs
angle between secants or tangents—
half the difference of the intercepted arcs

The Isoperimetric Theorems relate perimeters, areas, and volumes of figures. In two dimensions: Of all figures with the same perimeter, the circle has the most area. Of all figures with the same area, the circle has the least perimeter. In three dimensions: Of all figures with the same surface area, the sphere has the most volume. Of all figures with the same volume, the sphere has the least surface area. Many properties of real objects can be explained by these theorems.

Vocabulary

Below are the most important terms and phrases for this chapter.
For the starred (*) term you should be able to give a definition of the term.
For the other terms you should be able to give a general description and a specific example of each.

Lesson 15-1
intercepted arc
measure of the intercepted arc
Chord-Center Theorem
Arc-Chord Congruence Theorem
inscribed polygon
circumscribed polygon

Lesson 15-2
round-robin, bye, pairing

Lesson 15-3
picture angle of a lens
inscribed angle
Inscribed Angle Theorem

Lesson 15-4
right angle method
for finding center of circle
perpendicular bisector method
for finding center of circle

Lesson 15-5
Angle-Chord Theorem
*secant
Angle-Secant Theorem
pentagram

Lesson 15-6
Tangent-Chord Theorem
Tangent-Secant Theorem

Lesson 15-7
Secant Length Theorem
power of a point
Tangent Square Theorem

Lesson 15-8
Isoperimetric Theorem
Isoperimetric Inequality

Lesson 15-9
Isoperimetric Theorem
(space version)

SUMMARY

The Summary gives an overview of the entire chapter and provides an opportunity for students to consider the material as a whole. Thus, the Summary can be used to help students relate the various concepts presented in the chapter.

VOCABULARY

Terms, symbols, and properties are listed by lesson to provide a checklist of concepts a student must know. Emphasize to students that they should read the vocabulary list carefully before starting the Progress Self-Test. If students do not remember the meaning of a term or statement of a theorem, they should refer back to the individual lesson.

Whereas end-of-chapter materials may be considered optional in some texts, they should not be considered optional in UCSMP *Geometry*. The Progress Self-Test provides the opportunity for feedback and correction; the Chapter Review provides additional opportunities for practice. It is at this point that the material "gels" for many students, allowing them to solidify skills and concepts before a test. In general, student performance is markedly improved after these pages.

USING THE PROGRESS SELF-TEST

Assign the Progress Self-Test as a one-night assignment. Worked-out *solutions* for all questions are in the Selected Answers section of the student text. Encourage students to take the Progress Self-Test honestly, grade themselves, and then be prepared to discuss the test in class.

Advise students to pay special attention to those Chapter Review questions (pages 788-791) which correspond to questions missed on the Progress Self-Test. A chart provided with the Selected Answers keys the Progress Self-Test questions to the lettered SPUR Objectives in the Chapter Review or to the Vocabulary. It also keys the questions to the corresponding lessons where the material is covered.

ADDITIONAL ANSWERS
1. See Additional Answers in the back of this book.

2.
wk 1	2-5	3-4	1 bye
wk 2	3-1	4-5	2 bye
wk 3	4-2	5-1	3 bye
wk 4	5-3	1-2	4 bye
wk 5	1-4	2-3	5 bye

Progress Self-Test

See margin for answers not shown below.

Directions: Take this test as you would take a test in class. Then check your work with the solutions in the Selected Answers section in the back of the book. You will need a straightedge, compass, and protractor.

1. Find the center of the circle that contains points *C, D,* and *E* as shown below.

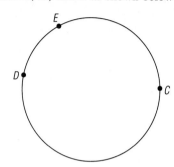

2. Schedule five teams for a round-robin tournament.

3. ℓ is tangent to $\odot O$ below at *Q*. If $\overline{OQ}$ intersects chord $\overline{XY}$ at the midpoint *M* of $\overline{XY}$, explain why $\ell \parallel \overline{XY}$.

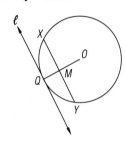

4. Square *JKLM* is inscribed in $\odot P$ below. If the radius of $\odot P$ is 30, find the perimeter of *JKLM*. $120\sqrt{2} \approx$ **169.7 units**

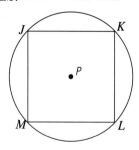

In 5 and 6, use the figure at the right, where m$\overarc{DC}$ = 80° and m$\angle DEC$ = 110.

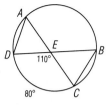

5. Find m$\angle B$. **40**
6. Find m$\overarc{AB}$. **140°**

7. In $\odot Z$ below, m$\overarc{US}$ = 30°, m$\overarc{UV}$ = 80°, and m$\overarc{ST}$ = 140°. Find m$\angle R$. **40**

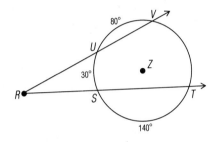

8. $\overrightarrow{PT}$ and $\overrightarrow{PU}$ are tangents to $\odot O$ below at *T* and *U*. If m$\overarc{UT}$ = 90°, explain why *PUOT* is a square.

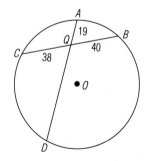

9. In circle *O* below, if *AQ* = 19, *BQ* = 40, and *CQ* = 38, find *QD*. **80 units**

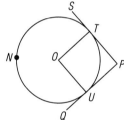

10. In ⊙G below, if WX = 12, XY = 16, and WZ = 10, find ZV. **23.6 units**

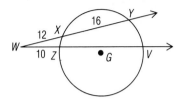

11. A clerk has 30 cm of a small wire screen to "fence in" some supplies on a desk.
   a. How should the screen be shaped to fence in the most area? **a circle**
   b. What is this area? $\frac{225}{\pi} \approx$ **71.6 cm²**

12. A sphere and a cube both have volume 240 cubic feet. Which has the larger surface area? **the cube**

In 13 and 14, refer to the stage below. You have a camera lens with a 64° picture angle.

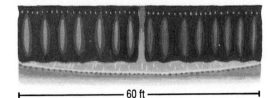

├─────── 60 ft ───────┤

13. Draw a picture indicating where you can stand so that the entire stage will be seen in your picture.

14. How near to the center of the stage in the middle of the audience can you stand and still photograph the entire stage? $\frac{30}{\tan 32°} \approx$ **48 ft**

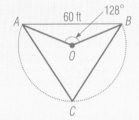

CHAPTER REVIEW

The main objectives for the chapter are organized here into sections corresponding to the four main types of understanding this book promotes: Skills, Properties, Uses, and Representations. We call these the SPUR Objectives. The four types of understanding are not in increasing order of difficulty. There may be hard skills and easy representations; some uses may be easier than anything else; and so on.

USING THE CHAPTER REVIEW

Students should be able to answer questions like these with about 85% accuracy by the end of the chapter.

You may assign these questions over a single night to help students prepare for a test the next day, or you may assign the questions over a two-day period.

If you assign the questions over two days, then we recommend assigning the *evens* for homework the first night so that students get feedback in class the next day. Then assign the *odds* for the second night (the night before the test) so that students can use the answers provided in the book as a study aid.

Chapter Review

Questions on **SPUR** Objectives

See margin for answers not shown below.

SPUR stands for **S**kills, **P**roperties, **U**ses, and **R**epresentations. The Chapter Review questions are grouped according according to the SPUR Objectives for this chapter.

SKILLS deal with the procedures used to get answers.

■ **Objective A:** *Calculate lengths of chords of arcs.* (Lesson 15-1)

1. A regular hexagon is inscribed in ⊙O below at the left. If the radius of ⊙O is 12, what is the length of each side of the hexagon? **12 units**

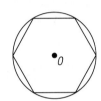
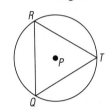

2. Equilateral triangle QRT is inscribed in circle P above at the right. If QP = 15, find the perimeter of △QRT. **45√3 ≈ 77.9 units**

In 3 and 4, ABCD is a square inscribed in ⊙O at the right below. AB = 12√2.

3. Find OB. **12 units**

4. Find the area of the shaded region.
144π − 288 ≈ 164.4 units²

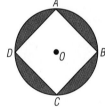

5. A circle has radius 55 mm. Find the length of a chord of a 144° arc.
110 sin 72° ≈ 104.6 mm

6. Regular octagon STOPZIGN is inscribed in ⊙Q at the right.
a. What is m$\widehat{IZ}$? **45°**
b. If QT = 15, find the perimeter of the octagon.
240 sin 22.5° ≈ 91.8 units

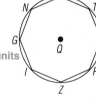

■ **Objective B:** *Calculate measures of inscribed angles from measures of intercepted arcs, and vice-versa.* (Lesson 15-3)

In 7–9, use the circle at the right.

7. Find m$\widehat{CB}$. **106°**
8. Find m$\widehat{ADC}$. **179°**
9. Find m∠D. **91**

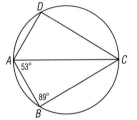

In 10 and 11, △PQR is inscribed in the circle below at the right.

10. Find m∠Q. **81**
11. Find m∠P. **52**

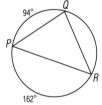

■ **Objective C:** *Calculate measures of angles between chords, secants, or tangents, from measures of intercepted arcs, and vice-versa.* (Lessons 15-3, 15-5, 15-6)

In 12 and 13, use circle Z at the right.

12. If m$\widehat{DG}$ = 100° and m$\widehat{EF}$ = 140°, what is m∠EHF?
120

13. If m∠EHD = 51 and m$\widehat{GF}$ = 37°, what other arc measure can be found, and what is that measure? **m$\widehat{DE}$ = 65°**

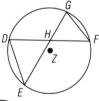

788

14. Below, m$\overparen{BC}$ = 30° m$\overparen{DE}$ = 125°. Find the measures of as many angles in the figure as you can.

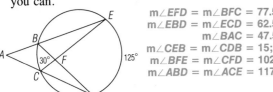

m∠EFD = m∠BFC = 77.5;
m∠EBD = m∠ECD = 62.5;
m∠BAC = 47.5;
m∠CEB = m∠CDB = 15;
m∠BFE = m∠CFD = 102.5;
m∠ABD = m∠ACE = 117.5

In 15–17, use ⊙L below with measures as marked.

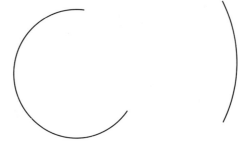

15. Find m∠PJQ. 14
16. Find m$\overparen{ON}$. 40
17. Find m∠PJM. 78

■ **Objective D:** *Locate the center of the circle given sufficient information using the right angle or perpendicular bisector method. (Lesson 15-4)*

In 18 and 19, trace the circle. Then find its center using the right angle method.

18.

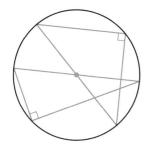

19.

20. Trace the three points below. Draw the circle through them.

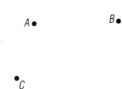

21. Trace the figure below. Draw the circle containing all vertices of △DEF.

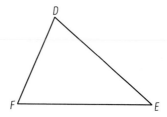

In 22 and 23, find the center of the circle containing the circular arc. Draw the entire circle.

22.   **23.**

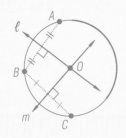

■ **Objective E:** *Apply the Secant Length Theorem. (Lesson 15-7)*

24. *A, B, C,* and *D* all lie on ⊙*Q* below. If *AX* = 12, *XB* = 40, and *DX* = 48, find *CX*.
10 units

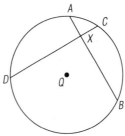

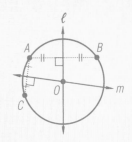
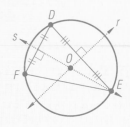
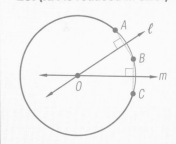

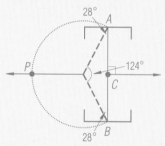
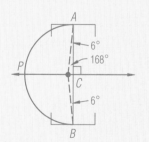
In 25 and 26, refer to ⊙O.

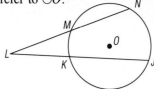

25. If $LN = 20$, $MN = 15$, and $LJ = 25$, find KJ. **21 units**

26. If $LM = 6$, $MN = 7$, and $KJ = 8$, find LK. $\sqrt{94} - 4 \approx$ **5.7 units**

27. $\overrightarrow{QR}$ is tangent to ⊙Z below at R. If $QR = 8$ and $QX = 4$, find YX. **12 units**

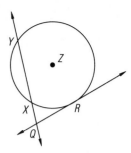

PROPERTIES deal with the principles behind the mathematics.

▪ **Objective F:** *Make deductions from properties of radii perpendicular to chords, and know sufficient conditions for radii to be perpendicular to them.* *(Lesson 15-1)*

In 28–30, given ⊙O, $\overline{AB} \perp \overline{CD}$, and $\overline{OA} \perp \ell$. Justify each statement. Be careful. One statement cannot be justified.

28. $DE = EC$
29. $OE = EB$
30. $\ell \parallel \overline{CD}$

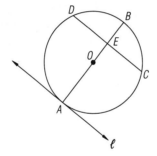

31. Use ⊙P below.
Given: W is the midpoint of $\overline{XY}$.
Prove: $\triangle ZYX$ is isosceles.

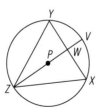

▪ **Objective G:** *Make deductions from properties of inscribed angles formed by chords, tangents, or secants.* *(Lessons 15-3, 15-5, 15-6)*

In 32 and 33, $ABCD$ at the right is a rectangle.

32. Explain why $\overline{BC}$ is a diameter.

33. Suppose m$\overparen{AB} = x$. What is m∠ACB? $\frac{x}{2}$

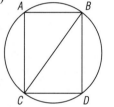

34. Below, $\overleftrightarrow{AB}$ is tangent to circle O at B. Prove: m∠ABD = m∠C.

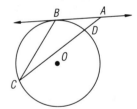

▪ **Objective H:** *Apply the Isoperimetric Inequalities to determine which figures have the most or least area, perimeter, or volume.* *(Lessons 15-8, 15-9)*

35. Consider all plane figures with area of 800 square feet.
   a. Which has the least perimeter? **a circle**
   b. What is the perimeter? $\sqrt{\frac{800}{\pi}} \cdot 2\pi \approx$ **100 ft**

36. a. Of all rectangles with perimeter 2000 centimeters, which has the most area? **a square**
   b. What is that area? **250,000 cm²**

37. A circle and a square both have perimeters of 32 inches. **a)** sq: 64 in.²; ⊙: π($\frac{32}{2π}$)² ≈ 81.5 in.²
   a. Calculate their areas.
   b. Which has the larger area? the circle

38. The surface area of a solid is 10,000 square meters. What figure has the largest volume for this surface area? a sphere

39. a. Of all boxes with surface area 48 square feet, which has the most volume? a cube
   b. What is that volume? ($\sqrt{8}$)³ ≈ 22.6 ft.³

40. A sphere and a cylinder both have volume 20,000 cubic meters.
   a. Can you tell which has the larger surface area? Yes, the cylinder.
   b. Why or why not? The sphere has the smallest surface area of any solid with a given volume.

USES deal with applications of mathematics in real situations

■ **Objective I:** *Given the angle width of a lens and the width of an object, determine the set of points from which the object will fit in the picture.* *(Lesson 15-4)*

In 41 and 42, a photographer wants to take a picture the entire length of a football field (from *A* to *B*). A scale drawing is made. The 50-yard line bisects the segment connecting the goal posts. Let *AB* = 120 yards.

41. a. Locate all points where the photographer could stand to exactly fit $\overline{AB}$ if the camera lens has a picture angle of 62°.
   b. At least how far from *C* will the photographer be if he stands on the 50-yard line? $\frac{60}{\tan 31°}$ ≈ 100 yards

42. a. Locate all points where the photographer could stand to exactly fit $\overline{AB}$ if the camera lens has a picture angle of 84°.
   b. At least how far from *C* will the photographer be if he stands on the 50-yard line? $\frac{60}{\tan 42°}$ ≈ 66.6 yards

■ **Objective J:** *Apply the Isoperimetric Inequalities in real situations.* *(Lessons 15-8, 15-9)*

43. a. Of all containers that can hold a liter of orange juice, what shape container has the least surface area?
   b. Why is this shape seldom used?

44. A farmer is making a pigpen with 60 feet of fencing.
   a. What is the area of the most efficient rectangle? 225 ft²
   b. What is the area of the most efficient shape? $\frac{900}{π}$ ≈ 286 ft²

45. Draw a figure with a large perimeter for its area.

46. Identify a figure with a large surface area for its volume.

REPRESENTATIONS deal with pictures, graphs, or objects that illustrate concepts.

■ **Objective K:** *Make a schedule for a round-robin tournament.* *(Lesson 15-2)*

47. Four teams need to be scheduled for a round-robin tournament. Picture the schedule using chords of circles, and write a complete schedule.

48. Schedule a round-robin tournament for 11 teams, *A*–*K*.

49. Schedule a round-robin tournament for 12 teams, *A*–*L*.
   Use the answer to Question 48.
   Replace the "bye" with the 12th team *L*.

EVALUATION
Three forms of a Chapter Test are provided in the Teacher's Resource File. Chapter 15 Test, Forms A and B cover just Chapter 15. The third test is Chapter 15 Test, Cumulative Form. About 50% of this test covers Chapter 15, 25% covers Chapter 14, and 25% covers previous chapters. A fourth test, Comprehensive Test, Chapters 1-15, that is multiple choice in format, is also provided. The Comprehensive Test may be used as part of a course exam.

45. sample:

46. samples: a concrete block, a sheet of notebook paper

47., 48. See Additional Answers in the back of this book.

This glossary contains definitions or descriptions of many of the terms used in this book. The numbers in parentheses following each term indicate a page on which that term is further discussed.

Named theorems are not listed here. To find the page number on which they are located, consult the index or the section in the back entitled THEOREMS.

acute angle   An angle whose measure is greater than 0 and less than 90. (113)

adjacent angles   Two nonstraight and nonzero angles are adjacent if and only if a common side is interior to the angle formed by the noncommon sides. (114)

algorithm   A sequence of steps leading to a desired end. (141)

alternate interior angles   Angles formed by two lines and a transversal whose interiors are partially between the lines and on different sides of the transversal. (234)

altitude   The distance between the bases of a trapezoid (384); the segment from a vertex perpendicular to the line containing the opposite side; also, the length of that segment (379). The distance between the planes of the solid (422); the length of a segment from the vertex perpendicular to the plane of the base of a pyramid or cone (429). Also called *height*.

angle   The union of two rays (its **sides**) that have the same endpoint (its **vertex**). (106)

antecedent   The "if" clause in an if-then statement. Also called *hypothesis*. (65)

arc   A path from one point (node) of a network to another point (its endpoints or vertices) (20). A part of a circle connecting two points (its endpoints) on the circle. (396)

area   The number of nonoverlapping unit squares or parts of unit squares that can be fit into a region. (355)

automatic drawer   Computer software that enables a geometric figure to be constructed from input by the user. (170)

auxiliary figure   A figure that is added to a given figure. (658)

axis of a cone   The line through the cone's vertex and the center of its base. (428)

base angles of a trapezoid   Two angles whose vertices are the endpoints of a base of the trapezoid. (215)

base angles of an isosceles triangle   Two angles of an isosceles triangle whose vertices are the endpoints of a base of the triangle. (206)

base of a trapezoid   Either of two parallel sides of a trapezoid. (215)

base   See *cylindric solid*. See *conic solid*.

betweenness of numbers   A number is between two others if it is greater than one of them and less than the other. (40)

betweenness of points   A point is between two other points on the same line if its coordinate is between their coordinates. (40)

biconditional statement   An if and only if statement that includes a conditional and its converse. (83)

bisector of a segment   The midpoint or any plane, line, ray, or segment which intersects a segment at its midpoint. (141)

bisector of an angle   The ray in the interior of an angle that divides the angle into two angles whose measures are equal. (116)

box   A right parallelepiped whose base is a rectangle. (424)

Cartesian plane   See *coordinate plane*.

center of a regular polygon   The point in the plane of the polygon which is equidistant from all its vertices. (335)

center of rotation   A point which is its own image under the rotation. (267)

center   See *circle*. See *rotation*.

central angle of a circle   An angle whose vertex is the center of the circle. (396)

chord   A segment whose endpoints are on a given circle. (397)

circle   The set of all points in a plane at a certain distance (its **radius**) from a certain point (its **center**). (84)

circumference of a circle   The perimeter of a circle, which is the limit of the perimeters of inscribed polygons. (397)

circumscribed polygon about a circle   A polygon with each of its sides tangent to the circle. (739)

clockwise orientation   The order in which the vertices of a polygon are given whereby the interior of the polygon is on the right. Also, the direction in which the hands move on a nondigital clock. (188)

clockwise rotation   The direction designated as the negative direction from a preimage to its corresponding image in a rotation; expressed by a negative magnitude. (267)

coincide   Contain exactly the same points. (192)

collinear points   Points that lie on the same line. (6)

compass   An instrument for drawing circles. (141)

complementary angles   Two angles whose measures sum to 90. (114) Also called *complements.*

composite   The result of applying the operation of composition to two transformations s followed by t, denoted by t ∘ s. (260)

composition   The operation of combining two transformations s followed by t by mapping each point *P* onto t(s(*P*)). (260)

concentric circles   Two or more circles with the same center. (331)

conclusion   The result of a deduction. (65) See *consequent.*

conditional   A statement of the form If-then... (65)

cone   The surface of a conic solid whose base is a circle. (428)

congruence transformation   A transformation that is a reflection or composite of reflections; also called *isometry* or *distance-preserving transformation.* (280)

congruent figures   Two figures such that one is the image of the other under a translation, a reflection, a rotation, or any composite of these. (279, 439)

conic section   The intersection of a plane with the union of two right conical surfaces that have the same vertex and whose edges are opposite rays. (436)

conic solid   The set of points between a given point (its **vertex**) and all points of a given region (its **base**), together with the vertex and the base. (428)

conjecture   An educated guess or opinion. (218)

consecutive angles   In a polygon, two angles whose vertices are endpoints of the same side.

consecutive sides   In a polygon, two sides with an endpoint in common. (93)

consecutive vertices   In a polygon, endpoints of a side. (93)

consequent   The "then" clause in an if-then statement. Also called *conclusion.* (65)

construction   A drawing which is made using only an unmarked straightedge and a compass following certain prescribed rules. (141)

contraction   A size change with magnitude less than one. (570)

contradiction   A situation in which two contradictory statements are both asserted. (646)

contradictory statements   Two statements that cannot both be true at the same time. (646)

contrapositive   A conditional resulting from negating and switching the antecedent and consequent of the original conditional. (636)

converse   The conditional statement formed by switching the antecedent and consequent of a given conditional. (76)

convex polygon   A polygon whose interior is a convex set. (94)

convex set   A set in which all segments connecting points of the set lie entirely in the set. (61)

coordinate axes   A pair of perpendicular coordinatized lines in a plane (14); three mutually perpendicular coordinatized lines in space (521).

coordinate geometry   Reasoning done with figures whose points are identified with coordinates in the plane or space. (521)

coordinate plane   A plane on which points are described as ordered pairs of real numbers. Also called *Cartesian plane.* (14)

coordinatized line   A line on which every point is identified with exactly one number and every number is identified with a point on the line. (8)

coplanar   Figures that lie in the same plane. (10)

corollary   An easily proved theorem that follows from another theorem. (230)

corresponding parts   Angles and sides that are images of each other under a transformation or other correspondence. (292)

cosine of an acute angle   The ratio $\dfrac{\text{leg adjacent to the angle}}{\text{hypotenuse}}$ in a right triangle. (702)

counterclockwise orientation   The order taken of the vertices of a polygon when the interior is on the left. (188)

counterclockwise rotation   The direction designated by a positive magnitude to indicate the rotation from a preimage to its corresponding image. (267)

counterexample to a conditional   A situation for which the antecedent is true and the consequent is false. (66)

cube   A box whose dimensions are all the same. (10)

cube root   The number whose cube is a given number. (480)

cylinder   The surface of a cylindric solid whose base is a circle. (423)

cylindric solid   The set of points between a region (its **base**) and its translation image in space, including the region and its image. (422)

decagon   A polygon with ten sides. (93)

deduction   The process of making justified conclusions. (521)

degree   Unit of measure used for the measure of an angle, arc, or rotation. (107)

degree measure of a major arc $\overset{\frown}{ACB}$ of $\odot O$ $360° - mAB$. (396)

degree measure of a minor arc $\overset{\frown}{AB}$ of $\odot O$ The measure of the central angle AOB. (396)

diagonal of a polygon   A segment connecting nonconsecutive vertices of the polygon. (93)

diameter of a circle or sphere   A segment connecting two points on the circle or sphere and containing the center of the circle or sphere; also, the length of that segment. (84, 433)

dilation   Also called *dilatation*. See *size change*.

dimensions of a box   The lengths of the three edges of a box which meet at a single vertex. (421)

dimensions of a rectangle   The lengths of the two sides of a rectangle which meet at a single vertex. (367)

direct reasoning (proofs)   Reasoning (proofs) using the Law of Detachment and/or the Law of Transitivity. (645)

direction of a translation   The direction given by any ray from a preimage point through its image point. (261)

discrete line   A line made up of points with space between them. (5)

distance between two points   The absolute value of the difference of their coordinates on a coordinatized line. (9)

dodecahedron   A polyhedron with twelve faces. (454)

edge   Any side of a polyhedron's faces. (449)

ellipse   The conic section formed by a plane which intersects only one of the right conical surfaces. (436)

empty set   See *null set*.

endpoint   See *arc*; *segment*.

ends of a kite   The common vertices of the equal sides of the kite. (223)

equiangular polygon   A polygon with all angles of equal measure. (360)

equidistant   At the same distance. (82)

equilateral polygon   A polygon with all sides of equal length. (358)

equilateral triangle   A triangle with all three sides equal. (94)

Euclidean geometry   The collection of propositions about figures which includes or from which can be deduced those given by the mathematician Euclid around 250 B.C. (36, 176)

expansion   A size change with magnitude greater than one. (570)

exterior angles   Angles formed by two lines and a transversal whose interiors contain no points between the two lines. (234) Angles which form linear pairs with angles of a polygon. (665)

extremes of a proportion   The first and fourth terms of the proportion. (582)

face of a polyhedron   Any of the polygonal regions that form the surface of the polyhedron. (449)

figure   A set of points. (30)

fundamental region   A region used to tessellate a plane. (362)

geometric mean of the positive numbers a and b   The positive number g such that $\dfrac{a}{g} = \dfrac{g}{b}$. (690)

glide reflection   The composite of a reflection and a translation parallel to the reflecting line; also called a *walk*. (287)

great circle of a sphere   The intersection of a sphere and a plane that contains the center of the sphere. (433)

height of a cylindric solid   The distance between the planes of the bases. Also called *altitude*. (422)

height of a conic solid   The length of a segment from the vertex perpendicular to the plane of the base. Also called *altitude*. (429)

heptagon   A polygon with seven sides. Also called *septagon*. (93)

hexagon   A polygon with six sides. (93)

hexahedron   A polyhedron with six faces. (449)

horizontal component of a vector   The first component in the ordered pair description of a vector. (714)

horizontal line   A line parallel to the horizon. (5)   A line with equation $y = k$. (16)

hyperbola   The conic section formed by a plane which intersects both of the right conical surfaces. (436)

hypotenuse   The side opposite the right angle in a right triangle. (327)

hypothesis   See *antecedent*.

icosahedron   A polyhedron with twenty faces. (454)

identity transformation   A transformation in which each point coincides with its image. (570)

if and only if statement   A statement consisting of a conditional and its converse. (83)

if-then statement   See *conditional*.

image   The result of applying a transformation to a preimage. (254)

image of a figure   The set of all images of points in the figure. (163)

included angle   The angle of a polygon whose vertex is the common point of two consecutive sides of the polygon. (311)

included side   The side of a polygon which is the intersection of two consecutive angles of the polygon. (312)

indirect reasoning (proofs)   Reasoning (proofs) using the Law of the Contrapositive, the Law of Ruling Out Possibilities, or the Law of Indirect Reasoning. (647)

inscribed angle in a circle   An angle whose vertex is on the circle and whose sides each intersect the circle at a point other than the vertex. (746)

inscribed polygon   A polygon whose vertices all lie on the same circle. (737)

instance of a sentence   A situation for which the sentence is true. (65)

interior angles   Angles formed by two lines and a transversal whose interiors are partially between the lines. (234)

interior of a figure   If a figure separates the plane into two parts, one bounded and one not, the bounded part (94)

interior of an angle   A nonzero angle separates the plane into two sets of points. If the angle is not straight, the convex set is the interior of the angle. (106)

intersection of two sets   The set of elements which are in both the sets. (87)

inverse   A conditional resulting from negating the antecedent and consequent of the original conditional. (636)

isometry   A transformation that is a reflection or composite of reflections. Also called *congruence* or *distance-preserving transformation*. (280)

isosceles trapezoid   A trapezoid with a pair of base angles equal in measure. (215)

isosceles triangle   A triangle with two or more equal sides. (94)

justification   The definition, postulate, or theorem which enables a conclusion to be drawn. (120)

kite   A quadrilateral with two distinct pairs of consecutive sides of the same length. (214)

lateral edge of a conic surface   Any segment connecting its vertex to a point on its base. (428)

lateral face of a polyhedron   Any face other than a base. (427)

lateral surface   The surface of a conic or cylindric solid other than the base. (422, 428)

lattice point   Points in the coordinate plane with integer coordinates. (18)

leg   A side of a right triangle that includes the right angle. (327)

length   The distance between two points measured along the segment or an arc joining them. (41)   A side of a rectangle. (357)

line   An undefined geometric term. (35). See *Point-Line-Plane Postulate* on p. 35 or p. 801.

line of reflection   The line over which a preimage is reflected. Also called *reflecting line*. (156)

linear pair   Two nonstraight and nonzero angles that are adjacent and whose noncommon sides are opposite rays. (114)

Logo   A computer language used to create drawings. (672)

magnitude   See *size change*.

magnitude of a rotation $\pm m\angle POP'$, where P' is the image of P under the rotation and O is its center. (267)

magnitude of a translation   The distance between any point and its image. (261)

major arc $\overset{\frown}{AB}$ of $\odot O$ The points of $\odot O$ that are on or exterior to $\angle AOB$. (396)

mapping   A transformation; a transformation *maps* a preimage onto an image. (255)

matrix   A rectangular array of rows and columns. (4)

mean   The sum of a set of numbers divided by the number of numbers in the set. Also called *average* or *arithmetic mean*. (537)   See also *geometric mean*.

meaning half of a definition   The conditional in a definition whose antecedent includes the word being defined. (83)

means of a proportion   The second and third terms of the proportion. (582)

median of a triangle   The segment connecting a vertex of the triangle to the midpoint of the opposite side. (208)

midpoint of a segment   The point on the segment equidistant from the segment's endpoints. (81)

minor arc $\overset{\frown}{AB}$ of $\odot O$ The points of $\odot O$ that are on or interior to $\angle AOB$. (396)

n-gon   A polygon with n sides. (93)

negation of a statement   A statement (called *not-p*) that is true whenever statement p is false and is false whenever statement p is true. (635)

net   A two-dimensional figure that can be folded on its segments or curved on its boundaries into a three-dimensional surface. (449)

network   A union of points and segments (arcs) in which each segment or arc contains only its endpoints. (20)

node   The endpoint of an arc in a network. (20) See also *vertex*.

non-Euclidean geometries   A geometry in which the theorems are not the same as those in Euclidean geometry. (241)

nonagon   A polygon with nine sides. (93)

nonconvex set   A set that is not convex. (61)

nonoverlapping regions   Regions that do not share interior points. (368)

null set   The set with no elements. Also called *empty set*. (88)

oblique cylinder   A non-right cylinder. (423)

oblique line   A line that is neither horizontal nor vertical. (5)

oblique prism   A non-right prism. (423)

obtuse angle   An angle whose measure is greater than 90 and less than 180. (113)

obtuse triangle   A triangle with an obtuse angle. (118)

octagon   A polygon with eight sides. (93)

octahedron   A polyhedron with eight faces. (454)

opposite rays $\overrightarrow{AB}$ and $\overrightarrow{AC}$ are opposite rays if and only if A is between B and C. (42)

opposite vectors   Two vectors whose sum is the zero vector. (716)

ordered pair   The pair of numbers (a, b) identifying a point on a coordinate plane. (14)

ordered triple   Three numbers (a, b, c) identifying a point in a three-dimensional coordinate system. (550)

overlapping triangles   Triangles that have interior points in common. (323)

parabola   The conic section formed by a plane parallel to an edge of the conical surface. (436)

parallel lines   Two coplanar lines which have no points in common or are identical. (36)

parallelepiped   A prism whose base is a parallelogram. (424)

parallelogram   A quadrilateral with two pairs of parallel sides. (213)

parallelogram rule The sum of two noncollinear vectors $\overrightarrow{OA}$ and $\overrightarrow{OB}$ is the vector $\overrightarrow{OC}$ such that $OACB$ is a parallelogram. (711)

pentagon A polygon with five sides. (93)

perimeter of a polygon The sum of the lengths of its sides. (356)

perpendicular Two segments, rays, or lines such that the lines containing them form a 90° angle. (132)

perpendicular bisector of a segment The line passing through the midpoint of the segment and perpendicular to the segment. (141) The plane that is perpendicular to the segment and contains the midpoint of the segment. (439)

perpendicular line to a plane A line perpendicular to every line in the plane through their intersection. (418)

perspective drawing A drawing of a figure made to look as it would in the real world. (25)

pi, π The ratio of the circumference to the diameter of a circle. (397)

picture angle of a camera lens An angle measure indicating how wide a field of vision can be captured in one photo. (745)

pixel A dot on a TV or computer screen or other monitor. (4)

plane An undefined geometric term. (35) See *Point-Line-Plane Postulate* on p. 35 or p. 801.

plane figure A set of points that are all in one plane. (10)

plane geometry The study of figures which lie in the same plane. (30)

plane section The intersection of a three-dimensional figure with a plane. (434)

point An undefined geometric term. (35) See *Point-Line-Plane Postulate* on p. 35 or p. 801.

point of tangency The point at which a tangent to a circle (sphere) intersects the circle (sphere). (653)

polygon The union of three or more coplanar segments (its **sides**) such that each segment intersects exactly two others, one at each of its endpoints (its **vertices**). (92)

polygonal region The union of a polygon and its interior. (94)

polyhedron A three-dimensional surface which is the union of polygonal regions and which has no holes. (Plural **polyhedra**) (449)

postulate A statement assumed to be true. Also called *axiom*. (35)

power of the point P for the circle O For any secant through P intersecting circle O at A and B, the product $PA \cdot PB$. (771)

preimage The original figure in a transformation. (156)

prism The surface of a cylindric solid whose base is a polygon. (423)

proof A sequence of justified conclusions, leading from what is given or known to a final conclusion. (120)

proportion A statement that two ratios are equal. (581)

proportional numbers Four numbers that form a true proportion. (581)

proposition A postulate or theorem.

protractor A tool commonly used to measure angles. (107)

pyramid The surface of a conic solid whose base is a polygon. (428)

Pythagorean triple A set of three numbers that can be lengths of sides of a right triangle. (394)

quadrilateral A polygon with four sides. (93)

radius of a circle or sphere A segment connecting the center of a circle or a sphere with a point on that circle or sphere; also, the length of that segment. (plural **radii**) (84, 433)

ratio A quotient of two numbers, $\frac{m}{n}$, $m{:}n$ or m/n. (581)

ratio of similitude The ratio of the lengths of corresponding segments in similar figures. (587)

ray The ray with endpoint A and containing B is the union of $\overline{AB}$ and the set of all points for which B is between each of them and A. (42)

rectangle A quadrilateral with four right angles. (213)

rectangular solid The union of a box and its interior. (421)

reflecting line The line over which a preimage is reflected. Also called *line of reflection*. (156)

reflection The transformation which associates each point with its reflection image. (164)

reflection image of a point P over a line m If P is not on m, the point Q such that m is the perpendicular bisector of $\overline{PQ}$. If P is on m, P itself. (157)

reflection image of a point A over a plane M   If A is not on M, the point B such that M is the perpendicular bisector of $\overline{AB}$. If A is on M, the point A itself. (439)

reflection-symmetric figure   A figure F for which there is a reflection r_m such that $r_m(F) = F$. (192, 440)

region   The union of a polygon or circle and its interior. More generally, any connected two-dimensional figure that has an area. (94)

regular polygon   A convex polygon whose angles are all congruent and whose sides are all congruent. (334)

regular polyhedron   A convex polyhedron whose faces are all congruent regular polygons. (454)

regular pyramid   A pyramid whose base is a regular polygon and whose lateral faces are congruent isosceles triangles. (473)

rhombus   A quadrilateral with four equal sides. (213)

right angle   An angle whose measure is 90. (113)

right triangle   A triangle with one right angle. (118)

right cylinder   A cylinder formed when the direction of translation of the base is perpendicular to the plane of the base. (423)

right prism   A prism formed when the direction of translation of the base is perpendicular to the plane of the base. (423)

rotation   The composite of two reflections over intersecting lines; the transformation "turns" the preimage onto the final image about a fixed point (its **center**). Also called *turn*. (267)

round-robin tournament   A tournament in which each competitor plays each other competitor exactly once. (740)

scalar multiplication   The operation combining the real number k and the vector (a, b) resulting in the vector (ka, kb). (717)

scalene triangle   A triangle with no sides of the same length. (94)

secant to a circle   A line that intersects the circle in two points. (759)

segment   The set consisting of the distinct points A and B (its **endpoints**) and all points between A and B. Also called *line segment*. (40)

semicircle   An arc of a circle whose endpoints are the endpoints of a diameter of the circle. (396)

side   One of the segments whose union is a polygon; also, the length of that segment. (93) See *angle*.

similar figures   Two figures for which there is a similarity transformation mapping one onto the other. (586)

similarity transformation   A composite of size changes and reflections. (586)

sine of an acute angle   The ratio $\dfrac{\text{leg opposite the angle}}{\text{hypotenuse}}$ in a right triangle. (702)

size change   The transformation S such that, for a given point P and a positive real number k (its **magnitude**) and any point O (its **center**), $S(P) = P'$ is the point on $\overrightarrow{OP}$ with $OP' = k \cdot OP$.   The transformation in which the image of (x, y) is (kx, ky). Also called *size transformation* or *dilation*. (570)

skew lines   Lines that do not lie in the same plane. (421)

slant height of a cone   The length of a lateral edge of the cone. (429)

slant height of a regular pyramid   The altitude from the vertex on any one of the lateral faces of the pyramid. (429)

slide   See *translation*.

slope   For a line in the coordinate plane containing (x_1, y_1) and (x_2, y_2), the number $\dfrac{y_2 - y_1}{x_2 - x_1}$. (128)

small circle of a sphere   The intersection of a sphere and a plane that does not contain the center of the sphere. (433)

solid   The union of the boundary and the region of space enclosed by a surface. (421)

solid geometry   The study of figures in three-dimensional space. (30)

space   The set of all possible points. (30)

sphere   The set of points in space at a fixed distance (its **radius**) from a point (its **center**). (433)

square   A quadrilateral with four equal sides and four right angles. (213)

square root   The number whose square is a given number. (390)

straight angle   An angle whose measure is 180. (113)

straightedge   An instrument for drawing the line through two points and which has no marks for determining length. (141)

subroutine   An algorithm used within another algorithm. (143)

sufficient condition p is a sufficient condition for q means "if p, then q." (340)

sufficient condition half of a definition   The conditional in a definition whose consequent includes the word being defined. (83)

sum of two vectors   See *vector addition*.

supplementary angles   Two angles whose measures sum to 180. Also called *supplements*. (114)

surface   The boundary of a three-dimensional figure.(421)

symmetry line   A reflecting line for a reflection-symmetric figure. (192)

symmetry plane   A plane M for a space figure F such that $r_M(F) = F$.   (440)

tangent of an acute angle   The ratio

$$\frac{\text{leg opposite the angle}}{\text{leg adjacent to the angle}}$$ in a right triangle. (697)

tangent to a circle or sphere   A line or plane which intersects the circle or sphere in exactly one point. (651)

tessellation   A covering of a plane with congruent nonoverlapping copies of the same region. (362)

tetrahedron   A polyhedron with four faces. (449)

theorem   A geometric statement deduced from postulates, definitions, or previously deduced theorems. (36)

three-dimensional figure   A geometric figure or real object that does not lie in a single plane. (10)

torus   A surface formed by rotating a circle about a line in space which contains no point on or interior to the circle. (456)

transformation   A correspondence between two sets of points such that each point in the preimage set has a unique image, and each point in the image set has exactly one preiamge. (255)

translation   The composite of two reflections over parallel lines. Also called *slide*. (261)

trapezoid   A quadrilateral with at least one pair of parallel sides. (214)

traversable network   A network in which all the arcs may be traced exactly once without picking up the tracing instrument. (20)

triangle   A polygon with three sides. (93)

triangulate   To split a polygon into nonoverlapping triangles. (384)

two-dimensional figures   Plane figures that do not lie in a single line. (10)

turn   See *rotation*.

union of two sets   The set of elements which are in either or both of the sets. (87)

unit cube   A cube in which every edge has length one unit. (478)

unit square   A square in which each side has length one unit. (367)

vanishing point (line)   The point (line) at which several lines of a drawing appear to meet at a distance from the viewer's eye. (25)

vector   A quantity that has both magnitude and direction. (708)

vector addition   The operation combining two vectors (a, b) and (c, d), resulting in ($a + c$, $b + d$) (their **sum**). (714)

vertex (plural **vertices**)   The endpoint of an arc of a network. (20)   See also *angle*; *node*; *polygon*.

vertex angle   The angle included by equal sides in an isosceles triangle. (206)

vertex of a polyhedron   Any vertex of the polyhedron's faces. (449)

vertical angles   Two nonstraight and nonzero angles whose sides form two lines. (114)

vertical component of a vector   The second component in the ordered pair description of a vector. (714)

vertical line   A line perpendicular to the horizon. (5) A line with equation $x = h$. (16)

volume   The number of unit cubes or parts of unit cubes that can be fit into a solid. (478)

walk   See *glide reflection*.

zero angle   An angle whose measure is zero. (113)

zero vector   The vector with zero magnitude; the vector (0, 0). (716)

Arithmetic and Algebra

$>$	is greater than
$<$	is less than
$\neq$	is not equal to
$\leq$	is less than or equal to
$\geq$	is greater than or equal to
$\approx$	is approximately equal to
π	pi
$|x|$	absolute value of x
$\sqrt{n}$	positive square root of n
$\sqrt[3]{n}$	cube root of n

Geometric Figures and Measures

$\overleftrightarrow{AB}$	line through A and B
$\overrightarrow{AB}$	ray starting at A and containing B
$\overline{AB}$	segment with endpoints A and B
AB	distance from A to B
$\angle ABC$	angle ABC
m $\angle ABC$	measure of angle ABC
$\urcorner$	right angle symbol
$n°$	n degrees
$\overarc{AB}$	minor arc with endpoints A and B
$\overarc{ADB}$	arc with endpoints A and B containing D
$m\overarc{AB}$	measure of arc AB in degrees
Area(F)	area of figure F
Volume(F)	volume of figure F
$\triangle ABC$	triangle with vertices A, B, and C
$ADCD...$	polygon with vertices A, B, C, D, ...
$\odot O$	circle with center O

Geometric Relations

$//$	is parallel to
$\perp$	is perpendicular to
$\cong$	is congruent to
$\sim$	is similar to

Logic and Sets

$\Rightarrow$	if-then (implication)
$\Leftrightarrow$	if and only if
$\{ ... \}$	set
$\{ \}, \emptyset$	empty or null set
N(E)	the number of elements in set E
P(E)	the probability of an event E
$\cap$	intersection (of sets)
$\cup$	union (of sets)

Trigonometry

tan A	tangent of $\angle A$
sin A	sine of $\angle A$
cos A	cosine of $\angle A$

Transformations

r_m	reflection over line m
$r_m(P)$	reflection image of point P over line m
$r(P)$	reflection image of point P
$T(P)$	tranformation image of point P
$T_1 \circ T_2$	composite of transformation T_2 followed by T_1
S_k	size change of magnitude k
A'	image of point A
A''	image of point A'

Coordinates and Vectors

(x, y)	ordered pair x, y
(x, y, z)	ordered triple x, y, z
$\overrightarrow{AB}$	vector with initial point A and terminal point B
$\mathbf{v}$	vector $\mathbf{v}$
(a, b)	vector with initial point $(0, 0)$ and endpoint (a, b)
$\mathbf{u} + \mathbf{v}$	resultant of two vectors
$k(a, b)$	scalar k times vector (a, b)

Calculator keys

$\boxed{\pm}$ or $\boxed{+/-}$	opposite
$\boxed{y^x}$ or $\boxed{x^y}$	powering function
$\boxed{INV}$, $\boxed{2nd}$, or $\boxed{F}$	second function
$\boxed{EE}$ or $\boxed{EXP}$	scientific notation
$\boxed{1/x}$ reciprocal	$\boxed{INV}$ inverse function
$\boxed{\sqrt{}}$ square root function	$\boxed{sin}$ sine function
$\boxed{x^2}$ squaring function	$\boxed{cos}$ cosine function
$\boxed{tan}$ tangent function	$\boxed{\pi}$ pi

Computer commands

2 * 3	$2 \cdot 3$
4 / 3	$4 \div 3$
3 ^ 5	3^5
> =	$\geq$
< =	$\leq$
< >	not equal to
SQR(N)	$\sqrt{n}$
IF...THEN	THEN statement to be executed only if IF part is true.

Postulates are statements that are assumed true. The postulates listed below may be different from those found in other geometry books.

Postulates of Euclidean Geometry

Point-Line-Plane Postulate:
a. **Unique line assumption:** Through any two points, there is exactly one line.
b. **Dimension assumption:** Given a line in a plane, there exists a point in the plane not on the line. Given a plane in space, there exists a point in space not on the line.
c. **Number line assumption:** Every line is a set of points that can be put in a one-to-one correspondence with the real numbers, with any point on it corresponding to 0 and any other point corresponding to 1.
d. **Distance assumption:** On a number line, there is a unique distance between two points.
(Lesson 1–7, p. 35)

Some Postulates from Arithmetic and Algebra

Postulates of Equality
Reflexive Property of Equality: $a = a$
Symmetric Property of Equality: If $a = b$, then $b = a$.
Transitive Property of Equality: If $a = b$ and $b = c$, then $a = c$.

Postulates of Equality and Operations
Addition Property of Equality: If $a = b$, then $a + c = b + c$.
Multiplication Property of Equality: If $a = b$, then $ac = bc$.
Substitution Property of Equality: If $a = b$, then a may be substituted for b in any expression.

Postulates of Inequality and Operations
Addition Property of Inequality: If $a < b$, then $a + c < b + c$.
Multiplication Property of Inequality: If $a < b$ and $c > 0$, then $ac < bc$.
If $a < b$ and $c < 0$, then $ac > bc$.
Equation to Inequality Property: If a and b are positive numbers and $a + b = c$, then $c > a$ and $c > b$.
Transitive Property of Inequality: If $a < b$ and $b < c$, then $a < c$.

Postulates of Operations
Commutative Property of Addition: $a + b = b + a$
Commutative Property of Multiplication: $ab = ba$
Distributive Property: $a(b + c) = ab + ac$ *(Lesson 1–7, p. 37)*

Triangle Inequality Postulate: The sum of the lengths of two sides of any triangle is greater than the length of the third side. *(Lesson 1–9, p. 46)*

Angle Measure Postulate:
a. **Unique measure assumption:** Every angle has a unique measure from $0°$ to $180°$.
b. **Two sides of line assumption:** Given any ray $\overrightarrow{VA}$ and any number x between 0 and 180, there are unique rays $\overrightarrow{VB}$ and $\overrightarrow{VC}$ such that $\overleftrightarrow{BC}$ intersects line $\overleftrightarrow{VA}$ and $m\angle BVA = m\angle CVA = x$.
c. **Zero angle assumption:** If $\overrightarrow{VA}$ and $\overrightarrow{VB}$ are the same ray, then $m\angle AVB = 0$.
d. **Straight Angle Assumption:** If $\overrightarrow{VA}$ and $\overrightarrow{VB}$ are opposite rays then $m\angle AVB = 180$.
e. **Angle Addition Property:** If $\overrightarrow{VC}$ (except for point V) is in the interior of $\angle AVB$, then $m\angle AVC + m\angle CVB = m\angle AVB$. *(Lesson 3–1, p. 108)*

Corresponding Angles Postulate: If two coplanar lines are cut by a transversal so that two corresponding angles have the same measure, then the lines are parallel. *(Lesson 3–4, p. 127)*

Parallel Lines Postulate: If two lines are parallel and are cut by a transversal, corresponding angles have the same measure. *(Lesson 3–4, p. 127)*

Reflection Postulate:

Under a reflection:

a. There is a 1–1 correspondence between points and their images.
This means that each preimage has exactly one image and each image comes from exactly one preimage.

b. If three points are collinear, then their images are collinear.
Reflections preserve collinearity. The image of a line is a line.

c. If B is between A and C, then the image of B is between the images of A and C.
Reflections preserve betweeness. The image of a line segment is a line segment.

d. The distance between two preimages equals the distance between their images.
Reflectons preserve distance.

e. The image of an angle is an angle of the same measure.
Reflections preserve angle measure. (Lesson 4-2, p. 164)

f. A polygon and its image, with vertices taken in corresponding order, have opposite orientations.
Reflections switch orientation. (Lesson 4-6, p. 189)

Area Postulate:

a. Uniqueness Property: Given a unit region, every polygonal region has a unique area.

b. Rectangle Formula: The area of a rectangle with dimensions ℓ and w is ℓw.

c. Congruence Property: Congruent figures have the same area.

d. Additive Property: The area of the union of two non-overlapping regions is the sum of the ares of the regions. *(Lesson 8-3, p. 368)*

Volume Postulate:

a. Uniqueness Property: Given a unit cube, every polyhedral solid has a unique volume.

b. Box Volume Formula: The volume of a box with dimensions ℓ, w, and h is ℓwh.

c. Congruence Property: Congruent figures have the same volume.

d. Additive Property: The volume of the union of two nonoverlapping solids is the sum of the volumes of the solids. *(Lesson 10-3, p. 479)*

e. Cavalieri's Principle: Let I and II be two solids included between parallel planes. If every place P parallel to the given planes intersects I and II in sections with the same area, then
Volume (I) = Volume (II). *(Lesson 10-5, p. 490)*

Postulates of Logic:

Law of Detachment: If you have a statement or given information p and a justification of the form $p \Rightarrow q$, you may conclude q. *(Lesson 13-1, p. 630)*

Law of Transitivity: If $p \Rightarrow q$ and $q \Rightarrow r$, then $p \Rightarrow r$. *(Lesson 13-1, p. 631)*

Law of the Contrapositive: A statement $p \Rightarrow q$ and its contrapositive   not $q \Rightarrow$ not p are either both true or both false. *(Lesson 13-2, p. 636)*

Law of Ruling Out Possibilities: When p or q is true and q is not true, then p is true. *(Lesson 13-3, p. 640)*

Law of Indirect Reasoning: If Reasoning from a statement p leads to a false conclusion, then p is false.
(Lesson 13-4, p. 647)

Postulates of Euclid:

1. Two points determine a line segment.

2. A line segment can be extended indefinitely along a line.

3. A circle can be drawn with any center and any radius.

4. All right angles are congruent.

5. If two lines are cut by a transversal, and the interior angles on the same side of the transversal have a total measure less than 180, then the lines will intersect on that side of the transversal.
(Lesson 13-6, p. 661)

Theorems are statements that have been proved, or can be proved, from the postulates. They are given here in order of appearance.

Theorem: Two different lines intersect in at most one point. *(Lesson 1-7, p. 36)*

Betweenness Theorem: If B is between A and C, then $AB + BC = AC$. *(Lesson 1-8, p. 41)*

Theorem: If A, B, and C are distinct points and $AB + BC = AC$, then B is on $\overline{AC}$. *(Lesson 1-9, p. 48)*

Theorem: For any three points A, B, and C, $AB + BC \geq AC$. *(Lesson 1-9, p. 48)*

Linear Pair Theorem: If two angles form a linear pair, then they are supplementary. *(Lesson 3-2, p. 115)*

Vertical Angle Theorem: If two angles are vertical angles, then they have equal measures. *(Lesson 3-2, p. 115)*

Parallel Lines and Slopes Theorem: Two nonvertical lines are parallel if and only if they have the same slope. *(Lesson 3-4, p. 128)*

Transitivity of Parallelism Theorem: In a plane, if $\ell \mathbin{//} m$ and $m \mathbin{//} n$, then $\ell \mathbin{//} n$. *(Lesson 3-4, p. 129)*

Two Perpendiculars Theorem: If two coplanar lines ℓ and m are each perpendicular to the same line, then they are parallel to each other. *(Lesson 3-5, p. 133)*

Perpendicular to Parallels Theorem: In a plane, if a line is perpendicular to one of two parallel lines, then it is perpendicular to the other. *(Lesson 3-5, p. 133)*

Perpendicular Lines and Slopes Theorem: Two nonvertical lines are perpendicular if and only if the product of their slopes is -1. *(Lesson 3-5, p. 134)*

Figure Reflection Theorem: If a figure is determined by certain points, then its reflection image is the corresponding figure determined by the reflection images of those points. *(Lesson 4-2, p. 165)*

Theorem: The triangle constructed in Euclid's *Elements* is an equilateral triangle. *(Lesson 4-4, p. 177)*

Perpendicular Bisector Theorem: If a point is on the perpendicular bisector of a segment, then it is equidistant from the endpoints of the segment. *(Lesson 4-5, p. 183)*

Flip-Flop Theorem: If F and F' are points or figures and r(F) = F', then r(F') = F. *(Lesson 4-6, p. 188)*

Segment Symmetry Theorem: A segment has exactly two symmetry lines: **1.** its perpendicular bisector, and **2.** the line containing the segment. *(Lesson 4-7, p. 193)*

Side-Switching Theorem: If one side of an angle is reflected over the line containing the angle bisector, its image is the other side of the angle. *(Lesson 4-7, p. 194)*

Angle Symmetry Theorem: The line containing the bisector of an angle is a symmetry line of the angle. *(Lesson 4-7, p. 194)*

Isosceles Triangle Symmetry Theorem: The line containing the bisector of the vertex angle of an isosceles triangle is a symmetry line for the triangle. *(Lesson 5-1, p. 207)*

Theorem: In an isosceles triangle, the bisector of the vertex angle, the perpendicular bisector of the base, and the median to the base determine the same line. *(Lesson 5-1, p. 208)*

Isosceles Triangle Theorem: If a triangle has two equal sides, then the angles opposite them are equal. *(Lesson 5-1, p. 208)*

Kite Symmetry Theorem: The line containing the ends of a kite is a symmetry line for the kite. *(Lesson 5-4, p. 223)*

Kite Diagonal Theorem: The symmetry diagonal of a kite is the perpendicular bisector of the other diagonal and bisects the two angles at the ends of the kite. *(Lesson 5-4, p. 224)*

Rhombus Symmetry Theorem: Every rhombus has two symmetry lines, the bisectors of its diagonals. *(Lesson 5-4, p. 225)*

Trapezoid Angle Theorem: In a trapezoid, consecutive angles between a pair of parallel sides are supplementary. *(Lesson 5-5, p. 228)*

Theorem: In an isosceles trapezoid, both pairs of base angles are equal in measure. *(Lesson 5-5, p. 229)*

Isosceles Trapezoid Symmetry Theorem: The perpendicular bisector of one base of an isosceles trapezoid is the perpendicular bisector of the other base and a symmetry line for the trapezoid. *(Lesson 5-5, p. 230)*

Isosceles Trapezoid Theorem: In an isosceles trapezoid, the non-base sides are equal in measure. *(Lesson 5-5, p. 230)*

Rectangle Symmetry Theorem: Every rectangle has two symmetry lines, the perpendicular bisectors of its bases. *(Lesson 5-5, p. 231)*

// Lines ⇒ AIA = Theorem: If two parallel lines are cut by a transversal, then alternate interior angles are equal in measure. *(Lesson 5-6, p. 234)*

AIA = ⇒ // Lines Theorem: If two lines are cut by a transversal and form equal alternate interior angles, then the lines are parallel. *(Lesson 5-6, p. 235)*

Theorem: If a quadrilateral is a rhombus, then it is a parallelogram. *(Lesson 5-6, p. 236)*

Quadrilateral Hierarchy Theorem: If a figure is of any type on the hierarchy, it is also of all types connected above it. *(Lesson 5-6, p. 236)*

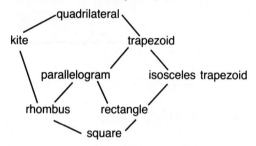

Triangle-Sum Theorem: The sum of the measures of the angles of a triangle is 180°. *(Lesson 5-7, p. 240)*

Quadrilateral-Sum Theorem: The sum of the measures of the angles of a convex quadrilateral is 360°. *(Lesson 5-7, p. 242)*

Polygon-Sum Theorem: The sum of the measures of the angles of a convex polygon of n sides is $(n - 2) \cdot 180°$. *(Lesson 5-7, p. 243)*

Two Reflection Theorem for Translations: If m // ℓ, the translation $r_m \circ r_\ell$ slides figures two times the distance between ℓ and m, in the direction from ℓ to m perpendicular to those lines. *(Lesson 6-2, p. 261)*

Two Reflection Theorem for Rotations: The rotation $r_m \circ r_\ell$ where m intersects ℓ, "turns" figures twice the non-obtuse angle between ℓ, and m, measured from ℓ to m, about the point of intersection of the lines. *(Lesson 6-3, p. 267)*

Equivalence of Properties of ≅ Theorem: For any figures F, G, and H:
   Reflexive Property of Congruence: F ≅ F.
   Symmetry Property of Congruence: if F ≅ G, then G ≅ F.
   Transitive Property of Congruence: If F ≅ G and G ≅ H, then F ≅ H. *(Lesson 6-5, p. 280)*

A-B-C-D Theorem: Every isometry preserves Angle measure, Betweenness, Collinearity (lines), and Distance (lengths of segments). *(Lesson 6-5, p. 281)*

Segment Congruence Theorem: Two segments are congruent if and only if they have the same length. *(Lesson 6-5, p. 281)*

Angle Congruence Theorem: Two angles are congruent if and only if they have the same meausre. *(Lesson 6-5, p. 282)*

Glide Reflection Theorem: Let $G = T \circ r_m$ be a glide reflection, and let $G(P) = P'$. Then the midpoint of $\overline{PP'}$ is on m. *(Lesson 6-6, p. 287)*

Corresponding Parts in Congruent Figures (CPCF) Theorem: If two figures are congruent, then any pair of corresponding parts is congruent. *(Lesson 6-7, p. 292)*

Theorem: If two triangles have two pairs of angles congruent, then their third pair of angles is congruent. *(Lesson 7-1, p. 306)*

SSS Congruence Theorem: If, in two triangles, three sides of one are congruent to three sides of the other, then the triangles are congruent. *(Lesson 7-2, p. 310)*

SAS Congruence Theorem: If, two triangles, two sides and the included angle of one are congruent to two sides and the included angle of the other, then the triangles are congruent. *(Lesson 7-2, p. 311)*

ASA Congruence Theorem: If in two triangles two angles and the included side of one are congruent to two sides and the included angle of the other, then the triangles are congruent. *(Lesson 7-2, p. 312)*

AAS Congruence Theorem: If, in two triangles, two angles and a non-included side of one are congruent respectively to two angles and the corresponding non-included side of the other, then the triangles are congruent. *(Lesson 7-2, p. 312)*

Theorem: If two angles of a triangle are congruent, then the sides opposite them are congruent. *(Lesson 7-3, p. 319)*

Diagonal of a Box Formula: In a box with dimensions a, b, and c, the length of the diagonal is $\sqrt{a^2 + b^2 + c^2}$ *(Lesson 11-6, p. 552)*

Theorem (Equation for a Sphere): The sphere with center (h, k, j) and radius r is the set of points (x, y, z) satisfying $(x - h)^2 + (y - k)^2 + (z - j)^2 = r^2$. *(Lesson 11-6, p. 553)*

Midpoint Formula in Three Dimensions: If a segment has endpoints (a, b, c) and (d, e, f), then its midpoint is $\left(\dfrac{a + d}{2}, \dfrac{b + e}{2}, \dfrac{c + f}{2}\right)$ *(Lesson 11-6, p. 553)*

Theorem: Let S_k be the transformation mapping (x, y) onto (kx, ky), $k > 0$.
Let $P' = S_k(P)$ and $Q' = S_k(Q)$. Then
(1) $\overline{P'Q'} \mathbin{/\mkern-4mu/} \overline{PQ}$,
(2) $P'Q' = k \cdot PQ$. *(Lesson 12-1, p. 565)*

Theorem: The transformation S_k, where $S_k(x, y) = (kx, ky)$ is the size change with center $(0, 0)$ and magnitude k. *(Lesson 12-2, p. 571)*

Size Change Distance Theorem: Under a size change with magnitude $k > 0$, the distance between any two image points is k times the distance between their preimages. *(Lesson 12-3, p. 575)*

Theorem: Size transformations preserve betweenness and collinearity. *(Lesson 12-3, p. 576)*

Theorem: A line and its image under a size transformation are parallel. *(Lesson 12-3, p. 576)*

Size Change Theorem: Under a size transformation:
(a) angles and their measures are preserved;
(b) betweenness is preserved;
(c) collinearity is preserved; and
(d) lines and their images are parallel. *(Lesson 12-3, p. 577)*

Figure Size Change Theorem: If a figure is determined by certain points, then its size change image is the corresponding figure determined by the size change images of those points. *(Lesson 12-3, p. 578)*

Theorem (Means-Extremes Property): If $\dfrac{a}{b} = \dfrac{c}{d}$, then $ad = bc$. *(Lesson 12-4, p. 582)*

Theorem (Means Exchange Property): If $\dfrac{a}{b} = \dfrac{c}{d}$, then $\dfrac{a}{c} = \dfrac{b}{d}$.

(Reciprocals Property): If $\dfrac{a}{b} = \dfrac{c}{d}$, then $\dfrac{b}{a} = \dfrac{d}{c}$. *(Lesson 12-4, p. 583)*

Similar Figures Theorem: If two figures are similar, then: (a) corresponding angles are congruent; (b) corresponding lengths are proportional. *(Lesson 12-5, p. 587)*

Fundamental Theorem of Similarity: If $G \sim G'$ and k is the ratio of similtude, then
(a) Perimeter $(G') = k \cdot$ Perimeter(G) or $\dfrac{\text{Perimeter}(G')}{\text{Perimeter}(G)} = k$
(b) Area$(G') = k^2 \cdot$ Area(G) or $\dfrac{\text{Area}(G')}{\text{Area}(G)} = k^2$
(c) Volume $(G') = k^3 \cdot$ Volume(G) or $\dfrac{\text{Volume}(G')}{\text{Volume}(G)} = k^3$. *(Lesson 12-6, p. 594)*

SSS Similarity Theorem: If the three sides of one triangle are proportional to the three sides of a second triangle, then the triangles are similar. *(Lesson 12-8, p. 605)*

AA Similarity Theorem: If two triangles have two angles of one congruent to two angles of the other, then the triangles are similar. *(Lesson 12-9, p. 610)*

SAS Similarity Theorem: If, in two triangles, the ratios of two pairs of corresponding sides are equal and the included angles are congruent, then the triangles are similar. *(Lesson 12-9, p. 611)*

Side-Splitting Theorem: If a line is parallel to a side of a triangle and intersects the other two sides in distinct points, it "splits" these sides into proportional segments. *(Lesson 12–10, p. 615)*

Side-Splitting Converse: If a line intersects $\overrightarrow{OP}$ and $\overrightarrow{OQ}$ in distinct points X and Y so that $\dfrac{OX}{XP} = \dfrac{OY}{YQ}$, then $\overleftrightarrow{XY} \parallel \overleftrightarrow{PQ}$. *(Lesson 12–10, p. 616)*

Theorem: If a line is perpendicular to a radius of a circle at the radius's endpoint on the circle, then it is tangent to the circle. *(Lesson 13–5, p. 652)*

Theorem: If a line is tangent to a circle, then it is perpendicular to the radius drawn to the point of tangency. *(Lesson 13–5, p. 652)*

Radius-Tangent Theorem: A line is tangent to a circle if and only if it is perpendicular to a radius at the radius's endpoint on the circle. *(Lesson 13–5, p. 653)*

Uniqueness of Parallels Theorem (Playfair's Parallel Postulate): Through a point not on a line, there is exactly one parallel to the given line. *(Lesson 13-6, p. 660)*

Theorem: In a glide reflection, the midpoint of the segment connecting a point to its image lies on the glide-reflection line. *(Lesson 13-6, p. 661)*

Exterior Angle Theorem: In a triangle, the measure of an exterior angle is equal to the sum of the measures of the two nonadjacent interior angles. *(Lesson 13-7, p. 665)*

Exterior Angle Inequality: In a triangle, the measure of an exterior angle is greater than the measure of either nonadjacent interior angle. *(Lesson 13-7, p. 666)*

Unequal Sides Theorem: If two sides of a triangle are not congruent, then the angles opposite them are not congruent, and the larger angle is opposite the longer side. *(Lesson 13-7, p. 667)*

Unequal Angles Theorem: If two angles of a triangle are not congruent, then the sides opposite them are not congruent, and the longer side is opposite the larger angle. *(Lesson 13-7, p. 667)*

Exterior Angles of a Polygon Sum Theorem: In any convex polygon, the sum of the measures of the exterior angles, one at each vertex, is 360. *(Lesson 13-8, p. 671)*

Isosceles Right Triangle Theorem: In an isosceles right triangle, if a leg is x then the hypotenuse is $x\sqrt{2}$. *(Lesson 14-1, p. 684)*

30-60-90 Triangle Theorem: In a 30-60-90 right triangle, if the short leg is x then the longer leg is $x\sqrt{3}$ and the hypotenuse is $2x$. *(Lesson 14-1, p. 685)*

Geometric Mean Theorem: The geometric mean of the positive numbers a and b is $\sqrt{ab}$. *(Lesson 14-2, p. 691)*

HL Congruence Theorem: If, in two right triangles, the hypotenuse and a leg of one are congruent to the hypotenuse and a leg of the other, then the two triangles are congruent. *(Lesson 7-5, p. 328)*

SsA Congruence Theorem: If, in two triangles, two sides and the angle opposite the longer of the two sides in one are congruent respectively to two sides and the angle opposite the corresponding side in the other, then the triangles are congruent. *(Lesson 7-5, p. 330)*

Properties of a Parallelogram Theorem: In any parallelogram: **a.** each diagonal forms two congruent triangles; **b.** opposite sides are congruent; **c.** the diagonals intersect at their midpoints. *(Lesson 7-6, p. 334)*

Theorem: The distance between parallel lines is constant. *(Lesson 7-6, p. 334)*

Center of a Regular Polygon Theorem: In any regular polygon there is a point (its center) which is equidistant from all its vertices. *(Lesson 7-6, p. 335)*

Sufficient Conditions for a Parallelogram Theorem: If, in a quadrilateral: (a) both pairs of opposite sides are congruent, or (b) both pairs of opposite angles are congruent, or (c) the diagonals bisect each other, or (d) one pair of sides is parallel and congruent, then the quadrilateral is a parallelogram. *(Lesson 7-7, p. 341)*

SAS Inequality Theorem: If two sides of a triangle are congruent to two sides of a second triangle, and the measure of the included angle of the first triangle is less than the measure of the included angle of the second, then the third side of the first triangle is shorter than the third side of the second. *(Lesson 7-8, p. 344)*

Equilateral Polygon Perimeter Formula: In an equilateral polygon with n sides of length s, the perimeter $p = ns$. *(Lesson 8-1, p. 358)*

Right Triangle Area Formula: The area of a right triangle is half the product of the lengths of its legs. *(Lesson 8-5, p. 378)*

Triangle Area Formula: The area of a triangle is half the product of a side and the altitude to that side. *(Lesson 8-5, p. 379)*

Trapezoid Area Formula: The area of a trapezoid equals half the product of its altitude and the sum of the lengths of its bases. *(Lesson 8-6, p. 385)*

Parallelogram Area Formula: The area of a parallelogram is the product of one of its bases and the altitude for that base. *(Lesson 8-6, p. 386)*

Pythagorean Theorem: In any right triangle with legs a and b and hypotenuse c, $a^2 + b^2 = c^2$ *(Lesson 8-7, p. 391)*

Pythagorean Converse Theorem: If a triangle has sides of lengths a, b, and c, and $a^2 + b^2 = c^2$, then the triangle is a right triangle. *(Lesson 8-7, p. 393)*

Circle Circumference Formula: If a circle has circumference C and diameter d, then $C = \pi d$. *(Lesson 8-8, p. 398)*

Circle Area Formula: The area A of a circle radius r is $A = \pi r^2$. *(Lesson 8-9, p. 402)*

The Four-Color Theorem: Suppose regions which share a border of some length must have different colors. Then any map of regions on a plane or a sphere can be colored in such a way that only four colors are needed. *(Lesson 9-8, p. 456)*

Right Prism-Cylinder Lateral Area Formula: The lateral area L.A. of a right prism (or cylinder) is the product of its height h and the perimeter (circumference) p of its base.   L.A. $= ph$ *(Lesson 10-1, p. 469)*

Prism-Cylinder Surface Area Formula: The total surface area S.A. of any prism or cylinder is the sum of its lateral area L.A. and twice the area B of a base.   S.A. $=$ L.A. $+ 2B$ *(Lesson 10-1, p. 470)*

Regular Pyramid-Right Cone Lateral Area Formula: The lateral area L.A. of a regular pyramid (or right cone) is half the product of the slant height and the perimeter p (circumference) of its base.   L.A. $= \frac{1}{2}\ell p$ *(Lesson 10-2, p. 475)*

Pyramid-Cone Surface Area Formula: The total surface area S.A. of any pyramid or cone is the sum of its lateral area L.A. and the area B of its base.   S.A. $=$ L.A. $+ B$ *(Lesson 10-2, p. 475)*

Cube Volume Formula: The volume of a cube with edge s is s^3. *(Lesson 10-3, p. 480)*

Prism-Cylinder Volume Formula: The volume V of any prism or cylinder is the product of its height h and the area B of its base. $V = Bh$ *(Lesson 10-5, p. 490)*

Pyramid-Cone Volume Formula: The volume V of any pyramid or cone equals $\frac{1}{3}$ the product of its height h and its base area B. $V = \frac{1}{3}BH$ *(Lesson 10-7, p. 501)*

Sphere Volume Formula: The volume V of any sphere is $\frac{4}{3}\pi$ times the cube of its radius. $V = \frac{4}{3}\pi r^3$ *(Lesson 10-8, p. 506)*

Sphere Surface Area Formula: The surface area S.A. of a sphere with radius r is $4\pi r^2$.   S.A. $= 4\pi r^2$ *(Lesson 10-9, p. 511)*

Distance Formula: The distance between two points (x_1, y_1) and (x_2, y_2) in the coordinate plane is $\sqrt{(x_2 - x_1)^2 + (y_2 - y_1)^2}$. *(Lesson 11-2, p. 528)*

Theorem (Equation for a Circle): The circle with center (h, k) and radius r is the set of points (x, y) satisfying $(x - h)^2 + (y - k)^2 = r^2$. *(Lesson 11-3, p. 533)*

Midpoint Formula: If a segment has endpoints (a, b) and (c, d), its midpoint is $\left(\dfrac{a + c}{2}, \dfrac{b + d}{2}\right)$ *(Lesson 11-4, p. 538)*

Midpoint Connector Theorem: The segment connecting the midpoints of two sides of a triangle is parallel to and half the length of the third side. *(Lesson 11-5, p. 545)*

Distance Formula in Three Dimensions: The distance between two points (x_1, y_1, z_1) and (x_2, y_2, z_2) is $\sqrt{(x_2 - x_1)^2 + (y_2 - y_1)^2 + (z_2 - z_1)^2}$. *(Lesson 11-6, p. 551)*

Right Triangle Altitude Theorem: In a right triangle, **a.** the altitude to the hypotenuse is the geometric mean of the segments into which it divides the hypotenuse; and **b.** each leg is the geometric mean of the hypotenuse and the segment of the hypotenuse adjacent to the leg. *(Lesson 14-2, p. 692)*

Theorem: Two vectors are equal if and only if their initial and terminal points are preimages and images under the same translation. *(Lesson 14-5, p. 709)*

Vector Addition Theorem: The sum of the vectors (a, b) and (c, d) is the vector $(a + c, b + d)$. *(Lesson 14-6, p. 714)*

Properties of Vector Addition Theorem: (1) Vector addition is commutative. (2) Vector addition is associative. (3) $(0, 0)$ is an identity for vector addition. (4) Every vector (a, b) has an additive inverse $(-a, -b)$. *(Lesson 14-6, p. 715)*

Chord-Center Theorem: a. The line containing the center of a circle perpendicular to a chord bisects the chord. **b.** The line containing the center of a circle and the midpoint of a chord bisects the central angle determined by the chord. **c.** The bisector of the central angle of a chord is perpendicular to the chord and bisects the chord. **d.** The perpendicular bisector of a chord of a circle contains the center of the circle. *(Lesson 15-1, p. 735)*

Arc-Chord Congruence Theorem: In a circle or in congruent circles: **a.** If two arcs have the same measure, they are congruent and their chords are congruent. **b.** If two chords have the same length, their minor arcs have the same measure. *(Lesson 15-1, p. 736)*

Inscribed Angle Theorem: In a circle the measure of an inscribed angle is one-half the measure of its intercepted arc. *(Lesson 15-3, p. 746)*

Theorem: An angle inscribed in a semicircle is a right angle. *(Lesson 15-3, p. 748)*

Angle-Chord Theorem: The measure of an angle formed by two intersecting chords is one-half the sum of the measures of the arcs intercepted by it and its vertical angle. *(Lesson 15-5, p. 758)*

Angle-Secant Theorem: The measure of an angle formed by two secants intersecting outside a circle is half the difference of the arcs intercepted by it. *(Lesson 15-5, p. 759)*

Tangent-Chord Theorem: The measure of an angle formed by a tangent and a chord is half the measure of the intercepted arc. *(Lesson 15-6, p. 764)*

Tangent-Secant Theorem: The measure of an angle between two tangents, or between a tangent and a secant, is half the difference of the intercepted arcs. *(Lesson 15-6, p. 764)*

Secant Length Theorem: Suppose one secant intersects a circle at A and B, and a second secant intersects the circle at C and D. If the secants intersect at P, then $AP \cdot BP = CP \cdot DP$. *(Lesson 15-7, p. 769)*

Tangent Square Theorem: The power of point P for $\odot O$ is square of the length of a segment tangent to $\odot O$. *(Lesson 15-7, p. 771)*

Isoperimetric Theorem: Of all plane figures with the same perimeter, the circle has the most area. *(Lesson 15-8, p. 776)*

Isoperimetric Inequality: If a plane figure has area A and perimeter p, then $A \le \dfrac{p^2}{4\pi}$. *(Lesson 15-8, p. 776)*

Isoperimetric Theorem: Of all plane figures with the same area, the circle has the least perimeter. *(Lesson 15-8, p. 777)*

Isoperimetric Theorem (space version): Of all solids with the same surface area, the sphere has the most volume. *(Lesson 15-8, p. 780)*

Isoperimetric Theorem (space version): Of all solids with the same volume, the sphere has the least surface area. *(Lesson 15-9, p. 781)*

Angle Formulas

n = number of sides, θ = measure of angle

Triangles:	Sum = $180°$	*(Lesson 5-7)*
Convex n-gons:	Sum = $(n - 2) \cdot 180°$	*(Lesson 5-7)*

Regular polygons: $\theta = \dfrac{(n - 2) \cdot 180°}{n}$ *(Lesson 7-6)*

Perimeter Formulas

p = perimeter, w = width, s = side, n = number of sides, ℓ = length, a, b, c = sides of triangles or kites, C = circumference, r = radius, d = diameter

Triangles:	$p = a + b + c$	*(Lesson 8-1)*
Right triangles:	$c^2 = a^2 + b^2$	*(Lesson 8-7)*
Kites:	$p = 2a + 2b$	*(Lesson 8-1)*
Parallelograms:	$p = 2\ell + 2w$	*(Lesson 8-1)*
Regular polygons:	$p = ns$	*(Lesson 8-1)*
Circles:	$C = \pi d = 2\pi r$	*(Lesson 8-8)*

Area Formulas

A = area, b = base, ℓ = length, s = side, h = height, b_1, b_2 = base, w = width, r = radius

Rectangles:	$A = \ell w$	*(Lesson 8-3)*
Squares:	$A = s^2$	*(Lesson 8-3)*
Triangles:	$A = \frac{1}{2}hb$	*(Lesson 8-5)*
Trapezoids:	$A = \frac{1}{2}h(b_1 + b_2)$	*(Lesson 8-6)*
Parallelograms:	$A = hb$	*(Lesson 8-6)*
Circles:	$A = \pi r^2$	*(Lesson 8-9)*

Hero's Formula:

$$\text{Area}(\triangle ABC) = \sqrt{s(s - a)(s - b)(s - c)}$$
where a, b, and c are sides of $\triangle ABC$ and s is half the perimeter *(Lesson 10-6)*

Lateral Area and Surface Area Formulas

L.A. = lateral area, S.A. = surface area, B = area of base, h = height, ℓ = slant height or length of box, p = perimeter, r = radius, s = edge, w = width

Right prisms:	L.A. = ph	*(Lesson 10-1)*
Prisms:	S.A. = L.A. + $2B$	*(Lesson 10-1)*
Right cylinders:	L.A. = $ph = 2\pi rh$	*(Lesson 10-1)*
Cylinders:	S.A. = L.A. + $2B$	*(Lesson 10-1)*
Pyramids:	L.A. = $\frac{1}{2}\ell p$	*(Lesson 10-2)*
	S.A. = L.A. + B	*(Lesson 10-2)*
Right cones:	L.A. = $\frac{1}{2}\ell p = \pi r\ell$	*(Lesson 10-2)*
Cones:	S.A. = L.A. + B	*(Lesson 10-2)*
Boxes:	S.A. = $2\ell h + 2wh + 2\ell w$	*(Lesson 10-6)*
Cubes:	S.A. = $6s^2$	*(Lesson 10-1)*
Spheres:	S.A. = L.A. = $4\pi r^2$	*(Lesson 10-9)*

Volume Formulas

V = volume, B = area of base, h = height, ℓ = length, r = radius, s = edge, w = width

Boxes:	$V = \ell wh$	*(Lesson 10-3)*
Cubes:	$V = s^3$	*(Lesson 10-3)*
Prisms:	$V = Bh$	*(Lesson 10-5)*
Cylinders:	$V = Bh = \pi r^2 h$	*(Lesson 10-5)*
Pyramids:	$V = \frac{1}{3}Bh$	*(Lesson 10-7)*
Cones:	$V = \frac{1}{3}Bh = \frac{1}{3}\pi r^2 h$	*(Lesson 10-7)*
Spheres:	$V = \frac{4}{3}\pi r^3$	*(Lesson 10-8)*

CONVERSION FORMULAS

	Customary	Metric

Length

ft = foot, in. = inch, yd = yard, mi = mile

$$1 \text{ ft} = 12 \text{ in.}$$
$$1 \text{ yd} = 3 \text{ ft}$$
$$1 \text{ mi} = 5280 \text{ ft}$$

cm = centimeter, mm = millimeter, m = meter, km = kilometer

$$1 \text{ cm} = 10 \text{ mm}$$
$$1 \text{ m} = 100 \text{ cm}$$
$$1 \text{ km} = 1000 \text{ m}$$

$$1 \text{ inch} = 2.54 \text{ centimeters}$$

Area

$$1 \text{ sq ft} = 144 \text{ sq in.}$$
$$1 \text{ sq yd} = 9 \text{ sq ft}$$

$$1 \text{ sq cm} = 100 \text{ sq mm}$$
$$1 \text{ sq m} = 10{,}000 \text{ sq cm}$$

Land area

$$1 \text{ sq mi} = 640 \text{ acres}$$

$$1 \text{ hectare} = 10{,}000 \text{ sq m}$$

Volume

$$1 \text{ ft}^3 = 1728 \text{ in.}^3$$
$$1 \text{ yd}^3 = 27 \text{ ft}^3$$

$$1 \text{ cm}^3 = 1000 \text{ mm}^3$$
$$1 \text{ m}^3 = 1{,}000{,}000 \text{ cm}^3$$

Liquid volume

pt = pint, qt = quart, gal = gallon

$$1 \text{ pt} = 28.875 \text{ in.}^3$$
$$1 \text{ qt} = 57.75 \text{ in.}^3$$
$$1 \text{ gal} = 231 \text{ in.}^3$$

mL = milliliter, L = liter

$$1 \text{ mL} = 1000 \text{ mm}^3$$
$$1 \text{ L} = 1000 \text{ cm}^3$$

$$1.06 \text{ quarts} \approx 1 \text{ liter}$$

Weight (Mass)

lb = pound, oz = ounce

$$1 \text{ lb} = 16 \text{ oz}$$
$$1 \text{ ton} = 2000 \text{ lb}$$

g = gram, kg = kilogram, mg = milligram

$$1 \text{ g} = 1000 \text{ mg}$$
$$1 \text{ kg} = 1000 \text{g}$$
$$1 \text{ metric ton} = 1000 \text{ kg}$$

$$2.2 \text{ pounds} \approx 1 \text{ kilogram}$$

LESSON 1-1 (pp. 3–7)
11. Sample: **See below. 13.** The one with 200 rows and 300 columns **15. a.** black squares (black ink on white paper). **b.** by clustering the squares **17.** Sample: **See below. 19.** 7.5 **21. a.** 23 **b.** 15 **c.** 8.3 **d.** 12

11.

17.

LESSON 1-2 (pp. 8–13)
7. 353 **9.** $|x - y|$ or $|y - x|$ **13.** Sample: The makers of the almanac may have chosen different points of reference within New York and Los Angeles from which to compute the road mileage or may have used different routes. **15.** 67 miles **17. a.** $AB = 150$, $BC = 225$, $AC = 375$ **b.** True **19.** 72,960 **21.** a line made up of points with space between their centers

23. $(3, -\frac{2}{3})$, $(-2, -\frac{7}{3})$, $(5,0)$

LESSON 1-3 (pp. 14–18)
3. oblique **5.** vertical **9. See below. 11. See below.**
13. $y = -5$ **15. a. b: See below. c.** $(3, -2)$ **17.** The Macintosh has 175,104 pixels and the IBM PC has 61,440 pixels. So the Macintosh has better resolution (if the dimensions are the same). **19.** about 1.8 cm **21. a.** 94 miles **b.** about 1.7 hours

9.

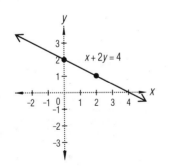

11.

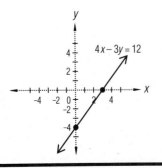

15.

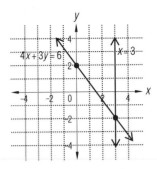

LESSON 1-4 (pp. 19–24)
11. T to R to S to T to U to R **13. a.** Sample: from A to C to B to D to A to E to B **b.** either A or B **15. a.** 0 even, 4 odd **b.** No **17. See below. 19. See below. 21. See below. 23.** 20 **25.** 5

17. a. sample:

b. sample: •————•

19.

Dots	Ordered Pairs	Locations	Nodes
S	A	A	N
A	A	A	N
S	A	A	S

21.

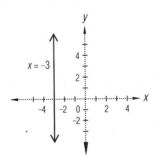

LESSON 1-5 (pp. 25–29)

7. See below. **9. a.** I, IV **b.** See below. **11.** See below. **13.** not traversable; more than 2 odd nodes **15. a.** See below. **b.** No **17. a.** See below. **b.** Answers may vary; the actual point of intersection is $(\frac{9}{7}, \frac{13}{7})$. **19.** 56 cm

7. a. sample: **b.** sample:

9. b.

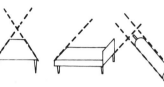

11.

15. a.

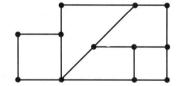

17. a.

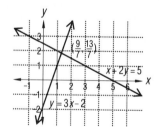

LESSON 1-6 (pp. 30–34)

9. Sample: 3; concord, harmony, agreement, concord. **11.** Sample: 2; satire, irony, satire. **13.** Sample: quanity. **15.** See below. **17.** See below. **19.** 5.3 **21. a.** 1 **b.** 2 **c.** 0 **d.** 3 **23.** See below.

15. a. **b.**

17.

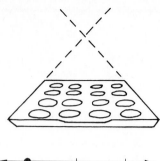

23.

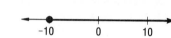

LESSON 1-7 (pp. 35–39)

3. No **5.** Yes **7.** True **9.** $\overrightarrow{XA}$ or $\overleftrightarrow{AX}$ **11.** a set of books of postulates and theorems by Euclid **13.** Transitive Property of Equality **15.** Addition Property of Equality **17.** Equation to Inequality Property **19.** Distributive Property **21.** Addition Property of Equality **23.** Sample: 3; proboscis, snout, nose, snout. **25. a.** See below. **b.** No **27. a.** horizontal **b.** oblique

25.

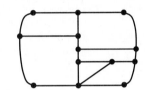

LESSON 1-8 (pp 40–45)

1. C is between A and B since $-2 < \sqrt{2} < 2$. **5.** M, N **7.** (d) **9.** $AB = |3 - 14| = 11$, $BC = |14 - 82| = 68$, $AC = |3 - 82| = 79$. Since $11 + 68 = 79$, $AB + BC = AC$. **11. a.** See below. **b.** a segment **13.** 38 **15.** 16 or -26 **17.** $4x$ **19.** Multiplication Property of Equality **21. a.** True **b.** True **c.** False **23.** See below. **25.** parts (a), (c), (d)

11. a.

23.

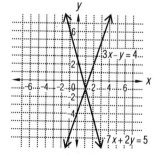

Point of intersection is (1, -1).

3. a. Yes **b.** Yes **c.** No **d.** No **5. a.** No **b.** Yes **c.** Yes **7.**
$BC = BA + AC$ **11.** True **13. a.** Yes **b.** No **15.** $x - y$,
$x + y$ **17.** 15 **19.** Commutative Property of Addition **21.**
a. See below. b. Yes **23.** 28

21. a. sample:

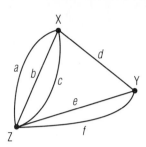

CHAPTER 1 PROGRESS SELF-TEST (p. 53)

1. $AB = |-8 - -4| = |-4| = 4$ units **2. See below. 3. See
below. 4.** The Triangle Inequality states that the sum of two
sides of a triangle must be longer than the third side. Since
$4.8 + 3.7 = 8.5 < 9.2$, the three lengths cannot be the sides
of a triangle. **5. See below. 6.** "A line contains infinitely
many points" is always true for dots, locations, and ordered
pairs (because the lines have no ends) and is never true for
nodes (an arc has only two nodes). **7.** "A point has size" is
always true for points as dots, and never true for locations,
ordered pairs, and nodes. **8.** Space has three dimensions:
length, width, and depth. **9.** Ignoring thickness, a sheet of
paper is "flat," like a plane, so it has two dimensions. **10.** If,
in defining a word, you return to that original word, circularity
has occurred. **11. a.b.** The screen that is 180 × 310 pixels has
55,800 pixels; the screen that is 215 × 350 pixels has 75,250
pixels. The screen with more pixels per unit of area, which is
the 215 × 350 screen, has better resolution. **12. See below.
13.** The distances are different because the air distance may be
measured along a straight path, perhaps between airports, and
the road distance may be measured along a path that follows
highways, perhaps between two downtown locations. **14. See
Below. 15.** Two points on $x = \frac{3}{2}$ are $(\frac{3}{2}, 0)$ and $(\frac{3}{2}, 10)$; the
line determined by these points is vertical. **16.** Two points on
$11x + y = 3$ are $(0, 3)$ and $(\frac{3}{11}, 0)$; the line determined by
those points is oblique. **17. a.** The network has no more than
two odd vertices, so it is traversable. **b.** Sample: V to Z to T
to V to W to Z to X to W **18. a. See below. b.** The network
has more than two odd vertices, so it is not traversable. **19.
See below. 20.** If $3x > 11$, the Addition Property of
Inequality lets you conclude that $3x + 6 > 17$. **21.** If $AB +
BC = 10$ and $AB = 7$, then Substitution lets you conclude that
$7 + BC = 10$. **22. See below. 23. See below. 24.** EF is a
number; that is choice (a). $\overline{EF}$, $\overrightarrow{EF}$, and $\overleftrightarrow{EF}$ are sets of points.

2. a. sample:

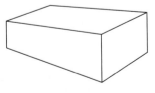

b. sample:

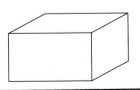

3.

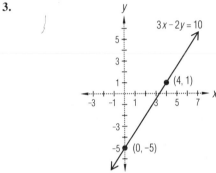

5. Extremes;

The distance d from Manilla to Shanghai is less than or
equal to $1115 + 1229$ and greater than or equal to
$1229 - 1115$, or $114 \le d \le 2344$.

12.

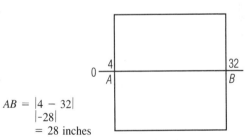

$AB = |4 - 32|$
$\quad\ \ |-28|$
$\quad = 28$ inches

14.

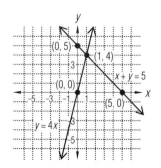

18. a.

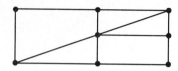

19. Extremes:

The time t needed to get from H to C is less than or equal to $8 + 6$ and more than or equal to $8 - 6$, so $2 \le t \le 14$.

22.

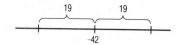

The coordinate of a point 19 units from -42 is either $-42 - 19 = -61$ or $-42 + 19 = -23$.

23.

The set of points is a ray.

The chart below keys the **Progress Self-Test** questions to the objectives in the **Chapter 1 Review** on pages 54–57. This will enable you to locate those **Chapter Review** questions that correspond to questions you missed on the **Progress Self-Test**. The lesson where the material is covered is also indicated in the chart.

Question	1	2	3	4	5	6–7	8–9	10
Objective	J	B	K	G	I	D	C	E
Lesson	1-2	1-5	1-3	1-9	1-9	1-1, 1-2, 1-3, 1-4	1-2	1-6

Question	11	12–13	14–16	17–18	19	20–21	22–23	24
Objective	C	H	K	A	I	E	F	J
Lesson	1-2	1-2	1-3	1-4	1-9	1-7	1-8	1-2

CHAPTER 1 REVIEW (pp. 54–57)

1. a. 5 **b.** 2 **3. a.** No **b.** It has more than two odd nodes. **5. See below. 7. a.** not in perspective. **9.** 2 **11.** 0 **13.** 1 **15–19. See below. 21.** point, line, plane **23.** to determine what descriptions of points, lines, and planes will be used **25.** Distributive Property **27.** Addition Property of Equality **29.** Addition Property of Inequality **31.** Transitive Property of Equality **33.** Multiplication Property of Equality **35. a. See below. b.** ray **37.** 78.5 **39.** -6 or 28 **41.** 16 **43.** No **45.** Yes **47.** Yes **49. a.** Yes **b.** longer than 9" and shorter than 11" **51.** 8° **53.** 96 miles **55.** at least 10 minutes and no more than 40 minutes **57.** at least 1.8 light years and no more than 10.4 light years **59.** 2.5 **61.** 42 **63.** 78 **65.** $|x - y|$ or $|y - x|$ **67. See below. 69.** oblique **71.** oblique **73.** $y = 1$

5. sample: a.

b.

	Dot	Location	Ordered Pair	Node
15.	N	A	A	A
17.	S	A	A	N
19.	S	N	N	S

35. a.

67.

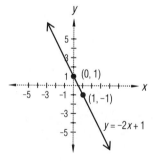

LESSON 2-1 (pp. 58–64)
5. 9 (not including the pictures at the beginning of the lesson or in the questions) **7.** No **9.** Yes **11. See below. 19.** -6
21. $x = 101.5$ **23.** $15z = m$

11. Sample:

LESSON 2-2 (pp. 65–69)
1. If a parallelogram has a right angle, then <u>it is a rectangle.</u>
3. If a figure is a square, then it is a polygon. **9.** 1 **11.** If a figure is a square, then it is a quadrilateral. **13.** $40 = 37 + 3$ or $40 = 29 + 11$ or $40 = 23 + 17$ **15.** No **17. a.** Sample: the line $y = x + 1$ **b.** the line $x = 2$ or the line $y = 3$ **19.**
a. nonconvex **b.** nonconvex **c.** convex **21.** longer than $9x$ but shorter than $17x$ **23.** $-32 < z < 58$

LESSON 2-3 (pp. 70–75)
5. See below. 7. The statement says nothing about polygons with 4 or fewer sides. **9.** True **11. a.** No **b.** It is changed to "yes." **13. a.** The formula gives an approximation of the area of a circle of radius R. **b.** when $R \le 0$ **15.** If a figure is a cube with side s, then its volume is s^3. **17. a.** $|x| = 10$ **b.** $x = -10$ **19.** A counterexample is a traversable network with no odd nodes. **(See art below.) 21. See below.**
23. $161 > q > 71$
5. COMPUTE NUMBER OF DIAGONALS IN POLYGON
ENTER THE NUMBER OF SIDES
? 100
THE NUMBER OF DIAGONALS IS 4850

19.

A   B
          C

21.

   ⊕   ⊕
0   25   57

LESSON 2-4 (pp. 76–80)
3. a. If you are at least 13 years old, then you are a teenager.
b. False **5. a.** A counterexample is a 10×3 rectangle. **b.** A counterexample is a 21×2 rectangle. **7. a.** $p \Rightarrow q$: If $2x + 31 = 4 - x$, then $x = -9$. $q \Rightarrow p$: If $x = -9$, then $2x + 31 = 4 - x$. **b.** $p \Rightarrow q$ and $q \Rightarrow p$ are both true. **9. a.** $p \Rightarrow q$: If $AB + BC = AC$, then B is between A and C. $q \Rightarrow p$: If B is between A and C, then $AB + BC = AC$. **b.** $p \Rightarrow q$ and $q \Rightarrow p$ are both true. **11. a.** $p \Rightarrow q$: If B is between A and C, then A is between C and B. $q \Rightarrow p$: If A is between C and B, then B is between A and C. **b.** Both $p \Rightarrow q$ and $q \Rightarrow p$ are false. **13.** No **15. a. See below. b.** Same two first lines, then: ? 1 [The program merely ends if n<3.] **17.** If a person was born in New York City, then that person is a U.S. citizen. **19.** a segment **(See art below.) 21.** Beta

15. a. COMPUTE SUM OF ANGLE MEASURES IN POLYGON
ENTER THE NUMBER OF SIDES
? 6
THE SUM OF THE ANGLE MEASURES (IN DEGREES) IS 720

19.

             ● ●   → y
           3 3.01

LESSON 2-5 (pp. 81–86)
9. a. 7 **b.** 7 **c.** $\frac{1}{2}$ **d.** $\frac{1}{2}$ **11.** Choice (d) contains all the points inside the circle as well as the circle itself, so it violates the definition. **13.** sufficient condition **15.** meaning **17.** A set is convex if and only if all segments connecting points of the set lie entirely in the set. **19.** Sample: A bisector of a segment is a line, ray, or segment that intersects the segment at its midpoint and at no other point. **21. a.** If $x^2 = \frac{4}{9}$, then $x = -\frac{2}{3}$.
b. No **23. a.** If A is between B and C, then $\overrightarrow{AB}$ and $\overrightarrow{AC}$ are opposite rays. **b.** Yes **25. See below.**

25.

                20
       ⎰‾‾‾‾‾‾‾‾‾‾‾‾⎱
   ●   ● ●
  P   14   **R** 6 **Q**

LESSON 2-6 (pp. 87–91)
3. A ∪ B = {-3, 0, 2, 5, 8}; A ∩ B = {-3, 2} **7.** the points A and B **11.** G ∪ H = all residents of Indonesia; G ∩ H = all residents of Jakarta. **13.** G ∪ H = students in all geometry classes; G ∩ H = ∅. **15.** $\overline{GH}, \overline{HI}, \overline{IJ}, \overline{GJ}, \overline{GI}$ **17. a.** violates property II **b.** violates property III **c.** violates property I **19.** sufficient condition half **21. See below. 23.** Antecedent: You work more than 40 hours a week. Consequent: You will receive time-and-a-half for overtime. **25. See below.**

21. Sample:

      (hexagon figure)

25.

           ⊕
    0   158

LESSON 2-7 (pp. 92–97)
9. convex **11.** convex **13.** (a) **15.** figure, two-dimensional figure, polygon, triangle, isosceles triangle, equilateral triangle **17. See below. 19.** $AEYD$, $ABXE$, $EXCY$, $ABCD$ **21.** If a figure is a union of three or more segments in the same plane such that each segment intersects exactly two others, one at each of its endpoints, then it is a polygon. **23. See below.**
25. Sides are not segments in this definition. **27. See below.**
29. a. 605.5 miles **b.** 1243.5 miles

17. sample:

23. sample: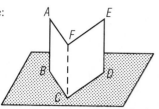

27. sample:

CHAPTER 2 PROGRESS SELF-TEST (pp. 99-100)

1. The "definition" contains too much information (not needed is "$\frac{1}{2}AB = AM$, and $\frac{1}{2}AB = MB$"). That is a violation of the third listed property. **2. See below. 3.** The antecedent is the "if clause" and the consequent is the "then clause": <u>Two angles have equal measure</u> if <u>they are vertical angles.</u> **4.** In if-then form: If a figure is a trapezoid, then it is a quadrilateral. **5. See below. 6. See below. 7.** $p \Leftrightarrow q$: There are over 10 books on that shelf if and only if the shelf falls. In simpler language: The shelf will not hold more than 10 books. **8. a.** Every triangle is a polygon, so the statement "If a figure is a triangle, then it is a polygon" is true. **b.** Converse: If a figure is a polygon, then it is a triangle. **c.** A counterexample to the converse is any quadrilateral, pentagon, or other polygon with more than three sides. **9.** The statement is "If you do your homework every night, you will be guaranteed passing grade." If you only know that the consequent is satisfied (Liane received a passing grade), it is impossible to tell if the antecedent (she did her homework every night) is true. **10.** If 6 is entered for V, then the antecedent in line 20 is satisfied, so the computer prints 36 (which is V^2). The antecedent in line 30 is not satisfied, so the computer ignores line 30. **11.** If 5 is entered for V, then the computer ignores line 20 because the antecedent is not satisfied. In line 30, the antecedent *is* satisfied, and the computer prints TOO SMALL (then the program ends). **12.** In the statement, the defined term (convex set) is in the antecedent, so the statement is the sufficient condition half. **13. See below. 14. a.** Hexagons have six sides; that is figure (iii). **b.** Quadrilaterals have four sides; that is figure (i). **c.** Octagons have eight sides; that is figure (iv). **15.** A figure is an isosceles triangle if and only if it is a triangle with two (or more) sides of equal length. **16. See below. 17. See below. 18.** The figure outlined has 18 sides, so it is an 18-gon.

2. sample:

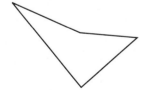

5.

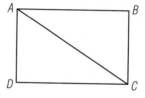

$r \cup t = ABCD \cup \triangle ADC$
$= \{\overline{AB}, \overline{BC}, \overline{CD}, \overline{DA}\} \cup \{\overline{AD}, \overline{DC}, \overline{AC}\}$
$= \{\overline{AB}, \overline{BC}, \overline{CD}, \overline{DA}, \overline{AC}\}$

So $r \cup t$ is the rectangle and its diagonal $\overline{AC}$.

6.

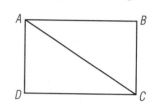

$r \cap t = \{\overline{AB}, \overline{BC}, \overline{CD}, \overline{DA}\} \cap \{\overline{AD}, \overline{DC}, \overline{AC}\}$
$= \{\overline{AD}, \overline{DC}\}$

So $r \cap t$ consists of segments $\overline{AD}$ and $\overline{DC}$.

13.

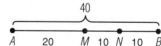

$AN = 20 + 10 = 30$

16. sample:

17.

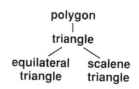

polygon
|
triangle
equilateral   scalene
triangle   triangle

The chart below keys the **Progress Self-Test** questions to the objectives in the **Chapter 2 Review** on pages 101–103. This will enable you to locate those **Chapter Review** questions that correspond to questions you missed on the **Progress Self-Test**. The lesson where the material is covered is also indicated in the chart.

Question	1	2	3–4	5–6	7	8	9	10–11
Objective	D	A	E	F	G	C	H	J
Lesson	2-1	2-7	2-2	2-6	2-4	2-4	2-4	2-3

Question	12	13	14–15	16	17	18
Objective	D	D	B	A	K	I
Lesson	2-5	2-5	2-7	2-7	2-7	2-7

CHAPTER 2 REVIEW QUESTIONS (pp. 101–103)

1. nonconvex **3.** convex **5. See below. 7. See below. 9. See below. 11. a.** If M is the midpoint of $\overline{AB}$, then $AM = MB$. **b.** True **13.** so people can agree on what things mean **15.** It is inaccurate. **17.** circle, line, interesects, two, point **19.** If a figure is a radius, then it is a segment **21.** If $AB = 7$, then $BA = 7$. **23.** If p, then q. **25. See below. 27. a.** $-15 \le n \le 15$ **b.** the set of all real numbers **29. a.** If $\triangle ABC$ has three 60° angles, then $\triangle ABC$ is equilateral. **b.** $\triangle ABC$ is equilateral if and only if $\triangle ABC$ has three 60° angles. **31.** true, false **33.** True **35.** pentagon **37. See below. 39.** 0.8 **41. See below.**

5. sample:

7. sample:

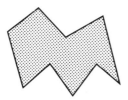

9.

25. sample:

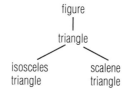

37. COMPUTE NUMBER OF DIAGONALS IN POLYGON
?20
THE NUMBER OF DIAGONALS IS 170

41.

figure
|
triangle
/   \
isosceles   scalene
triangle   triangle

LESSON 3-1 (pp. 104–112)

3. a. P **b.** $\overrightarrow{PR}$ or $\overrightarrow{PT}$ and $\overrightarrow{PS}$ or $\overrightarrow{PM}$ or $\overrightarrow{PN}$ **c.** Sample: $\angle 1$, $\angle RPM$, $\angle TPS$, $\angle NPT$, $\angle P$. **7. a.** ≈ 22 **b.** ≈ 100 **9. a.** 120 **b.** Angle Addition Property **11. a.** $\angle CAB$, $\angle BAD$, and $\angle DAC$ **b.** 120 **13. a. See below. b.** part (b) of the postulate **15. a.** sample: 175 **b.** sample: 30 **17. a.** Answers may vary. **b.** 35° **19. a. See below. b.** 14 **21.** 19 **23. a.** If a line, ray, or segment is a bisector of $\overline{AB}$, then it contains the midpoint of $\overline{AB}$. **b.** If a line, ray, or segment contains the midpoint of $\overline{AB}$, then it is a bisector of $\overline{AB}$.

13. a.

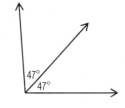

19. a.

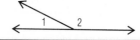

LESSON 3-2 (pp. 113–119)

3. obtuse **5.** vertical **7. a.** $180 - x$ **b.** x **c.** $180 - x$ **9. See below. 11. See below. 13. a.** If two angles are supplementary, then they form a linear pair. **b. See below. c.** The converse is not true. **15. a.** right **b.** acute **c.** obtuse **17.** 95 **19.** $\approx 19°$ **21. a.** 8 **b.** 6 **c.** 5 **d.** 3 **e.** 4 **f.** 7 **g.** 9 **h.** 10 **i.** 35 **j.** n **23. a.** 7 **b.** 1

9. sample:

11.

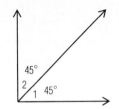

13. b.

LESSON 3-3 (pp. 120–125)
5. Vertical Angle Theorem **9.** Sample: **a.** $y = 8$ **b.** Multiplication Property of Equality **11.** (a) **13.** definition of supplementary angles (meaning) **15.** definition of angle bisector (sufficient condition) **17.** The segment with endpoints A and B is the set consisting of the distinct points A and B and all points between A and B. **19.** m$\angle$T = 15 **21.** 38.5 **23.** 45 **25.** 59 **27.** If X and Y are two angles, then they cannot be both acute and supplementary.

LESSON 3-4 (pp. 126–131)
1. $\angle$3 **3.** Lines m and n should be drawn parallel. **5.** True

7. $-\frac{2}{5}$ **11.** 4 **15. a.** $\angle$1, $\angle$4, $\angle$7 **b.** $\angle$2, $\angle$3, $\angle$5, $\angle$8

17. $\angle$FCD **19.** True **21.** corr. $\angle$s = $\Rightarrow$ $\parallel$ lines **23. See below. 25.** -35

23. sample:

LESSON 3-5 (pp. 132–139)
5. Two Perpendiculars Theorem **7.** $-\frac{3}{2}$ **11. a.** 90 **b.** 50 **13. a.** $\parallel$ lines $\Rightarrow$ corr. $\angle$s = **b.** $\ell \perp m$ and $m \parallel n \Rightarrow \ell \perp n$ **c.** $\parallel$ lines $\Rightarrow$ corr. $\angle$s = **d.** $\ell \perp m \Rightarrow$ 90° angle **15.** $\frac{9}{2}$ **17.** m$\angle$2 = 70, m$\angle$3 = 110, m$\angle$4 = 70, m$\angle$5 = 110, m$\angle$6 = 110, m$\angle$7 = 70, m$\angle$8 = 110 **19.** corr. $\angle$s = $\Rightarrow$ $\parallel$ lines **21.** m$\angle$6 $\approx$ 100 **23.** {D, H}

25.

LESSON 3-6 (pp. 140–145)
7. See below. 9. See below. 11. See below. 13. See below. 15. See below. 17. Meaning: If two lines are perpendicular, then they form a 90° angle at the point of intersection. Sufficient condition: If two lines form a 90° angle at their point of intersection, then the lines are perpendicular. **19.** m$\angle$1 = 84

7. sample:

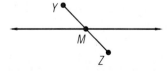

9.

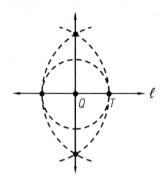

11.

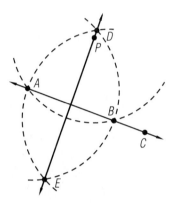

13.

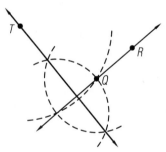

15. $\triangle$ABC is an equilateral triangle.

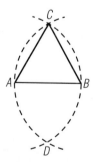

1. See below. 2. m∠3 = m∠4 because of the Vertical Angle Theorum. So if m∠3 = 77, then m∠4 = 77 by the Transitive Property of Equity. **3.** ∠3 and ∠4 are called Vertical Angles. **4.** ∠3 and ∠5 form a linear pair, so m∠3 + m∠5 = 180. If m∠3 = 2x, then m∠5 = 180 − 2x by the Addition Property of Equality. **5.** From eye level (horizontal) to straight up (vertical) is 90°. So from 15° to 90° is (90−15)° = 75°. **6.** If ∠1 and ∠2 are complementary, then m∠1 + m∠2 = 90 (definition of complementary (meaning)). Substituting m∠1 = 5x − 7 and m∠2 = 4x + 16, then (5x − 7) + (4x + 16) = 90, or 9x + 9 = 90, so 9x = 81 and x = 9. Finally, m∠1 = 5x − 7 = 5(9) − 7 = 45 − 7 = 38. **7. See below. 8. See below. 9. See below. 10.** For two adjacent angles, the statement that the sum of the measures of the two smaller angles equals the measure of the large angle is the Angle Addition Property; that is choice (d). **11. See below. 12.** $\overrightarrow{BC}$ bisects ∠ABD, so m∠ABC = m∠CBD or 14y − 3 = 37 − y. So 15y = 40, and y = $\frac{40}{15}$ = $\frac{8}{3}$. **13. See below. 14. See below. 15.** The slope of $\overline{AB}$ is $\frac{y_2 - y_1}{x_2 - x_1}$ = $\frac{1 - 0}{4 - 0}$ = $\frac{1}{4}$. **16.** The slope of any line, segment, or ray perpendicular to $\overline{AB}$ is -4, because ($\frac{1}{4}$)(-4) = -1. **17.** Two points on 2x − y = 6 are (0, -6) and (3, 0). The slope of the line through those points is $\frac{y_2 - y_1}{x_2 - x_1}$ = $\frac{0 - -6}{3 - 0}$ = $\frac{6}{3}$ = 2. **18.** The slope of any line perpendicular to 2x − y = 6 is -$\frac{1}{2}$, because (2)(-$\frac{1}{2}$) = -1. **19.** m∠4 = m∠3 because ∥ lines ⇒ AIA =. ∠3 is supplementary to a 40° angle, so m∠4 = 140 by the Transitive Property of Equality. **20.** m∠5 = 40 because ∥ lines ⇒ AIA =. **21.** The shortest path from point H to the street is the length of the ⊥ segment from H to the street, or segment x ; that is choice (b). **22. See below. 23.** If Q is the midpoint of $\overline{OP}$, then OQ = OP; that is the definition of midpoint (meaning).

1. sample:

7.

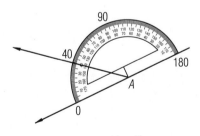

m ∠A ≈ 40

8.

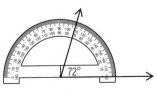

m∠A ≈ 40

9.

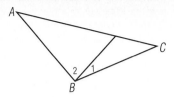

m∠ABC = 110, so m∠1 + m∠2 = 110.
m∠2 = 4 · m∠1, so m∠1 + 4m∠1 = 110.
$$5m∠1 = 110$$
$$m∠1 = 22$$

11. ∠1 is acute, so 0 < 21 + x < 90.
$$-21 < x < 69$$

13. Two lines (ℓ and m) perpendicular to the same line (n) are parallel to each other.

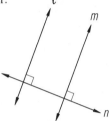

14. Two lines (ℓ and m) parallel to the same line (n) are parallel to each other.

22.

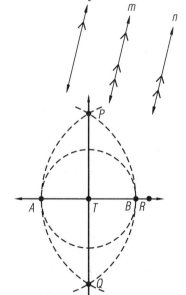

Step 1: ⊙T, intersecting $\overleftrightarrow{TR}$ at
     A and B.   (Compass rule)
Step 2: ⊙A containing B, ⊙B
     containing A; they
     intersect at P and Q.   (Compass rule)
Step 3: $\overleftrightarrow{PQ}$ (Straightedge rule)

The chart below keys the **Progress Self-Test** questions to the objectives in the **Chapter 3 Review** on pages 149–153. This will enable you to locate those **Chapter 3 Review** questions that correspond to questions you missed on the **Progress Self-Test**. The lesson where the material is covered is also indicated in the chart.

Question	1–4	5	6	7–8	9	10	11–12	13	14
Objective	A	G	C	B	C	F	C	F	F
Lesson	3-2	3-2	3-2	3-1	3-1	3-3	3-2	3-5	3-4

Question	15	16	17	18	19–20	21	22	23
Objective	I	J	I	J	D	H	E	F
Lesson	3-4	3-5	3-4	3-5	3-4	3-6	3-6	3-3

CHAPTER 3 REVIEW (pp. 149–153)

1. a. ∠LPO or ∠NPM **b.** sample: ∠LPL **c.** sample: ∠LPM and ∠MPO **d.** ∠MPL, ∠LPM **3. See below. 5. a.** 102 **b.** 102 **c.** 78 **7.** m∠R ≈ 52 **9. See below. 11. See below.**

13. $x = -168$ **15.** m∠1 = 144, m∠2 = 36 **17.** $x = \frac{47}{17}$

19. 16 **21.** 69 **23.** $w = \frac{17}{2} z$ **25.** 135 **27. See below. 29. See**

below. 31. a. See below. b. the center of the circle containing X, Y, and Z **c.** Step 1: Straightedge rule;   Step 3, Straightedge rule;   Step 5: Point rule **33.** (a) **35.** (a) **37.** Linear Pair Theorem **39.** Angle Addition Property **41. See**

below. 43. 135 **45. See below. 47.** -1 **49.** $\frac{5}{3}$ **51.** $y = 3x$

53. $-\frac{2}{3}, \frac{3}{2}$ **55.** (c)

3. sample:

9.

11.

27.

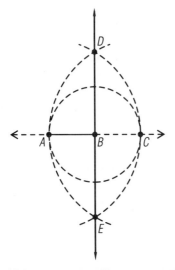

29.

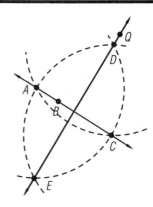

31. a.

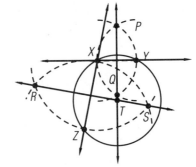

41.

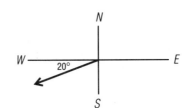

45.

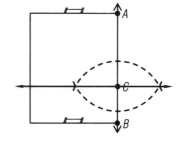

5. See below. **9.** See below. **11. a.** (3, -5) **b.** (-3, 5) **13.
a.** (*c*, -*d*) **b.** (-*c*, *d*) **15.** See below.

17. a. HELP! I'M TRAPPED INSIDE THIS PAGE. **b.** N
19. See below. **21.** (b) **23.** 25

5. a.

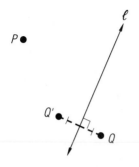

b.

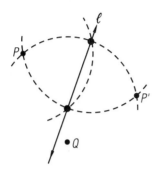

9.

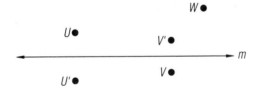

15.

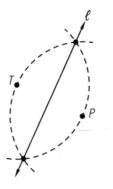

19.

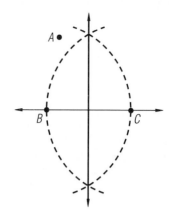

3. *V'* will be between *A'* and *Z'*. **5. a.** No **b.** Reflections
preserve angle measure, and these angles have different
measures. **7.** $\overline{ZS}$ **9. a.** $\overline{D'E'}$ and $\overline{D'F'}$ **b.** at *G* and *H* **11.** See
below. **13.** 3 **15.** None are needed. **17.** (d) **19.** (e) **21.** See
below. **23.** See below. **25.** See below. **27.** -3, $\frac{1}{3}$ **29.** If *a* = *b*
and *b* = *c*, then *a* = *c*.

11.

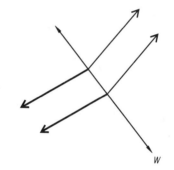

21.

23.

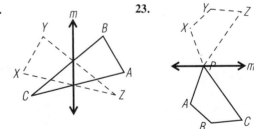

25.

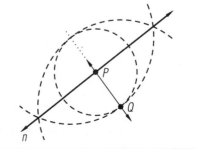

821

LESSON 4-3 (pp. 170–175)
3. a. $AB = AD \approx 21$ mm; $BC = DC \approx 16$ mm **b.**
Reflections preserve distance. **5. a.** They are equal. **b.**
Reflections preserve distance. **7. a.** They have the same
measure. **b.** Reflections preserve angle measure. **9. a.**
Answers may vary. **b.** $\angle 1$ and $\angle 3$, $\angle 2$ and $\angle 4$, $\angle 8$ and $\angle 6$,
$\angle 7$ and $\angle 5$ **c.** ∥ lines $\Rightarrow$ corr. $\angle$s = (Parallel Lines Postulate)
11. a-c. See below. d. $BC = DC = FE = EB$ because
reflections preserve distance. **e.** Samples: $m\angle DAC =$
$m\angle CAB = m\angle BAE = m\angle FAE$; $m\angle ADC = m\angle ABC =$
$m\angle ABE = m\angle AFE$; $m\angle DCA = m\angle BCA = m\angle BEA =$
$m\angle FEA$. **13. See below. 15.** $P' = (2, 0)$, $Q' = (4, 3)$, $R' =$
$(-2, 7)$ **19.** $\angle ABC$, $\angle CBA$, $\angle B$, $\angle 1$ **21.** A $\cap$ B = {I,N,S}

11. a-c. Answers may vary. Sample:

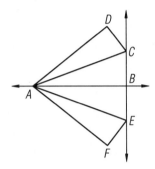

13.

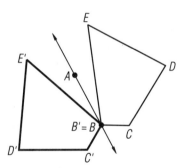

LESSON 4-4 (pp. 176–182)
3. definition of $\odot$ (meaning) **5. a.** ∥ lines $\Rightarrow$ corr. $\angle$s =
(Parallel Lines Postulate) **b.** Vertical Angle Theorem **c.**
Transitive Property of Equality (steps a and b) **7.** No **9.** No
11. No **13.** $m \parallel n$ and $\angle 5$ and $\angle 7$ are vertical angles. **15. See
below. 17. a. See below. b.** Reflections preserve distance.
19. 35 **21.** Addition Property of Equality **23.** All angles of
$\triangle ABC$ and $\triangle ABD$ have measure 60. All sides of $\triangle ABC$
and $\triangle ABD$ have equal lengths (which for the sample shown is
$\frac{1}{2}$ inch). **(See art below.)**

15.

Conclusions	Justifications
1. $m\angle ABE = m\angle CBD$	Vertical Angle Theorem
2. $m\angle ABE = m\angle D$	Transitive Property of Equality (given and step 1)

17. a.

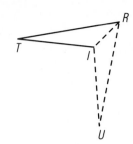

23.

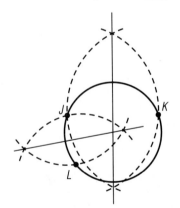

LESSON 4-5 (pp. 183–186)
1. a. The reflection image over a line of a point on the line is
the point itself. **b.** definition of reflection (sufficient condition)
c. Reflections preserve distance. **5.** Construct the $\perp$ bisector
of $\overline{JK}$ and $\overline{JL}$ to find the center O. Construct $\odot O$ through J.
(See art below.) **7. See below. 9. See below. 11.** K, N **13.**
$m\angle 1 = m\angle 3 = m\angle 8 = m\angle 6$, $m\angle 4 = m\angle 2 = m\angle 5 = m\angle 7$

5.

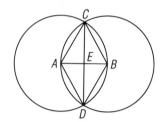

7.

Conclusions	Justifications
1. $r_{\overleftrightarrow{QR}}(Q) = Q$	The reflection over a line of a point on the line is the point itself.
2. $CQ = DQ$	Reflections preserve distance.

9.

Conclusions	Justifications
1. $BC = AC$	Def. of equilateral triangle (meaning)
2. $AC = CD$	Def. of midpoint (meaning)
3. $BC = CD$	Transitive Property of Equality

LESSON 4-6 (pp. 187–191)

1. See below. **3.** See below. **5. a.** clockwise **b.** clockwise **c.** counterclockwise **7.** True **9. a.** I **b.** $\angle XSI$ **c.** $\overrightarrow{IS}$ **d.** $\overline{XS}$ **11.** counterclockwise **13.** See below. **15. a.** (iii) **b.** (iii) **c.** (i) **d.** (ii) **17. a.** definition of reflection (meaning) **b.** definition of reflection (meaning) **c.** Two Perpendiculars Theorem **19. a.** $\frac{-3}{2}$ **b.** $\frac{2}{3}$ **21.** Let x be 45.

1.

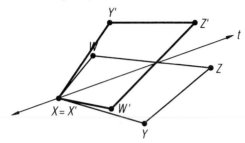

3. Sample:

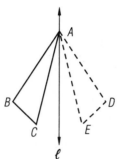

13. Sample:

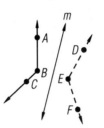

LESSON 4-7 (pp. 192–197)

3. See below. **5.** See below. **7.** See below. **9. a.** $\overrightarrow{FG}$ **b.** $\overrightarrow{FJ}$ **c.** $\angle GFJ$ **11.** See below. **13.** See below. **15. a.** See below. **b.** True **17.** See below. **19.** (d) **21. a.** m$\angle AOB$ = m$\angle BOC$ **b.** definition of angle bisector (meaning) **c.** m$\angle AOB$ = m$\angle COD$ **23.** 2 **25.** See below.

3.

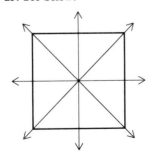

5.

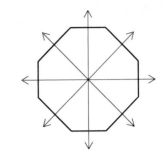

7.

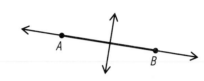

11.

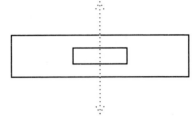

13.   **15. a.**

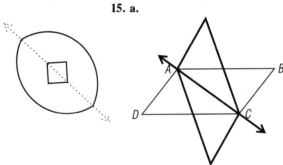

17.

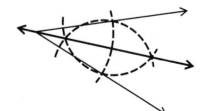

25.

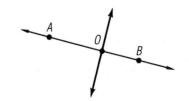

CHAPTER 4 PROGRESS SELF-TEST (p. 199)

1. Point *B* is the reflection image of *A*, and point *D* is the reflection of *C*. So $\overline{BD}$ is the reflection image of $\overline{AC}$, and *AC* = *BD* because reflections preserve distance. **2.** Point *B* is the reflection image of *A* over line *m*, so $m \perp \overline{AB}$ by the definition of reflection (meaning). **3.** The image of *X* is *D*, so $r_m(X) = D$. **4.** The images of points *A*, *B*, and *C* are *W*, *Z*, and *Y*, respectively, so $r_m(\angle ABC) = \angle WZY$. **5.** The orientation of *WXYZ* is clockwise, so the orientation of the image of *WXYZ* is counterclockwise. **6.** Polygon *ABCD* is symmetric across line *n*, so *A* and *B* are images of each other, and so are *D* and *C*. So $r_n(ABCD) = BADC$. **7.** $r_n(\angle BDA) = \angle ACB$, so if m$\angle BDA$ = *x*, then m$\angle ACB$ = *x*, because reflections preserve angle measure. **8. See below. 9.** In general, a reflection over the *x*-axis of (*x*, *y*) is (*x*, -*y*). So if *M* = (2, 0), then *M'* = (2, -0) = (2, 0); if *N* = (5, -1), then *N'* = (5, -(-1)) = (5, 1); if *P* = (-3, 4), then *P'* = (-3, -4). **10–15. See below.**

8.

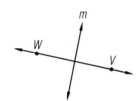

m is the $\perp$ bisector of $\overline{WV}$.

10.

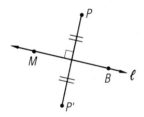

$\overleftrightarrow{MB}$ is the $\perp$ bisector of $\overline{PP'}$.

11.

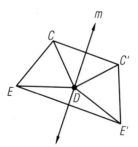

m is the $\perp$ bisector of $\overline{CC'}$, $\overline{EE'}$.

12.

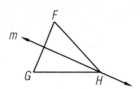

$\triangle FGH$ is isosceles, with vertex $\angle H$. There is one line of symmetry, the $\perp$ bisector of base $\overline{FG}$.

13.

The figure appears to be a regular pentagon. That figure has 5 lines of symmetry, the $\perp$ bisectors of the sides.

14.

Conclusions	Justifications
1. m$\angle 1$ = m$\angle 2$	Given
2. m$\angle 1$ = m$\angle 3$	Vertical Angle Theorem
3. m$\angle 3$ = m$\angle 2$	Transitive Property of Equality (steps 1, 2)

15.

Conclusions	Justifications
1. $\ell \perp \overline{YZ}$	definition of reflection (meaning)
2. $\ell \perp \overline{WX}$	definition of reflection (meaning)
3. $\overline{WX} \parallel \overline{YZ}$	Two perpendiculars Theorem

The chart below keys the **Progress Self-Test** questions to the objectives in the **Chapter 4 Review** on pages 200–203. This will enable you to locate those **Chapter Review** questions that correspond to questions you missed on the **Progress Self-Test**. The lesson where the material is covered is also indicated in the chart.

Question	1	2	3–5	6	7	8	9	10
Objective	E	E	E	F	D	A	I	A
Lesson	4-2	4-1	4-6	4-7	4-6	4-1	4-2	4-1

Questions	11	12	13	14	15
Objective	B	C	H	G	G
Lesson	4-2, 4-3	4-7	4-7	4-4	4-5

CHAPTER 4 REVIEW (pp. 200–203)

1. See below. **3.** See below. **5.** See below. **7.** See below. **9.** See below. **11.** See below. **13.** $180 - x$ **15.** ℓ is the $\perp$ bisector of $\overline{AB}$. **17.** Figure Reflection Theorem **19.** Reflections preserve distance. **21.** clockwise **23.** $\angle Y$ and $\angle W$, $\angle YXZ$ and $\angle WXZ$, $\angle YZX$ and $\angle WZX$ **25.** True **27.** True **29.** Conclusion 1: Flip-Flop Theorem   Conclusion 2: Reflections preserve distance. **31.** See below. **33.** See below. **35.** See below. **37.** $(3, -7)$ **39.** $(-a, b)$

1.

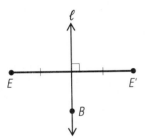

3.

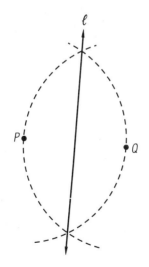

5.

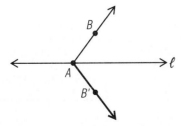

7.

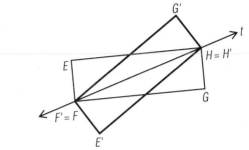

9.

11.

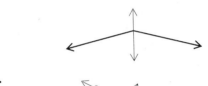

31.

Conclusions	Justifications
1. $m\angle 1 = m\angle 4$	$\parallel$ lines $\Rightarrow$ corr. $\angle$s =
2. $m\angle 4 = m\angle 6$	Vertical Angle Theorem
3. $m\angle 1 = m\angle 6$	Transitive Property of Equality (steps 1 and 2)

33.

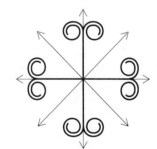

35.

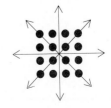

LESSON 5-1 (pp. 204–212)
1. a. $\overline{WN}$ **b.** $\angle I$ **c.** $\angle W$ and $\angle N$ **d.** $\angle W$ and $\angle N$ **3.** (d) **5. See below. 7. a.** (iii) **b.** (i) **c.** (iv) **9.** $\angle P$ and $\angle H$, $\angle HOE$ and $\angle POE$, $\angle HEO$ and $\angle PEO$ **11. See below. 13.** (d) **15.** F **17. See below. 19.** equilateral triangle, rectangle, pentagon, 7-gon, octagon, nonagon

5.

Conclusions	Justifications
1. $m\angle 1 = m\angle XYZ$	Vertical Angle Theorem
2. $m\angle XYZ = m\angle 2$	Isosceles Triangle Theorem
3. $m\angle 1 = m\angle 2$	Transitive Property of Equality (steps 1 and 2)

11.

Conclusions	Justifications
1. $m\angle B = m\angle ACB$	Isosceles Triangle Theorem
2. $m\angle ACB = m\angle ECD$	Vertical Angle Theorem
3. $m\angle ECD = m\angle CED$	Isosceles Triangle Theorem
4. $m\angle B = m\angle CED$	Transitive Property of Equality (steps 1, 2, and 3)

17. sample:

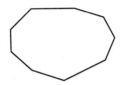

LESSON 5-2 (pp. 213–217)
17. $\overline{WZ} \perp \overline{WX}$; $\overline{WX} \perp \overline{XY}$; $\overline{XY} \perp \overline{ZY}$; $\overline{ZY} \perp \overline{WZ}$; rectangle **19.** $\overline{FG} \perp \overline{GH}$; $\overline{GH} \perp \overline{HE}$; $\overline{HE} \perp \overline{EF}$; $\overline{EF} \perp \overline{FG}$; $FG = GH = EH = EF$; square **21. a.** definition of circle (meaning) **b.** definition of circle (meaning) **c.** definition of kite (sufficient condition) **25. a.** 10 **b.** 33 **27. See below.**

27. sample:

LESSON 5-3 (pp. 218–222)
3. counter example **5. a.** $ABCD$ **b.** $PQRS$ **7.** The diagonals of a rectangle have equal length. **9. See below. 11. See below. 13. See below. 15.** Opinions will vary. **17.** Opinions will vary. **19.** A quadrilateral is a parallelogram if and only if both pairs of its opposite sides are parallel. **21.** A triangle is isosceles if and only if it has two (or more) sides of equal length. **23.** polygon, quadrilateral, kite, rhombus, square **25. a.** E **b.** $FEHG$ **c.** $\angle FHG$

9. Sample conjecture: A diagonal of a rhombus forms 4 equal angles with the sides of the rhombus.

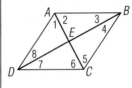

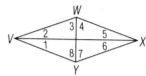

	ABCD		JKLM		VWXY
	angle measure		angle measure		angle measure
	1	60	1	45	1	20
	2	60	2	45	2	20
	3	30	3	45	3	70
	4	30	4	45	4	70
	5	60	5	45	5	20
	6	60	6	45	6	20
	7	30	7	45	7	70
	8	30	8	45	8	70

11. sample:

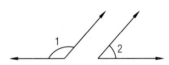

13. sample:

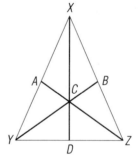

LESSON 5-4 (pp. 223–227)
5. a. I and E **b.** $\overline{EI}$ **c.** $\angle ITE$ **7.** $ED = 15$; $BD = 30$; $m\angle BAC = 50$; $m\angle DCA = 30$; $m\angle BEA = m\angle AED = m\angle DEC = m\angle BEC = 90$; $m\angle BAD = 100$; $m\angle BCD = 60$ **9. a.** Kite Symmetry Theorem **b.** Kite Diagonal Theorem **c.** definition of reflection (suff. cond.) **d.** definition of reflection (suff. cond.) **e.** Figure Reflection Theorem **f.** Reflections preserve angle measure. **11. a. See below. b.** Yes **c.** Yes **13. See below. 15.** A quadrilateral is a trapezoid if and only if it has one pair of parallel sides. **17.** isosceles trapezoids, rectangles, squares **19. See below. 21.** 15

11. a. sample:

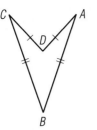

13. sample:

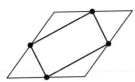

19.

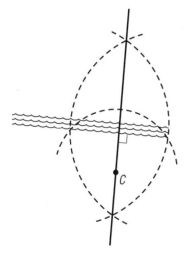

LESSON 5-5 (pp. 228–233)
5. m∠I = 125; m∠Z = m∠D = 55; DI = 12 cm **9. a.** definition of trapezoid (sufficient condition) **b.** Isosceles Triangle Theorem **c.** definition of isosceles trapezoid (sufficient condition) **11. See below. 13. a.** True **b.** True **c.** True **15.** RT = 3; IT = 4; KE = 8; KT = 6; m∠KIE = 49; m∠KIT = 98; m∠KEI = m∠TEI = 22; m∠TRE = m∠TRI = m∠KRE = m∠KRI = 90 **17. a.** B and D **b.** Yes **c.** Yes **19. a.** angle measure, betweenness, collinearity, distance **b.** orientation **21. a.** 16 **b.** 134

11.

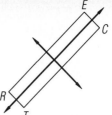

LESSON 5-6 (pp. 234–239)
1. a. ∠7, ∠2, ∠3, ∠6 **b.** ∠7 and ∠6, ∠2 and ∠3 **3.** ∠5, ∠6, ∠7, ∠8 **9.** ABCD is a parallelogram, from the Quadrilateral Hierarchy Theorem. Therefore, $\overline{AD} \parallel \overline{BC}$ by the definition of parallelogram (meaning). **11. a.** Vertical Angle Theorem **b.** Transitive Property of Equality **c.** Corresponding ∠s = ⟹ ∥ lines **13.** m∠4 = 135; m∠7 = 140; m∠2 = 95; m∠3 = 40; m∠1 = 45 **15.** m∠DEG = m∠BEC = m∠FGE = 123; m∠EHI = m∠AED = m∠BEH = 137; m∠BEG = m∠CED = 57; m∠GEH = m∠AEC = 80; m∠DEH = m∠AEB = 43; m∠AEG = m∠CEH = 100 **17. a.** Yes **b.** No **19.** isosceles right triangle **21.** 97 **23.** 0°, 180°

25. sample:

LESSON 5-7 (pp. 240–245)
1. a. ∥ Lines ⟹ AIA = Theorem **b.** ∥ Lines ⟹ AIA = Theorem **c.** substitution **3.** 20, 60, 100 **7. a.** Sample: a triangle formed by two north-south lines and the equator. **b.** non-Euclidean geometries **9. a.** 180 **b.** Triangle-Sum Theorem **11. a.** 3240 **b.** Polygon-Sum Theorem **13.** 82°26′ **15. a.** 60 **b.** The sum of the measure of the interior angles is 180, and they are all of the same measure, so any one angle measures $\frac{180}{3}$ = 60. **17.** 39 and 102 or 70.5 and 70.5 **19. See below. 21.** A quadrilateral is a trapezoid if and only if it has at least one pair of parallel sides. **23.** R: 15°E of S; Q: 30°S of W

19.

	Conclusions	Justifications
	1. m∠CBE = m∠E	∥ Lines ⟹ AIA = Theorem
a.	2. m∠D = m∠E	Transitive Property of Equality (step 1 and given)
	3. ABED is a trapezoid	def. of trapezoid (suff. cond.)
	4. ABED is an isosceles trapezoid.	def. of isosceles trapezoid (suff. cond.)
b.	5. ∠A and ∠D are supplementary.	Trapezoid Angle Theorem

CHAPTER 5 PROGRESS SELF-TEST (p. 249)
1. Squares are below rectangles in the Quadrilateral Hierarchy, so it is true that every square is a rectangle. **2. See below.**
3. a. The sum of the three angle measures is 180, so (5x) + (90 − x) + (x) = 180, or 5x + 90 = 180, so 5x = 90 and x = 18. **b.** m∠A = x = 18; m∠B = (90 − x) = 90 − 18 = 72; m∠C = 5x = 5(18) = 90. (To check: m∠A + m∠B + m∠C = 18 + 72 + 90 = 180.) **4. See below. 5. See below.**
6. a. △MNP is equilateral, so it is also equiangular; m∠M = 60. **b.** The two acute angles at point N, ∠MNP and ∠PNO, are parts of equilateral triangles. So each angle has measure

60, and m∠MNO = 120. **7.** △MNO is equilateral, so MN = MP = NP, and △NOP is equilateral so NO = PO = NP. By the Transitive Property of Equality, MN = NO = OP = MP, So MNOP is a rhombus (*True*) by the definition of rhombus (sufficient condition). **8. See below. 9. a.** ABCD is a parallelogram, so it is also a trapezoid. So m∠A + m∠B = 180 by the Trapezoid Angle Theorem. **b.** ADCB is a parallelogram, so $\overleftrightarrow{AD} \parallel \overleftrightarrow{BC}$. So m∠D = m∠DCE because ∥ lines ⟹ AIA =. **10. See below. 11. a.** ∠5 and ∠6 form a linear pair, so m∠5 + m∠6 = 180. Since ℓ∥m, ∠6 = ∠3 by ∥ lines ⟹ AIA =. So m∠5 + m∠3 = 180 or (9z − 52) +

$(2z + 45) = 180$. Then $11z - 7 = 180$ or $11z = 187$, so $z = 17$. **b.** $m\angle 3 = 2z + 45 = 2(17) + 45 = 34 + 45 = 79$.
12. See below. 13. See below. 14. a. For most briefcases, the top has the shape of a rectangle. **b.** Opinions may vary. One explanation is that the rectangular outline of the briefcase is convenient for carrying books and papers. **15. See below.**
2.

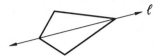

False; a kite has only one line of symmetry.

4. a. Sample:

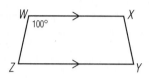

b. $m\angle X = 100$ by the Isosceles Trapezoid Theorem. The sum of $m\angle W + m\angle X + m\angle Y + m\angle Z = 360$ because of the Quadrilateral Sum Theorem, so $m\angle Y + m\angle Z = 160$ by the Addition Property of Equality. By the Isosceles Trapezoid Theorem, $m\angle Y = m\angle Z$, so $m\angle Y = m\angle Z = 80$.

5.

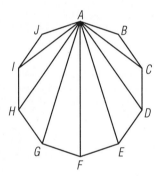

$ABCDEFGHIJ$, a convex decagon, can be triangulated into 8 triangles. The sum of the measures of the 8 triangles is $8(180) = 1440$.

8. a-b.

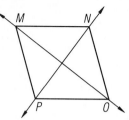

$MNOP$ has two symmetry lines, $\overleftrightarrow{MO}$ and $\overleftrightarrow{NP}$.

10.

Conclusions	Justifications
1. $AB = BC$	Given
2. $m\angle A = m\angle ACB$	Isosceles Triangle Theorem
3. $m\angle ACB = m\angle ECD$	Vertical Angle Theorem
4. $m\angle A = m\angle ECD$	Transitive Property of Equality (Steps 2 and 3)

12. sample:

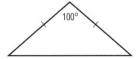

13. a-b. Counterexample:

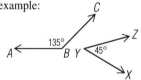

The counterexample shows that the conjecture is false. $\angle 1$ and $\angle 2$ are supplementary, but they do not form a linear pair.

15.

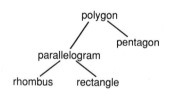

The chart below keys the **Progress Self-Test** questions to the objectives in the **Chapter 5 Review** on pages 249–251. This will enable you to locate those **Chapter Review** questions that correspond to questions you missed on the **Progress Self-Test**. The lesson where the material is covered is also indicated in the chart.

Question	1	2	3	4a	4b	5	6	7	8
Objective	D	E	C	A	B	C	C	D	E
Lesson	5-2	5-4	5-7	5-5	5-5	5-7	5-1	5-2	5-4

Question	9a	9b	10	11	12	13	14	15
Objective	B	B	G	B	A	F	H	I
Lesson	5-5	5-6	5-1	5-6	5-1	5-3	5-2	5-2

CHAPTER 5 REVIEW (pp. 249–251)
1. See below. **3.** See below. **5.** m∠T = 120; m∠R = 60
7. a. 53 **b.** 127 **9.** 57 **11.** 27 **13.** 42 **15.** 46 **17. a.** 58 **b.**
m∠D = 59, m∠E = 60, and m∠F = 61 **19.** 1080 **21.**
polygon, quadrilateral, parallelogram, rhombus, square **23.**
isosceles trapezoid **25.** True **27.** Yes **29.** (c) **31.** False
33. True **35.** Answers may vary. **37.** Answers may vary.
39. a. False **b.** See below. **41.** See below. **43.** See below.
45. See below. **47. a.** square **b.** Answers may vary. On a
major league field, the dimensions are 90 feet on a side. **c.**
Answers may vary. **49.** See below.

1. sample:

3. sample:

39. b. counterexample:

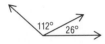

41. <u>Conclusions</u>
  1. $\overline{EF} \parallel \overline{GH}$
  2. EFHG is a trapezoid.

<u>Justifications</u>
AIA = ⇒ ∥ Lines Theorem
definition of trapezoid
(sufficient condition)

43. <u>Conclusions</u>
  1. AB = AC

  2. AC = CD

  3. AB = CD

<u>Justifications</u>
definition of isosceles
triangle (meaning)
definition of isosceles
triangle (meaning)
Transitive Property of
Equality

45. <u>Conclusions</u>
  1. OQ = OR

  2. PQ = PR

  3. OQPR is a kite.

<u>Justifications</u>
definition of circle
(meaning)
definition of circle
(meaning)
definition of kite
(sufficient condition)

49.

LESSON 6-1 (pp. 252–258)
9. a. (7,0) **b.** Yes **11. a.** See below. **b.** slide **13.** Two of the
outside vertices do not move, while the others do. This
makes, for example, ∠O different from ∠O′. **15. a.,b. See
Below. c.** turn
17. (b) **19. a.** Yes **b.** The right angle has measure 90; the
other two have measure 45. **21.** See below. **23.** 16

11. a.

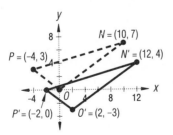

15. a.,b.

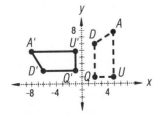

21. sample:

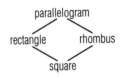

LESSON 6-2 (pp. 259–265)
5. a. D **b.** E **9. a.** 2 cm **b.** vertically up **11.** $\overline{AB}$ **13.** Slide
each preimage point 6 inches to the left, or reflect it across
each of two parallel, vertical lines where the second reflecting
line is 3 inches to the left of the first. **15.** about 8′8″ **17.**
a. (6, -1) **b.** (x + 4, y − 6) **19.** (-12, 15) **21. a.** True
b. False **23.** A circle is the set of points in a plane at a certain
distance (its radius) from a certain point (its center).

LESSON 6-3 (pp. 266–272)
5. a. Reflections preserve distance. **b.** Reflections preserve
distance. **c.** Transitive Property of Equality **7.** 80 **9.** See
below. **11.** See art below. **a.** (-4, -2) **b.** 180°(or -180°) with
center at the origin **13.** See below. **15. a.** -172° **b.** 172°
c. 86 **17.** (d) **19.** (13, -212) **21.** 135.75° **23. a.** 24° **b.** 2°

9.

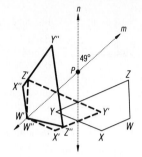

11.

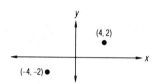

13.

Conclusions	Justifications
1. $\overline{MN} = PQ$; $PQ = ST$	Reflections preserve distance.
2. $MN = ST$	Transitive Property of Equality

LESSON 6-4 (pp. 273–278)
3. See below. **5.** See below. **7.** See below. **9.** See below.
11. See below. **13.** $m\angle 1 = m\angle 2 = 45$ **15.** See below.
17. center: (6, 2); magnitude: 180° **19. a.** 80 **b.** acute

3.

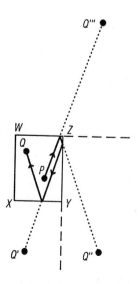

5.

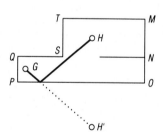

7.

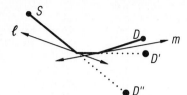

9.

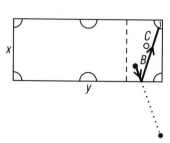

11.

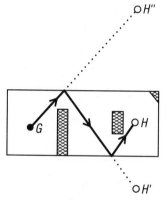

15.

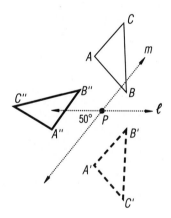

LESSON 6-5 (pp. 279–284)
3. a. $\overline{GH}$ **b.** $\angle HFG$ **c.** $\triangle GHE$ **5.** Symmetric Property of
Congruence **7. a.** $r_n \circ r_p$ **b.** $r_p \circ r_n$ **13.** $m\angle C = m\angle T$ **15.** An
isosceles triangle has two congruent sides. **17. See below.**
19. Yes **21.** maps it onto itself **23. a.** $\overline{AC}$ and $\overline{AD}$ **b.** $\angle ACB$
25. See below. 27. a. 60° **b.** -120° **29. a.** Yes **b.** 30

17. samples:

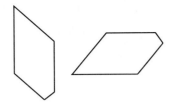

25.

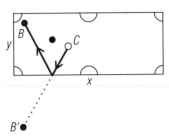

LESSON 6-6 (pp. 285–291)

7. See below. 9. See below. 11. reflection, rotation, translation, glide reflection **13. a.** angle measure, betweenness, collinearity, distance **b.** orientation **15. a. See below. b.** No **17.** Segment Congruence Theorem **19.** The bisector of an angle splits it into two congruent angles. **21. a.** C and I **b.** $\overleftrightarrow{CI}$ **c.** $\triangle CIH$ **d.** $\triangle CIH$ **23. a.** $89 < m\angle T \leq 180$ **b.** Yes

7.

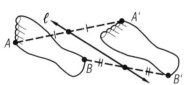

Figure I   Figure II

9. sample:

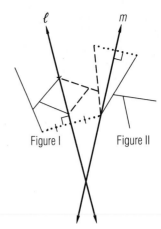

Figure I   Figure II

15. a.

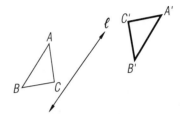

LESSON 6-7 (pp. 292–295)

5. a. $\angle C$ **b.** $\angle IMC$ **c.** $\overline{VT}$ **7.** $\overline{FA}$ **9.** $\angle ETG$ **11. a.** $\triangle ABD \cong \triangle CBD$ **b.** $\overline{AB} \cong \overline{CB}$, $\overline{BD} \cong \overline{BD}$, $\overline{AD} \cong \overline{CD}$; $\angle A \cong \angle C$, $\angle ABD \cong \angle CBD$, $\angle ADB \cong \angle CDB$ **13. a.** $\triangle MNO \cong \triangle PON$ **b.** $\overline{MN} \cong \overline{PO}$, $\overline{MO} \cong \overline{PN}$, $\overline{ON} \cong \overline{NO}$, $\angle M \cong \angle P$, $\angle PNO \cong \angle MON$, $\angle PON \cong \angle MNO$ **15. See below. 17.** translation, rotation, reflection, glide reflection **19. a.** $-\frac{1}{3}$ **b.** 3

21. translation **23.** If a triangle has two congruent sides, then the angles opposite them are congruent. **25.** $(2x, 3y)$

15. samples:

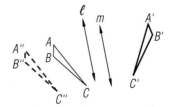

CHAPTER 6 PROGRESS SELF-TEST (pp. 297–298)

1. See below. 2. The composition of two reflections is a rotation, so $r_\ell \circ r_m(\triangle ABC)$ is a rotation; that is choice (b). **3. See below. 4. See below. 5.** The image of $\angle C$ is $\angle H$, and the image of $\angle H$ is $\angle L$. Because reflections preserve angle measure, the angle in $\triangle JKL$ with the same measure as $\angle C$ is $\angle L$. **6.** $\overline{FG}$ is the image of $\overline{AB}$, and the image of $\overline{FG}$ is $\overline{KJ}$. Because reflections preserve length, the segments with the same length as FG are $\overline{AB}$ and $\overline{KJ}$. **7.** $r_m(\triangle ABC) = \triangle FED$, and $r_\ell(\triangle FED) = \triangle HGI$. So $\triangle ABC \cong \triangle FED \cong \triangle HGI$. **8.** According to the CPCF (Corresponding Parts of Congruent Figures) Theorem, if $\triangle ABC \cong \triangle DEF$, then all six pairs of corresponding parts are congruent: $\angle A \cong \angle D$, $\angle B \cong \angle E$, $\angle C \cong \angle F$, $\overline{AB} \cong \overline{DE}$, $\overline{AC} \cong \overline{DF}$, and $\overline{BC} \cong \overline{EF}$. **9.** Five properties preserved by translations are angle measure, betweenness of points, collinearity of points, distances between points, and orientation. **10.** Four kinds of isometries are slides, rotations, reflections, and glide reflections.

11. True. Since reflections are isometries, and isometries preserve congruence, then a series of reflections results in congruent figures. **12. See below. 13.** A hexagon has six sides and six vertices, so V(hexagon) = 6. **14–17. See below.**

1. a.

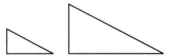

$$r_\ell \circ r_m(\triangle ABC) = r_\ell(\triangle A'B'C')$$
$$= \triangle A''B''C''$$

b. The transformation is a translation, in the direction $\perp$ to ℓ and m, in the direction from m to ℓ, with a distance twice that between ℓ and m.

3.

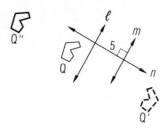

$$r_\ell \circ r_m(Q) = r_\ell(Q')$$
$$= Q''$$

The transformation is a translation, in the direction n, from m to ℓ, with a distance 10, which is twice the distance from m to ℓ.

4.

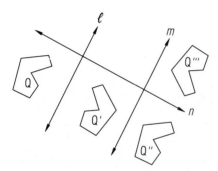

$$r_n \circ r_m \circ r_\ell(Q) = r_n \circ r_m(Q')$$
$$= r_n(Q'')$$
$$= Q'''$$

The transformation is a glide reflection, over the reflecting line n, at a distance twice that from ℓ to m, in the direction from ℓ to m.

12. a.

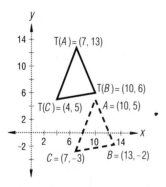

b. The transformation is a translation of 3 units to the left and 8 units up.

14.

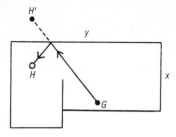

15.

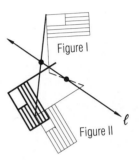

16.

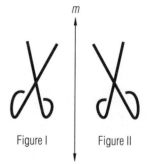

This isometry is a glide reflection: reflection over ℓ followed by a translation parallel to ℓ.

17.

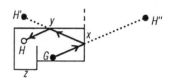

The isometry is a reflection across line m.

The chart below keys the **Progress Self-Test** questions to the objectives in the **Chapter 6 Review** on pages 299–301. This will enable you to locate those **Chapter 6 Review** questions that correspond to questions you missed on the **Progress Self-Test**. The lesson where the material is covered is also indicated in the chart.

Question	1	2	3,4	5	6	7	8	9	10	11
Objective	A	C	B	D	D	B	D	D	C	C
Lesson	6-2	6-3	6-3	6-5	6-7	6-2	6-6	6-5	6-2	6-6

Question	12a	12b	13	14,15	16,17
Objective	G	G	G	F	E
Lesson	6-1	6-2	6-1	6-4	6-6

CHAPTER 6 REVIEW (pp. 299–301)

1. See below. 3. a. See below. b. a translation ⊥ to m and n, in the direction from m to n, with a magnitude twice the distance from m to n. **5. See below. 7.** (a) **9.** ∠B **11.** a rotation with center Q, magnitude 180° **13.** 15°, C **15.** ∠F, ∠H **17.** True **19.** translation, rotation, reflection, glide reflection **21.** *CDAB, KLIJ* **23.** definition of congruence (sufficient condition) **25.** Reflexive Property of Congruence **27.** glide reflection **29.** translation **31.** glide reflection **33. See below. 35. See below. 37. a., b. See below. c.** The transformation stretches the figure by a factor of 2 in the horizontal direction only and then reflects it about the line $y = x$. **39.** 4 **41.** (a)

1. a rotation with center Z and magnitude ≈98°, in the positive direction

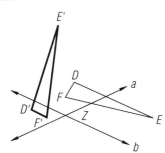

3. a.

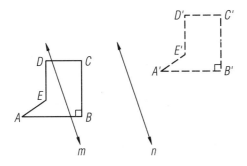

5. sample (two images are possible):

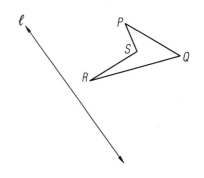

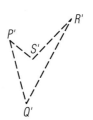

33.

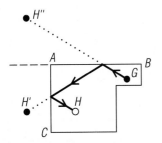

35.

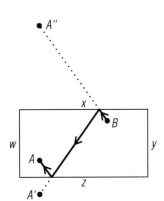

37. a., b.

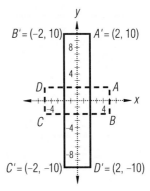

LESSON 7-1 (pp. 302–309)

7–19. See below. 21. translation **23.** The line containing the ends of a kite is a symmetry line for the kite. **25.** greater than 53 cm but less than 129 cm

7. sample:

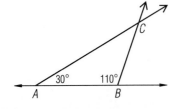

9.

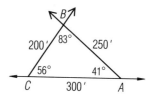

11. a. samples:

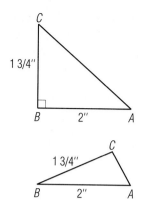

b. No

13. a. samples:

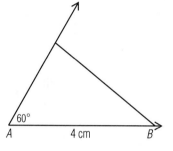

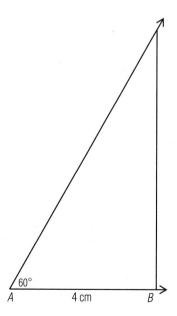

b. No

15. a. samples:

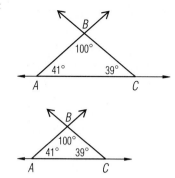

b. No

17. a.

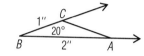

b. Yes

19. a.

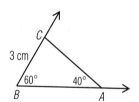

b. Yes

LESSON 7-2 (pp. 310–316)
9. a. Side-Switching Theorem **b.** Side-Switching Theorem
c. △*GFH* **11.** not necessarily congruent **13.** by the ASA
Congruence Theorem, △*OYN* ≅ △*YOX* **15.** by the ASA
Congruence Theorem, △*CGO* ≅ △*IPN* **17. See below. 19.
See below. 21.** because of the ASA Congruence Theorem
23. figure, quadrilateral, kite, rhombus, square

17. a.

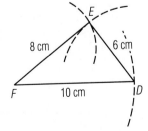

b. Yes, because of the SSS Congruence Theorem

19. a.

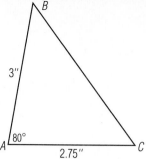

b. Yes, because of the SAS Congruence Theorem

LESSON 7-3 (pp. 317–322)
3. See below. 5. a. Reflexive Property of Congruence **b.** CPCF Theorem **7. See below. 9. See below. 11.a.** True **b.** False **13. See below. 15.** This is not possible since it violates the Triangle Inequality. **17.** $\frac{x}{4}$ **19. See below.**

3. Conclusions	Justifications
1. $\overline{AC} \cong \overline{AC}$	Reflexive Property of Congruence
2. $\triangle ABC \cong \triangle CDA$	SSS Congruence Theorem (step 1 and given)
3. $\angle 2 \cong \angle 4$	CPCF Theorem
4. $\overleftrightarrow{BC} \parallel \overleftrightarrow{AD}$	AIA $= \Rightarrow \parallel$ Lines Theorem

7. Conclusions	Justifications
1. $AB = CD$; $BC = AD$	Given
2. $AC = AC$	Reflexive Property of Congruence
3. $\triangle ABC \cong \triangle CDA$	SSS Congruence Theorem (steps 1 and 2)

9. Conclusions	Justifications
1. $BA = BC$	definition of isosceles triangle (meaning)
2. $AD = DC$	definition of midpoint (meaning)
3. $\overline{BD} \cong \overline{BD}$	Reflexive Property of Congruence
4. $\triangle ABD \cong \triangle CBD$	SSS Congruence Theorem (steps 1, 2, and 3)

13. Conclusions	Justifications
1. $BC = CD$	definition of midpoint (meaning)
2. $\triangle ABC \cong \triangle EDC$	SAS Congruence Theorem (step 1 and given)

19. a. sample:

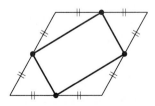

b. Opinions may vary, but diagrams like the one above show a counterexample to the conjecture. (A true conjecture is that the resulting figure is a rectangle.)

LESSON 7-4 (pp. 323–326)
1. a. 8 **b.** $\triangle DAU$ **c.** $\triangle QUD$, $\triangle DAQ$ **3–7. See below.**
9. a. Vertical Angle Theorem **b.** SAS Congruence Theorem (step 1 and given) **c.** CPCF Theorem **d.** Vertical Angle Theorem **e.** Transitive Property of Equality **11.** $\triangle PCA \cong \triangle PCB$ by the SAS Congruence Theorem. So $PA = PB$ by the CPCF Theorem. **13.** True **15.** acute

3. Conclusions	Justifications
1. $\angle H \cong \angle K$, $\angle GJI \cong \angle GIJ$	Isosceles Triangle Theorem
2. $\triangle GHJ \cong \triangle GKI$	AAS Congruence Theorem (step 1 and given)
3. $\angle HGJ \cong \angle KGI$	CPCF Theorem

5. Conclusions	Justifications
1. $\angle A \cong \angle A$	Reflexive Property of Congruence
2. $\triangle AEB \cong \triangle ADC$	ASA Congruence Theorem (given and step 1)
3. $EB = CD$	CPCF Theorem

7. Conclusions	Justifications
1. $RS = RS$	Reflexive Property of Equality
2. $\triangle PRS \cong \triangle QSR$	SSS Congruence Theorem (given and step 1)
3. $m\angle P = m\angle Q$	CPCF Theorem

LESSON 7-5 (pp. 327–332)
1. See below. 3. (c) **5. a.** HL Congruence Theorem **b.** $\triangle ABC \cong \triangle FED$ **7. a.** HL Congruence Theorem **b.** $\triangle ABD \cong \triangle CBD$ **9. See below. 11. a.** definition of a circle (meaning) **b.** definition of a circle (meaning) **c.** SsA Congruence Theorem (steps 1, 2, 3, and given) **13.** Let T be the top of the maypole, M the point on the maypole that is the same height as June's and April's hands, J the position of June's hands, and A the position of April's hands. $\overline{JA}$ is parallel to the ground, since J and A are equal in height (given). So $\overline{JA} \perp \overline{TM}$ by the Perpendicular to Two Parallels Theorem. Since $\overline{TM} \cong \overline{TM}$ (by the Reflexive Property) and $\overline{TJ} \cong \overline{TA}$ (given), $\triangle TJM \cong \triangle TAM$ by the HL Congruence Theorem. So $\overline{JM} = \overline{AM}$ by the CPCF Theorem.

1. samples:

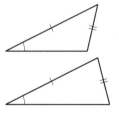

9.

Conclusions	Justifications
1. △WXZ ≅ △VXY	HL Congruence Theorem (given)
2. ∠W ≅ ∠V	CPCF Theorem

15. a.

Conclusions	Justifications
1. AB = AC	given
2. m∠B = m∠C	Isosceles Triangle Theorem
3. △ABD ≅ △ACE	SAS Congruence Theorem (Step 2 and given)
4. $\overline{AD} ≅ \overline{AE}$	CPCF Theorem
5. ∠ADE ≅ ∠AED	Isosceles Triangle Theorem

b. 6. △ADE is isosceles. — definition of isosceles triangle (sufficient condition)

17. a.

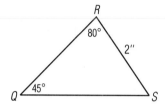

b. The drawings will be congruent because of the AAS Congruence Theorem.

LESSON 7-6 (pp. 333–338)

1. a. definition of parallelogram (meaning) **b.** ∥ Lines ⇒ AIA = Theorem **c.** Reflexive Property of Congruence **d.** ASA Congruence Theorem (steps 2, 4, and 5) **3. a.** $\overline{AB}, \overline{AC}, \overline{CD}, \overline{BD}$ (all are ≅) **b.** ∠A ≅ ∠D, ∠B ≅ ∠C **c.** $\overline{AD}, \overline{BC}$ **7. See below. 9.** $OS = SQ = RS = SP = \frac{x}{2}$ **11–17. See below.**

19. ∠B ≅ ∠X for ASA; $\overline{AC} ≅ \overline{YZ}$ for SAS; ∠C ≅ ∠Z for AAS

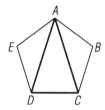

7.

Conclusions	Justifications
1. $\overline{AB} ≅ \overline{AE}$	definition of regular pentagon (meaning)
2. $\overline{BC} ≅ \overline{ED}$	definition of regular pentagon (meaning)
3. ∠B ≅ ∠E	definition of regular pentagon (meaning)
4. △ABC ≅ △AED	SAS Congruence Theorem (steps 1,2,3)
5. $\overline{AC} ≅ \overline{AD}$	CPCF Theorem

11. a. sample:

b. 1440° **c.** 144°

13.

Conclusions	Justifications
1. △AEF ≅ △BDC	HL Congruence Theorem (step 1 and given)
2. ∠F ≅ ∠C	CPCF Theorem

15.

Conclusions	Justifications
1. $\overline{MX} = \overline{NX}$	definition of midpoint (meaning)
2. ∠M ≅ ∠N; ∠MXZ ≅ ∠NXY	Given
3. △MXZ ≅ △NXY	ASA Congruence Theorem (steps 1 and 2)
4. ∠Y ≅ ∠Z	CPCF Theorem

17. a.

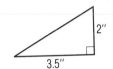

b. Yes, by the SAS Congruence Theorem

LESSON 7-7 (pp. 339–343)

5. Step 6: CPCF Theorem   Step 7: AIA = ⇒ ∥ Lines Theorem **7. See below. 9.** kite, parallelogram **11.** Since the vertical sides of V, W, X, and Y are congruent and parallel, the vertical sides of Z are both congruent and parallel by the transitivity of congruence and parallelism. **13.** If both pairs of opposite sides are congruent, then the figure is a parallelogram, by the Sufficient Conditions for a Parallelogram Theorem. Then both pairs of opposite angles are congruent by the Properties of a Parallelogram Theorem. **15–19. See below.**

7.

Justifications
1. Point-Line-Plane Postulate
2. Reflexive Property of Equality
3. ∥ lines ⇒ AIA = Theorem
4. SAS Congruence Theorem (steps 2,3, and given)
5. CPCF Theorem
6. AIA = ⇒ ∥ Lines Theorem
7. definition of parallelogram (sufficient condition)

15. Use rectangle ABCD.

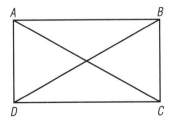

Conclusions	Justifications
1. *ABCD* is a parallelogram.	Quadrilateral Hierarchy Theorem
2. $\overline{AD} \cong \overline{BC}$	Properties of a Parallelogram Theorem
3. $\angle ADC \cong \angle BCD$	Both are right angles (def. of rect.).
4. $\overline{DC} \cong \overline{DC}$	Reflexive Property of Congruence
5. $\triangle ADC \cong \triangle BCD$	SAS Congruence Theorem (parts 2, 3, and 4)
6. $\overline{AC} \cong \overline{BD}$	CPCF Theorem

17. a.

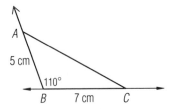

b. Yes **c.** SAS Congruence Theorem

19. a. sample:

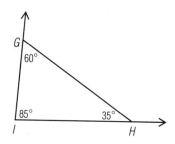

b. No **c.** Triangles with longer or smaller sides could still have these same angle measures.

LESSON 7-8 (pp. 344–347)
3. (c) **5. a.** Yes **b.** trigonometry **7.** $QT = TS$ and $RT = RT$, but m$\angle QTR = 75$ while m$\angle STR = 105$. So, applying the SAS Inequality Theorem in $\triangle QTR$ and $\triangle STR$, $RS > QR$.
9. 5 cm **11. See below. 13.** can't conclude congruence **15. See below. 17.** rotation

11. Use quadrilateral *ABCD*:

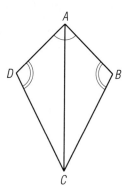

Conclusions	Justifications
1. $\overline{AC} \cong \overline{AC}$	Reflexive Property of Congruence
2. $\angle D \cong \angle B$	Given
3. $\angle DAC \cong \angle BAC$	Definition of bisector
4. $\triangle DAC \cong \triangle BAC$	AAS Congruence Theorem (parts 1, 2, 3)
5. $\overline{AD} \cong \overline{AB}; \overline{DC} \cong \overline{BC}$	CPCF Theorem
6. *ABCD* is a kite.	Definition of kite (sufficient condition)

15. a.

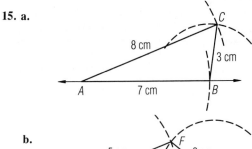

b.

c. m$\angle A$ = m$\angle D \approx 22$; m$\angle C \approx 30$, m$\angle F \approx 150$, so $\angle C$ and $\angle F$ are supplementary.

CHAPTER 7 PROGRESS SELF-TEST (p. 349)
1.a. Since $\angle 1 \cong \angle 3$ and $\angle 2 \cong \angle 4$ (given) and $\overline{AC} \cong \overline{AC}$ (Reflexive Property of Congruence), $\triangle ABC \cong \triangle CDA$. **b.** The justification for the congruence is the ASA Congruence Theorem. **2.a.** Since it is given that M is the midpoint of $\overline{AC}$, then $AM = MC$ by the definition of midpoint (meaning). **b.** $\angle AMB \cong \angle CMD$ because of the Vertical Angle Theorem. **c.** Since it is given that $\overline{AB} \parallel \overline{CD}$, then $\angle MBA \cong \angle MDC$ because $\parallel$ lines $\Rightarrow$ AIA =. **d.** $\triangle MBA \cong \triangle MDC$ by the AAS Congruence Theorem (from parts **a, b, c**). **3. See below. 4. See below. 5.** Each of the following conditions is sufficient for a quadrilateral to be a parallelogram: both pairs of opposite sides are parallel; both pairs of opposite angles are congruent; both pairs of opposite sides are congruent; one pair of opposite sides are parallel and congruent; two pairs of consecutive

angles are supplementary. **6.** If, in two triangles, two pairs of sides are congruent, then for the angles contained by those sides, the side opposite the greater angle has the greater length. (Exact wordings may differ.) **7–10. See below. 11.** In $\triangle ADB$ and $\triangle ADC$, $\overline{AD} \cong \overline{AD}$ (by the Reflexive Property of Equality), $\overline{BD} \cong \overline{CD}$ (given), and $\angle ADB \cong \angle ADC$ (they are both right angles). So $\triangle ADB \cong \triangle ADC$ by the SAS Congruence Theorem, and $AB = AC$ by the CPCF Theorem.

3. a.

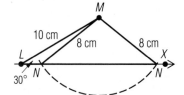

b-c. There are two possible triangles, so it is not necessarily so that everyone else's triangle will be congruent to yours.

4. a.

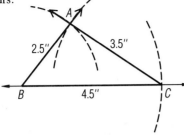

b-c. Given the lengths of 3 sides (and after checking that those three lengths can be the lengths of sides of a triangle), every triangle having sides with those lengths must be congruent, because of the SSS Congruence Theorem.

7.

	Conclusions	Justifications
a.	1. $\overline{QP} = \overline{QP}$	Reflexive Property of Congruence
	2. $\triangle QPS \cong \triangle QPT$	HL Congruence Theorem (step 1 and given)
	3. $QS = QT$	CPCF Theorem
b.	4. $\angle SQP \cong \angle TQP$	CPCF Theorem
	5. $\overrightarrow{QP}$ bisects $\angle SQT$.	Definition of angle bisector (sufficient condition)

8. If $\overline{AB}$ and $\overline{CD}$ are both parallel and congruent, then $ABDC$ is a parallelogram by the Sufficient Conditions for a Parallelogram Theorem, part d.

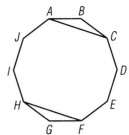

9.

	Conclusions	Justifications
	1. $\overline{AB} \cong \overline{FG}$, $\overline{BC} \cong \overline{GH}$, $\angle B \cong \angle G$	Definition of regular polygon (meaning)
	2. $\triangle ABC \cong \triangle FGH$	SAS Congruence Theorem (step 1)
	3. $AC = FH$	CPCF Theorem

10.

	Conclusions	Justifications
	1. $\angle W \cong \angle W$	Reflexive Property of Congruence
	2. $\triangle WYU \cong \triangle WXV$	AAS Congruence Theorem
	3. $\overline{WU} \cong \overline{WV}$	CPCP Theorem
	4. $\triangle WUV$ is isosceles.	Definition of isosceles triangle (sufficient condition)

The chart below keys the **Progress Self-Test** questions to the objectives in the **Chapter 7 Review** on pages 350–353. This will enable you to locate those **Chapter 6 Review** questions that correspond to questions you missed on the **Progress Self-Test**. The lesson where the material is covered is also indicated in the chart.

Question	1	2	3a	3bc	4a	4bc	5	6
Objective	B	C	A	A	A	A	E	Voc
Lesson	7-2	7-3	7-1	7-2	7-1	7-2	7-7	7-8

Question	7	8	9	10	11			
Objective	D	E	D	D	F			
Lesson	7-5	7-7	7-3	7-4	7-2			

CHAPTER 7 REVIEW (pp. 350–353)

1. a. See below. **b.** Yes **c.** SSS Congruence Theorem **3. a.** See below. **b.** Yes **c.** ASA Congruence Theorem **5. a.** See below. **b.** Yes **c.** HL Congruence Theorem **7. a.** See below. **b.** No **c.** There are two noncongruent triangles that fit the given information. **9. a.** See below. **b.** Yes **c.** SsA Congruence Theorem **11. a.** AAS Congruence Theorem **b.** $\triangle MOP \cong \triangle PNM$ **13. a.** SAS Congruence Theorem **b.** $\triangle GFE \cong \triangle GIH$ **15. a.** ASA Congruence Theorem **b.** $\triangle NOP \cong \triangle ORQ$ **17.** See below. **19.** See below. **21. a.** Reflexive Property of Congruence **b.** SSS Congruence Theorem (given and step 1) **c.** CPCF Theorem **23.** See below. **25.** See below. **27.** congruent **29.** bisect each other **31.** See below. **33.** $\triangle XBD \cong \triangle XBA \cong \triangle XBC$ by use of the AAS Congruence Theorem, so $DB = AB = CB$. **35.** SAS Inequality Theorem **37.** parallelogram

1. a.

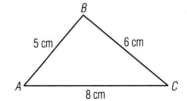

3. a.

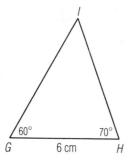

5. a.

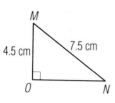

7. a.

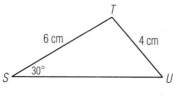

9. a.

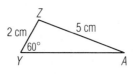

17.

Conclusions	Justifications
1. $\overline{AC} \cong \overline{AC}$	Reflexive Property of Congruence
2. $\triangle ADC \cong \triangle ABC$	HL Congruence Theorem (step 1 and given)

19.

Conclusions	Justifications
1. $\angle YUX \cong \angle WUV$	definition of angle bisector (meaning)
2. $\triangle UVW \cong \triangle UXY$	AAS Congruence Theorem (step 1 and given)

23.

Conclusions	Justifications
1. $\angle KJM \cong KJL$	definition of angle bisector (meaning)
2. $\overline{JK} \cong \overline{JK}$	Reflexive Property of Congruence
3. $\triangle KJM \cong \triangle KJL$	SAS Congruence (steps 1, 2, and given)
4. $\angle M \cong \angle L$	CPCF Theorem

25.

Conclusions	Justifications
1. $\overline{BC} \cong \overline{BC}$	Reflexive Property of Congruence
2. $\triangle ABC \cong \triangle DCB$	AAS Congruence Theorem (step 1 and given)
3. $\overline{AC} \cong \overline{DB}$	CPCF Theorem

31.

Conclusions	Justifications
1. $BD = BD$	Reflexive Property of Equality
2. $m\angle ABD = m\angle CDB$	// Lines $\Rightarrow$ AIA = Theorem
3. $\triangle ABD \cong \triangle CDB$	AAS Congruence Theorem (steps 1,2, and given)
4. $AB = DC$	CPCF Theorem
5. $ABCD$ is a parallelogram.	Sufficient Conditions for a Parallelogram Theorem

---

LESSON 8-1 (pp. 354–361)
3. a. 1199 miles **b.** 23 hours, 1 minute **5.** 8 miles **7.** $4t$ **9.**
$7(x + 1)$ or $7x + 7$ **11.** 0.9 meters **13.** 1.25 ft **15. a.** $8s +$
$18m + 2\ell$ **b.** 1300 meters **c.** 1200 meters **17. See below.**

19. (d) **21.** Yes **23. a.** $\frac{2}{2.54} \approx .79$ inch **25.** 1.5 **27.** Sample
counterexample: If $x = -1$, then $(x + 1)(2x - 3) = 0$, but $2x^2$
$- 3 = -1$. **29. a.** ≈ 60 mph **b.** ≈ 51 mph **c.** Sample: the
route from Dallas to Atoka has more stops or slower speed
limits.

17.

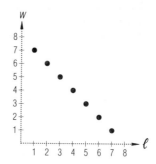

LESSON 8-2 (pp. 362–366)
11. the roughly triangular region determined by connecting the noses of the fish **(See below for art.) 13.** (c) **15.** 2.6 **17.** 108
19. See below. 21. $\sqrt{27} \approx 5.2$, $-\sqrt{27} \approx -5.2$

11.

19.

Conclusions	Justifications
1. $\overline{BD} \cong \overline{BD}$	Reflexive Property of Congruence
2. $\triangle BAD \cong \triangle DCB$	ASA Congruence Theorem (Step 1 and given)
3. $AB = CD$	CPCF Theorem

LESSON 8-3 (pp. 367–372)
1. a. 27 units² **b.** 75 units² **3. a.** 9200 miles **b.** 4,800,000 sq miles **7. See below. 9. a.** 100 units² **b.** k^2 units² **11.** $\frac{1}{2}$ yard
13. a. 288 sq in. **b.** 2 sq ft **c.** 144 **15.** $3w^2$ units² **17. See below. 19.** 4, -4 **21.** (b) **23.** 10, 15, 20 units

7. $45 \times 43 = 1935$
    $1320 + 120 + 345 + 150 = 1935$

17.

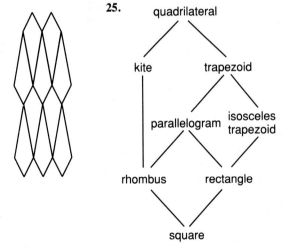

25.

quadrilateral

kite   trapezoid

parallelogram   isosceles trapezoid

rhombus   rectangle

square

LESSON 8-4 (pp. 373–377)
7. $\approx$ 4,245 dots/in.² **9.** $\approx$14.25 km² **11.** about $\frac{1}{3}$ or about .34 mi² **13.** farm in U.S. **15.** $(x - y)(x + y)$ **17.** 56 linear units **19. See below. 21.** x = -4 or 4 **23.** (a)

19.

Conclusions	Justifications
1. $\triangle PQA \cong \triangle DRA$	AAS Congruence Theorem (given)
2. $\overline{PA} \cong \overline{DA}$	CPCF Theorem
3. $\triangle PAD$ is isosceles.	definition of isosceles triangle (suff. cond.)

LESSON 8-5 (pp. 378–383)
7. a. 24 units² **b.** 60 units² **c.** 84 units² **9.** 12 units² **11. a.** 9 units² **b.** 15 units² **c.** 24 units² **13. See below. 15.** $\frac{48}{7} \approx$ 6.86 units **17.** 23 units² **19. a.** 288,000 sq miles, answers may vary ± 25,000 sq miles **b.** 266,400 sq miles, answers may vary ± 10,000 sq miles **21.** 124 units² **23.** $3\sqrt{5}$

13. a. Shown below is the construction of the altitude from Z.

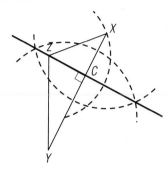

b. $XY \approx 8.1$ cm: $CZ \approx 2.3$ cm; area ≈ 9.3 cm² (Measurements are based on Students' Edition text.)

LESSON 8-6 (pp. 384–389)
3. a. bases: $\overline{EF}$ and $\overline{GH}$; altitude: $\overline{IF}$ **b.** 6720 units² **9.** 57 units² **13.** 16,800 units² **15.** $\frac{1}{2}bc$ units² **17.** (d) **19.** Place a grid over the fabric. Add the number of squares entirely inside the figure to half the number of squares partially covering the figure, and multiply the result by the area of each square.
21. 12x **23.** $ac + ad + bc + bd$

LESSON 8-7 (pp. 390–395)
3. a. $\frac{1}{2}ab$ **b.** $(a + b)^2$ or $a^2 + 2ab + b^2$ **c.** $a^2 + b^2$ **d.** $\sqrt{a^2 + b^2}$ **5.** (c) **7.** $\sqrt{18} = 3\sqrt{2} \approx 4.24$ units **9.** 12 units **11.** 24″ **13.** Yes **15.** No **17.** Yes **19.** Yes **21.** 54″ **23.** 74 meters **25.** $\frac{1400}{90} \approx 15.56$ minutes **27.** 16,320 sq ft **29.** 4.5 units² **31.** 1 unit and 12 units

LESSON 8-8 (pp. 396–401)
1. $\overparen{RS}$, $\overparen{SP}$, $\overparen{PQ}$, $\overparen{QR}$, $\overparen{QS}$ **3. a.** 180° **b.** 180° **c.** 150° **5.** central **13. a.** 8π units **b.** 25.1 units **15. a.** $\frac{15\pi}{6}$ units **b.** 2.62 units **17. a.** 8640° **b.** 940$\pi \approx$ 3016 ft **19.** 20 units **21.** $A = \frac{1}{2}h(b_1 + b_2)$ **23.** $p = 4s$ **25.** $\frac{(n - 2) \cdot 180}{n}$ **27.** (b) **29.** $\approx$20 mph

LESSON 8-9 (pp. 402–406)
1. a. 10 units **b.** $10\pi \approx 31.42$ units **c.** $100\pi \approx 314.2$ units² **3.** 4900π sq in. **5.** 15,394 in.² **7. a.** $3600\pi \approx 11,300$ sq meters **b.** 377 meters **9. a.** $64 - 8\pi \approx 38.87$ units² **b.** $24 + 4\pi \approx 36.57$ units **11. a.** $\frac{1}{16}$ **b.** $\frac{15}{16}$ **13. a.** 72° **b.** $6\pi \approx 18.8$ units **15.** $90\pi \approx 282.74$ units **17. a.** $18x^2$ units² **b.** $(13 + \sqrt{97})x \approx 22.8x$ units **19. a.** 24,200 sq miles, answers may vary ± 3500 sq miles **b.** 22,300 sq miles, answers may vary ± 900 sq miles **21.** m∠E = 130, m∠D = m∠F = 50 **23. a.** .01 **b.** 36 **c.** 1760

1. See below. 2. Using formula $A = \ell \times w$, Area $= 200\text{m}^2$ and length $= 25\text{m}$; $200 = 25 \times w$, then $w = 8\text{m}$. **3.** In a regular polygon, all sides have the same length. So if a regular hexagon has perimeter q, then each of its 6 sides has length one-sixth of the perimeter, or $\frac{q}{6}$. **4.** Using the formula $A = \frac{1}{2}bh$ with $b = 210$ units and $h = 80$ units, $A = \frac{1}{2}(210)(80) = (105)(80) = 8400$ units^2. **5.** Using the formula $A = bh$ with $b = 40$ units and $h = 11$ units, $A = (40)(11) = 440$ units^2. **6.** Using the formula $A = \frac{1}{2}h(b_1 + b_2)$ with height h and bases a and c, $A = \frac{1}{2}h(a + c)$. **7. See below. 8. See below. 9.** The perimeter of the square is $p = 4s = 4(10) = 40$ units. The circumference of the circle is $C = 2\pi r = 2\pi(5) = 10\pi$. The difference is $p - C = 40 - 10\pi \approx 8.6$ units. **10.** The area of the circle is $A = \pi r^2 = \pi(5)^2 = 25\pi$. The area of the square is $A = s^2 = 10^2 = 100$. The probability that a point inside the square is also inside the circle is $\frac{25\pi}{100} = \frac{\pi}{4} \approx .785$. **11.** The entire circumference is $C = 2\pi r = 2\pi 20 = 40\pi$. $\overset{\frown}{CD}$ represents $45°$ or $\frac{1}{8}$ of the circle, so the length of $\overset{\frown}{CD}$ is $\frac{40\pi}{8} = 5\pi \approx 15.7$ units. **12.** $\text{m}\overset{\frown}{CBD} = 360° - \text{m}\overset{\frown}{CD}$. Since $\overset{\frown}{CD}$ is $\frac{1}{8}$ of the circle, or $45°$, then $\text{m}\overset{\frown}{CBD} = 360° - 45° = 315°$. **13.** There seem to be 00 unit squares inside the lake and 00 unit squares on the lake's boundary, and each unit square represents $10^2 = 100$ miles^2. Adding half the number of boundary squares to the number of squares inside the lake, and multiplying by 100, the area of the lake can be approximated as 000 square miles. (Answers may vary.) **14. See below. 15.** Using the formula $A = \pi r^2$ with $r = 80$ miles, $A = \pi(80)^2 = 6400\pi \approx 20,100$ miles^2. **16.** In yards, 9 ft by 15 ft is 3 yds by 5 yds; that product is 15 yds.^{2} **17.** If the perimeter of a square is 2640 ft, then each side has length $\frac{2640}{4} = 660$ ft. The area of a square with side 660 ft is $660^2 = 435,600$ ft^2. **18. See below. 19.a.** $11^2 + 60^2 = 121 + 3600 = 3721 = 61^2$. Since $a^2 + b^2 = c^2$, the three lengths (11, 60, 61) can be the lengths of sides of a right triangle. **b.** The statement, if $a^2 + b^2 = c^2$, then a, b, and c can be the lengths of sides of a right triangle, is the Pythagorean Converse Theorem. **20. See below. 21. See below.**

1. sample:

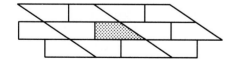

7.

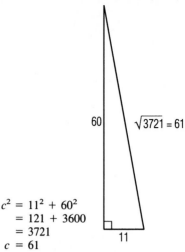

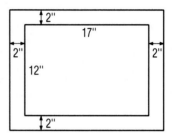

$c^2 = 11^2 + 60^2$
$\quad = 121 + 3600$
$\quad = 3721$
$c = 61$

The perimeter of the triangle is $60 + 11 + 61 = 132$ units.

8.

2"

17"

2"   2"

12"

2"

The outside dimensions are $12 + 4$ and $17 + 4$, or $16''$ and $21''$. The outside perimeter is $2(16 + 21) = 2(37) = 74''$.

14.

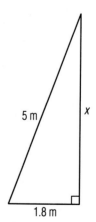

5 m x

1.8 m

$x^2 + 1.8^2 = 5^2$
$\quad\quad x^2 = 25 - 3.24$
$\quad\quad\quad = 21.76$
$\quad\quad x \approx 4.66476$
$\quad\quad\quad \approx 4.7$ meters

18.

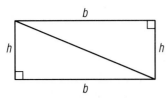

The area of a rectangle with height h and base b is $A = bh$. Two right triangles, each with base b and height h, make up that rectangle, so a formula for the area of either right triangle is $A = \frac{1}{2}bh$.

20.

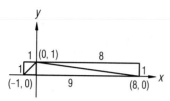

The horizontal base has length 9, and the height is 1, so the area of the triangle is $A = \frac{1}{2}bh = \frac{1}{2}(9)(1) = 4.5$ units^2

21.

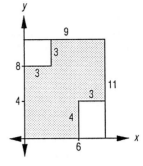

The area of the shaded octagon is the area of the large rectangle ($\ell = 9$, $w = 11$, $A = \ell \times w = 99$), less the area of the small rectangle at the upper left ($\ell = 3$, $w = 3$, $A = \ell \times w = 9$), then less the area of the small rectangle at the lower right ($\ell = 3$, $w = 4$, $A = \ell \times w = 12$). So the area of the octagon is $99 - 9 - 12 = 78$ units^2.

The chart below keys the **Progress Self-Test** questions to the objectives in the **Chapter 8 Review** on pages 410–413. This will enable you to locate those **Chapter 8 Review** questions that correspond to questions you missed on the **Progress Self-Test**. The lesson where the material is covered is also indicated in the chart.

Question	1	2	3	4	5–6	7	8	9	10	11–12
Objective	A	E	C	D	D	G	J	F	M	F
Lesson	8-2	8-3	8-1	8-5	8-6	8-7	8-1	8-8	8-9	8-8

Question	13	14	15	16–17	18	19	20	21
Objective	B	K	M	L	I	H	N	N
Lesson	8-4	8-7	8-9	8-3	8-5	8-7	8-5	8-3

CHAPTER 8 REVIEW (pp. 410-413)
1. See below. 3. See below. 5. 900,000 ± 2500 sq ft **7.** 32 units **9.** 235 meters **11.** 10 cm **13.** 12.5 units and 25 units **15.** 625 sq ft **17.** $288x^2$ units^2 **19.** 84 units^2 **21.** 20 mm **23.** 3.5s units **25. a.** $C = 20\pi$ units, $A = 100\pi$ units^2 **b.** $C \approx 62.83$ units, $A \approx 314.16$ units^2 **27.** 24 units **29. a.** 20° **b.** 160° **c.** 200° **31.** $\sqrt{5} \approx 2.24$ units **33.** $13x + x\sqrt{85} \approx 22.2x$ units **35.** 75 cm **37.** Yes **39.** No **41.** Area of trapezoid: $A = \frac{1}{2}h(b_1 + b_2)$, but in a parallelogram $b_1 = b_2 = b$, so $A = \frac{1}{2}h(b + b) = \frac{1}{2}h \cdot 2b = hb$. **43.** (b) **45.** $8s^2$ units^2 **47.** 80 cm **49.** 37 feet **51.** ≈ 8.7 ft **53.** 44,100 m^2 **55.** 780,000 sq ft **57.** $\frac{1}{9}$ or $11.\overline{1}\%$ **59.** 1885 feet **61.** $\frac{100}{\pi} \cong 32$ ft **63.** 2025 units^2 **65.** 32 units^2

1. sample:

3. sample:

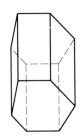

LESSON 9-1 (pp. 414–420)

11. a. always (unless the center of gravity is not above the triangular region determined by the legs) **b.** when the ends of the legs are coplanar **c.** Through three noncollinear points, there is exactly one plane. (part f) **13.** by measuring the length of a segment perpendicular to both walls with one endpoint on each wall **15.** sample: the floor and a wall **17.** sample: the ceiling and intersecting line of the south and west walls **19. See below. 21. a.** 90° **b.** 30° **23.** A polygon is the union of three or more segments in the same plane such that each segment intersects exactly two others, one at each of its endpoints. **25.** A figure is a rectangle if and only if it is a quadrilateral with four right angles. **27.** $x = 67.5$, $y = 112.5$

19. sample:

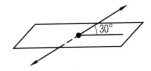

23. sample:

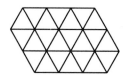

LESSON 9-2 (pp. 421–426)

3. a. edge **b.** six **c.** *ABCD* and *GHEF,* or *ABHG* and *DCEF,* or *ADFG* and *BCEH* **d.** 12. **e.** samples: $\overline{AD}$ and $\overline{HE}$, $\overline{AG}$ and $\overline{CE}$ **5–7. See below. 9.** box **11.** solid right prism (often hexagonal) **13. See below. 15. a.** 15 units **b.** $36\pi \approx 113.1$ square units **17. See below. 19.** intersecting planes **21.** an infinite number of planes **23. See below. 25.** $2w(l + h)$ **27.** $\pi r(r + 2h)$

5. sample:

7. sample:

13. sample:

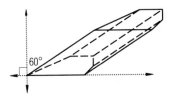

LESSON 9-3 (pp. 427–431)

1. a. *ABDE* **b.** *C* **c.** $\overline{BC}$ or $\overline{AC}$ or $\overline{DC}$ or $\overline{EC}$ **d.** △*BCD* or △*ACB* or △*ACE* or △*DCE* **3. a.** right cone **b.** $\overleftrightarrow{MO}$ **c.** $\overline{MN}$ or $\overline{ML}$ **d.** *M* **e.** ⊙*O* **f.** *MO* **g.** *ML* or *MN* **5.** hexagonal pyramid **7. See below. 9. a.** 10 units **b.** $\sqrt{116} \approx 10.77$ units **11. See below. 13. See below. 15. a.** above the vertex **b.** left of front in the plane of the base **c.** in front of a corner in the plane of the base **17.** In a right cylinder, the direction of the translation is perpendicular to the base; in an oblique cylinder it is not. **19. a.** Triangle-Sum Theorem **b.** definition of perpendicular (sufficient condition) **c.** definition of right triangle (sufficient condition) **d.** Pythagorean Theorem **21.** Larger has six times the area of smaller. **23.** $h(l + w)$

7. sample:

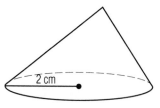

11. a.

b. $\sqrt{130} \approx 11.4$ cm **c.** $9\pi \approx 28.3$ cm^2

13. sample:

LESSON 9-4 (pp. 433–438)

5. the intersection of a sphere and a plane not containing the center of the sphere **7. See below. 9.** the plane sections of two congruent right conical surfaces, with the same axis, joined at their vertices: circle, ellipse, parabola, and hyperbola **13–21. See below. 23. a.** 10 **b.** 10 **c.** $\sqrt{200} \approx$ 14.14 units **25. a.** the point Q such that ℓ is the perpendicular bisector of $\overline{PQ}$ **b.** A plane figure F is a reflection-symmetric figure if and only if there is a line m such that $r_m(\text{F}) = \text{F}$.

7. a. sample:

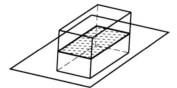

b. They are congruent.

13. a. sample:

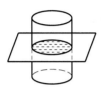

b. sample:

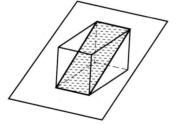

c. rectangles

15. a. sample:

b. sample:

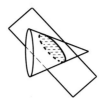

c. circle and ellipse

17.

21. sample:

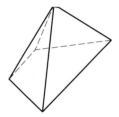

LESSON 9-5 (pp. 439–443)

1. a. Yes **b.** infinitely many **3. a.** Yes **b.** infinitely many **5. a.** Yes **b.** infinitely many **11.** 9 **13. See below. 15. See below. 17.** solid right cylinder **19. a.** a square pyramid **b.** *FOUR* **c.** Z **d.** $\overline{ZF}, \overline{ZO}, \overline{ZU}, \overline{ZR}$ **e.** $\triangle ZRF, \triangle ZRU, \triangle ZUO, \triangle ZOF, FOUR$ **21. See below. 23.** $x(xy - 4)$

13.

15. a. sample:

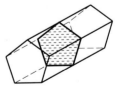

b. sample:

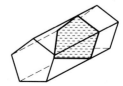

c. Part (a) is a pentagon congruent to the bases. Part (b) is a pentagon.

21. a.

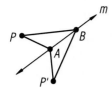

b. kite

LESSON 9-6 (pp. 444–448)

3–9. See below. 11. ≈ 28 ft **13.** 9 **15.** 6 units **17.** regular heptagonal prism **19. a.** $\sqrt{11} \approx 3.32$ units **b.** $\sqrt{22} \approx 4.69$ units **21. See below. 23.** $\pi(r^2 + 2rh - h)$

3.

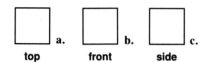

top   **a.**   front   **b.**   side   **c.**

5.

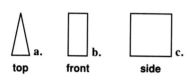

top   **a.**   front   **b.**   side   **c.**

7. a.

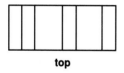

top

b.

front

c.

side

9. sample:

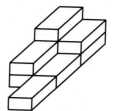

21.

Conclusions	Justifications
1. $\overline{AB} \cong \overline{CD}$	Properties of a Parallelogram Theorem
2. $\overline{AB} \parallel \overline{CD}$	definition of parallelogram (meaning)
3. $\angle ABQ \cong \angle CDQ$, $\angle QAB \cong \angle QCD$	$\parallel$ Lines $\Rightarrow$ AIA = Theorem
4. $\triangle AQB \cong \triangle CQD$	ASA Congruence Theorem (steps 1 and 3)

LESSON 9-7 (pp. 449–455)

5. a. back **b.** up **c.** left **7. See below. 9. a.** cone without a base **b.** Answers may vary slightly. **11. See below. 13. a.** 9 **b.** 16 **c.** 9 **15. See below. 17. a.** 3 **b.** 3 **c.** middle, left section **19. a.** Yes **b.** one **21. a.** 4 units **b.** 3 units **c.** 12 units^2 **23.** definition of a rhombus (sufficient condition)

7.

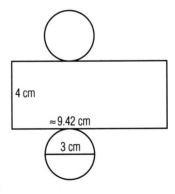

4 cm

≈9.42 cm

3 cm

11. sample:

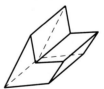

15. sample:

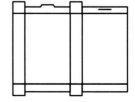

3. 124 **5.** See below. **9.** See below. **11.** See below. **13.** surface, polyhedron, prism, right prism, box **15.** See below.

17. See below. **19. a.** $\sqrt{136} \approx 11.7$ units **b.** $\sqrt{1800} \approx 42.4$ square units **21.** 23

5. sample:

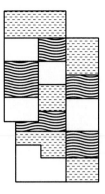

9. sample:

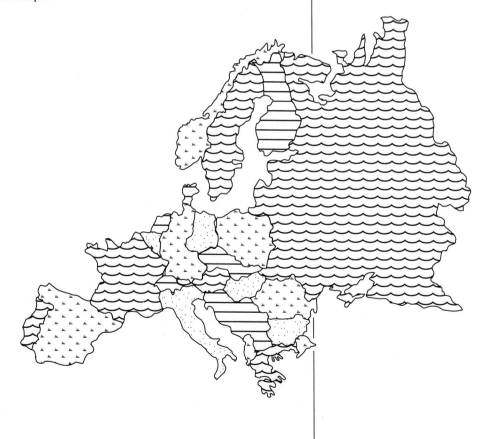

11. sample:

15. sample:

17. sample:

The chart below keys the **Progress Self-Test** questions to the objectives in the **Chapter 9 Review** on pages 462–465. This will enable you to locate those **Chapter 9 Review** questions that correspond to questions you missed on the **Progress Self-Test**. The lesson where the material is covered is also indicated in the chart.

Question	1–5	6	7–8	9	10	11–12	13	14	15
Objective	G	A	A	B	J	G	D	C	B
Lesson	9-2	9-1	9-2	9-4	9-5	9-3	9-7	9-6	9-4

Question	16	17	18	19	20	21		22	23
Objective	D	E	E	H	I	K		F	L
Lesson	9-7	9-3	9-2	9-7	9-2	(prev. course)		9-6	9-8

CHAPTER 9 PROGRESS SELF-TEST (p. 461)

1. The figure is a prism, since it has parallel bases. Moreover, the bases are triangles, and are ⊥ to the planes of the sides. So the figure is a right triangular prism. **2.** The edges are $\overline{AD}$, $\overline{BE}$, $\overline{CF}$, $\overline{AB}$, $\overline{BC}$, $\overline{AC}$, $\overline{DE}$, $\overline{EF}$, and $\overline{DF}$; there are 9 edges.
3. The faces are *ABC, DEF, ABED, BCFE,* and *ACFD;* there are 5 faces. **4.** The vertices are *A, B, C, D, E,* and *F;* there are 6 vertices. **5.** A solid is the union of a surface and all the points in the interior of the surface. **6–10. See below.**
11. a. There are four lateral edges; $\overline{GI}$, $\overline{GJ}$, $\overline{GK}$, and $\overline{GH}$.
b. The vertex is point *G.* **12–16. See below. 17.a.** The height of the cone is represented by segment $\overline{AD}$. **b.** The base of the cone is a circle with radius *OB* = 10 cm. The area of the base is $A = \pi r^2 = \pi(10)^2 = 100\pi \approx 314.16$ cm^2.
18.a. *FIHG* is a rectangle with height 22″. The length is the leg of a right triangle with hypotenuse 9″ and leg 4″, or $\sqrt{9^2 - 4^2} = \sqrt{81 - 16} = \sqrt{65}$ inches. So Area(*FIHG*) = $22\sqrt{65} \approx 177.4$ inches^2. **b.** The area of right triangle *EFG* is one-half the product of the legs, or $\frac{1}{2}(4)(\sqrt{65}) = 2\sqrt{65} \approx 16.12$ inches^2. **19.** A box is a hexahedron, which is a prism, which is a polyhedron. A box is not a pyramid; that is choice (b). **20. See below. 21.** $\pi r^2 + 2\pi rh = \pi r(r + 2h)$
22–23. See below.

6. sample:

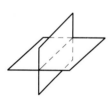

7. sample:

8. sample:

9. sample:

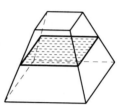

10. view from above:

There are 4 symmetry planes. Each is ⊥ to the bases of the pyramid. Two planes bisect opposite pairs of angles of the bases, and two planes bisect opposite pairs of sides of the bases.

12.

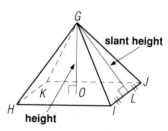

GO is the height of the pyramid and *GL* is the slant height.

13.

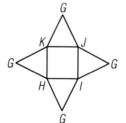

14.

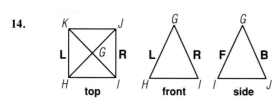

15.

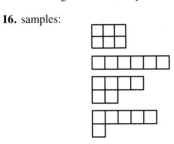

The intersection of sphere O and plane m containing O is called a great circle of sphere O.

16. samples:

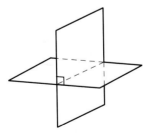

20.

The figure is a solid, right, square prism.

22. sample:

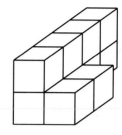

a. The building is two stories tall.
b. It is 4 sections from front to back.
c. The tallest parts are all the sections on the left side.

23. sample:

CHAPTER 9 REVIEW (pp. 462–465)
1–13. See below. **15.** (c) and (d) only **17.** See below.
19. a. ≈62.4 square units **b.** 8 units **21. a.** $9\pi \approx 28.3$ square cm **b.** $\sqrt{32} \approx 5.66$ cm **23.** See below. **25. a.** 2 **b.** 3
c. back section **27. a.** box, rectangular parallelipiped, or hexahedron **b.** twelve **c.** sample: $\overline{BC}$ and $\overline{HE}$ **29. a.** 7
b. 13 **c.** 2 **d.** octahedron **31.** Yes; any face could be the base.
33. solid pentagonal prism **35.** sphere **37.** rectangular solid
39. a. Yes **b.** infinitely many **41.** See below. **43.** $\ell w(h + 2)$
45. $\pi r^2(4 + r)$ **47.** in a plane or on a sphere **49.** See below.

1. sample:

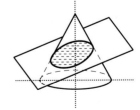

3. sample:

5.

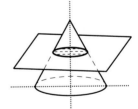

7. a. sample:

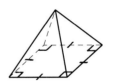

b. sample:

c. Part a is a circle; part b is an ellipse.

9. a. sample:

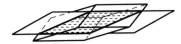

b. sample:

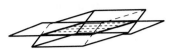

c. part a is a parallelogram; part b is a parallelogram.

11. a.

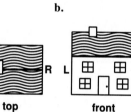

top

b.

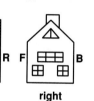

front

c.

F [ ] B

right

13. a.

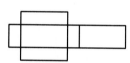

L [ ] R

top

b.

L [ ] R

front

c.

F [ ] B

right

17. sample:

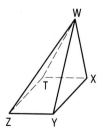

23. a.

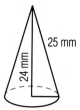

25 mm
24 mm

b. $49\pi \approx 153.9$ square mm

41.

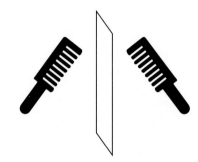

49. sample:

LESSON 10-1 (pp. 466–472)
3. 1040 cm² **5. a.** cube **b.** 100 square units **c.** 150 square
units **7. a.** right cylinder **b.** $15\pi \approx 47$ square units **c.** 19.5π
≈ 61 square units **9. a.** $B = \pi r^2$ **b.** L.A. $= 2\pi rh$ **c.** S.A. $=$
$2\pi rh + 2\pi r^2$, or $2\pi r(h + r)$ **11.** L.A. ≈ 154 in.²; S.A. $\approx$
174 in.² **13.** surface area **15.** surface area **17.** 598 cm² **19.**
$6s^2$ **21.** Exactly: $2 \cdot \frac{4375\pi}{45} \approx 611$ gallons; about 610–620
gallons are needed. **23.** the point in the interior of the polygon
that is equidistant from all of its vertices **25.** $\frac{8}{27}$

LESSON 10-2 (pp. 473–477)
1. See below. **7.** sides of the base **9.** the center of the base
11. a. ≈ 587.4 ft **b.** $\approx 887,000$ ft² **13.** (a) **15.** See below.
17. See below. **19. a.** ≈ 47.5 cm² **b.** ≈ 164 cm² **21.** See
below. **23.** See below.

1. sample:

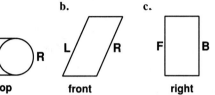

15. a.

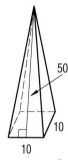

50
10
10

b. 1000 units² **c.** 1100 units²

17. a.

17
14

b. $119\pi \approx 374$ units²
c. $168\pi \approx 528$ units²

23. a.

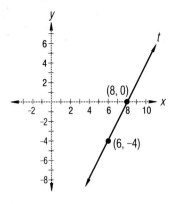

b. 2 **c.** $-\frac{1}{2}$

LESSON 10-3 (pp. 478–482)

1. 176,400 cm³ **3.** No **7.** $\sqrt[3]{50}$ **9. a.** adds 84 in.² **b.** no change **11.** 12 inches **13.** 7.57 **15. a.** 3 **b.** 9 **c.** 27 **17. See below. 19. a.** $156\pi \approx 490$ in.² **b.** 4 square feet **21. a.** polyhedron **b.** radius **c.** vertex

17. a.

b. $48\pi \approx 150.8$ units²

LESSON 10-4 (pp. 483–487)

7. $2x^2 + 21x + 27$ **9.** $a^3 + 6a^2 + 11a + 6$ **11.** multiplied by 3 **13.** The volume is increased by 6 times the product of the width and the height. **15. a.** Bag X holds about twice as much as bag Y. **b.** Bag X should cost about twice as much as bag Y. **17.** $y^2 - x^2$ **19.** $a^2 + b^2 + c^2 + 2ab + 2ac + 2bc$ **21.** 1.46 **23.** about 1.8 cm³ **25.** $\pm\sqrt{\frac{10}{\pi}} \approx \pm 1.8$

LESSON 10-5 (pp. 488–493)

3. (d) **7.** $225\pi \approx 707$ cubic units **9.** 500 m³ **11.** 210 ft³ **13. See below. 15.** 189 m³ **17.** The plane sections parallel to but not including the base will not be of the same area. **19.** doubles the volume **21.** $4x^2 + 3xy + 28x - 10y^2 - 35y$ **23.** 20 cm³ **25.** 108 square units **27. See below.**

13. Answers may vary; samples are shown here. The volume of each is 252π cubic units.

27.

Conclusions	Justifications
1. $\overline{CE} \cong \overline{CE}$	Reflexive Property of Congruence
2. $\angle FEC \cong \angle DCE$	∥ Lines $\Rightarrow$ AIA = Theorem
3. $\triangle FEC \cong \triangle DCE$	SAS Congruence Theorem (steps 1,2,and given)
4. $\angle FCE \cong \angle DEC$	CPCF Theorem

LESSON 10-6 (pp. 494–498)

7. L.A. $= 2\pi rh$ **11. a.** L.A. $= \frac{1}{2}\ell(2\pi r) = \pi r\ell$ **b.** S.A. $= \pi r\ell + \pi r^2 = \pi r(\ell + r)$ **13. a.** $\sqrt{(18)(9)(6)(3)} = 54$ units² **b.** The triangle is a right triangle, so Area $= \frac{1}{2}hb = \frac{1}{2}(9)(12) = 54$ units². **15.** $\sqrt{600 \cdot 200 \cdot 200 \cdot 200} \approx 69{,}282$ units² **17.** $39{,}366\pi \approx 123{,}672$ cubic units **19.** The volume is decreased by $8a^2$ cubic units. **21. See below. 23.** $-\frac{b}{a}$

21. a.

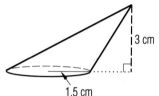

b. $16 + 2.25\pi \approx 23$ cm²

LESSON 10-7 (pp. 499–504)

3. 114 units³ **5.** $\frac{32\pi}{3} \approx 33.5$ ft³ **7.** 56 units³ **9.** $\sqrt{\frac{24}{\pi}} \approx 2.8$ cm **11.** $\approx 116{,}000{,}000$ ft³ **13.** The volume is multiplied by 49. **15. a.** 6 units **b.** $128\pi \approx 402$ units³ **17.** L.A. $= 4(\frac{1}{2}\ell s) = 2\ell s$ **19.** $(x + z)(y + 8) = xy + 8x + zy + 8z$ **21.** 15

LESSON 10-8 (pp. 505–509)

1. a. $20\pi \approx 62.8$ units² **b.** $20\pi \approx 62.8$ units² **7.** 4 m **9. a.** 10.7, or almost 11 days **b.** 4.3, or just over 4 days **11.** $\frac{500\pi}{3} \approx 524$ units³ **13.** Additive Property **15.** boxes, cylinders, prisms **17. a.** True **b.** False **19. a.** It is multiplied by 9. **b.** It is multiplied by 27. **21. a.** 64 units² **b.** 16 **c.** 8 **d.** none **e.** none **23.** x

LESSON 10-9 (pp. 510–513)

5. a. 10,000 π sq in. **b.** 31,416 sq in. **7.** $\approx 1.84\%$ **9.** $\approx 75\%$ of the surface area of the sphere yields a cost of about $9200. **11. a.** The moon has about $\frac{1}{16}$ the surface area of the earth. **b.** The moon has about $\frac{1}{64}$ the volume of the earth. **13.** They are the same; both are $4\pi r^2$. **15. a. See below. b.** $\frac{62.5\pi}{3} \approx 65.45$ cubic cm **17.** The wider, shorter jar holds twice as much jam. **19.** 22.2 units **21. See below.**

21. $A' = (6, 3)$; $B' = (-3, -3)$; $C' = (0, -9)$

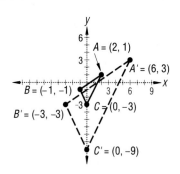

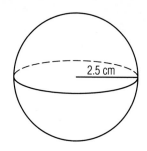

15. a.

b. $\frac{62.5\pi}{3} \approx 65.45$ cubic cm

CHAPTER 10 PROGRESS SELF-TEST (p. 515)

1-2. See below. 3. Using $V = \frac{4}{3}\pi r^3$ with $r = \frac{1}{2}(620) = 310$ mi, $V = \frac{4}{3}\pi(310)^3 = \frac{119,164,000\pi}{3} \approx 124,788,249 \approx 1.25 \times 10^8$ mi^3. **4. See below. 5.** The figure is a right cylinder with radius $3''$ and height $20''$. Using $V = Bh$, $V = \pi(3^2)(20) = 180\pi \approx 565.5$ in.^{3} **6.** Using $V = \frac{1}{3}Bh = \frac{1}{3}\pi r^2 h$ with $r = 8$ and $h = 15$, $V = \frac{1}{3}\pi(8)^2(15) = 320\pi \approx 1005.3$ units^3. **7-10. See below. 11.** Using S.A. $= 4\pi r^2$ with S.A. $= 100\pi$, $100\pi = 4\pi r^2$ so $25 = r^2$ and $r = 5$ units. **12.** $\sqrt[3]{400} = 400$ $\boxed{y^x}$ 3 $\boxed{1/x}$ $\boxed{=}$ $7.368063 \approx 7$. **13.** Cavalieri's Principle: Let I and II be two solids included between parallel planes. If every plane P parallel to the given planes intersects I and II in sections with the same area, then Volume (I) = Volume (II). **14. See below. 15.** The ratio of surface areas is the square of the ratio of similitude, so Jupiter's surface area is 11^2 or 121 times as large as the earth's. **16.** S.A. $=$ L.A. $+ B$ is the formula for a figure with one base, so it is the formula for pyramids and cones. **17.** L.A. $= ph$ is the formula for right cylindric solids, so it is the formula for prisms (including boxes and cubes) and right cylinders. **18.** The volume can be expressed as a product of its three dimensions or as a sum of the volumes of the eight small boxes. So $V = (x + 1)(y + 2)(z + 6) = xyz + yz + 2z + 2xz + 6xy + 6y + 12 + 12x$.

1. a. sample

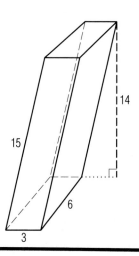

The formula for the volume of a prism is $V = Bh$.

b. Using $V = Bh$ with $B = (6)(3) = 18$ and $h = 14$, $V = (18)(14) = 252$ cm^3.

2. a.

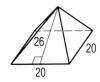

The formula for the lateral area of a regular prism is L.A. $= \frac{1}{2}p\ell$.

b. Using L.A. $= \frac{1}{2}p\ell$ with $p = 4(20) = 80$ and $\ell = 26$, L.A. $= \frac{1}{2}(80)(26) = 1040$ units^2.

4.

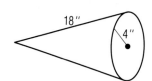

Using L.A. $= \frac{1}{2}C\ell$, with $C = 2\pi r = 8\pi$ and $\ell = 18$, L.A. $= \frac{1}{2}(8\pi)(18) = 72\pi \approx 226$ in^2.

7. Using L.A. $= ph$ with $p = 32$ and $h = 30$, L.A. $= (32)(30) = 960$ units^2.

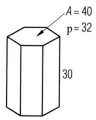

8. Using $V = Bh$ with $B = 40$ and $h = 30$, $V = (40)(30) = 1200$ units^3.

9.

Using $V = \ell wh$, $400 = \ell(5)(10)$ so $400 = 50\ell$
and $\ell = 8$ cm.

10. Using the figure from Question 9,
S.A. $= 2B + ph$
$= 2(5 \times 8) + 2(5 + 8)(10)$
$= 80 + 260$
$= 340$ cm²

14.

By the Pyramid-Cone Volume Formula, the volume of the pyramid is one-third the volume of the prism.

The chart below keys the **Progress Self-Test** questions to the objectives in the **Chapter 10 Review** on pages 516–519. This will enable you to locate those **Chapter 10 Review** questions that correspond to questions you missed on the **Progress Self-Test**. The lesson where the material is covered is also indicated in the chart.

Question	1a	1b	2a	2b	3	4	5	6	7	8
Objective	A	B	A	C	J	I	J	C	B	B
Lesson	10-1	10-5	10-2	10-2	10-8	10-2	10-5	10-7	10-1	10-5

Question	9	10	11	12	13	14	15	16-17	18
Objective	B	B	D	E	H	H	G	F	K
Lesson	10-5	10-1	10-9	10-3	10-5	10-7	10-4	10-6	10-4

CHAPTER 10 REVIEW (pp. 516–519)
1. See below. 3. See below. 5. a. $72\pi \approx 226$ units² **b.** $104\pi \approx 327$ units² **c.** $144\pi \approx 452$ units³ **7.** 720 units³ **9.** 150 units² **11.** S.A. $= \pi(3.5)\sqrt{112.25} + \pi(3.5)^2 \approx 155$ units²; Volume $= 10 \cdot (3.5)^2 \cdot \frac{\pi}{3} \approx 128.3$ units³ **13. a.** 50 units **b.** 8000 units² **c.** 14,400 units² **15.** 200 units² **17.** S.A. $= 20,736\pi \approx 65,144$ units²; Volume $= 497,644\pi \approx 1,563,458$ units³ **19.** 6 units **21.** 30 **23.** 5.04 **25.** $s^2 + 2s\ell$ **27. a.** It is multiplied by 9. **b.** It is multiplied by 27. **29.** The new volume is 4 times as large. **31.** Plane sections at any level other than at the bases will not have the same area.
33. a. True **b.** False **35.** 8 ft² **37.** $200\sqrt{5000} \approx 14,142$ cubits² **39.** $300\pi \approx 942.5$ cm³ **41.** $\frac{500,000}{3} \approx 167,000$ cubits³

43. See below. 45. $(2x + 7)(x + 12) = 2x^2 + 7x + 24x + 84 = 2x^2 + 31x + 84$

1.

3.

43. $20xy + 15x + 8y + 6$

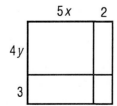

LESSON 11-1 (pp. 520–526)
7–13. See below. 15. (5, -2) **17. a.** $200\pi \approx 628.3$ sq ft
b. ≈ 1257 bushels **19.** Pythagorean Theorem **21. a.** 450 **b.**
450

7.

Conclusions	Justification
1. slope of $\overline{XY} = -\frac{1}{2}$ slope of $\overline{XZ} = 2$	definition of slope (meaning)
2. The product of their slopes is -1, so $\overline{XY} \perp \overline{XZ}$.	Perpendicular Lines and Slopes Theorem
3. $\triangle XYZ$ is a right triangle.	definition of right triangle (sufficient condition)

9.

Conclusions	Justifications
1. slope of $\overline{EF} = 1$ slope of $\overline{FG} = -1$ slope of $\overline{GH} = 1$ slope of $\overline{EH} = -1$	definition of slope (meaning)
2. The product of their slopes is -1, so $\overline{EF} \perp \overline{FG}$, $\overline{FG} \perp \overline{GH}$, $\overline{GH} \perp \overline{EH}$, and $\overline{EH} \perp \overline{EF}$.	Perpendicular Lines and Slopes Theorem
3. $EFGH$ is a rectangle.	definition of a rectangle (sufficient condition)

11.

Conclusions	Justifications
1. slope of $\overline{WX} = 0$ slope of $\overline{XY} = \frac{c}{b}$ slope of $\overline{YZ} = 0$ slope of $\overline{ZW} = \frac{c}{b}$	definition of slope (meaning)
2. $\overline{WX} \parallel \overline{YZ}$, $\overline{XY} \parallel \overline{ZW}$	Parallel Lines and Slopes Theorem
3. $WXYZ$ is a parallelogram.	definition of parallelogram (sufficient condition)

13. a.

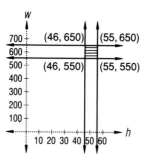

b. The graph is the rectangular region with vertices (46, 550), (55, 550), (55, 650), and (46, 650).

LESSON 11-2 (pp. 527–531)
1. 11 **3.** $\sqrt{146} \approx 12.08$ **5.** $\sqrt{52} \approx 7.21$ **7.** $\sqrt{65} \approx 8.06$
miles **9. See below. 11. a.** False; sample counterexample: Let
$x_1 = 4$; $x_2 = 1$. Then $|x_2 - x_1| = 3$, but $x_2 - x_1 = -3$.
b. True **c.** True **d.** True **13.** $BC = \sqrt{145}$ and $BA = \sqrt{145}$.

Thus, by the definition of circle (sufficient condition), C and A
are on the same circle with center B. **15. See below. 17.**
(12.25, 13) **19.** The area of the triangle is one-half the area of
the parallelogram. **21.** 90

9.

Conclusions	Justifications
1. $AB = \sqrt{20}$ $BC = \sqrt{20}$ $CD = \sqrt{212}$ $AD = \sqrt{212}$	Distance Formula
2. $AB = BC$, $CD = AD$	Transitive Property of Equality
3. $ABCD$ is a kite.	definition of kite (sufficient condition)

15.

Conclusion	Justifications
1. slope of $\overline{PQ} = -\frac{1}{2}$ slope of $\overline{QR} = 2$	definition of slope (meaning)
2. $\overline{PQ} \perp \overline{QR}$	Perpendicular Lines and Slopes Theorem
3. $\triangle PQR$ is a right triangle.	definition of right triangle (sufficient condition)

LESSON 11-3 (pp. 532–536)
1. a. Yes. **b.** Yes. **c.** No. **d.** Yes. **3. See below. 9. a.**
(-6, -2) **b.** 1 **c.** sample: (-6, -3) **11–13. See below. 15.** $41x$
17. See below. 19. They are collinear. **21. See below.**

3. a. $\sqrt{(x-7)^2 + (y-1)^2}$ **b.** $(x-7)^2 + (y-1)^2 = 25$

c.

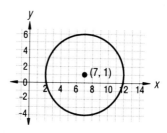

d. samples: (2, 1), (12, 1), (7, 6), (7, -4)

11. (0, 5), (3, 4), (4, 3) (5, 0), (4, -3), (3, -4), (0, -5),
(-3, -4), (-4, -3), (-5, 0) (-4, 3), (-3, 4)

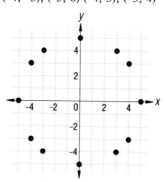

13.

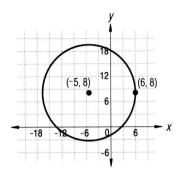

17.

Conclusions	Justifications
1. slope of $\overline{TQ} = \frac{9b}{5a}$	definition of slope (meaning)
slope of $\overline{SR} = \frac{9b}{5a}$	
2. $\overline{TQ} \parallel \overline{SR}$	Parallel Lines and Slopes Theorem
3. $QRST$ is a trapezoid.	definition of trapezoid (sufficient condition)

21. sample:

LESSON 11-4 (pp. 537–543)

1. $\frac{350}{3} = 116\frac{2}{3}$ **3.** 1634 **5.** (5.5, 5) **7. a.** (5, -6) **b.** The distance from (12, -4) to (5, -6) = $\sqrt{53}$. The distance from (-2, -8) to (5, -6) = $\sqrt{53}$. The slope between (12, -4) and (5, -6) = $\frac{-2}{-7} = \frac{2}{7}$. The slope between (-2, -8) and (5, -6) = $\frac{2}{7}$. **9. See below. 11.** $\frac{a + c - 2a}{2}$ or $\frac{c - a}{2}$ **13.** $\frac{2d - (b + d)}{2c - (a + c)}$ or $\frac{d - b}{c - a}$ **15.** $-\frac{23}{5}$ = -4.6 **17.** 46 or 54, depending on which piece was cut from each end. **19. a.** (0, 0) **b.** $\sqrt{75} \approx 8.66$ units **c.** sample: $(\sqrt{75}, 0)$ **d.** 75π **21.** (3, -5) **23. a.** 2560 cm³ **b.** ≈1249.6 cm² **25. a.** x **b.** $2x$ **c.** $x\sqrt{5}$

9. a. $L = (6.5, 0)$, $M = (8, 6)$, $N = (1.5, 6)$

b.

Conclusions	Justifications
1. slope of $\overline{LM} = 4$	definition of slope (meaning)
slope of $\overline{DE} = 4$	
2. $\overline{LM} \parallel \overline{DE}$	Parallel Lines and Slopes Theorem

c.

Conclusions	Justifications
1. slope of $\overline{MN} = 0$	definition of slope (meaning)
slope of $\overline{EF} = 0$	
2. $\overline{MN} \parallel \overline{EF}$	Parallel Lines and Slopes Theorem

d.

Conclusions	Justifications
1. $MN = 6.5$	Distance Formula
$EF = 13$	
2. Since $6.5 = \frac{1}{2}(13)$, $MN = \frac{1}{2}EF$.	Substitution

LESSON 11-5 (pp. 544–549)
1. $AL = AN = BC = 6$ **5. See below 7. See below 9.** $(a^2 + b^2)$, 4, $a^2 + b^2$ **11. See below 13.** 30 units **15.** $DC = 20$, $EC = RT = 40$, $YD = 29$, $EY = RY = 21$, $ER = TC = 42$ **17.** (3.2, 3) **19. a.** 13 **b.** $-\frac{12}{5}$ = -2.4 **c.** (8.5, 27) **21.** $(x + 2)^2 + y^2 = 25$

5. sample:

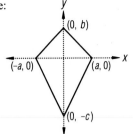

7. sample:

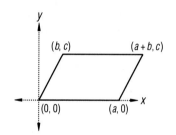

11. samples:

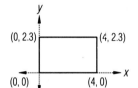

LESSON 11-6 (pp. 550–556)
3. See below. 5. $\sqrt{227} \approx 15.07$ units **7.** (4, -2, -1) **9. See below. 11.** $\sqrt{149} + \sqrt{338} + \sqrt{275} \approx 47.17$ **13.** $\sqrt{2025} = 45$ inches **15.** (0, 0), (12, 0) and (0, 16) or (0, 0), (0, 12) and (16, 0) **17. See below. 19. a.** (14, 5) **b.** $\sqrt{109} \approx 10.44$ units **c.** True **21.** (5.4, 6)

3.

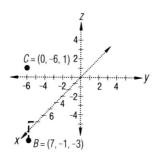

$C = (0, -6, 1)$

$B = (7, -1, -3)$

9. a.

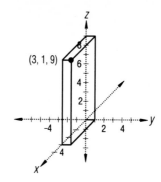

$(3, 1, 9)$

b. 27 units^3

17.

Conclusions	Justifications
1. $\overline{PL} \parallel \overline{MN}$	Midpoint Connector Theorem
2. $\angle QLP \cong \angle QNM$	$\parallel$ lines $\Rightarrow$ corr. $\angle$s $=$

CHAPTER 11 PROGRESS SELF-TEST (p. 558)

1. $\overline{FD}$ connects the midpoints of $\overline{BC}$ and $\overline{AC}$, so $\overline{FD} \parallel \overline{AB}$ and $FD = \frac{1}{2}AB$ by the Midpoint Connector Theorem. $EB = \frac{1}{2}AB$ by the definition of midpoint (meaning), so $FD = EB$ by the Transitive Property of Equality. Then $EBDF$ is a parallelogram by the Sufficient Conditions for a Parallelogram Theorem, part d. **2.** If $AB = 11$ and $BC = 22.3$, then $AE = EB = 5.5$ and $BD = DC = 11.15$ by the definition of midpoint (meaning), and $FD = 5.5$ and $ED = 11.15$ by the Midpoint Connector Theorem (while the lengths $AF = FC = ED$ and $AC = 2AF$ are not known, a restriction is that $11.15 - 5.5 = 5.65 < AC < 11.15 + 5.5 = 16.65$.) **3. See below. 4.** The coordinates of the center of gravity are the means of the x- and y-coordinates: $(\frac{-5 + 6 + 9 + 6 + -8}{5}, \frac{4 + 4 + 0 + -4 + -4}{5}) = (\frac{8}{5}, \frac{0}{5}) =$ $(1.6, 0)$. **5. a. b.** Comparing $(x + 1)^2 + (y - 9)^2 = 25$ with the general equation $(x - h)^2 + (y - k)^2 = r^2$, where (h, k) is the center and r is the radius, the center is $(-1, 9)$ and the radius is 5. **c.** Four points on the circle can be found by moving 5 units from the center; those four points are $(-6, 9)$, $(4, 9)$, $(-1, 14)$, and $(-1, 4)$. **6–7. See below. 8.** E is the midpoint of $\overline{HR}$; its coordinates are $(\frac{6 + 16}{2}, \frac{8 + 8}{2}) = (\frac{22}{2}, \frac{16}{2}) =$ $(11, 8)$. I is the midpoint of $\overline{RB}$; its coordinates are $(\frac{10 + 16}{2}, \frac{0 + 8}{2}) = (\frac{26}{2}, \frac{8}{2}) = (13, 4)$. O is the midpoint of MB; its coordinates are $(\frac{0 + 10}{2}, \frac{0 + 0}{2}) = (5, 0)$. U is the midpoint of $\overline{MH}$; its coordinates are $(\frac{0 + 6}{2}, \frac{0 + 8}{2}) = (3, 4)$. **9.** Here is one proof (of many possible) that $EIOU$ is a rectangle: First, $EI = UO$ and $UE = OI$ (by drawing $\overline{HB}$ and $\overline{MR}$, and using the Midpoint Connector Theorem). So $EIOU$ is a parallelogram by the Sufficient Conditions for a Parallelogram Theorem. The slope of $\overline{UO}$ is $\frac{y_2 - y_1}{x_2 - x_1} = \frac{0 - 4}{5 - 3} = \frac{-4}{2} = -2$ and the slope of $\overline{OI}$ is $\frac{y_2 - y_1}{x_2 - x_1} = \frac{4 - 0}{13 - 5} = \frac{4}{8} = \frac{1}{2}$. Then $\overline{UO} \perp \overline{OI}$ by the Perpendicular Lines and Slopes Theorem, so $EIOU$ is a rectangle by the definition of rectangle (sufficient condition).

10. See below. 11. For $P = (3, -1, 8)$ and $Q = (-4, 9, 0)$,

$\overline{PQ} = \sqrt{(x_2 - x_1)^2 + (y_2 - y_1)^2 + (z_2 - z_1)^2} =$

$\sqrt{(-4 - 3)^2 + (9 - -1)^2 + (0 - 8)^2} =$

$\sqrt{(-7)^2 + (10)^2 + (-8)^2} = \sqrt{49 + 100 + 64} = \sqrt{213} \approx$

14.59 units. **12.** Using the formula $(x - h)^2 + (y - k)^2 + (z - j)^2 = r^2$ with $(h, k, j) = (0, -19, 4)$ and $r = 6$, the equation is $(x - 0)^2 + (y - -19)^2 + (z - 4)^2 = 6^2$ or $x^2 + (y + 19)^2 + (z - 4)^2 = 36$. **13. See below. 14.** The midpoint of $\overline{WY}$ is $(\frac{0 + (2a + 2b)}{2}, \frac{0 + (2c)}{2}) = (a + b, c)$, and the midpoint of $\overline{XZ}$ is $(\frac{2b + 2a}{2}, \frac{2c + 0}{2}) = (a + b, c)$. So $\overline{WY}$ and $\overline{XZ}$ have the same midpoint.

3.

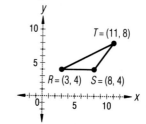

$T = (11, 8)$

$R = (3, 4)$ $S = (8, 4)$

$RS = |3 - 8| = |-5| = 5$

$ST = \sqrt{(x_2 - x_1)^2 + (y_2 - y_1)^2}$

$\qquad = \sqrt{(11 - 8)^2 + (8 - 4)^2}$

$\qquad = \sqrt{3^2 + 4^2}$

$\qquad = 5$

$RT = \sqrt{(x_2 - x_1)^2 + (y_2 - y_1)^2}$

$\qquad = \sqrt{(11 - 3)^2 + (8 - 4)^2}$

$\qquad = \sqrt{8^2 + 4^2}$

$\qquad = \sqrt{64 + 16}$

$\qquad = \sqrt{80}$

The perimeter is $5 + 5 + \sqrt{80} = 10 + \sqrt{80} \approx 18.94$ units.

6.

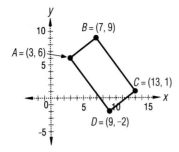

The slope of $\overline{AB} = \frac{y_2 - y_1}{x_2 - x_1} = \frac{9 - 6}{7 - 3} = \frac{3}{4}$.

The slope of $\overline{BC} = \frac{y_2 - y_1}{x_2 - x_1} = \frac{1 - 9}{13 - 7} = \frac{-8}{6}$.
$$= \frac{4}{-3}.$$

The slope of $\overline{CD} = \frac{y_2 - y_1}{x_2 - x_1} = \frac{-2 - 1}{9 - 13} = \frac{-3}{-4}$.

The slope of $\overline{DA} = \frac{y_2 - y_1}{x_2 - x_1} = \frac{6 - -2}{3 - 9} = \frac{8}{-6}$.
$$= \frac{4}{-3}.$$

Since opposite sides are parallel (by the Parallel Lines and Slope Theorem), $ABCD$ is a parallelogram. Since adjacent sides are $\perp$ (by the Perpendicular Lines and Slopes Theorem), $ABCD$ is a rectangle. The answer is choice (a).

7. Place Selkirk at $(0, 0)$. Then $G = (-12, 60)$ and $C = (39, -36)$.

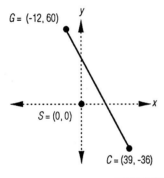

The distance GC $= \sqrt{(x_2 - x_1)^2 + (y_2 - y_1)^2} =$
$\sqrt{(39 - -12)^2 + (-36 - 60)^2} = \sqrt{51^2 + (-96)^2} =$
$\sqrt{2601 + 9216} = \sqrt{11817} \approx 108.7$ miles.

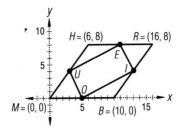

10.

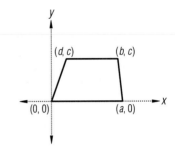

13. $2x - 3y = -8$.
$4x - 5y = 20$
Multiply the first equation by -2 to eliminate the x-variable:
$-4x + 6y = -16$
$\underline{4x - 5y = 20}$
$y = 4$
$2x - 3(4) = 8$
$2x - 12 = 8$
$2x = 20$
$x = 10$
The solution is $(10, 4)$.

The chart below keys the **Progress Self-Test** questions to the objectives in the **Chapter 11 Review** on pages 559-561. This will enable you to locate those **Chapter 11 Review** questions that correspond to questions you missed on the **Progress Self-Test**. The lesson where the material is covered is also indicated in the chart.

Question	1, 2	3	4	5	6	7
Objective	C	F	D	G	A	E
Lesson	11-5	11-2	11-4	11-3	11-2	11-2
Question	**8**	**9**	**10**	**11, 12**	**13**	**14**
Objective	H	A	I	J	K	B
Lesson	11-4	11-1	11-5	11-6	11-1	11-4

CHAPTER 11 REVIEW (pp. 559-561)

1. $AB = \sqrt{145}$; $AC = \sqrt{145}$. Since $AB = AC$, $\triangle ABC$ is isosceles by the definition of an isosceles triangle (sufficient condition). **3.** trapezoid **5.** Let the midpoint of $\overline{PQ}$ be $K = (0, 2b)$; of $\overline{QR}$ be $L = (2a, 0)$; of $\overline{RS}$ be $M = (0, -2b)$; of $\overline{PS}$ be $N = (-2a, 0)$. Then $KL = \sqrt{4a^2 + 4b^2}$; $LM = \sqrt{4a^2 + 4b^2}$; $MN = \sqrt{4a^2 + 4b^2}$; and $NK = \sqrt{4a^2 + 4b^2}$. So $KL = LM = MN = NK$. **7.** slope of $\overline{WY} = \frac{s - 0}{s - 0} = \frac{s}{s} = 1$; slope of $\overline{XZ} = \frac{s - 0}{0 - s} = \frac{s}{s} = -1$. Since $1 \cdot -1 = -1$, $\overline{WY} \perp \overline{XZ}$ by the Perpendicular Lines and Slopes Theorem. **9.** $WX = 41$, $VX = 82$, $VZ = 80$ **11.** Applying the Midpoint Connector Theorem to $\triangle BCD$, $\overline{EF} \parallel \overline{BD}$. Thus $BDEF$ is a trapezoid by the definition of trapezoid (sufficient condition). **13.** $(0, -1.2)$ **15.** at its midpoint **17.** $\sqrt{146} \approx 12.1$ miles **19.** 28 inches **21.** $\sqrt{136} \approx 11.66$ units **23.** $10 + \sqrt{90} \approx 19.49$ units **25.** $(x - 8)^2 + (y + 1)^2 = 225$ **27. a.** $(6, -3)$ **b.** 13 **c.** sample: $(19, -3)$ **29.** See below. **31.** $(4.5, 0)$ **33.** $\frac{30}{55} = \frac{6}{11}$ **35.** (a, b), $(a, -b)$, $(-a, -b)$, $(-a, b)$ **37.** $(25, 5)$ **39.** See below. **41.** $(x - 4)^2 + (y + 3)^2 + z^2 = 100$ **43.** $(4, -3)$ **45.** $(7, 29)$

29.

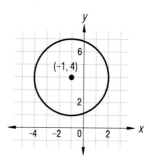

39. a.

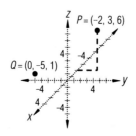

b. $(-1, -1, 3.5)$
c. $\sqrt{93} \approx 9.64$ units

LESSON 12-1 (pp. 562–568)

3. $BC = \sqrt{(-15 - 0)^2 + (-6 - 3)^2} = 3\sqrt{34}$; $B'C' = \sqrt{(-10 - 0)^2 + (-4 - 2)^2} = 2\sqrt{34} = \frac{2}{3}BC$. **5.** See below. **7.** $OA = \sqrt{(-9 - 0)^2 + (15 - 0)^2} = \sqrt{306} = 3\sqrt{34}$; $OA' = \sqrt{(-6 - 0)^2 + (10 - 0)^2} = \sqrt{136} = 2\sqrt{34}$; $AA' = \sqrt{(-9 - -6)^2 + (15 - 10)^2} = \sqrt{34}$. Since $OA' + AA' = OA$, then A' is between O and A. **9. a.** (x, y) **b.** S_1 is the identity size change transformation. **11. a.** $P' = (-15, 60, 20)$ **b.** $Q' = (10, -40, 0)$ **c.** $QP = \sqrt{(2 - -3)^2 + (-8 - 12)^2 + (0 - 4)^2} = \sqrt{441} = 21$; $Q'P' = \sqrt{(10 - -15)^2 + (-40 - 60)^2 + (0 - 20)^2} = \sqrt{11025} = 105 = 5QP$. **13.** If a figure is determined by certain points, then its reflection image is the corresponding figure determined by the reflection images of those points. **15.** $x = 13.5$ **17.** $AB = 36$

5. a.

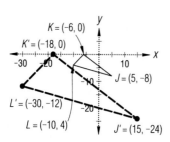

b. The sides of $\triangle J'K'L'$ are parallel to and 3 times the length of the corresponding sides of $\triangle JKL$. Each preimage-image pair is collinear with the origin.

LESSON 12-2 (pp. 569–574)

3. See below. **5.** 6 **11.** $\frac{3}{5}$ **13.** $\frac{3}{4}$ **15–19.** See below. **21.** 1200' **23. a.** 63,360 **b.** 1,000,000

3.

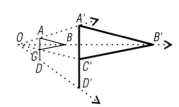

15. $k \approx \frac{3}{4}$

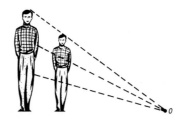

17.

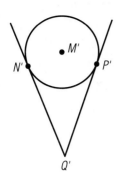

19. $A' = (0, -12)$, $B' = (-39, 1)$, $C' = (21, 33)$

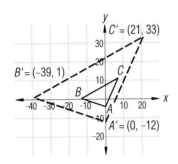

LESSON 12-3 (pp. 575-580)
1. Divide the length of the image segment by the length of the preimage segment. **3.** False **7.** They are parallel. **9.** $TXJ = 73$ **11. a.** 2.5 **b.** 15 **c.** 12 **13–15.** See below. **17.** $AC = \frac{24}{7} \approx 3.43$; $OD \approx 7.117$; $CD \approx 1.017$; $OB = 7$ **19.** $.00001 = 10^{-5}$ **21.** $\sqrt{306} \approx 17.5$ ft **23.** $k = \frac{900}{7} \approx 128.57$ **25.** $t = -11$

13. $k = \frac{5}{6}$

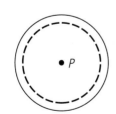

15. $k = 4$.

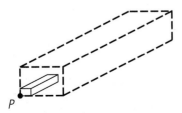

LESSON 12-4 (pp. 581–585)
5. a. $ru = st$ **b.** $\frac{r}{t} = \frac{s}{u}$ **c.** $\frac{s}{r} = \frac{u}{t}$ **7.** $\frac{2}{4} \neq \frac{6}{8}$, $\frac{2}{6} \neq \frac{4}{8}$, $\frac{2}{8} \neq \frac{4}{6}$ **9.** 12.5
11. Samples: $\frac{u}{v} = \frac{w}{x}$; $\frac{w}{x} = \frac{y}{z}$; $\frac{u}{v} = \frac{y}{z}$; $\frac{w}{u} = \frac{y}{v}$, $\frac{x}{v} = \frac{w}{u}$, $\frac{v}{u} = \frac{x}{w}$ **13.**
a. True **b.** True **c.** False **15.** $\approx \$1.83$ **17.** Any three of the following: $\frac{w}{y} = \frac{z}{x}$; $\frac{w}{z} = \frac{y}{x}$, $\frac{y}{w} = \frac{x}{z}$, or $\frac{z}{w} = \frac{x}{y}$ **19.** $S(A) = (8, -3)$, $S(B) = (5, 4)$, $AB = \sqrt{6^2 + 14^2} = \sqrt{232} = 2\sqrt{58}$ $S(A)S(B) = \sqrt{3^2 + 7^2} = \sqrt{58}$; $\sqrt{58} = \frac{1}{2} \cdot 2\sqrt{58}$

21. 10 in. **23. a.** Since $GHJKL$ is regular, $\overline{GL} \cong \overline{HJ}$. Since triangles FGL and HIJ are regular, $\overline{FG} \cong \overline{GL} \cong \overline{FL}$; $\overline{HI} \cong \overline{JI} \cong \overline{HJ}$. Thus, by the Transitive Property of Congruence, all six of these segments are congruent. So by the SSS Congruence Theorem, $\triangle FGL \cong \triangle HIJ$. **b.** 168

LESSON 12-5 (pp. 586–592)
1. a similarity transformation **3.** congruent, similar **7.** Yes
9. No **11.** Yes **13.** Yes **15.** False **17.** $\frac{4x}{7}$ **19. See below.**
21. $w = \sqrt{32} \approx 5.66$ cm **23.** 6 **25.** $\approx \$3.34$ **27. a.** True
b. True **c.** 15 **29. a.** No **b.** The triangles could be similar with a ratio of similitude not equal to 1.

19. a.

b. It is the image under an expansion with scale factor 3.

LESSON 12-6 (pp. 593–598)
1. a. $\frac{5}{7}$ (or $\frac{7}{5}$) **b.** $\frac{25}{49}$ (or $\frac{49}{25}$) **c.** $\frac{125}{343}$ (or $\frac{343}{125}$) **5.** 2176 units^3 **7.** $\frac{5}{13}$ (or $\frac{13}{5}$) **9. a.** $20 + \sqrt{40} \approx 26.32$ units **b.** $100 + 5\sqrt{40} \approx$ 131.62 units **11. a.** 337.5 in.^{3} **b.** ≈ 29.63 in.^{3} **13. a.** 18 cm^2 **b.** 1000 cm^3 **15.** (b) **17.** $DE = 7.5$; $EF = 12.5$; m$\angle E = 135$ **19.** $\frac{x}{11} = \frac{10}{y}$; $\frac{10}{x} = \frac{y}{11}$; $\frac{11}{x} = \frac{y}{10}$ **21.** $33\frac{1}{3}$ percent

LESSON 12-7 (pp. 599–603)
3. 144; $144^3 = 2,985,984$ **5.** The giantess would weigh about 125 times the weight of the woman. **7.** The giantess's standing area would be about 25 times the area of the woman's. **9.** False **11.** The weight of the animal increases as the cube of their heights; thus, to support this greater weight, the cross-section of the skeleton of the larger animal, which signals the strength of the skeleton, must be correspondingly larger. **13.** 15.625 kg **15. a.** No **b.** The taller box has twice

b. The taller box has twice the volume of the shorter. **c.** The taller box has more surface area than the shorter, but you cannot express the ratio of their surface areas as a simple fraction. **17. a.** $\sqrt{13} \approx 3.6$ **b.** $(\sqrt{13})^3 \approx 46.9$ **19.** $m\angle R = 42$; $m\angle T = 42$; $m\angle S = 43$; $MT = 12.24$; $RQ \approx 29.8$

21.

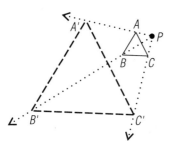

LESSON 12-8 (pp. 604–608)

1. a. $\triangle DEF \sim \triangle UVW$ **b.** $\frac{10}{33}$ or $\frac{33}{10}$ **c.** $UV = 7.\overline{57}$; $VW = 9.\overline{69}$
3. $\frac{ST}{VW}$, $\frac{TR}{WU}$ **7.** False **9. a.** $\triangle PQR \sim \triangle TVU$ **b.** Sample: apply S_3 to $\triangle PQR$ with center Q. Take the image and reflect over the $\perp$ bisector of $\overline{P'T}$. Then rotate with magnitude $m\angle Q''TV$ with center T. **11. See below. 13.** 43.94 lb **15.** 972π units^3
17. a. volume of a pyramid or cone with height h and base of area B **b.** surface area of a rectangular solid with sides l, w, h **c.** perimeter of a triangle with sides a, b, c **d.** volume of a cylinder of height h and base of radius r **e.** lateral area of a cone with base of radius r and slant height l

11. Consider these two triangles:

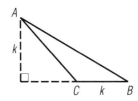

LESSON 12-9 (pp. 609–614)

1. a. $\triangle ABC \sim \triangle YXZ$ **b.** $\frac{1}{2}$ or 2 **c.** $m\angle Y = 60$ **9. a.** Yes
b. SSS Similarity Theorem **11–13. See below. 15. a.** No
b. $\frac{12}{8} \neq \frac{16}{12} \neq \frac{20}{16}$

11.

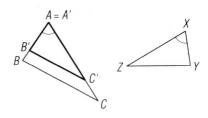

Let $k = \frac{XY}{AB}$, and then find $\triangle A'B'C' \sim \triangle ABC$ with ratio of similitude k.

Then $A'B' = k \cdot AB$ $\qquad A'C' = k \cdot AC$
$\quad\quad\;\; = \frac{XY}{AB} \cdot AB$ $\qquad\quad\;\; = \frac{XY}{AB} \cdot AC$
$\quad\quad\;\; = XY$ $\qquad\qquad\quad\; = \frac{XZ}{AC} \cdot AC$
$\qquad\qquad\qquad\qquad\qquad\;\; = XY$

So $\triangle A'B'C' \cong \triangle XYZ$ by the SAS Congruence Theorem. Thus $\triangle ABC$ can be mapped onto $\triangle XYZ$ by a composite of size changes and reflections, so $\triangle ABC \sim \triangle XYZ$.

13.

Conclusions	Justifications
1. $m\angle WYZ = m\angle ZYV$	Vertical Angle Theorem
2. $\frac{WY}{XY} = \frac{3 \cdot VY}{3 \cdot YZ} = \frac{VY}{YZ}$	Mult. Prop. of Equality
3. $\triangle WXY \sim \triangle VZY$	SAS Similarity Theorem

17.

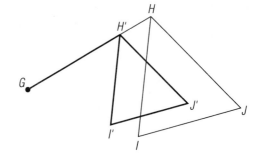

LESSON 12-10 (pp. 615–620)

1. a. $\frac{AB}{AY} = \frac{CB}{XY}$ **b.** $\frac{AC}{CX}$ **3.** 24 **5.** $\frac{7}{6}$ **7.** (c) **9.** $AC = 24$, $CE = 36$
11. $\frac{y}{x} = \frac{w}{z}$; $\frac{x}{z} = \frac{y}{w}$; $\frac{z}{x} = \frac{w}{y}$; $\frac{x}{x+y} = \frac{z}{z+w}$; $\frac{x+y}{x} = \frac{z+w}{z}$ **13.** $x = 125$ m; $y = 100$ m **15.** No **17.** Yes, $\triangle STO \sim \triangle XYZ$ by the SSS Similarity Theorem **19.** 93.75 miles

CHAPTER 12 PROGRESS SELF-TEST(pp. 622–623)
1. See below. 2. See below. 3. A size change is a similarity transformation. It does not necessarily preserve distance, area, and volume, but it does preserve angle measure (also betweenness, collinearity, and orientation). The answer is choice (a) **4.** Under a size change of magnitude $\frac{3}{4}$, the area of the image changes by the square of the ratio of similitude, so Area$(\triangle A'B'C') = (\frac{3}{4})^2$ Area$(\triangle ABC) = \frac{9}{16}$ Area$(\triangle ABC)$.

5. Two figures are similar if and only if there is a similarity transformation (that is, a composite of size changes and reflections) mapping one onto the other. **6.** $\overleftrightarrow{WX} \parallel \overleftrightarrow{YZ}$, so $\overleftrightarrow{WX}$ divides $\overline{YV}$ and $\overline{ZV}$ proportionally. So $\frac{VW}{WY} = \frac{VX}{XZ}$. **7.** Using $\frac{VW}{VY} = \frac{VX}{VZ}$ with $VW = 11$, $VY = VW + WY = 11 + 13 = 24$, and $VZ = 30$, then $\frac{11}{24} = \frac{VX}{30}$, so $330 = 24VX$, and $VX = 13.75$ units.

8. Using $\frac{VW}{VY} = \frac{WX}{YZ}$ with $WX = 8$, $YZ = 20$, and $WV = 10$, then $\frac{10}{VY} = \frac{8}{20}$ so $8VY = 200$ and $VY = 25$ units. **9.** If $\frac{a}{b} = \frac{c}{d}$, then some other true proportions are $\frac{a}{c} = \frac{b}{d}$, $\frac{d}{b} = \frac{c}{a}$, $\frac{b}{a} = \frac{d}{c}$, $\frac{c}{a} = \frac{d}{b}$. (To check, the means-extremes product should be $ad = bc$.) **10.** $\triangle ACB \sim \triangle ECD$ ($\angle BAC \cong \angle DEC$ by $\parallel$ lines $\Rightarrow$ AIA $=$; $\angle ACB \cong \angle ECD$ by the Vertical Angle Theorem), so $\frac{AC}{EC} = \frac{BC}{DC}$. Using $AC = 32$, $CE = 24$, and $DC = 20$, then $\frac{32}{24} = \frac{BC}{20}$ so $640 = 24BC$ and $BC = 26.\overline{6} = 26\frac{2}{3}$ units. **11.** $\angle AUQ$ corresponds to $\angle O$, so m$\angle AUQ =$ m$\angle O = 37$. The ratio of similitude can be found using $\frac{DQ}{RF} = \frac{6}{8} = \frac{3}{4}$. So $DA = \frac{3}{4}RU = \frac{3}{4}(27) = \frac{81}{4} = 20.25$ units, and $AU = \frac{3}{4}UO$ or $24 = \frac{3}{4}UO$, $UO = \frac{4}{3}(24) = 4(8) = 32$ units. **12.** The ratio of volumes is the cube of the ratio of sides, so the ratio of volumes is $5^3 : 1^3 = 125 : 1$. **13.** Using the proportion $\frac{w_1}{w_2} = \left(\frac{h_1}{h_2}\right)^3$, where w represents weight and h represents height, $\frac{5}{w_2} = \left(\frac{4}{12}\right)^3 = \frac{64}{1728}$. So $64w_2 = 8640$ and $w_2 = 135$ lb. **14.** The ratios of side lengths can be written as $\frac{8}{12} = \frac{2}{3}$, $\frac{12}{18} = \frac{2}{3}$, and $\frac{18}{27} = \frac{2}{3}$. Since all 3 ratios are equal, the two triangles are similar by the SSS Similarity Theorem. **15.** $\angle A \cong \angle E$ and $\angle B \cong \angle D$ because $\parallel$ lines $\Rightarrow$ AIA $=$ (also, $\angle BCA \cong \angle DCE$ by the Vertical Angle Theorem). So the triangles are similar by the AA Similarity Theorem. **16.** The parallel streets, Washington, Adams, and Jefferson, divide Martha Lane and Abigail Avenue proportionally. So $\frac{200}{150} = \frac{x}{165}$ and $150x = 33,000$, so $x = 220$ m. **17.** The slides are similar figures, so $\frac{5}{3} = \frac{x}{25}$ (note that both shorter sides, 3 cm and 25 cm, appear in corresponding positions in the fractions). Then $3x = 125$ and $x = 41.\overline{6} = 41\frac{2}{3}$ cm. **18.** The ratio of the lengths of feet equals the ratio of heights, because each is a linear measurement. So $\frac{2}{30} = \frac{0.4}{x}$ (note that both numerators are in meters, while both denominators are in centimeters). Then $2x = 12$ and $x = 6$ cm. **19.** The ratio of weights is the cube of the ratio of heights, and the ratio of (foot) areas is the square of the ratio of heights. So the weight would be $6^3 = 216$ times as much and corresponding areas would differ by a factor of $6^2 = 36$. **20. See below.**

1.

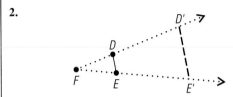

Draw $\overline{OA}$, $\overline{OB}$, and $\overline{OC}$. Then find A', B', and C' so that $AA' = \frac{3}{4}AO$, $BB' = \frac{3}{4}BO$, and $CC' = \frac{3}{4}CO$.

2.

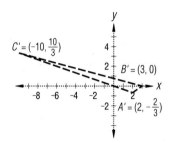

Draw $\overrightarrow{FD}$ and $\overrightarrow{FE}$. Then find D' and E' so that $FD' = 2.8FD$ and $FE' = 2.8FE$.

20.

Under a size change of magnitude $\frac{2}{3}$, centered on the origin,
$A = (6, -2)$ so $A' = (2, -\frac{2}{3})$;
$B = (9, 0)$ so $B' = (3, 0)$;
$C = (-30, 10)$ so $C' = (-10, 3\frac{1}{3})$.

The chart below keys the **Progress Self-Test** questions to the objectives in the **Chapter 12 Review** on pages 624–627. This will enable you to locate those **Chapter 12 Review** questions that correspond to questions you missed on the **Progress Self-Text**. The lesson where the material is covered is also indicated in the chart.

Questions	1,2	3	4	5	6–8	9	10,11		
Objective	A	D	D	D	B	E	C		
Lesson	12-2	12-3	12-6	12-5	12-10	12-4	12-5		

Question	12	13	14	15	16	17,18	19	20
Objective	D	H	F	F	G	G	H	I
Lesson	12-6	12-7	12-8	12-9	12-10	12-5	12-7	12-1

1. See below. **3.** See below. **5.** It is *DEFG* itself. **7.** 100
9. 8 **11.** 12 **13.** m∠*H* = 100, *PE* = 4.1$\overline{6}$, *OU* = 7.92
15. 90, 57, 33 **17.** 625 units² **19. a.** *J* **b.** 1.5 **c.** True **21.** If
the ratio of similitude is *k*, the ratio of the volumes is k^3.

23. 2:1 **25.** $\frac{a}{m} = \frac{e}{t}$, $\frac{m}{t} = \frac{a}{e}$, $\frac{t}{m} = \frac{e}{a}$ **27.** $\frac{8}{12} = \frac{16}{24}$, $\frac{8}{16} = \frac{12}{24}$,
$\frac{16}{8} = \frac{24}{12}$, $\frac{12}{8} = \frac{24}{16}$ **29. a.** Yes **b.** by the SSS Similarity

Theorem **31.** Yes, by the SAS Similarity Theorem **33.** See
below. **35.** 6.25″ **37.** 15 meters **39.** 20.$\overline{2}$″ **41.** ≈ $15.08
43. ≈ 3.4 lb **45.** True **47.** See below. **49. a.** *P*′ = (-20,
-32, 44) **b.** *OP* = $\sqrt{25 + 64 + 121}$ = $\sqrt{210}$; *OP*′ =
$\sqrt{400 + 1024 + 1936}$ = $\sqrt{3360}$ = $\sqrt{16 \cdot 210}$ = 4$\sqrt{210}$ =
4 · *OP*.

1.

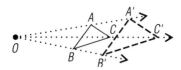

3.

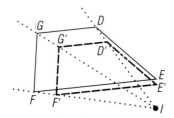

33.

Conclusions	Justifications
1. ∠*ACB* and ∠*ACD* are right angles.	definition of perpendicular (meaning)
2. m∠*ACB* = 90 m∠*ACD* = 90	definition of right angle (meaning)
3. m∠*ACB* = m∠*ACD*	Transitive Property of Equality
4. $\frac{BC}{AC} = \frac{x}{2x} = \frac{1}{2}$ $\frac{AC}{DC} = \frac{2x}{4x} = \frac{1}{2}$	Multiplication Property of Equality
5. $\frac{BC}{AC} = \frac{AC}{DC}$	Transitive Property of Equality
6. △*ABC* ~ △*DAC*	SAS Similarity Theorem

47.

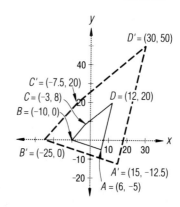

LESSON 13-1 (pp. 628–634)
7. If you use Toothdazzle, the more popular you will be with
the opposite sex. **9.** If 7(*x* − 12) < 70, then *x* − 12 < 10. If
x − 12 < 10, then *x* < 22. Using the Law of Transitivity, we
conclude: If 7(*x* − 12) < 70, then *x* < 22. **11.** Boris Becker
is world class. **13.** No conclusion can be made. **15.** Joe is 16
or older. **17.** Nothing can be concluded. **19.** See below. **21.**
a. 10 **b.** $\sqrt{116}$ **c.** $\sqrt{216}$ **d.** (iv) **23.** It is multiplied by 18.

25. 540 **27.** See below. **29. a.** $x^2 - 2xy + y^2$ **b.** $4a^2$

19. sample:
   a. *p*: ∠*ABE* and ∠*ABC* are a linear pair.
      p ⇒ *q*: If two angles form a linear pair, then they are
      supplementary.
      Conclusion *q*: ∠*ABE* and ∠*ABC* are supplementary.
   b. Sample: *x* + m∠*ABC* = m∠*EBD* + m∠*DBC*.

27. sample:

LESSON 13-2 (pp. 635–639)
1. The perimeter of an *n*-gon with side *s* is not *ns*. **3.** You
were late for school today. **9. a.** If you can get $10 for that
old tape recorder, then you will bring it in Saturday. **b.** If you
cannot get $10 for that old tape recorder, you will not bring it
in Saturday. **c.** If you do not bring that old tape recorder in

Saturday, you cannot get $10 for it. **11.** (a) **13.** If the
Pythagorean Theorem holds for △*ABC*, then △*ABC* is a right
triangle. **15. a.** *x* ≠ 3 **b.** Detachment and Contrapositive
17. Yes **19.** None of these apples was grown in the shade.
21. From a statement or given information *p* and a
justification of the form *p* ⇒ *q*, you may conclude *q*. **23.** See
below. **25.** -2 **27.** 5, -5

23.

Conclusions	Justifications
1. m∠*DAC* = m∠*BCA*	∥ Lines ⇒ AIA = Theorem
2. m∠*ACD* = m∠*CAB*	∥ Lines ⇒ AIA ⇒ Theorem
3. *AC* = *AC*	Reflexive Property of Equality
4. △*ACD* ≅ △*CAB*	ASA Congruence Theorem (steps 1, 2, 3)
5. $\overline{AB}$ ≅ $\overline{CD}$	CPCF Theorem

LESSON 13-3 (pp. 640–644)
3. *s* and *t* have exactly one point in common. **5.** Sample: The
teller is male, either Farmer or Guinness; Shirley is Ms Edwards.
7. Carol plays the clarinet, Sue plays the trombone,
Jill plays the flute, Dave plays the tuba, Jim plays the cornet.
9. Sample: $\overline{BC}$ is not parallel to $\overline{AD}$. **11.** Mike—chemist,
Darlene—dentist, Gary—teacher, Wanda—car dealer,
Ken—farmer, Brad—doctor, Joyce—lawyer **13. a.** If I eat
my hat, then Jackie is a good cook. **b.** If Jackie is not a good
cook, I will not eat my hat. **c.** If I don't eat my hat, then
Jackie is not a good cook. **15.** Diagonals in a square are
perpendicular.

17.

Conclusions	Justifications
1. $\overline{AC} = \overline{BC}$, $\overline{DC} = \overline{EC}$	definition of isosceles triangles (meaning)
2. $\angle ACD \cong \angle BCE$	Vertical Angle Theorem
3. $\triangle ACD \cong \triangle BCE$	SAS Congruence Theorem (steps 1 and 2)

LESSON 13-4 (pp. 645–650)

5. (a) **7.** Either $\sqrt{9800} = 99$ or $\sqrt{9800} \neq 99$. Assume $\sqrt{9800} = 99$. Then squaring both sides: $9800 = 99^2$. But, by the definition of power, $99 \cdot 99 = 9801$. These last two equations are contradictory, so by the Law of Indirect Reasoning, the assumption $\sqrt{9800} = 99$ is false, so $\sqrt{9800} \neq 99$. **9.** $\triangle ABC$ is scalene. **11.** contradictory **13.** not contradictory **15. a.** $x < {}^-21$ **b.** direct reasoning **17.** Isobel—5′11″—brunette; Mary—5′10″—black; Ruth—5′8″—auburn; Marcia—5′7″— blond; Grace—5′6″—red **19. a.** If $\angle A$ is not congruent to $\angle D$, then $\triangle ABC$ is not similar to $\triangle DEF$. **b.** If $\angle A \cong \angle D$, then $\triangle ABC \sim \triangle DEF$. **c.** If $\triangle ABC$ is not similar to $\triangle DEF$, then $\angle A$ is not congruent to $\angle D$. **d.** The contrapositive is true. **21.** 12

LESSON 13-5 (pp. 651–657)

7. 9 **9.** sample: a ball on a floor **11.** $\sqrt{136} \approx 11.7$
13. a. Yes **b.** infinitely many **15.** See below. **17.** (b) **19. a.** Julie walks to school. **b.** Law of Ruling Out Possibilities **21. a.** If the diagonals of a figure are not congruent, then it is not a rectangle. **b.** Yes

15.

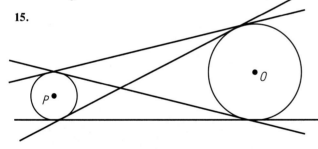

LESSON 13-6 (pp. 658–664)

3. not uniquely determined **5.** See below. **13–19.** See below. **21.** Compass Rule **23.** 12 units **25.** In 1960, Richard Nixon did not win the majority of electoral votes. **27.** rectangles

5.

13., 15., 17.

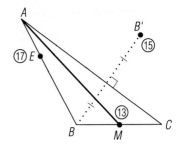

⑰ is the only figure not uniquely determined.

19. sample:

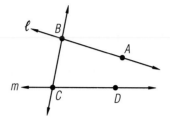

If $m\angle ABC + m\angle DCB < 180$, then ℓ and m intersect on the same side of $\overleftrightarrow{BC}$ as A and D are.

LESSON 13-7 (pp. 665–670)

1. a. 40 **b.** 140 **c.** 40 **3.** $\angle 2$ and $\angle 1$ **5.** $\angle 2$ and $\angle 3$ **7.** $\angle B$ **9.** $\overline{FE}$ **11.** True **13.** $\overline{GJ}$ **15.** $m\angle Q = 90$ (given). So, $m\angle 2 < 90$, since $m\angle 2 + m\angle SPQ = 90$. Therefore, $m\angle 2 < m\angle Q$, by substitution. So $PQ < PS$, by Unequal Angles Theorem. **17. a.** x **b.** $x + y$ **c.** $180 - 2x - y$ **19.** Through a point not on a line, there is exactly one parallel to the given line. **21.** 5 **23.** 32 cm

LESSON 13-8 (pp. 671–674)

5. See below. **7.** a regular 30-gon with sides of length 4 **9.** Assume a given figure is a convex decagon with 4 right interior angles. The corresponding exterior angles would also be right angles, and so the sum of their measures would be 360°. So the sum of the measures of all 10 exterior angles would exceed 360°, which contradicts the Exterior Angles of a Polygon Sum Theorem. Therefore, the assumption is false. So no convex decagon can have 4 right interior angles. **11.** $\angle 3$ is an exterior angle of $\triangle XYV$, so $m\angle 3 > m\angle 2$ (from the Exterior Angles Inequality Theorem). Similarly, $\angle 2$ is an exterior angle of $\triangle WXV$, so $m\angle 2 > m\angle 1$. Transitivity gives $m\angle 3 > m\angle 2 > m\angle 1$. So $\angle 1$ is the smallest. **13.** See margin. **15.** the square **17.** $\angle ACD$, $\angle CBP$

5. TO OCT
  REPEAT 8 [FORWARD 12 RIGHT 45]
  END

13. not uniquely determined; sample:

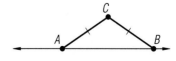

CHAPTER 13 PROGRESS SELF-TEST (pp. 676–677)
1.a. A hexagon is a specific kind of polygon, so the statement is true. **b.** Inverse: If a figure is not a hexagon, then it is not a polygon. **c. See below. 2.** If two angles do not form a linear pair, then they are not adjacent angles. **b. See below. 3.a.** An angle may be acute, right, or obtuse. If it is neither acute nor obtuse, then it must be a right angle. **b.** The conclusion in part **a** is based on the Law of Ruling Out Possibilities. **4.** If all three angles of a triangle are less than 50°, then the sum of the measures of the angles of the triangle must be under 150. This is a contradiction, since the sum of the measures of the three angles in a triangle must be 180. Therefore the original assumption, that the measures of the three angles in a triangle can all be under 50°, must be false. **5.** Suppose $\sqrt{80} = 40$. Then $80 = (\sqrt{80})^2 = 40^2 = 1600$. But $80 \neq 1600$. So the original assumption, that $\sqrt{80} = 40$, is false, and $\sqrt{80} \neq 40$. **6-9. See below. 10.a.** $\angle ABD$ and $\angle CBD$ form a linear pair, so they are supplementary. So if $m\angle ABD = 120$, then $m\angle CBD = 60$. **b-c.** In $\triangle BCD$, $\angle ABD$ is an exterior angle and $\angle C$ and $\angle D$ are the nonadjacent interior angles. So $m\angle C < 120$ and $m\angle D < 120$ by the Exterior Angle Inequality. **11.** Until the discovery of non-Euclidean geometries, postulates were thought to be *definitely* true. Now it is realized that they are only *assumed* true. **12-13. See below. 14.** $\overline{PT}$ and $\overline{PU}$ are tangents to $\odot O$, so $\overline{PT} \perp \overline{QT}$ and $\overline{PU} \perp \overline{OU}$. $\angle P$ is given to be a right angle, and $\angle O$ is a right angle because the sum of the four angles in quadrilateral *OUPT* is 360°. So *OUPT* is a rectangle by the definition of rectangle (sufficient condition). Moreover, $PT = PU$ because two tangents to a circle from an external point have the same length. So *OUPT* is a square by the definition of square (sufficient condition). **15.** Drawing $\overline{AE}$ and $\overline{DB}$, each is $\perp$ to the common tangent $\overleftrightarrow{CE}$. So $\triangle CBD \sim \triangle CAE$ by the AA Similarity Theorem (each triangle contains $\angle C$, and $\angle CDB$ and $\angle CEA$ are right angles). Then $\frac{CD}{CE} = \frac{DB}{EA}$. Using $BD = 9$, $CD = 20$, and $CE = 50$, $\frac{20}{50} = \frac{9}{EA}$ or $20EA = 450$ and $EA = 22.5$. So the radius of $\odot A$ is 22.5 units. **16. See below.**

1.c. counterexamples: 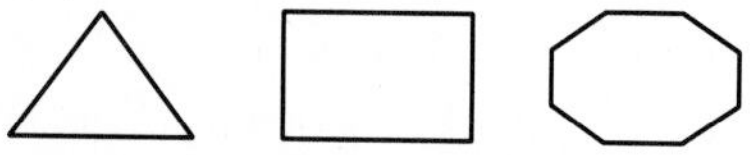

Any *n*-gon, where $n \neq 6$, is not a hexagon (so the antecedent of the inverse is satisfied), but it is a polygon (so the consequent is not satisfied).

2.b. counterexample:

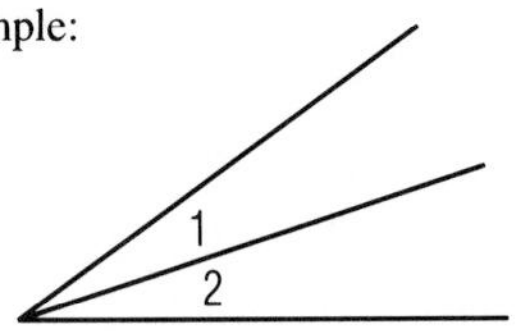

Angles 1 and 2 do not form a linear pair (so the antecedent of the contrapositive is satisfied), but they are adjacent (so the consequent is not satisfied).

6.

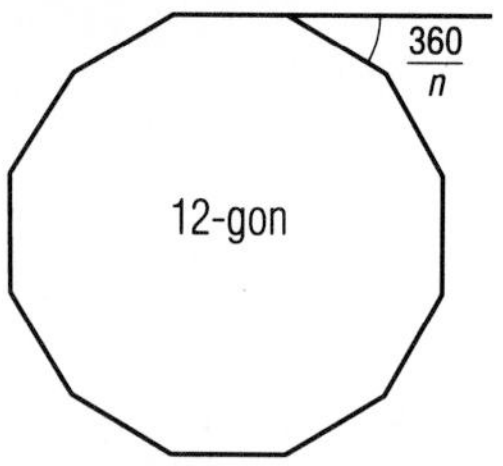

The measure of the exterior angle of a regular duodecagon (12-gon) is $\frac{360}{12} = 30$.

7. Sample:

```
TO REGOCT
  REPEAT 8 [FORWARD 6 RIGHT 45]
END
```

This program draws a side of length 6, then moves through an exterior angle of 45° (because $\frac{360}{8} = 45$). The program does this 8 times.

8. Assign letters to statements:

$b \Rightarrow h$ (All babies are happy.)
$t \Rightarrow b$ (If someone is teething, that person is a baby.)
$n \Rightarrow$ *not-h* (Nate is sad.)

Then starting with *n*, the fourth statement lets you conclude *not-h*. From the contrapositive of the first conditional, you can conclude *not-b*. From the contrapositive of the second conditional, you can conclude *not-t*. Thus you can state $n \Rightarrow$ *not-t*, or "Nate is not teething."

9.

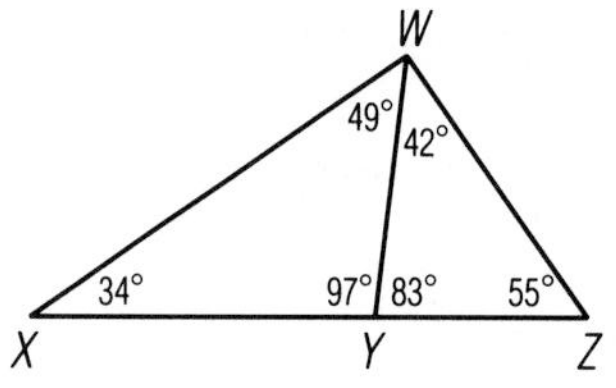

Fill in the measures of the angles: $m\angle XWY = 180 - (34 + 97) = 49$, $m\angle WYZ = 180 - 97 = 83$; $m\angle YWZ = 180 - (83 + 55) = 42$. Then, in $\triangle XYW$, $\overline{WY}$ is opposite the smallest angle, so it is the shortest of the three segments. Then, in $\triangle WYZ$, $\overline{YZ}$ is shorter than $\overline{WY}$ because $\overline{YZ}$ is opposite the smaller angle. So $\overline{YZ}$ is the shortest segment; that is choice (f).

12.

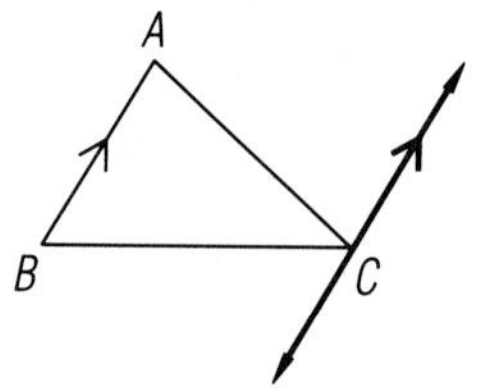

There is a unique line through *C* parallel to $\overleftrightarrow{AB}$; that is the Uniqueness of Parallels Theorem.

13.

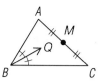

The bisector $\overrightarrow{BQ}$ of $\angle B$ does not necessarily contain the midpoint M of $\overline{AC}$. ($\overrightarrow{BQ}$ does contain M if $AB = BC$.)

16.

	20th	19th	18th	17th
Jack	X_2	X_2	O	X_3
Queen	X_1	O		
King	O			X_1
Ace	X_3			O

From clue 1, the Queen is not from the 20th century and the King is not from the 17th century. From clue 2, the Jack is not from the 20th century and is not from the 19th century. From clue 3, the Jack is not from the 17th century, and the Ace is not from the 20th century. That means that the Jack must be from the 18th century, which makes the Queen from the 19th century, the King from the 20th century, and the Ace from the 17th century.

The chart below keys the **Progress Self-Test** questions to the objectives in the **Chapter 13 Review** on pages 678–681. This will enable you to locate those **Chapter 13 Review** questions that correspond to questions you missed on the **Progress Self-Test**. The lesson where the material is covered is also indicated in the chart.

Question	1–2	3	4–5	6	7	8
Objective	C	D	E	B	A	J
Lesson	13-2	13-3	13-4	13-8	13-8	13-2

Question	9	10	11	12–13	14–15	16
Objective	H	I	K	G	F	J
Lesson	13-7	13-7	13-6	13-6	13-5	13-3

CHAPTER 13 REVIEW (pp. 678–681)
1. See below. 3. a. 46 **b.** 92 **5. a.** If $x^2 = 9$, then $x = 3$. **b.** If $x \neq 3$, then $x^2 \neq 9$. **c.** If $x^2 \neq 9$, then $x \neq 3$. **d.** original, contrapositive **7. a.** All people in the U.S. live in New York. **b.** If a person is not a New Yorker, then that person does not live in the U.S. **c.** If a person does not live in the U.S., then that person is not a New Yorker. **d.** original, contrapositive. **9. a.** *LOVE* is a trapezoid. **b.** Law of Detachment **11. a.** $x \neq 11$ **b.** Law of Contrapositive and Law of Detachment **13. a.** ℓ is not perpendicular to m. **b.** Law of Contrapositive and Law of Detachment **15. a.** All names on this list are melodious. **b.** Laws of Transitivity, Detachment, Contrapositive, and Ruling Out Possibilities **17. a.** The teacher is incorrect. **b.** Law of Indirect Reasoning **19.** Assume that in quadrilateral $ABCD$, $\angle A$, $\angle B$, $\angle C$, and $\angle D$ are acute. Thus $m\angle A < 90$, $m\angle B < 90$, $m\angle C < 90$, and $m\angle D < 90$. So $m\angle A + m\angle B + m\angle C + m\angle D < 360$, which contradicts the Quadrilateral-Sum Theorem. So by the Law of Indirect Reasoning, the assumption is false; a

quadrilateral cannot have four acute angles. **21.** Either $\sqrt{2} = \frac{239}{169}$ or $\sqrt{2} \neq \frac{239}{169}$. Assume $\sqrt{2} = \frac{239}{169}$. Then $2 = (\frac{239}{169})^2 = \frac{57,121}{28,561}$. Then $2 \cdot 28,561 = 57,121$; so $57,122 = 57,121$. This is a false conclusion, so by the Law of Indirect Reasoning, the assumption is false. So $\sqrt{2} \neq \frac{239}{169}$. **23.** $18\pi \approx 56.5$ units **25.** $3025\pi \approx 9503.3$ mm^2 **27.** Uniqueness of Parallels Theorem **29.** cannot be justified **31.** $\angle C$ **33.** $\overline{HI}$ **35.** $\angle 3$ is larger than $\angle 4$, because it is an exterior angle $\triangle TYZ$. Similarly, $\angle 2$ is larger than $\angle 3$, and $\angle 1$ is larger than $\angle 2$. So $\angle 1$ is the largest. **37.** Mary is too old for camp. **39. a.** Law of Ruling Out Possibilities **b.** He may not have included all possibilities. **41.** Through a point not on a line, there is exactly one line parallel to the given line.

1. TO HEXAGON
   REPEAT 6 [FORWARD 10 RIGHT 60]
   END

LESSON 14-1 (pp. 682–689)
3. $\overline{DG}, \overline{EH}, \overline{IF}, \overline{DH}, \overline{EG}$; $\triangle DIJ$, $\triangle DJL$, $\triangle HIJ$, $\triangle HJL$, $\triangle EKL$, $\triangle EKF$, $\triangle GKL$, $\triangle GKF$ $\triangle EHG$, $\triangle DHG$, $\triangle HED$, and $\triangle GED$ **5.** 105 **7.** $10\sqrt{2} \approx 14.14$ cm **9.** 10.4 cm, 12.0 cm **11.** $\frac{E\sqrt{3}}{2}$ units **13.** $\frac{100}{\sqrt{2}} \approx 70.71$ ft **15.** $\triangle CBA$, $\triangle BPA$, $\triangle CPB$ (and also $\triangle ADC$) **17.** $DE = \pm\sqrt{150} \approx \pm 12.25$ (But if DE is a length, it must be positive.) **19.** (a) **21.** square

LESSON 14-2 (pp. 690–695)
1. 10.00 **3.** True **5.** 4 **7. a.** 13 **b.** $\frac{25}{13} \approx 1.92$ **c.** $\frac{60}{13} \approx 4.62$
9. a. Yes **b.** True **11. a.** Right Triangle Altitude Theorem **b.** Geometric Mean Theorem **c.** Addition Property of Equality **d.** Distributive Property **e.** Substitution Property of Equality **13. a.** $\frac{5\sqrt{3}}{2} \approx 4.33$ units **b.** $\frac{25\sqrt{3}}{4} \approx 10.83$ units^2 **15.** The prism

$\cong \triangle MEC$ by the SSS Congruence Theorem, so $\angle D \cong \angle E$ by CPCT. Thus $\triangle ADE$ is isosceles, with $AD = AE$. By the Betweenness Property and subtraction, $AB = AD - BD$ and $AC = AE - CE$. So $AB = AC$, by substitution, and $ABMC$ is a kite because it has two distinct pairs of congruent consecutive sides. **19.** 2 or 1

LESSON 14-3 (pp. 696–701)
1. See below. 3. 3.271 **5.** $\frac{7}{24} \approx .292$ **7.** $\frac{1}{\sqrt{3}}$ or $\frac{\sqrt{3}}{3}$ **9. See below. 11. a.** $\angle 4$ **b.** $\angle 1$ **13. a.** $\frac{x}{h}$ **b.** $\frac{h}{y}$ **c.** $\frac{x}{h} = \frac{h}{y}$ **d.** part a
15. $\triangle ACD$, $\triangle CBD$ **17.** $\sqrt{89} \approx 9.43''$

1. sample: $\tan 40° \approx \frac{30}{36} = .8\overline{3}$.

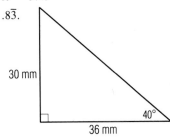

30 mm
36 mm
40°

9.

4
6

a. between 30° and 35° **b.** between 55° and 60°

LESSON 14-4 (pp. 702–707)
3. a. $\frac{2}{2\sqrt{5}} = \frac{1}{\sqrt{5}} \approx .447$ **b.** $\frac{4}{2\sqrt{5}} = \frac{2}{\sqrt{5}} \approx .894$ **c.** 2
d. $\frac{4}{2\sqrt{5}} = \frac{2}{\sqrt{5}} \approx .894$ **5. a.** $\frac{1}{\sqrt{2}}$ or $\frac{\sqrt{2}}{2}$ **b.** $\frac{1}{\sqrt{2}}$ or $\frac{\sqrt{2}}{2}$ **c.** 1
7. a. .228 **b.** .974 **9.** ≈ 8.5 ft **11. a.** Sample: $\sin B \approx \frac{25}{46} \approx$
.543; $\sin B' \approx \frac{17}{32} \approx .531$. **b.** They will probably not be equal due to measurement error, but very close. **13.** ≈ 20.1 ft **15.** ≈ 670 ft **17.** ≈ 86.60 **19. a.** Converse: If $PM + MQ = PQ$, then M is between P and Q. Inverse: If M is not between P and Q, then $PM + MQ \neq PQ$. Contrapositive: If $PM + MQ \neq PQ$, then M is not between P and Q. **b.** All are true. **21.**
a. $50\sqrt{2}$ **b.** $58\sqrt{2}$

LESSON 14-5 (pp. 708–713)
1. a. Winds in the upper atmosphere affect the flying time.
b. The trip east to west usually takes longer. **3.** initial point: O; terminal point: A; magnitude: 400; direction: 20° south of east **7.** $-4 + -2 = -6$ **13–17. See below.**
19. $\tan R = \frac{35}{15} \approx 2.33$; $\sin R = \frac{35}{38} \approx 0.92$; $\cos R = \frac{15}{38} \approx 0.39$
21. ≈ 11.7 meters **23.** $576\pi \approx 1810$ units^2

13.

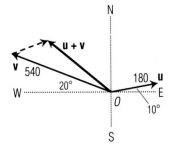

N
u + v
V 540
20°
180 u
W
E
O
10°
S

15.

150
N
37°
W
E
S

17.

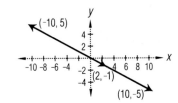

v
u
W
u + v + w

LESSON 14-6 (pp. 714–719)
5. $(\frac{1}{2} - \frac{\sqrt{3}}{2})$ **9–15. See below. 17.** $\approx -.032$ (or .032, depending on the direction of the plane) **19.** horizontal: $\sqrt{3}$; vertical: 1 **21. See below. 23.** False **25.** 1

9. a.

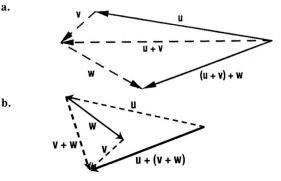

v
u
u + v
w
(u + v) + w

b.

u
w
V + W
v
u + (v + w)

c. Vector additon is associative.

11.

y
(-10, 5)
4
2
x
-10 -8 -6 -4   4 6 8 10
-2 (2, -1)
-4
(10, -5)

13.

A   B

15.

Conclusions	Justifications
$(a, b) + (c, d) = (a + c, b + d)$	Vector Addition Theorem
$= (c + a, d + b)$	Commutativity of Real Number Addition
$= (c, d) + (a, b)$	Vector Addition Theorem

21.

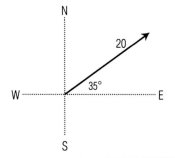

N
20
W   35°   E
S

LESSON 14-7 (pp. 720–724)

3. horizontal: $-10\cos 20° \approx -9.4$; vertical: $10\sin 20° \approx 3.42$ **5.** horizontal: 0; vertical: -3 **7.** magnitude $= 2\sqrt{10} \approx$ 6.32; direction: $\approx 18.4°$ N of E (or 71.6° E of N) **9.** magnitude ≈ 183 lbs; direction: $\approx 17°$ S of E (or 73° E of S) **11.** about 93.6 feet away; $\approx 20°$ below horizontal **13–15.** See below. **17.** $\frac{225\sqrt{3}}{4} \approx 97.4$ units^2 **19.** The $\frac{1}{8}$-size cello is $\frac{1}{2}$ the height of a full-size cello.

13.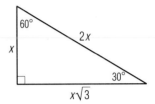

15.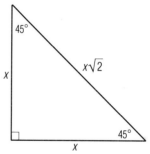

CHAPTER 14 PROGRESS SELF-TEST (pp. 726–727)

1. The three sides have lengths $XY \approx 5.5$ cm, $XZ \approx 1.6$ cm, and $YZ \approx 5.3$ cm. So $\cos Y = \frac{\text{side adjacent to } \angle Y}{\text{hypotenuse}} = \frac{YZ}{XY} \approx \frac{5.3}{5.5} \approx$ 0.96. **2.** The tangent ratio is $\frac{\text{opposite side}}{\text{adjacent side}}$. For the three numbered angles, the opposite side is constant, so the smallest tangent will be associated with the shortest adjacent side; $\angle 3$ will have the smallest tangent. **3.** $\sin B = \frac{\text{side opposite } \angle B}{\text{hypotenuse}} = \frac{AC}{AB}$ $= \frac{\text{side adjacent to } \angle A}{\text{hypotenuse}} = \cos A$. So if $\sin B = \frac{9}{11}$, then $\cos A = \frac{9}{11}$. **4–5.** To find WZ and WY, use the property that each leg is the mean proportional between the hypotenuse and its segment adjacent to the leg. For WZ, $\frac{YZ}{XZ} = \frac{XZ}{WZ}$ or $\frac{75}{45} = \frac{45}{WZ}$. So $75WZ = 2025$, or $WZ = 27$ units. For WY, $\frac{YZ}{XY} = \frac{XY}{WY}$ or $\frac{75}{60} = \frac{60}{WY}$. So $75WY = 3600$, or $WY = 48$ units. **6.** In right triangle CDB, $CD^2 = \sqrt{CB^2 - DB^2} = \sqrt{6^2 - 2^2} = \sqrt{36 - 4} = \sqrt{32}$. Then, since the altitude is the mean proportional to the segments of the hypotenuse, $\frac{AD}{CD} = \frac{CD}{DB}$ or $\frac{AD}{\sqrt{32}} = \frac{\sqrt{32}}{2}$. So $2AD = 32$ and $AD = 16$. Since $AB = AD + DB$, then $AB = 16 + 2 = 18$ units. **7.** CD, the altitude to the hypotenuse of a right triangle, is the mean proportional to the lengths of the segments of the hypotenuse, which are the distances AD and DB. **8.** $\triangle ABC$ is an isosceles triangle with legs $\overline{AB}$ and $\overline{BC}$. Since AB is given to be 7 units, then $BC = 7$ units. **9.** $\triangle ABC$ is a 45-45-90 triangle, so its hypotenuse is $\sqrt{2}$ times the length of a leg. So $AC = 7\sqrt{2} \approx 9.9$ units. **10.** $\triangle ACD$ is a 30-60-90 triangle so AD is twice the length of the side $\overline{AC}$ opposite the 30° angle. Since $AC = 7\sqrt{2}$ (from Question 9), then $AD = 2(7\sqrt{2}) = 14\sqrt{2} \approx 19.8$ units. **11.** $\tan D = \frac{\text{side opposite } \angle D}{\text{side adjacent to } \angle D} = \frac{EF}{DF} = \frac{48}{14} \approx 3.43$. **12.** $\cos E = \frac{\text{side adjacent to } \angle E}{\text{hypotenuse}} = \frac{EF}{DE} = \frac{48}{50} = .96$. **13–14.** See below. **15.** $\frac{18}{x} = \frac{x}{30}$ so $x^2 = (18)(30) = 540$ and $x = \sqrt{540} \approx 23.2379 \approx 23.24$. **16.** To find the height of the tree above eye level, use $\tan 35° = \frac{h}{40}$. Using a calculator (in degree mode), 35 $\boxed{\tan}$ $\boxed{\times}$ 40 $\boxed{=}$ 28.0083 $\approx$ 28 feet. Adding the five feet for eye level, the height of the tree is about 33 feet. **17–21.** See below. **22.** For the horizontal component, $\cos 35° = \frac{x}{50}$ so $x = 50\cos 35 \approx 40.958 \approx 41$; since the horizontal component is in the negative direction, it is ≈ -41. For the vertical component: $\sin 35° = \frac{y}{50}$ so $y = 50\sin 35 \approx$

28.6788 $\approx$ 28.7; it is in the negative direction, so it is about -28.7. **23–25.** See below.

13.

In a 30-60-90 triangle, the lengths of the sides are x, $x\sqrt{3}$, and $2x$. so $\sin 60° = \frac{x\sqrt{3}}{2x} = \frac{\sqrt{3}}{2}$.

14.

In a 45-45-90 triangle, the lengths of the sides are x, x, and $x\sqrt{2}$. So $\tan 45° = \frac{x}{x} = 1$.

17.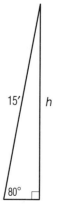

$\sin 80° = \frac{h}{15}$

$h = 15\sin 80$

$= 80$ $\boxed{\sin}$ $\boxed{\times}$ 15 $\boxed{=}$

≈ 14.772116

≈ 14.77 ft

18. Use the parallelogram rule:

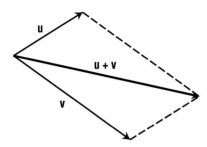

19. Use equal vectors such that the endpoint of one vector is the initial point of the next.

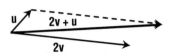

a. For the sum **2v + u,** its initial point is the initial point of the starting vector **v,** and its terminal point is the terminal point of vector **u.**

b.

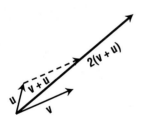

Find **v + u** using the parallelogram method. Then find 2(**v + u**) by starting another vector **v + u** at the terminal point of **v + u.**

20. The opposite of a vector has the same length but opposite direction. Below are vectors $\vec{AB}$ and several opposite vectors $\vec{CD}$ and $\vec{EF}$.

21.

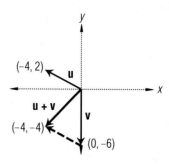

Find **u + v** either by the parallelogram rule or by adding the x- and y-coordinates: **u + v** = (-4 + 0, 2 + -6) = (-4, -4).

23.

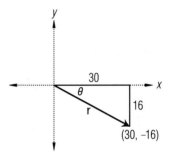

$\tan \theta = \frac{16}{30}$, so $\theta = 16 \boxed{\div} 30 \boxed{=} \boxed{\text{inv}} \boxed{\tan} \approx 28$ °.
$r = \sqrt{16^2 + 30^2} = \sqrt{256 + 900} = \sqrt{1156} = 34.$

The direction of the vector is about 28° south of east (or 62° east of south) and its magnitude is 34.

24.

The resultant speed is $700 - 150 = 550$ km/hr. In $3\frac{1}{2}$ hours, the plane could travel (550)(3.5) = 1925 km.

25.

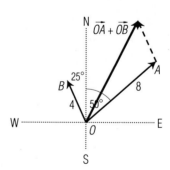

Using the Parallelogram Rule, the kayaker will be moving in a direction east of north.

Trigonometry can give a more exact answer.

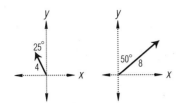

For the current vector, horizontal component is $-4 \sin 25°$ ≈ -1.69 and the vertical component is $4 \cos 25° = 3.63$, so its terminal point is $(-1.69, 3.63)$. For the kayaker, the horizontal component is $8 \sin 50 \approx 6.13$ and the vertical component is $8 \cos 50 \approx 5.14$, so its terminal point is $(6.13, 5.14)$. The components of the sum of the

vectors are $(-1.69 + 6.13, 3.63 + 5.14) = (4.44, 8.77)$.

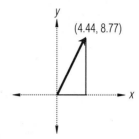

The direction of the resultant vector is $8.77 \boxed{\div} 4.44$ $\boxed{=} \boxed{inv} \boxed{tan} \approx 61.5°$ north of east, and its magnitude is $\sqrt{4.44^2 + 8.77^2} = \sqrt{96.6265} \approx 9.83$ mph.

The chart below keys the **Progress Self-Test** questions to the objectives in the **Chapter 14 Review** on pages 728–731. This will enable you to locate those **Chapter 14 Review** questions that correspond to questions you missed on the **Progress Self-Test**. The lesson where the material is covered is also indicated in the chart.

Question	1	2	3	4–6	7	8–10	11	12–13	14	
Objective	B	B	F	D	G	A	C	C	C	
Lesson	14-4	14-3	14-4	14-2	14-2	14-1	14-3	14-4	14-3	

Question	15	16	17	18	19	20	21	22–23	24	25
Objective	Voc.	I	I	E	E	H	K	L	J	J
Lesson	14-2	14-3	14-4	14-5	14-6	14-6	14-6	14-7	14-5	14-7

CHAPTER 14 REVIEW (pp. 728–731)

1. $AC = 4\sqrt{3} \approx 6.93$; $BC = 8$ **3.** $12\sqrt{2}$ **5. a.** $7\sqrt{2}$ **b.** 7 **c.** $7\sqrt{3}$ **d.** 14 **7.** $25\sqrt{3} \approx 43.30$ units **9.** Answers may vary. Appoximate measures are $m\angle E \approx 76$, $\sin E \approx .97$, $\cos E \approx .24$, $\tan E \approx 4.01$. **11.** $\angle 1$ **13.** $\frac{24}{26} = \frac{12}{13}$ **15.** $\frac{10}{24} = \frac{5}{12}$ **17.** .843 **19.** 1.000 **21.** $\sqrt{3}$ **23.** $\frac{1}{\sqrt{2}}$ or $\frac{\sqrt{2}}{2}$ **25.** $\frac{49}{12} \approx 4.08$ **27.** $x = \frac{49}{25} = 1.96$; $z = \frac{576}{25} = 23.04$; $y = \frac{168}{25} = 6.72$ **29–35. See below. 37.** $\frac{AC}{AB}$ **39.** $\frac{BC}{AC}$ **41.** sine **43.** x **45.** BD, DC **47.** DBA, DAC **49. See below 51.** Yes **53.** ≈ 21.56 yards **55.** ≈ 66 feet **57.** 1750 km **59. See below. 61.** magnitude ≈ 6.2 mph; direction: $\approx 32°$ E of S (or $58°$ S of E) **63-65. See below. 67.** $\approx(-12.5, 21.65)$ **69.** magnitude $= \sqrt{1637} \approx 40.5$; direction: $\approx 50°$ W of S (or $\approx 40°$ S of W)

29.

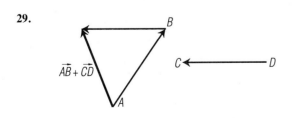

31.

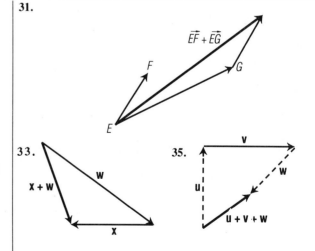

49. sample:

59. The boat will move in the direction $\overrightarrow{OM}$.

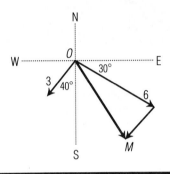

63.

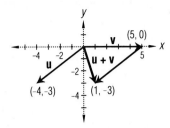

65.

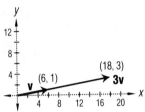

LESSON 15-1 (pp. 732–739)

3. 98° **5.** bisects **7. b.** median to the base, bisector of the vertex angle. **c.** bisector of the vertex angle, perpendicular bisector of the base **d.** perpendicular bisector of the base, altitude of the triangle **9.** False **11.** $25\sqrt{2} \approx 35.4$ m **13.** ≈ 22.3 m **15.** $\sqrt{2.75} \approx 1.66$ ft **17.** 12 units **19.** 360° **21.** $\frac{28}{15} \approx 1.87$ m³ **23. a.** $\frac{(n-2) \cdot 180}{n}$ **b.** 135

LESSON 15-2 (pp. 740–744)

1. 2 plays 7, 3 plays 5, 4 plays 6, 1 bye **3.** parallel **5.** 6–1, 5–2, 4–3, 7 bye **7. See below. 9.** True **11.** Two chords have the same length, so after 3 weeks, the pairings will be repeated. **13.** (c) and (d) **15.** $45\sqrt{3} \approx 77.9$ mm **17. See below. 19.** 1.8 miles **21. See below.**

7. Sample:

1st week	2nd	3rd	4th	5th	6th	7th
7–2	1–3	2–4	3–5	4–6	5–7	6–1
6–3	7–4	1–5	2–6	3–7	4–1	5–2
5–4	6–5	7–6	1–7	2–1	3–2	4–3
1–8	2–8	3–8	4–8	5–8	6–8	7–8

17.

Conclusions	Justifications
1. $\ell \perp \overline{CE}$	Tangent to Circle Theorem
2. $\overline{AB} \perp \overline{CE}$	Chord-Center Theorem (parts b and c)
3. $\overline{AB} \parallel \ell$	Two Perpendiculars Theorem

21.

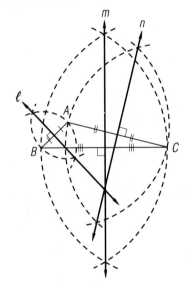

LESSON 15-3 (pp. 745–751)

3. 48.5 **7. a.** 25 **b.** 65 **c.** 90 **d.** right **9. a.** n **b.** $\frac{n}{2}$ **11. See below. 13.** m∠D = 90, m∠DCA = 60, m∠ACB = 45, m∠DCB = 105, m∠B = 90, m∠BAC = 45, m∠BAD = 75 **15. a.** Inscribed Angle Theorem **b.** Inscribed Angle Theorem **c.** Transitive Property of Equality (steps 1 and 2) **17. See below. 19. a.** 72° **b.** 500sin36° ≈ 294 units **21.** $\sqrt{700} \approx$ 26.46 yards

11.

Conclusions	Justifications
m∠ABC = m∠ABD − m∠CBD	Angle Addition Postulate
= ½m$\widehat{AD}$ − ½m$\widehat{CD}$	by Case I
= ½(m$\widehat{AD}$ − m$\widehat{CD}$)	Distributive Property
= ½m$\widehat{AC}$	Arc Addition

17. Sample: 2–11, 3–10, 4–9, 5–8, 6–7, 1–12. For the remaining weeks, rotate the chords of the diagram below:

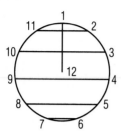

LESSON 15-4 (pp. 752–757)

1–7. See below. 11. a. m∠1 = 30, m∠2 = 30, m∠3 = 30, m∠4 = 30 **b.** True **13.** perpendicular bisector **15. a.** m∠A = m∠CDA = 30, m∠ACD = 120, m∠ADB = 90, m∠BCD = m∠BDC = m∠CBD = 60 **b.** x **c.** 7√3 ≈ 12.12 **17.** 625π ≈ 1963.5 square feet

1.

3. anywhere on $\widehat{ACB}$

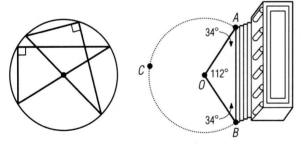

5. a. The photographer should stand at point P, which is about 25.9 m from the steps.

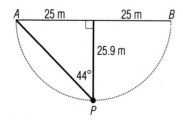

b. They can stand anywhere on $\widehat{APB}$.

7.

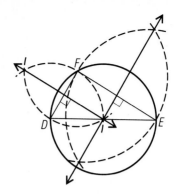

LESSON 15-5 (pp. 758–762)

1. a. 12.5 **b.** 48 **c.** 60.5 **d.** 119.5 **3.** 100 **5. a.** 65 **b.** 15 **7.** infinitely many **9. a.** 40 **b.** 70 **11. See below.**
13. m∠A = 122.5, m∠B = 85, m∠C = 95, m∠D = 102.5, m∠E = 135 **15.** 2√107.25 ≈ 20.71 inches **17.** x = 8 or -8

11.

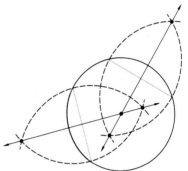

LESSON 15-6 (pp. 763–768)

1. a. 90 **b.** 55 **3.** 54 **5. a.** 142.5 **b.** 60 **c.** 97.5 **7.** m$\widehat{QTR}$ = 205°; m$\widehat{QSR}$ = 155° **9.** If the measure of the major arc $\widehat{BD}$ is x°, and the measure of the minor arc $\widehat{BD}$ is y°, then m∠C = ½(x − y), by Tangent-Secant Theorem. Rearranging this, y = x − 2m∠C. But x = 360 − y. So, substitution gives y = 360 − y − 2m∠C. This simplifies to 2y = 360 − 2m∠C, or y = 180 − m∠C. **11.** 110° **13. a.** 65 **b.** 92.5 **c.** 87.5 **d.** 22.5 **15. a.** Yes **b.** not necessarily **17.** 25π ≈ 78.5 in.² **19.** BC = 15; JG = 16; m∠G = 81 **21. a.** 2304π ≈ 7238.2 mm³ **b.** 576π ≈ 1809.6 mm²

LESSON 15-7 (pp. 769–774)

3. 8 **7.** 4 **9.** 6 **11.** True; PA · PC = PB · PD, so dividing by PA = PD, the result is PC = PB. **13.** Yes; since D, C, and P are collinear, and B, A, and P are collinear, then D, C, P, B, and A are coplanar. Points D, C, A, and B lie on the circle which is the intersection of that plane and the sphere. Apply the Secant Length Theorem to this circle. **15.** 135° **17. See below. 19. a.** 20 **b.** $\frac{20}{21}$ ≈ .952 **c.** $\frac{21}{29}$ ≈ .724 **d.** $\frac{21}{29}$ ≈ .724

17. You can stand anywhere on the part of the circle drawn below.

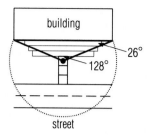

LESSON 15-8 (pp. 775–779)

1. a square with side 10 ft **3.** The minimum area is as close to zero as you like. **5. See below. 7.** $6\pi \approx 18.8$ cm **9.**

Question 8 **11. a.** 540 ft^2 **b.** $\frac{2025}{\pi} \approx 645$ ft^2 **13. a.** 12.4 units

b. 224 **15. a.** 130° **b.** 50° **17.** 64 **19. a.** If our class has done every lesson in the book, then we will have finished the next lesson. **b.** If we do not finish the next lesson, then our class will not have done every lesson in the book. **c.** If our class has not done every lesson in the book, then we will not have finished the next lesson.

CHAPTER 15 PROGRESS SELF-TEST (pp. 786–787)

1. See below. 2. See below. 3. Points O and M are equidistant from points X and Y, so $\overleftrightarrow{OM}$ is the $\perp$ bisector of $\overline{XY}$. Line ℓ is a tangent line, so $\ell \perp \overline{OQ}$. So $\ell \parallel \overline{XY}$ by the Two Parallels Theorem. **4.** Draw segments $\overline{JL}$ and $\overline{KM}$. In each of the four small right isosceles triangles, the side is 30 (the radius of the circle) so the hypotenuse is $30\sqrt{2}$. So the perimeter of $JKLM$ is $4(30\sqrt{2}) = 120\sqrt{2} \approx 169.7$ units. **5.** $\angle B$, an inscribed angle, is measured by half its intercepted arc. So m$\angle B = \frac{1}{2}(\overset{\frown}{DC}) = \frac{1}{2}(80) = 40$. **6.** To find m$\overset{\frown}{AB}$, use the property that $\angle DEC$ is measured by half the sum of the intercepted arcs. So m$\angle DEC = \frac{1}{2}(\text{m}\overset{\frown}{DC} + \text{m}\overset{\frown}{AB})$ or $110 = \frac{1}{2}(80 + \text{m}\overset{\frown}{AB})$. Then $220 = 80 + \text{m}\overset{\frown}{AB}$ and m$\overset{\frown}{AB} = 140°$, **7.** To find m$\angle R$, first find m$\overset{\frown}{VT}$: m$\overset{\frown}{VT} = 360° - \text{m}\overset{\frown}{VUT} = 360° - (80° + 30° + 140°) = 360° - 250° = 110°$. Then m$\angle R = \frac{1}{2}(\text{m}\overset{\frown}{VT} - \text{m}\overset{\frown}{US}) = \frac{1}{2}(110 - 30) = \frac{1}{2}(80) = 40$. **8.** $\overline{PT}$ and $\overline{PU}$ are tangents to $\odot O$, so $\overline{PT} \perp \overline{OT}$ and $\overline{PU} \perp \overline{OU}$. Given that m$\overset{\frown}{UT} = 90$, then m$\angle O = 90$ and $\angle P$ is a right angle because the sum of the four angles in quadrilateral $OUPT$ is 360°. So $OUPT$ is a rectangle by the definition of rectangle (sufficient condition). Moreover, $PT = PU$ because two tangents to a circle from an external point have the same length. So $OUPT$ is a square by the definition of square (sufficient condition). **9.** For the two chords $\overline{BC}$ and $\overline{AD}$, $(AQ)(DQ) = (CQ)(BQ)$. Using $AQ = 19$, $BQ = 40$, and $CQ = 38$, then $(19)(DQ) = (38)(40)$ so $19(DQ) = 1520$ and $DQ = 80$ units. **10.** For the two secants $\overline{WY}$ and $\overline{WV}$, $(WX)(WY) = (WZ)(WV)$. Using $WX = 12$, $XY = 16$, and W2 = 10, then $(12)(12 + 16) = (10)(10 + ZV)$ so $(12)(28) = 100 + 10(ZV)$ or $336 = 100 + 10(ZY)$ and $236 = 10(XY)$ so $ZV = 23.6$ units. **11. a.** The figure with the greatest area for a fixed perimeter is a circle. **b.** Using $C = 2\pi r$ with $C = 30$ cm,

---

5. sample:

LESSON 15-9 (pp. 780–784)

5. The minimum volume is as close to zero as you like. **9.**
a. $36\pi \approx 113$ m^2 **b.** Sample: radius of 2 m, height of 9 m; surface area: $44\pi \approx 138$ m^2 **c.** Sample: radius of 6 m, height of 3 m; surface area; $36\pi + 18\pi\sqrt{5} \approx 240$ m^2 **d.** less

11. $\frac{\pi\sqrt{x^3}}{6}$ or $\frac{\pi x\sqrt{x}}{6}$ units^3 **13. a.** circle: $\frac{2304}{\pi} \approx 733$ in.^{2}; square: 576 in.^{2} **b.** square **15.** $AC \cdot CB = CD \cdot CE$ by the Secant Length Theorem, and $AC = CB$ by the Chord-Center Theorem, parts b and c. So, substitution gives $AC \cdot AC = CD \cdot CE$ or $\frac{CD}{AC} = \frac{AC}{CE}$. This means that AC is the geometric mean of CD and CE. **17.** $\overline{BC}$ **19.** It is between 21 and 893 miles.

$30 = 2\pi r$ and $r = \frac{15}{\pi}$. Then using $A = \pi r^2$, $A = \pi\left(\frac{15}{\pi}\right)^2 = \frac{225\pi}{\pi^2} = \frac{225}{\pi} \approx 71.6$ cm^2. **12.** For a given volume, a sphere has the smallest surface area. So if a cube and sphere have the same volume, the cube will have the larger surface area. **13–14. See below.**

1.

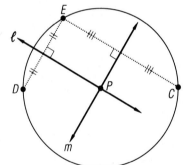

Construct the $\perp$ bisectors of $\overline{DE}$ and $\overline{EC}$. They meet at P, the center of the circle. Use point D, E, or C to draw the circle.

2. Start with 5 points equally spaced around a circle:

Draw chords connecting 5-2 and 4-3. This gives the first week's pairings:
Round 1: 2-5, 3-4, 1 bye
Rotate the chords around the circle for the next 4 rounds:
round 2: 1-3, 4-5, 2 bye
round 3: 2-4, 1-5, 3 bye
round 4: 3-5, 1-2, 4 bye
round 5: 1-4, 2-3, 5 bye.

13.

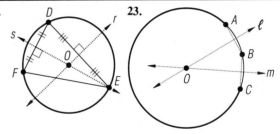

To find point T on the $\perp$ bisector of $\overline{AB}$: tan $32° = \frac{30}{TD}$, so TD $= 30 \boxed{\div} 32 \boxed{\tan} \boxed{=} \approx 48$. Find the circle through A, B, and T; then at any point on $\overset{\frown}{ATB}$ the entire stage will fit and fill the camera angle. **14.** From Question 13, you can stand 48 feet from the center of the stage.

The chart below keys the **Progress Self-Test** questions to the objectives in the **Chapter 15 Review** on pages 788–791. This will enable you to locate those **Chapter 15 Review** questions that correspond to questions you missed on the **Progress Self-Test**. The lesson where the material is covered is also indicated in the chart.

Question	1	2	3	4	5	
Objective	D	K	F	A	B	
Lesson	15-4	15-2	15-1	15-1	15-3	
Question	6–7	8	9,10	11	12	13,14
Objective	C	G	E	J	H	I
Lesson	15-5	15-6	15-7	15-8	15-9	15-4

CHAPTER 15 REVIEW (pp. 778–791)

1. 12 units **3.** 12 units **5.** 110sin72° $\approx$ 104.6 mm **7.** 106° **9.** 91 **11.** 52 **13.** mDE = 65° **15.** 14 **17.** 78 **19–23. See below. 25.** 21 units **27.** 12 units **29.** not necessarily true and so unjustifiable **31.** m$\angle ZWY$ = m$\angle ZWX$, since both are right angles, by the Chord-Center Theorem, parts b and c. YW = WX, since W is the midpoint of $\overline{XY}$. $ZW = ZW$, so $\triangle ZWY$, $\cong$ $\triangle ZWX$, by SAS Congruence. Therefore, $\overline{ZY} \cong \overline{ZX}$, from the CPCT Theorem, and so $\triangle ZYX$ is isosceles. **33.** $\frac{x}{2}$ **35. a.** a circle **b.** $\sqrt{\frac{800}{\pi}} \cdot 2\pi$, or about 100 feet **37. a.** square: 64 sq in.; circle: $\pi(\frac{32}{2\pi})^2 \approx 81.5$ sq in. **b.** the circle **39. a.** a cube **b.** $(\sqrt{8})^3 \approx 22.6$ in.^{3} **41. See below 43. a.** a sphere **b.** Sample answer: the container could easily roll off a shelf. **45–47. See below. 49.** Use the answer to Question 48. Replace the "bye" with the 12th team L.

19.

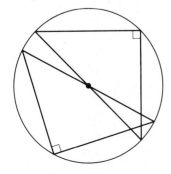

21. **23.**

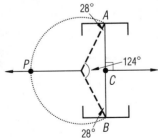

41. a. anywhere on $\overset{\frown}{APB}$ (or its reflection image over $\overleftrightarrow{AB}$)

b. $\frac{60}{\tan 31°} \approx 100$ yards

45. sample:

47. sample:

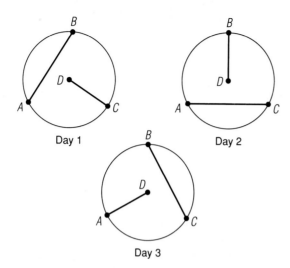

Day 1

Day 2

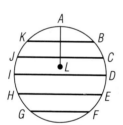

Day 3

Day 1: *A* vs. *B*, *C* vs. *D*
Day 2: *A* vs. *C*, *B* vs. *D*
Day 3: *A* vs. *D*, *B* vs. *C*

49.

1 Overview of UCSMP

The Reasons for UCSMP

■ Recommendations for Change

The mathematics curriculum has undergone changes in every country of the world throughout this century, as a result of an increasing number of students staying in school longer, a greater number of technically competent workers and citizens being needed, and because of major advances in mathematics itself. In the last generation, these developments have been accelerated due to the widespread appearance of computers with their unprecedented abilities to handle and display information.

In the last 100 years, periodically there have been national groups examining the curriculum in light of these changes in society. (A study of these reports can be found in *A History of Mathematics Education in the United States and Canada*, the 30th Yearbook of the National Council of Teachers of Mathematics, 1970.) The most recent era of reports can be said to have begun in the years 1975–1980, with the publication of reports by various national mathematics organizations calling attention to serious problems in the education of our youth.

Beginning in 1980, these reports were joined by governmental and private reports on the state of American education with broad recommendations for school practice. Two of these are notable for their specific remarks about mathematics education.

1983: National Commission on Excellence in Education. *A Nation At Risk.*

"The teaching of mathematics in high school should equip graduates to: (a) understand geometric and algebraic concepts; (b) understand elementary probability and statistics; (c) apply mathematics in everyday situations; and (d) estimate, approximate, measure, and test the accuracy of their calculations. In addition to the traditional sequence of studies available for college-bound students, new, equally demanding mathematics curricula need to be developed for those who do not plan to continue their formal education immediately." (p. 25)

1983: College Board (Project EQuality). *Academic Preparation for College: What Students Need to Know and Be Able to Do.*

All students (college-bound or not) should have:
"The ability to apply mathematical techniques in the solution of real-life problems and to recognize when to apply those techniques.
Familiarity with the language, notation, and deductive nature of mathematics and the ability to express quantitative ideas with precision.
The ability to use computers and calculators.
Familiarity with the basic concepts of statistics and statistical reasoning.
Knowledge in considerable depth and detail of algebra, geometry, and functions." (p. 20)

The specific remarks about school mathematics in these documents for the most part mirror what appeared in the earlier reports. Thus, **given what seemed to be a broad consensus on the problems and desirable changes in pre-college mathematics instruction, it was decided at the outset of UCSMP, that UCSMP would not attempt to form its own set of recommendations, but undertake the task of translating the existing recommendations into the reality of classrooms and schools.**

At the secondary (7–12) level, these reports respond to two generally perceived problems pursuant to mathematics education.

GENERAL PROBLEM 1: Students do not learn enough mathematics by the time they leave school.

Specifically:

(A) Many students lack the mathematics background necessary to succeed in college, on the job, or in daily affairs.

(B) Even those students who possess mathematical skills are not introduced to enough applications of the mathematics they know.

(C) Students do not get enough experience with problems and questions that require some thought before answering.

(D) Many students terminate their study of mathematics too soon, not realizing the importance mathematics has in later schooling and in the marketplace.

(E) Students do not read mathematics books and, as a result, do not learn to become independent learners capable of acquiring mathematics outside of school when the need arises.

These situations lead us to want to
upgrade students' achievement.

GENERAL PROBLEM 2: The school mathematics curriculum has not kept up with changes in mathematics and the ways in which mathematics is used.

Specifically:

(A) Current mathematics curricula have not taken into account today's calculator and computer technology.

(B) Students who do succeed in secondary school mathematics are prepared for calculus, but are not equipped for the other mathematics they will encounter in college.

(C) Statistical ideas are found everywhere, from newspapers to research studies, but are not found in most secondary school mathematics curricula.

(D) The emergence of computer science has increased the importance of a background in discrete mathematics.

(E) Mathematics is now applied to areas outside the realm of the physical sciences, as much as within the field itself, but these applications are rarely taught and even more rarely tested.

(F) Estimation and approximation techniques are important in all of mathematics, from arithmetic on.

These existing situations lead us to a desire to
update the mathematics curriculum.

Since the inception of UCSMP, reports from national groups of mathematics educators have reiterated the above problems, and research has confirmed their existence. Three reports are of special significance to UCSMP.

Universities have for many years had to recognize that mathematics encompasses far more than algebra, geometry, and analysis. The term **mathematical sciences** is an umbrella designation which includes traditional mathematics as well as a number of other disciplines. The largest of these other disciplines today are statistics, computer science, and applied mathematics. In 1983, the Conference Board of the Mathematical Sciences produced a report, *The Mathematical Sciences Curriculum: What Is Still Fundamental and What Is Not*. THE UCSMP GRADES 7–12 CAN BE CONSIDERED TO BE THE FIRST MATHEMATICAL SCIENCES CURRICULUM.

The Second International Mathematics Study (SIMS) was conducted in 1981–82 and involved 23 populations in 21 countries. At the eighth-grade level, virtually all students attend school in all those countries. At the 12th-grade level, the population tested consisted of those who are in the normal college preparatory courses, which, in the United States, include precalculus and calculus classes.

The UCSMP grades 7–12 can be considered to be the first mathematical sciences curriculum.

At the eighth-grade level, our students scored at or below the international average on all five subtests: arithmetic, measurement, algebra, geometry, and statistics. We are far below the top: Japan looked at the test and decided it was too easy for their 8th-graders, and so gave it at 7th grade. Still, the median Japanese 7th-grader performed at the 95th percentile of United States 8th-graders. These kinds of results have been confirmed in other studies, comparing students at lower-grade levels.

At the twelfth-grade level, about 13% of our population is enrolled in precalculus or calculus; the mean among developed countries is about 16%. Thus, the United States no longer keeps more students in mathematics than other developed countries, yet our advanced placement students do not perform well when compared to their peers in other countries. SIMS found:

1987: Second International Mathematics Study (SIMS). *The Underachieving Curriculum.*

In the U.S., the achievement of the Calculus classes, the nation's **best** mathematics students, was at or near the average achievement of the advanced secondary school mathematics students in other countries. (In most countries, **all** advanced mathematics students take calculus. In the U.S., only about one-fifth do.) The achievement of the U.S. Precalculus students (the majority of twelfth grade college-preparatory students) was substantially below the international average. In some cases the U.S. ranked with the lower one-fourth of all countries in the Study, and was the lowest of the advanced industrialized countries. (*The Underachieving Curriculum, p. vii.*)

The situation is, of course, even worse for those who do not take precalculus mathematics in high school. Such students either have performed poorly in their last mathematics course, a situation which has caused them not to go on in mathematics, or they were performing poorly in junior high school and had to take remedial mathematics as 9th-graders. If these students go to college, they invariably take remedial mathematics, which is taught at a faster pace than in high school, and the failure rates in such courses often exceed 40%. If they do not go to college but join the job market, they lack the mathematics needed to understand today's technology. IT IS NO UNDERSTATEMENT TO SAY THAT UCSMP HAS RECEIVED ITS FUNDING FROM BUSINESS AND INDUSTRY BECAUSE THOSE WHO LEAVE SCHOOLING TO JOIN THE WORK FORCE ARE WOEFULLY WEAK IN THE MATHEMATICS THEY WILL NEED.

SIMS recommended steps to renew school mathematics in the United States. **The UCSMP secondary curriculum implements the curriculum recommendations of the Second International Mathematics Study.**

In 1986, the National Council of Teachers of Mathematics began an ambitious effort to detail the curriculum it would like to see in schools. The "NCTM Standards," as they have come to be called, involve both content and methodology. The *Standards* document is divided into four sections, K–4, 5–8, 9–12, and Evaluation. Space limits our discussion here to just a few quotes from the 5–8 and 9–12 standards.

It is no understatement to say that UCSMP has received its funding from business and industry because those who leave schooling to join the work force are woefully weak in the mathematics they will need.

1989: National Council of Teachers of Mathematics. *Curriculum and Evaluation Standards for School Mathematics*

"The 5–8 curriculum should include the following features:

■ Problem situations that establish the need for new ideas and motivate students should serve as the context for mathematics in grades 5–8. Although a specific idea might be forgotten, the context in which it is learned can be remembered and the idea can be re-created. In developing the problem situations, teachers should emphasize the application to real-world problems as well as to other settings relevant to middle school students.

■ Communication with and about mathematics and mathematical reasoning should permeate the 5–8 curriculum.

■ A broad range of topics should be taught, including number concepts, computation, estimation, functions, algebra, statistics, probability, geometry, and measurement. Although each of these areas is valid mathematics in its own right, they should be taught together as an integrated whole, not as isolated topics; the connections between them should be a prominent feature of the curriculum.

■ Technology, including calculators, computers, and videos, should be used when appropriate. These devices and formats free students from tedious computations and allow them to concentrate on problem solving and other important content. They also give them new means to explore content. As paper-and-pencil computation becomes less important, the skills and understanding required to make proficient use of calculators and computers become more important." (pp. 66–67)

"The standards for grades 9–12 are based on the following assumptions:

■ Students entering grade 9 will have experienced mathematics in the context of the broad, rich curriculum as outlined in the K–8 standards.

The UCSMP secondary curriculum is the first full mathematics curriculum that is consistent with the recommendations of the NCTM Standards.

■ The level of [paper-and-pencil] computational proficiency suggested in the K–8 standards will be expected of all students; however, no student will be denied access to the study of mathematics in grades 9–12 because of a lack of computational facility.

■ Although arithmetic computation will not be a direct object of study in grades 9–12, conceptual and procedural understandings of number, numeration, and operations, and the ability to make estimations and approximations and to judge the reasonableness of results will be strengthened in the context of applications and problem solving, including those situations dealing with issues of scientific computation.

■ Scientific calculators with graphing capabilities will be available to all students at all times.

■ A computer will be available at all times in every classroom for demonstration purposes, and all students will have access to computers for individual and group work.

■ At least three years of mathematical study will be required of all secondary school students.

■ These three years of mathematical study will revolve around a core curriculum differentiated by the depth and breadth of the treatment of topics and by the nature of applications.

■ Four years of mathematical study will be required of all college-intending students.

■ These four years of mathematical study will revolve around a broadened curriculum that includes extensions of the core topics and for which calculus is no longer viewed as *the* capstone experience.

■ All students will study appropriate mathematics during their senior year." (pp. 124–125)

THE UCSMP SECONDARY CURRICULUM IS THE FIRST FULL MATHEMATICS CURRICULUM THAT IS CONSISTENT WITH THE RECOMMENDATIONS OF THE NCTM STANDARDS.

■ Accomplishing the Goals

We at UCSMP believe that the goals of the various reform groups since 1975 can be accomplished, but not without a substantial reworking of the curriculum. It is not enough simply to insert applications, a bit of statistics, and take students a few times a year to a computer. Currently the greatest amount of time in arithmetic is spent on calculation, in algebra on manipulating polynomials and rational expressions, in geometry on proof, in advanced algebra and later courses on functions. These topics—the core of the curriculum—are the most affected by technology.

It is also not enough to raise graduation requirements, although that is the simplest action to take. Increases in requirements characteristically lead to one of two situations. If the courses are kept the same, the result is typically a greater number of failures and even a greater number of dropouts. If the courses are eased, the result is lower performance for many students as they are brought through a weakened curriculum.

The fundamental problem, as SIMS noted, is the curriculum, and the fundamental problem in the curriculum is **time.** There is not enough time in the current 4-year algebra-geometry-algebra-precalculus curriculum to prepare students for calculus, and the recommendations are asking students to learn even more content.

Fortunately, there is time to be had, because the existing curriculum wastes time. It underestimates what students know when they enter the classroom and needlessly reviews what students have already learned. This needless review has been documented by Jim Flanders, a UCSMP staff member ("How Much of the Content in Mathematics Textbooks is New?" *Arithmetic Teacher,* September, 1987). Examining textbooks of the early 1980s, Flanders reports that at grade 2 there is little new. In grades 3–5, about half the pages have something new on them. But over half the pages in grades 6–8 are totally review.

And then in the 9th grade the axe falls. Flanders found that almost 90% of the pages of first-year algebra texts have content new to the student. The student, having sat for years in mathematics classes where little was new, is overwhelmed. Some people interpret the overwhelming as the student "not being ready" for algebra, but we interpret it as the student being swamped by the pace. When you have been in a classroom in which at most only 1 of 3 days is devoted to anything new, you are not ready for a new idea every day.

This amount of review in grades K–8, coupled with the magnitude of review in previous years, effectively decelerates students at least 1–2 years compared to students in other countries. It explains why almost all industrialized countries of the world, except the U.S. and Canada (and some French-speaking countries who do geometry before algebra), can begin concentrated study of algebra in the 7th or 8th grade.

Thus we believe that ALGEBRA SHOULD BE TAUGHT ONE YEAR EARLIER TO MOST STUDENTS THAN IS CURRENTLY THE CASE.

However, we do not believe students should take calculus one year earlier than they do presently. It seems that most students who take four years of college preparatory mathematics successfully in high schools do not begin college with calculus. As an example, consider the data reported by Bert Waits and Frank Demana in the *Mathematics Teacher* (January, 1988). Of students entering Ohio State University with exactly four years of college preparatory high-school mathematics, only 8% placed into calculus on the Ohio State mathematics placement test. The majority placed into pre-calculus, with 31% requiring one semester and 42% requiring two semesters of work. The remaining 19% placed into remedial courses below precalculus.

Those students who take algebra in the 8th grade and are successful in calculus at the 12th grade are given quite a bit more than the normal four years of college preparatory mathematics in their "honors" or "advanced" courses. It is not stretching the point too much to say that they take five years of mathematics crammed into four years.

Thus, even with the current curriculum, four years are not enough to take a typical student from algebra to calculus. Given that the latest recommendations ask for students to learn more mathematics, **we believe five years of college preparatory mathematics** *beginning with algebra* **are necessary to provide the time for students to learn the mathematics they need for college in the 1990s.** The UCSMP secondary curriculum is designed with that in mind.

. . . algebra should be taught one year earlier to most students than is currently the case.

The UCSMP Secondary Curriculum

The UCSMP curriculum for grades 7–12
consists of these six courses:

Transition Mathematics

Algebra

Geometry

Advanced Algebra

Functions, Statistics, and Trigonometry with Computers

Precalculus and Discrete Mathematics

EACH COURSE IS MEANT TO STAND ALONE. Each course has
also been tested alone. HOWEVER, TO TAKE BEST ADVAN-
TAGE OF THESE MATERIALS, AND TO HAVE THEM
APPROPRIATE FOR THE GREATEST NUMBER OF STUDENTS, IT
IS PREFERABLE TO USE THEM IN SEQUENCE.

Each course is meant to stand alone. . . . However, to take best advantage of these materials, and to have them appropriate for the greatest number of students, it is preferable to use them in sequence.

■ Content Features

Transition Mathematics: This text weaves three themes—
applied arithmetic, pre-algebra and pre-geometry—by focusing on arithmetic operations in mathematics and the real
world. Variables are used as pattern generalizers, abbreviations in formulas, and unknowns in problems, and are
represented on the number line and graphed in the coordinate
plane. Basic arithmetic and algebraic skills are connected to
corresponding geometry topics.

Algebra: This text has a scope far wider than most other algebra texts. It uses statistics and geometry as settings for
work with linear expressions and sentences. Probability provides a context for algebraic fractions, functions, and set
ideas. There is much work with graphing. Applications motivate all topics, and include exponential growth and
compound interest.

Geometry: This text presents coordinates, transformations,
measurement formulas, and three-dimensional figures in the
first half of the book. Concentrated work with proof-writing
is delayed until midyear and later, following a carefully sequenced development of the logical and conceptual precursors
to proof.

Advanced Algebra: This course emphasizes facility with algebraic expressions and forms, especially linear and quadratic
forms, powers and roots, and functions based on these concepts. Students study logarithmic, trigonometric, polynomial,
and other special functions both for their abstract properties
and as tools for modeling real-world situations. A geometry
course or its equivalent is a prerequisite, for geometric ideas
are utilized throughout.

**Functions, Statistics, and Trigonometry with Computers
(FST):** FST integrates statistical and algebraic concepts, and
previews calculus in work with functions and intuitive notions of limits. Computers are assumed available for student
use in plotting functions, analyzing data, and simulating experiments. Enough trigonometry is available to constitute a
standard precalculus course in trigonometry and circular functions.

Precalculus and Discrete Mathematics (PDM): PDM integrates the background students must have, to be successful in calculus, with the discrete mathematics helpful for computer study. The study of number systems, three-dimensional coordinate geometry, and some linear algebra is also included. Mathematical thinking, including specific attention to formal logic and proof, is a theme throughout.

■ General Features

Wider Scope: Geometry and discrete mathematics are present in all courses. Substantial amounts of statistics are integrated into the study of algebra and functions. The history of concepts and recent developments in mathematics and its applications are included as part of the lessons themselves.

Reality Orientation: Each mathematical idea is studied in detail for its applications to the understanding of real-world situations, or the solving of problems like those found in the real world. The reality orientation extends also to the approaches allowed the student in working out problems. Students are expected to use scientific calculators. Calculators are assumed throughout the series (and should be allowed on tests), because virtually all individuals who use mathematics today use calculators.

Problem Solving: Like skills, problem solving must be practiced. When practiced, problem solving becomes far less difficult. All lessons contain a variety of questions so that students do not blindly copy one question to do the next. Explorations are a feature of the first four years, and Projects are offered in the last two years. Some problem-solving techniques are so important that at times they (rather than the problems) are the focus of instruction.

Enhancing Performance: Each book's format is designed to maximize the acquisition of both skills and concepts, with lessons meant to take one day to cover. Within each lesson there is review of material from previous lessons from that chapter or from previous chapters. This gives the student more time to learn the material. The lessons themselves are sequenced into carefully constructed chapters. Progress Self-Test and Chapter Review questions, keyed to objectives in all the dimensions of understanding, are then used to solidify performance of skills and concepts from the chapter, so that they may be applied later with confidence. (See pages T35–T36 for more detail.)

Reading: Reading is emphasized throughout. Students can read; they must learn to read mathematics in order to become able to use mathematics outside of school. Every lesson has reading and contains questions covering that reading. (See page T37 for more detail.)

Understanding: Four dimensions of understanding are emphasized: skill in carrying out various algorithms; developing and using mathematical properties and relationships; applying mathematics in realistic situations; and representing or picturing mathematical concepts. We call this the SPUR approach: **S**kills, **P**roperties, **U**ses, **R**epresentations. On occasion, a fifth dimension of understanding, the historical dimension, is discussed. (See pages T38–T39 for more detail.)

Technology: Scientific calculators are recommended because they use an order of operations closer to that found in algebra and have numerous keys that are helpful in understanding concepts at this level. Work with computers is carefully sequenced within each year and between the years, with gradual gain in sophistication until FST, where computers are an essential element. In all courses, integrated computer exercises show how the computer can be used as a helpful tool in doing mathematics. Students are expected to run and modify programs, but are not taught programming. (See pages T40–T43 for more detail.)

■ Target Populations

We believe that all high-school graduates should take courses through *Advanced Algebra*, that all students planning to go to college should take courses through *Functions, Statistics, and Trigonometry with Computers*, and that students planning majors in technical areas should take all six UCSMP courses.

The fundamental principle in placing students into the first of these courses is that entry should not be based on age, but on mathematical knowledge. Our studies indicate that about 10% of students nationally are ready for *Transition Mathematics* at 6th grade, about another 40% at 7th grade, another 20% at 8th grade, and another 10–15% at 9th grade. We caution that these percentages are national, not local percentages, and the variability in our nation is enormous. We have tested the materials in school districts where few students are at grade level, where *Transition Mathematics* is appropriate for no more than the upper half of 8th-graders. We have tested also in school districts where as many as 90% of the students have successfully used *Transition Mathematics* in 7th grade.

However, the percentages are not automatic. Students who do not reach 7th-grade competence until the 9th-grade level often do not possess the study habits necessary for successful completion of these courses. At the 9th-grade level, *Transition Mathematics* has been substituted successfully either for a traditional pre-algebra course or for the first year of an algebra course spread out over two years. It does not work as a substitute for a general mathematics course in which there is no expectation that students will take algebra the following year.

On page T27 is a description of this curriculum and the populations for which it is intended. The percentiles are national percentiles on a 7th-grade standardized mathematics test using 7th-grade norms, and apply to students entering the program with *Transition Mathematics*. Some school districts have felt that students should also be reading at least at a 7th-grade reading level as well. See page T28 for advice when starting with a later course.

Top 10%: The top 10% nationally reach the 7th-grade level of competence a year early. They are ready for *Transition Mathematics* in 6th grade and take it then. They proceed through the entire curriculum by 11th grade and can take calculus in 12th grade. We recommend that these students be expected to do the Extensions suggested in this Teacher's Edition. Teachers may also wish to enrich courses for these students further with problems from mathematics contests.

50th–90th percentile: These students should be expected to take mathematics at least through the 11th grade, by which time they will have the mathematics needed for all college majors except those in the hard sciences and engineering. For that they need 12th-grade mathematics.

30th–70th percentile: These students begin *Transition Mathematics* one year later, in 8th grade. The college-bound student in this curriculum is more likely to take four years of mathematics because the last course is hands-on with computers and provides the kind of mathematics needed for any major.

15th–50th percentile: Students who do not reach the 7th-grade level in mathematics until 9th grade or later should not be tracked into courses that put them further behind. Rather, they should be put into this curriculum and counseled on study skills. The logic is simple: mathematics is too important to be ignored. If one is behind in one's mathematical knowledge, the need is to work more at it, not less.

Even if a student begins with *Transition Mathematics* at 9th grade, that student can finish *Advanced Algebra* by the time of graduation from high school. That would be enough mathematics to enable the student to get into most colleges.

UCSMP Target Populations in Grades 7–12

Each course is meant to stand alone. However, to take best advantage of these materials, and have them appropriate for the greatest number of students, it is preferable to use them in sequence. Although it is suggested that students begin with *Transition Mathematics*, students may enter the UCSMP curriculum at any point. Below is a brief description of the UCSMP curriculum and the populations for which it is intended.

The top 10% of students are ready for *Transition Mathematics* at 6th grade. These students can proceed through the entire curriculum by 11th grade and take calculus in the 12th grade.

Students in the 50th–90th percentile on a 7th-grade standardized mathematics test should be ready to take *Transition Mathematics* in 7th grade.

Students who do not reach the 7th-grade level in mathematics until the 8th grade **(in the 30th–70th percentile)** begin *Transition Mathematics* in 8th grade.

Students who don't reach the 7th-grade level in mathematics until the 9th grade **(in the 15th–50th percentile)** begin *Transition Mathematics* in the 9th grade.

Grade				
6	Transition Mathematics			
7	Algebra	Transition Mathematics		
8	Geometry	Algebra	Transition Mathematics	
9	Advanced Algebra	Geometry	Algebra	Transition Mathematics
10	Functions, Statistics, and Trigonometry with Computers	Advanced Algebra	Geometry	Algebra
11	Precalculus and Discrete Mathematics	Functions, Statistics, and Trigonometry with Computers	Advanced Algebra	Geometry
12	Calculus (Not part of UCSMP)	Precalculus and Discrete Mathematics	Functions, Statistics, and Trigonometry with Computers	Advanced Algebra

Starting in the Middle of the Series

From the beginning, every UCSMP course has been designed so that it could be used independently of other UCSMP courses. Accordingly, about half of the testing of UCSMP courses after *Transition Mathematics* has been with students who have not had any previous UCSMP courses. We have verified that any of the UCSMP courses can be taken successfully following the typical prerequisite courses in the standard curriculum.

ALGEBRA:
No additional prerequisites other than those needed for success in any algebra course are needed for success in UCSMP *Algebra*. Students who have studied *Transition Mathematics* tend to cover more of UCSMP *Algebra* than other students because they tend to know more algebra, because they are accustomed to the style of the book, and because they have been introduced to more of the applications of algebra.

UCSMP *Algebra* prepares students for any standard geometry course.

GEOMETRY:
No additional prerequisites other than those needed for success in any geometry course are needed for success in UCSMP *Geometry*. UCSMP *Geometry* can be used with faster, average, and slower students who have these prerequisites. Prior study of *Transition Mathematics* and UCSMP *Algebra* insures this background, but this content is also found in virtually all existing middle school or junior high school texts.

Classes of students who have studied UCSMP *Algebra* tend to cover more UCSMP *Geometry* than other classes because they know more geometry and are better at the algebra used in geometry.

Students who have studied UCSMP *Geometry* are ready for any second-year algebra text.

ADVANCED ALGEBRA:
UCSMP *Advanced Algebra* should not be taken before a geometry course but can be used following any standard geometry text. Students who have studied UCSMP *Advanced Algebra* are prepared for courses commonly found at the senior level, including trigonometry or precalculus courses.

FUNCTIONS, STATISTICS, AND TRIGONOMETRY WITH COMPUTERS:
FST assumes that students have completed a second-year algebra course. **No additional prerequisites other than those found in any second-year algebra text are needed for success in *FST*.**

PRECALCULUS AND DISCRETE MATHEMATICS
PDM can be taken successfully by students who have had *FST*, by students who have had typical senior level courses that include study of trigonometry and functions, and by top students who have successfully completed full advanced algebra and trigonometry courses.

PDM provides the background necessary for any typical calculus course, either at the high school or college level, including advanced placement calculus courses.

Development Cycle for UCSMP Texts

The development of each text has been in four stages. First, the overall goals for each course are created by UCSMP in consultation with a national advisory board of distinguished professors, and through discussion with classroom teachers, school administrators, and district and state mathematics supervisors.

The Advisory Board for the Secondary Component at the time of this planning consisted of Arthur F. Coxford, Jr., University of Michigan; David Duncan, University of Northern Iowa; James Fey, University of Maryland; Glenda Lappan, Michigan State University; Anthony Ralston, State University of New York at Buffalo; and James Schultz, Ohio State University.

As part of this stage, UCSMP devoted an annual School Conference, whose participants were mathematics supervisors and teachers, to discuss major issues in a particular area of the curriculum. Past conferences have centered on the following issues:

1984   Changing the Curriculum in Grades 7 and 8

1985   Changing Standards in School Algebra

1986   Functions, Computers, and Statistics in Secondary Mathematics

1987   Pre-College Mathematics

1988   Mathematics Teacher Education for Grades 7–12

At the second stage, UCSMP selects authors who write first drafts of the courses. Half of all UCSMP authors currently teach mathematics in secondary schools, and all authors and editors for the first five courses have secondary school teaching experience. The textbook authors or their surrogates initially teach the first drafts of Secondary Component texts, so that revision may benefit from first-hand classroom experience.

After revision by the authors or editors, materials enter the third stage in the text development. Classes of teachers not connected with the project use the books, and independent evaluators closely study student achievement, attitudes, and issues related to implementation. For the first three years in the series, this stage involved a formative evaluation in six to ten schools, and all teachers who used the materials periodically met at the university to provide feedback to UCSMP staff for a second revision. For the last three years in the series, this stage has involved a second pilot.

The fourth stage consists of a wider comparative evaluation. For the first three books, this evaluation has involved approximately 40 classrooms and thousands of students per book in schools all over the country. For the last three books in the series, this stage has involved a careful formative evaluation. As a result of these studies, the books have been revised for commercial publication by Scott, Foresman and Company, into the edition you are now reading. (See pages T46–T50 for a summary of this research.)

T30

2 UCSMP *Geometry*

Problems UCSMP *Geometry* Is Trying to Address

This book is different from many other geometry books. The differences are due to our attempt to respond to seven serious problems which cannot be treated by small changes in content or approach.

PROBLEM 1:
Large numbers of students do not see why they need geometry.

In the past, the content and sequence of a geometry course has been determined almost exclusively by the desire to teach abstract deductive reasoning. This motivation is insufficient for today's world, in which geometrical ideas are found in all branches of mathematics and its applications.

The UCSMP *Geometry* response: Logical thinking is not downplayed in this course, but the ability to apply geometry is made as important a priority. This is not as difficult a task as it may seem, for geometry is *the* branch of mathematics that connects mathematics with the real physical world. Indeed, Euclidean geometry has been mathematically described as the study of shape, and shapes are everywhere. We believe many geometry books have purposely avoided that which could help them the most — the experiences that everyone has had with shapes and forms.

Teachers of UCSMP *Geometry* report that this emphasis on applications has three particularly important effects. First, it virtually eliminates the question "Why do we have to study this?" Second, it helps develop mathematical intuition from visual intuition and, thereby, makes the material easier. Third, it encourages class discussion and helps students to become more involved in the content. We believe that we have developed a course that is accessible to a greater number of students — all students who complete algebra — without watering down the content.

PROBLEM 2:
Too many students leave geometry with not enough knowledge that they can apply in later courses.

Much of the content students will encounter in later mathematics courses deal with functions and relations. Transformations are examples of functions and, in UCSMP *Geometry*, function notation is used with them. There is evidence from the doctoral work of Anthone Kort at Northwestern University in 1970 that the kind of work we do with transformations in UCSMP *Geometry* increases the competence of students with function ideas in algebra and trigonometry. In UCSMP *Geometry*, study of transformations begins in Chapter 4 and is integrated throughout the remainder of the book. Coordinates are important for picturing functions and relations, so work with coordinates is integrated throughout UCSMP *Geometry*.

We keep a logical system going through the course, but we do not feel it necessary to have to prove every result that students use. An elementary school teacher can tell students about the infinitude of primes, without having to prove it. An algebra teacher can speak of the irrationality of π again without proof. Likewise, there are many nice and important geometry results that are simple to state, helpful to know, yet difficult to prove at this level. If theorems are important, we think they deserve mention. For example, a lesson is devoted to the Four-Color Theorem, but, of course, without its proof.

PROBLEM 3:
Students are not skillful enough, regardless of what they are taught.

A study conducted from the University of Chicago in 1980-81 (Usiskin, 1982) using almost 2700 geometry students from 11 schools in 5 states showed that the mean score of geometry students in some schools at the beginning of the year is higher that the mean score of geometry students in other schools at the end of the year. That is how poor their knowledge is to begin with. The geometry course itself is often taught with such an emphasis on proof that the content and applicability of theorems is ignored. Finally, geometry ideas are seldom reviewed in succeeding math courses.

The UCSMP response: Obviously the first step is to increase the knowledge of students entering geometry. Geometrical ideas are developed throughout the preceding UCSMP courses, *Transition Mathematics* and *Algebra*. In these courses, consistent with the van Hiele model of learning geometry (Hoffer, 1981; van Hiele, 1986), UCSMP *Geometry* provides experiences to help students identify and draw geometric figures and observe and identify their properties to help students master levels 1 and 2 in the van Hiele scheme. The evidence from our studies is that study from these books raises the level of knowledge of average students to the level of the best of entering geometry students. That is, based on geometry knowledge, average incoming UCSMP Geometry students test quite a bit like "honors" students.

During the geometry course itself, we believe that the most important content must come early enough so that it can be reviewed. For this reason, area and volume ideas are found earlier in UCSMP *Geometry* than in most books. To develop competence with a concept, we employ a four-stage process.

■ **Stage 1** involves a concentrated introduction to the ideas surrounding the concept: why it is needed, how to work with it, and the kinds of problems that can be solved with it. Most books are organized to have this stage, because teachers recognize that explanations of an idea require time, but few tell why ideas are needed. At the end of this stage, typically only the best students have mastered the concept. But in UCSMP *Geometry* this is only the beginning.

■ **Stage 2** occupies the following lessons in the chapter and consists of questions designed to increase competence in the concept. These are found in the review exercises. By the end of the lessons of the chapter, most students should have good competence, but some may not have enough.

■ **Stage 3** involves mastery learning. At the end of each chapter is a Progress Self-Test for students to take and judge how they are doing. Worked-out solutions are included to provide feedback and help to the student. This is followed by a list of objectives with review questions for students to acquire those skills they didn't have when taking the Progress Self-Test. Teachers are expected to spend 1-3 days on these sections to give students time to reach mastery. By the end of this stage, all students

should have gained mastery at least at the level of typical students covering the content, and some will have very high levels of mastery.

■ **Stage 4** continues the review. Vital concepts receive consistent emphasis throughout the book. The evidence (see pages T44-48) is that this four-stage process enables students to gain competence over a wider range of content than comparable students normally possess.

Many goemetric ideas, including area, volume, congruence, similarity, coordinates, and transformations, are applied in the next course in the UCSMP curriculum, *Advanced Algebra*. Thus unlike most second-year albegra courses which ignore a student's having taken geometry, the UCSMP curriculum reinforces that work.

PROBLEM 4:
Despite great effort, many students do not learn to do proofs.

The evidence from a nationwide study of proofwriting ability is that about one-third of all geometry students in proof-oriented courses do learn how to do proofs and about one-third cannot do even the simplest triangle congruence proof. (For a description of this unique study, see an article by Sharon Senk in the September 1985 *Mathematics Teacher*.) This is true despite the fact that about half of the school year (October through January or February) is devoted to teaching proofs. Obviously something is wrong, and it is not fixed by putting more time on this task. After six weeks, virtually every teacher knows that some students have learned to do proofs, and the others will not. For those others, the rest of the time spent on proof is misery.

Research (Senk, 1989; Wirszup, 1976) indicates that students' difficulties in learning to write proofs are due in part to unfamiliarity with prerequisite content. Geometry students generally have no idea why they should do proofs or what writing a proof will accomplish, and most have never before had to write any mathematical argument. We do not believe that difficulties with proof are caused by mathematical immaturity. Imagine if you were asked to take a course in Yang-Mills theory (which is actually a new theory in mathematics itself), prove things on the first day using a new form you weren't sure you understood using a manual of style and grammar written in another country. You would probably have quite a bit of trouble despite your maturity in mathematics.

The UCSMP *Geometry* response: We try to increase proof competence by carefully sequencing the writing of proof arguments, first with one-step justifications, then short proofs involving transitivity, then short congruence proofs, and finally some longer proofs. That is, we provide experiences to help students with van Hiele level 3 ideas before introducing level 4 activities. There is quite a bit of discussion of the system in which proofs are done; it makes no sense for a student to prove something if he or she does not understand the nature of assumptions in mathematics. We show flexibility in how the proofs are written — two-column proofs and proofs in paragraphs form are exemplified.

PROBLEM 5:
Students don't read.

Students using traditional texts tell us they don't read because (1) the text is uninteresting, and (2) they don't have to read — the teacher explains it for them. Some teachers think students are not capable of learning mathematics on their own. But students *must* learn to read for future success in mathematics.

Our response to (1): Every lesson of this book contains reading that we think is informative and interesting. This reading is a resource for information, for examples of how to do problems, for the history of major ideas, for applications of ideas, for connections between ideas in one place in the book and in another, and for motivation. Questions Covering the Reading test students' comprehension of the text.

Our response to (2): Because evidence shows that our students can read and understand the text, teachers have the freedom to teach in a variety of ways. It is not necessary for the teacher to explain every day what the text says. In particular, the teacher should not say "You don't have to do problems x to y because we haven't covered them yet." The teacher can focus on developing examples and explanations specifically tailored to his or her students and the teacher's special strengths.

Some teachers of UCSMP courses are skeptical at first about the amount of reading in the book. Yet, as the year progresses, they tend to view the reading as one of the strongest features of this series. Some teachers have felt that UCSMP materials help students develop reading comprehension, but we do not have evidence to back this up. Our evidence does show

that students of UCSMP *Geometry* are more willing to read and read more often than students using other books.

PROBLEM 6:
Students lose algebra skills during the year they study geometry.

The UCSMP *Geometry* response: The work with coordinates and transformations provides almost continual contact with algebraic ideas, skills and graphing. (It is so well-integrated into the course that many people viewing the text do not realize how much is there.) In addition to this work, there is conscious effort to review manipulative algebra skills, including linear equations and quadratics. A lesson is included dealing with the geometric representation of polynomial multiplication. There is quite a bit of work with square roots and proportions, and some with cube roots. Our evidence (see pages T44-T48) is that students are at least as well-prepared for their next algebra course as other students.

PROBLEM 7:
The mathematics curriculum has been lagging behind today's widely available and inexpensive technology.

Despite the nearly universal availability of calculators and widespread availability of computers, most contemporary textbooks still do not integrate this technology into the course scheme. All UCSMP secondary courses assume that students have access to scientific calculators at all times (including tests). Although scientific calculators are not needed as often in geometry as they might be in algebra, there are many times during UCSMP *Geometry* when they are necessary.

UCSMP *Geometry* incorporates the use of an automatic drawer like the *Geometric Supposer* distributed by Sunburst, IBM's *Geodraw,* or the drawer developed by UCSMP and Scott, Foresman and Company. This enables students to explore figures, develop conjectures, and confirm theorems in a way that is difficult to do otherwise.

Connections with computers in this course include templates for Logo programs and programs written in BASIC for if-then statements. In this we are following current practices in schools. But the influence of computers ranges further than this. Certain content has been included because of its importance in a computer age, including points as dots and pixels, interpretations of algorithms, as well as a great deal of graphing.

Goals of UCSMP *Geometry*

It would be too easy and somewhat misleading to state that the goals of UCSMP *Geometry* are to remove forever the problems detailed above. Obviously we want to make headway on these. It is better to think of this book as an attempt to attack all the dimensions of the understanding of geometry: the skills of drawings, measurement, and visualization; the properties and deductive nature; its many uses; and the algebraic and numeric representations.

The guiding principles for including a topic in UCSMP *Geometry* were: (1) suitable level of difficulty for average 9th graders; (2) the importance of the topic for daily living, career development, or future study of mathematics; and (3) the extent to which the topics as a whole provide a balanced view of geometry as describing the visual world, as representing algebra, and as a mathematical system.

We attempt to convey to the student, through historical references and references to recent mathematical work (e.g., the four-color problem), that geometry continues to develop as an area of human activity. This is to reach for a more lofty goal. WE WANT STUDENTS TO VIEW THEIR STUDY OF MATHEMATICS AS WORTH-WHILE, AS FULL OF INTERESTING AND ENTERTAINING INFORMATION, AS RELATED TO ALMOST EVERY ENDEAVOR. We want them to realize that mathematics is still growing and is changing fast. We want them to look for and recognize mathematics in places they haven't before, to use the library, to search through newspapers or almanacs, to get excited by knowledge.

We want students to view their study of mathematics as worthwhile, as full of interesting and entertaining information, as related to almost every endeavor.

Who Should Take UCSMP *Geometry*?

Virtually every student who expects to graduate high school should take this course. A year of geometry is required for admission to almost all colleges; geometry is found on all college-entrance examinations; and geometry is necessary to understand science, art and architecture, engineering, and many other disciplines. In fact, most colleges today either require or want students to have a second year of algebra after geometry. A student who has not passed two years of algebra and a year of geometry has the choice of only a few majors.

There are just as many reasons for non-college-bound students to take geometry. Technical schools, such as those for the trades, require that students be familiar with formulas, graphs, and trigonometry. Geometry is the language of design; without it a student has difficulty describing anything physical. The way that geometry is taught in most places also provides students with the language of logic and deduction, one of the great gifts of mathematical study to thinking.

Students who take UCSMP *Geometry* should have as a prerequisite UCSMP *Algebra* or another full-year algebra course, including substantial work with solving linear equations and inequalities, solving linear systems, translating from English to mathematical symbols and vice-versa, making and reading graphs, and using the Quadratic Formula.

The pace of the course assumes that students are familiar with various types of angles, with parallel lines and transversals, the Pythagorean Theorem, the Triangle-Sum Theorem, and the names of many of the special quadrilaterals. Familiarity with a scientific calculator is assumed and some familiarity with the BASIC computer language is desired. All of these are found in previous UCSMP courses. Students who do not have all these prerequisites can succeed in UCSMP *Geometry*. However, you may need to spend more time on certain lessons than suggested in the pacing chart. For instance, teachers in our studies whose students had weak backgrounds in geometry prior to UCSMP *Geometry* found it necessary to spend more time on Chapter 3, Angles and Lines, than did teachers whose students had studied from UCSMP texts.

3 General Teaching Suggestions

While it is true that most of the content in this book is found in other geometry texts, both the content and the approach of UCSMP *Geometry* represents rather significant departures from standard practice. *A teacher should not expect to use this book to teach exactly the same material in exactly the same way he or she has been accustomed to teaching.*

UCSMP *Geometry*, like any good mathematics text, can be adapted to a variety of models of teaching from direct instruction through cooperative learning. The suggestions found in this and the following pages provide ideas which lead to success and discourage practices which do not lead to success. They should not be construed as rigid: students, teachers, classes, schools, and school systems vary greatly. But they should not be ignored. These suggestions come from users, from our extensive discussion with teachers of earlier versions of these materials, and from test results.

Optimizing Learning

■ Pace

Students adjust to the pace set by the teacher. There is a natural tendency, when using a new book, to go more slowly, to play it safe should you forget something. Teachers using these materials for the first time have almost invariably said that they would move more quickly the next year. Do not be afraid to move quickly. **Each lesson is meant to be covered in a day.** We know from our studies that this pace produces the highest performance levels. Students need to be exposed to content in order to learn it. To set a tone of high expectations, it is especially important that Chapter 1 be taught at a one day per lesson pace. At the end of the chapter, spend a few days on the Progress Self-Test, Objectives, and Review to cinch the major ideas.

We recommend that a typical homework assignment be one of the following:

> 1. read Lesson n; write answers to all Questions in Lesson n; or
> 2. read Lesson n; write answers to Questions Covering the Reading in Lesson n, and Applying the Mathematics, Review, and Exploration in Lesson n-1.

Thus, virtually every day students should be expected to do the equivalent of a complete set of questions from a lesson. The questions have been designed to cover the key skills, properties, uses and representations in the lesson. Questions were not written with an odd-even assignment plan in mind. Skipping questions may lead to gaps in student understanding. The Exploration questions may be assigned for all to do, or left as optional work for extra credit. David R. Johnson's booklet *Every Minute Counts* and *Making Minutes Count Even More* (see reference list) giving excellent practical suggestions on making use of class time.

There are times when it will be difficult to maintain this pace. But be advised: a slow pace can make it too easy to lose prespective and relate ideas. You need to get to later content to realize why you were asked to learn earlier content! If you spend too much time in the lessons, you may find that your slowest students may have learned more by having gone through content slowly, but all the other students will have learned less. The wise teacher strikes a balance, goes quickly enough to keep things interesting but slowly enough to have time for explanations.

Average students who have studied from *Transition Mathematics* and USCMP *Algebra* should be able to cover 13 chapters of UCSMP *Geometry*. Classes with better students have been able to complete all 15 chapters. Classes with average students should complete 13 or 14 chapters, depending on their earlier background. The minimal course for the slowest students is through Lesson 12-7.

If you need to go through the chapters more slowly than recommended, rather than omitting an entire chapter, we suggest omitting certain lessons. However, please be aware that these lessons are reviewed later. You will need to adjust your homework assignments accordingly.

Review

Every lesson includes review questions. These questions serve a variety of purposes. First, they develop competence in a topic. Because we do not expect students to master a topic on the day they are introduced to it, these questions, coming *after* introduction of the topic, help to solidify the ideas. Second, they maintain competence from preceding chapters. This review is particularly effective with topics that have not been studied for some time.

At times, we are able to give harder questions in reviews than we could expect students to be able to do on the day they were introduced to the topic. Thus the reviews sometimes serve as questions which integrate ideas from previous lessons.

Finally, we occasionally review an idea that has not been discussed for some time, just before it is to surface again in a lesson. The Notes on Questions usually alert you to this circumstance.

Teachers in classes that perform the best assign all the review questions, give students the answers each day, and discuss them when needed. Those who do not assign all reviews tend to get poorer performance; their students never get enough practice to solidify and master the ideas and, even when mastered, the ideas are forgotten. **The review questions must be assigned to ensure optimum performance.**

Mastery

The mastery strategy used at the end of each chapter of UCSMP *Geometry* is one that has been validated by a great deal of research. Its components are a Progress Self-Test (the "formative test" in the parlance of some mastery learning literature), solutions to the test in the student's textbook (the "feedback"), review questions tied to the same objectives used to make up the self-test (the "correctives"), and finally a chapter test covering the same objectives.

Following the strategy means assigning the Progress Self-Test as a homework assignment to be done *under simulated test conditions*. The next day should be devoted to answering student questions about the problems and doing some problems from the Review Questions if there is time. If a particular topic is causing a great deal of trouble, the corresponding Lesson Master (in the Teacher's Resource File) may be of help.

For most classes, as a second night's assignment, we suggest the *even-numbered* Review questions on the SPUR Objectives. Neither solution nor answers to these questions are in the student text and students will have to work on their own without these aids. The next day, discuss these review questions in class.

Give the test on the third day. The odd-numbered Review questions, for which answers are given in the student text, can be useful for studying for that test. If at all possible, return the test to students so they see where they made errors and can better study for midterm and final exams. In some classes, a third day before the test may be needed. If so, either the odd-numbered Review questions or selected Lesson Masters can be used as sources of additional questions.

We strongly recommend that, except for classes of exceptionally talented students (where less review may be needed), teachers follow this strategy. THE EVIDENCE IS SUBSTANTIAL THAT USE OF THE CHAPTER END-MATTER MATERIALS PROMOTES HIGHER LEVELS OF PERFORMANCE.

The evidence is substantial that use of the chapter end-matter materials promotes higher levels of performance.

■ Reading

The typical geometry student who has not used previous UCSMP materials has never been asked to read mathematics. As a result, it is common for students to ask why they have to read.

We tell them: You must read because you must learn to read for success in all future courses that use mathematics, not just in mathematics; because you must learn to read for success in life outside of school and on any job; becuase the reading will help you understand the uses of mathematics; because the reading contains interesting information; because the reading tells you how the material from one lesson is related to other material in the book; because there is not enough time in class to spend doing something that you can do in a study period or at home.

Students often do not know how to read a mathematics text. They read too quickly and they gloss over little words ("if", "but", and so on) that may be very important to the meaning of a statement. They may be unable to verbalize mathematical symbolism, such as $3x + 5 = 2$ ("three ex plus five equals 2") or $m//n$ (m and n are parallel).

To teach students how to read mathematics, we suggest that at the beginning of the school year some class time be spent each day reading the lesson in class. Some days you can have students read out loud; on others have them read silently to themselves. When students read out loud, provide feedback on their ability to read technical symbols correctly. The first few times students read in class, it may help to give them an overview (advance organizer) of what they are about to read. After they have read, ask students to summarize the key ideas in the lesson, and encourage them to ask questions about anything that is not clear.

The questions Covering the Reading at the end of each lesson are meant to test comprehension of the material in the text. They can be used as oral exercises during or after oral reading of the text, or as part of a written assignment. Once students are comfortable with the format of the lessons, we suggest you begin to expect that reading be done outside the class on a regular basis.

It is not uncommon for students who are using UCSMP materials for the first time to resist your suggestions to read the text. However, in our trials of earlier versions of this text, teachers have reported that even the most recalcitrant students have learned to read the text by the end of the first marking period. Furthermore, teachers report that UCSMP *Geometry* students who have studied from previous UCSMP texts where they were expected to read carry this expectation over into UCSMP *Geometry*. That is, students' willingness to read regularly carries over into their study of mathematics in following years.

Although we believe that reading their text is an important strategy by which students learn mathematics, we know that it is not the only way they learn. In particular, if you want to give a brief overview of the new lesson before students read it, please do. We do, however, wish to discourage the practice of *always* explaining how to do questions before the students have had the opportunity to learn on their own. Particularly counterproductive is to tell students that certain problems do not have to be tried "because we have not yet done them in class." This only teaches students that they cannot learn on their own and to be dependent on you.

Students also learn enormous amounts from discussing alternate strategies to problems with you and their classmates, from engaging in well-constructed computer laboratory activities, and from struggling with open-ended Exploration and the extra extension questions to be found in this Teacher's Edition. By teaching students to read outside of class, you are free to use class time more creatively and effectively than if you were compelled to develop all major ideas yourself in class.

Our testing indicates that almost all lessons in UCSMP *Geometry* an be read by students on their own. However, some of the longer proofs need to be covered in the classroom. *Specific reading comprehension tips and strategies and other comments on reading are provided in the Teacher's Edition margin notes for appropriate lessons.*

Understanding — The SPUR Approach

"Understanding" is an easy goal to have, for who can be against it? Yet understanding means different things to different people. In UCSMP texts an approach is taken that we call the SPUR approach. It involves four different aspects, or dimensions, of understanding.

Skills: For many people, understanding mathematics means simply knowing *how* to get an answer to a problem with no help from any outside source. But in classrooms, when we speak of understanding how to use a calculator or a computer, we mean using a computer to do something for us. In UCSMP texts, these are both aspects of the same kind of understanding, the understanding of algorithms (procedures) for obtaining a result. This is the S of SPUR, the Skills dimension, and it includes visualization, drawings, and constructions of figures.

Properties: It is obvious that some students have skills without knowing what it is they are doing. During the 1960s, understanding *why* emerged to become at least as important as understanding *how*. Mathematicians often view this kind of understanding as the ultimate goal. For instance, mathematics courses for prospective elementary school teachers assume these college students can do arithmetic and instead teach the properties and principles behind the arithmetic. This the P of SPUR, the Properties dimension, and it ranges from the rote identification of properties to the discovery of new proofs. Geometry has often been taught with this dimension of understanding as its sole goal.

Uses: To the person who applies mathematics, neither knowing how to get an answer nor knowing the mathematical reasons behind the process is as important as being able to *use* the answer. For example, a person does not possess full understanding of similarity until that person can apply the Fundamental Theorem of Similarity (see pages 593-603 of the student text) appropriately in real situations. This dimension ranges from the rote application of ideas (for instance, the shape of a stop sign is a regular octagon) to the discovery of new applications or models for mathematical ideas. UCSMP *Geometry* is notable for its attention to this dimension of understanding.

Representations: To some people, even having all three dimensions of understanding given above does not comprise full understanding. They require that students represent a concept and deal with the concept in that representation in some way. Ability to use concrete materials and models, or graphs and other symbolic representations deomstrates this dimension of understanding. This is the R of SPUR, the Representations dimension, and it ranges from the use of algebra in geometry (as in coordinate geometry) to the invention of new representations of concepts (as in Lesson 15-2, where regular polygons help to schedule teams).

The four types of understanding have certain common qualities. For each there are people for whom that type of understanding is preeminent, and who believe that the other types do not convey the *real* understanding of mathematics. Each has aspects that can be memorized and the potential for the highest level of creative thinking. Each can be, and often is, learned in isolation from the others. We know there are students who have S and none of the others; in the 1960s some students learned P and none of the others; there are people on the street who have U and none of the others; and some people believe that children cannot really acquire any of the others without having R. There are continual arguments among educators as to which dimension should come first and which should be emphasized.

Because of this, in UCSMP texts we have adopted the view that the understanding of mathematics is a multi-dimesional entity. We believe each dimension is important, that each dimesion has its easy aspects and its difficult ones. Some skills (for example, long division) take at least as long to learn as geometry proofs; some uses are as easy as putting together beads.

For a specific example of what understanding means in these four dimensions, consider what would constitute evidence of understanding of congruent figures. (The *Representations* for congruence are done in UCSMP *Advanced Algebra* and later courses.)

Skills understanding means visualizing, drawing, or constructing figures. (For example, draw a figure congruent to a given figure but with opposite orientation.)

Properties understanding means knowing properties which you can apply. (Apply a congruence theorem in a proof.)

Uses understanding means knowing situations in which you could apply the idea. (Explain why it is useful to have assembly lines make congruent parts.)

Representations understanding means having a representation of the solving process or a graphical way of interpreting the solution. (Explain why the graph of $y = \cos x$ is congruent to the graph of $y = \sin x$.)

We believe there are students who prefer one of these dimensions over the others when learning mathematics. Some students prefer applications, some would rather do drawings, some prefer to know the theory, and still others like the models and representations best. Many students need to work with several dimensions of understanding before a concept makes sense to them. Thus the most effective teaching allows students opportunities in all these dimensions.

The SPUR approach is not a perfect sorter of knowledge; many ideas and many problems involve more than one dimension. For instance, the mathematics behind a construction may involve both S and P. And some understandings do not fit any of these dimensions. In some chapters, we add a fifth dimension H — the Historical dimension — for it provides still another way of looking at knowledge. (As far as we know, the greek mathematician Euclid was the first to organize the triangle congruence propositions as we know them today.)

In this book, you see the SPUR categorization at the end of each chapter in a set of Objectives and corresponding Chapter Review questions. The Progress Self-Test for each chapter and the Lesson Masters (in the Teacher's Resource File) are keyed to these objectives. We never ask students (or teachers) to categorize tasks into the various kinds of understanding; that is not a suitable goal. The categorization is meant only to be a convenient and efficient way to ensure that the book provides the opportunity for teachers to teach and for students to gain a broader and deeper understanding of mathematics than is normally the case.

You may wonder why the Review Questions (at the end of each chapter) and *Lesson Masters* (in the TRF) are organized using the SPUR categorization. It is because we believe that practice is essential for mastery, but that blind practice, in which a student merely copies what was done in a previous problem to do a new one, does not help ultimate performance. The practice must be accompanied by understanding. The properties, uses, and representations enhance understanding and should be covered to obtain mastery, even of the skills.

The Lesson Masters are particularly appropriate for students who wish more practice; for helping students individually with problems they have not seen; after a chapter test has been completed, if you feel that students' performance was not high enough; and for in-class work on days when a normal class cannot be conducted. However, they should be used sparingly. *The Lesson Masters should not be part of the normal routine* and should seldom be used when they would delay moving on to the next lesson.

Using Technology

We use calculators and computers in UCSMP because they make important mathematical ideas accessible to students at an early age; they relieve the drudgery of calculation and graphing, partcularly with numbers and equations encountered in realistic contexts; and they facilitate exploration and open-ended problem solving by making multiple instances easy to examine. Furthermore, our use of technology has resulted in no loss of paper-and-pencil skill in arithmetic, and has freed up time in the curriculum to spend on other topics that lead to overall better performances by UCSMP students.

■ Calculators

Hand-held calculators first appeared in 1971. Not until 1976 did the price for a four-function calculator come below $50 (equivalent to well over $100 today). Still, in 1975, a national commission recommended that hand calculators be used on all tests starting in eighth grade, and in 1980 the National Council of Teachers of Mathematics recommended that calculators be used in all grades of school from kindergarten on. It is reported that the Achievement section of the College Board exams and the Advanced Placement exams will allow calculators in the near future. Several standardized test batteries are being developed with calculators. And slowly but surely calculators are being expected on more and more licensing exams outside of school.

The business and mathematics education communities generally believe that paper and pencil algorithms are becoming obsolete. Do not be surprised. The long division algorithm we use was born only in the late 1400s; it can have a death as well. (Before that time, the abacus was used almost exclusively to get answers to problems — note the relationship of the abacus to Roman numerals. So mechanical means to do problems are really older than paper-and-pencil means.) Increasingly, businesses do not want their employees to use paper-and-pencil algorithms to get answers to arithmetic problems. Banks require that their tellers do all arithmetic using a calculator.

Inevitably, calculators will be considered as natural as pencils for doing mathematics. A century from now people will be amazed when they learn that some students as recent as the 1990s went to schools where calculators were not used. Students of the future would no doubt consider it cruel and unusual punishment.

In UCSMP *Geometry* we use calculators in the following ways: to calculate the value of expressions that could be done by hand at this level, but would be tedious, such as finding the volume of a box with large dimensions; to generate decimal approximations to quantities which we do not expect students to be able to do by hand, such as $\sqrt{37}$, $\tan 40°$, or $\sqrt[3]{2.5}$; and to estimate values of expressions involving π, such as one finds in many area and volume formulas. We asume that students have access to scientific calculators for work in and out of class. Students will be hampered in their study of UCSMP *Geometry* if scientific calculators are not permitted.

There are five basic reasons why 4-function non-scientific calculators do not suffice.

(1) Uses require the ability to deal with large and small numbers. On many 4-function calculators, a number as large as the area of the U.S. or the distance to the sun cannot be entered. The calculator must have the ability to display numbers of scientific notation.

(2) 4-function calculators give error messages which do not distinguish between student error and calculator insufficiency. This restricts the kind of problems one can assign.

(3) There are keys on scientific calculators that are very useful in this course. Keys for π, cube root, trigonometric functions, and parentheses are all utilized in this book.

(4) Order of operations on a scientific calculator is the same as in algebra, so this kind of calculator motivates and reinforces algebra skills. In contrast, order of operations on a 4-function calculator is often different from that used in algebra and could confuse students.

(5) A scientific calculator can be used for later courses a student takes; it shows the student there is much more to learn about mathematics.

Students will overuse calculators. Part of learning to use any machine is to make mistakes: using it when you shouldn't, not using it when you should. Anyone who has a word processor has used it for short memos that could much more easily have been hand-written. Anyone who has a microwave has used it for food that could have been cooked either in a conventional oven or on top of the stove.

The overuse dies down, but it takes some months. In the meantime, stress that there are three ways to get answers to arithmetic problems: by paper and pencil, mentally, or by using some automatic means (a table, a calculator, a trusty friend, etc.) Some problems require more than one of these means, but the wise applier of arithmetic knows when to use each of these ways.

Good arithmeticians do a lot of calculations mentally, either because they are basic facts (e.g., 3 x 5) or because they can be gotten by simple rules (e.g., 2/3 x 4/5 or 100 x 4.72). They may not use a calculator on these because the likelihood of making an error entering or reading is greater than the likelihood of making a mental error. As a rule, we seldom say, "Do not use calculators here." We want students to learn for themselves when calculator use is appropriate and when not. However, you may feel the need to prod some students to avoid the calculator. An answer of 2.9999999 for $\sqrt{9}$ should be strongly discouraged.

■ Computers and Automatic Drawers

The computer is a powerful tool in the classroom. We recommend that you have access to a microcomputer with BASIC, Logo, and automatic drawing software and the capability to set the computer up for classroom demonstrations. Ideally you should have access to a group of microcomputers so that students can work individually or in pairs occasionally in a laboratory setting.

A desirable computer is one with the ability to deal with a good amount of data and to show drawings with accuracy and precision. Today, the Apple II family is at the *lower* end of such computers, and the IBM-PC or PC/2 compatible or Macintosh families are at the upper end. We expect that computers will be available in the next couple of years which will again raise the level of performance one can purchase rather inexpensively.

In the second chapter of this book, computer programs appear in examples and exercises as contemporary representations of the logic of if-then statements. The BASIC computer language is used because it is usually packaged for the microcomputers which are most popular in American schools. The programs have been kept short so that they can be typed relatively quickly. It is not necessary for every student to type and run each program. Many programs can be used as classroom demonstrations.

Throughout the book, students are asked to explore conjectures and verify theorems with drawings. (For instances, consider Question 24 on page 162 or Question 14 on page 221.) All of these exercises can be done by hand, but many are enhanced with the use of an automatic drawer, that is, using software which enables figures to be drawn. Automatic drawers are the subject of Lesson 4-3.

An appropriate automatic drawer for UCSMP *Geometry* should (1) enable the user to follow the procedure for any construction (such as perpendicular bisectors), (2) perform reflec-

tions, rotations, translations, and size change transformations, (3) measure segments and angles of figures that appear on the screen, and (4) allow a procedure to be repeated with a new starting figure so as to enable students to test conjectures and explore. The Geometric Supposer software distributed by Sunburst and IBM's Geodraw have most of these features, and the state-of-the-art drawer being developed by UCSMP and Scott, Foresman will have all of these features (but not all features will exist in its Apple version).

In Chapter 13, some Logo programs are given. Although the student does not have to have a computer to do most of the questions, the impact of the lesson is increased if the programs are demonstrated. Optimally the student will have the opportunity to run a program. Since this is an geometry course, not a programming course, you should emphasize whether students can follow the steps of a program and tell what the output will be. Students should be able to modify a given program to answer a question with different given information. Do not ignore the computer questions even if you do not have computers available. The computer provides a concrete illustration of the role of technology.

If you have never done much work with computers, do not be alarmed. This is a geometry course, not a programming course. Computer language is explained in the text whenever needed. Whether you are a novice or expert, we encourage you to try the programs we provide on your own system. The various versions of BASIC and Logo and each computer have slightly different characteristics, and our generic programs may need to be modified slightly for your system. Check with a computer expert in your school on how this might be done.

In addition to the references in the text to BASIC, Logo, and automatic drawers, Computer Masters are provided in the Teacher's Resource File. These blackline masters are keyed to specific lessons in each of Chapters 1-15, with almost all requiring automatic drawing software. They are meant for use by a class in a laboratory setting, or by individuals for extra credit work. It is not necessary to do these masters to be successful in UCSMP *Geometry*. Since each one stands alone, you may do as many or as few as you think appropriate for your class.

T41

Evaluating Learning

▪ Grading

No problem seems more difficult than the question of grading. If a teacher has students who perform so well that they all deserve As and the teacher gives them As as a result, the teacher will probably not be given plaudits for being successful but will be accused of being too easy. This suggests that the grading scale ought to be based on a fixed level of performance, which is what we recommend. We recommend this because the performance that gives an A in one school or with one teacher may only rate a C in another, and we think it unfair.

Seldom in this book are there ten similar questions in a row. To teach students to be flexible, the wording of questions is varied, and principles are applied in many contexts. The problems are varied because that is the way problems come in later courses and in life outside of school. Furthermore, in UCSMP *Geometry* we emphasize the relations between algebra and geometry and between various aspects of geometry. Learning to solve problems in a variety of contexts or to discern relationships between properties is more difficult that learning to perform a routine skill. Thus, a natural question that arises is "How should I grade students in UCSMP courses?".

We believe a student should be able to do each set of objectives at about the 85% level. An 85% score on a test deserves no less than a high B, and probably an A. In the past, our tests have often led us to the following grading scale: 85-100 = A, 72-84 = B, 60-71 = C, 50-59 = D, 0-49 = F. Such a scale may alarm some teachers, but students in UCSMP courses generally learn more mathematics overall than students in comparison classes. We believe that the above grading policy rewards students fairly for work well done.

Some teachers are accustomed to the grading scale 90-100 = A, 80-90 = B, 70-79 = C, 60-69 = D, and 0-59 = F. One January a teacher of *Transition Mathematics* presented us with a problem. She had to make out grades for the fall semester. Her quandary was as follows: "I've never had a class that learned so much, but my grades are lower." Later she said, "I have students who are failing. But I can't switch them to another class [using another book at the same level] because they know too much." Her problem is not unusual: percentages correct on tests of higher order thinking are generally lower than scores on tests of routine skills. We often make a basketball analogy. In many courses all the shots students ever have are lay-ups (exercises) and an occasional free throw (easy problems).

They shoot these over and over again, from the same spot ("Do the odd-numbered exercises from 1-49."). In UCSMP *Geometry*, almost every question is a different shot (a problem), some close in, some from middle distance, a few from half-court. To expect percentages of correct shots to be the same is unrealistic.

There are times, however, when you want to practice one specific shot to make it automatic. We suggest focusing in on a few topics for quizzes. The Teacher's Resource File contains quizzes and tests for each chapter. If students perform well on quizzes and tests, it has a real effect on interest and motivation. You should endeavor to use grading as a vehicle for breeding success as well as for rating students.

In the light of all this, we strongly urge you to let students know what they need to know in order to get good grades. All research on the subject indicates that telling students what they are supposed to learn increases the amount of material covered and tends to increase performance. Also, let students know that you expect *all of them* to perform well. Do not arbitrarily consign some of your students to low grades. Let them know that it is possible for all of them to get As if they learn the material.

Some teachers have found that because of the way that the review questions maintain and improve performance, cumulative tests at the end of each marking period give students an opportunity to do well. For your convenience, the Teacher's Resource File has Chapter Tests in Cumulative Form (in addition to the regular Chapter Tests) for each chapter, beginning with Chapter 2. These Cumulative Tests allow students a chance to show what they have learned about a topic since they studied the chapter discussing that topic. Beginning with Chapter 3, the questions in the Cumulative Tests are about 50% from the current chapter, 25% from the preceding chapter, and 25% from all other earlier chapters.

■ Standardized Tests

At our first conference with school teachers and administrators early in the project, we were told in the strongest terms, "Be bold, but remember that you will be judged by old standardized tests."

There are many types of standardized tests in high school mathematics: (1) standardized geometry tests; (2) general test batteries in which there may be a mathematics subtest; (3) local school or state assessments; and (4) college entrance examinations. There is strong evidence that performance on any of these can be enhanced by practice on questions like those which will appear. Since these tests often have bearing on student placement you should, when possible, inform students of the kinds of questions they are likely to encounter.

Based on our testing and what teachers and schools have reported, here is what we concluded about these various kinds of tests. (1) As reported on the following pages, students in UCSMP *Geometry* perform as well as students from other classes on traditional standardized tests. Yet, since UCSMP students outperform other students on applications, graphing, and some other content found in UCSMP *Geometry*, it is unfair to UCSMP students if they are judged only by a traditional standardized test.

(2) We have done no controlled studies of performance on UCSMP students in test batteries like the ITBS, CAT, SAT, or MAT. Anecdotal evidence suggests that 8th graders who have been through *Transition Mathematics* and UCSMP *Algebra* perform much higher on concepts and slightly lower on paper-and-pencil computation than counterparts of equal ability from previous years in these schools. The total mathematics score has tended to significantly improve for the school.

(3) Assessments differ so much from district to district and state to state that we can offer no generalizations. Obviously, we believe UCSMP students will tend to perform well on assessments which are in agreement with the content suggested in the NCTM *Standards*.

(4) We believe that students studying UCSMP courses are likely to do better on the College Board SAT-M than other students. The SAT-M is a problem-solving test, and far more questions on the SAT-M cover content likely to be unfamiliar to other students than to UCSMP students. The ACT exams seem at least as favorable to our students as to students in other books. Furthermore, if UCSMP suggestions are followed and more students take *Geometry* in the 9th grade, then there is no question that students in the UCSMP curriculum will far outscore comparable students who are a course behind. Preliminary evidence with PSAT scores indicates that 10th graders who have had all UCSMP courses through *Advanced Algebra* score as well as non-UCSMP juniors of equivalent ability in second-year algebra.

Finally, a note about curriculum projects. Many people treat books from curriculum projects as "experimental". Few commercial textbooks, however, have been developed on the basis of large scale testing. Few have been produced as part of a coherent 7-12 curriculum design. This text has gone through extensive prepublication analysis and criticism. It has been revised on the basis of comments and evaluations of the many teachers who have been in our evaluation studies. It is the intention of UCSMP to provide materials which are successful as well as teachable.

UCSMP *GEOMETRY* SHOULD BE VIEWED AS A NEW TEXT, NOT AS AN EXPERIMENTAL TEXT.

UCSMP *Geometry* should be viewed as a new text, not as an experimental text.

4 Research and Development of UCSMP *Geometry*

Arthur F. Coxford, Jr., and Zalman Usiskin, two of the authors of USCMP *Geometry*, wrote a geometry text in the late 1960s which went through three years of testing before a revised version was published commercially in 1971. That text was the first textbook published in the United States for average students that employed transformations as part of the postulate system, and it incorporated algebra and function ideas. The way that book was developed has served as a model for the development and testing of all UCSMP secondary texts.

These authors had long desired to write a new geometry textbook which would combine the best of that previous work with new developments in geometry and geometry teaching, particularly the incorporation of applications and technology and the latest research on student learning of geometry. Placing this work in the UCSMP curriculum presented a new challenge and a new opportunity, since the mathematics in this book had to coordinate with the other courses in the curriculum but could use ideas developed in the previous books. Fortunately, first drafts of both UCSMP *Algebra* and *Advanced Algebra* had been completed before writing began on UCSMP *Geometry*.

Writing of UCSMP *Geometry* began in the spring and summer of 1986 and continued through the 1986-87 school year. Daniel Hirschhorn, an experienced high school teacher and doctoral student at the University of Chicago, joined the writing team at this time.

During the 1986-87 year the first draft was used in three Chicago public schools and three suburban public schools in the Chicago area. (Names of these schools and teachers can be found on page iii of the student text.) Teachers received the loose-leaf materials a chapter at a time, sometimes just a few days before they needed to be used. The Chicago public school classes presented perhaps the ultimate test for these pilot materials; *all* students in Chicago public high schools are required to take geometry. The only students who had taken any previous UCSMP courses were in one of the suburban schools, and none of the teachers had ever taught other UCSMP courses.

One of the authors observed a class every day during that year. Also, the teachers in this pilot study periodically met at the University of Chicago to report on how the materials were going in their classes. All classes were observed and students were interviewed by independent evaluators, and at the end of the year various tests were given, but there was no comparison group.

The pilot teachers generally found the materials to be appropriate, interesting, and engaging and were particularly delighted with the applications and the earlier appearance of the measurement topics. They were satisfied with student performance except on proof-writing, which in this first draft was entirely delayed until the second semester. The Chicago teachers found the materials to be no more difficult and much more appropriate than any other geometry text familiar to them, but still too difficult for many of their students. All the teachers gave many suggestions for improvement and indicated what should not be changed.

The pilot study exposed a difficulty that any book might have in dealing with the range of backgrounds of geometry students. Some of the pilot students had never graphed a line; some had never measured angles; some could not solve a simple linear equation; some had not encountered square roots in algebra. Some students had good algebra skills but knew little geometry upon entering the course. Those students who studied from previous UCSMP courses were at a decided advantage.

The revised version was guided by the suggestions of the teachers. Work on proof was placed earlier in the text. Work with algebraic skills was more evenly spread through the chapters. Some lessons were deleted; others were expanded. Thousands of small changes were made.

National Field Studies and Test Results

The pilot study was jointly conducted by the Secondary and Evaluation Components of UCSMP. The national field studies were conducted independently by the Evaluation Component. The only input of the Secondary Component into the national field studies was in advising on selection of sites and test instruments, and in constructing special content tests for this study.

It was felt there would not be enough students in 1987-88 who had taken both previous UCSMP courses to allow a broad study of both types of students. Consequently, it was decided to stretch the national field study of UCSMP Geometry over two years, with the first year (1987-88) focusing on students who had no previous UCSMP courses and the second year (1988-89) involving students who had both *Transition Mathematics* and UCSMP *Algebra*.

Between the two national field studies the text was again revised. In Year 1 the text was printed in three parts and spiral bound. In Year 2 the text was printed in two parts and soft cover bound. The major changes made after Year 1 was to integrate materials on inequalities throughout the text and to give earlier attention to proofs applying the triangle congruence theorems. A few other lessons were added or deleted, but the scope of the course was not markedly affected.

The same general procedures were used in both years. A matched-pair design of UCSMP and comparison classes was desired. UCSMP classes were selected to provide a representative sample of schools and students from across the nation. In Year 1, all classes were predominantly 10th grade; in Year 2, both 9th and 10th grade UCSMP classes were involved. At each site, potential comparison classes were selected by a supervisor at the site. In each year, comparison classes could not be found in one of the schools and a neighboring school was used.

At the beginning of the year, students were given pretests on geometry knowledge and on algebra skills. These pretests were used to create matched pairs of classes at each site. As in previous UCSMP studies, only about half the classes that began the study wound up as one of a well-matched pair. However, the results for matched pairs are almost identical to those for the entire sample (this too has been the case in other UCSMP studies), and so the entire sample for each year is discussed here.

The implementation of the design of the Year 2 study met with problems. In the design, each site was to have some classes in which virtually all students had taken both previous UCSMP courses and comparison classes with comparable students who did not have this experience. This required that the school keep a relatively small number of students together in classes for three years, in some cases even through a transfer from a feeder school to a senior high school. There were only a small number of potential sites to begin with and, as the evaluators determined only after the study began, most of the sites could not supply classes meeting these criteria.

Of the 22 UCSMP classes, in only 4 did 80% or more of the students have previous UCSMP experience (and only 8 had a majority of students with previous UCSMP experience). In 1 of these 4 classes, a comparison class could not be found in the same school. The three remaining classes were from an inner city school, a small town, and an affluent suburb. The inner city school class was composed of 11th graders; the other two were composed of 9th graders. All could only be matched with comparison classes mostly populated with 10th graders or older students.

From the interviews and class observations during Year 2 it was deteremined that classes in which all or virtually all students have the previous UCSMP courses begin with expectations which do not appear as readily when many students have not had the same experience. These expectations include doing a lesson a day, completing all questions of that lesson, and engaging in dicussions about the mathematics (i.e., being active, not passive in class).

Consequently, though these three classes constitute a small subsample, results from their schools are included below. But in general, the students in the Year 2 closely resembled those in the Year 1 study, and so for the purpose of the following discussion the two years are treated together, unless otherwise specified.

The studies involved schools from Arizona, California, Georgia, Illinois, Michigan, New Jersey, Ohio, and Pennsylvania. The SES of these schools were: upper middle, 4; middle, 11; lower middle, 5; mixed, 4. Twelve schools were classified as urban, 8 as suburban, and 4 as rural or small town. There were no substantial differences among the teachers in experience, though 16 of 23 UCSMP teachers who completed the forms had master's degrees while 14 of 26 comparison teachers had master's degrees. Both UCSMP and comparison classes averaged 47 minutes in length.

During the school year, each UCSMP and comparison class was observed by a member of the evaluation team. All teachers and a sample of students from each class were interviewed. Towards the end of the year, a Teacher Questionnaire was given to all teachers and a 28-item Student Opinion Survey was administered to all students. There is space here only to give a representative sampling of the results, and we focus on those things on which the results are most interesting or on which there were the greatest differences between groups.

In general, the comparison teachers in both years spent the greatest part of class time introducing new topics, while the UCSMP teachers for both years spent the greater proportion of their time reviewing homework. Experienced UCSMP teachers tended to spend less time reviewing homework than non-experienced UCSMP teachers and more time introducing new topics and more time on cooperative learning activities. They were also more likely to assign the learning activities. They were also more likely to assign the reading as homework; over two-thirds assigned reading every night.

All UCSMP teachers but one allowed calculators at all times. Almost all comparison classes allowed calculators, too. There was great desire to use computers but only a minority employed them significantly.

Table 1 gives teachers' opinions about the text UCSMP *Geometry* using criteria from an instrument developed by Iris Weiss for the 1985-86 National Survey of Science and Mathematics Education. The order of items is based on the national percents. (The national ratings, for mathematics texts for grades 10-12, are uniformly higher than the ratings given by comparison teachers to their texts.)

Table 1:
Percent of teachers giving favorable ratings about textbooks

Item	UCSMP (n = 26)	National (n = 517)
appropriate reading level	88	87
clear and well-organized	88	82
explains concepts clearly	81	73
develops problem-solving skills	77	68
has exercises for practice of drill	42	60
good suggestions for activities/ assignments	73	55
interesting to students	65	43
examples of applications	62	40
good suggestions for computers	31	31
good suggestions for calculators	62	27

The student opinion survey was completed by 1050 UCSMP *Geometry* students (590 in Year 1, 460 in Year 2) and 918 comparison students (570 in Year 1, 348 in Year 2). The results from the two years are very similar, except that UCSMP students in Year 2 generally reported that the text was easier than students in Year 1 reported and that they did not spend as much time on homework. (About three-quarters of the students in the two years reported spending 30 minutes or less on homework.) UCSMP students were significantly (.01 level) *more likely* to agree that their text has helped them to understand proof; that their text encourages them to find different ways to solve a problem; and that calculators and applications help in learning math. They were *less likely* to agree that the problems in their text are uninteresting. There was *no difference* on interest in mathematics, on perceived utility of geometry, on ease of understanding explanations, and on liking for geometry.

Three tests were given at the end of the year to each student to assess knowledge of geometry: (1) the American Testronics Test — Geometry, a 40-item standardized test; (2) a 34-item project-constructed multiple-choice test (below called UCSMP Geometry Test) focusing on areas of content not felt to be adequately covered by the standardized test, namely reasoning and proof, transformations, visualization and 3-dimensional ideas, coordinates, and applications; and (3) Form 1 or Form 2 of a project-constructed 11-item test. Five of the items in the project-constructed tests were multiple-choice; on one form they were algebra skill items and on the other form they dealt with mathematical systems. The other six were open-ended items dealing with proofs, including some proof-writing items. Each item was worth 4 points; a score of 3 of 4 on an item is considered correct. Half of the students in each class were randomly given one form; the other half took the other form.

Mean scores on these tests for each year are given in **Table 2.** The analysis is limited to students who took all the tests; in Year 2 a second analysis includes all students from the three classes containing three-year UCSMP students and the corresponding comparison classes in the same schools.

Table 2: **Mean scores on content tests**

YEAR 1 — ALL STUDENTS WHO TOOK ALL TESTS

	UCSMP 25 classes			Comparison 25 classes		
	n	Mean	s.d.	n	Mean	s.d.
Pretest	349	14.6	6.0	360	14.5	5.9
Amer. Testronics	349	14.3	5.5	360	14.7	5.8
UCSMP Geometry	349	14.2	5.3	360	11.0	4.5
Algebra	184	2.1		197	2.0	
Math. systems	165	2.1		163	1.9	
Proof A	184	6.5		197	5.0	
Proof B	165	7.6		163	7.1	

YEAR 2 — ALL STUDENTS WHO TOOK ALL TESTS

	UCSMP 20 classes			Comparison 18 classes		
	n	Mean	s.d.	n	Mean	s.d.
Pretest	228	16.1	6.6	181	15.0	5.7
Amer. Testronics	228	13.4	6.2	181	13.1	5.6
UCSMP Geometry	228	10.9	5.8	181	8.9	5.0
Algebra	118	2.1	1.7	92	1.5	1.2
Math. systems	110	1.9	1.3	89	1.9	1.2
Proof A	118	7.1	6.2	92	7.3	5.4
Proof B	110	7.2	5.5	89	5.2	4.3

YEAR 2 — CLASSES IN WHICH 80% OF UCSMP STUDENTS HAD PRIOR UCSMP COURSES

	UCSMP 3 classes			Comparison 3 classes		
	n	Mean	s.d.	n	Mean	s.d.
Pretest	39	19.7	7.1	53	17.0	6.5
Amer. Testronics	39	17.9	6.5	53	17.7	6.3
UCSMP Geometry	39	17.3	6.7	53	13.5	6.0
Algebra	19	2.4	1.8	26	1.8	1.1
Math. systems	20	2.8	1.7	27	2.6	1.1
Proof A	19	11.7	8.1	26	10.6	6.0
Proof B	20	9.8	6.3	27	8.1	5.1

There are a number of striking aspects to these data. When UCSMP *Geometry* is taught and the teacher cannot take advantage of the previous UCSMP experience (either because there is none or because there are too many students in the class that do not have this experience), UCSMP students perform about 5% lower than comparison students on a standardized test and about 28% higher than comparison students on a test emphasizing reasoning and proof, transformations, visualization and 3-dimensional ideas, coordinates, and applications. The performance of UCSMP students on algebra was the same in Year 1 and higher (perhaps due to changes in the materials) in Year 2. The performance on proof was uneven. A detailed look at the scores by individual class (tables not given here) suggests that the teacher has more effect on student proof-writing than on other areas tested. Some teachers emphasize proof considerably more than others who teach from the same books. In both UCSMP and comparison groups, there were teachers who did not expect their students to be able to write proofs.

The broad sample is by no means a select group of students. Almost half of UCSMP teachers in Year 1 rated their classes at the beginning of the year as *below* average in ability. The overwhelming majority of UCSMP classes in Year 2 and comparison classes in both years were identified by their teachers as consisting of average ability students. The performance of both groups on the geometry items of the pretest is well below the mean performance that we found in our nationwide study of 1980-81.

The performance of those students in classes where students had the previous UCSMP courses is strikingly different. They tend to begin with substantially more algebra and geometry knowledge and they maintain that superiority in all aspects of the course. Comparison students can catch up on a traditional standardized multiple-choice test but do not tend to catch up on proof-writing or algebra and perform at substantially lower levels on the topics covered in the UCSMP Geometry Test. All of this substantiates research we had done before UCSMP began — that to increase performance in geometry and in proof, students need to encounter geometry before beginning a geometry course.

Item analyses were done with the entire sample. With a difference of almost 30% on the UCSMP Geometry Test as a whole, one can expect a large number of items on which UCSMP students outperformed comparison students by at least 10% or at least a .01 significance level). Only a few items on the American Testronics test showed such a large difference. From the two tests, items favoring UCSMP students by at least 10% dealt with:

> the measure of the angle between two tangents
> fourth vertex of parallelogram in the coordinate plane
> circularity of definitions
> reading a road mileage chart
> the converse of a statement
> rewriting a statement in if-then form
> lines of symmetry
> the reflection image of a point in the coordinate plane
> slopes of perpendicular lines
> relating types of quadrilaterals
> reflections off a wall
> traversable networks
> graph of a line
> slope of a line given its equation
> definition of a postulate
> need for undefined terms
> coordinate proof

Comparison students outperformed UCSMP students by at least 10% on items dealing with:

> the definition of median
> sufficient conditions for congruence of angles
> justifying statements in a congruent triangles proof
> generality of a theorem

Scores of boys were compared with scores of girls on each test for each group. On the American Testronics test, comparison boys outperformed comparison girls ($p = .02$) but UCSMP boys and girls performed equally. On the UCSMP Geometry test and the project-designed proof tests, comparison boys and girls performed equally well but UCSMP girls outperformed UCSMP boys.

Readability

Many people are concerned about the reading level of UCSMP texts. Three general caveats are in order: First, the *amount* to be read is independent of the reading level; UCSMP texts have more to be read but this does not affect the readability level. Second, reading experts are in general agreement that there does not exist a reliable method for evaluating the reading level of mathematics texts; graphs, symbols, equations, and technical vocabulary affect readability but no formula takes these into account. Third, the placement of text on a page, the type font, and many other physical characteristics can affect the readability of text, and these factors are ignored in readability formulas.

A reading analysis was done using the readability test developed by Edward Fry at the Rutgers University Reading Center. Four text samples were randomly selected from UCSMP *Geometry* and from the most widely used text in comparison classes. The test samples of UCSMP *Geometry* were evaluated to be at grades 8, 9, 7 and 5 (in order of appearance in the text). The samples from the comparison text were at grades 9, 7, 9, and 9.

Continuing Research and Development

UCSMP is committed to continual study of its materials. During the 1989-90 school year, we are studying students who have studied from *Transition Mathematics*, UCSMP *Algebra*, and UCSMP *Geometry* and are currently enrolled in UCSMP *Advanced Algebra*. (This includes some students who were not in the geometry study.) We are particularly interested in comparing these students with similar students who have not had any UCSMP experience.

USCMP is also committed to modifications of its materials based on its studies, based on the continual changes in mathematics and its applications, or based on developments in the learning of geometry.

The current student edition of UCSMP *Geometry* incorporates two major content additions from the project's test versions. The use of automatic drawing software has been integrated into the text, beginning in Chapter 4 and three lessons on vectors have been added. The first five chapters have been reorganized into seven, and many lessons have been reordered. Many other changes have been made for this edition, based on the teaching of the soft cover version of the text by one of the authors, on careful readings given to the matierals by UCSMP and Scott, Foresman editors, on the test results reported above, and on remarks by the teachers in the national field studies.

The Scott, Foresman edition of UCSMP *Geometry* also includes the appearance of four colors and of attractive pictures, which for a subject as visual as geometry can be a particularly effective learning enhancement. Also, there are available many supplements, including Lesson Masters for teachers who wish more questions on a particular lesson, Visual Masters to help in explanations, and extra quizzes and tests. Because of these changes, we expect students to perform as well, if not better with the Scott, Foresman version than with our previous versions. We also expect that these changes will ease the transition into this text for students who have not had previous UCSMP materials.

Each November since 1985, we have held a conference at the University of Chicago at which users and prospective users of secondary component UCSMP materials can meet with each other and with authors. Beginning in August 1989, we have conducted a free full day in-service for any teachers or supervisors who will be using the materials. We encourage new users to attend one of these meetings.

We desire to know of any studies school districts conduct using these materials. UCSMP will be happy to assist school districts by supplying a copy of the noncommercial tests we have used in our evaluations (except for certain open-ended items) and other information as needed.

Both Scott, Foresman and Company and UCSMP welcome comments on these books. Please address comments either to Mathematics Product Manager, Scott, Foresman and Company, 1900 East Lake Avenue, Glenview, IL 60025, or to Zalman Usiskin, University of Chicago, 5835 S. Kimbark Avenue, Chicago, IL 60637.

5 Bibliography

REFERENCES for Sections 1-4 of Professional Sourcebook

College Board, *Academic Preparation for College: What Students Need To Know and Be Able To Do.* New York: College Board, 1983.

Coxford, Arthur F., and Usiskin, Zalman P. *Geometry—A Transformation Approach.* River Forest, IL: Laidlaw Brothers, 1971, 1975.

Flanders, James. **"How Much of the Content in Mathematics Textbooks Is New?"** *Arithmetic Teacher,* September 1987, pp. 18-23.

Hoffer, Alan. **"Geometry Is More Than Proof."** *Mathematics Teacher,* January 1981, pp. 11-18.

Jones, Philip and Coxford, Arthur F. *A History of Mathematics Education in the United States and Canada.* 30th Yearbook of the National Council of Teachers of Mathematics. Reston VA: NCTM, 1970.

Kort, Anthone. **Transformation vs. nontransformation geometry: Effects on retention of geometry and on transfer in eleventh-grade mathematics.** Unpublished doctoral dissertation, Northwestern University, 1970.

McNight, Curtis, et. al. *The Underachieving Curriculum: Assessing U.S. School Mathematics from an International Perspective.* Champaign, IL: Stipes Publishing Company, 1987.

National Commission on Excellence in Education. *A Nation at Risk: The Imperative for Educational Reform.* Washington, DC: U.S. Department of Education, 1983.

National Council of Teachers of Mathematics. *Curriculum and Evaluation Standards for School Mathematics.* Reston, VA: NCTM, 1989.

Senk, Sharon L. **"How Well Do Students Write Geometry Proofs?"** *Mathematics Teacher,* September 1985, pp 448-456.

Senk, Sharon L. **"Van Hiele Levels and Achievement in Writing Geometry Proofs."** *Journal for Research in Mathematics Education,* May 1989, pp. 309-321.

Usiskin, Zalman. *Van Hiele Levels and Achievement in Secondary School Geometry.* Chicago: CDASSG Project, Department of Education, 1982.

Van Hiele, Pierre Marie. *Structure and Insight.* New York: Academic Press, 1986.

Waits, Bert and Demana, Franklin. **"Is Three Years Enough?"** *Mathematics Teacher,* January 1988, pp. 11-15.

Weiss, Iris R. *Report of the 1985-86 National Survey of Science and Mathematics Education.* Research Triangle Park, NC: Research Triangle Institute, 1987.

Wirszup, Izaak. **"Breakthroughs in the psychology of learning and teaching geometry."** In J.L. Martin (ed.), *Space and Geometry: Papers from a Research Workshop.* Columbus, OH: ERIC/SMEAC, 1976, pp. 75-97.

Section 5: Bibliography

REFERENCES from Student Edition or Teaching Notes

Abbott, Edwin Abbott, *Flatland.* New York: Dover Publications, 1952.

Birkhoff, George David, and Beatley, Ralph. *Basic Geometry.* Chicago: Scott, Foresman and Company, 1940.

Coxford, Arthur. **"A Transformation Approach to Euclidean Geometry."** In *Geometry in the Mathematics Curriculum,* 36th Yearbook of the National Council of Teachers of Mathematics. Reston, VA: NCTM, 1973.

Grünbaum, Branko, **"Geometry Strikes Again,"** *Mathematics Magazine,* January 1985, pp. 12-17.

Haldane, J.B.S. **"On Being the Right Size."** In *The World of Mathematics,* James R. Newman, editor, pp. 952-957. New York: Simon and Schuster, 1956.

Hirschhorn, Daniel B. **"Why is the SSA Triangle Congruence Theorem not Included in Textbooks?"** *Mathematics Teacher,* May 1990, pp. 358-361.

Litwiller, Bonnie H., and Duncan, David R. **"SSA: When Does It Yield Triangle Congruence?"** *Mathematics Teacher,* February 1981, pp. 106-108.

Loomis, Elisha A. *The Pythagorean Proposition.* Reston, VA: NCTM, 1968.

MacGillavry, Caroline H. *Fantasy & Symmetry: The Periodic Drawings of M.C. Escher.* New York: Harry N. Abrams, 1976.

Senk, Sharon L., and Hirschhorn, Daniel B. **"Multiple Approaches to Geometry: Teaching Similarity."** *Mathematics Teacher,* April 1990, pp. 274-280.

Thompson D'Arcy Wentworth. **"On Magnitude."** In *The World of Mathematics,* James R. Newman, editor, pp. 1001-1056. New York: Simon and Schuster, 1956.

Yeshurun, Shraga, and Kay, David C. **"An Improvement on SSA Congruence for Geometry and Trigonometry."** *Mathematics Teacher,* May 1983, pp. 364-367.

Additional General References

Altshiller-Court, Nathan. *College Geometry.* College Outline Series. New York: Barnes and Noble, 1952.

Coxeter, H.S.M., and Greitzer, Samuel. *Geometry Revisited.* New Mathematical Library, Volume 19. Washington, DC: Mathematical Association of America, 1967.

Heath, Sir Thomas L. *The Thirteen Books of Euclid's Elements.* New York: Dover Publications, 1956.

Hirsch, Christian R., and Zweng, Marilyn J., editors. *The Secondary School Mathematics Curriculum.* 1985 Yearbook of the National Council of Teachers of Mathematics. Reston, VA: NCTM, 1985.

Johnson, David R. *Every Minute Counts.* Palo Alto, CA: Dale Seymour Publications, 1982.

Johnson, David R. *Making Minutes Count Even More.* Palo Alto, CA: Dale Seymour Publications, 1986.

Johnson, Roger A. *Advanced Euclidean Geometry.* New York: Dover Publications, 1960.

Lindquist, Mary Montgomery, and Shulte, Albert P. *Learning and Teaching Geometry K-12*. 1987 Yearbook of the National Council of Teachers of Mathematics. Reston, VA: NCTM, 1987.

The Mathematics Teacher, National Council of Teachers of Mathematics. 1906 Association Drive, Reston, VA 22091.

SOURCES for Additional Problems

Carroll, Lewis. *Symbolic Logic and the Game of Logic*. New York: Dover Publications, 1958.

The Diagram Group. *Comparisons*. New York, St. Martin's Press, 1980.

Eves, Howard. *An Introduction to the History of Mathematics*. 5th ed. Philadelphia. Saunders College Publishing, 1983.

Garfunkel, Solomon and Steen, Lynn A., editors. *For All Practical Purposes: An Introduction to Contemporary Mathematics*. New York: W.H. Freeman, 1988.

Hanson, Viggo P., and Zweng, Marilyn J, editors. *Computers in Mathematics Education*. 1984 Yearbook of the National Council of Teachers of Mathematics. Reston, VA: NCTM, 1984.

Hoffman, Mark, editor. *The World Almanac and Book of Facts, 1990*. New York: World Almanac, 1990.

Johnson, Otto, executive ed. *The 1990 Information Please Almanac*. Boston: Houghton Mifflin Company, 1990.

Joint Committee of the Mathematical Association of America and the National Council of Teachers of Mathematics. *A Sourcebook of Applications of School Mathematics*. Reston, VA: NCTM, 1980.

Kastner, Bernice. *Applications of Secondary School Mathematics*. Reston, VA: National Council of Teachers of Mathematics, 1978.

Kastner, Bernice. *Space Mathematics*. Washington, D.C.: U.S. Government Printing Office, 1985.

Sharron, Sidney, and Reys, Robert E., editors. *Applications in School Mathematics*. 1979 Yearbook of the National Council of Teachers of Mathematics, Reston, VA: NCTM, 1979.

U.S. Bureau of the Census. *Statistical Abstract of the United States: 1990*. 110th ed. Washington D.C., 1990.

Williams, Wayne. *Quizzles*. New York: Grosset & Dunlap, Inc., 1956.

SOFTWARE AND VISUAL AIDS

Education Development Center, Schwartz, Judah L., and Yerushalmy, Michal. *The Geometric Supposer.* Pleasantville, NY: Sunburst Communications, 1985.

Geodraw. Boca Raton, Florida, IBM, 1987.

Polydrons. Polydron UK Ltd., 11 Scotia Close, Brackmills Industrial Estate, Northampton NN4 0HR.

UCSMP Geometry Drawing Software. Scott, Foresman and Company. 1900 East Lake Avenue, Glenview, IL 60025.

LESSON 1-1   (pages 4-7)
20.

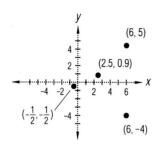

CHAPTER 1 PROGRESS SELF-TEST
(page 53)
3.

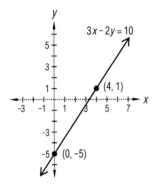

13. The airport distance is measured directly from airport to airport; the road distance is probably measured from two other points and is not a straight path.
14.

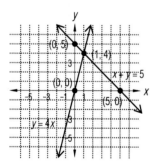

17. b. sample: V to Z to T to V to W to Z to X to W
18. a.

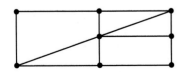

b. No, it has more than 2 odd vertices.
20. Addition Property of Inequality
21. Substitution Property of Equality
22. -23 or -61

LESSON 4-4   (pages 176-182)
14.

Conclusions	Justifications
1. m∠4 = m∠2	∥ lines ⇒ corr. ∠s =
2. m∠2 = m∠8	Vertical Angle Thm.
3. m∠4 = m∠8	Transitive Prop. of Eq. (steps 1 and 2)

15.

Conclusions	Justifications
1. m∠ABE = m∠CBD	Vertical Angle Thm.
2. m∠ABE = m∠D	Transitive Prop. of Eq. (given and step 1)

16.

Conclusions	Justifications
1. AB = BC	def. of equilateral △ (meaning)
2. BC = DC	def. of equilateral △ (meaning)
3. AB = DC	Transitive Prop. of Eq. (steps 1 and 2)

LESSON 4-5   (pages 183-186)
9.

Conclusions	Justifications
1. BC = AC	def. of equilateral △ (meaning)
2. AC = CD	def. of midpoint (meaning)
3. BC = CD	Transitive Prop. of Eq.

10. sample:

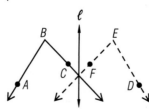

m∠ABC = m∠DEF because reflections preserve angle measure.
12. If B is between A and C, and if r(A) = A′, r(B) = B′, and r(C) = C′, then B′ is between A′ and C′.

15. a.

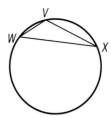

c. If the largest angle is acute, right, or obtuse, the center of the circle is inside, on, or outside the triangle, respectively.

LESSON 5-2   (pages 213-217)
1. a. If both pairs of a quadrilateral's opposite sides are parallel, then it is a parallelogram.
b. sample:

2. a. If a quadrilateral's four sides are equal in length, then it is a rhombus.
b. sample:

3. a. If a quadrilateral has four right angles, then it is a rectangle.
b. sample:

4. a. If a quadrilateral has four equal sides and four right angles, then it is a square.
b. sample:

5. a. If a quadrilateral has two distinct pairs of consecutive sides of the same length, then it is a kite.
b. sample:

6. a. If a quadrilateral has at least one pair of parallel sides, then it is a trapezoid.

ADDITIONAL ANSWERS

6. b. sample:

7. a. If a trapezoid has a pair of base angles equal in measure, then it is an isosceles trapezoid.
b. sample:

16. $\overline{ST} \parallel \overline{VU}$; $\overline{SV} \parallel \overline{TU}$
17. $\overline{WZ} \perp \overline{WX}$; $\overline{WX} \perp \overline{XY}$; $\overline{XY} \perp \overline{ZY}$; $\overline{ZY} \perp \overline{WZ}$
18. $AB = BC = CD = AD = 1$ cm
19. $\overline{FG} \perp \overline{GH}$; $\overline{GH} \perp \overline{HE}$; $\overline{HE} \perp \overline{EF}$; $\overline{EF} \perp \overline{FG}$; $FG = GH = EH = EF$
22. trapezoid, isosceles trapezoid, parallelogram, rectangle
23. trapezoid, isosceles trapezoid, parallelogram, kite, rhombus, rectangle, square
24. trapezoid, isosceles trapezoid
28. kites; sample:

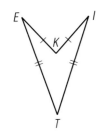

29.

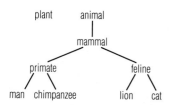

30.

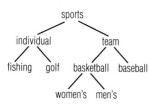

LESSON 5-3 (pages 218-222)
9. samples:

ABCD

angle	measure
1	60
2	60
3	30
4	30
5	60
6	60
7	30
8	30

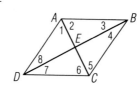

JKLM

angle	measure
1	45
2	45
3	45
4	45
5	45
6	45
7	45
8	45

VWXY

angle	measure
1	20
2	20
3	70
4	70
5	20
6	20
7	70
8	70

Sample conjecture: A diagonal of a rhombus bisects the angles of the rhombus.

22.

Conclusions	Justifications
1. $r_m(R) = R$, $r_m(S) = S$	def. of reflection (suff. cond.)
2. $RT = RU$; $ST = SU$	Reflections preserve distance.
3. $RUST$ is a kite.	def. of kite (suff. cond.)

24.

Conclusions	Justifications
1. $AC = BC$	def. of isosceles $\triangle$ (meaning)
2. $BC = CD$	def. of isosceles $\triangle$ (meaning)
3. $AC = CD$	Transitive Prop. of Eq.
4. C is the midpoint of AD.	def. of midpoint (suff. cond.)
5. $\overline{BC}$ is a median in $\triangle ABD$.	def. of median (suff. cond.)

CHAPTER 5 REVIEW (pages 249-251)
42.

Conclusions	Justifications
1. $ABCD$ has a line of symmetry (call it m), which is the $\perp$ bisector of $\overline{AB}$ and $\overline{DC}$.	Isosceles Trapezoid Symmetry Thm.
2. $r_m(A) = B$, $r_m(C) = D$	def. of reflection (suff. cond.)
3. $AC = BD$	Reflections preserve distance.

43.

Conclusions	Justifications
1. $AB = AC$	def. of isosceles $\triangle$ (meaning)
2. $AC = CD$	def. of isosceles $\triangle$ (meaning)
3. $AB = CD$	Transitive Prop. of Eq.

44. a. Kite Diagonal Theorem
b. definition of bisector (meaning)
c. definition of midpoint (meaning)

45.

Conclusions	Justifications
1. $OQ = OR$	def. of circle (meaning)
2. $PQ = PR$	def. of circle (meaning)
3. $OQPR$ is a kite.	def. of kite (suff. cond.)

46. b. Answers may vary.

47. a. square

b. Answers may vary. On a major league field, the dimensions are 90 feet on a side.

c. Answers may vary.

48. a. octagon, rectangle, pentagon

49.

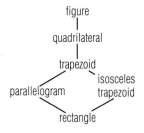

50.

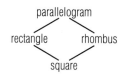

LESSON 6-2 (pages 259-265)

10. a.-d.

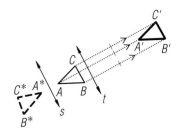

LESSON 6-4 (pages 273-278)

7.

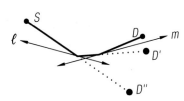

9.

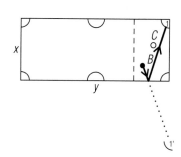

10.

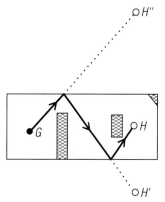

11.

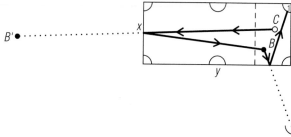

12. Aim at (11, 10).

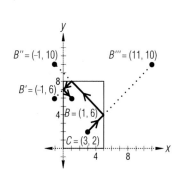

15.

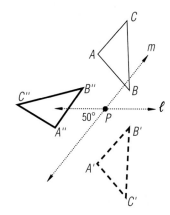

20. sample:

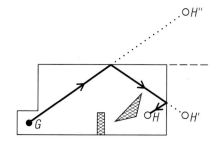

LESSON 6-6 (pages 285-291)

20.

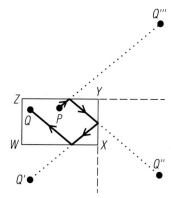

ADDITIONAL ANSWERS

CHAPTER 6 REVIEW (pages 299-301)

3. a.

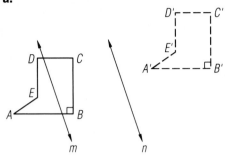

4. a.

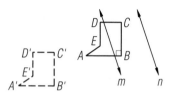

5. sample: (Two images are possible.)

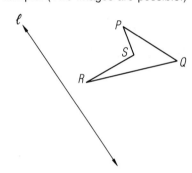

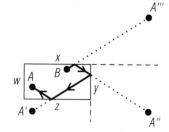

34.

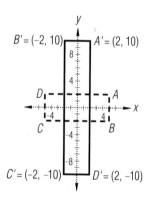

35.

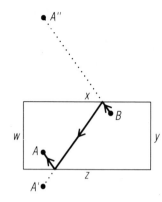

36. a.

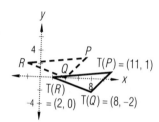

37. a. and b.

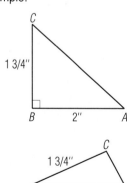

LESSON 7-1 (pages 304-309)

11. a. sample:

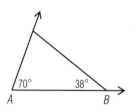

b. No

12. a. sample:

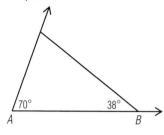

b. No

13. a. sample:

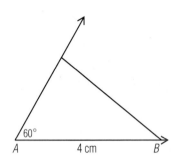

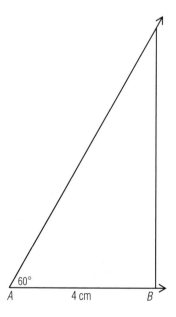

b. No

14. a.

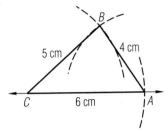

b. Yes

15. a. sample:

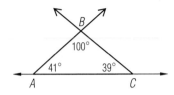

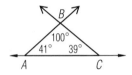

b. No

16. a. sample:

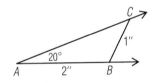

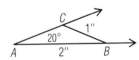

b. No

17. a.

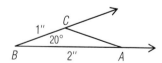

b. Yes

18. a.

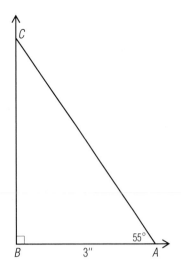

b. Yes

19. a.

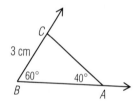

b. Yes

LESSON 7-7 (pages 339–343)

8. Use parallelogram *ABCD*:

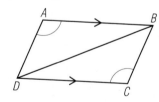

Conclusions	Justifications
1. Draw $\overline{BD}$.	Point-Line-Plane Post.
2. $\overline{BD} \cong \overline{BD}$	Reflexive Prop. of Congruence
3. m∠ABD = m∠CDB	∥ Lines ⇒ AIA = Thm.
4. △ABD ≅ △CDB	AAS Congruence Thm. (steps 2, 3, and given)

5. m∠ADB = m∠CBD	CPCF Thm.
6. $\overline{AD} \parallel \overline{BC}$	AIA = ⇒ ∥ Lines Thm.
7. *ABCD* is a parallelogram.	def. of parallelogram (suff. cond.)

11. Since the vertical sides of V, W, X, and Y are congruent and parallel, the vertical sides of Z are both congruent and parallel by the transitivity of congruence and parallelism.

13. (1) If both pairs of opposite sides are congruent, then the figure is a parallelogram (Sufficient Conditions for a Parallelogram Theorem). (2) If it is a parallelogram, then opposite angles are congruent (Properties of a Parallelogram Theorem).

15. Use rectangle *ABCD*.

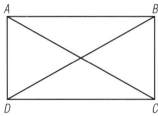

Conclusions	Justifications
1. *ABCD* is a parallelogram.	Quad. Hier. Thm.
2. $\overline{AD} \cong \overline{BC}$	Prop. of a Parallelogram Thm.
3. ∠ADC ≅ ∠BCD	Both are right angles (def. of rect.).
4. $\overline{DC} \cong \overline{DC}$	Reflexive Prop. of Congruence
5. △ADC ≅ △BCD	SAS Congruence Thm. (steps 2, 3, and 4)
6. $\overline{AC} \cong \overline{BD}$	CPCF Thm.

16. If, in two right triangles, the hypotenuse and a leg of one are congruent to the hypotenuse and a leg of the other, then the two triangles are congruent.

ADDITIONAL ANSWERS

17. a. (Art is reduced in size.)

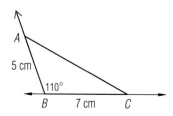

b. Yes
c. SAS Congruence Theorem

18. a. (Art is reduced in size.)

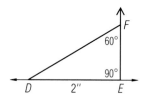

b. Yes
c. AAS Congruence Theorem
19. a. sample: (Art is reduced in size.)

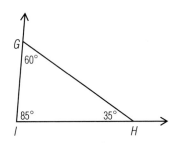

b. No
c. Triangles with longer or smaller sides could still have these same angle measures.

LESSON 7-8 (pages 344–347)
11. Use quadrilateral *ABCD:*

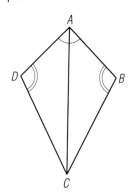

Conclusions	Justifications
1. $\overline{AC} \cong \overline{AC}$	Reflexive Prop. of Congruence
2. $\angle DAC \cong \angle BAC$	def. of angle bisector (meaning)
3. $\triangle DAC \cong \triangle BAC$	AAS Congruence Thm. (steps 1, 2, and given)
4. $\overline{AD} \cong \overline{AB}$; $\overline{DC} \cong \overline{BC}$	CPCF Thm.
5. *ABCD* is a kite.	def. of kite (suff. cond.)

12. a.

Conclusions	Justifications
1. $\overline{QS} \cong \overline{QS}$	Reflexive Prop. of Congruence
2. $\triangle QTS \cong \triangle SRQ$	SSS Congruence Thm. (step 1 and given)

b.

3. $\angle TQS \cong \angle RSQ$	CPCF Thm.
4. $\overline{QT} \parallel \overline{RS}$	AIA $= \Rightarrow \parallel$ Lines Thm.

15. (Art is reduced in size.)
a.

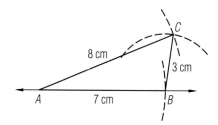

b.

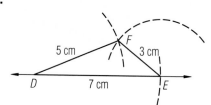

c. $m\angle A = m\angle D \approx 22$; $m\angle C = 30$ and $m\angle F = 150$, so $\angle C$ and $\angle F$ are supplementary.

CHAPTER 7 PROGRESS SELF-TEST
(page 349)
4. c. by the SSS Congruence Theorem
5. Any 3 of the following: both pairs of opposite sides parallel; both pairs of opposite sides congruent; both pairs of opposite angles congruent; the diagonals bisect each other; or one pair of opposite sides parallel and congruent.
6. Sample: If an angle gets bigger, but its adjacent sides stay the same length, then the side opposite that angle gets longer.
7. a.

Conclusions	Justifications
1. $\overline{QP} \cong \overline{QP}$	Reflexive Prop. of Congruence
2. $\triangle QSP \cong \triangle QTP$	HL Congruence Thm. (step 1 and given)
3. $QS = QT$	CPCF Thm.

b.

4. $m\angle SQP = m\angle TQP$	CPCF Thm.
5. $\overline{QP}$ is the angle bisector of $\angle SQT$.	def. of angle bisector (suff. cond.)

8. From the Sufficient Conditions for a Parallelogram Theorem (part d), *ABDC* is a parallelogram.
9. Draw decagon *ABCDEFGHIJ* and diagonal $\overline{AC}$ and $\overline{FH}$.

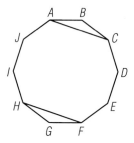

$\overline{AB} \cong \overline{BC} \cong \overline{FG} \cong \overline{GH}$, and $\angle B \cong \angle G$ (since *ABCDEFGHIJ* is given to be regular). So, $\triangle ABC \cong \triangle FGH$ (by the SAS Congruence Theorem). Therefore, $AC = FH$ (by the CPCF Theorem).

10.

Conclusions	Justifications
1. $\angle W \cong \angle W$	Reflexive Prop. of Congruence

2. $\triangle WUY \cong$ AAS
$\triangle WVX$ Congruence
Thm. (step 1
and given)
3. $WU = WV$ CPCF Thm.
4. $\triangle WUV$ is   def. of
isosceles.   isosceles $\triangle$
(suff. cond.)

11. Since $BD = DC$, $AD = AD$, and $\angle ADB$ and $\angle ADC$ are both right angles, $\triangle ADB \cong \triangle ADC$ by the SAS Congruence Theorem. Thus, the length of the ropes $AB = AC$ by the CPCF Theorem.

CHAPTER 7 REVIEW (pages 350-353)
5. a. (Art is reduced in size.)

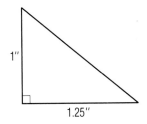

b. Yes
c. HL Congruence Theorem
6. a. (Art is reduced in size.)

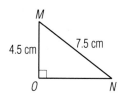

b. Yes
c. SAS Congruence Theorem
7. a. (Art is reduced in size.)

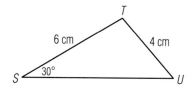

b. No
c. There are two noncongruent triangles that fit the given information.
8. a. (Art is reduced in size.)

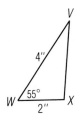

b. Yes
c. SAS Congruence Theorem
9. a. (Art is reduced in size.)

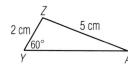

b. Yes
c. SsA Congruence Theorem
11. a. AAS Congruence Theorem
b. $\triangle MOP \cong \triangle PNM$
16. a. Reflexive Property of Congruence
b. ASA Congruence Theorem (step 1 and given)
17.

Conclusions	Justifications
1. $\overline{AC} \cong \overline{AC}$	Reflexive Property of Congruence
2. $\triangle ADC \cong \triangle ABC$	HL Congruence Thm. [step 1 and given]

18.

Conclusions	Justifications
1. $QA = QB$; $PA = PB$	def. of a circle (meaning)
2. $\overline{PQ} \cong \overline{PQ}$	Reflexive Prop. of Congruence
3. $\triangle APQ \cong \triangle BPQ$	SSS Congruence Thm. (steps 1 and 2)

19.

Conclusions	Justifications
1. $\angle YUX \cong \angle WUV$	def. of angle bisector (meaning)
2. $\triangle UVW \cong \triangle UXY$	AAS Congruence Thm. (step 1 and given)

20.

Conclusions	Justifications
1. $\overline{BC} \cong \overline{BC}$	Reflexive Prop. of Congruence
2. $\triangle ACB \cong \triangle DBC$	SAS Congruence Thm. (step 1 and given)

21. a. Reflexive Property of Congruence
b. SSS Congruence Theorem (step 1 and given)
c. CPCF Theorem
22.

Conclusions	Justifications
1. $\angle ABC \cong \angle BCD$; $\overline{AB} \cong \overline{BC} \cong \overline{CD}$	def. of regular polygon
2. $\triangle ABC \cong \triangle DCB$	SAS Congruence Thm. (step 1)
3. $\overline{AC} \cong \overline{BD}$	CPCF Thm.

LESSON 8-4 (pages 373-377)
25.

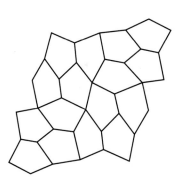

CHAPTER 8 PROGRESS SELF-TEST
(page 408)
1.

ADDITIONAL ANSWERS

LESSON 9-1 (pages 416-420)
18. sample:

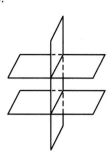

or

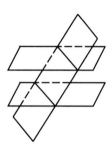

19. sample:

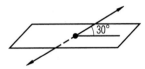

26. By the definition of bisector (suff. cond.), the diagonals of *ABDC* bisect each other. This is known to be a sufficient condition for a parallelogram.

LESSON 9-2 (pages 421-426)
20. sample:

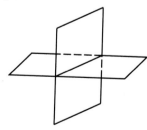

23. sample:

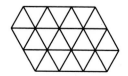

LESSON 9-4 (pages 433-438)
15. a. sample:

b. sample:

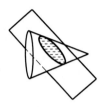

c. circle and ellipse
21. sample:

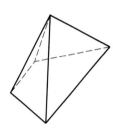

22. sample:

LESSON 9-5 (pages 439-443)
16. a. sample:

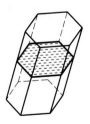

b. sample:

c. Part (a) is a hexagon congruent to the base. Part (b) is a hexagon.

LESSON 9-6 (pages 444-448)
3. a.-c.

top   front   side

4. a.-c.

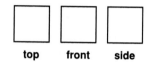

top   front   side

5. a.-c.

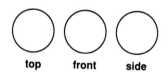

top   front   side

6. a.-c.

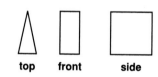

top   front   side

7. a.-c.

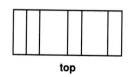

top

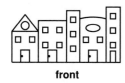

front

side

9. sample:

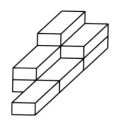

14. b. sample:

c. sample:

21.

Conclusions	Justifications
1. $\overline{AB} \cong \overline{CD}$	Prop. of a Parallelogram Thm.
2. $\overline{AB} \parallel \overline{CD}$	def. of a parallelogram (meaning)
3. $\angle ABQ \cong \angle CDQ$, $\angle QAB \cong \angle QCD$	$\parallel$ Lines $\Rightarrow$ AIA $=$ Thm.
4. $\triangle AQB \cong \triangle CQD$	ASA Congruence Thm. (steps 1 and 3)

LESSON 9-8   (pages 455-459)

15. sample:

16. sample:

17. sample:

18. sample:

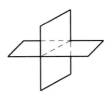

23. a. Oregon, Arizona, Colorado, S. Dakota, Missouri, Mississippi, Ohio, Virginia, New Jersey, Rhode Island
b. Nevada, Wyoming, Oklahoma, Louisiana, Iowa, Kentucky, Georgia, Maryland, Massachusetts
c. Idaho, New Mexico, Nebraska, N. Dakota, Arkansas, Wisconsin, Indiana, Alabama, N. Carolina, W. Virginia, Delaware, New York, New Hampshire
d. Washington, California, Utah, Montana, Kansas, Texas, Minnesota, Illinois, Michigan, Tennessee, Pennsylvania, Florida, S. Carolina, Connecticut, Vermont, Maine
e. Hawaii, Alaska

CHAPTER 9 PROGRESS SELF-TEST
(page 461)
8. sample:

9. sample:

12.

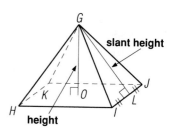

13.

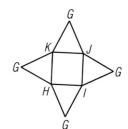

14.

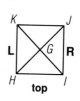

top   **front**   **side**

16. sample:

20. sample: a rectangular solid

ADDITIONAL ANSWERS

23. sample:

CHAPTER 9 REVIEW (pages 462-465)

12. c.

right

13. a.-c.

top

front

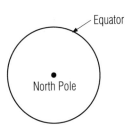

right

14.

16. sample:

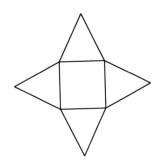

17. sample:

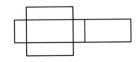

18. sample:

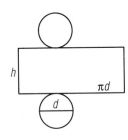

21. a. $9\pi \approx 28.3$ sq cm

23. a.

24. a. 2

46. Thomas Guthrie

49. sample:

LESSON 10-2 (pages 473-477)

2. sample:

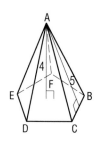

3. sample:

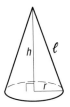

15. a. sample:

16. a. sample:

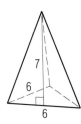

17. a. sample:

T62

20. sample:

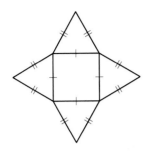

23. a.

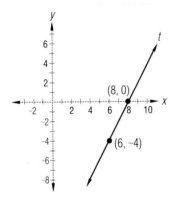

LESSON 10-3 (pages 478-482)

16. b. The printout would be:
GIVE DIMENSIONS OF BOX
7, 12, 17
THE VOLUME IS 1428 CUBIC UNITS.
THE SURFACE AREA IS 814 SQUARE UNITS.
The answer for volume agrees with Example 1 of this lesson. The surface area of 814 square units is 84 more than that of Example 1 of Lesson 10-1. The difference represents the area of the top base which the example did not call for.

CHAPTER 10 PROGRESS SELF-TEST
(page 515)

13. Let I and II be two solids included between parallel planes. If every plane P parallel to the given planes intersects I and II in sections with the same area, then Volume (I) = Volume (II).

14. The volume of the pyramid is one-third the volume of the prism.

LESSON 11-1 (pages 522-526)

13. a.

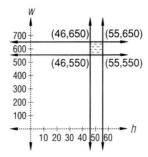

LESSON 11-3 (pages 532-536)

13.

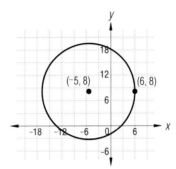

17.

Conclusions	Justifications
1. slope of $\overline{TQ} =$ $\frac{-14b-4b}{-a-9a} = \frac{9b}{5a}$ slope of $\overline{SR} =$ $\frac{-7b-2b}{a-6a} = \frac{9b}{5a}$	def. of slope (meaning)
2. $\overline{TQ} \parallel \overline{SR}$	Parallel Lines and Slopes Thm.
3. $QRST$ is a trapezoid.	def. of trapezoid (suff. cond.)

20. sample:

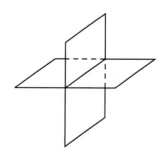

21. sample:

22.

Conclusions	Justifications
1. $XY = XZ$	def. of isosceles $\triangle$ (meaning)
2. $\frac{1}{2} \cdot XY =$ $\frac{1}{2} \cdot XZ$	Mult. Prop. of Equality
3. $VX = \frac{1}{2} \cdot XY$, $WX = \frac{1}{2} \cdot XZ$	def. of midpoint (meaning)
4. $VX = WX$	substitution (step 3 into step 2)
5. $\triangle XVW$ is isosceles.	def. of isosceles $\triangle$ (suff. cond.)

LESSON 11-6 (pages 550-556)

16. b.

Conclusions	Justifications
1. The mid-points are located at (b, c) and $(a + d, c)$.	def. of midpoint (meaning)
2. The slope of the segment joining the midpoints is 0. The slope of the base segments is 0.	def. of slope (meaning)
3. The segment joining the midpoints is parallel to the bases.	Parallel Lines and Slopes Thm.

ADDITIONAL ANSWERS

CHAPTER 11 REVIEW (pages 559-561)
18. a.

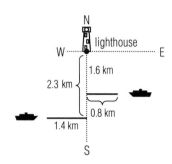

b. $\sqrt{5.33} \approx 2.3$ km
29.

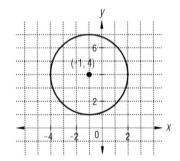

30.

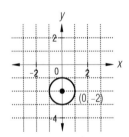

39. a.

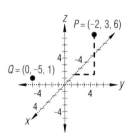

b. (-1, -1, 3.5)
c. $\sqrt{93} \approx 9.64$ units

40. a.

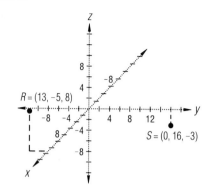

b. (6.5, 5.5, 2.5)
c. $\sqrt{731} \approx 27.04$ units

LESSON 12-1 (pages 564-568)
8.

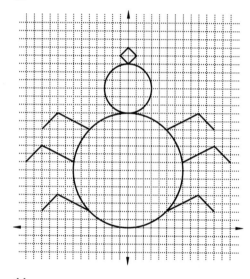

11. c.
$$QP = \sqrt{(2 - \text{-}3)^2 + (\text{-}8 - 12)^2 + (0 - 4)^2}$$
$$= \sqrt{441} = 21$$
$$Q'P' =$$
$$\sqrt{(10 - \text{-}15)^2 + (\text{-}40 - 60)^2 + (0 - 20)^2}$$
$$= \sqrt{11{,}025} = 105 = 5 \cdot QP$$

14. (Art is reduced in size.)

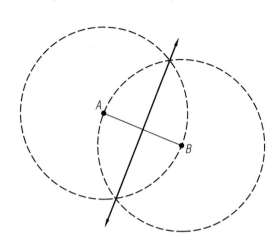

LESSON 12-2 (pages 569-574)
14. $k = \frac{1}{3}$

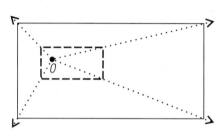

15. $k \approx \frac{3}{4}$

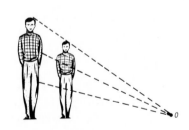

LESSON 12-3 (pages 575-580)
15.

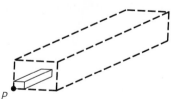

LESSON 12-5 (pages 586-592)
19. a.

LESSON 12-10 (pages 615-620)
20.

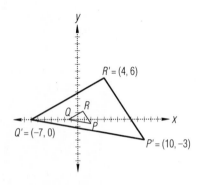

CHAPTER 12 REVIEW (pages 624-627)
24. b. Sample: Below is a counterexample.

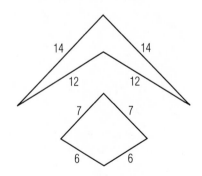

LESSON 14-5 (pages 708-713)
14.

9.8

15.

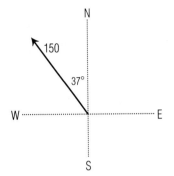

16.

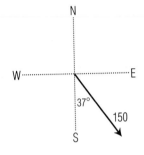

17.

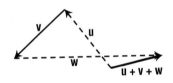

LESSON 14-6 (pages 714-719)
27. b. Samples: The mean of (-8, 3) and (-2, -5) is (-5, -1).

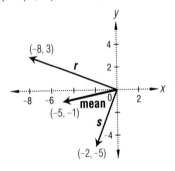

The mean of (3, 3) and (3, -1) is (3, 1).

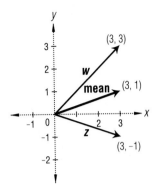

When **u** and **v** have the same initial points, their mean is the vector whose initial point is the initial point of **u** and **v** and whose terminal point is the midpoint of the terminal points of **u** and **v**.

CHAPTER 14 PROGRESS SELF-TEST
(pages 726-727)
18.

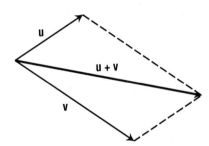

CHAPTER 14 REVIEW (pages 728-731)
29.

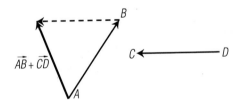

32.

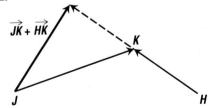

T65

ADDITIONAL ANSWERS

59. The boat will move in the direction $\overrightarrow{OM}$.

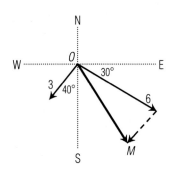

63.

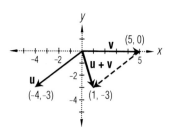

64.

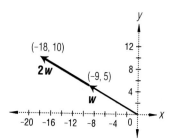

65.

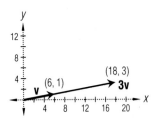

LESSON 15-2 (pages 740-744)

7. sample:

1st wk	2nd wk	3rd wk	4th wk	5th wk	6th wk	7th wk
7-2	1-3	2-4	3-5	4-6	5-7	6-1
6-3	7-4	1-5	2-6	3-7	4-1	5-2
5-4	6-5	7-6	1-7	2-1	3-2	4-3
1-8	2-8	3-8	4-8	5-8	6-8	7-8

LESSON 15-3 (pages 745-751)

11. m∠ABC

= m∠ABD − m∠CBD	Angle Add. Post.
= $\frac{1}{2}$m$\widehat{AD}$ − $\frac{1}{2}$ m$\widehat{CD}$	by Case I
= $\frac{1}{2}$ (m$\widehat{AD}$ − m$\widehat{CD}$)	Distributive Prop.
= $\frac{1}{2}$ m$\widehat{AC}$	Arc Addition

LESSON 15-4 (pages 752-757)

9. sample:

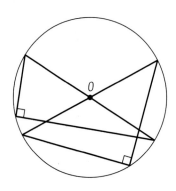

CHAPTER 15 PROGRESS SELF-TEST
(pages 786-787)

1.

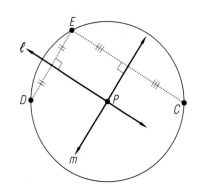

CHAPTER 15 REVIEW (pages 788-791)

47. sample:

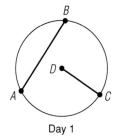

Day 1

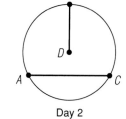

Day 2

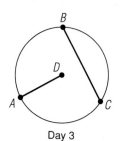

Day 3

Day 1: A vs. B, C vs. D
Day 2: A vs. C, B vs. D
Day 3: A vs. D, B vs. C

48. Sample:
Rotate the chords:

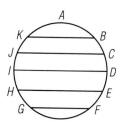

1.	K-B	J-C	I-D	H-E	G-F	A bye
2.	A-C	K-D	J-E	I-F	H-G	B bye
3.	B-D	A-E	K-F	J-G	I-H	C bye
4.	C-E	B-F	A-G	K-H	J-I	D bye
5.	D-F	C-G	B-H	A-I	K-J	E bye
6.	E-G	D-H	C-I	B-J	A-K	F bye
7.	F-H	E-I	D-J	C-K	B-A	G bye
8.	G-I	F-J	E-K	D-A	C-B	H bye
9.	H-J	G-K	F-A	E-B	D-C	I bye
10.	I-K	H-A	G-B	F-C	E-D	J bye
11.	J-A	I-B	H-C	G-D	F-E	K bye

Page references in **bold face type** indicate the location of the definition of the term.

AA Similarity Theorem, 609
AAA condition, 307
AAS Congruence Theorem, 312, 609
A-B-C-D Theorem, 281
absolute value, 9, 82
acre, 376
acute,
   angle, **113**
   nonmathematical meaning, 119
   triangle, 118
Addition Property
   of Equality, 37, 72, 78
   of Inequality, 37
addition of vectors, 714, 715, 720
Additive Property,
   of Area, 368
   of Volume, 479
adjacent,
   angles, **114,** 115, 116
   sides and angles in a right triangle, 696
Africa (map), 465
AIA = ⇒ ∥ Lines Theorem, 234
algorithm, 141, 143, 363
   for constructing an equilateral triangle, 176
   for dividing a segment into *n* congruent parts, 620
   for getting the area of any polygon, 384
Alhambra, 363
Alice in Wonderland, 632
alternate exterior angles, 234-235
alternate interior angles, 234-235
altitude, 379
   of a solid, 422
   of a trapezoid, 384
   of a triangle, 379
analytic geometry, 521
analyze step, 177-178
anamorphic art, 29
angle(s), 105, **106,** 164, 261, 304-306, 310-312, 587
   acute, **113**
   adjacent, **114,** 115, 116
   alternate exterior, 234-235
   alternate interior, 234-235
   base, 206, 215
   bisector, **116,** 196, 207, 208
   complementary, **114,** 116
   corresponding, 126, 127

of depression, 706
exterior, formed by a transversal, **234**
exterior of, 106
exterior, of a polygon, 665, 671
of inclination, 420
interior, formed by a transversal, **234**
interior of, 106
measure, 107, 164, 188, 240-243, 281, 587
measure postulate, 108
obtuse, **113**
postulates pertaining to, 368
right, **113,** 132
sides of, 106
straight, 106-109, **113**
supplementary, **114,** 115, 116
vertex, 206
vertex of, 106
vertical, **114,** 115
zero, 106, 108, **113**
Angle Addition Property, 108, 109
Angle-Chord Theorem, 758
Angle Congruence Theorem, 281
Angle Measure Postulate, 108
Angle-Secant Theorem, 759
Angle Symmetry Theorem, 194
ante, 69
antecedent, 65-67, 71, 72, 76, 83, 84
   as the given, 121
Appel, Kenneth, 456
Applications. Every set of questions features applications problems.
arc, 24
   endpoints, 396
   length, 397
   major, 396, 734
   measure, 734
   minor, 396, 734
   in a network, 20-21
Arc-Chord Congruence Theorem, 736
Archimedes, 497
area, 355, 367, 390, 483, 775
   of a circle, 595
   fundamental properties of, 367-370
   of a kite, 383
   lateral, 427, 469-470, 473-475
   of a rectangle, 595
   of a rhombus, 383
   surface, 468, 470, 475
Area Postulate, 368
arithmetic mean, 691
Art Institute of Chicago, 3
ASA Congruence Theorem, 312, 609
Associative Property of Vector Addition, 715

assumption(s), 121. *See also* postulates.
   from a diagram, 178
   straight angle, 108
   two sides of a line, 108
   unique line, dimension, distance, number line, 35
   unique measure, 108
   zero angle, 108
automatic drawer, drawing tool, 170-173, 182 (ex. 23-24), 186 (ex. 15), 212 (ex. 21), 308 (ex. 11-19), 383 (ex. 25)
auxiliary,
   line(s), 658
   nonmathematical meaning, 664
axis (axes),
   of a cone, 428
   of a coordinate system, 14, 550
   x- and *y*-, 14
   x-, *y*-, and *z*-, 550

Baha'i House of Worship, 100
bar graph, 563
base,
   angles, 206, 215
   of conic solid, 427, **428**
   of cylindric solid, 422
   of isosceles triangle, 206
   of trapezoid, 215
   line for a protractor, 107
BASIC, 70, 71. *See also* computer programs.
between, betweenness, 40, 82, 163, 164, 188, 261, 281, 587
Betweenness Theorem, 41, 46
biconditional, 84. *See also* if and only if statements.
bilateral symmetry, 440
billiards, 273-275
binomial, 484
bisector, 112, 116, 128, 141, 439
   angle, **116**
   perpendicular, **141,** 439
   of a segment, **112**
box, 10, 339, 421, 424, 449, 484, 494, 495, 511
Box Volume Formula, 479, 483
Brobdingnagians, 599
bye (tournament), 740

calculator,
   cube root key, 480
   inverse key, 722
   trigonometric ratio(s), 697, 699, 703, 707

calculus, 375
camera picture angle, 745
capacity, 478, 810
Carroll, Lewis, 632, 637
Cartesian plane, 14
Cavalieri, Francesco Bonaventura, 490
Cavalieri's Principle, 490, 505
center, 569
  of a circle, **84,** 184, 752
  of gravity, 537
  for a protractor, 107
  of a regular polygon, **335**
  of a rotation, 267
  of a size transformation, 569, **570**
  of a sphere, **433**
Center of Regular Polygon Theorem, 335
central angle, 396, 734
centroid, 212
Ceres, 515 (ex. 3)
Chapter Review, 54-57, 101-103, 149-153, 200-203, 249-251, 299-301, 350-353, 410-413, 462-465, 516-519, 559-561, 624-627, 678-681, 728-731, 788-791
Chapter Summary, *See* Summary.
Chapter Test. *See* Progress Self-Tests.
Chasles, Michel, 253
chord
  of arc, 734
  of circle, 734
Chord Center Theorem, 735
circle(s), 10, 60, **84,** 107, 396-398, 402, 403, 415, 433, 436, 532-534, 651-654, 733-737
  area of, 402
  center of, **84**
  concentric, 331, 397
  congruent, 735
  diameter of, **84**
  equation of, 533
  great, 433
  radius of, **84**
  small, 433
  tangent, 535, 651-653, 739
Circle Area Formula, 402
Circle Circumference Formula, 398
circularity, 31
circumference of a circle, 397, 777
circumscribed polygon, 739
clockwise, 188, 267
closed curve, simple, 222
coincide, 192
collinear points, 6, 163, 164, 188
collinearity, 261, 281
  preserving, 576, 587
common tangents, 654

Commutative Property of Addition, 37
Commutative Property of Multiplication, 37
compass, 141
Compass rule, 141, 142
complementary angles, complements, 114, 116
component vectors, 714, 721
composite, composition, 259, **260,** 279
composite of reflections, 280
computer,
  automatic drawer, 170-173, 182 (ex. 23-24), 186 (ex. 15), 212 (ex. 21), 308 (ex. 11-19), 383 (ex. 25)
  programs, BASIC, 70, 71, 74 (ex. 12-13), 75 (ex. 25), 80, (ex. 15), 99 (ex. 10-11), 103 (ex. 36-40), 482 (ex. 16)
  programs, Logo, 672, 673 (ex. 7), 674 (ex. 18), 676 (ex. 7), 678 (ex. 1-2)
  screens, 4, 17, 375
concave, 61
concentric circles, 331, 397
conclusion(s), 65, 121, 177
  justifying, 120-122
  the logic of making, 630-632
conditional statement, 65, 72, 76, 121
  contrapositive of, 636-637
  converse of, **76,** 77-78, 127
  inverse of, 636
  negation of, 635
cone, 415, **428,** 429, 435, 451, 475, 494, 499-501, 511
  lateral area, 475
  surface area, 475
congruence, congruent,
  arcs, 736
  circles, 736
  figures, **279, 439**
  reflexive, symmetric, transitive properties of, 280
  space figures, **439**
  transformation, 280
  triangles, 310-322
Congruence Property, of area, 368
  of volume, 479
conic
  section, 436
  solid, **428**
  surface, 428
conjecture, 218-220, 227 (ex. 14), 233 (ex. 23), 248 (ex. 13), 250 (ex. 35-37), 251 (ex. 38-39), 322 (ex. 19), 580 (ex. 27), 701 (ex. 19), 719 (ex. 28), 757 (ex. 18), 784 (ex. 21)
  Four Color, 455
  unsolved, 222

consecutive,
  angles, 228
  sides, 93, 214
  vertices, 93
consequent, 65-67, 72, 76
  as a conclusion, 121
construction, 141-143
  altitude of a triangle, 182
  angle bisector, 196
  center of a circle, 184
  dividing a segment into *n* congruent parts, 620
  and drawing, 140
  duplicating the cube, 145
  impossible, 145
  perpendicular bisector of segment, 142
  a perpendicular, 142-143
  squaring a circle, 145
  a triangle, given 3 sides, 305
  trisecting an angle, 145
contracting, 570
contradiction, contradictory, 645, **646**
contrapositive, 636, 667
converse, 76, 77-78, 127
conversion formulas, 810
convex, 94
  polyhedron, 452
  set, **61**
coordinate(s), 8, 522
  geometry, 521
  graphing, 14
  plane, 14
  and proofs, 522-523
  system, 3-dimensional, 550
  z-, 550
coordinatized line, 9
coplanar, 10
corollary, 230
correspondence, one-to-one, 35, 164, 255, 416
corresponding angles,
  formed by a transversal, 126, 127
  in congruent triangles, 292
  in similar triangles, 606
  and nonincluded sides, 312
Corresponding Angles Postulate, 127
corresponding parts, 292
Corresponding Parts in Congruent Figures (CPCF) Theorem, 292
cosine, 702, 703
counterclockwise, 188, 267
counterexample, 66, 67, 77, 120, 239
CPCF Theorem, 292
Crawford, Ralston, 25
cube, 10, 26, 449, 454, 781
cube root, 480
Cube Volume Formula, 480

cubic unit, 478
curve, simple closed, 222, 415
cycloid, (*i*)
cylinder, 415, 422, **423**, 424, 429, 435,
    451, 488-490, 494, 495, 505, 511,
    780
    lateral area, 469
    surface area, 470
cylindric solid, **422,** 423
cylindric surface, 422, 424

debugging, 71
decagon, 93
deduce, 521
definitions,
    good, 81-84
    meaning half and sufficient condition
        half, 83
    need for, 30-31, 60-61
degree,
    measure of an angle, **107**
    measure of a major arc, **396**
    measure of a minor arc, **396**
    measure of a semicircle, **396**
Dell Big Book of Crosswords and
    Pencil Puzzles, 139
dense, 10
depression, angle of, 706
Desargues, Gerard, 131
Desargues' Theorem, 131
Descartes, René, 14, 451, 521
determine, 35, 417, 658
diagonal,
    of a kite, 224
    of a polygon, 70, 71, 93
    of a quadrilateral, 72
Diagonal of a Box Formula, 522
diagram, assumptions from, 178
diameter,
    of a circle, 84
    of a sphere, 433
Dido of Carthage, 784
dilatation, dilation, 570
Dimension assumption, 35
dimensions, 15
    of a box, 421
    of a rectangle, 367
direct proof, 645
direct reasoning, 645
directed line segment, 708
direction,
    of a translation, 261
    of a vector, 708
discrete line(s), 5
    intersection of, 88
distance, **9,** 15, 43, 82, 84, 163, 164,
    188, 261, 281, 587
    formula, 528
    formula in three dimensions, 551
    unique, assumption, 35

distinct, 192
Distributive Property, 37
dividing a segment into *n*
    congruent parts, 620
dodecahedron, 454
Dodgson, Charles L., 632
dot, 4, 5, 6
dot product, 725
dot-matrix printer, 4
double implication, 83
drawer, automatic, 170-173
drawing, 140, 157
    perspective, 26, 256
duplicating a cube, 145

earth, 45 (ex. 25), 152 (ex. 40), 242,
    515 (ex. 15), 518 (ex. 30), 602
    (ex. 17), 654, 657 (ex. 23-24), 768
    (ex. 22)
eclipse, 657, 768
edge,
    of a box, 421
    of a polyhedron, 449
    of a prism, 421
    of a pyramid, 427
Egypt, 427, 432, 474
elements, 30
Elements, The, 36, 176, 691
elevation, 444
ellipse, 435, 436
elliptical region, 355
empty set, 88
endpoint, **40,** 92, 93
ends of a kite, 223
equal vectors, 708
Equality, Postulates of, 37
equation,
    of a circle, 533
    of a line, 16
    of a sphere, 553
Equation to Inequality Property,
    37, 41
equiangular, 209
equidistant, 82, 335
equilateral,
    hexagon, 358
    pentagon, 358
    polygon, 358
    triangle, 94, 177, 209, 335, 365
Equilateral Polygon Perimeter
    Formula, 358
Equivalence Properties of ≅
    Theorem, 280
Escher, Maurits, 253, 288, 289, 300,
    365
Euclid, 36, 37, 176, 177, 253, 601, 651,
    662, 691
Euler, Leonard, 19-22, 253, 453, 703
Euler's Formula, 453
Europe, (map), 457

even node, 21
even vertex, 21
events (probability), 403
expansion, 570
Exploration question, 7, 13, 18, 24,
    29, 34, 39, 45, 51, 64, 69, 75, 80,
    86, 91, 97, 112, 119, 125, 131, 139,
    145, 162, 169, 175, 182, 186, 191,
    197, 212, 217, 222, 227, 233, 239,
    245, 258, 265, 272, 278, 284, 291,
    295, 309, 316, 322, 326, 332, 338,
    343, 347, 361, 366, 372, 377, 383,
    389, 395, 401, 406, 420, 426, 432,
    438, 443, 448, 454, 459, 472, 477,
    482, 487, 493, 498, 504, 509, 513,
    526, 531, 536, 543, 549, 556, 568,
    574, 580, 585, 592, 598, 603, 608,
    614, 620, 634, 639, 644, 650, 657,
    664, 670, 674, 689, 695, 701, 707,
    713, 719, 724, 739, 744, 751, 757,
    762, 768, 774, 779, 784
exponential growth curve, 16
extended ratio, 241
exterior,
    of an angle, 106
    of a polygon, 94
exterior angle,
    formed by a transversal, 234
    of a polygon, **665,** 671
Exterior Angle Inequality, 666
Exterior Angles of a Polygon Sum
    Theorem, 671
Exterior Angle Theorem, 665
extremes, 582, 583

face
    of a polyhedron, 449
    of a box, 421
    of a pyramid, 427
family tree, 94
Fermat, Pierre de, 14, 521
fifth postulate (of Euclid), 661-662
figure(s), **30**
    congruent,
    one-dimensional, 415
    plane, 10
    similar, 563
    space, 10
    three-dimensional, 10, 415
    two-dimensional, 10, 415
Figure Reflection Theorem, 165, 187
Figure Size Change Theorem, 578
Flip-Flop Theorem, 188
flowchart display of a proof, 180
formulas, 358, 368
    conversion, list of, 810
    for three-dimensional figures,
        494-495, 511
    See also p. 809 for list.
Four Color Conjecture, 455

Four Color Theorem, 456
fundamental region, 362
Fundamental Theorem of
    Similarity, 593-595, 599

Galileo, 601, 733
Games, 644
Gardner, Martin, 91
Gauss, Karl Friedrich, 240, 241
geometer, 27, 86
geometric mean, **690**
Geometric Mean Theorem, 691
geometry, 3
    analytic, 521
    coordinate, 521
    non-Euclidean, 241, 662
    plane, 30
    solid, 30
giants, 599-600
given, 121
glide reflection, 253, 286, **287**, 587,
    660, 661
Glide Reflection Theorem, 287
Goldbach's Conjecture, 66, 67
Goldbach, Christian, 66
golf, miniature, 273-275
good definitions, 80-84
graceful network, 24
grade, 126
graph theory, 455
graphing, 15
great circle, 433, 434
grid for solving logic puzzles, 641
Guinness Book of World Records,
    599
Gulliver's Travels, 599, 600
Guthrie, Thomas, 455

Haken, Wolfgang, 456
hard copy, 173
harmonic mean, 695
Hawaii (map), 408
height,
    of a cone, 429, 473
    of a cylindric solid, 422
    of a pyramid, 429, 473
    slant, 427, 473
    of a solid, 422
hemisphere, 433
heptagon, 93, 335
Hero's (Heron's) Formula, 497
hexagon, 65, 70, 93, 335, 358, 365
hexagonal prism, 423
hexahedron, 449
hidden lines, 27, 256, *See also*
    illustrations: 415, 418, 421, 422,
    427, 428, 433, 434, 436.
hierarchy, 94, 236, 246, 288, 494-495,
    587
    of conic surfaces, 429

    of cylindric surfaces, 424
    of isometries, 288
    of quadrilaterals, 213-215, 223
Hilbert, David, 523
Hinge Theorem, 347
history of mathematics, 14, 19-22,
    36, 66, 91, 131, 253, 364, 377, 455,
    456, 497, 521, 523, 601, 632, 660,
    661, 703, 733
HL condition, 328
HL Congruence Theorem, 328
HL Similarity Theorem, 614
homonym, 119
horizontal component, 714
horizontal line, 5, 16, 126
humerus, 111
hyperbola, 436
hypercube, 556
hypersphere, 556
hypotenuse, 327
hypotenuse-leg condition, 328
hypothesis, 65

IBM PC computer, 4
icosahedron, 454
identity, 587
identity transformation, 570
if and only if statements, 83
if-then statements, 65-67, 120
    in computer programs, 70-72
image, 254
Imhotep, 427
implication, implies, 67, 630
    See also contrapositive, converse,
    inverse.
    double, 83
Implication, Transitive Property of,
    630
included angle, 311
included side, 312
indirect proof, 645-648
indirect reasoning, 635, 645, 647
inequality
    isoperimetric, 776
    postulates of, 37, 46
    quadrilateral, 51
    transitive property, 37
    triangle, 46-49
initial point, 708
inscribed angle, 745, **746**
Inscribed Angle Theorem, 746
inscribed polygon, 737
instance, 65
intercepted arc, 734
interior,
    of an angle, 106, 234
    of a polygon, 94
interior angle, 665, 671
intersection, 93
    of lines, 88

    of planes, 418
    of sets, **87**
inverse, 636
irregular regions, 373-375
isometry, 280, 281, 285-288, 587
Isoperimetric Inequality, 776
Isoperimetric Theorem, 776, 777
Isoperimetric Theorem (space
    version), 780, 781
Isosceles Right Triangle Theorem,
    684
isosceles trapezoid, 215, 223, 228,
    230, 236
Isosceles Trapezoid Symmetry
    Theorem, 230
Isosceles Trapezoid Theorem, 230
isosceles triangle, 94, 206-209
Isosceles Triangle Bisector
    Theorem, 208
Isosceles Triangle Symmetry
    Theorem, 207
Isosceles Triangle Theorem, 208

Jack and the Beanstalk, 599
justifications, justifying conclusions,
    120-122, 177
    steps in parentheses, 318
Jupiter, 515 (ex. 15), 614 (ex. 16)

kite, **214,** 215, 218, 223-225, 236, 357
    area, 383
Kite Diagonal Theorem, 224
Kite Symmetry Theorem, 223
Königsberg Bridge Problem, 19-22

labyrinth, 139
Lake Michigan (map), 426
lateral area, 469, 473
lateral edge,
    of a cone, 428
    of a pyramid, 427
lateral face,
    of a prism, 423
    of a pyramid, 427
lateral surface, 422
    of a cone, 428
    of a cylindric solid, 422
lattice points, 18, 377, 535
Law of the Contrapositive, 636
Law of Cosines, 592
Law of Detachment, 630
Law of Indirect Reasoning, 647
Law of Ruling Out Possibilities, 640
Law of Transitivity, 630, 631
lean-to roof, 304
Leaning Tower of Pisa, 118
leg, 327
length, 41
Lilliputians, 600
limit, 375

line(s), 5, 6, 8, 10, 15, 20, 31, 82, 87, 88, 115, 126, 416-418
  auxiliary, 658
  coordinatized, 9
  coplanar, 10
  dense, 10
  discrete, 5
  of dots, 5
  equation of, 15
  hidden, 27
  horizontal, 5
  in networks, 20
  oblique, 5
  one-dimensional, 10
  parallel, 5, 126-129
  perpendicular, **132,** 133-135
  of reflection, 156, 158, 165, 192
  secant, **759,** 769
  segment, **40**
  of sight, 25
  skew, 421
  and tilt, 105
  unique, assumption, 35
  vanishing, 26
  vertical, 5
linear pair, 114, 115, 116
Linear Pair Theorem, 115, 116, 120
lines of sight, 25
logic. *See* Chapter 13; conjecture; deductive reasoning; if and only if statements; if-then statements; indirect reasoning
Logo, 672. *See also* computer programs
Loyd, Sam, 91

Macintosh, 4, 375
magnitude,
  of a rotation, 267
  of a size change, 565, 569
  of a translation, 261
  of a vector, 708
Magritte, René, 265
major arc, 396, 734
map
  Africa, 465
  Europe, 457
  Hawaii, 408
  Lake Michigan, 406
  Nevada, 389
  Ohio, 12
  Texas, 385
  United States, 455
mapping, 255. *See also* transformation.
Mathematical Puzzles of Sam Loyd, 91
matrix (computer screens), 4
maze, 139
mean(s), 537, 582, 583

  arithmetic, 691
  geometric, **690**
  harmonic, 695
  of a proportion, 581-583
meaning half (of a definition), 83, 84
Means Exchange Property, 583
Means-Extremes Property, 582
measure,
  of an angle, 107
  degree, 107
  of an intercepted arc, 734
  unique, assumption, 108
median, 208
  nonmathematical meanings, 212
menu, 170
Mercator projection, 509
midpoint, 81, 82, 83, 544-546
Midpoint Connector Theorem, 545
Midpoint Formula, 538
Midpoint Formula in Three Dimensions, 553
miniature golf, 273-275
minor arc, 396, 734
minute (as angle measure), 112
model, 483
moon, 448 (ex. 18), 602 (ex. 17), 654, 657 (ex. 23-24), 768 (ex. 22)
Moors, 363
multiplication of binomials or trinomials, 484
Multiplication Property
  of Equality, 37, 72, 78
  of Inequality, 37

n-**gon,** 93
Napoleon III with His Children, 29
negation, 635
net, 449, 504
network, 20
  graceful, 24
Nevada (map), 389
New York Bridge Problem, 33
nodes, 20, 24
  even and odd, 21
nonadjacent angles,
  with exterior angle theorem, 665
nonagon, 93, 335
noncollinear points, 417
nonconvex set, 61
non-Euclidean geometries, 241, 662
non-included side, 312
nonoverlapping regions, 368
nonoverlapping triangles, 333
not-p, 635, 636
null set, 88
number, 82
  of diagonals in a polygon, 70
number line, 8, 15, 416
  unique, assumption, 35

Objectives, *See* Chapter Review.
oblique,
  cone, 428
  cylinder, 424
  line, 5, 16
  prism, 424
obtuse,
  angle, **113**
  nonmathematical meaning, 119
  triangle, 118
octagon, 93, 335
octahedron, 454
odd node, 21, 22
odd vertex, 22
Ohio (map), 12
Olympics, (Seoul Summer), 5
one-dimensional, 10, 25, 415
one-to-one correspondence, 15, 416
opposite,
  face of a box, 421
  rays, **42,** 115
  sides and angles in a right triangle, 696
  vectors, 716
ordered pair, 14, 16
  description of a vector, 714
ordered triple, 550
orientation, 188, 191
origin, 35
Osgood, Charles, 58, 65, 81
overlapping triangles, 323, 333

pair, linear, 114
pairing, 741
parabola, 16, 436
parallel lines, 5, **36,** 126, 127, 135
  // lines $\Rightarrow$ corr. $\angle$s = Postulate, 127
  // lines $\Rightarrow$ AIA = Theorem, 234
Parallel Lines Postulate, 127
Parallel Lines and Slopes Theorem, 128
parallel planes, 418, 419
parallelepiped, 424
parallelogram, 60, 94, **213,** 214-215, 223, 228, 234, 236, 333, 334, 339-341, 386
  rule (for vectors), 711
Parallelogram Area Formula, 386
parentheses in proof justifications, 318
Pencil Puzzle Treasury, 644
pentagon, 93, 335, 358, 365
pentagonal prism, 422
pentagonal pyramid, 427
pentagram, 762
perimeter,
  of a circle, 777
  of an equilateral polygon, 358
  of a kite, 357

of a polygon, 355, **356,** 357
of a rectangle, 358
perpendicular, 132
bisector, 141, 142, 183, 208, 439
constructing, 140-143
lines, **132,** 133-135
planes, **418,** 419
to a plane, 418
perpendicular bisector method,
144, (ex. 15), 752
Perpendicular Bisector Theorem,
183, 184
Perpendicular Lines and Slopes
Theorem, 134
Perpendicular to Parallels
Theorem, 133
perspective, 25
drawing, 26, 29 (ex. 20)
hidden lines, 27, 256. *See also*
illustrations: 415, 418, 421, 422,
427, 428, 433, 434, 436
pi, 397, 398
Pick's Theorem, 377
picture angle, 745
picture graph, 563
pixels, 4, 17
plane, 10, 31, 416-419, 421
figure, 10
geometry, 30
postulates pertaining to, 35
section, **434**
Playfair's Parallel Postulate, 660,
662
Playfair, John, 662
point(s), 3, **5,** 6, **8,** 10, **14,** 15, 16, **20,**
31, 40, 43, 82, 87, 88, 135, 164,
416-418
dots as, 5
equidistant, 82
lattice, 18
locations as, 8
in networks, 20
as nodes, 20
noncollinear, 417
ordered pairs as, 14
of tangency, 651, 653
vanishing, 25
Point-Line-Plane Postulate, 35, 36,
40, 416, 417, 658
Point rule, 141, 142
pointillism, 7
polygon, 60, 65, 70, 71, **92,** 93, 94,
187, 188, 205, 243, 358, 378, 384,
421, 671. *See also* kite;
parallelogram; quadrilateral;
rectangle; regular polygon;
rhombus; square; trapezoid;
triangle.
equilateral, 358
regular, 334

polygonal region, 94, 421
Polygon-Sum Theorem, 243
polyhedron, polyhedra, 449. *See*
also prism; pyramid.
polynomial, 484
postulate(s), 35-37. *See* pp. 801-802
for list.
angle measure, 108
area, 368
from arithmetic and algebra, 37
of Euclid, 661
Point-Line-Plane, 35
reflection, 164, 189
volume, 479, 490
power of a point, 771
preimage, 156, 163-165, 254
preserved properties, 163, 164, 281,
576, 577, 587
printer, dot-matrix, 4
prism, 415, **423,** 424, 429, 435,
488-490, 494, 495, 500, 511
Prism-Cylinder Surface Area
Formula, 470
Prism-Cylinder Volume
Formula, 490
probability, 403
Proclus, 662
product, dot, 725
Progress Self-Test, 53, 99-100,
147-148, 199, 248, 297-298,
349, 408-409, 461, 515, 558,
622-623, 676-677, 726-727,
786-787
proof, 120, 177, 317-320, 522-523,
630-632, 645-648
Properties. *See* Chapter Review.
Properties of a Parallelogram
Theorem, 334
Properties of Vector Addition
Theorem, 715
proportion, 581-583
protractor, 107
Ptolemy, Claudius, 703
pyramid, 415, 427, **428,** 429, 435, 494,
499-501, 511
Egyptian, 427, 432 (ex. 24), 474
Mayan (Mexico), 498 (ex. 20),
503 (ex. 11)
Pyramid-Cone Surface Area
Formula, 475
Pyramid-Cone Volume
Formula, 501
Pythagoras, 390
Pythagorean Converse
Theorem, 393
Pythagorean Theorem, 390-393
Pythagorean triple, 395

quadrangular pyramid, 438
quadrilateral, 51, 60, 70, 72, 93,

213-215, 223, 228, 236,
339-341, 415. *See also* kite;
parallelogram; rectangle; rhombus;
square; trapezoid.
Quadrilateral Hierarchy Theorem,
215, 236
Quadrilateral-Sum Theorem, 242
Quetzalcóatl, 503
Quizzles, 649

radius,
of a circle, **84**
perpendicular to a tangent, 652
of a sphere, 433
Radius-Tangent Theorem, 653
ratio, 581, 609
of similitude, 587
ray, 10, 40, **42,** 43, 87, 95, 164, 708
reciprocal, 583
Reciprocals Property, 583
rectangle, 60, 61, 213, 214-215, 223,
228, 231, 236, 339, 367, 369
area of, 368, 595
perimeter of, 358
Rectangle Formula (for area), 368
Rectangle Symmetry Theorem, 231
rectangular parallelepiped, 424
rectangular pyramid, 445
rectangular solid, 421
reference sources,
Dell Big Book of Crosswords and
Pencil Puzzles, 139
Guinness Book of World Records,
599
Information Please Almanac
(1989), 8, 11
Pencil Puzzle Treasury, 644
Quizzles, 649
Rand McNally Road Atlas (1973),
361
Rand McNally Road Atlas (1988),
361
Rand McNally Road Atlas (1989),
356, 361
Sports Illustrated, 205
USA Weekend, 58, 59
World Almanac (1989), 8, 11
refining a conjecture, 219
reflecting line, 156, 158, 165, 192
reflection, 255, 259, 260, 280, 439,
440, 587
image, 156, 158, 164-165, 189, **439**
image of a figure, 163
image of a point, **157**
image of polygons, 187-188
in space, **439**
Reflection Postulate, 164, 189
reflection-symmetric figure, 155,
192, 193, **440**
Reflexive Property

of Congruence, 280
of Equality, 37
Regiomontanus, 703
region,
elliptical, 355
fundamental, 362
irregular, 373-375
polygonal, 94
regular polygon, 334, 335
regular polyhedron, 454
regular pyramid, 473-475, 494, 511
Regular Pyramid-Right Cone Lateral Area Formula, 475
Representations. See Chapter Review.
resolution, 4, 17
resultant, 709
Review, Chapter. See Chapter Review.
Review question, 7, 13, 17-18, 24, 28-29, 32-34, 39, 44-45, 50-51, 64, 69, 75, 80, 86, 90-91, 96-97, 112, 118-119, 124-125, 131, 138, 145, 161-162, 169, 174-175, 181-182, 186, 190-191, 196-197, 212, 217, 222, 227, 232-233, 238-239, 245, 257-258, 265, 272, 278, 283-284, 290-291, 294-295, 308, 316, 321-322, 325-326, 332, 337-338, 343, 347, 360-361, 366, 372, 376-377, 383, 388-389, 395, 400-401, 405-406, 420, 426, 431-432, 438, 442-443, 447-448, 453, 458-459, 472, 477, 482, 487, 493, 498, 503-504, 508-509, 513, 525-526, 531, 536, 542-543, 549, 555-556, 568, 574, 579-580, 585, 592, 598, 602-603, 608, 614, 619, 634, 639, 644, 649-650, 656-657, 664, 669-670, 674, 689, 694-695, 701, 706-707, 713, 718-719, 724, 739, 743-744, 751, 756-757, 761-762, 767-768, 774, 779, 783-784
rhombus, 60, **213,** 214-215, 220, 223, 225, 228, 234, 236
area, 383
rhombus Symmetry Theorem, 225
Rice, Marjorie, 364, 377
right,
angle, **113,** 132
angle method, 752
cone, 428, 494, 495, 511
conical surface, 436
cylinder, 423, 424, 440, 469, 470, 494, 495, 511
prism, 423, 424, 469, 494, 495, 511
Right Prism-Cylinder Lateral Area Formula, 469

right triangle, 118, 378, 390-393, 692, 696-699
30-60-90, 685
45-45-90, 685
Right Triangle Altitude Theorem, 692
Right Triangle Area Formula, 378
Rorschach, Hermann, 155
rotation, 253, **267,** 280, 587
round-robin, 740
route, 88
rule,
compass, 141
parallelogram, 711
point, 141
straightedge, 141, 142

SAS condition, 307
SAS Congruence Theorem, 310, 344, 609
SAS Inequality Theorem, 344, 347
SAS Similarity Theorem, 611
scalar multiple, 717
scalar multiplication, 716, **717**
scale factor, 569
scale model, 592
scalene triangle, 94
secant, 759, 769
Secant Length Theorem, 769
section,
conic, 436
plane, 434-435
sector, 402
segment, 10, **40,** 43, 82, 84, 87, 89, 92, 93
Segment Congruence Theorem, 281
Segment Symmetry Theorem, 193
semicircle, 396, 734
sequens, 69
set(s), 30
empty, 88
intersection and union of, **87**
Seurat, Georges, 3, 4
sides,
of an angle, 106
consecutive, 93
opposite an angle in a triangle, 696
of a polygon, 93
Side-Splitting Converse, 616
Side-Splitting Theorem, 615
Side-Switching Theorem, 194
sight, lines of, 25
similar, similarity, 563, **586**
chords, 736
circles, 736
figures, 563, 586
Similar Figures Theorem, 587
similitude, ratio of, 587
similarity transformation, 586, 587

simple closed curve, 222
sine, 702, 703
size change, 564-565, **568,** 570, 587
Size Change Distance Theorem, 575
size change factor, 569
size change image, 569
Size Change Theorem, 577
size transformation, 569, 570, 576, 577
skew lines, 421
Skills. See Chapter Review.
slant height,
of a pyramid, 427, 473
of a cone, 427, 473
slide, 253, 259, **261.** See also translation.
slope, 128, 134
small circle of a sphere, 433
solar eclipse, 654
solid, 30, 421. See also cone; cylinder; polyhedron; prism; pyramid; sphere.
space, 30, 416-419
coordinates in, 550
figures, 10, 421-424, 427-429, 444-446, 449-451
plane sections in, 433-436
reflections in, 439-441
sphere, 10, 242, 415, 494, 495, 505, 510, 511, **433,** 434, 780, 781
center of, 433
diameter of, 433
great circle of, 433
radius of, 433
Sphere Surface Area Formula, 511
Sphere Volume Formula, 506
sponge, 782
SPUR Review. See Chapter Review.
square, 10, 60, 61, 94, **213,** 214-215, 223, 228, 335, 365, 367
pyramid, 450
root, 390
squaring a circle, 145
SSA condition, 327
SsA Similarity Theorem, 614
SsA Theorem, 330
SSS condition, 307
SSS Congruence Theorem, 310, 604, 609
SSS Similarity Theorem, 604, 605, 609
statement(s),
conditional, 65, 72, 76, 121
contrapositive of a, 636, 637
converse of a, **76,** 77-78, 127
if and only if, 83
if-then, 65-67, 120
negation of a, 635
Stein, Rolf, 354, 364, 366
straight angle, 106-109, **113**

Straight Angle Assumption, 108
Straightedge rule, 141, 142,
subroutine, 143
Substitution Property of Equality,
    37, 115
sufficient condition half (of a
    definition), 83, 84, 340
Sufficient Conditions for a
    Parallelogram Theorem, 341
sum,
    of angle measures in polygons,
    240-243
    of vectors, **709**
Summary, Chapter, 52, 99, 146, 198,
    246, 296, 348, 407, 460, 514, 557,
    627, 675, 725, 785
sun, 518 (ex. 30), 614 (ex. 16), 654,
    657 (ex. 23-24), 768 (ex. 22)
Sunday Afternoon on Grande Jatte
    Island, 2, 3
supplementary angles,
    supplements, 114, 115, 116
surface, 421, 422, 424
    area, 467, 468
Swift, Jonathan, 599
symbols
    See p. 800 for list.
Symmetric Property of
    Congruence, 280
Symmetric Property of
    Equality, 37, 72
symmetry,
    bilateral, 440
    line, **192,** 193, 207
    plane, 440

tangent(s), tangency, 535, 651-654
    angles formed by, 763-765
    ratio, **697,** 698, 699, 701
    to a circle, **651**
    to a sphere, 653
Tangent-Chord Theorem, 764
Tangent-Secant Theorem, 764
Tangent Square Theorem, 771
Teotihuacán, 498
terminal point, 708
terms, undefined, 30-31
tessellate, tessellation, 252-253,
    362, 364, 365
tetrahedron, 449, 454
Texas (map), 383
theorem, 36. *See* pp. 803-808 for list.
three color problem, 456. *See also*
    four color problem.
three-dimensional, 10, 25, 30, 415,
    421, 439, 468
    coordinate system, 550
    figures, 494, 511
tiling, 362-364
tilt, 105, 126, 133

torus, 456
Transamerica Building, 427
transformation, 254, **255,** 256, 259,
    280, 587
    congruence, 280
    glide reflection, 253, 286, **287,** 587,
    660, 661
    reflection, **157,** 255, 259, 260, 280,
    439, 440, 587
    rotation, 253, **267,** 280, 587
    similarity, **586,** 587
    size change, 569, **570,** 576, 577
    slide, 253, 259, **261**
    translation, 253, 259, **261,** 280, 587
Transitive Property
    of Congruence, 280
    of Equality, 37
    of Implication, 630
    of Inequality, 37
Transitivity of Parallelism
    Theorem, 129
translation, 253, 259, **261,** 280, 587
transversal, 126
trapezoid, 60, **214,** 215, 223, 228-230,
    384-386
    base angles of, 229
    isosceles, **215**
Trapezoid Angle Theorem, 228
Trapezoid Area Formula, 385
traversable, 20, 22
tree, family, 94
triangle(s), 10, 60, 89, 92, 93, 94,
    177, 240, 303-307, 310-312,
    317-319, 323, 328-330, 344,
    345, 378, 379, 415, 665, 666,
    684-686, 691, 696-699. *See*
    also right triangle.
    30-60-90, 685
    45-45-90, 684
    acute, 118
    congruence proofs, 317-319
    congruent, 306, 307, 310-313,
    317-320, 327-330
    drawing, 304-307
    equilateral, 94, 177, 335
    inequality, 46-49
    isosceles, 94, 206-209, 229
    obtuse, 118
    overlapping, 323-324
    right, 118, 378, 390-393, 684-687,
    692, 696-699
    scalene, 94
    similar, 604-606, 609-611, 615-616
Triangle Area Formula, 378
Triangle Inequality Postulate, 46
Triangle-Sum Theorem, 240
triangular prism, 500
triangular pyramid, 499-501, 440
triangulate, triangulation, 303, 384
Trichotomy Law, 643

trigonometric ratio, 699
trigonometry, 346, 683
trinomial, 484
tripod, 417
trisecting an angle, 145
truncated cone, 431
truncated pyramid, 431
turn, 253
two column form, 177
two-dimensional, 10, 25, 30, 415,
    439, 468
Two Perpendiculars Theorem, 133
Two Reflection Theorem
    for rotations, 267
    for translations, 261
Two sides of line assumption, 108

ulna, 111
undefined terms, 30-31, 36, 188
Unequal Angles Theorem, 667
Unequal Sides Theorem, 667
union, 87-89, 92
Unique line assumption, 15, 35
Unique measure assumption, 108
uniqueness, 658
Uniqueness of Parallels, 660
Uniqueness Property(ies), 368, 479
unit cube, 478
unit square, 367
United States (map), 455
Uses. *See* Chapter Review.

value, absolute, 82
vanishing line, 26
vanishing point, 25, 26
variables and equations, 521
vector(s), 683
    addition, 714, 715, 720
    components of, 714, 721
    and coordinates, 720-721
    direction, 708
    dot product, 724
    equal, 709
    initial point of, 708
    magnitude of, 708
    opposite, 716
    ordered pair description, 714
    parallelogram rule, 711
    resultant, 708
    scalar multiple, 717
    sum of, 708
    terminal point of, 708
    zero, 716
Vector Addition Theorem, 714
Venus, 518 (ex. 34)
vertex (vertices), 20, 21, 22, 93,
    427, **428**
    angle, 206, 207
    of an angle, 106
    of a box, 421

consecutive, 93
even and odd, 21
in networks, 20
of a polygon, 93
of a polyhedron, 449
vertical angles, 114, 115
Vertical Angle Theorem, 115, 116, 120
vertical line, 5, 16
Vieté, François, 521
view, 444
Vocabulary, 52, 99, 146, 198, 247, 297, 348, 407, 460, 514, 557, 621, 675, 725, 785
volume, 467, 478-480, 484, 485

of a box, 505, 595
of a cone, 499-501, 505, 595
of a cylinder, 488-490, 505
of a prism, 488-490, 505
of a pyramid, 499-501, 505, 595
of a sphere, 595
Volume Postulate, 479, 490

Wadlow, Robert, 599
walk, 253, 286
wedge, 402
weightlifters, 599, 603
whole greater than parts, 37
Who Owns the Zebra, 629
Williams, Wayne, 644, 649

Wilmer, Elizabeth, 456
window, 170
write step in a proof, 177-178

x-axis, 14-16, 550

y-axis, 14-16, 550

z-axis, 550
z-coordinate, 550
zero angle, 106, 108, **113**
Zero angle assumption, 108
zero vector, 716
zero-dimensional, 8
Zoser, 427

INDEX

ACKNOWLEDGEMENTS

Illustrator's Acknowledgements

For permission to reproduce indicated information on the following pages, acknowledgement is made to:

Roger Boehm
344, 628

Paul Dolan
23, 25, 27, 49, 51, 73, 80, 91, 152, 245, 264, 372, 383, 508, 513, 529, 537, 562, 573, 614, 615, 698, 712, 718, 755, 787

Scott Donaldson
274, 277, 284, 298

David Ebinger
444

Chuck Gonzales
7, 137, 194, 260, 277, 332, 342, 354, 413, 448, 579, 604, 671, 699, 700, 704, 713, 727, 731, 767

Susan Hahn
567

Bryan Haynes
9, 10, 373

Min Jae Hong
79, 112, 227, 234, 276, 530, 598, 609, 694

Daniel Pelavin
591

Robert Pizzo
204

Sally Vitsky
33

Picture Acknowledgements

Unless otherwise acknowledged, all photographs are the property of Scott, Foresman and Company. The following abbreviations indicate position of photos on page: L (left), R (right), T (top), C (center), and B (bottom).

2-3 Georges Seurat, *Sunday Afternoon on the Island of La Grande Jatte,* 1884-1886, oil on canvas, 207.6 X 308.0 cm, Helen Birch Bartlett Memorial Collection, 1926.224. © The Art Institute of Chicago. All Rights Reserved. 3 Georges Seurat, *Sunday Afternoon on the Island of La Grande Jatte.* 1884-86, oil on canvas, 207.6 X 308.0 cm, Helen Birch Bartlett Memorial Collection, 1926.224: detail view #12. © The Art Institute of Chicago. All Rights Reserved. 4 David R. Frazier 5L Bob Daemmrich/The Image Works 5R David R. Frazier 8 Jon Feingersh/Stock Boston 12 Arthur Bilsten/Stock Imagery 13 R. Lebeck/The Image Bank 14 Groninger Museum, Groningen, The Netherlands 18 Courtesy Cadott Lions Club and the Cadott Chamber of Commerce from *The Cadott Sentinel* 22 Roger Ressmeyer/Starlight 23 Lionel Delevingne/Stock Boston 25T Tony Stone/Click/Chicago/Tony Stone 25B The Regis Collection, Minneapolis, MN 29 Michael Schuyt 30 AP/Wide World Photos 34 Arnold J. Kaplan/The Picture Cube 39 Philip A. Savoie/Bruce Coleman Inc. 40 Dominique Sarraute/The Image Bank 41 David Madison/Bruce Coleman Inc. 46 F. Hidalgo/The Image Bank 49 Lawrence Migdale 50 J. Clark/The Stock Market 54 John Kelly/The Image Bank 58-59 John S. Abbot 62 Terry Ashe/Uniphoto 64 Children's Television Workshop 68R Walter Chandoha 69 David R. Frazier 70 Lawrence Migdale 75 Don & Pat Valenti/DRK Photos 76 Robert Landau/West Light 81 Geoffrey Gove/The Image Bank 86 D. Rowan/FPG 88 David R. Frazier 90T Billy E. Barnes/FPG 90B David R. Frazier 93 Courtesy Watertown Historical Society 97 Peter Eisenman, FAIA/Courtesy Eisenman Architects 99T Susan Van Etten, PhotoEdit 100 Courtesy Baha'i House of Worship, Wilmette, IL 102 Focus On Sports 104-105 Walter Hodges/Allstock 105B Wendell Metzen/Bruce Coleman Inc. 106 John Running/Stock Boston 110 Jeff Foott Productions 112B NASA 113 Elsilrac Enterprises 118 J. Ehlers/Bruce Coleman Inc. 126L David R. Frazier 126R Vince Streano/The Stock Market 139 Reprinted courtesy of Dell Magazines 1989, a division of Bantam Doubleday Dell Publishing Group, Inc. 140 Steve Niedorf/The Image Bank 143 Educational Directions/FPG 154-155 Tom Tracy/The Stock Market 155T Card IV Rorschach, *Psychodiagnostics,* Verlagttans Huber Bern, © 1921, renewed 1948 155C Courtesy Chrysler Corporation. Used with permission. 155B Charles Seaborn/Odyssey Productions 156T Rob Atkins/The Image Bank 156B Larry Reynolds 163 Eric Meola/The Image Bank 170 Hank

Morgan/Rainbow 176 Scala/Art Resource 181 Ronnie Kaufman/The Stock Market 190 Bob Daemmrich, Stock Boston 191 Focus On Sports 192 Erwin & Peggy Bauer 194L The Cleveland Museum of Art, Purchase, Edward L. Whittemore Fund 199 Courtesy Chrysler Corporation. Used with permission. 206 David R. Frazier 211 Bohdan Hrynewych/Stock Boston 217TC David R. Frazier 217B Robert Frerck/Odyssey Productions 223 Jamie Tanaka/Bruce Coleman Inc. 231 Cliff Hollenbeck 240 Steve Monti/Bruce Coleman Inc. 244 Tony Freeman, PhotoEdit 252-253 © 1990 M.C. Escher/Heirs/Cordon Art—Baarn—Holland 259 Peter Angelo Simon/the Stock Market 265 Museum Boymans van Beuningen, Rotterdam, Herscovici/Art Resource 266 Manfred Kage/Peter Arnold Inc. 267 Ken & Miriam Rose/The Image Bank 271 Manfred Kage/Peter Arnold Inc. 273 © John Margolies/Esto 288, 289, 300 © 1990 M.C. Escher Heirs/Cordon Art—Baarn—Holland 302-303 Charles Osgood/Copyrighted Chicago Tribune Company. All rights reserved. Used with permission. 307 Peter F. Runyon, The Image Bank 309 Used by permission of Highlights for Children, Inc. Columbus, OH. Copyrighted 1986. 310 Robert Fried/Stock Boston 323 Gary Braasch 327 Ken Sherman/Bruce Coleman Inc. 331 Gabe Palmer/The Stock Market 345 Walter Chandoha 349 Ellis Herwig/Stock Boston 352 Peter Pearson/Click/Chicago/Tony Stone 356 Brent Jones 365 © 1990 M.C. Escher Heirs/Cordon Art—Baarn—Holland 368 Adam Woolfitt/Woodfin Camp & Associates, Inc. 378 John I. Koivula 389B Grant Heilman 391 The Bettmann Archive 392 David R. Frazier 396 Peter Menzel/Stock Boston 398 David Madison 400 Alan Magayne-Roshar/Third Coast Stock 401 Beringer/Dratch/the Image Works 402 Leslye Borden/PhotoEdit 405 Bill Robert/PhotoEdit 409 Chuck O'Rear/West Light 414-415 L.L.T. Rhodes/Click/Chicago/Tony Stone 416 California Institute of Technology 423 Charles Harbutt/Actuality Inc. 427T Roger Ressmeyer/Starlight 427C Larry Lee/West Light 432 Dallas & John Heaton/Click/Chicago/Tony Stone 439 Patti Murray/Animals Animals 440 Donald R. Specker/Animals Animals 444 David Ebinger 447 Milt & Joan Mann/Cameramann International Ltd. 472 David R. Frazier 473T John Kinser/Bruce Coleman Inc. 473C Courtesy General Dynamics, Fort Worth Division 474 Carl Purcell 483 Cameron Davidson/Bruce Coleman Inc. 487 David Austen/Stock Boston 488 Martin Rogers/Stock Boston 497 The Bettmann Archive 498 John S. Flannery/Bruce Coleman Inc. 505 Kelly/Mooney Photography 512 Richard Pasley/Stock Boston 518 M. Timothy O'Keefe, Bruce Coleman Inc. 519 Harry Wilks/Stock Boston 520-521 T. Hoirata & T. Horiguchi/Siggraph 523 The Bettmann Archive 525 Len Rue Jr./Leonard Rue Enterprises 526 Reprinted with permission from: Medenbach, Olaf: *The Magic of Minerals,* 1988, © 1988 Springer-Verlager Berlin-Heidelberg. 527 David Lissy/Sportschrome, Inc. 532 Elisa Leonelli/Bruce Coleman Inc. 536 Tony Freeman, PhotoEdit 542 Bob Daemmrich 544 © 1986 Dale Seymour Publications 548 Mark Sherman/Bruce Coleman Inc. 550 Richard Pasley/Stock Boston 562-563 Jean Pragen/Click/Chicago/Tony Stone 575 Mary Kate Denny, PhotoEdit 581 Tony Freeman/PhotoEdit 585 Phil Degginger/Photo Kinetics 597 Ernest Hass/Magnum Photos 599 UPI/Bettmann Newsphotos 601 Donald R. Specker/Animals Animals 603 Leo Mason/*Sports Illustrated* 625 Runk/Schoenberger from Grant Heilman 630 Giraudon/Art Resource 632 Library of Congress 633 UPI/Bettmann Newsphotos 635 Robert Frerck/Odyssey Productions 637 Dr. E.R. Degginger/Color-Pic, Inc. 638 Richard Hutchings, InfoEdit 640 Erika Stone 641 Owen Franken/Stock Boston 643 Bob Daemmrich/The Image Works 645 Billy E. Barnes/Stock Boston 649 Bob Daemmrich/Stock Boston 651 NASA 657T Dr. E.R. Degginger/Color-Pic, Inc. 657B Dr. Brook Sandford and William H. Regan/Los Alamos Scientific Library 658 Superstock/Shostal Associates 664 UPI/Bettmann Newsphotos 674 Julian Baum/Bruce Coleman Inc. 676 Phil Degginger/Photo Kinetics* 677 Colonial Williamsburg 678 Michael George/Bruce Coleman Inc. 681 David R. Frazier 682-683 Dr. E.R. Degginger/Bruce Coleman Inc. 684 John Griffin/The Image Works 687 David R. Frazier 688 Jeff Foott Productions 690 Bill Gallery/Stock Boston 694 Steve Hansen/Stock Boston 695 Tim Carlson/Stock Boston 702 Miro Vintoniv/Stock Boston 708 David H. Wells/The Image Works 711 Bob Daemmrich/Stock Boston 714 Dr. Harold Edgerton (1990)/Courtesy Palm Press, Inc. 723 D.P. Hershkowitz/Bruce Coleman Inc. 724 Bob Daemmrich/The Image Works 727 D.H. Hessell/Stock Boston 732-733 Michael Ventura/Bruce Coleman Inc. 734 Norman Owen Tomalin/Bruce Coleman Inc. 740 David R. Frazier 744 Mitchell B. Reibe/Sportschrome, Inc. 745 Underwood & Underwood/The Bettmann Archive 751 Ellis Herwig/Stock Boston 755 Patsy Davidson/The Image Works 763 Gary Brettnacher/Click/Chicago/Tony Stone 775 David R. Frazier 780 John Eastcott & Yva Momatiuk/The Image Works.